A GUIDE TO NUCLEAR POWER TECHNOLOGY

A GUIDE TO NUCLEAR POWER TECHNOLOGY

A RESOURCE FOR DECISION MAKING

FRANK J. RAHN
ACHILLES G. ADAMANTIADES
JOHN E. KENTON
CHAIM BRAUN

The Electric Power Research Institute
Palo Alto, California

KRIEGER PUBLISHING COMPANY
MALABAR, FLORIDA

Original Edition 1984
Reprint Edition 1992

Printed and Published by
KRIEGER PUBLISHING COMPANY
KRIEGER DRIVE
MALABAR, FLORIDA 32950

Library of Congress Cataloging-In-Publication Data
A Guide to nuclear power technology : a resource for decision making /
Frank J. Rahn ... [et. al.].
p. cm.
Originally published: New York : Wiley, c1984.
Includes index.
ISBN 0-89464-652-4
1. Nuclear engineering. I. Rahn, Frank J.
TK9145.G82 1991
621.48'3--dc20 91-22459
CIP

10 9 8 7 6 5 4 3

PREFACE

The purpose of this book is to describe the various aspects of the technology associated with the production of nuclear power. Many facets of nuclear technology are not treated in an integrated form in any existing book with the amount of technical detail we have used. On the other hand, there exists a large audience of people in the United States and abroad who, without being specialists, have an interest and often a responsibility in this field. Consequently, the breadth of coverage attempted here is quite comprehensive, whereas the technical depth is tuned to the person who has some technical background but is not a specialist in the field.

The topics covered in this guidebook include not only the reactor itself but also the external fuel cycle, economics, and proliferation concerns. Several chapters are devoted to radiation effects, the behavior of radioactivity in the environment, uranium mining, reactor operations, waste disposal, and decommissioning, subjects that are seldom covered adequately.

To our knowledge, there is no single book on the market today with the breadth of coverage and the adequate technical detail discussed above to fulfill the need. On the other hand, there seems to be a growing list of groups and institutions that deal with nuclear energy and would, therefore, find such a book useful. Such groups include:

1. Federal agencies dealing with domestic energy issues.
2. Federal agencies dealing with international energy issues.
3. Technology assessment groups (federal, state, private).
4. Technological forecasting groups.
5. Economic and financial consultants.
6. Planning staff on federal, state, and regional levels.
7. Planning staff of private corporations dealing in the energy and environmental fields.
8. State legislators and commissions.
9. Legal persons involved in nuclear issues.
10. Technical writers of newspapers and magazines.
11. Engineers without a special training in nuclear technology.
12. Nuclear engineers who may need a wider exposure to certain aspects of nuclear technology (for example, health or environmental concerns).

A book like this oviously cannot provide a complete and detailed description of all areas in a varied and complex field such as nuclear power. Rather it attempts to serve as a guide to the basic concepts without lapsing into superficial coverage. To aid the reader in obtaining further information, an extensive bibliography has been prepared for each chapter.

We are indebted to the editorial review board for their many fine suggestions, in addition to many others who were kind enough to help us improve the manuscript. While much of the credit belongs to them, we, of course, accept full responsibility for the material appearing in the book. Most of all, we wish to thank our wives and families, whose patience and encouragement sustained us throughout this work.

FRANK J. RAHN
ACHILLES G. ADAMANTIADES
JOHN E. KENTON
CHAIM BRAUN

Palo Alto, California
July 1984

CONTENTS

A GUIDE TO NUCLEAR POWER TECHNOLOGY

CHAPTER 1
INTRODUCTION

1.1. HISTORICAL PERSPECTIVE

Whether one is pro- or antinuclear, objective appraisal demands recognition that the development of civilian nuclear electric power shares—with powered flight, television, and the space program's manned landings on the moon and explorations of distant planets—a position as one of the most epoch-making achievements of this century.

This is not said to praise nor to tout nuclear power, but only to seek the perspective of a historian 100 or 200 years from now looking back at our century.

It is true that nuclear power was born of wartime torment and tragedy. So also, the historian would say, were fire, tempered metals, rockets, and the gunpowder that is the base of today's explosives used in construction projects.

In one sense, the history of radioactivity goes back to the foundation of the earth, for since the earth existed it has been bathed in a sea of radioactivity in the form of cosmic rays from the sun and other stars. In another sense, the *known* history of radioactivity began in 1895 with the discovery of X-rays by the German physics professor Wilhelm Roentgen of the University of Würzburg. He reported a glow at the broad end of the pear-shaped Crookes tube he was using to study the effects of electrical discharges in a vacuum. This glow was not what he was interested in so he covered the tube with a tightly fitting black cardboard shield. By chance a fluorescent screen that glowed when excited by ultraviolet or other rays was lying nearby outside the shield, and Roentgen noticed that it also glowed when the tube was operating. By chance, an iron rod used to support apparatus standing between the outside of the shield and the fluorescent screen cast a shadow on the screen. Roentgen investigated, and found that the rays from the tube penetrated not only the black cardboard shield, but also wood and other substances, but not metals. The rays also penetrated the flesh of his hand but not the bones, so that the bones were outlined on the screen. Not knowing what the rays were, he named them X-rays after the mathematical symbol for the unknown. He soon discovered that the rays could make a record on a photographic plate, as light does, and make images of bones through flesh. Thus were X-rays discovered. Their value to medicine was recognized at once.

Many scientists began experimenting with the mysterious new X-rays. It was eventually shown that they are a form of radiation like visible light, but with very much shorter wavelength.

One of those who became interested in investigating X-rays was a French physicist, Henri Becquerel. He began to explore the effect of the rays on fluorescent minerals, of which his father had collected many samples. One of those he chose was a uranium salt, which he exposed to sunlight until it showed a visible fluorescence, and then he placed it on a photographic plate wrapped in black paper. Upon development the plate was blackened. Then Becquerel discovered that the uranium salt would produce the same effect even without first being exposed to sunlight to make it fluoresce. He then showed that any uranium compound would behave in the same way.

His work inspired a doctoral student in physics, Marie Sklodowska Curie—a young Polish woman married to French physicist Pierre Curie—to make a systematic study of Becquerel radiation. She found that a natural ore of uranium, pitchblende, was several times more active than purified uranium oxide. She began fractioning pitchblende to discover the reason for this phenomenon, and with her husband discovered two new, highly radioactive, elements. The first they named polonium for Marie's native country; the second they named radium.

The Curies went on to investigate the new phenomenon that Marie named "radioactivity." They did much to investigate and clarify the properties of radium and its transformation products, or decay products. In this connection, it should be stated that radioactivity is nothing more than a natural process of decay, as certain heavy elements—the so-called naturally radioactive elements—spontaneously throw off "alpha," "beta," or "gamma" particles which are, respectively, helium atoms, electrons, and an electromagnetic radiation of much shorter wavelength than ultraviolet.

In 1903 the Curies and Becquerel jointly won the Nobel Prize. Their work had caused great excitement in the world of science and inspired those who followed: Rutherford and Soddy in England, Hahn and Meitner in Germany, Fermi in Italy, and Bohr in Denmark, among a number of others, worked feverishly to explore this new frontier.

It is ironic that Rutherford, one of the greatest contributors to our understanding of the structure of the atom and its nucleus, declared in 1933 before the British Association for the Advancement of Science that "The energy produced by the breaking down of the atom is a very poor kind of thing. Anyone who expects a source of power from the transformation of these atoms is talking moonshine."

Lord Rutherford (as he was to become for his contributions to atomic science) did not live to see the discovery of fission when it was calculated that the energy from 1 pound of uranium-235 is equivalent to the energy available from 3 million pounds of coal, 2 million pounds of gasoline, or 20 million pounds of TNT.

It was only six years after Rutherford's "moonshine" statement (and two years after his death), in 1939 in Berlin, that Otto Hahn and Fritz Strassman performed the epochal experiment that was to open the door to the nuclear power age. Following up work done in 1936 by Enrico Fermi in Rome, they directed a stream of neutrons on a target of common uranium. The result mystified them at first, for they found barium—a much lighter weight element—in the target residue. It took further experimentation, and consultation with Lise Meitner (see Figure 1.1) and Otto Frisch in Denmark, Curie in Paris, and Fermi in Rome, before the correct solution was arrived at. And even then, it was not until the following year, 1940, that Nier, Dunning, and Booth at the University of Minnesota and Columbia University performed the decisive experiment.

The clue to the solution was that uranium has a slightly lighter weight isotope, uranium-235. Natural uranium mined in the ground everywhere in the world and refined from the ore is consistently found to be composed of 99.3% uranium-238, and 0.7% uranium-235. The existence of isotopes of some elements was known at that time, but uranium-235 was so rare that very little was known about it. In fact, before 1939 the greatest amount of uranium-235 concentrated weighed less than 0.02 millionths of a gram, too small to see under the most powerful microscope. (A dime weighs 2.5 g.) Otto Hahn's autobiography conveys very graphically the sense of excitement and ferment among physicists in the late 1930s when they were trying to unravel the mysterious identities of what were known then as uranium-X, uranium-Y, and uranium-Z. This research culminated in the discovery of the element protactinium.

The startling and unexpected answer to what had taken place in the Hahn–Strassmann experiment was that some of the ^{235}U contained in the uranium target had fissioned—that is, some of the ^{235}U nuclei had split apart under neutron bombardment to form new pairs of other, lighter weight, elements. The barium that Hahn and Strassmann had found in the target was in fact one of the fission fragments of the fissioned uranium.

The news of this event created a sensation when it was reported by Niels Bohr to the Fifth Washington (D.C.) Conference on Theoretical Physics—the more so as the fission process appeared to be accompanied by the release of a significant amount of energy. Soon after, John Dunning of Columbia University in New York repeated the experiment, and calculated that the fission of each atom released more than 150 million electron-volts. This meant that a pound of uranium when fissioned could release the energy equivalent of 3 million pounds of coal.

It became obvious to many physicists that there might be a real danger that German scientists would harness this new and vast energy source for construction of a bomb of unprecedented power. Understandably, it was principally emigré physicists who had fled to the United States from Nazi Germany and fascist Italy who were the most acutely concerned. They met to share their concern that the United States should do something, and their concern was hardly alleviated by news that Germany had prohibited sales of uranium from Czech mines. The British, too, had sobering reports of large quantities of paraffin ordered by Germany to be made using "heavy water" (water in which the hydrogen component is the isotope "heavy hydrogen," to be discussed later) and it was difficult to imagine a use for this other than in uranium research.

In September 1939, Hitler invaded Poland and World War II was under way. This, incidentally, was only nine months after the discovery of uranium fission, so rapidly were events moving.

Leo Szilárd and Eugene Wigner, Hungarian emigré scientists in the United States, decided that the uranium matter had to be brought to President Roosevelt's notice, and by someone who would command his attention. They turned to Albert Einstein and asked him to write a letter to the president, which he did (see Figure 1.2). They then approached a friend of the president, New York economist Alexander Sachs, and asked him to deliver it personally. Sachs carried the letter to the White House in October. Roosevelt called in his aide, "Pa" Watson, and declared, "This requires action." He thereupon appointed an Advisory Committee on Uranium, to be chaired by Lyman Briggs, director of the National Bureau of Standards, with two ordnance officers—one from the Army and one from the Navy—as members. The group met on October 21 with Szilárd, Wigner, Edward Teller, and others. Their report to the president, dated November 1, mentioned an atomic bomb as a possibility, and recommended a program of experiments.

Figure 1.1. Lise Meitner and Otto Hahn in their laboratory in the 1930s.

To begin, 50 tons of uranium oxide and 4 tons of graphite were procured, using $6000 made available by the Navy for the purpose. Experiments at Columbia University had shown that graphite would be effective in slowing neutrons to the optimum velocities required. When George Pegram of Columbia University was asked what use the uranium project could be to the Navy, he replied that a submarine using nuclear energy could travel around the world underwater without surfacing.

During this eventful year, a parallel series of events had been taking place which stemmed also from the Washington Conference on Theoretical Physics in January, 1939. While many were focusing attention on the bomb potential of uranium fission, the technical advisor to the director of the Naval Research Laboratory, Ross Gunn, immediately saw other implications for the Navy. A fission engine would not require oxygen, and would therefore free submarines of the need to

Albert Einstein
Old Grove Rd.
Nassau Point
Peconic, Long Island

August 2nd, 1939

F.D. Roosevelt,
President of the United States,
White House
Washington, D.C.

Sir:

Some recent work by E.Fermi and L. Szilard, which has been communicated to me in manuscript, leads me to expect that the element uranium may be turned into a new and important source of energy in the immediate future. Certain aspects of the situation which has arisen seem to call for watchfulness and, if necessary, quick action on the part of the Administration. I believe therefore that it is my duty to bring to your attention the following facts and recommendations:

In the course of the last four months it has been made probable - through the work of Joliot in France as well as Fermi and Szilard in America - that it may become possible to set up a nuclear chain reaction in a large mass of uranium,by which vast amounts of power and large quantities of new radium-like elements would be generated. Now it appears almost certain that this could be achieved in the immediate future.

This new phenomenon would also lead to the construction of bombs, and it is conceivable - though much less certain - that extremely powerful bombs of a new type may thus be constructed. A single bomb of this type, carried by boat and exploded in a port, might very well destroy the whole port together with some of the surrounding territory. However, such bombs might very well prove to be too heavy for transportation by air.

The United States has only very poor ores of uranium in moderate quantities. There is some good ore in Canada and the former Czechoslovakia, while the most important source of uranium is Belgian Congo.

In view of this situation you may think it desirable to have some permanent contact maintained between the Administration and the group of physicists working on chain reactions in America. One possible way of achieving this might be for you to entrust with this task a person who has your confidence and who could perhaps serve in an inofficial capacity. His task might comprise the following:

a) to approach Government Departments, keep them informed of the further development, and put forward recommendations for Government action, giving particular attention to the problem of securing a supply of uranium ore for the United States;

b) to speed up the experimental work, which is at present being carried on within the limits of the budgets of University laboratories, by providing funds, if such funds be required, through his contacts with private persons who are willing to make contributions for this cause, and perhaps also by obtaining the co-operation of industrial laboratories which have the necessary equipment.

I understand that Germany has actually stopped the sale of uranium from the Czechoslovakian mines which she has taken over. That she should have taken such early action might perhaps be understood on the ground that the son of the German Under-Secretary of State, von Weizsäcker, is attached to the Kaiser-Wilhelm-Institut in Berlin where some of the American work on uranium is now being repeated.

Yours very truly,

A. Einstein

(Albert Einstein)

Figure 1.2. A facsimile of a letter from Albert Einstein to President Franklin D. Roosevelt on the subject of uranium as a "new and important source of energy." (Courtesy Franklin D. Roosevelt Museum.)

surface each night to recharge the electrical batteries they use for propulsion when submerged and unable to use their diesels. Gunn contacted Merle Tuve of the Carnegie Institution (who was to win fame as the inventor of the proximity fuse).

The Navy made $1500 available for a study of the concept of a nuclear-propelled submarine. In 1940 Tuve reported that a nuclear engine for submarines appeared practical—in fact, more so at that time than an atomic bomb. The Navy was to continue its interest in nuclear propulsion throughout the war, although the decision was made early to try to develop a bomb first.

The Advisory Committee on Uranium in its November 1, 1939 report concluded "If it [chain reaction of uranium fission] could be achieved and controlled, it might supply power for submarines. If the reaction should be explosive, it would provide a possible source of bombs with a destructiveness vastly greater than anything now known."

In June 1940 the Uranium Committee became a subcommittee of the National Defense Research Committee which was responsible for much of the U.S. scientific effort during the war.

Even before Pearl Harbor, more and more projects were started to study methods of separating the fissionable ^{235}U isotope from natural uranium which is 99.3% ^{238}U not readily fissionable, and only 0.7% ^{235}U. By the time that Pearl Harbor dramatically showed the need for an all-out effort, there were 16 research programs under way.

One of the results of this work, achieved prior to Pearl Harbor, was the discovery by E. M. McMillan at the University of California cyclotron that a thin layer of uranium oxide exposed to charged particles yields a new isotope of uranium, ^{239}U, which has a very short life and spontaneously emits an electron. This had the effect of raising the substance's atomic number from 92 (that of uranium, until then the last and heaviest in the list of known elements) to 93. This new element, number 93, was named neptunium because Neptune is the next planet in the solar system after Uranus for which uranium was named.

Only minute amounts were available for study. Nevertheless, a research team at the University of California at Berkeley, under Glenn Seaborg, observed that neptunium also has a very short life and also throws off an electron spontaneously, thereby producing another new element, number 94. This second transuranium element was named—in the same way, for the next planet after Neptune, Pluto—plutonium.

Theoretical work on the properties attaching to different combinations of protons and neutrons in an atomic nucleus led to the prediction that plutonium, like ^{235}U, would be fissionable. The Berkeley team confirmed this prediction by experiments in 1941.

This fact had considerable significance for the coming atomic bomb effort. It meant that instead of just one, there were now two possible materials from which to try to fashion a crushing, war-ending weapon before the enemy did, ^{235}U and plutonium.

In 1942 it was decided to assign the atomic bomb project to the Army. On June 18, Colonel J. C. Marshall of the Army Corps of Engineers was assigned to form a new engineer district to undertake a full-scale development program. The new organization was code named the Manhattan Engineering District, and was officially established on August 13, 1942, in deepest secrecy. The following month, Brigadier General Leslie R. Groves of the Corps of Engineers was selected to command it.

The Manhattan District was granted unprecedented priorities to requisition materials and men, that is, scientific brainpower. It was also given a virtually unlimited drawing account on War Department funds. By war's end, the Manhattan District's investment totaled $2.23 billion.

The story of the mammoth Manhattan District "crash program" on learning a new and unknown technology and producing a weapon for the war effort has been told too often† to require more than a brief, summary retelling here.

There were four principal tasks before Groves and his new organization: procurement of uranium; production of the ^{235}U separated from natural uranium; production of plutonium; and the fashioning of these new kinds of explosives into practical, reliable, and deliverable weapons. (It should be recalled that in September 1942 it had not yet even been demonstrated that a chain reaction of uranium nuclei, releasing their latent energy, was feasible.)

At the end of 1942 came a major breakthrough for the atomic development program. A team of physicists under Enrico Fermi had built the world's first reactor (see Figure 1.3) in a squash court under the west stands of Chicago University's Stagg Field (see Figure 1.4). This was a structure of uranium emplaced in carefully ordered array in graphite blocks stacked in a roughly pyramidal shape. Only 6 tons of refined uranium metal were available, and the assembly was completed with 24 tons of uranium oxide—the whole emplaced in 385 tons of graphite. The graphite served as "moderator," to slow the neutrons to optimum velocity. Strips of cadmium served as control rods; they were held out of the assembly by ropes, and a physicist was poised with an axe ready to sever the ropes and drop the cadmium control strips into the assembly should it be necessary to shut it down quickly.

At 3:25 p.m. on December 2, 1942, Fermi's monitoring of the instruments (see Figure 1.5)

†See Bibliography.

Figure 1.3. December 2, 1942, the world's first nuclear reactor operates. (Courtesy DOE.)

showed that the reactor had become chain reacting (''had gone critical'' was the phrase that gained currency for start of a chain reaction, after natural physical laws concerning the minimum concentration of fissionable material, a ''critical mass,'' had been learned).

This was the demonstration that the chain reaction, conjectured since Hahn and Strassmann's discovery of fission, could indeed be instigated. The Stagg Field ''pile'' was operated at a level of only half a watt of thermal power (of course there was no provision for electricity generation, as this was a proof-of-principle experiment), and up to 200 W thermal for brief intervals.

Because the ''Chicago Pile'' was built by piling up successive layers of graphite moderator and uranium, for a few years chain-reacting systems generally were called ''piles.'' The term ''reactor,'' borrowed from the chemical engineering industry, soon replaced it.

The news of Fermi and his team's success was transmitted to Washington by the prearranged code message ''The Italian navigator has landed in the New World.'' To the prearranged question,

Figure 1.4. Chicago University's Stagg Field, site of the first nuclear reactor. (Courtesy DOE.)

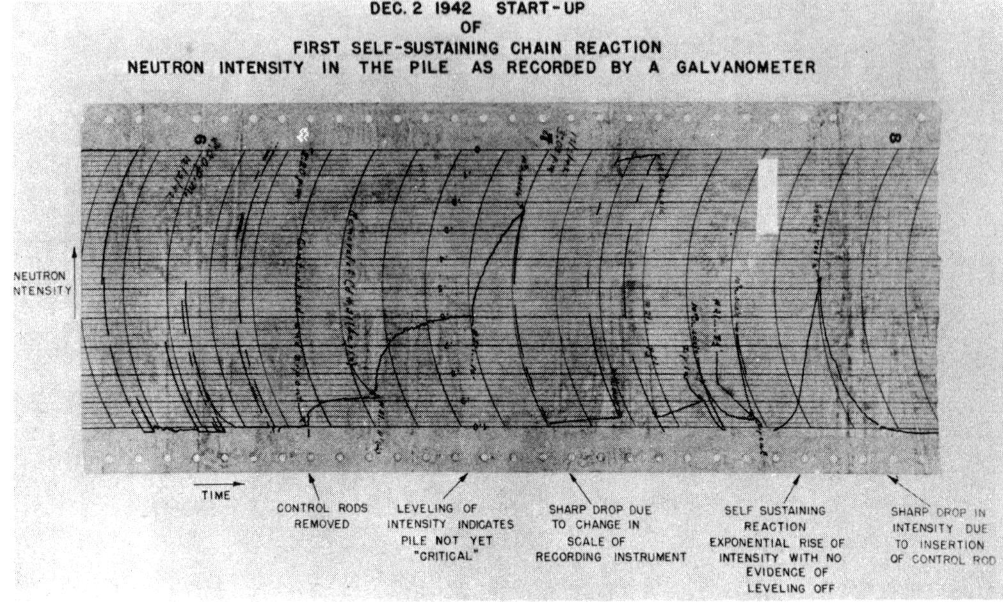

Figure 1.5. December 2, 1942 start-up of first self-sustaining chain reaction. Neutron intensity in the pile was recorded by a galvanometer. (Courtesy DOE.)

"How were the natives?" came the code reply, "Friendly," meaning that the experiment had worked. With the chain reaction demonstrated, the Manhattan District's work was now cut out for it.

Uranium Supply

The chief sources of uranium ore were the Shinkolobwe mines in Katanga province, Belgian Congo (today know as Zaire), and Canada. Various organizations worked on problems in refining the ore to pure metal, and on processes required to transform it to other forms as needed, such as feed material to isotope separation plants.

Producing usable quantities of the two fissionable materials presented quite different problems. ^{235}U, being an isotope—or variant form—of uranium, has the same chemical properties as all isotopes of uranium (its fissionability is a *physical,* not a *chemical* property) and therefore it cannot be separated from the predominant bulk of ^{238}U found in natural uranium by chemical means. The only leverage the scientists had to try to pry the two isotopes apart was by a physical characteristic, the very slight difference in weight between the two—a mere 3/238ths. Plutonium, on the other hand, being a "new" element, had to be obtained by the means by which it had been discovered, but on a far larger scale: neutron bombardment of uranium.

^{235}U Production

The scientific teams working on the ^{235}U problem considered and tried seven different methods of isotope separation: centrifuging, chemical exchange, electrolytic, electromagnetic, fractional distillation, gaseous diffusion, and thermal diffusion. In the long run the most effective—despite the gigantic scale of the facilities required—proved to be gaseous diffusion. This is treated in detail in Chapter 6; let us merely summarize very briefly here.

Purified uranium oxide is chemically converted to a uranium compound, uranium hexafluoride, which has the very convenient property that it becomes a gas above 140°F, but solidifies below about 104°F. Uranium hexafluoride gas (or "hex" as it is called in the field) is pumped through miles of piping and many hundreds of porous barriers finer than any ever made before. The gas contains atoms of ^{235}U and ^{238}U in their natural proportions of 0.7% and 99.3%, respectively. At each barrier, the slightly heavier ^{238}U has a slight tendency to remain behind while the slightly lighter ^{235}U atoms within the gas tend to pass through a little more readily. At each stage the gas that passes through, slightly richer in ^{235}U, is pumped to the next barrier while the gas that remained behind is pumped back to the entrance side of the previous barrier. Thus the lighter isotope keeps progressing forward, gradually becoming more and more concentrated, while the heavier gas, depleted in ^{235}U, keeps moving backward while being stripped of more and more of its ^{235}U content. In this laborious way, the lighter ^{235}U is gradually separated from the heavier ^{238}U. The process is called "enriching," as the total amount of uranium product is enriched in the ^{235}U isotope. The fraction left behind is called "depleted" uranium, depleted of most of its ^{235}U, and almost pure ^{238}U. It is not practical to produce 100% pure ^{235}U, but separation to greater than 90% is carried out to make weapons material. For electric power fuel, however, uranium is enriched to only 2% to 4% in ^{235}U. So it can be seen that uranium for weapons use is a quite different material from uranium used as fuel for electric power.

The Manhattan District engaged a contractor to build a huge gaseous diffusion plant.† For security reasons, a remote forest area along the Clinch River about 30 miles west of Knoxville, Tennessee, had been selected and code named "Clinton Engineer Works." To provide housing for permanent employees, a town, Oak Ridge, was built; in the 1980 census it was the tenth largest city in Tennessee. Construction of a large-scale gaseous diffusion facility (dubbed "K-25") was begun in 1943; it began operating in early 1945. In the meantime large-scale electromagnetic and thermal diffusion plants ("Y-12" and "S-50," respectively) were also built at the Clinton Works.

The K-25 plant, three-quarters of a mile long and a quarter of a mile wide to house the miles of pipes, pumps, and filters of the gaseous diffusion project, is still in operation today after many modifications, along with K-27, an annex built in six months to enlarge the capacity of the plant, and postwar additions.

Plutonium Production

A pilot-scale reactor designed for the sole purpose of producing plutonium was built at the Clinton Works; it was designated X-10. This was a considerably larger version of the Chicago Pile, but with air cooling and radiation shielding added. Cartridges of jacketed natural uranium were slid into channels into the center of the graphite; the reactor operated for a period of time during which the uranium was bombarded by neutrons from the chain reaction, and then the cartridges or slugs of uranium were unloaded and replaced by fresh ones. The irradiated slugs were subjected to chemical processing to separate the plutonium that some of the ^{238}U had been transmuted into from the remainder of the uranium. The reactor began operation in November 1943, and successful performance of the chemical separation process was demonstrated by early 1944. Here were produced the first significant quantities of plutonium available anywhere to that time—milligrams, later gram amounts.

The X-10 reactor design was scaled up considerably, with the exception that the production-scale reactors were cooled by water rather than air. Three of these production reactors were built, again at a remote site: the desertlike southeast corner of Washington state, along the Columbia River which supplied cooling water.

As for the fourth major task before the Manhattan District, development and design of a bomb, that is outside the scope of this book. Suffice it to say that the first proof-of-principle detonation, the Trinity shot at Alamogordo, New Mexico, took place on July 16, 1945.

We have been reviewing, at bird's-eye level, the history of the Manhattan District's massive effort to develop a war-ending nuclear weapon before the Nazis. However the history of the peaceful uses of atomic energy, and of nuclear power, did not begin after the end of World War II.

On the contrary, even while the crash program to make a bomb was under way with unprecedented dedication of materials, manpower, and funds, many scientific minds involved in the program were already turning their thoughts to the postwar peacetime potential of the new energy source, well before the bomb had ever been designed or demonstrated.

Enrico Fermi wrote that on the very day that he and his team achieved the world's first controlled nuclear chain reaction in the Stagg Field reactor, "We all hoped that with the end of the war, emphasis would be shifted decidedly from the weapon to the peaceful aspects of atomic energy."

By 1944, a year before the end of the war, at least five different types of nuclear reactors to produce electric power were being considered. Small demonstration or pilot plants of all five types were built—the predecessors of the commercial-size demonstration plants that followed. The first token amount of electricity, 100 W, was generated by the EBR-1 experimental reactor on December 20, 1951 (see Figure 1.6); and the nation's first commercial-scale reactor, the Shippingport nuclear plant, first reached full power on December 23, 1957. Thus the elapsed time to bring nuclear power to reality was less than 12½ years from the first weapon detonation, and only 15 years from Fermi's first demonstration of the chain reaction and of reactor operation at Stagg Field.

†Although the gaseous diffusion process development received major attention during World War II, the diffusion plant was not finished in time to yield the first bomb material which was obtained using electromagnetic and thermal diffusion techniques.

Figure 1.6. Electricity was first produced at EBR-I on December 20, 1951.

One of the first types was the so-called breeder reactor (discussed in Chapter 13). Another was Farrington Daniels' plan for a high-temperature reactor cooled by helium, a design descendant of the so-called "Mae West" pile proposed in 1942 by Thomas Moore and Miles Leverett for production of plutonium. Groves' Advisory Committee on Research and Development felt that Daniels' project had great promise, and recommended that it be assigned to a contractor for construction at the Clinton Works. The Daniels pile failed to see fruition; however, the concept survived. Two commercial versions of the HTGR, or High-Temperature Gas-cooled Reactor, were built in the United States. Britain and France adopted the gas-cooled reactor type, and Britain is still using that type today.

In the United States, Philadelphia Electric Co. operated a 40,000-kW (net electric) HTGR successfully from 1964 to 1974. Colorado Public Service Co. has been operating a 330,000-kW HTGR at Fort St. Vrain near Denver since 1974.

Besides the breeder and the gas-cooled types, there were three other kinds of reactors proposed.

First was a proposal at Los Alamos Scientific Laboratory in New Mexico to build a reactor using plutonium as fuel, and so-called fast neutrons (i.e., unmoderated neutrons having the very high energy and velocity that they have at the moment of their release in fission) to bombard and fission the fuel. In the water-cooled and gas-cooled reactors, the neutrons are slowed down, or "moderated," to increase the likelihood of their causing new fission reactions in ^{235}U fuel (more about this in the section "What is Fission?").

Second was a novel and radically different concept, in which the fuel would be in a homogeneous state such as a solution of ^{235}U salts in water. This differs from all the previously mentioned reactor concepts in which the fuel is heterogeneous, in the form of discrete metal rods, cartridges, or strips, and a liquid or gaseous coolant is pumped past the fuel rods or strips to carry away the heat of fission. The homogeneous reactor, on the other hand, circulates the fuel itself in fluid form. The fuel is made critical, or chain reacting, in a spherical tank, heats up from its own fission heat, and is pumped out of the tank through narrow pipes too narrow to permit formation of a critical mass therefore becoming subcritical. Still hot, nevertheless, it is passed through a heat exchanger in which a separate water loop is boiled to steam to turn the turbine. The cooled fuel fluid is returned to the spherical reactor tank to repeat the process.

Third and last of these early proposals (there were to be many, many more ideas subsequently) was a reactor using a metallic coolant that becomes liquid at about 52°F: a sodium–potassium alloy called NaK after the two metals' chemical symbols. This concept originated in the Naval Research Laboratory, and the Navy was to try it for submarine propulsion as we shall see.

So by January 1947 there had been two years of work and activity on controlled nuclear energy for electric power.

In 1946 Congress passed the McMahon Act, introduced by Senator Brien McMahon of Connecticut, after a protracted debate over the issue of civilian control of atomic energy. The Army fought against losing control of atomic development, but did not prevail. General Groves turned over the facilities and resources of the Manhattan District to a new Atomic Energy Commission established by the act. This was headed by five civilian commissioners; however the Commission staff included a statutory Division of Military Application which looked after those aspects of atomic energy relating to defense and national security.

The act also established within the Congress a Joint Committee on Atomic Energy, with nine members each from the House and the Senate, and the chairmanship to rotate biennially between a senator and a representative.

Under the 1946 act, however, atomic energy remained a subject classified secret, and private industry's only role was as contractors to the AEC.

In the late 1940s, much of AEC's power reactor design and engineering was going into two projects: the Materials Testing Reactor (MTR) and the Experimental Breeder Reactor (EBR-1), both located near Idaho Falls, Idaho. The MTR was a low-temperature water reactor the purpose of which was to study irradiation effects and irradiation damage of materials in (what were then) high neutron fields. The MTR provided much useful information on the behavior of fuel, materials, and various nuclear steam supply components.

The other project, EBR-1, was built near MTR on federal land in the Idaho desert (that was to become AEC's National Reactor Testing Station). Since the early 1940s, some nuclear scientists had been thinking that the breeder reactor concept had considerable benefits. Its advantage is that it can transmute nonfissionable ^{238}U into fissionable plutonium: a great advantage because 99.3% of all natural uranium in the earth is the nonfissionable ^{238}U variety, and because in theory more fuel is created than is used (see Chapter 13). So EBR-1 was built to test the breeder concept. In December 1951, the first electricity ever generated from nuclear power came from EBR-1. Its site is now a historical monument.

By 1954, circumstances had changed to the point where fundamental changes in the Atomic Energy Act seemed desirable. Not only had the United States lost its monopoly in nuclear weapons, but sufficient progress had been made in the development of civilian uses of atomic energy, particularly in the electric power area, that the time seemed ripe to open the door to private enterprise and to international cooperation in continuing that development.

And so Congress replaced the Atomic Energy Act of 1946 with the Atomic Energy Act of 1954. Its most notable feature was that it opened the door to private enterprise, and permitted private ownership of specified types of atomic energy facilities, including electric power plants, subject to licensing requirements. Uranium, plutonium, and other sensitive nuclear materials ("special nuclear material" in the language of the act) could still only be owned by the federal government, but it could be leased by private firms, on payment of use-charges to be set by AEC.

Accompanying these changes was another necessary change: private access to specified categories of hitherto secret information was authorized subject to compliance with AEC regulations.

Also in 1954, AEC's Reactor Development Division proposed, and Congress approved, a "five-reactor program" to test the technical and economic feasibility of commercial nuclear power by building five small demonstration plants of as many different types (see Table 1.1).

The five types selected were:

1. A Pressurized Water Reactor (PWR).
2. A variant of the PWR called the Experimental Boiling Water Reactor (EBWR).
3. A molten-sodium cooled reactor (SRE).
4. A second, larger Homogeneous Reactor Experiment (HRE-2).
5. A second, larger breeder reactor experiment (EBR-2).

Table 1.1. AEC Five-Reactor Demonstration Program, 1954

Reactor	Contractor	Location	Start-up	Shutdown	Capacity, net kWe
Experimental Boiling Water Reactor (EBWR)	Argonne National Laboratory	Arco, ID	1956	1967	4,000
Experimental Breeder Reactor No. 2 (EBR-2)	Argonne National Laboratory	Argonne, IL	1964	—[a]	16,500
Homogeneous Reactor Experiment No. 2 (HRE-2)	Oak Ridge National Laboratory	Oak Ridge, TN	1957	1961	300
Pressurized Water Reactor (PWR)	Duquesne Light Co.	Shippingport, PA	1957	1982	90,000
Sodium Reactor Experiment (SRE)	Atomics International	Santa Susana, CA	1957	1966	5,700

[a] Still in operation (as of October 1982).

Figure 1.7. Shippingport plant. (Courtesy DOE.)

This "five-year plan" (in fact it was to be 10 years before the last of the five reactors was completed) was the proving ground of American commercial nuclear power, along with work by the Navy on submarine propulsion reactors. Four of the five reactors were small, laboratory-scale experiments or demonstration plants, but one was a commercial-scale reactor. This was the only one of the five built on the power network of an electric power utility. It was the PWR, built by the Atomic Energy Commission and Westinghouse Electric Co. on the electrical system of Duquesne Light Co. of Pittsburgh (see Figure 1.7). The utility supplied a site at Shippingport, Pennsylvania, west of Pittsburgh. It has an electric output of 60 MWe (a MWe or megawatt electric is a million watts, or thousand kilowatts, of electric power); thus it could produce power at a rate of 60,000 kWh.

It operated successfully from December 18, 1957, until 1982 when it was shut down permanently. The Shippingport reactor was a direct descendant of the Naval Reactors program; the commercial success of PWR technology is in large part due to this demonstration project.

All five demonstration reactor types resulted in a second-generation, commercial, scaled-up project, four of which were built and operated. However, only the two water reactor types, the PWR and BWR, were widely adopted by electric utilities and widely used. To a certain extent this is due as much to certain shortcomings of the other three concepts. However there was another factor that played a role in helping to determine this outcome, and that was the Navy propulsion program.

Following up its early interest in the idea of a nuclear-propelled submarine dating back to the news of the first fissioning of uranium in Berlin in 1939, the Navy, after a number of paper studies in June 1946, assigned an eight-man team, five officers and three civilian engineers and physicists, to the Manhattan District's Clinton Works. Their assignment was to learn the fundamentals of nuclear technology and to lay the groundwork for a possible nuclear submarine engine. This was to prove a key event, for the senior officer (not by appointment but by force of personality) was a Navy electrical engineer, Captain H. G. Rickover, a hard-driving perfectionist who was to win fame as the "father of the Nuclear Navy."

Although the group was assigned to work with the Farrington Daniels team on the gas-cooled Daniels Pile—the first formal nuclear power project—Rickover and his men were more impressed with the potential of a concept proposed by Alvin Weinberg (later director of Oak Ridge National Laboratory), using water under high pressure rather than gas as the heat-transfer medium. This

Figure 1.8. A submarine hull section built in a tank of water on land in the Idaho desert to simulate a submarine engine room. Inside this cylinder is the land-based prototype of the nuclear plant for the *Nautilus*. (Courtesy DOE.)

judgment by the Rickover group was to shape the future of commercial nuclear power for some 40 years, from that time until today.

In 1948, the first formal submarine reactor construction project was established at Argonne National Laboratory, with Westinghouse Electric as the prime industrial contractor. The Navy also had Westinghouse establish a separate laboratory, the Bettis Atomic Power Laboratory outside Pittsburgh, for classified naval work exclusively and to keep its work for the Navy sharply separated from its commercial work in nuclear power development.

The project was based on use of pressurized water as the reactor coolant medium. (It must be recalled that this was six years before the AEC five-reactor program in which the Shippingport plant figured.) The Navy and Westinghouse built a land-based prototype of the submarine reactor, full scale, in a simulated submarine hull section on a federal reservation in the southeastern Idaho desert near Idaho Falls (see Figure 1.8).

On completion of the prototype, a crew of Navy reactor operator trainees simulated a transatlantic submerged trip from the East Coast to Europe. The reactor performed faultlessly. A duplicate of this propulsion unit was built and installed in the submarine *Nautilus*, designed and built to receive it. The *Nautilus* left the General Dynamics Corp.'s Electric Boat shipyard on January 17, 1955—a mere 17 days past the date of January 1 that had been set in 1948, seven years earlier, no mean feat for a first-of-a-kind facility that was an amalgam of hitherto unknown science and engineering (see Figure 1.9).

The signal success of this project gave the pressurized water reactor concept a lead over other proposed U.S. reactor concepts which proved insuperable.

In the meantime, General Electric Co. had become interested in the NaK, or sodium–

Figure 1.9. The first nuclear-propelled submarine leaving her home port, Groton, Conn., on sea trials. (Courtesy DOE.)

potassium, cooled reactor and the prospects of developing a civilian power plant based on use of a NaK-cooled reactor which would also be a breeder of plutonium. The company made a proposal to the Navy to build a submarine propulsion plant using a sodium-cooled reactor. This was not to be a fast reactor, rather it used intermediate energy neutrons.

Until the *Nautilus*, the overall state of nuclear technology appeared to favor the sodium-cooled or breeder reactors. The primary systems of these did not require advances in pressure-vessel technology. In addition, PWR fuel cladding had to be both corrosion resistant and have a low affinity for parasitic neutron capture. Such a cladding material was not yet available. Finally, a PWR required enriched uranium, and the United States did not then have adequate enrichment facilities.

However, the state of cold war tensions in the 1950s, together with the perseverance of Admiral H. G. Rickover, produced a shift in research and development efforts toward the PWR. Rickover's nuclear submarine program funded the development both of zirconium alloys as suitable materials for PWR fuel cladding, and of the necessary advances in pressure-vessel technology. Also, the government—spurred mostly by the cold war—greatly expanded its uranium enrichment facilities.

(It may be worth noting that although a submarine is an engine of destruction, its *propulsion plant*, distinct from its armament, torpedoes, or missiles, does not know whether it is driving a warship, a luxury passenger ship, an oil tanker, or a tugboat; therefore a submarine's nuclear propulsion unit can be just as truly a prototype for, and progenitor of, a civilian, commercial nuclear power plant as any pilot-scale power plant built by private industry.)

The Navy's second nuclear-propelled submarine, *Seawolf*, did use a sodium-cooled reactor when it was built. Although the propulsion plant performed in exemplary fashion, there were some problems with steam generators; the Navy decided that it was not logical to build a submarine fleet using two different types of nuclear power units each requiring its own separate replacement-part inventory and its own training school for engineers, maintenance personnel, and officers. So the *Seawolf* was converted to use a pressurized water reactor power plant, and the lead of the PWR reactor type over other power reactor types was further confirmed.

By the mid-1950s, the PWR technology had gained—through massive government funding—an edge over other technologies. In 1953, while *Nautilus* was still under construction, Rickover, acting in his dual role as head of AEC's naval reactors branch and the Navy's head of nuclear propulsion, expanded the submarine contract with Westinghouse to include development of a nuclear power plant to drive aircraft carriers. At the close of fiscal year 1953 the military requirement for the large surface-ship reactor was eliminated. However, it was felt that the PWR design that was to be scaled up from submarine size held enough promise for central station power that AEC decided to continue research and development on it.

In early 1954, when AEC announced its "five-year, five-reactor program" (see above), one of the five was the PWR. AEC adapted for the utility industry's use the design work that had been done on the "large ship reactor." Because of the submarine program, PWR development was still directed within AEC by Rickover's naval reactors branch. Thus Westinghouse continued its work and became the principal nuclear contractor for the plant that was eventually built at Shippingport, Pennsylvania.

Meanwhile, as mentioned, General Electric was developing the BWR technology that had been pioneered by Argonne National Laboratory and, following a series of reactor safety experiments called "Borax" (for Boiling Reactor Experiment), found expression in the Experimental Boiling Water Reactor (EBWR). This was another one of the five units in the five-year program.

A year after the five-year program was launched, AEC announced a "power Demonstration Reactor Program" to stimulate electric utilities to build large-scale nuclear power plants, using developed technologies such as the PWR or BWR. As incentives, AEC offered to waive the fuel-use charge, and to pay the cost of necessary research and development. This offer resulted in the construction of five plants, three of them taking advantage of financial aid offered by AEC, and two undertaken without any government financial assistance.

The first to respond to the invitation was Consolidated Edison Co. of New York, whose president, Hudson Searing, made a dramatic announcement in Washington before the Joint Committee on Atomic Energy on February 10, 1955, stating that Con Ed would build a 236-MWe nuclear power plant at Indian Point, New York, overlooking the Hudson River near Peekskill, and would do so using its own financial resources exclusively without any government help.

This proposal was quickly followed by four others. These were from:

1. Commonwealth Edison Co. of Chicago (in association with three other electric utilities and an architect/engineering firm). They proposed to build a 180-MWe boiling water reactor, about 47 miles southwest of Chicago, for completion in 1960. This was the Dresden 1 plant, which is still licensed to operate today.
2. Yankee Atomic Electric Co. of Boston, a consortium of 12 New England electric utilities, large and small, proposed to build a 100-MWe PWR at Rowe, Massachusetts, near Williamstown, for completion in late 1957. This unit is also still in operation today.
3. Consumers Public Power District of Columbus, Nebraska, proposed a 75-MWe sodium–graphite reactor—a scale-up of the Sodium Reactor Experiment (SRE), a unit in the AEC five-year program. The scale-up was to be built at Hallam near Beatrice, Nebraska, for completion in 1959.
4. Atomic Power Development Associates, a consortium of 16 electric utilities and four manufacturing companies, proposed a 100-MWe fast breeder reactor plant to be located at Monroe, Michigan, south of Detroit, for completion in late 1958. It was named for Enrico Fermi.

These plants were all completed and operated successfully. The builders of the Yankee plant took pride in the fact that their plant was completed ahead of schedule and under budget.

Meanwhile, at this time, other reactor types were being proposed and tried. AEC built an Organic Moderated Reactor Experiment (OMRE) at the National Reactor Testing Station it had established in southeastern Idaho. This used an organic material, terphenyl, as the coolant medium to bring the fission heat out of the reactor to a heat exchanger.

It was also disclosed after the fact that AEC, within the secret Aircraft Nuclear Propulsion program (secret because of its military implications), had built and successfully operated at Oak Ridge an Aircraft Reactor Experiment (ARE). In this reactor, the fuel was in the form of molten uranium salts, and was circulated through the reactor and the primary heat exchangers. This is analogous to the homogeneous reactor concept already mentioned, except that in the aqueous homogeneous reactor the uranium salts are in a water solution. After declassification of the ARE, AEC went on to build a Molten Salt Reactor Experiment (MSRE) at Oak Ridge to test the feasibility of this concept for civilian power use. This unit operated successfully, and had some advantages that found it friends in private industry, including the fact that, by bleeding off some of the uranium salts while the reactor was operating, they could be separated from the fission product wastes and returned to the reactor. This "on-line reprocessing" is both a great economic advantage and an antiproliferation advantage. However the concept was considered too exotic by others, and here again the early lead of the PWR and BWR concepts proved too much to overcome.

AEC announced a second and a third round of its Power Demonstration Reactor Program tailored to the needs of small utilities and publicly, municipally, or cooperatively owned utilities. Several reactors were built under these programs. Among them were these.

The city of Piqua, Ohio, built an 11.4-MWe scale-up of the organic moderated reactor that operated from 1963 to 1966. However, the organic coolant had a tendency to break down under irradiation and gum up in the piping. No more of this type were built.

A consortium of utilities in Virginia and the Carolinas undertook a reactor concept combining the superior moderating capacity of heavy water with the greater availability and economy of light water (i.e., ordinary water) for cooling. They built a 17-MWe plant that operated from 1963 to 1967, in which the fuel bundles, or core, were immersed in a tank of heavy water for moderation.

Entering the tank, passing along the fuel bundles and out again, were tubes in which pressurized water circulated. The concept was successful from the point of view of neutron economy, but was too complicated and costly to build and maintain. It is, however, a "first cousin" of the CANDU reactor type that Canada has developed to a high degree of success. In the CANDU, as in the Carolinas–Virginia reactor, the tank of moderator water is kept separated from the coolant water pumped through it within tubes; unlike it, the Canadian concept uses heavy water both as moderator and as coolant.

Speaking of maintenance, it must be mentioned that Pennsylvania Power & Light Co. undertook a 100-MWe commercial scale-up of the Oak Ridge aqueous homogeneous reactor design. The project was well advanced in research and development work and in licensing proceedings seeking a construction permit, when project engineers looking ahead discovered that there was no way that maintenance work could be carried out inside the reactor containment after the plant had begun operating and become radioactive. This resulted in termination of the project.

The point here is that all were searching for an "ideal" reactor concept that would be economic. The most debated question of the time at industry meetings on nuclear power was, "When will nuclear power become economic?" It must be remembered that this was the period of $3 per barrel imported fuel oil, before the Arab oil embargo and the Suez crisis. A number of additional PWR and BWR power plants were built with AEC assistance in the second and third rounds of the Power Demonstration Reactor Program.

During this period of slow, wary growth, utilities studied and pondered the implications of nuclear power for their systems. Six mils per kilowatt-hour (kWh) was the generally accepted target that nuclear power had to achieve to become competitive with then-prevailing fossil fuel prices.

The breakthrough occurred in February 1963, when Jersey Central Power & Light Co. in New Jersey published a painstakingly detailed economic analysis explaining its choice of nuclear over coal for its next generating station. Using standard utility accounting methods, it calculated that nuclear generating cost would be less than 4 mils/kWh. This "Oyster Creek Report," so called after the site of the proposed nuclear power plant, caused a sensation in the power field. For the first time, a utility had made a decision to use nuclear fuel rather than coal or oil on strictly economic grounds, as distinct from learning, or "getting in on the ground floor," of a new technology that was then widely regarded as the wave of the future.

The effect of the Oyster Creek Report was as that of a logjam breaking up. In 1963, three other nuclear plants were ordered after Oyster Creek. In 1965, seven; in 1967, 20; in 1968, 14. By the end of 1969, utilities had ordered 91 nuclear power units. In that year also, the plants ordered in 1963 began operation (see Figure 1.10), and the utilities began to be able to judge the performance of these first commercial—as distinguished from demonstration—nuclear power plants. By the end of 1972, 160 plants had been ordered, including those already operating.

Figure 1.10. The Maine Yankee nuclear power plant at Wiscasset, Maine, one of the pioneers in the field. (Courtesy Maine Yankee.)

Meanwhile, other countries were not oblivious to this new energy source. In December 1966, when 16 U.S. nuclear plants were generating electricity, there were 11 nuclear stations operating in Britain; most of them were multiunit stations, and in fact there were 24 individual power reactors grouped at these 11 stations. In France there were two stations, consisting of six reactors, in operation; three single-unit stations in Italy; two in Japan; five in the U.S.S.R. known to the West; and one each in Belgium, Canada, West Germany, and Sweden. The British and French units were all of the gas-cooled graphite-moderated type. Italy, Japan, and the Soviet Union all had combinations of water-moderated and gas–graphite reactors; Canada was operating the 22-MWe pilot plant of its CANDU concept.

Beginning in 1972, although the Arab oil embargo and other perturbing events in the Mideast spurred U.S. utilities to order new plants, two contrary currents also set in. In 1972 38 reactors were ordered (although about 22 have since been canceled), and in 1973 there were 41 reactor orders (and about 24 of those canceled). The contrary currents were the electric utility's 1974 financial crisis, which denied utilities much of their budgeted construction funds, as well as making them of necessity less tolerant to regulatory delays.

Second, environmentalists and conservationists stepped up their opposition to nuclear power at every turn. They made shrewd use of every available legal tactic to delay licensing hearings, and in so doing deterred a number of utilities from continuing planned nuclear power construction projects. They formed alliances and strove, successfully, to make nuclear power a political issue. The antinuclear movement is one factor that has brought nuclear power to a standstill in the United States. Cost of money, construction delays, and weak management practices are some of the others which have helped sidetrack new commercial nuclear power plant orders.

United Kingdom

While the United States was busily occupied in comparing and evaluating this great number of different reactor concepts, Canada and Britain, who played a small but important role in the Manhattan District, and France and the Soviet Union were already getting to work on nuclear power projects of their own.

Because of the high cost and inaccessible technology of building gaseous diffusion plants to enrich natural uranium in ^{235}U, Britain opted to build power plants using the same concept that Fermi had used in his first chain reaction experiment in Chicago. This is the graphite-moderated, gas-cooled reactor type which uses natural uranium, unenriched, as fuel. Because the moderating properties of graphite are superior to those of water, it is possible to build a large chain-reacting system using unenriched uranium fuel moderated by graphite. However, for this a larger quantity of uranium is required than the 2–4% enriched fuel used in American light-water reactors (LWRs, a combining term that includes both PWRs and BWRs). As a result the gas–graphite power reactor is much bulkier than the LWRs, massive as those are. The gas–graphite reactor vessel is so huge it cannot be transported even by barge, as American reactor vessels are, from the factory to the plant site. The British had to learn to weld their reactor vessels together from steel plates in the field, on site, and anneal the welds in huge temporary sheds built around the vessel on site, to relieve stresses in the plates caused by welding. (In the United States, stress relieving is done in the factory, before shipment.)

The Calder Hall power station, Britain's equivalent of Shippingport, was opened by Queen Elizabeth on October 17, 1956, to become the world's first industrial-scale nuclear power station. It beat Shippingport to that honor by about 14 months. Shippingport first achieved criticality on December 2, 1957—which, as it happened, was the fifteenth anniversary of Fermi's epochal chain-reactor experiment in Chicago. It began generating electricity later that month.

In the British gas–graphite reactor, carbon dioxide is the coolant gas. A big development program was carried out on the circulators, or pumps, to push a sufficient quantity of coolant gas through the core to cool it and bring out its useful fission heat. The hot gas is piped to a heat exchanger, analogous to the American PWR heat exchangers (today called steam generators) in which water is boiled to steam to drive the turbine.

Britain's Atomic Energy Authority (UKAEA) built three more reactors at Calder Hall, in the hills of Cumberland, and four more identical ones at Chapel Cross in Dumfriesshire. In addition to providing electricity to the national network, these reactors served also as plutonium production reactors for the British defense effort.

Since that time, the two utilities in Britain—the Central Electricity Generating Board (CEGB) and the South of Scotland Electricity Board (SSEB)—have placed in service and are operating 18 additional Calder-type nuclear power plants. These have become known in British as the "magnox" type, after the *magn*esium alloy used to clad the *ox*ide fuel cartridges. In addition, CEGB and SSEB are each operating two Advanced Gas-cooled Reactors (AGR), and 10 more AGRs are under construction, six of them near completion (as of the end of 1982).

After long consideration, study, and deliberation, the CEGB decided in the latter part of 1982 to build its first water-cooled nuclear power plant, a PWR to be located at the Sizewell nuclear power station alongside two older magnox units. A formal inquiry on PWR safety began in Britain in November 1982.

France

France was not far behind. In a certain sense, France may be seen as the place where it all began, with the discovery of radioactivity by Becquerel in 1894 when he found that uranium salts or ores will expose a photographic plate, and with the subsequent discovery of radium by Pierre and Marie Curie. Their many other discoveries extended knowledge about radioactivity and set the stage for the progress in atomic physics that led to the harnessing of atomic energy.

Although their country lay devastated after World War II, the French still were so conscious of the importance of atomic energy that only five months after VE Day, before a new permanent government had yet been fashioned, the provisional government established the Commissariat à l'Energie Atomique (CEA).

After establishing laboratories equipped with research reactors, the CEA undertook construction of two power plants at Marcoule near Avignon in the southern Rhone valley. The first, called G-1, was graphite moderated like Calder Hall, but air-cooled. Next to it were built G-2 and G-3, also graphite moderated but cooled by pressurized carbon dioxide, like the British magnox reactors.

G-1 generated less than enough electricity to power its own air circulators, but G-2 and G-3 each developed 40,000 kWe net power.

The French national utility, Electricité de France, went on to build five larger, industrial-scale gas–graphite nuclear power units. But in the early 1960s it decided to try a PWR, to be located near the Belgian border, in collaboration with a Belgian utility. This unit was built by a French industrial syndicate under Westinghouse license. The reactor's performance impressed the French sufficiently that they switched over completely from gas–graphite to PWR units.

For a number of reasons—principally because its domestic fossil fuel reserves were diminishing or running out—France became the first major nation to declare that it was government policy to build no more coal, oil, or natural gas power plants, but only nuclear. The country has built up its own industrial infrastructure to manufacture PWRs and fabricate PWR fuel, has built an enrichment plant, and is one of the world's leaders in the application of nuclear power. Nineteen PWRs were placed in service within a four-year period, 1977–1981, and 29 more are under construction, for completion by 1988. As a result of this prodigious construction program, France expects to get 85% of its electricity from nuclear power by the turn of the century.

Soviet Union

Winston Churchill's wartime description of the Kremlin as "a mystery wrapped in a riddle wrapped in an enigma" applies to a large degree even to the peacetime applications of nuclear energy, including power generation, in the Soviet Union. What is known about the Soviet nuclear program is what the Russians choose to disclose—which is not notably copious. A large proportion of what we do know was disclosed in the Soviet presentations to the three United Nations Conferences on the Peaceful Uses of Atomic Energy, held in Geneva in 1955, 1958, and 1964. All the proceedings of those conferences were published in book form.

On July 1, 1954, the Moscow newspaper *Pravda* said in a terse but triumphant announcement that four days earlier, "an atomic driven electric power station was put into operation and generated electricity for use in industry and agriculture in adjoining districts. This is the first time that an industrial turbine is working not on coal or other fuel but on atomic energy." There was considerable skepticism in the West about this because details were withheld and no Westerners were permitted to see the plant—or even to learn its location.

In September 1955, however, at the Geneva conference, details were supplied in a 61-page paper that contained photographs and design drawings, and minutiae of the design and operation of the 5000-kWe plant. It was learned that the plant is located at Obninsk, about 66 miles southwest of Moscow; and that it is graphite moderated but water cooled, with the water circulated internally through each fuel element, instead of flowing freely past the outside of the fuel bundle in the reactor vessel, as in Western PWRs. The fuel used is 5% enriched uranium, which indicated that the U.S.S.R. must have a gaseous diffusion plant or some other facility for uranium isotope separation and enrichment.

In the following years, the Russians quickly scaled up the size of the plants they built, just as did the United States, Britain, and France. They built a 210-MWe PWR at Novo-Voronezh, and one 50-MWe BWR at Dimitrovgrad. They apparently were not impressed by the latter because they are not known to have built any more BWRs; however the first PWR was followed by a 365-MWe unit and then a 440-MWe unit, both also at Novo-Voronezh, a suburb of Voronezh on the Don River south of Moscow. This 440-MWe PWR has been exported by the U.S.S.R. to East Germany,

Poland, Hungary, Czechoslovakia, Rumania, Bulgaria, Finland, and a 300-MWe version has been reported sold to Libya.

Meanwhile at home, the Russians built 13 more PWRs, in sizes up to 1000 MWe. However, they have also continued to develop the Obninsk graphite-moderated, light-water-cooled type of reactor, and have built 20 of that type, including 14 of 1000-MWe capacity. By 1985 the USSR expects about 15% of its electricity to come from nuclear power; and roughly twice that amount by 1990.

Britain, France, and the U.S.S.R., as well as Germany, are also building reactors of the breeder type. These will be discussed in Chapter 13.

Canada

One other early starter in nuclear power development was Canada. The Canadian government began in January 1955 to design an experimental type of reactor, with a generating capacity of 20 MWe.

This Nuclear Power Demonstration (NPD) unit was completed in 1959 at Rolphton, Ontario, on the Ottawa River 150 miles northwest of Ottawa but near the principal Canadian nuclear laboratories at Chalk River, Ontario. It was an original concept. Heavy water (water, it will be recalled, in which the hydrogen atoms are heavy hydrogen rather than common hydrogen) is used as both moderator and coolant. The motive for this was the same as that for Britain using graphite-moderated reactors: the moderating characteristics of heavy water, like those of graphite, are sufficiently better than those of ordinary water to permit the use of unenriched uranium as fuel. Canada is blessed with abundant deposits of uranium, but did not have an enrichment plant in the early 1950s, and—like Britain—did not wish to be dependent on imports of enriched uranium from another country.

Canada had numerous difficulties to overcome in the development of the heavy-water (also called deuterium) reactor type, but persisted, under the single-minded and dedicated leadership of Dr. W. Bennett Lewis, head of its atomic energy organization. The effort paid off, since the Canadian Natural Uranium Deuterium reactor (called CANDU) has been very successful.

A scale-up of the NPD with a power output of 206 MWe net, was completed at Douglas Point, Ontario, in 1968. Two larger stations followed, one at Pickering near Toronto with four 515-MWe units and four 740-MWe units, called the Bruce station, at the Douglas Point site. These were built and are being operated by Ontario Hydro, which has 12 more under construction, the last to be in service by 1990. Hydro Quebec and the New Brunswick Electric Power Commission are also going nuclear. Hydro Quebec has built and is operating one 250-MWe BWR, and a 638-MWe CANDU unit. The New Brunswick utility has also built a 630-MWe CANDU.

One of the difficulties the Canadians encountered in establishing their CANDU reactors was the construction of plants to separate heavy water from ordinary water. All ordinary water contains 0.03% heavy water, and the chemical process for separating the latter is straightforward and not difficult. However, the construction and shakedown of large plants to do it on an industrial scale proved to have some hurdles. The problems were eventually solved, and today Canada is the world's major producer of heavy water.

Worldwide Perspective

Other countries are also actively pursuing the commercial development of nuclear power. Particularly aggressive have been Japan and Sweden. In 1982, Japan produced 17% of its electricity from nuclear power, Sweden 39%. Table 1.2 shows the fraction of electric energy produced by nuclear

Table 1.2. Percentage of Electricity Generated in Nuclear Reactors in 1982

Country	%	kWh per Capita	TWh
France	39	1800	108
Sweden	39	4200	39.1
Finland	39	2900	16.7
Switzerland	28	2300	15.1
Belgium	31	1200	15.6
Taiwan	19		
Japan	17	700	102
W. Germany	17	800	63.5
United Kingdom	16	600	43.9
United States	12	1200	299.4

power in the other major nuclear producing countries. By 1990, France plans to produce between 60 and 70% of its electricity from nuclear power. Other countries, for example, Czechoslovakia, will rely even more heavily than the French on nuclear power. The Czechs have commissioned their last fossil fuel unit in 1982. All future plants (19 currently in planning and construction) will be nuclear. On the other hand, Sweden, which now gets over 40% of its electricity, and produces 4200 kWh/yr per capita from nuclear power, has declared that it will build no more nuclear units, and presumably will phase out all of its nuclear units by 2010.

In 1982, 281 units with some 162,000 MWe of nuclear capacity were operating around the world. The total is scheduled to surpass 650 units (550,000-MWe capacity) by 1990. The largest 1990 programs in GWe are: United States (117), France (50), Japan (25), and Federal Republic of Germany (19).

1.2. WHAT IS FISSION?

The basic principle of fission and the chain rection may have to be explained here for the benefit of those readers not already familiar with it.

A nuclear power plant is, in many respects, not very unlike a conventionally fueled power plant. In both, the first step is to heat water to boiling. The resulting steam is then piped to the blades of a high-speed turbine and made to spin them, much as a river or stream turns a water wheel. The shaft of the turbine is connected to the shaft of a generator and, in turning it, generates electricity.

The difference between the conventional and the nuclear power plant is in how the water is heated to boiling. In an oil-fired plant, the fuel oil is pumped into the boiler or combustion chamber. In a coal-fired plant, the coal is no longer shoveled into the boiler by perspiring stokers, but is pulverized and fed in by conveyor belts to the firebox.

In a uranium-fueled power plant the first aim is still to produce steam for the turbine, but the uranium is of course not burned in the conventional sense: there is no combustion. The uranium fuel must be treated and configured in a very precise and specific way to permit the fission chain reaction to occur, be harnessed, and controlled.

To begin at the beginning: there exist in nature 92 *elements* or elemental materials. Many, like the metals iron, copper, silver, gold, and tin, have been known since antiquity. Others, such as the gases oxygen, hydrogen, nitrogen, were identified only about two centuries ago; still other elements were discovered only recently.

The point is that the smallest identifiable unit of any of these elements—the smallest before it would lose its identity in further subdivision—is called an atom. If one could subdivide an atom, one would no longer have iron or copper or oxygen, but subatomic particles: protons, electrons, neutrons. From these particles all atoms, all matter, is built.

Imagine a single atom (about a hundred-millionth of an inch in diameter) as a submicroscopic solar system. In the center is the nucleus, composed of protons and neutrons densely packed together. Around the nucleus in orbiting rings are the "planetary" electrons. Protons and electrons carry infinitesimally small electric charges. For the sake of convenience, every proton is said to have a positive charge of 1, and every electron a negative charge of 1. Since opposite charges always attract, the total number of orbiting electrons around the nucleus in any atom must equal the total number of protons within the nucleus. Neutrons are electrically neutral, whence their name—and, incidentally, probably also why they were only discovered as recently as 1932 (by James Chadwick in England).

Another important characteristic of these particles is their weight, or mass. Here it is the protons and the neutrons—the particles composing the nucleus—that are each said to have a mass of 1, essentially equal, whereas the mass of an electron is so much less than even the infinitesimally small weight of a proton or neutron, that it is insignificant by comparison, and so the electron is said to have a mass of zero.

To summarize:

Particle	Charge	Mass
Proton	+1	1
Electron	−1	0
Neutron	0	1

No two elements' atoms are alike, although all atoms are made up of different numbers of protons and neutrons. Each element's atoms differ from those of every other element in the number of subatomic particles they contain. It is these differences that lend each element its own individual characteristics.

The 92 naturally occurring elements may be listed from 1 to 92 by the number of protons in their nucleus (which determines their weight) from hydrogen with 1 to uranium with 92. A hydrogen atom is composed of only one proton as nucleus and one orbiting electron. The actual mass of a hydrogen atom has been calculated to be 1.67×10^{-27} kg.

The next heavier element, helium, is said to have an "atomic weight" of 4, because its nucleus consists of two protons and two neutrons each with a mass of 1. Thus it can be seen that the total number of protons and neutrons in the nucleus of any atom of one element determines that element's "atomic weight."

This is the derivation of the familiar number 238 that most of us have read about in connection with "uranium-238" or, for short, "U-238," or as the physicist writes it, "^{238}U." It means simply that the common uranium nucleus has a total of 238 protons and neutrons.

Here, Nature throws a joker or wild card into the deck, in that some elements have variant forms, called "isotopes." (The number of protons does not change; their total positive charge attracts a fixed number of electrons, and it is the electrons that give the atoms of an element that element's characteristic chemical behavior.) The number of neutrons in the nucleus can vary, changing the atomic weight but not the chemical behavior of the atoms.

In 1939, Otto Hahn and Fritz Strassmann in Berlin, following up work begun in the 1930s by Enrico Fermi in Rome, discovered that if they accelerated a stream of neutrons and projected them into a target of common uranium (i.e., ^{238}U) a seemingly weird and at first inexplicable thing happened. Barium was found in the target, where none had been before. It took months of experimentation and conferences among physicists in several countries before the solution was discovered.

What had happened in Hahn and Strassmann's experiment was that they had split, or fissioned, some of the ^{235}U in their uranium target. When they fired neutrons at the target, some neutrons were absorbed into—or "captured" by—the ^{235}U atoms, which then had a total of 236 protons and neutrons. Since this combination is unstable, the nucleus broke apart into two lighter weight halves, each carrying the appropriate number of electrons with it, thus producing a variety of pairs of new atoms in such a way that the total of protons and neutrons in each pair added up to 236—or perhaps 234 or 235 since it was later shown that one or two neutrons were set free and remained free. The new atoms are called fission fragments, and these range predominantly in the list of elements from zinc, atomic weight 65, to gadolinium, atomic weight 157. The energy released in fission is equivalent to the mass lost in the process, since the weight of the total sum of the products is slightly less than that of the mass of the original nucleus plus the absorbed neutron.

The clue was that uranium has a slightly lighter weight isotope, ^{235}U. Until physicists developed accelerators, or "atom-smashers," earlier in this century to try to unlock the mysteries of matter, uranium was of interest only as a yellow–orange pigment for pottery, and to improve the whiteness of false teeth. But it became of interest to physicists after the French chemist Henri Becquerel discovered in 1896 that a uranium ore, pitchblende, would leave a picture of itself on a photographic plate, and an associate, Marie Curie, called the effect "radioactivity." She also isolated the unknown element radium in the pitchblende.

Natural uranium mined in the ground everywhere in the world and refined from the ore consistently is composed of 99.3% ^{238}U. The nuclei of its atoms contain a total of 238 protons and neutrons. The other 0.7% is an isotope of uranium having three neutrons fewer in each nucleus, and therefore called ^{235}U.

A fission event is accompanied by a release of considerable energy in the form of heat. This is the heat used in a reactor to heat water to boiling. The source of the heat is the transformation of mass to energy in the form of heat as expressed in Einstein's famous formula $E = mc^2$ where E is energy, m is mass, and c is the speed of light, about 300,000 km/sec, or 186,270 miles/sec. The square of c, c^2, is that number multiplied by itself.

The energy released is mostly in the form of kinetic energy (energy of motion) carried by the moving fission fragments. These fragments, however, are quickly slowed by collisions with other nuclei, and in this bumping, colliding, process the kinetic energy is converted to heat, in the vicinity of the fission event—within a few micrometers (thousandths of a millimeter) of it. About 20% of the total energy released is carried away by the beta and gamma rays, as well as by fission neutrons. This energy is also eventually converted into heat, although this conversion takes place farther away from the fission event.

The amount of energy released in fission is of the order of 200 megaelectron volts (MeV), that is, 200,000,000 eV. This may be expressed as 3.2 hundred-billionth of a joule, a joule being a unit of work or energy equal to 0.738 ft-lb (a foot-pound is the amount of energy it requires to lift a 1-lb weight 1 ft high). In absolute terms, the 200 MeV released in one fission event is very small, but in relation to the amount of mass involved in the fission process it is extremely large.

To obtain a better conception of the amount of energy released in a fission event, let us compare it with more familiar quantities. To fuel for one day a 1-MW-thermal (about 0.33-MW electrical) electric power plant (that is, a plant capable of generating power at a rate of 330,000 kW, or producing 330,000 kWh in an hour) 1.24 g of U^{235} would have to be consumed. In a coal-fired plant of the same size, 2860 kg of coal each day would have to be consumed. The ratio of amount of fuel needed to produce the same amount of power is 2,300,000 to 1 (herein lies the great attraction of nuclear power).

As Enrico Fermi was later to show, when a nucleus of uranium is fissioned, two or three neutrons remain free and are not retained in the nucleus of one of the fission fragments. These free neutrons are then free to fission other nuclei of ^{235}U, and continue the fission process. This is why it is called a "chain reaction"—each group of simultaneous fission events sets loose free neutrons which trigger a subsequent group of fission events, and so on.†

The reaction is controlled by the use of rods or blades of an element that has a higher affinity for absorbing neutrons than does ^{235}U itself. Silver, indium, hafnium, gadolinium, and boron are among the materials used for this purpose. To slow down a chain reaction, the control rod is pushed part-way in among the reactor fuel bundles; to stop the reaction, it is pushed all the way in. The control elements "soak up" the free neutrons, which then become unavailable to carry on the chain reaction and the reaction is slowed or stopped.

In order for a chain reaction to take place, there must be a minimum amount of ^{235}U present and in a sufficiently close volume. This is called a critical mass. For ^{235}U, this is a sphere of about 15 kg of pure ^{235}U. However, in a power reactor there are a number of other materials required.

The various geometrical configurations required for criticality have been worked out in great detail, as a necessary safety measure. Fifteen kilograms of ^{235}U in the form of a 1-in.-thick metal plate, or in a long 1-in. diameter pipe, will not permit criticality, since the neutrons are too diffusely spread. The largest size containers and their shape which are safe for holding liquid compounds of uranium in the laboratory are well known, and the observance of the rules for their use are very strictly enforced.

Although an average of two or three neutrons are emitted in each fission, the continuation of the chain reaction is not always guaranteed. Neutrons can be "lost" by nonfission reactions in the fuel, to materials of the reactor core, or by leakage of neutrons out through the outer surface of the core. The fraction of neutrons leaking out can be reduced by increasing the size of the core, or the concentration of the fissionable material. The minimum amount of fissile material needed to sustain a chain reaction is called, as has been said, a *critical mass*. Its amount varies from about 15 kg (in a reactor with highly enriched uranium, i.e., nearly pure ^{235}U) to more than 200 kg (as in a natural uranium, graphite-moderated reactor). Natural uranium alone, without a moderator, can never reach critical size, because of the relatively high number of neutron reactions that do not lead to fission.

To measure criticality, the symbol k has been adopted. It represents the ratio of neutrons born in one "generation" to the neutrons born in the previous "generation," that is, those born in one simultaneous group of nuclear reactions. When $k = 1$, the reactor is critical, and the fission reaction can be sustained indefinitely. When k is larger than 1, the reactor is *supercritical* and the neutron population and power level rise until k is brought back to 1, by use of control rods or other means of control. Finally, if k is smaller than 1, the reactor is said to be *subcritical*, and any fission reaction that may start will eventually die. The only way to maintain a chain reaction when k is less than 1 is by the insertion of an independent neutron source.

The principle of neutron "moderation" is important to understand for a good comprehension of how reactors work. It was discovered early that the very energetic neutrons that are released at the moment of fission are not as likely to cause a new fission to take place in ^{235}U as a neutron that has lost some of its initial energy. For this purpose a "moderator," usually graphite or water, is used. In the early gas-cooled reactors and those still in use in France and Britain, the uranium fuel is distributed in a graphite structure, so that the free-flying neutrons, when released, bounce off—but are not absorbed in—atoms of the graphite, much as a billiard ball loses energy caroming off the edges of the pool table. In water-cooled reactors, the coolant water itself acts as moderator.

Another characteristic of our infinitely diversified natural elements is that although moderated neutrons (commonly called "thermal neutrons" because in this less-energetic state they are in thermal equilibrium with the substance in which they exist) have a high probability of causing fission of ^{235}U nuclei but will not fission ^{238}U nuclei, unmoderated or "fast" neutrons, however, can enter a ^{238}U nucleus. Such a nucleus now contains 239 protons and neutrons. In this condition the atom of which it is part is "uncomfortable" or unstable, throws off an electron, and becomes neptunium-239, which very quickly decays to plutonium-239. (We use the term "decay" because all radioactivity is in fact nothing other than decay—the loss of a proton, an electron, neutron, or an alpha or gamma particle.) This new material plutonium, into which the original ^{238}U has been

†This was very graphically demonstrated in an early training film showing the floor of a basketball court filled with mousetraps each holding a pingpong ball. The narrator on the court gallery tossed down one pingpong ball, which released the ball held by one mousetrap, which released another, and so on; immediately the air was filled with flying pingpong balls. This is an easy way to think of what happens in a fission chain reaction.

transformed (the mediaeval alchemists would have said "transmuted") is readily fissionable by the highly energetic "fast" neutrons. Thus it provides a second fuel for electric power generation. Plutonium is toxic (although by no means "the most toxic substance known to man" as it has been called, yielding that dubious distinction to cyanide, botulism, pure nicotine, curare, and other poisons).

Another comon misnomer applied to plutonium is that it is a "man-made" element, as though it had never existed in nature. In fact, however, as the discussion in Chapter 4 of the Oklo phenomenon in Gabon, Africa, will illustrate, plutonium once probably existed on earth, but by natural radioactivity it disappeared in nature.

How plutonium can be used as a nuclear fuel will be described in Chapter 11.

To achieve stable operation, a nuclear power plant must match the rate or level of heat produced by the reactor to the offsite electrical load demands. This requires that the energy being produced equal the energy being removed. The energy produced is a function of the rate of fission, and its associated heat production. The energy removed is a sum of electrical energy generated and sent out into the system, and thermal energy released to the environment (by friction and other nonproductive losses).

The rate of fission is controlled by the concentration of fissile atoms in the fuel (its enrichment), by the ratio of fuel to coolant, by the spacing of the fuel, and by the presence or absence of neutron absorbers. These absorbers can be used to control the fission process by capturing neutrons so that they are not available to cause fission. The actual fission rate is controlled in a dynamic mode by moving the neutron poisons, by moving the fuel, or by varying the ratio of moderator to fuel.

The energy removed is a function of the demand for electricity (from each plant on the network), the efficiency of conversion of the heat of fission to electricity, and the amount of energy being dissipated as waste energy. The efficiency of conversion is mostly dependent on plant design, but can also be affected by the weather: colder weather provides colder cooling water to the condenser circuit, resulting in higher thermodynamic efficiency of conversion.

The basic considerations of a nuclear power plant design are to provide a suitable medium in which the fission and heating will occur: fuel elements, a reliable means of controlling this process (control and safety rods), and a reliable method of coping with the energy generated, that is, heat transfer systems.

One last point that needs to be made is the distinction between nuclear weapons material and nuclear fuel material. For a nuclear bomb, one requires either uranium that has been enriched from the 0.3% of ^{235}U found in natural uranium refined from ore to higher than 90% ^{235}U or otherwise a sizable quantity of pure plutonium. Commercial nuclear power plants use as fuel uranium that has been enriched only to between 2 and 4% ^{235}U, the rest being ^{238}U which is, as we have seen, not fissionable by thermal neutrons. This fundamental difference is why a nuclear power plant simply *cannot* explode like a nuclear bomb. It uses as fuel a material that is as inert as a "dynamite" stick made of 2 to 4% dynamite and 96 to 98% beach sand.

BIBLIOGRAPHY

Benoit, C., *L'Industrie Atomique en France et dans le Monde,* Paris, Dunod, 1959, 159 pp.

Dean, G., *Report on the Atom,* Knopf, New York, 1957, 366 pp.

Ellis, R. H. Jr., *Nuclear Technology for Beginners,* McGraw-Hill, New York, 1959, 284 pp.

Glasstone, S., *Sourcebook on Atomic Energy,* Van Nostrand, New York, 1950, 546 pp.

Groves, L. R., *Now It Can Be Told* (The Story of the Manhattan Project), Harper & Row, New York, 1962, 465 pp.

Hahn, O., *A Scientific Autobiography,* Scribner's, New York, 1966, 296 pp.

Hewlett, R. G., and O. E. Anderson, Jr., *The New World 1939/1946,* Pennsylvania State University Press, University Park, Pennsylvania, 1962, 766 pp.

Hogerton, J. F., *The Atomic Energy Deskbook,* Reinhold, New York, 1963, 673 pp.

Reis, Th., *L'Energie Nucléaire dans le Monde,* Paris, Dunod, 1957, 296 pp.

Smyth, H. D., *Atomic Energy for Military Purposes* (official report of the Manhattan District), Princeton University Press, Princeton, New Jersey, 1946, 308 pp.

Wills, J. G., *Nuclear Power Plant Technology,* Wiley, New York, 1967, 323 pp.

CHAPTER 2
NUCLEAR TECHNOLOGY SUMMARY

Energy is produced in a nuclear plant from the splitting of heavy nuclei, primarily uranium. This process, known as nuclear fission, was first discovered by two German physicists, Hahn and Strassman, in 1939. On December 2, 1942, the first nuclear "chain reaction" was demonstrated at Stagg Field at the University of Chicago by Enrico Fermi and his associates. From Fermi's demonstration, it was proved that the fission reaction could be self-sustained and controlled, thus affording mankind an entirely new and very large source of energy. The energy released in fission is kinetic, but quickly converts to heat. From that point on, the method of generating electricity from the dissipated heat of the fission reaction is similar to that used in a coal, oil, or any other thermal power plant. The heat turns water to steam, and the steam drives a turbine generator to produce electricity.

In the following paragraphs, these basic physical processes will be discussed, and highlights of actual nuclear power systems will be given.

2.1. BASIC CONCEPTS AND PROCESSES

Nuclear Fuels

The only fissile material found in nature is the isotope uranium-235. A fissile nucleus is one that will fission when bombarded with slow-moving thermal neutrons. Fissile uranium-235 constitutes only 0.7% of uranium found in nature; the balance (99.3%) is a heavier isotope, uranium-238. Uranium-238 is not fissile, although it is fissionable since it can be split when bombarded with fast neutrons, that is, with neutrons of sufficiently high energy. In fact, many nuclei in the periodic table of the elements could fission when bombarded with very energetic neutrons.

Uranium-238 and thorium-232 (also found in nature) have another interesting property. Upon absorption of one neutron and after a series of radioactive decays, they give birth, respectively, to two artificial fissile isotopes, plutonium-239 and uranium-233.

These nuclear transformations are described in the following equations:

$$^{238}\text{U} + n \rightarrow [^{239}\text{U}]^* \rightarrow \beta^- + {}^{239}\text{Np} \rightarrow \beta^- + {}^{239}\text{Pu} \quad \text{(fissile)}$$
$$^{232}\text{Th} + n \rightarrow [^{233}\text{Th}]^* \rightarrow \beta^- + {}^{233}\text{Pa} \rightarrow \beta^- + {}^{233}\text{U} \quad \text{(fissile)}$$

Because of their potential to absorb a thermal neutron and hence to produce new fissile materials, uranium-238 and thorium-232 are called fertile materials. This important property is utilized in the converter and breeder reactor, discussed later. Thus there are three main fissile isotopes of interest in the nuclear industry: one found in nature, uranium-235, and two artificial, plutonium-239 and uranium-233, which are produced from the fertile isotopes uranium-238 and thorium-232.

Fission and Fission Energy

When a thermal neutron is absorbed by a fissile nucleus, the internal balance of the forces inside the nucleus is perturbed. The excited nucleus then may split into two lighter nuclei, much like a water droplet that has become too large splits into two smaller droplets (Figure 2.1). Beta and gamma rays, neutrons, two fission fragments, and energy are the products of fission (Figure 2.2).† The energy released is equivalent to the mass lost in the process, since the total sum of the products weighs slightly less than the mass of the original nucleus plus the absorbed neutron.

†Other particles, such as neutrinos, are also produced and carry with them a certain small fraction of energy. Because of zero cross section, these particles are nearly impossible to capture or detect.

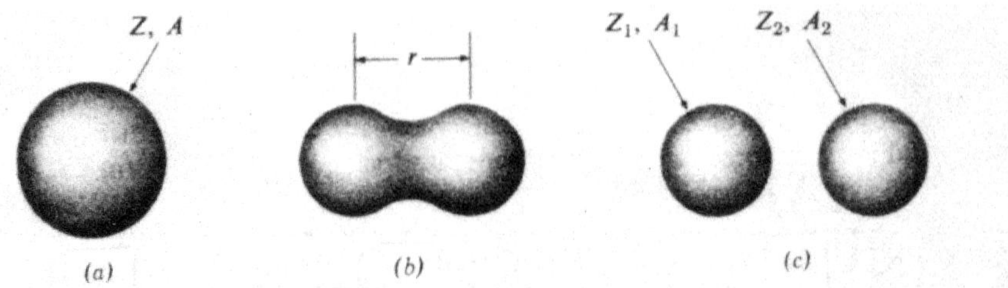

Figure 2.1. Stages in fission. The analogy between nuclei and liquid droplets was found to be useful when N. Bohr and J. Wheeler explained fission just months after its discovery by using the same model. The surface tension of a liquid causes a droplet to assume a spherical shape, but if energy is supplied in some fashion, this shape is distorted. If the attractive surface tension force is greater than the distorting force, the drop oscillates between spherical and elongated shapes. If, however, the distorting force becomes larger than the attractive force, the drop elongates past a threshold point and splits (fission).

In each fission event, two or three (or even more) neutrons are emitted, depending on laws of statistical distribution. The average number of neutrons generated per fission is between two and three. If, after accounting for neutron losses through leakage or neutron captures in nonfission events, at least one of the fission neutrons is caught by a fissile nucleus in a fission-causing absorption and the process continues, a self-sustained fission reaction is established, as shown schematically in Figure 2.2.

The mass deficit in the fission reaction emerges in the form of energy, according to Einstein's formula of mass energy equivalence, $E = mc^2$. The energy released is mostly in the form of kinetic energy carried by the moving fission fragments. These fragments, however, are quickly slowed by collisions with other nuclei; thus the kinetic energy is converted to heat in the vicinity of the fission event (within a few micrometers). About 20% of the total energy released is carried away by the beta and gamma rays, as well as by the fission neutrons (Table 2.1). The energy is also eventually converted into heat, although this conversion takes place farther away from the fission event.

The amount of energy released in fission is of the order of 200 MeV, or 3.2×10^{-11} joules (J). Although small in absolute terms, this amount of energy is extremely large in relation to the amount of mass involved in the fission process. To obtain a better conception of the amount of fission energy, let us compare it with more familiar quantities. To produce 1 megawatt-day (MWd) of thermal energy (i.e., to fuel a 1-MW thermal plant or a 0.33-MW electric plant for 1 day), 1.24 g of ^{235}U would have to be consumed. This quantity is called specific consumption (i.e., mass of fuel consumed per unit energy produced) and can be called *C*. The equivalent amount of coal (assuming

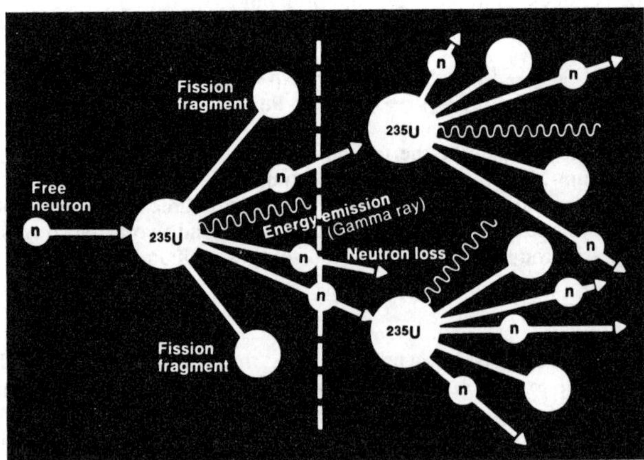

Figure 2.2. Schematic diagram of a fission chain reaction. Two large fission fragments, prompt neutrons, beta and gamma rays are released. The number of neutrons released per fission varies between 2 and 5 with an average value of about 2.43 for ^{235}U. (For ^{239}Pu the value is 2.90 and for ^{233}U it is 2.51. The value also varies with neutron energy).

Table 2.1. Emitted and Recoverable Energies for Fission of ^{235}U

Form	Emitted Energy, MeV	Recoverable Energy, MeV
Fission fragments	168	168
Fission product decay		
β-rays	8	8
γ-rays	7	7
neutrinos	12	—
Prompt γ-rays	7	7
Fission neutrons (kinetic energy)	5	5
Capture γ-rays	—	3–12
Total	207	198–207

a heating value of about 30,230 kJ/kg or 13,000 Btu/lb) would be 2860 kg/day, or a ratio of about 2,300,000:1. Expressed in another way, the inverse of C gives the amount of energy released per unit mass, or burnup:†

$$B = \frac{1}{C} = \frac{1}{1.24}\frac{\text{MWd}}{\text{g}} = \frac{10^6}{1.24}\frac{\text{g}}{\text{t}}\frac{\text{MWd}}{\text{g}} = 800{,}000\frac{\text{MWd}}{\text{t}}$$

This figure is expressed per ton (metric) of ^{235}U and is to be compared with 0.35 MWd/t of coal. This very large amount of energy can be released only if every nucleus of ^{235}U in fuel of pure ^{235}U is consumed. In practice, however, the fuel is a mixture of fissile and fertile isotopes and this must be periodically replaced. Thus the actual burnup achieved in light-water reactor (LWR) fuel is from 25,000 to 35,000 MWd/t of fuel. In breeder reactors, the burnup can be increased from 100,000 to 150,000 MWd/t, which implies a higher utilization of the energy inherent in the fuel.

Critical Mass

Although an average of two or three neutrons are emitted in each fission, the continuation of the chain reaction is not always guaranteed. Neutrons can be "lost" by nonfission reactions in the fuel, to materials of the reactor core, or by leakage of neutrons through the surface of the core. The fraction of neutrons leaking out can be reduced by increasing the size of the core or the concentration of the fissile material. The minimum amount of fissile material needed to sustain a chain reaction is called critical mass. Its amount varies from about 10 kg (in an assembly with highly enriched, that is, pure ^{235}U) to more than 200 kg (as in a natural uranium–graphite reactor).‡ Natural uranium alone (without a moderator) can never reach critical size, because of the relatively high number of neutron reactions that do not lead to fission.

To measure criticality, the symbol k is used. k is the ratio of neutrons born in one generation to the neutrons born in the previous generation. When $k = 1$, the reactor is critical, and the fission reaction can be sustained indefinitely. When k is larger than 1, the reactor is supercritical, and the neutron population and power level rises until k is brought back to 1 through means of control. Finally, when k is smaller than 1, the reactor is said to be subcritical; any fission reaction that may start will eventually die. The only way to maintain a chain reaction when $k < 1$ is by the insertion of an independent neutron source.

Two important considerations follow from the discussion above. First, it is essential to maintain an adequate fissile material inventory in the reactor core to achieve criticality throughout core life. Hence, whenever the fuel is depleted of fissile material below a certain level, replacement of at least part of the core is necessary. This refueling operation, according to present practice in the LWR industry, is done once a year. One-fourth or one-third of the core is replaced with fresh fuel during the refueling outage, which normally lasts between four and eight weeks. Other repair and maintenance operations are scheduled to coincide with refueling to minimize the loss of energy production. In the CANDU reactor, refueling is performed continuously and on-line.

The second consideration is the importance of maintaining adequate control of the chain reaction at all times and allowing it to become only slightly supercritical when an increase of power level is desired. An elaborate and redundant control system is, therefore, incorporated in all

†t is used to symbolize metric ton.

‡Large modern LWRs contain about 100 t of fuel of which about 2.5 t is fissile material.

nuclear reactors for the purposes of controlling power level and shutting the reactor down in normal and emergency situations. Materials with high neutron absorption, such as cadmium, boron, hafnium, and silver-indium, are used as control elements.

Prompt and Delayed Neutrons

Neutrons emitted as a result of the fission process may be divided into two classes: "prompt neutrons" and "delayed neutrons." Prompt neutrons appear at the moment of fission—within an interval perhaps as short as 10^{-14} sec. They constitute 99% of all fission neutrons. Delayed neutrons make up about 0.65% of the total number of neutrons from fission of ^{235}U, and appear as products of the radioactive decay of the fission fragments. They are emitted with gradually decreasing intensity for several minutes after the actual fission event. For nuclear engineering purposes, they have an importance far greater than might be thought from their relatively small number, in that they ease the task of controlling the chain reaction. At least six groups of delayed neutrons have been identified, with half-lives varying from 0.05 to 55.6 sec, and with varying relative yield.

Fission Fragments

Almost all fission results in two fragments of unequal mass. The heavier fragment has a mass number of around 140 while the lighter fragment has a mass number of about 95. The probability of any mass number appearing as a result of fission is shown in the double-humped curve shown in Figure 2.3. The law of conservation of nucleons means that the total sum of nucleons in the fission fragments plus the number of prompt neutrons must equal the number of nucleons in the original nucleus (235 in the case of a splitting ^{235}U). The laws of conservation of mass and momentum result in an unequal distribution of energy and the lighter fragment carries approximately 100 MeV of energy and the heavier fragment about 67 MeV as shown in the diagram in Figure 2.4.

The kinetic energy of the fission fragments propels them through the cloud of electrons of the original nucleus. Although they pick up a number of electrons as they move, they remain highly ionized as they continue their passage through the surrounding material. Because of the high charge

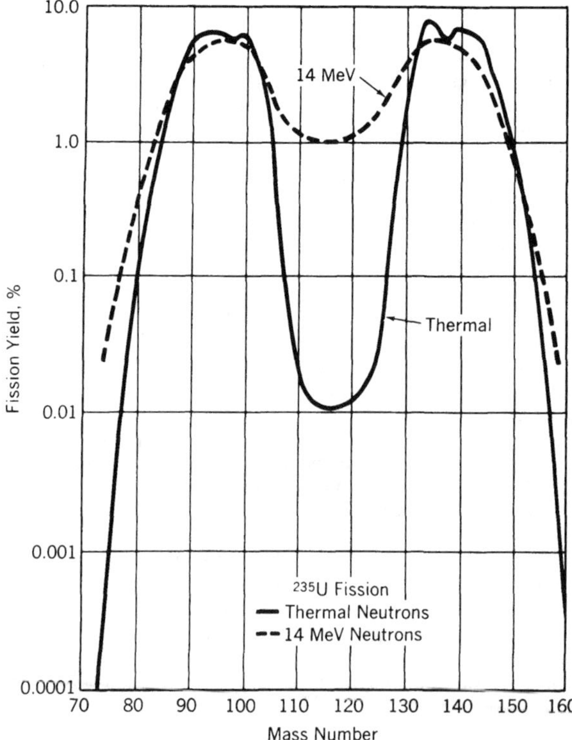

Figure 2.3. Mass distribution of fission products from fission of uranium-235.

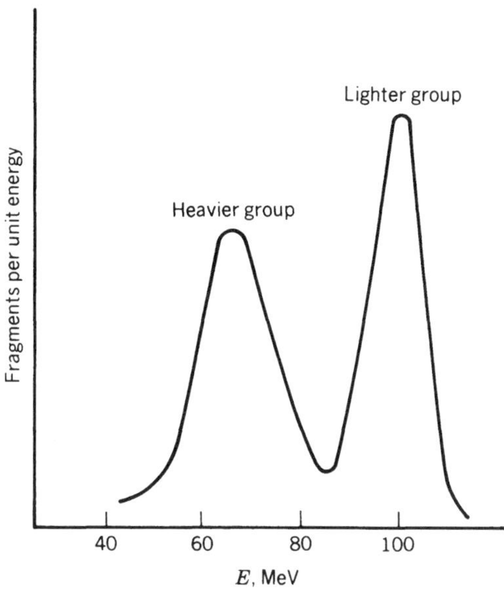

Figure 2.4. Energy distribution of fission fragments as a function of energy in MeV.

they carry, fission fragments are rapidly slowed down through the process of ionization and they finally come to a stop within a short distance of their origin. Their kinetic energy is thus dissipated as heat. Typical ranges of the lighter, more penetrating fission fragment are shown in Table 2.2.

The short range of fission fragments is quite significant in the exploitation of nuclear energy. First, it means that the production of heat is virtually local, that is, at the very point where fission occurred. Second, it makes it possible to stop fission fragments with very thin layers of materials. Thus, the cladding, a thin tube of zircaloy in which fuel pellets are stacked to form a fuel rod, can be quite adequate to stop fission fragments from the surface of the fuel pellet. Cladding thickness of 0.5 mm (500 μm) would be more than adequate for this purpose.

Radioactivity Produced in Fission

In addition to the prompt radiation emitted during fission, there is also radiation emanating from the fission products, of which there is a great variety. Some of these decay quickly (e.g., xenon-135 decays with a half-life of 9.23 hr and iodine-131 with a half-life of 8.08 days), whereas others have long half-lives (for krypton-85 it is 10.3 yr and for cesium-137, 30 yr). Radiation falls under three main categories: (1) alpha particles, consisting of helium nuclei—heavy particles with a large mass and easily stopped by a thin layer of matter; (2) beta particles, consisting of electrons of either positive or negative charge—light particles and more penetrating than alphas, but also easily stopped by a sheet of glass; and finally, (3) gamma rays, which consist of electromagnetic waves of relatively high frequency (and hence high energy) which are very penetrating. Since radiation is potentially harmful to living matter, measures must be taken to protect people from excessive exposure. Hence shielding consisting of concrete, water, steel, lead, and other dense materials is an important part of reactor design.

Table 2.2. Ranges of Fission Fragments in Various Materials

Medium	Range, μm
Aluminum	14
Copper	5.9
Silver	5.3
Uranium	6.3
Uranium oxide (U_3O_8)	14

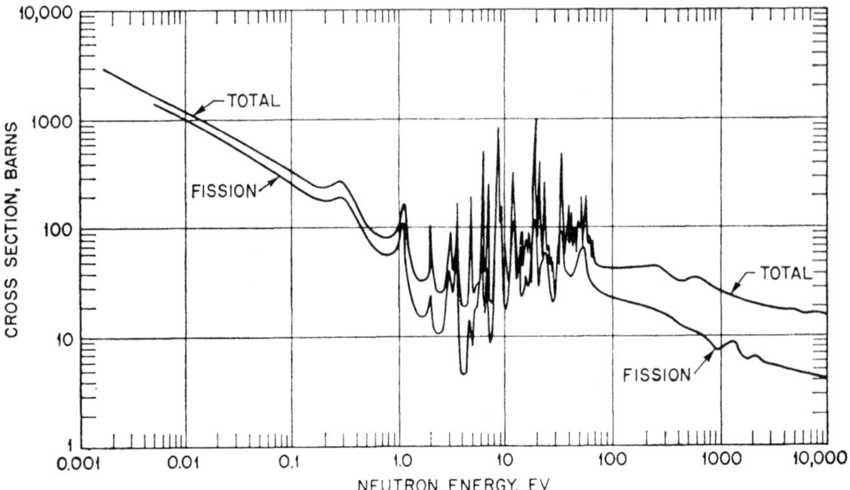

Figure 2.5. Total and fission cross sections of uranium-235 as function of neutron energy.

Nuclear Reactions—Cross Sections

Fission is one of several possible reactions of nuclei with neutrons. It occurs predominantly with thermal (slow-moving) neutrons.

The probability of any nuclear reaction occurring—that is, the probability that a neutron† will interact with the nucleus of any element or isotope—can be accurately measured. This probability is expressed in terms of a quantity called the nuclear "cross section." The term derives from the fact that the probability represents the effective area of cross section of a single nucleus of a given species for a particular reaction—or, in other words, the apparent size of the target that the nucleus presents to the oncoming particle. If the probability is high that the reaction will occur, the number expressing the cross section for that reaction will be large, and vice versa. Vast effort has been expended over the years, principally in the national laboratories, in measuring the cross sections of all possible nuclear reactions, and the results of this work have produced an essentially complete data base which is available in graphical or digital form.

The unit to express the cross section is a "barn," a name that was proposed in 1942 by the American physicists M. G. Holloway and C. P. Baker because of a humorous association of ideas. A barn is defined as an area 10^{-24} cm^2, roughly the geometric size of the nucleus.‡ So, for a nuclear reaction to take place, 10^{-24} seemed "as big as a barn," relatively speaking.

The cross sections of elements vary with the relative energy of the oncoming particle. When a neutron has certain specific energy values, there is a sharp increase in the reaction rate. For certain energy values, the probability of a neutron entering a nucleus is exceptionally large. This phenomenon is called resonance. It is very marked at low energies. At thermal energies, many nuclei have a very large probability of reaction (high cross section) which is inversely proportional to the velocity of the neutron. For these nuclei, the apparent cross section is much larger than the geometric cross section; hitting them with a thermal neutron then is as easy as "hitting the broad side of a barn."

Although it is convenient and simple to introduce the cross section as a target area, this must not be taken literally. The experimental meaning of the cross section comes from its use as a measure of the number of nuclear events that occur under a given set of conditions.

Nuclear cross sections are found to have values ranging from small fractions of a barn to hundreds of thousands of barns, and these values often differ greatly from the geometrical cross section. A given nucleus can have widely differing cross sections for different nuclear reactions, and the values represent the relative probabilities of those reactions taking place.

When ^{235}U is irradiated by neutrons, several different processes can occur: fission, neutron capture without fission, neutron scattering, and so on. As seen in Figure 2.5, the probability of any one of these reactions occurring depends on the energy of the incident neutron. For thermal neutrons, fission dominates over the other processes. For neutron energies up to 0.1 MeV, large capture and fission resonances can occur. For fast neutrons ($E > 0.1$ MeV) the cross section, small

†Or electron, gamma ray, or other radiating particle.
‡The size of an atom is found to be in the neighborhood of 10^{-16} cm^2.

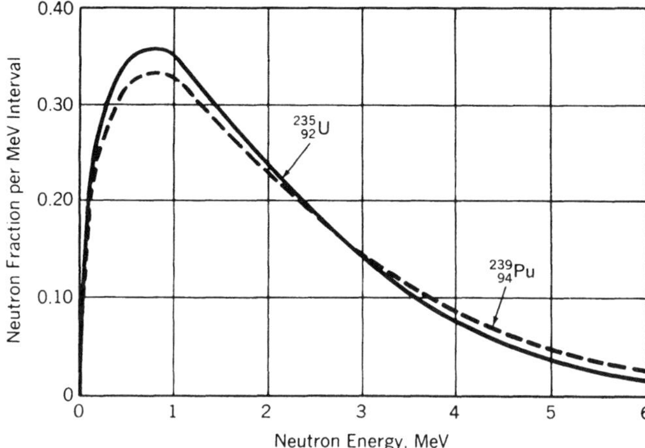

Figure 2.6. Fission neutron energy distribution.

for all processes, is approximately 1 barn. For ^{238}U, however, almost no fission occurs except at high neutron energies (hence ^{238}U is called fissionable rather than fissile). In this case, neutron capture dominates, resulting in the eventual transmutation of the ^{238}U into ^{239}Pu, as already mentioned above.

Neutron Spectrum

The neutrons that are produced in the fission process have relatively high energy, with an average value around 2 MeV. Their energies are, of course, spread as shown in Figure 2.6, which gives the spectrum of fission neutrons. These fast neutrons then may come into collision with other materials in the reactor such as water and gradually lose energy until their energies are reduced to thermal. A typical thermal neutron has a speed of 2200 m/sec. Under ideal conditions, the thermal spectrum is "Maxwellian," which means the neutron population is at equilibrium with the surrounding medium (e.g., water) at a given temperature. Depending on the amount of light nuclei in the reactor (e.g., hydrogen or deuterium) the reactor operates at a more or less thermalized neutron spectrum.

2.2. REACTOR COOLANT, MODERATOR, AND REACTOR CLASSIFICATION

The challenge presented to engineering science by the discovery of fission was how to harness and control the fission reaction for uses beneficial to human beings. The applications of nuclear reactors are many; the major application is for the production of electric power. Heat produced within the fuel must be constantly removed to (1) prevent the fuel temperature from rising to unacceptably high levels, and (2) transport the heat produced to another location, where it can be more readily converted into other forms, for example, electricity. This leads to the need for a reactor coolant and coolant pumps to circulate it through the system. Various liquids and gases have been used as coolants because of their physical, neutronic, and chemical characteristics. Ordinary and heavy water, organic waxes, carbon dioxide and helium, and liquid sodium have all been applied. A ^{235}U nucleus is more likely to absorb a slow-moving neutron that a fast one. Thus a slow (or thermal) neutron is more likely to induce a ^{235}U fission. For this reason, the majority of power reactors today utilize thermal neutrons in the core and hence are called thermal reactors. Neutrons produced from a fission, however, have high energies, mostly between 1 and 2 MeV. To slow the neutrons and make them better candidates to go on and cause other fissions, light nuclei must be introduced into the core. The neutrons are slowed down by numerous collisions with the light nuclei. The material that causes this slowing down and thermalization of neutrons is called the "moderator." Ordinary water, heavy water, graphite, and beryllium have been used as moderators in various reactors. The lighter the moderator, the more efficient it is; however, other properties, such as probabilities (called "cross sections") for scattering and absorption, must also be considered in estimating a figure of merit for moderators. In the LWR, ordinary water is used for both functions: as core coolant and moderator. The same is true with the heavy water of the CANDU reactor. In other reactors, combinations of materials are used. For example, graphite is the moderator and helium gas is the coolant in one version of the gas-cooled reactor.

In unmoderated reactors, the neutron spectrum lies in the high-energy region, mostly between

Table 2.3. Nuclear Reactor Components and Materials

Component	Function	Materials
Fuels	To undergo fission reactions to produce energy	^{233}U, ^{235}U, ^{239}Pu, ^{241}Pu
Coolant	To remove heat from the reactor core	Light water, heavy water, organic waxes, CO_2, air, helium, sodium, bismuth, sodium-potassium
Moderator	To slow down and thermalize fast fission neutrons	Light water, heavy water, graphite, beryllium, beryllium oxide
Reflector	To reduce neutron leakage	Same as moderator materials
Shielding	To protect personnel from ionizing radiation	Concrete, steel, lead, water, polyethylene
Control rods	To control criticality and power level	Cadmium, boron, hafnium, gadolinium, silver-indium
Structural elements	To provide containment of fuel and physical support of reactor core	Aluminum, stainless steel, zirconium

0.5 and 1.0 MeV. These neutrons move with fast velocities and hence the reactors are called "fast." The great advantage of fast reactors is that they can convert fertile materials (^{238}U and ^{232}Th) into fissile materials (^{239}Pu and ^{239}U) more quickly than is done in thermal reactors, because of favorable neutronic characteristics of fertile isotopes in the fast-energy region. It is also possible to design reactors with a neutron spectrum that lies between the thermal and the fast spectrum, namely in the "epithermal" region. These reactors are called "intermediate." They have been, and are being, investigated but have not attracted the interest and development effort of the other two types.

Burners, Converters, and Breeders

It is also common to classify reactors by the amount of new fissile material produced. Thermal reactors convert relatively little fertile material to fissile material compared to the amount they consume. They are, therefore, called "burners." If the ratio of fissile material produced to the fissile material consumed (which is called the conversion ratio) is substantial (between 0.5 and 1.0), the reactor can be called a converter. Finally, if this ratio exceeds unity, it follows that more fuel is produced than is consumed; hence the reactor is a breeder. A fast-neutron spectrum reactor can be used for the breeding of new fuel and affords the possibility of fueling additional fast breeders (in addition to replenishing its own fuel) without further mining of uranium.

The various materials used in reactors are summarized in Table 2.3. The main classification schemes of reactors are shown in Table 2.4. The last classification in Table 2.4 of homogeneous and heterogeneous reactors is based on the configuration of the reactor materials. Although reactors in industrial practice today are exclusively heterogeneous, a brief discussion of the subject affords useful insights into the problems inherent in the design and operation of nuclear reactors. In homogeneous reactors, fuel and moderator are mixed together. Uranium salt dissolved in water could be used in such a reactor. The proposed molten salt breeder reactor also belongs in the homogeneous category. Such a reactor could be designed in a spherical geometric shape, advantageous for both neutron economy and mathematical analytical simplicity. However, the same mixture which is heated in the core must then be circulated through a heat exchanger for the removal of

Table 2.4. Classification of Nuclear Reactors According to Neutron Spectrum, Fissile Material Consumption, and Nuclear Configuration

According to neutron spectrum:	Thermal Intermediate Fast
According to fissile material consumption and prediction:	Burners Converters Breeders
According to nuclear configuration:	Homogenous Heterogeneous

heat. This would imply that the whole plant must be shielded against radiation from fission products. An enormous amount of fluid mass would have to be circulated, and maintenance of the plant would be extremely difficult and costly. For these reasons, homogeneous reactors have not been developed for power production.

In heterogeneous reactors, the fuel is segregated from the coolant and/or moderator into fuel lumps (rods, spheres, or plates) which not only provide practical advantages such as containment of fission products, but also an increase in the neutron multiplication factor. A mixture of natural uranium and graphite at Stagg Field (known as CP-1) did go critical because it was designed as a heterogeneous assembly. The completed assembly included 3200 uranium metal cylinders and 14,500 uranium oxide lumps, with a total weight of 50 t of uranium and 470 t of graphite.

The reactor types to be described in the following are all of the heterogeneous type. The solid fuel is in the form of rods, plates, or pins assembled in bundles, spaced uniformly in a cylindrical core. The coolant circulates through channels among the fuel elements. This arrangement provides effective heat transfer, economy, and ease of refueling operations.

2.3. ENERGY CONVERSION

The heat released in the reactor core is stored as temperature and pressure in the coolant. The amount of stored thermal energy is called the "enthalpy" of the fluid. In a power plant, this thermal energy is converted into mechanical energy as steam expands in the turbine, which, in turn, moves the electric generator for the production of electricity. In most cases, the transfer of thermal energy takes place through one or two stages of heat exchangers. In a pressurized water reactor (PWR), the heat exchangers (usually called steam generators) separate the energy conversion system from the reactor core cooling circuit. In other cases, [such as in the boiling water reactor (BWR)], the coolant itself is vaporized and expands in the steam turbine without intermediate steps. The steam exiting from the turbine is condensed in the condenser and is fed back to the heat source (core or heat exchanger) to repeat the cycle. The condenser, a large component in power plants, requires a large supply of cooling water through which the remaining thermal energy of the steam at the turbine outlet is rejected. This water can be provided by a stream, lake, or ocean in an open system or by a closed system using a cooling pond or a cooling tower. The latter device is used in a variety of alternative designs to reject heat in the atmosphere. The thermal cycle for the transport and conversion of thermal energy is the main system of a thermal plant. A number of auxiliary systems are also incorporated into the plant to perform a variety of functions. These systems are described in more detail in Chapter 8.

The energy conversion part of the plant (often referred to as the Balance Of Plant, or BOP) incorporates a large number of components (heat exchangers, pumps, tanks, pipes, etc.) which are described in detail in Chapter 9. The BOP is nearly 90% of the total plant cost and must be designed properly and operated for compatibility and optimum interaction with the nuclear reactor proper.

Thermal Efficiency

The energy produced in the core is in the form of heat. Because of the second law of thermodynamics, it is impossible to convert all of this energy into "useful" mechanical or electrical energy. The ratio of mechanical energy in the turbine to the total thermal energy stored as enthalpy in steam is the thermal efficiency of the cycle. It depends on the temperature of steam as it enters the turbine and also on the temperature of the environment to which "useless" or "waste" heat must be rejected. In LWRs, because of the relatively low steam temperatures achievable, thermal efficiency is about 33%. In high-temperature gas-cooled reactors and in modern coal plants, thermal efficiency can be 40% or even higher.

2.4. BASIC REACTOR SYSTEMS AND COMPONENTS

It is obvious that the number of options available from the variety of materials listed in Table 2.3 as well as from the classification in Table 2.4, makes for a large number of possible combinations. For various reasons, mostly technical and economical but also historical, the number of reactor systems actually developed and put to practical use is rather small. By far the predominant type of reactor used for electric power production today is the light-water reactor (LWR), first developed in the United States by the joint efforts of industry and government. The LWR comes in two varieties: the pressurized water reactor (PWR) and the boiling water reactor (BWR), the PWR being more dominant in numbers than the BWR. Out of about 232 reactors operating worldwide, 150 (or 65%) are LWRs (see Table 2.5). Future plans for reactor construction are based almost exclusively on the LWR. Even countries that began their nuclear programs with other types of reactors (the United Kingdom and France started with graphite gas-cooled reactors) moved toward the LWR.

Table 2.5. Nuclear Reactors with Operating Licenses by Type as of December 31, 1983

			Percentage of Total
PWR[a]	(93 non-U.S. + 52 U.S.) =	145	49
BWR[b]	(35 non-U.S. + 29 U.S.) =	64	22
PHWR[c]		21	7
GCR[d]	(42 non-U.S. + 1 U.S.)	43	14
LMFBR[e]		4	1
Other[f]		22	7
		299	

[a]Pressurized water reactor.
[b]Boiling water reactor.
[c]Pressurized heavy-water reactor, also known as CANDU (CANadian Deuterium-Uranium reactor).
Number includes the boiling heavy-water reactor Gentilly 1.
[d]Gas-cooled, graphite-moderated reactor. This type (known as Magnox in Britain) was used in the first stages of the British and French programs. The category also includes a number of advanced gas-cooled reactors in the United Kingdom and the only high-temperature, gas-cooled, graphite-moderated reactor in the United States at Fort St. Vrain.
[e]Liquid-metal, fast breeder reactor.
[f]Includes 18 light-water-cooled, graphite-moderated reactors developed in the U.S.S.R.; five more are under construction.

Pressurized Water Reactor (PWR)

Figure 2.7 shows a simplified schematic diagram of a PWR plant. It consists mainly of (1) the reactor pressure vessel, which contains the nuclear core, and primary coolant circuit through which water, acting as both coolant and moderator, flows to remove the fission-produced heat; (2) a heat exchanger or steam generator, in which heat is transferred to a secondary loop where steam is generated; and (3) the energy conversion system, where steam is used to make electricity. The diagram shows, for simplicity, only one primary and one secondary loop. In actual practice, in order to increase the power output from the plant while keeping the components down to a reasonable (and available) size, several loops are attached to the pressure vessel. One-, two-, and three-loop configurations are utilized as shown in Figure 2.8. The primary system with all its piping and components is enclosed in a specially designed structure called the containment. Thus any radioactivity that may leak from the fuel into the primary water is isolated from the environment.

The name of the PWR derives from the fact that water in the primary circuit is kept at a pressure of about 2250 psi (or 15.5 MPa), and a maximum temperature of about 600°F (315°C). These conditions prevent any boiling, since the boiling point of water at 2250 psi is well above 600°F.

The fuel in a PWR consists of slightly enriched uranium oxide (UO_2) pellets in the form of 8 × 12 mm cylinders. The pellets are sintered (i.e., heated to a high temperature), machined to proper and exact dimensions, and then stacked and sealed (with helium gas) in the cladding to form fuel rods or pins which are about 12 ft (3.65 m) in length and about 0.374 in. (10 mm) in diameter (see Figure 2.9). The pins are then clustered in groups of 17 × 17 "bundles" or "assemblies"† held together by top and bottom metal structures and by several spacer grids, as shown in Figure 2.10. The bundle is the operational fuel unit and represents a large amount of energy. At a burnup of 35 MWd/kg, the amount of energy extracted from a fuel bundle is equivalent to about a quarter-million barrels of oil. A typical 1000-MWe plant contains about 200 fuel assemblies and between 40,000 and 50,000 fuel pins. Toward the end of its life, the fuel contains some plutonium converted from the ^{238}U in the fresh fuel. Some of this plutonium is burned in the core before the bundle is removed, but most of it remains in the fuel at the time of removal. This makes spent fuel a potential energy source. If a policy of recovery and reuse of the plutonium is adopted in the United States, fresh fuel could be a mixture of uranium and plutonium oxide in the same pellet. If one assumes complete utilization of all nuclei in a fuel bundle (both fissile and fertile), the potential equivalent energy content of a bundle amounts to a staggering 7 million barrels of oil. The total fuel in the core of a 1000-MWe PWR is about 100 to 110 t of uranium dioxide.

†Earlier designs provided 15 × 15 rod array. One manufacturer makes fuel in a 16 × 16 rod array.

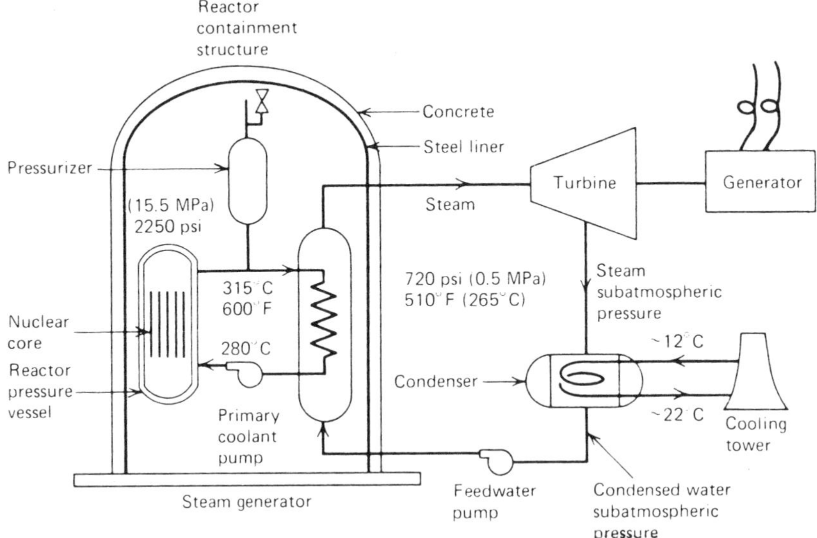

Figure 2.7. Schematic of a PWR power plant. Note how the heat transfer occurs within the containment building.

In each assembly, 16 to 25 positions (depending on the design) are left open for the insertion of control rods. The center position is left open for an instrumentation thimble. About 30% of all the assemblies contain control rods, connected at the top of the assembly to a metal piece with spiderlike arms. They are moved by control rod drives that penetrate the top of the vessel.

Another means of control is to introduce a boron solution in the primary coolant system. This method is used primarily to offset long-term reactivity changes caused by buildup of fission products (which act as neutron poisons) and reduction of fissile content because of burnup. It is also used for reactor shutdown. As reactivity becomes less with time, the boron concentration is gradually reduced (from an original value of about 12%) so that control rods are always capable of covering the necessary control range without having to compensate for long-term reactivity changes.

Fresh fuel in an LWR contains uranium enriched to 2 to 3% in ^{235}U. The enrichment varies across the core with the highest enrichment (a little over 3%) at the edge and with lower enrichment in the core interior. Such a dispersion is used to even out the power distribution with as small a variation as possible from an average value of about 100 kW/liter of core volume.

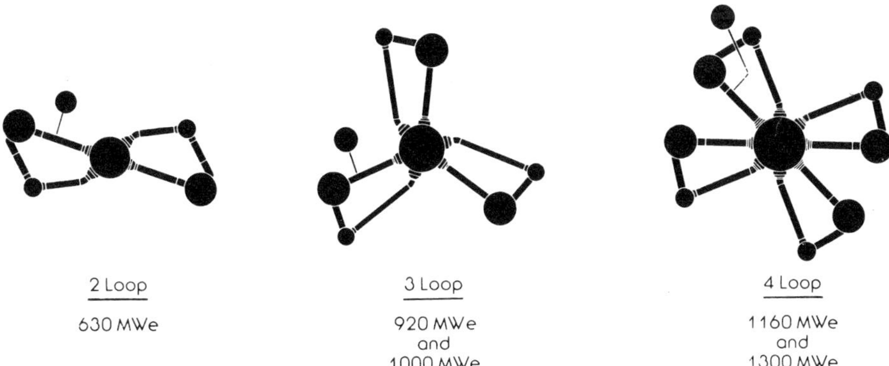

Figure 2.8. Plan view of three different configurations of PWR primary systems. (Courtesy Westinghouse Electric Corp.)

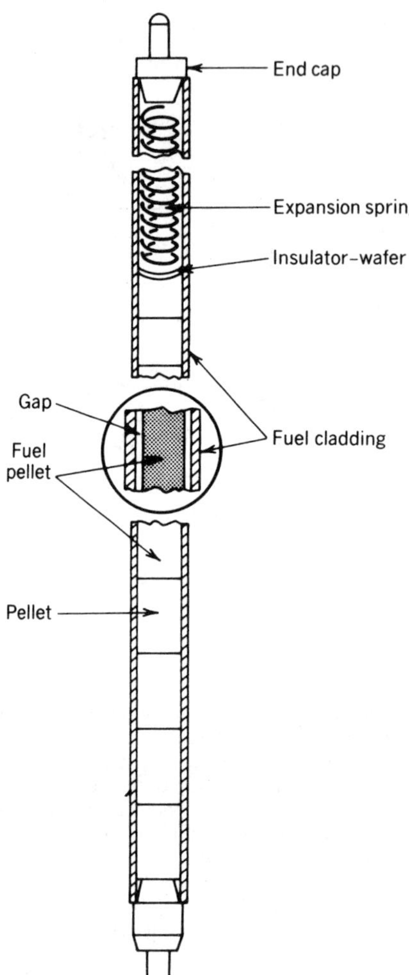

Figure 2.9. Illustration of oxide fuel as used in commercial LWR power plants.

Heat removal from a PWR core is accomplished through the primary circuit circulating water. A schematic of the reactor pressure vessel and the flow direction of the coolant is shown in Figure 2.11. A complete isometric diagram of a four-loop primary system is shown in Figure 2.12.

The Boiling Water Reactor (BWR)

In the BWR, water passing through the core is allowed to boil inside the reactor vessel, by use of a lower primary coolant pressure, typically about 1040 psi (7 MPa). Steam is piped directly to the turbine for the production of power and is returned to the reactor vessel via feed pumps. Figure 2.13 shows a simplified diagram of the plant, and Figure 2.14 shows a view of the pressure vessel, its internals, and its two recirculation loops. The fuel in a BWR is somewhat different from that used in a PWR, as shown in Figure 2.15. The assemblies are a little more than 12 ft in length and are made of 8 × 8 arrays (in earlier designs 7 × 7 arrays) of fuel pins about 0.482 in. (1.23 cm) in diameter. The fuel is again uranium oxide (UO_2) of varying enrichment (averaging about 2.8%) sealed in Zircaloy-2 tubes 34 mils (0.86 mm) thick. Total active fuel column height is 148 in. (3.76 m) with a 12-in. plenum for the collection of fission gases. A 9-mil (0.23-mm) gap is maintained between the tube's inner diameter and the pellets and a spring is inserted at the top of the fuel rod to ensure continuous contact between pellets. Whereas the PWR bundle is open, the BWR bundle is enclosed in a metal sheath (fuel channel) which contains the coolant flow in the assembly. The assemblies contain, in addition to the fuel rods, tie rods which, together with the upper and lower tie plates, provide the structural stability of the assembly. There are also water rods containing

Figure 2.10. Inspection of a nuclear fuel assembly for a large power reactor. (Courtesy Combustion Engineering Co.)

water moderator rather than fuel. A typical large BWR plant of 1220-MWe size may have more than 750 assemblies containing 40,000 to 50,000 individual rods, weighing more than 200 t.

Control in a BWR is provided by several means. Boron carbide-filled rods, assembled and sheathed into cruciform blades, are inserted into the core through the bottom of the vessel to provide both reactivity control and power shaping. This latter is particularly necessary in BWRs; as bubbles form toward the upper part of the core, power density tends to fall there. To provide for long-term reactivity changes, gadolinium (gadolinium oxide) is mixed with fresh fuel in several rods in each bundle. This neutron poison is burned gradually and is completely depleted toward the end of fuel life. Finally, reactivity control is provided by adjusting and recirculating flow rate. When this is decreased, the number of steam bubbles in the core increases, leading to undermoderation and to a decrease in power density and level. Compared to a PWR of comparable power, the BWR core has thicker rods, is larger, and has a power density about half that of a PWR (i.e., 50 kW/liter of core). The pressure vessel is accordingly much larger, about 20 ft (6.0 m) in diameter and 70 ft (22 m) in height. It is made of 6- to 7-in. (16-cm)-thick carbon steel clad internally with a $\frac{1}{8}$-in. (3-mm) stainless steel layer.

Feedwater enters near the top of the reactor vessel. Flow is induced downward through a set of jet pumps internal to the vessel, then upward through the core, via orifices at the assembly bottom. As water flows through the core, it is heated to a boil. It exits the core in a mixture of steam (10 to 13 wt%) and water (87 to 90%). The water fraction is recirculated down the annulus between the "shroud" surrounding the core region and the reactor vessel. Steam separators and dryers are placed over the core to separate steam and water and to provide a flow of dry steam to the turbine. The recirculating pumps handle about one-third of the total flow and are capable of regulating power between a 75 and 100% level with no control rod movement. (Natural circulation, alone, can accommodate power generation up to 30%.) To raise power levels, the recirculation flow rate is increased, thus reducing the void fraction in the core. This, in turn, provides more neutron modera-

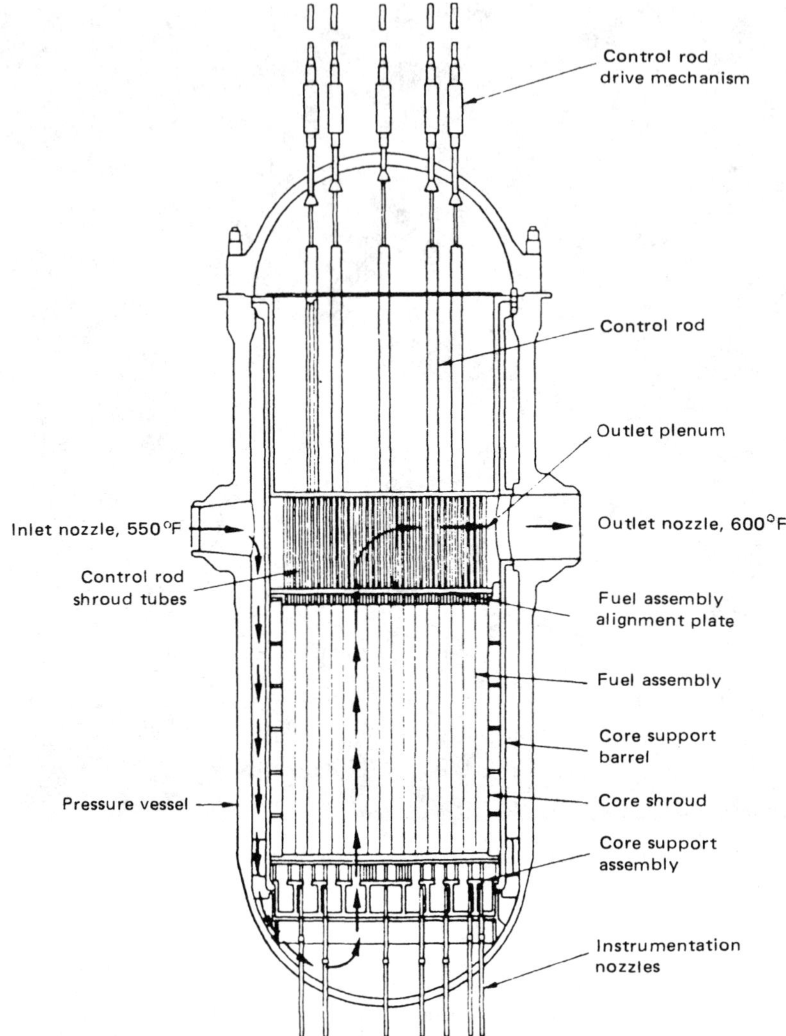

Figure 2.11. Cross-sectional view of a pressurized water reactor. (Courtesy Combustion Engineering, Inc.)

tion, shifts the spectrum toward a lower temperature, and increases reactivity. The power level will rise, stabilizing when the increased boiling reduces the reactivity back to zero. Conversely, a reduction in recirculation flow rate causes a reduction in power. The steam exiting the reactor vessel of a BWR is radioactive primarily from nitrogen-16 (with a 7-sec half-life) which is formed by neutron bombardment of oxygen-16, and possibly from radioactivity leaked from failed pins. Therefore, shielding must be provided for the entire coolant system, including the turbine and condenser, for the protection of personnel.

2.5. THERMAL DESIGN OF A NUCLEAR PLANT

Thermal Cycles and Thermal Efficiency

An LWR's thermal rating is determined by many factors: core size; peak power density; power shape and coolant distribution; efficiency of the recirculation pumps; operating temperature and pressure. The core adds thermal energy to the coolant. The turbine extracts some of it to produce electricity; the balance is rejected to the environment via the condensers.

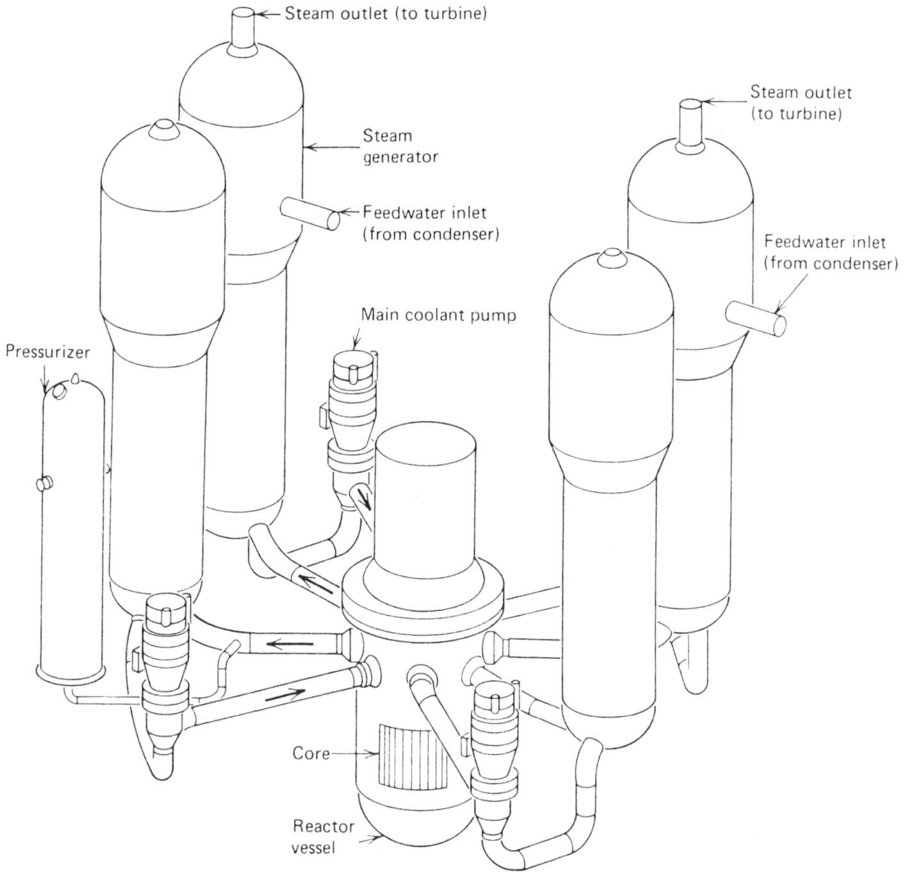

Steam outlet (to turbine)
Steam generator
Feedwater inlet (from condenser)
Steam outlet (to turbine)
Feedwater inlet (from condenser)
Main coolant pump
Pressurizer
Core
Reactor vessel

Figure 2.12. The primary system for a Westinghouse PWR. This constitutes the nuclear steam supply system for a PWR plant.

Figure 2.13. Schematic of a BWR power plant. The steam flows to the turbine-generator, and then is condensed and returned as feedwater to the reactor vessel.

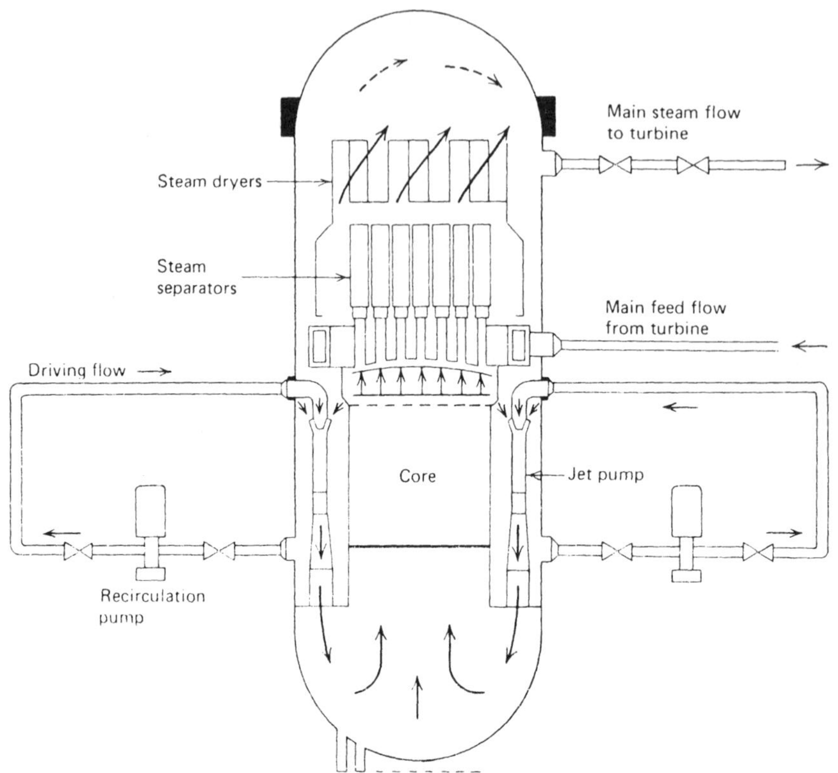

Figure 2.14. Jet pump system of a boiling water reactor. (Courtesy General Electric Co.)

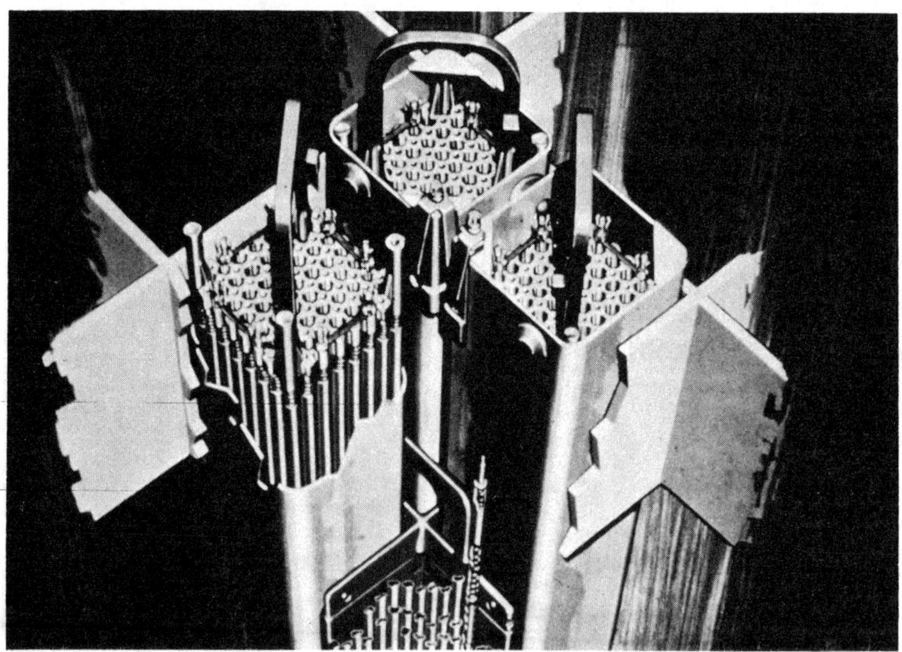

Figure 2.15. BWR module containing four fuel assemblies and a cruciform control rod. (Courtesy General Electric Co.)

Thermodynamic efficiency is increased by the use of feedwater heaters: coolant returning from the condenser is heated with steam extracted from the turbine before it enters the core (see Chapter 8). Even so, because of the relatively low steam temperature, the thermal efficiency of nuclear plants is limited to 33–34%.

PWRs use a forced circulation, indirect cycle system. The reactor primary system operates at about 2200 psi and 580°F; a coolant pump forces the coolant through the core, and a steam generator transfers the heat to a secondary coolant loop operating at somewhat lower temperature (530°F) and pressure (950 psi). The indirect cycle thus provides steam that is not radioactive, but it does require expensive steam generators. A PWR, however, has lower volume and a simpler control system than a BWR.

The high pressure in the primary system of a PWR prevents boiling. It also increases thermodynamic efficiency since the "ideal" efficiency of any system depends on the temperature difference between its hottest and coldest points. If the system were unpressurized, the boiling point would be quite low (100°C). The pressure is maintained by the pressurizer, a large component with a void space that can accommodate surges in the system's coolant volume.

PWRs generally produce dry, saturated steam in the secondary loop at the turbine entrance. In one design (Babcock & Wilcox) superheated steam is produced. A problem is that as the steam passes through the turbine, some of it condenses. The endpoint moisture (24%) is excessive, and can lead to low efficiency and turbine damage, blade erosion, and chemical corrosion. Steam moisture separators and reheaters, placed in the crossover piping between the high- and low-pressure turbine stages, have proved effective in reducing the moisture content of the steam in the turbine; they also improve cycle efficiency considerably (see Chapters 8, 9, and 10).

A BWR is characterized by the occurrence of boiling in the core. The steam generated in the core passes directly to the turbine (Figure 2.13). Forced recirculation of the coolant in the core is used. Most designs feature internal jet pumps with an external recirculation loop for this purpose (Figure 2.14), although one manufacturer now offers a recirculation system without the external lines.

There is also no steam generator between the core and the turbine; hence BWR plants are classified as forced circulation, direct cycle units.

During normal operation, BWRs are controlled by maintaining nearly constant system pressure. This is achieved in part by coupling the turbine to the reactor, in part by varying the recirculation flow. To maneuver, a BWR's power is varied by controlling the reactor coolant flow as explained above.

BWRs are, therefore, inherently stable† in normal transients, operating at essentially constant pressure. The need for control rod operation is minimized. At powers below about 30% of rated power, there is no need for forced recirculation of the coolant, and the plant operates on natural circulation. PWRs are also inherently stable because of the negative reactivity feedback caused by an increase in temperature.

Thermal Limits

A major limitation on the thermal design of a water reactor is the requirement on the heat flux in the core (see Chapter 17). If boiling occurs, the heat transfer from the core to the coolant increases and bubbles are produced. This is referred to as nucleate boiling (Figure 2.16). However, at very high powers, a Departure from Nucleate Boiling (DNB) can occur, causing film blanketing, and the heat transfer dramatically decreases, causing the core to overheat. The power at which this occurs is called the critical heat flux and is a major parameter in reactor design.

For PWRs, the ratio of the critical heat flux to the heat flux in the hottest part of the reactor, called the Departure from Nucleate Boiling Ratio (DNBR), is designed to be always greater than a given value (e.g., 1.30) for all conditions. Thus the possibility of a reactor reaching the critical heat flux is very small, and this would occur only in a very small part of the core.

BWRs treat critical heat flux somewhat differently than do PWRs because boiling occurs normally in the core. The channels around each BWR fuel assembly also affect the flow patterns.

The limiting thermal conditions are defined in terms of a Critical Power Ratio (CPR). The CPR is the ratio of the fuel assembly power at which critical heat flux occurs to the actual assembly power. A BWR must maintain a minimum CPR at all times for a given operating limit at rated conditions.

Since the maximum power level is determined by the rate at which heat can be removed, heat transfer is important in the design of the reactor core. Transfer of heat to the coolant is facilitated by increasing the fuel surface area and coolant velocity. These changes require increased pumping power which reduces system efficiency.

†During the early BWR forerunner experiments, there was concern about the possibility of the voids producing a feedback that might destabilize the core. This was observed at low pressure; however, at 1000 psi the effect was several orders of magnitude smaller.

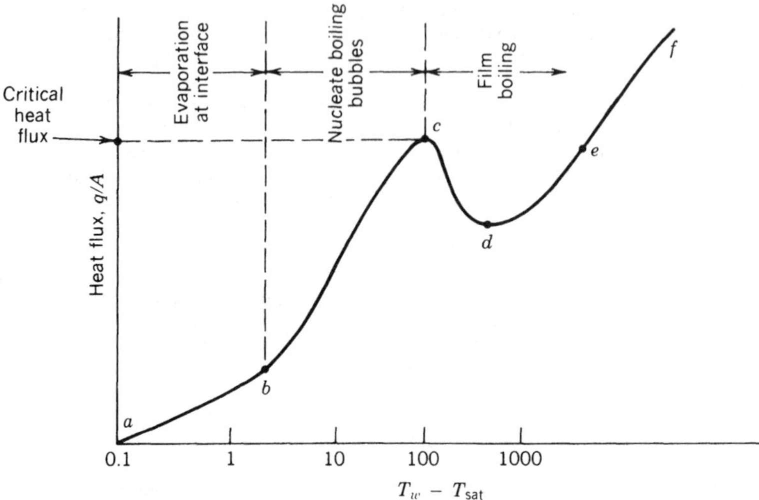

Figure 2.16. Pool boiling curve describes heat transfer phenomena when a uniformly heated rod is immersed in a pool of liquid at saturation temperature. The heat flux from the rod to the liquid is plotted against the temperature difference between rod surface and saturation. *ab:* natural convection; evaporation at liquid surface. *bc:* bubble formation; nucleate boiling. *cd:* unstable transition boiling. *def:* stable film boiling. *e:* burnout point.

Design limits for the fuel are set by its melting point (about 2800°C or 5072°F) and the allowable temperature of its protective cladding. Because fission energy is more or less uniformly produced over the cross section of the fuel rod, the maximum temperature occurs at the fuel rod's center (Figure 2.17) since it is the outer surface that is cooled. Because the thermal conductivity of uranium is low, the peak centerline temperatures are quite high—and this affects the design and safety of a reactor.

Other parameters must also be evaluated in the thermal design of a reactor. These include fuel and cladding temperature, primary system pressure, fuel pellet enthalpy, linear heat generation rates along a fuel rod's length, and core exit temperatures. Over the last 25 years, reactor thermal performance has increased significantly with the increase of outlet temperature. The margins for improvement of thermal efficiency are, however, limited, bounded by condenser cooling temperature and maximum allowable core coolant temperature, both of which are relatively fixed. Therefore, it is practically impossible to increase thermal efficiency beyond the 34% level. The advances in plant rating are also due to increased coolant flow rates and greater heat transfer area provided by its smaller rod diameter.

2.6. MATERIALS

In the design of a nuclear reactor, the proper choice of materials is of paramount importance for technical feasibility and economical and operational optimization. The materials must have the required physical properties, be readily available, offer economic advantages, and be able to withstand the stress of the environment over their intended lifetime.

As a moderator, ordinary water has many advantages, due to its hydrogen content, good heat removal capabilities, and, most important, because it is abundant and inexpensive. Its disadvantages are a fairly high neutron absorption cross section, the need for high purification, and its relatively low boiling point, which requires high pressures if high temperatures must be achieved.

The reactor vessel is a massive structure, up to 40 ft high (12 m) and 14 ft (4 m) in diameter with a thickness of 8 in. (20 cm) or more of carbon steel. The inner surface, which comes in contact with the coolant, is covered with a liner of stainless steel to minimize corrosion. Stainless steel is also used in all other inner parts of the primary systems where corrosion resistance and structural strength are required; such are the thermal shield and the reactor core supports.

Stainless steel was also used as fuel rod cladding in early PWRs (Connecticut Yankee and San Onofre 1). Zircaloy was later substituted, despite its high cost, because of its lower neutron absorption and the resulting improvement in neutron economy. However, stainless steel cladding, with its higher strength, has resulted in better fuel performance (i.e., a lower susceptibility to cracks and hence fewer "leaker" rods). Also, the zirconium in Zircaloy can interact chemically

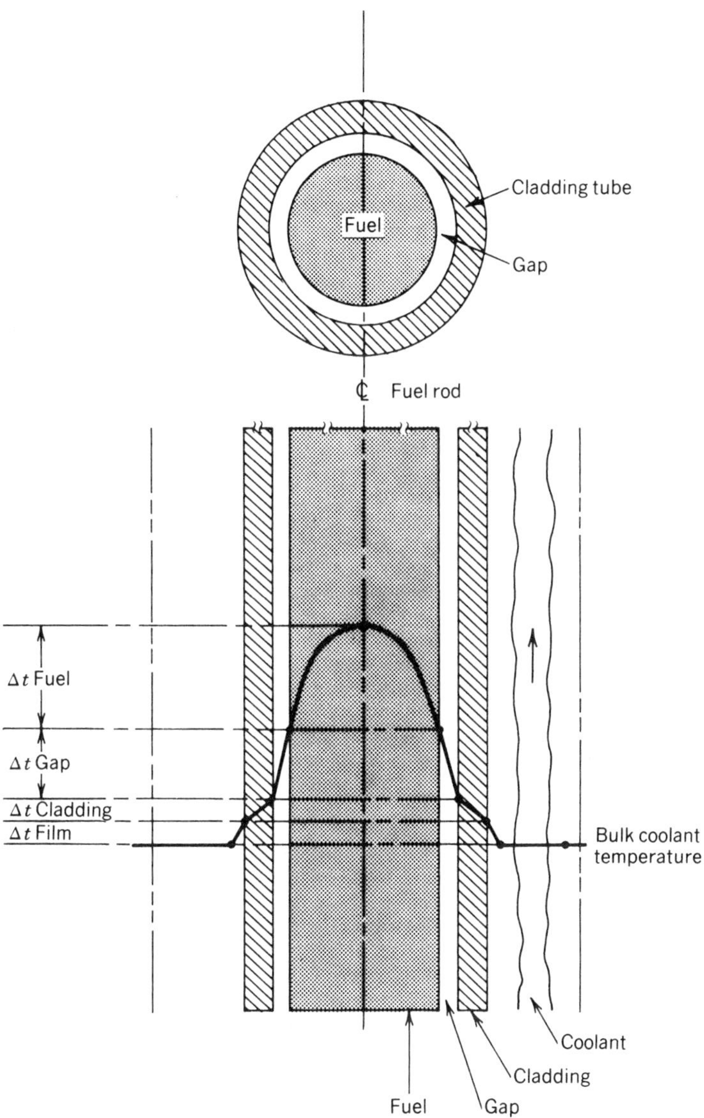

Figure 2.17. Temperature profile in fuel rod (not to scale).

with water to produce zirconium oxide and hydrogen at a temperature much lower than that for stainless steel. However, temperatures are kept well below this temperature limit.

The material for the control rods is usually a mixture of silver (80%), indium (15%), and cadmium (5%), clad in stainless steel. The strong neutron absorption is provided by cadmium. Other materials have been used or considered for control, such as gadolinium, europium, hafnium, and boron.

Concrete is used extensively in a power plant for its structural and shielding properties. The reactor vessel rests on, and is surrounded by, a concrete structure which provides the primary shielding against radiation from the core. The containment vessel is a massive reinforced concrete structure, often exceeding 4 ft (1.20 m) in thickness. This provides additional shielding against any radiation in the primary loop or in the containment atmosphere. It also provides protection against internal penetration from missiles (high-speed fragments from a failed turbine) and external threats from tornado-driven debris, earthquakes, floods, and so on, and, in certain cases, tsunamis and even aircraft crashes. A more detailed description of the variety of materials used in nuclear plants is presented in Chapter 10.

2.7. FUEL MANAGEMENT

One requirement in fuel management is to optimize the "neutron economy," which simply means to make each neutron liberated in fission do its part in continuing the chain reaction and in creating more heat energy. This involves avoiding parasitic—that is, useless—capture of neutrons, or allowing them to stray out of the core.

Another requirement is to ensure that the fission rate of the core is even to the highest degree possible, both axially (top to bottom) and radially (center to edge). This is necessary for good control of the reactor, and to ensure that the "burnup" of fuel in each area or "region" of the core proceeds at the most even possible rate. It can readily be seen how undesirable it would be to have one region or zone of the fuel burn out more quickly than the rest of the core: this would lead not only to thermal-hydraulic difficulties but also to reactor control difficulty and poor fuel utilization.

Since with each unit of heat produced some fissile material is destroyed, a reactor just critical would quickly become subcritical. To enable a reactor to run for some time (say one year) extra reactivity (i.e., extra fissile material) must be built into the core at the outset. To keep the reactor critical at all times, the extra reactivity must be counterbalanced. In PWRs, this is accomplished by a boron compound dissolved in the coolant. Its concentration is adjusted (lowered) over time to account for the drop in core reactivity. The same is accomplished in BWRs (and now also in PWRs) by the use of burnable poisons. These are solid materials with a relatively high neutron absorption cross section, which are mixed with the UO_2 fuel in selected fuel rods. As the fresh fuel gradually burns down (the word "burn" is, of course, use figuratively: there is no combustion), the burnable poison does likewise, so that the power distribution over the residence-time of the fuel in the core is smoothed out.

Early in the development of the first commercial PWRs, it was determined that a core enriched to 2–4% in ^{235}U can last effectively for about three years in a reactor, before the gradual accumulation of fission products (the new elements produced each time a ^{235}U nucleus fissions) becomes so high that the parasitic absorption of neutrons makes it uneconomical to continue operating that core. Very soon after this determination, however, the reactor designers and the user utilities decided that a better scheme than replacing an entire core every three years† would be to replace one-third of the core each year. A better fuel utilization results from annual batch refueling: the old depleted fuel compensates for the extra reactivity of the fresh, more reactive fuel. Because annual refueling reduces plant availability and hence the plant's economic productivity, many utilities are now going to 18-month refueling schedules. Also, neutron economy is served by this refueling plan. At each refueling, the fuel is "shuffled."

The arrangement of new and old fuel in the core can be quite complicated. The goal is to optimize (i.e., minimize) the cost of the fuel over the life of the plant. The optimum is a function of fuel enrichment, burnable poison content, outage time, cost of uranium, value of spent fuel,‡ probability of early fuel failure, and so on.

Early schemes placed fresh fuel on the outer edge of the core, gradually moving it toward the center as it "burned." In general, most current schemes involve the discharge of alternate adjacent fuel assemblies, with the surviving assemblies being moved to new locations. The first fueling cycle presents a special problem, since all the fuel is new. Special enrichments, poison loading, early discharge, and so on, can be used in this case. A detailed description of these fueling strategies is presented in Chapter 11.

The fuel discharged from the reactor is stored deep in a pool of water (for shielding) located adjacent to the reactor building. It is stored in racks of boron-loaded steel or some other neutron-poison-containing metal, to prevent inadvertent criticality. What happens to it from there on will be covered in detail in Chapter 15.

2.8. RADIATION PROTECTION

Another aspect of reactor operation is the minimization of the radiation dose to plant employees and to the surrounding population in general. The minimization of exposure to manmade radiation generally, whether occupational or to the public at large, has given rise to the science of "health physics" (which is also called "radiation protection").

Each nuclear plant has its own staff of professional health physicists who are responsible for monitoring radiation levels inside and outside the plant; maintaining employee exposure records; and ensuring the use of good practices with radioactive materials and environments, so that personnel exposure is kept to a minimum.

In the early 1970s, well before the Three Mile Island event, the U.S. Nuclear Regulatory Commission (NRC) promulgated its ALARA principle, which requires all NRC licensees to keep

†Four years and one-quarter core change for BWRs.

‡If spent fuel is considered waste, this value is negative. If spent fuel is considered as an ore (a source of Pu), then the value is positive.

radiation doses *A*s *L*ow *A*s *R*easonably *A*ttainable. This policy is carried out by reactor operators, and is enforced by the NRC. It must be noted that radiation is part of the natural environment. An average person is exposed yearly to about 100 to 120 mrems (see Chapter 3 for units and other details): 40 mrems/yr from cosmic rays, 30 mrems/yr from soils and buildings, and 20 mrems/yr from radioactive potassium in human blood. Medical X-rays give the average person 75 mrems/yr and additional exposure comes from airline flights (depending on elevation and trip duration). People residing at higher elevation (e.g., Denver) or near more radioactive soils (Kerala, India) receive multiples of the above average exposure of 100 mrems/yr.

A great variety of tools and methods have been developed to make possible the safe handling of radioactive components. A fundamental characteristic of radiation is that its intensity decreases as the distance from its source increases (inverse square law). Likewise, its intensity decreases with the density of the material the radiation must traverse to reach the point where it is to be measured. This basic law of physics results in the so-called "attenuation factor," which is a function of distance from the source of radiation times the density of the material (i.e., shielding) placed between the source of radiation and the material or body exposed to the radiation.† This is why reactors and other radiation sources are always so carefully shielded. (Similarly, maintenance personnel in a nuclear power plant wear protective clothing to guard against spreading low-level radioactivity through contamination.)

A third factor in determining radiation dose is time: obviously, the longer something or someone is exposed to radiation, the greater the amount of radiation will be absorbed.

One can distinguish between "exposure dose" and "absorbed dose." Exposure dose is the product of the intensity of the radiation field and the time of exposure; absorbed dose is the actual amount of energy absorbed by the sample or person. This can lead to confusion, because in practice, the number may sometimes be the same. Nevertheless, the conceptual difference is important. The nature of the medium exposed determines the absorbed dose; and if the exposure dose is known, the absorbed dose can readily be calculated (see Chapter 3).

Although the presence of atomic radiation is not detectable by human senses, it can easily be detected by various types of instruments. One of the simplest is ordinary photographic film, which darkens when exposed to radiation. This makes it convenient to use, and is the reason that it is used in the "film badges" that are the most common type of personal radiation detector used by workers in radiation areas. It also lends accuracy because it does not measure the exposure dose in a general area, room, or space, but rather the exposure dose specifically where the worker was, during his movements. From this, consequently, the absorbed dose by the worker can readily and more exactly be calculated.

Not as convenient for personal use because it is bulkier, but more convenient for measuring the radioactivity of an area or a specific item of material because it gives an instantaneous reading, is the Geiger–Müller counter, or G–M detector (named for Hans Geiger and Wilhelm Müller who invented it in the 1920s) (Figure 2.18*a*). This is a gas-filled tube containing electrodes between which there is an electrical voltage but no current flowing. When "ionizing radiation" passes through the tube, a short, intense pulse of current passes from the negative to the positive electrode and is counted, by making a "click." The number of pulses per second measures the intensity of radiation. (The term "ionizing radiation" refers to the fact that radioactive disintegrations, manifested by emission of alpha, beta, gamma, or X-rays, displace electrons from other atoms or molecules, thereby producing free ions.) Thus a slowly clicking G–M counter indicates relatively little radiation in the area; one clicking faster indicates a higher level of radiation present.

There are other types of radiation detectors: proportional counters, scintillation counters, and ThermoLuminescent Dosimeters (TLDs). TLDs are also widely used, like film badges, as pocket personal dosimeters.

Two other modes in which these devices may be configured are as "survey monitors" (Figure 2.18), which are usually hand-held and have a broad area of coverage, so they can be used to survey the general level of radioactivity in a given area before a worker enters the area, or in laboratories, nuclear power plants, and even inside an operating reactor, to report the level of radioactivity at a given location. (In the last application, needless to say, the reading is reported remotely to a meter in the plant control room, by electric circuitry.)

The ability of radiation detectors to count individual particles of radiation permits measuring radiation with a high degree of sensitivity—that is, to detect the presence of even very small amounts of radioactive materials. Detection is very sensitive in another way also, permitting the identification of specific radioactive materials. This can be done because every radioactive element, and even every different radioactive isotope of every element, has its own radiation "signature"—a characteristic pattern of radioactivity. Thus, by the type of particles emitted, and their energy levels, the emitting substance can be positively identified.

†For example, highly penetrating 2-MeV gamma rays can be attenuated tenfold by about 2 in. of lead, 4 in. of steel, or 12 in. of water. Each like increment of material reduces the radiation another tenfold, so that the radiation can very quickly be reduced to low levels.

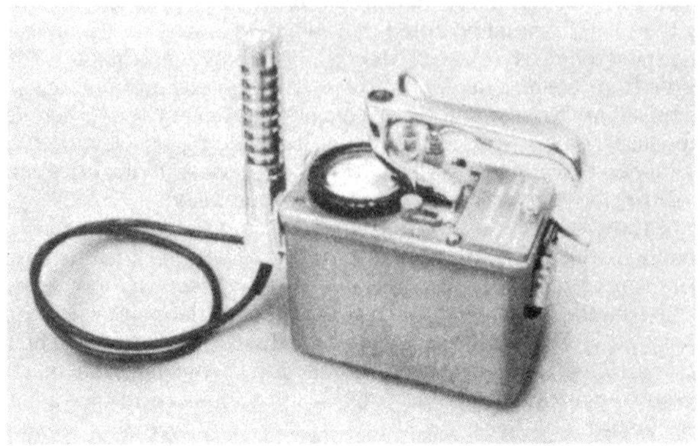

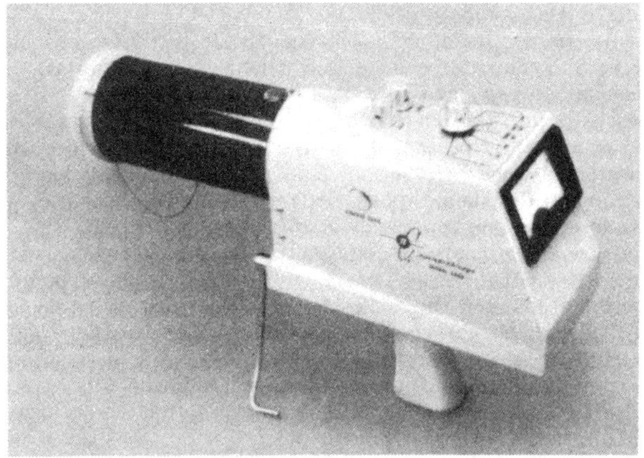

Figure 2.18. Radiation detection instruments. Top: Geiger–Müller counter. (Courtesy Eberline Instrument Corp.) Bottom: Radiation monitor. (Courtesy Nuclear Chicago Corp.)

This makes it possible for operators of nuclear power plants to maintain an extremely close and continuous check not only on the radiation levels in and around the plant, but also on the amount and identity of any fission products that may be released, or be present in plant effluents. Further, it makes it possible to tell positively whether any trace amount of radiation outside a nuclear plant originated within the plant, or from fallout or other background radiation having no connection with the plant.

2.9. CONTAINMENT

The principle of "defense in depth" design has been mentioned earlier. This principle also comes into play in nuclear plant design to minimize or avoid altogether the possible escape of any radiation from the plant. This is the concept of "containment."

All commercial reactors,† going back to the 1954 demonstration program, are built inside air-tight steel spheres or capsule-shaped concrete structures. This Reactor Containment Building (RCB) as it has come to be known, was usually built first, and the reactor assembled inside it (Figure 2.19). Once completed, special doors are used for passage of bulky equipment. Fuel is brought in by an underground conveyor from the adjacent clean-fuel vault, and personnel enter through an airlock. Permanent penetrations for steam lines and electrical connections are double sealed. Before a new reactor may be started up, the containment building must undergo pressure testing to prove that it is, in fact, completely air-tight.

Ventilation air from the RCB is made to pass through charcoal or other filter traps before it is exhausted via a high stack.

In summary, the defense-in-depth principle embodies four lines of defense. First, radiation is locked up in the fuel matrix; second, it is contained inside the fuel cladding; third, it is surrounded

†Exceptions are some older units in the U.S.S.R., where a different concept was used.

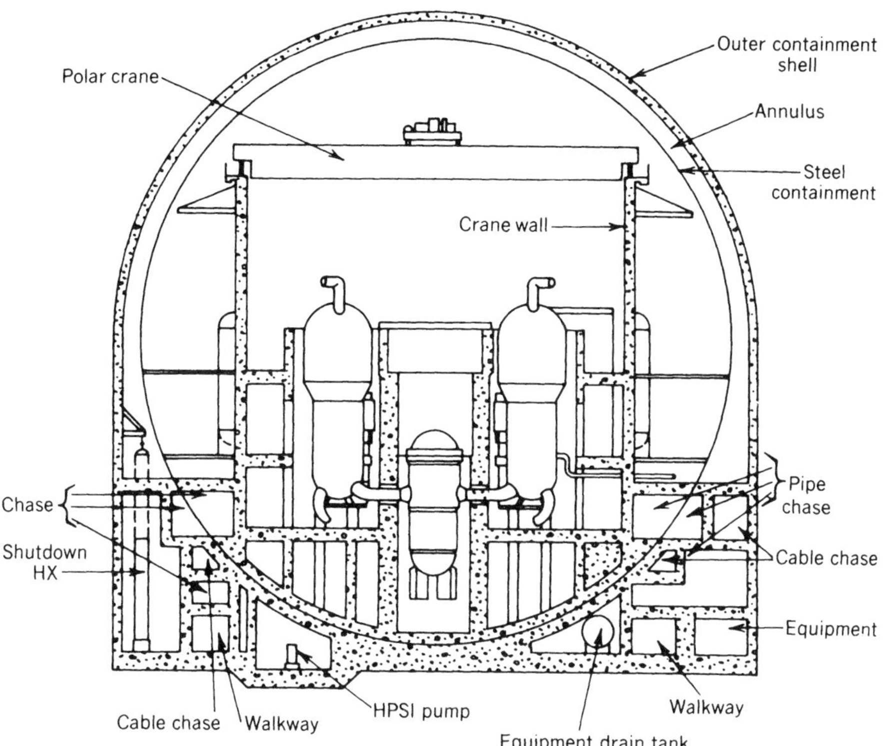

Figure 2.19. Cross section of PWR containment building. It consists of a spherical steel containment shell in which the entire primary system and various other auxiliary systems are enclosed, and an outer concrete shell, serving mostly as shielding against radiation. (Courtesy Combustion Engineering Co.)

by the reactor pressure vessel; and fourth, it is held within the reactor containment building. All four barriers would have to be breached, simultaneously, in order for any radiation from the reactor to leave the reactor and enter the biosphere, or environment.

2.10. THE NUCLEAR FUEL CYCLE

Although the main event of nuclear power is the fission process, which occurs in the reactor, there are a number of other important events both preceding and following fission. Together they constitute what is called the nuclear fuel cycle. (The term cycle may not be exactly appropriate in the case where the cycle is not closed, as is the case at the time of writing.)

The only fissionable material found in nature is ^{235}U. Plutonium becomes part of the cycle when the fertile material ^{238}U is converted into fissile ^{239}Pu. Thus the dominant fuel cycle is the uranium/plutonium cycle. If ^{232}Th is used in a reactor to produce fissile ^{233}U, another cycle emerges, the thorium/uranium cycle. Since the applications of the latter have been rather limited and a commercial thorium/uranium cycle has not been developed, the discussion below will concentrate on the uranium/plutonium cycle.

Front End of the Cycle

Mining

It all begins with the *mining of uranium*—or thorium. Geologists have estimated that uranium is present in the earth's crust to the extent of 4 ppm. The concentration of thorium is nearly three times greater. Therefore, a total of nearly 5×10^{13} t of fertile material is present within the top 3-mile layer of the earth's crust (Chapter 5).

This is a generalized approach, however, which does not consider the question of distribution of economically recoverable reserves. Uranium and thorium are so widely distributed that significant concentrations in workable deposits are more the exception than the rule. Exploitable deposits have on the average a concentration of 0.1 to 0.5% (2 to 10 lb of U_3O_8 per short ton of ore).

Large deposits of uranium-rich minerals are found in many places around the world: in central Africa and around the gold-mining areas of South Africa; in Canada's Great Bear Lake region in Ontario; and in Australia. Lower-grade ores have been mined extensively on the Colorado plateau in the United States since the 1940s. There are other deposits being worked in west-central France, in the western mountains of Czechoslovakia, in southwestern Hungary in Europe; in Gabon, West Africa, and in Madagascar. Also, in Africa rich deposits have been found in the Republic of Niger (north of Nigeria).

The chief sources of thorium are the coastal sands rich in monazite found at Travancore near the southern tip of India, and on the coast of Brazil. Monazite sands have also been found on the shores of Florida's panhandle.

Milling

After uranium ore has been mined, it is crushed and the host rock separated from the ore, usually by a flotation process. The uranium is milled and concentrated as uranium oxide (U_3O_8) which is generally known in the industry as "yellowcake."

Conversion

The yellowcake is then shipped to a "conversion plant" where it is fluorinated to produce the chemical compound uranium hexafluoride (UF_6). This is a convenient form for the gaseous diffusion enrichment process because the UF_6 sublimates (passes directly from the solid phase to the gaseous phase without liquefying) at 53°C.

Enrichment

The uranium hexafluoride, familiarly called "hex," is shipped in tanklike containers to one of the three U.S. gaseous diffusion enrichment plants: the original, since-expanded, one at Oak Ridge, or one of two new ones at Paducah, Kentucky and Portsmouth, Ohio; or to one of many other enrichment plants throughout the world. The enrichment process will be treated in detail in Chapter 6.

After enrichment, the two resulting streams, enriched uranium and depleted uranium, part company. The depleted uranium is stored adjacent to the diffusion plant, and the enriched material is converted back to an oxide again—this time uranium dioxide (UO_2)—and sent to a fuel fabrication plant.

Fabrication

Fuel fabrication plants for commercial fuel are operated in the United States at present by the four reactor manufacturers (Westinghouse, General Electric, Babcock & Wilcox, and Combustion Engineering Corp.) plus Exxon Nuclear Co. Other plants are operated in the major nuclear power user countries.

At these plants, UO_2 intended for LWR fuel is shaped into pellets about the size of the last joint on the little finger of a man's hand. The pellets are sintered, that is, baked, to obtain a hard, dense, consistency. After polishing, they are loaded into Zircaloy tubes. A number of tubes are put together with appropriate tie plates, fittings, and spacers to form fuel assemblies. More detailed description of fuel and fuel fabrication is given in Chapters 9 and 7.

Fuel Loading and Reactor Operations

Completed assemblies are shipped to the power plant in special criticality-proof containers, and on arrival are stored in a clean-fuel vault provided for the purpose.

Bolting or unbolting the head of a reactor vessel, to close or open it, is no mean undertaking. A ring of bolts about the size of a man's arm are used, with nuts of corresponding magnitude that are fastened in place with mechanical bolt tighteners.

At refueling time, the nuts are removed and a polar crane at the top of the reactor containment building eases the vessel head off its seating and hoists it to one side onto a pad provided for the purpose. The reactor cavity—the concrete pit in which the reactor vessel is moored in place—is filled with water to a height such that full-length (usually 12-ft long) fuel assemblies lifted out of the core can swing clear of the lip of the reactor vessel without any of their tops coming out of the water. The purpose of the water is to shield the workers from the radiation of the fuel assemblies. Those fuel assemblies removed are lowered into a canal that connects the reactor cavity with the spent-fuel pool by a bridge crane that spans the pool and runs on rails its full length, and as far as the reactor cavity. In this manner, the discharged assemblies are moved to open positions in the racks on the floor of the spent-fuel pool. These racks are made of a metal containing enough neutron poison material to make certain that the spent assemblies in the pool cannot go critical there.

The assemblies not ready for discharge are shuffled, as described earlier, and the fresh clean assemblies are then loaded into the core grid spaces freed. Underwater periscopes are provided for use in the reactor vessel and in the spent-fuel pool as required. Assemblies discharged are inspected visually by means of these periscopes to check their condition, and a log is kept recording the serial number of each assembly moved into or out of the core. The radioactive content of the water is also checked to make certain that none of the fuel rods has developed any pin-hole leaks that permit release of fission products into the water.

Should any trace amounts of fission products be found in the water, there is a sophisticated method called "sipping" that permits identification of the individual assembly or assemblies that are leaking radioactivity.

Any leakers are identified and isolated. If they had been scheduled to be reloaded into the reactor for further use, a different, sound assembly is substituted.

The fuel fabricators keep very close tabs on sipping operations, to make sure that their quality assurance programs are working effectively.

After the reactor has been "buttoned up" again, that is, the vessel head secured back in place after completion of reloading, the director of reloading operations turns the reactor back to the operating staff, for start-up.

In the process of starting up, a "start-up source"—a neutron emitter—is used since there are not enough spontaneous neutrons emitted to permit restarting the reactor in a timely and efficient fashion by simply waiting for the critical mass of fuel in the core to start up by "letting nature take its course." A neutron source (for example, a polonium–beryllium capsule, Chapter 9) which emits a large number of neutrons spontaneously, is used for this purpose, and put into the core through a guide tube while the control rods are slowly and carefully retracted. Radiation monitors around the core report remotely to the control room the neutron "flux" as it increases. Flux is the number of neutrons crossing a unit area per unit time and is proportional to the fission reaction rate.

Once the reactor has become critical, the control rods are retracted further to increase power until the reactor is back at 100% power. Reactor operations are described fully in Chapter 12.

Back End of the Cycle

Spent Fuel Storage

The predominant fueling strategy requires that either one-third or one-quarter of the fuel assemblies be discharged from the core each year. While fresh assemblies are placed in the core to replenish its reactivity, the spent fuel is transferred to an adjacent pool where it is stored for several years. Spent fuel is highly radioactive and the water serves as shielding and as a cooling medium, to remove the heat produced by the decaying fission products. After several years of cooling in the spent fuel pool, the assemblies are suitable for transportation to a reprocessing plant (see below). However, this option is not currently available and spent fuel must be stored indefinitely in the spent fuel pool at the reactor. Since the amount of stored fuel increases every year, and because utilities must maintain enough space in the pool for a full core discharge, the problem of spent fuel has become a critical one. Solutions proposed include: (a) redesigning or modifying the pools to allow for more dense storage patterns in the same total space available; (b) building more storage capacity at the reactor site; (c) allowing transfers between reactor sites or between utilities to complement needs and available space; and (d) building centralized storage capacity away from reactors (AFR) to accommodate the excess quantities.

Reprocessing and Refabrication

At the reprocessing center, the spent fuel rods are stripped of cladding, and the spent fuel pellets are dropped in a pool of nitric acid. The pellets dissolve in the acid. The solution is then fed to countercurrent extraction systems. Usually, in the first extraction cycle, about 99% of the fission waste products are removed. Then further purification and separation of the plutonium from the uranium is performed. The end products of this step are usually UO_2 and PuO_2 which can be recycled. The separation is a straightforward chemical process that has been carried out by the U.S. government for weapons material and for spent fuel from nuclear-propelled naval vessels for more than 30 years. The reprocessing of commercial fuel was to be done in order to return the unfissioned fuel material to the inventory of material to be used for fuel fabrication. Three commercial fuel reprocessing plants have been built in the United States, but only one has operated, and it has had to shut down. Public concern over the issue of nuclear weapons proliferation, and fear that chemically pure plutonium from reprocessed fuel could be used for fueling weapons caused Presi-

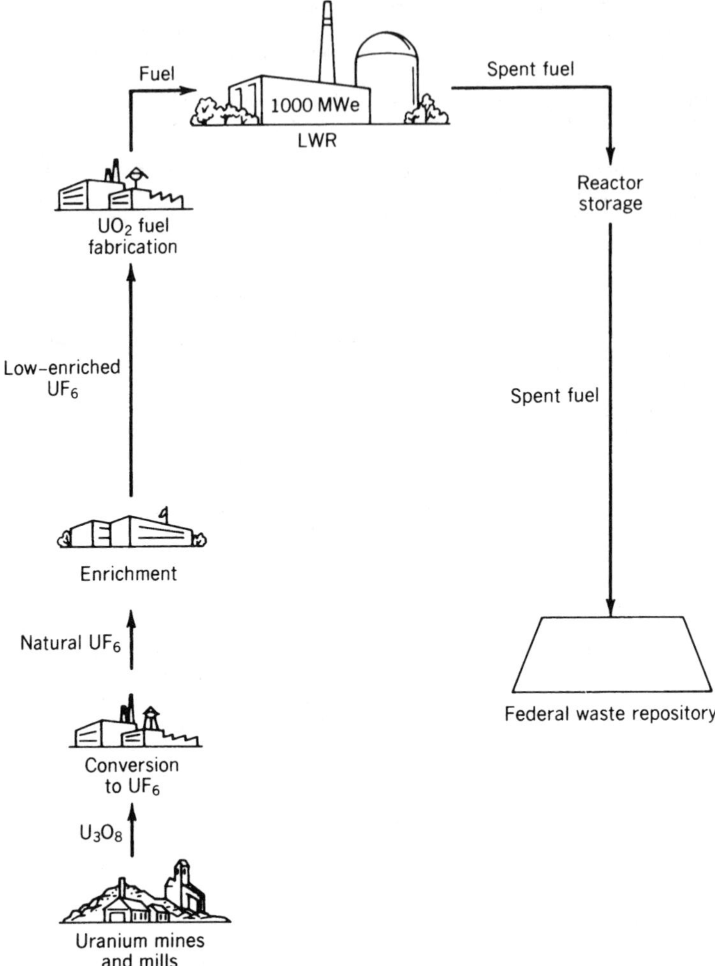

Figure 2.20. A once-through fuel cycle. In this cycle spent fuel is handled as waste and is prepared for permanent disposal.

dent Ford, on the eve of the 1976 elections, to place a ban on reprocessing that was continued in force by President Carter. This ban was lifed by President Reagan, but the companies that in 1970 saw a bright future in the reprocessing business by 1980 saw no economic incentive to enter or re-enter the field under the existing circumstances. This will be further explained in Chapter 14.

The separated ^{235}U from the reprocessing plant was to be blended with freshly enriched uranium for fabrication into new fuel rods. The separated plutonium had two possible uses as nuclear power plant fuel. One possibility is to use it in thermal LWRs. This scheme is generally known by the designation "plutonium recycle," and involves blending plutonium oxide and uranium oxide for the active fuel material. This, in the jargon of the industry, has become known as MO_x,† or "MOX."

Breeders

The other possibility is to use plutonium in breeder reactors using fast neutrons (hence the term "fast breeder"), and produce, or breed, new plutonium in a "blanket" of depleted uranium, that is,

†UO_2 and PuO_2 are the chemical forms of the uranium and plutonium used for fuel in LWRs. When blended together, they are referred to as mixed oxides, hence MOX.

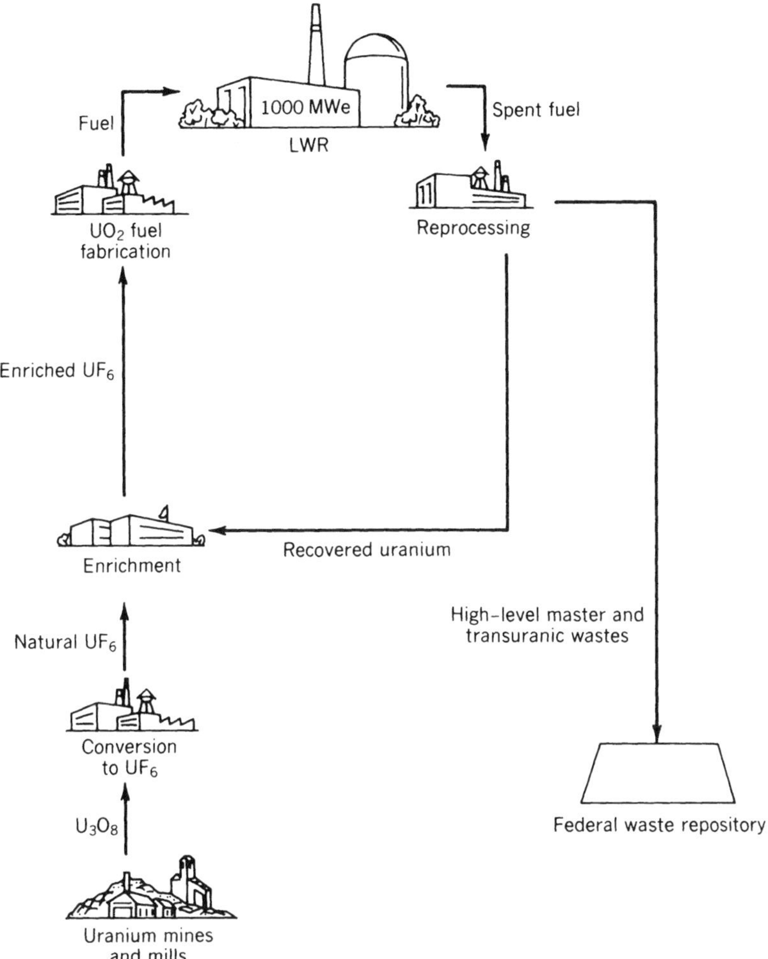

Figure 2.21. Fuel cycle with uranium recovery only.

the uranium left over after most of the ^{235}U has been removed in the enrichment process. This blanket in most breeder core designs either surrounds the central core of fissionable material (called the "driver") or is interspersed with it. Again, the reader is referred to Chapter 13 for a discussion of breeder history and technology in the United States and abroad.

Waste Disposal

The fission waste products are removed from the reprocessing plant and disposed of in various ways. High-level waste can be concentrated into a glassy bead form, and either buried in salt beds deep in the earth, or else shipped to a heavily guarded disposal site. Low-level wastes are stored in liquid form.

The role of the AEC in the high-level waste field, as originally conceived and generally accepted, was that it would take the high-level waste, after a cooling period, from the reprocessing plant, seal it in stainless steel canisters, and place the canisters in holes drilled in underground galleries a mile deep, carved out of bedded or domed salt deposits. Why this has not yet happened and is only now starting to be done will be detailed in Chapter 15. In essence, what had been a solvable technical problem of how to process the waste and prepare it for disposal has been, over the years, transformed into a major political debate focused on the question of where (i.e., in whose backyard) to locate the waste repository.

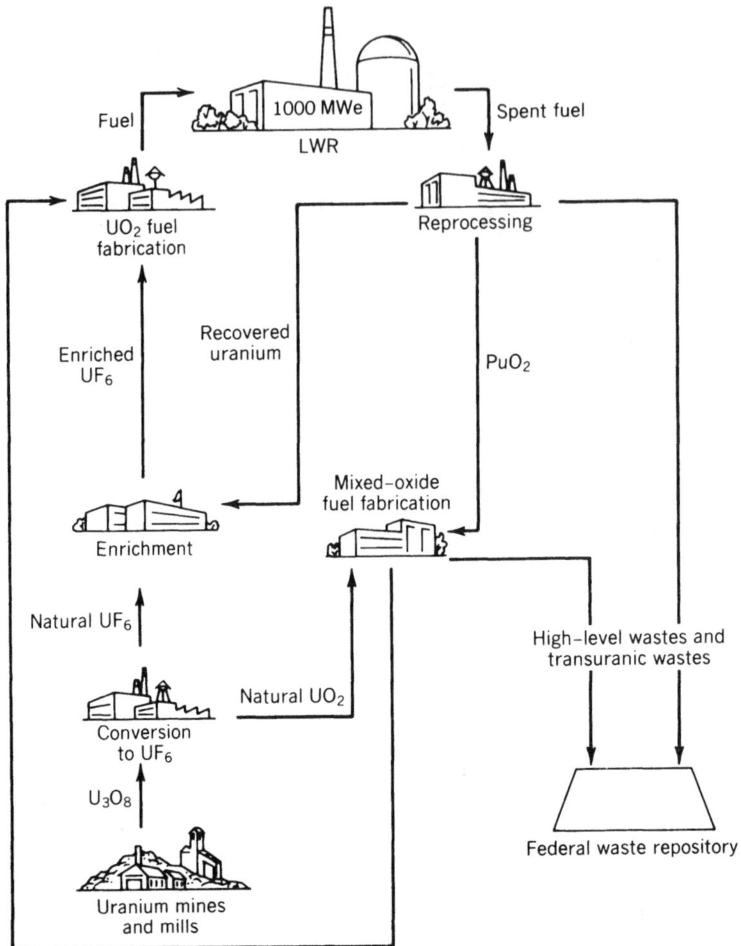

Figure 2.22. Fuel cycle with reprocessing and recycling of both uranium and plutonium.

2.11. FUEL CYCLE TYPES

A number of variations of the fuel cycle exist, depending on the type of reactor to be fueled and on the disposition of the spent fuel discharged from the reactor. Figure 2.20 illustrates the once-through (also called throwaway) cycle. Presently, a version of this cycle is actually used in the United States since spent fuel is being stored indefinitely at the reactor site. In this cycle, spent fuel is treated as waste and eventually provisions must be made for safe handling, packaging, and transfer of the spent fuel to a permanent waste repository assumed to be a federal facility. No reprocessing and no recovery of fissile materials is performed in this cycle.

Figure 2.21 shows a cycle in which spent fuel is reprocessed to allow recovery of the uranium only, while the high-level waste with the plutonium and higher transuranic elements are treated as waste. The uranium is shipped back to the enrichment plant to raise its enrichment from about 0.8 to 3% which is suitable for reuse as LWR fuel. The "wastes" require proper treatment, packaging, and shipment to a permanent repository. A more complete fuel cycle is shown in Figure 2.22. Here, in addition to uranium, plutonium is recovered. Since plutonium is a fissile material, it can be used as fuel. Plutonium oxide mixed with uranium oxide forms the so-called MOX (Mixed Oxide) fuel which can be recycled in LWRs. Mixed oxide fuel has been irradiated in test assemblies in a number of commercial reactors in the United States and overseas, to demonstrate that it can be used successfully and without problems as LWR fuel. However, the recycling of plutonium has not become a commercial reality in the United States because of a number of impediments and restrictions. A keener interest in plutonium recycle has been evinced in Japan and the Federal Republic of

Germany. In Japan, the main motivation was to enhance the country's energy independence while in the FRG it was claimed to simplify significantly the disposal of high-level wastes.

It is also possible to envision a symbiotic relationship of LWRs and fast breeders, based on this third version of the cycle. Plutonium recovered from LWR fuel can be used as first fuel loading of fast breeder reactors. This is the most efficient use of plutonium because plutonium's best properties occur in a fast neutron spectrum, encountered in fast breeders. Hence, this is the route chosen by the French. Plutonium recovered from the French reprocessing plants is reserved for use in their fast breeder development program.

The breeder requires its own fuel cycle, with its own specifications and features. These arise primarily from the high burnup of the breeder fuel (three times or higher than that of LWR fuel). Another cycle exploits thorium, which although not a fissile material per se generates fissile ^{233}U when in a reactor. Although thorium has been used in demonstrations at LWR plants (Indian Point 1 and at the Shippingport Reactor) the thorium cycle has not been developed commercially. Yet another fuel cycle would be needed to reprocess fuel from the high-temperature gas-cooled reactor where the fuel is imbedded in a matrix of graphite. More details on spent fuel and reprocessing techniques are presented in Chapter 15.

Nuclear Power and Proliferation

One of the principal reasons for stopping the reprocessing of spent fuel and recycling of plutonium in the United States has been a concern regarding the spread of nuclear explosives. The perception was that since plutonium can be chemically separated from other materials in spent fuel, it offered possibilities for theft or diversion, by individuals or groups, of fissile materials to illicit purposes. Furthermore, it was feared that countries with a technical capability for reprocessing spent fuel might find it tempting to cross the line and join the "nuclear club."† As a result of these concerns, the reprocessing of plutonium was banned in 1976 by President Ford. Other concerns were raised in connection with the breeder and the enrichment technologies. Intensive activity was mounted in the late 1970s to explore the issues, to examine the potential of alternative technologies, and to attempt to formulate an international consensus as to future nuclear developments. These issues are explored from a technical as well as from an institutional point of view in Chapter 20.

BIBLIOGRAPHY

Babcock & Wilcox Company, *Steam, its Generation and Use,* 39th ed., New York, 1978.

Ellis, R. Hobart, Jr., *Nuclear Technology for Engineers,* McGraw-Hill, New York, 1959.

Foster, A. R., and R. L. Wright, Jr., *Basic Nuclear Engineering,* 3rd ed., Allyn & Bacon, Boston, Massachusetts, 1978.

Glasstone, S., and A. Sesonske, *Nuclear Reactor Engineering,* Van Nostrand, New York, 1963.

Grenon, M., *Le Travail en Milieu Hostile [Work in Hostile Environments],* Presses Universitaires de France, Paris, 1968.

Hogerton, J. F., *Atomic Power Safety,* Atomic Industrial Forum, New York, 1964.

Kaplan, I., *Nuclear Physics,* 2nd ed., Addison-Wesley, Reading, Massachusetts, 1963.

Lahey, R. T., and F. J. Moody, *The Thermal-Hydraulics of a Boiling Water Nuclear Reactor,* American Nuclear Society, Chicago, 1977.

Lamarsh, J. R., *Introduction to Nuclear Engineering,* Addison-Wesley, Reading, Massachusetts, 1975.

Tong, L. S., and J. Weisman, *Thermal Analysis of Pressurized Water Reactors,* 2nd ed., American Nuclear Society, Chicago, 1979.

Wills, J. G., *Nuclear Power Plant Technology,* Wiley, New York, 1967.

†The five nations known to belong to the nuclear weapons club are: the United States, United Kingdom, U.S.S.R., France, and the People's Republic of China. India exploded a nuclear device in May of 1964 but has called it a "peaceful explosive" and has denied possession of or intentions to make nuclear bombs.

CHAPTER 3
HEALTH, RADIATION, AND NUCLEAR POWER

3.1. INTRODUCTION

Large amounts of radiation received over short periods of time can cause adverse effects, including cancer and genetic defects, to plants, animals, and humans. In this regard, radiation is no different than many other toxic agents present in our environment. People are perhaps more sensitized to the potential dangers of radiation than some of these other hazards. We all exist, however, in a continuous radiation field. Radioactivity is a natural phenomenon that surrounds us, and is in our food and water. The most highly irradiated worker group in the United States is airline flight crews who receive their dosage from cosmic rays.

Radiation concern is in part caused by conflicting reports and studies on its effects. Often apparently conflicting data are due to the fact that, at low-dose rates, the effects are so small, and thus they can be studied only in very large populations. The size (and therefore nonhomogeneity) of the study groups incorporate other possible causal agents that often confound the results.

One thing is clear—more is known about the effects of radiation than about any other hazard, including such pollutants as lead, mercury, and arsenic, which have posed poorly understood environmental hazards for centuries. Although radiation is the most studied of these hazards,† its significance for human health at very low doses is unknown. This is because health effects at low dose have not been directly observed, and therefore estimates of public risk must be extrapolated from observed effects at very high doses without the benefit of a verified theory to guide the extrapolation. This is roughly equivalent to trying to assess the health effect of a single aspirin from data obtained on a small group of people each of whom took 100 aspirin at a single time.

Does radiation resulting from nuclear power plant operations and its associated fuel cycle represent a significant hazard to the public and occupational workers? In this chapter, we will examine this question and the related issue of what increment over natural, or background, radiation is associated with nuclear power activities.

3.2. RADIATION IN THE WORLD

Radiation is a natural component of the world around us. People and animals have been exposed to radiation since the start of time. Low levels of radioactivity are in the air, water, and food necessary to sustain life. A fair amount of radiation comes from outer space in the form of cosmic rays.

The amount of background radiation at any particular place depends on the altitude at which we live and the ore deposits in the vicinity. The dose a person receives is further dependent on how he lives, what he eats, and the materials used in the construction of his home. Typical values for each of these components are given in Figure 3.1. This is further broken down according to dose rates to the various body organs in Table 3.1. As seen in these illustrations, the average per capita radiation dose in the United States exceeds 200 mrems/yr. For a life span of 70 yr the dose would exceed 14,000 mrems on average.

Over geologic periods of time, "background" radiation levels were probably much higher at certain times than they are today. Much of this was due to "terrestrial" radiation contained in rock which has gradually decayed over the eons, as well as "bursts" of cosmic radiation occurring when the earth's magnetic field changed polarity. The radiation from rock is pervasive in the environment. As seen in Table 3.2 all rock types contain radionuclides, primarily isotopes of potassium, rubidium, thorium, and uranium. These radionuclides are also found in coal, dissolved in river water, and taken up by vegetation. The radiation from nuclear plants is qualitatively no different

†For instance the International Commission on Radiological Protection has studied the effects and hazards of radiation for over 50 years.

		Your Annual Dose (mrems)
Where You Live	**Location:** Cosmic radiation at **sea level**	44
	Elevation: Add 1 mrem for each 100 ft of elevation .... Elevation of some U.S. cities (in ft): Atlanta 1050; Chicago 595; Dallas 435; Denver 5280; Las Vegas 2000; Minneapolis 815; Pittsburgh 1200; St. Louis 455; Salt Lake City 4400; Spokane 1890. (Coastal cities are assumed to be zero, or sea level.)	
	House Construction (based on $\frac{3}{4}$ of time indoors) .... Brick 45 Stone 50 Wood 35 Concrete 45	____
	Ground: (based on $\frac{1}{4}$ time outdoors): U.S. Average	15
What You Eat, Drink, and Breathe	**Food** **Water** **U.S. Average** **Air**	25
	Weapons test fallout	4
How You Live	**X-ray diagnosis** .... Number of Chest X-rays ____ ×10 Number of lower Gastrointestinal tract X-rays ____ ×500 U.S. Average Dose: Whole Body ____ 100	____ ____ ____
	Jet plane travel: For each 1500 miles add 1 mrem	____
	TV viewing: For each hour per day ____ ×0.15	____
How Close You Live to a Nuclear Plant	**At site boundary:** average number of hours per day ____ ×0.2 ...... **One mile away:** average number of hours per day ____ ×0.02 .... **Five miles away:** average number of hours per day ____ ×0.002 ..... **Over 5 miles away:** .... None........	____ ____ ____
	My total annual mrems dose	____

Compare your annual dose to the U.S. annual average of 228 mrems

1 mrem/yr is equal to: Moving to an elevation 100 ft higher.
Increasing your diet by 4%.
Taking a five-day vacation in the Sierra Nevada mountains.

Note: The above does not include the contribution from radon in the soil or building materials which can add about 100 mrems/yr to the average dose, and in some instances exceed 500 mrems/yr.

Figure 3.1. Common sources of radiation. (Courtesy American Nuclear Society.)

from this background radiation: it consists of either nuclear particles (electrons, neutrons, or ionized helium nuclei) or energetic electromagnetic waves (gamma rays) similar to X-rays (Table 3.3). A material that emits any of these radiations is termed radioactive. These various types of radiation vary considerably in their ability to produce harm.

As important as radiation type is the exposure pathway. External exposure, contamination, and internal deposition of radiation sources are critical concepts in understanding radiation effects. As an example of these concepts, consider an alpha particle (ionized helium atom). Because it is so massive, and is quickly stopped in tissue, it is referred to as a high LET (Linear Energy Transfer) radiation. Unless the exposure is very high, it poses no serious external hazard because it is stopped by the (dead) outer layers of the skin, but it can present a serious internal health hazard if injested or inhaled. The temporal nature of any alpha exposure must be also considered, as well as the method of entering the body. Finally, the total body burden (amount of radionuclides in the

Table 3.1. Summary of Average Dose Equivalent Rates (mrems/yr) from Various Sources of Natural Background Radiation for the United States (NCRP) and for the World (Beninson)

United States Source	Gonads	Lungs	Bone Surfaces	Bone Marrow	G.I. Tract
Cosmic radiation	28	28	28	28	28
Cosmogenic radionuclides	0.7	0.7	0.8	0.7	0.7
External terrestrial	26	26	26	26	26
Inhaled radionuclides	—	100	—	—	—
Radionuclides in the body	27	24	60	24	24
U.S. totals (rounded)	80	180	120	80	80
Average world totals (mrems/yr)	91	539	112	86	

Source: From *Rev. Mod. Physics* **50** (1978).

Table 3.2. Summary of Concentrations of Major Radionuclides in Major Rock Types and Soil

Rock Type	Potassium-40: Percent total Potassium	Potassium-40: pCi/g	Rubidium-87: ppm total Rubidium	Rubidium-87: pCi/g	Thorium-232: ppm	Thorium-232: pCi/g	Uranium-238: ppm	Uranium-238: pCi/g
Igneous rocks								
Basalt	0.8	7	40	0.9	3	0.3	0.5	0.2
Mafic	1.1	9	50	1	1.6, 2.7	0.2	0.5	0.2
Salic	4–5	30–40	200	5	16, 20	1.7	3.9	1.3
Granite	>4	>30	200	5	17	1.9	3	1
Sedimentary rocks								
Shale	2.7	22	120	3	12	1.3	3.7	1
Sandstones:								
Clean quartz	<1	<8	<40	<1	<2	<0.2	<1	<0.3
Dirty quartz	2	10	90	2	3–6	0.3	2	1
Arkose	2	16–24	80	2	2	0.2	1	0.3
Beach sands	<1	<8	<40	<1	6	0.7	3	1
Carbonate rocks	0.3	2	10	0.2	2	0.2	2	0.7
Soils	1.5	12	65	1.4	9	1	1.8	0.6

Source: Adapted from NCRP-45.

Table 3.3. Properties of Nuclear Radiation

Type	Nature	Range in Air	Stopped by
α-rays	Ionized He atoms very densely ionizing can produce high local damage	2 cm	A sheet of paper
β-rays	Energetic electrons sparsely ionizing except at end of range	50 cm	2 cm of wood
γ-rays	Electromagnetic waves sparsely ionizing	Many tens of meters	5 cm of lead
Neutrons	Nuclear particle can produce dense ionization at great depths, depending on energy; can produce transmutation of atoms which affects chemical bonding	Many meters[a]	Up to 30 cm of water

[a]Depends on energy.

body, usually relative to some permissible level) is significant in assessing the extent of radiological health problems.

3.3. RADIATION FROM NUCLEAR POWER PLANTS

Radioactive materials occur in solid, liquid, and gaseous forms in nuclear power plants. Solid forms include irradiated nuclear fuel, or low-level wastes such as water purification resins and work clothing. Liquid wastes include tritium† and reactor coolant water, which contain either dissolved radioactivity or suspended radioactive solids. These liquid wastes are usually processed to remove water and then stored pending disposal. Gaseous wastes contain some fission products (krypton, xenon, iodine) and tritium. The gases are collected and stored according to the applicable federal regulations. During this time, they undergo decay prior to their release to the environment. In this way the radioactivity is reduced to background levels. The time it takes for the radioactivity to decrease to half its starting level is termed its half-life. Each radioisotope has a unique half-life.

Radiation occurs in a nuclear reactor when a uranium atom fissions. The fissioning produces neutrons and fission products. Fission products emit high-energy β- and γ-rays which are quite penetrating forms of radiation. The neutrons not only present a potential radiation hazard themselves, but can lead to radioactivity in other elements by three processes:

1. *Neutron Capture Resulting in Transmutation.* This causes one isotope to be changed into another, sometimes more hazardous, isotope. An example is neutron capture by ^{238}U which eventually results in ^{239}Pu. This is illustrated in Figure 3.2. The plutonium is an α-ray emitter, with a long half-life of 24,400 yr. This process can be continued to produce a number of transuranic elements (^{240}Pu, ^{241}Pu, etc.) which present a potential biological hazard because of their α-radiation and long lives.
2. *Neutron Capture Resulting in Activation.* The structural members of a reactor are usually composed of various steel alloys. Iron and various trace elements in the alloy (e.g., cobalt) can capture neutrons and become radioactive. An example is the neutron capture reaction in ^{59}Co, which produces ^{60}Co, a potent γ-ray emitter.‡ Subsequently, corrosion processes can redistribute such isotopes throughout a nuclear plant's coolant system. The entire primary coolant system can thus become moderately radioactive, making maintenance difficult, and sometimes hazardous.
3. *Fissioning of Uranium.* Results in two or more lighter atoms, called fission products. Fission products accumulate in the reactor fuel during operation, and remain there until the fuel is reprocessed. Occasionally, fission products escape from the fuel into the coolant water. These are subsequently collected in the liquid or gaseous wastes of the reactor.

Commercial nuclear power production is not the only (or even the largest) source of man-made radiation to which the public is exposed. Other sources include medical diagnosis and therapy, mining activities, power production from coal and geothermal plants, fallout from nuclear weapons, and so on. As seen in Table 3.4, radiation associated with nuclear power represents on average less than 0.2% of that from all sources. Radiation can be a positive or negative factor in the human environment. Radiation, which is harmful at very high doses, can be used to reveal tumors and broken bones for medical treatment, and to treat cancer.

Forms of Radiation

Four radiation types arise from various reactor sources. Alpha and beta particles, gamma rays, and neutrons can all cause ionization in human tissue. Alpha particles (a helium atom without electrons) are heavy and fast moving, but travel only about 1 in. in air and can be stopped by a sheet of paper or regular clothing. Even those alpha particles that get past the clothing will be stopped by the first few layers of skin. Since the surface layers of skin are dead (except for the lips and eyes), no measurable damage will usually occur, although burns can occur at high doses. The real danger of alpha particles occurs when they enter the body, through a skin puncture, ingestion, or inhalation. Once inside the body, the alpha-emitting nuclides can have a long residence time, affect living cells, and do considerable biological damage. The residence time is heavily dependent on the elements involved and on metabolic activity.§ Plutonium, one of the more important alpha emitters of concern, is insoluble in body fluid and is not easily absorbed into the body from the digestive

†Tritium is a radioactive form of hydrogen. Because of its half-life (12.3 yr) and because it can become a part of water molecules, it is a potential biological hazard. However, the beta rays it emits are weak, which reduces the hazard.

‡^{60}Co is an isotope widely used for industrial radiography because of its high gamma energies.

§Many alpha emitters are actinides, which are bone seekers. Bone marrow generates blood cells. The destruction of bone marrow is one mechanism of alpha damage.

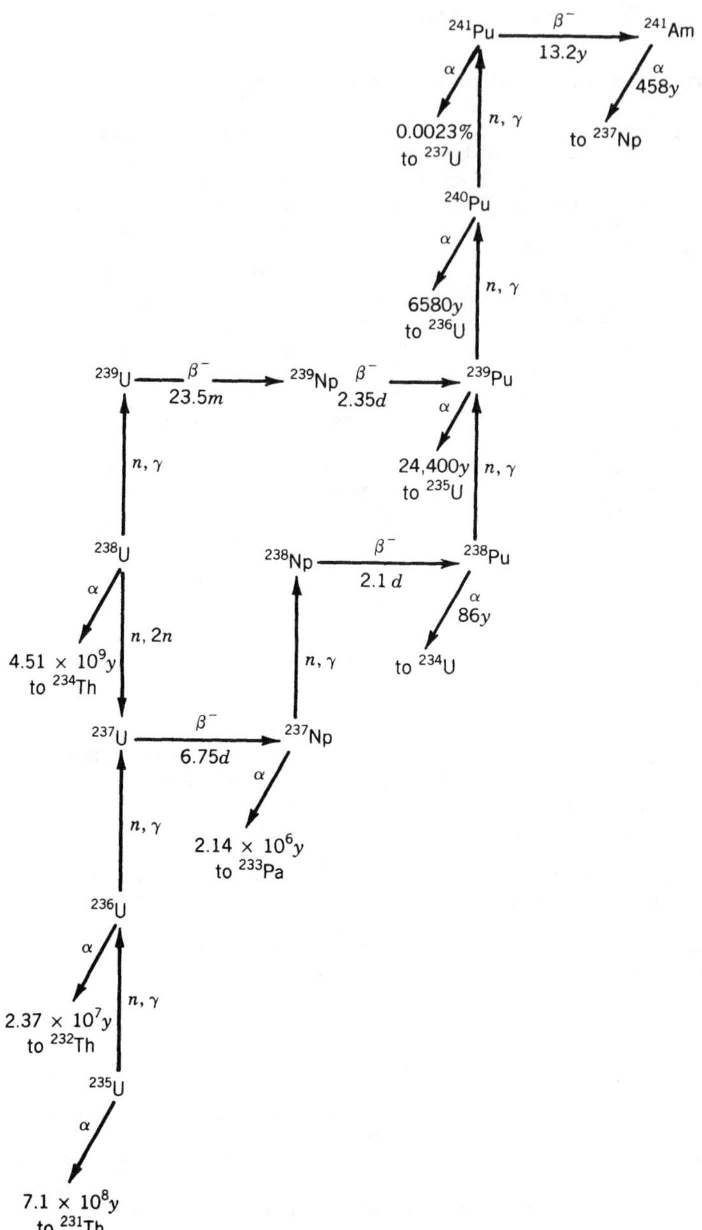

Figure 3.2. Major actinide chains in the uranium nuclear fuel cycle. Many long-lived transuranic elements can be produced in a nuclear reactor. Some, such as ^{241}Am and ^{237}Np, can present potential long-term hazards. The various transuranic elements build up over time as fuel is burned in a reactor. [Adapted from *Rev. Mod. Physics* **50** (1978).]

Table 3.4. Annual Radiation Exposure to U.S. Population

	Dose		Statistical Projection	
	Average, mrems	Total, person-rems	Cancer	Genetic Defect
Source				
Natural background	100	21,700,000	3,050	193
Technologically enhanced[a]	5	1,000,000	150	10
Medical diagnostics	85	18,500,000	2,600	164
Nuclear power (general public)[b]	0.03	6,000	1	0.05
Nuclear power (workers)	600	33,000	5	0.3
Nuclear weapons (development and fallout)	6	1,400,000	200	13
Consumer products	0.03	6,500	1	0.06
Effects				
Total from all radiation sources			6,007	381
Total from all causes, known and unknown			400,000	356,000
Percent from all radiation sources			1.5%	0.1%

Source: From *EPRI Journal*, Sept. 1979.

Note: Calculations by Ralph Lapp, based on estimates of the BEIR committee.

[a]Mainly from naturally occurring radionuclides redistributed by human activities, such as mining and milling of phosphate and burning coal.

[b]Assuming normal operation, normal exposure. The radiation from the TMI accident (50-mile radius) was, 3,300 person-rems, expected to produce 1 cancer, 0.05 genetic defect.

system. However, it is a problem as an aerosol,‡ since it tends to get trapped in the lungs. On the other hand, radium, also an alpha emitter but rarely associated with nuclear power activities, is more efficiently absorbed from the gastrointestinal tract. Exposure to alpha particles is therefore an extremely important consideration in the handling of radioactive material, although prevention is quite simple. "Gloveboxes" operated at subatmospheric pressures is a common example of an effective preventive measure against the transfer of radioactive particles.

Beta particles are fast-moving electrons that can penetrate up to an inch of wood, and travel some feet in the air at sea-level conditions. As such, beta particles can penetrate the skin and must therefore be protected against. Relatively modest shielding (a few inches of wood) can usually prevent bodily penetration and the resultant cell ionization damage. Beta-emitting elements are not usually of concern unless they are ingested. An example of such a beta emitter is tritium (an isotope of hydrogen), which can easily enter the body unless protective actions are taken.

Gamma rays are essentially the same as strong X-rays; their high energy gives them high penetrating powers. Many of the fission products created when uranium is burned in a reactor are potent gamma emitters. High-gamma-ray fields exist in nuclear reactors and must be protected against by a few feet of concrete or a few yards of water. Heavy metals, such as lead, are more effective shields and, where their use is warranted, can greatly reduce the thickness of shielding required. Most of the components associated with the primary cooling system in a reactor are in compartments which provide shielding. The most radioactive material is the fuel itself, which is shielded by water, steel, and concrete.

Radiation Units

Two kinds of units are used to quantify radioactivity. The first is related to the strength of the radioactive source, that is, the number of particles emitted per unit time. This activity is measured in curies, named after Madame Curie who discovered radium. One curie (Ci) is the amount of radioactivity associated with 1 g of radium—approximately 3.7×10^{10} disintegrations/sec. Small amounts of radiation are measured in millicuries (10^{-3} Ci), or microcuries (10^{-6} Ci), or even picocuries (10^{-12} Ci).

‡Because of its density and refractory melting point, plutonium is difficult to create as an aerosol and thus rarely encountered.

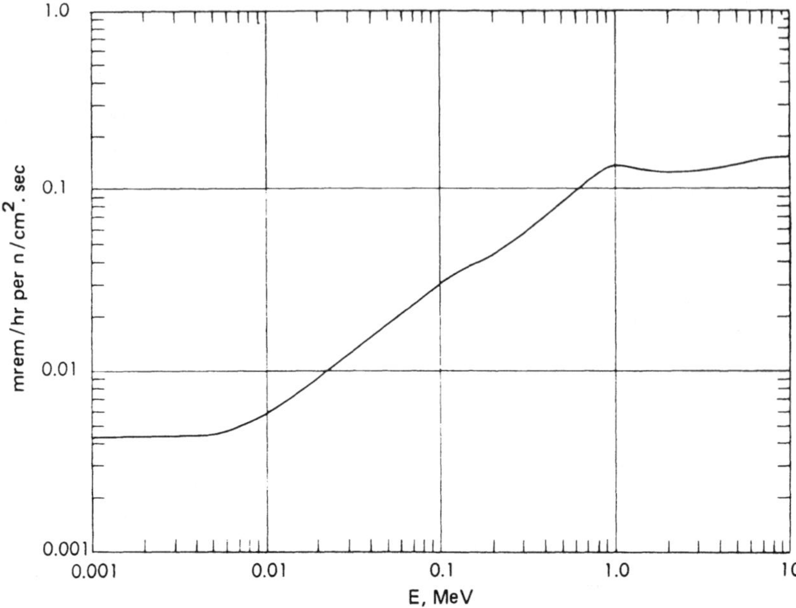

Figure 3.3. Conversion between neutron flux (the number of neutrons crossing a unit area per unit time) and biological dose. (From H. Goldstein, *Fundamental Aspects of Reactor Shielding*, Addison-Wesley, Reading, Massachusetts, 1959.)

The second set of units relates to the dose of radiation absorbed by a person or object. For the absorbed dose, the rad is the unit used and corresponds to 100 ergs of energy absorbed per gram of material. For biological dose, the situation is more complex, because biological systems respond differently according to the type of radiation received. The ideal unit for specifying biological dose should be independent of the nature of the radiation and its energy. Moreover, different biological effects might be the basis for such a unit. Such effects might include chromosome breakage, white blood cell damage, or localized energy deposition in a cell. One would like a unit that would give the same biological effect independent of the radiation type, the dose rate, or the effect being measured.

A biological unit was first needed for the use of medical X-rays. It was called a roentgen,† after the discoverer of X-rays, Wilhelm Roentgen, and was related to the amount of radiation that would produce 1 esu‡ of ionization in 1 cm^3 of air at standard temperature and pressure. This unit was not suitable for other types of radiation, such as neutrons, but served as the basis for all subsequent standards. The current unit is the rem, an acronym for *r*oentgen-*e*quivalent *m*an. One rad of gamma radiation in tissue corresponds to a biological dose of 1 rem. Different types of radiation can be weighted by their relative efficiency to find their equivalent rem exposure. A representative example of this weighting process is shown in Figure 3.3 for neutrons. The relative biological efficiency for photons (X- and γ-rays) and electrons is approximately unity.

A relationship also exists between activity and the dose rate; the latter depends on both attenuation and distance (Figure 3.4). A rough rule-of-thumb is that 1 Ci of 1-MeV gamma rays at 1-m distance in air would produce a dose rate of about 1 rem/hr. For small doses of radiation, the units of millirem (10^{-3} rem) and microrem (10^{-6} rem) are used. Millirem (mrem) is the term most used in discussion of nuclear power because the amounts usually discussed are generally small. Although the curie, roentgen, rad, and rem are in current usage, they are being replaced in the scientific literature by a set of consistent metric units (Table 3.5).

†The roentgen unit has been in use for over 50 years and is still commonly used in medicine. It can be easily measured in air ionization chambers. The radiation which gives 1 roentgen in air gives an absorbed dose in body tissue of 0.93 rad. The rad is the common unit of *absorbed* dose; the roentgen refers to the intensity of the radiation field.

‡*e*lectro*s*tatic *u*nit, an outdated measure of electrical charge.

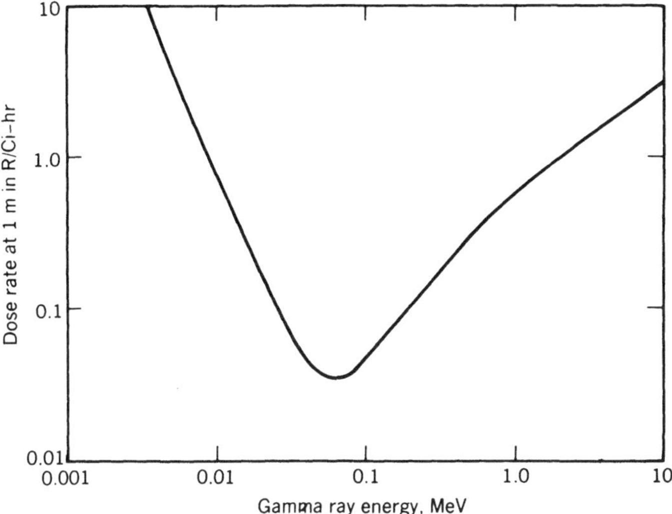

Figure 3.4. Exposure in air at 1 m from a point isotopic γ-source of 1 Ci. (From TID-7004.)

Radiation Detectors

There are a variety of instruments that can be used to detect radiation. One of the simplest, and the one widely used for personnel protection, is the film badge (Figure 3.5). This is simply a piece of photographic film that can be conveniently worn. When developed, the film appears cloudy if it has been exposed to radiation. When small masks of various materials, such as lead and cadmium, are used, the film can distinguish between β-rays, γ-rays, and neutrons. To determine the dose received, the film is developed and the "fogging" caused by the radiation exposure determined. Chemical dosimeters and various other special detectors are sometimes included. Although they are quite accurate, film badges do not give instantaneous readouts, and are therefore unsuitable for many purposes, such as radiation alarms.

Most direct reading radiation instruments are gas-filled counters of one type or another. They work because of the ionizing properties of radiation: the radiation entering the instrument produces ions in the gas which are collected on an electrode maintained at high voltage. A current "pulse" results, which then can be processed electronically to produce a "count," an electronic analogue to the *dose rate* the instrument is being exposed to. A well-known example is the Geiger counter, although greatly improved versions are now available. Solid-state detectors have also become available over the last two decades. They can be made extremely sensitive to the energy of the incoming radiation. Since they do not perform well in very high radiation fields, they are generally used for specialized applications in reactor technology. Ion chambers are used when only the dose rate is important, as is the case for the area radiation monitors used in nuclear plants.

A useful device for personnel protection is the pen dosimeter. This instrument is a small condenser ion chamber about the size and shape of a fountain pen. The ion pairs produced by radiation cause the discharge of a capacitor proportional to the dose the instrument sees. The

Table 3.5. New Units for Radiation Quantities

Quantity	New Named Unit and Symbol	In Other SI units	Old Special Unit and Symbol	Conversion Factor
Exposure	—	C/kg	roentgen (R)	1 C/kg ~ 3876 R
Absorbed dose	gray (Gy)	J/kg	rad (rad)	1 Gy = 100 rad
Dose equivalent	sievert (Sv)	J/kg	rem (rem)	1 Sv = 100 rem
Activity	becquerel (Bq)	s^{-1}	curie (Ci)	1 Bq ~ 2.7×10^{-11} Ci

Note: As of 1 April 1978, NRPB adopted the International System of Units (SI). The relationships between the new SI units and previous units are shown. The old units are still in common use.

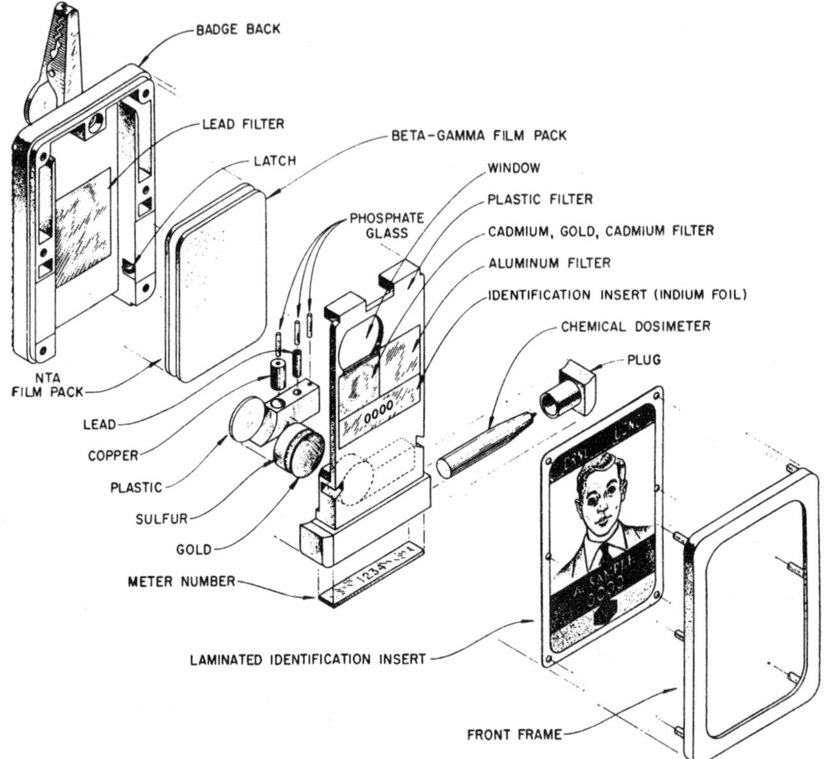

Figure 3.5. A well-designed film badge. (From ORNL-2777.)

convenience of the device (it requires no electronics, and is easily read on the spot) has led to its wide use. Pen dosimeters with ranges up to 1000 rads are available, although most have a range between 0 and 500 mrems. They are commonly carried by plant personnel. More and more, however, these simple devices are being upgraded with sophisticated electronics, so that they can be read as a worker enters and leaves a radiation area. In this way a computer can keep a running total of exposure, and what plant operations are leading to personnel exposure.

3.4. RADIOLOGICAL RISK

The concept of radiological risk is based on two quantities: dose and dose rate. Effects of radiation must be estimated at low levels by various theories since there are no detectable effects. Just as radiation effects are modified by dose, they are also sensitive to the time over which the dose is delivered—the dose rate. Animal experimentation has shown that protracting the exposure of some animals (low-dose rates) results in little or no biological damage compared with those animals receiving the same dose but at high-dose rates. This effect is similar to the biological response of any agent.

The linear theory refers to a straightline extrapolation from high doses with demonstrable effects to low doses where there are no demonstrable effects or, at least, questionable effects. This postulates that the health effects of low-dose radiation (on a statistical basis) will be proportional to, or linear with, those that occur at high doses and dose rates. For example, if a dose of 100 rems to 1000 people (10^5 person-rem) produced 10 additional cancers, then a dose of 0.1 rem to one million people (10^5 person-rem) would also produce 10 additional cancers. Studies of the radiation effects in human beings have generally been carried out following exposures that were very intense (i.e., high dose and high-dose rate). Notable examples include the Japanese survivors of the atomic bombings and those persons treated with radiation for rheumatoid spondylitis—two populations on whom the greatest reliance is placed in developing risk estimates. No radiation effects have been detected in persons exposed to low-dose rates similar to that experienced in the operation of nuclear power plants. For instance, in some sections of India where background radiation levels

Table 3.6. Quantitative Factors Affecting Biological Damage

1. *Total dose.*
2. *Dose rate.* To a certain extent the body can repair radiation damage, and the rate at which the total dose is given will therefore be important. A dose which may be lethal when given in a period of a few hours may have no obvious effect when spread over a lifetime.
3. *Previous exposure history.* The separation of damage into reparable and permanent means that the effect of any given exposure depends on the history of previous exposures: magnitude, duration, interval between exposures, etc.
4. *Radiation type and energy.* For a given dose the biological effect may depend on the energy of the radiation and its type, e.g., whether gamma rays or neutrons. The outstanding physical property involved here is the stopping power of the ionizing particles produced by the passage of the radiation. The effects of mixed radiation (neutrons and gamma rays) may be different than when the two radiations are used separately.
5. *Physical and chemical environment.* Temperature and oxygen pressure have been shown to have a definite effect on the damage produced by radiation.
6. *Portion of organism exposed.* The effects depend sharply on whether the whole body or only a portion of the body is exposed. Genetic effects obviously cannot occur if the gonads are not irradiated, and shielding of the eyes prevents cataract formation. Therapeutic exposures have been used for selected portions of the body which would produce death rapidly if given as whole body doses. Certain organs (such as the spleen, which is closely involved in blood formation) have been shown to be particularly sensitive to radiation.
7. *Species exposed.* The results of a given exposure may vary considerably from one species to the next. Even among warm-blooded mammals the lethal dose varies over a factor of three.
8. *Individual variations.* There are large variations in the reactions of individuals to radiation. As a result, the observation of radiation damage must be statistical in nature. Predictions can only be made for a population, not the individual.

Source: Adapted from H. Goldstein, *Fundamental Aspects of Reactor Shielding,* Addison-Wesley, Reading, Massachusetts, 1959.

exceed 5 rems/yr due to the presence of thoria sands, no apparent effects have been observed in the population. The important issue is how to extrapolate from the high-dose, high-dose-rate exposure to the low-dose, low-dose-rate exposure. The linear assumption is widely used. Much of the recent data studied by the NCRP† suggest that this assumption of linearity probably leads to exaggerated estimate of risk. Other models, such as a quadratic model or a linear quadratic model, have also been proposed. These models give lower estimates of risk at lower exposures.

Biological Effects of Radiation

Biological systems are extremely complex. As a result, the effect of radiation on such systems is equally complex. While total radiation dose is often used as the measure of radiation damage, this use should be viewed as one of convenience since effects on different individuals can vary. These variations can be experimentally observed. It is not uncommon to observe response differences of factors of two or three in supposedly identical biota. As a result, statistical predictions are used. These statistical effects, sometimes referred to as risk, are intended to be used over a large population, where statements about average response take on meaning.

Besides total dose, other qualitative factors shown to cause radiation effects are: the dose rate, previous irradiation history, type of radiation, environment, organ/type of organism involved, and extent of the body exposed. These factors are summarized in Table 3.6. The large number of variables involved make quantitative assessment of radiation effects difficult. Moreover, there are many forms of damage that organisms can incur.

The biological effects in humans due to radiation exposure are usually categorized into early somatic effects, late somatic effects, and genetic effects. These are as follows:

1. *Early Somatic Effects.* These include radiation-induced illness and early fatality which occur a few days to a few months after exposure. The usual expression is the LD_{50} dose, that is, the dose expected to be lethal to 50% of the exposed population. Bone marrow and other blood-forming organs are the most sensitive in humans and damage to these can lead to early fatalities when an LD_{50} dose is about 300 rems. Some deaths at 150 rems occur, and without medical treatment nearly total fatality will occur at 600 rems. (It is interesting to note that doses well above

†The U.S. National Committee on Radiation Protection.

Table 3.7. Radiation Dosimetry and Biological Response

Dosimetry			
Dose, rems	Dose Rate	Exposure[a]	Biological Response
0.3	Weekly	*T*	Probably none
1	Daily (for years)	*T*	Leukopenia
1.5	Weekly	*L*	Probably none
25	Single dose	*L*	Chromosome break in tumor cells (tissue culture)
50–100	In accumulated small dose	*L*	Gene mutations to double spontaneous rate per generation
200	Single dose	*T*	Nausea
300–500	Single dose	*T*	LD_{50} for man
400	Single dose	*L*	Reversible epilation
400–500	10–50 rems/day	*T*	Clinical recovery
600–900	300 rems/day or small doses	*L*	Radiation cataract
1000–2500	200–300 rems/day	*L*	Response of markedly radiosensitive cancer
2500–6000	200–300 rems/day	*L*	Response of moderately radiosensitive cancer
4000–5000	200–300 rems/day	*L*	Limits of nervous tissue
5000–6000	200–300 rems/day	*L*	Limits of gastrointestinal tract

Source: After *Radiation Dosimetry,* G. J. Hine and G. L. Brownell, eds., Academic Press, New York, 1956.

[a]*T* = total body; *L* = local.

600 rems are routinely administered in organ transplant operations. Such large doses temporarily destroy the white blood cells and immunosuppression mechanisms in the body, which would lead to death if not closely monitored by physicians.)

Apart from the blood-forming organs, radiation doses to the other body organs of a few thousand rems are required before a high probability of death occurs. At the other end of the scale, few human health effects have been noted at single-exposure doses below 25 rems. Moreover, continuous exposures at the rate of about 0.3 rem/week (300 mrems/week) result in effects difficult to observe. Animal experimentation is usually performed at rates about 10 rems/min, although some long-term experiments have been performed at dose rates of 0.3 rem/day. Below 0.3 rem/day, animal health effects become rare, and difficult to observe. Most experimental data, therefore, exist at high dose rates. Typical biological response to various radiation doses are given in Table 3.7.

Heavy doses of radiation, that is, above 100 rems, will produce what is called "radiation sickness" in humans. Almost nothing is felt during exposure until the dose is nearly lethal. When the dose is large enough to cause eventual death, nausea and shock are common during the exposure. Within a few days, various effects appear, such as a decrease in the number of blood cells, hemorrhaging, and loss of hair. (These are all common reactions in the radiotherapy treatment of cancer.) The suppression of the immune system reduces the usual defenses to bacteria. Secondary complications, such as infection, are a primary cause of death. Recovery from a sublethal dose usually occurs within a month or two. Radiation illness can also be treated by bone marrow transplants, drugs, and other known procedures.

2. *Late (or Latent) Somatic Effects.* Cancer is likely to be the most important latent somatic effect of radiation, although other effects such as thyroid nodules, birth defects, growth deficiency, and chromosomal aberration are known in animals or man. Eye cataracts in humans from high-energy neutron radiation exposure have been observed. Because cancer and these other effects take some years to develop, they are called latent health effects. Some of these effects, such as thyroid nodules, are highly treatable.† Others, such as chromosomal aberration, have unobserved consequences. Still others, such as birth defects caused by pelvic X-ray therapy to women in the early stages of pregnancy, have led to the discontinuation of such medical practices. But the most controversial and difficult to resolve effect is that of latent cancer.

†A roughly 95% cure rate is routinely achieved in treating thyroid nodules.

Table 3.8. Cancer-Causing Agents Which May Be Associated with Various Occupations

Agent	Sites of Cancer
Arsenicals	Skin, lung
Auramine	Bladder
Coal tar, pitch	Skin, lung
High boiling petroleum oils	Skin
Shale oils	Skin
Tars	Skin
Creosote oils	Skin
Anthracene oils	Skin
Soot (carbon black)	Skin
Mustard gas	Lung
Cutting oils	Skin, possibly respiratory and upper alimentary tract
Various combustion products	Lung
Chromates	Lung
Asbestos	Lung, pleura, peritoneum, GI tract
Sunlight	Skin
Aromatic amines	Bladder, possibly biliary tract, salivary glands
X-rays and radium	Skin, lung, leukemia
Nickel	Lung, nasal cavity
Isopropyl oil	Lung, larynx, nasal sinus
Radioactive chemicals	Bones, nasal sinus
Bis(chloromethyl) ether	Lung
Vinyl chloride	Liver

Cancer is the second leading cause of death in the United States; only heart disease is greater. Roughly 20% of the population will die from cancer, although about 25% will contract it some time in their lifetime (this ranges from 23.4% for nonwhite males, to 29.8% for white females). Various agents, including radiation, are known or suspected to contribute to cancer (Table 3.8).

Understanding the relationship between radiation and cancer is complicated by the facts that: (1) a significant fraction of the population will develop cancer under normal conditions, (2) the incremental occurrence of radiation-induced cancer is very small, and (3) there is usually no way to differentiate radiation-induced cancers from those that occur spontaneously. Upper limits of radiation risk exist, based on what are thought to be conservative estimates (Table 3.9). How conservative these estimates are is the subject of great and heated controversy.

Radiation-caused thyroid nodules are of special interest in the discussion of nuclear power safety. This is because many early studies have identified radioactive iodine (a thyroid-seeking element) as a high contributor to public consequences in the event of a major reactor accident. This seems less the case today since the early studies assumed radioiodine would exist as molecular iodine (I_2), a gas, while more recent studies, as well as the accident results at Three Mile Island (TMI), have indicated that the chemical form of iodine in an accident is nongaseous CsI, which is not easily dispersed and therefore much less a hazard to the general population. In any case, thyroid nodules are estimated to occur at the rate of about one per million persons per rem for internal radiation doses to children, the most sensitive population. About one-third of the total number of nodules would be malignant. Malignant thyroid nodules, as discussed above, are highly curable since they are well differentiated and slow growing.

3. *Genetic Effects.* Various studies on therapeutic radiation patients and atom bomb victims have shown that ionizing radiation will cause breaks in chromosomes. Most of these aberrations are unstable, but some persist for many years. Although the association between chromosomal aberrations and human health is increasing, its significance is unknown but thought to be very small. Genetic defects have not been linked with cancer, and there is no evidence† to date that associates possible mutagenic effects with birth defects in the children of radiation victims.

†See, for example, Beebe, *American Scientist* **70,** 35 (1982).

Table 3.9. Upper Bound Estimate[a] of Expected Latent Cancer (Excluding Thyroid) Deaths per Million Person-rems of External Exposure

Type of Cancer	Expected Deaths per 10^6 person-rems
Leukemia	28.4
Lung	22.2
Stomach	10.2
Alimentary canal	3.4
Pancreas	3.4
Breast	25.6
Bone	6.9
All other	21.6
Total (excluding thyroid)	121.6

Source: From U.S. Nuclear Regulatory Commission, 1975.

[a]Upper-bound estimates are made on the basis of the linear hypothesis. That is to say, the probability of contracting cancer is assumed to be proportional to the dose.

Radiation exposure does not appear to induce new kinds of genetic changes in individuals. That is, the changes observed are no different than changes that occur spontaneously. Radiation does increase the frequency of such genetic aberrations. The National Academy of Science estimates that the dose doubling the number of spontaneous aberrations is between 20 and 200 rems.

Radiation Health Studies

Studies on radiation health effects are reviewed by the International Commission on Radiological Protection (ICRP) and its American counterpart, the National Committee on Radiation Protection (NCRP). These organizations were set up in the 1920s to set guidelines for radiation exposure. After the Second World War, two other prestigious groups were formed to help assess the scientific data. These are the National Academy of Science's Committee on the Biological Effects of Ionizing Radiation (BEIR) and the United Nations Scientific Committee on the Effects of Atomic Radiation (UNSCEAR).

During the early years, most of the radiation data came from studies on small animals rather than on man. Such animal studies will always have problems when extrapolated to humans for two reasons: (1) the differences in radiosensitivity between animals and man and (2) many types of cancer are thought to have incubation periods much longer than the lifespan of most experimental animals. As a result, a great deal of reliance is placed on studies of atomic bomb survivors of Hiroshima and Nagasaki, and of medical patients treated with X-rays for ankylosing spondylitis (a spine disease).

The Japanese survivors of the atomic bomb were exposed to approximately 5 million person-rems of radiation. Between 1950 and 1974, there were 204 excess cancer deaths in this population of which 73 were from leukemia. This is about 10% more than the expected cancer death incidence. The risk estimate derived from these numbers is 95 cancer cases/million person-rems. The Japanese data show a strong correlation with the victims' age (Figure 3.6) and dose received (Figure 3.7).

The studies on the atomic bomb victims are somewhat difficult to interpret because of the dosimetry involved. The two bombs were of different types. Their yield and radiation distributions are still not completely agreed upon. Most recent studies rely on the Tentative-1965 (T-65) dose estimate made at Oak Ridge National Laboratory. Using this dose model, leukemia mortality appeared much higher at Hiroshima than Nagasaki. This was attributed to the higher neutron component in the T-65 estimates. Some newer calculations show a much lower neutron component than the T-65 study. This would imply that neutrons at low dose are more carcinogenic for some forms of cancer than previously thought. With the old dosimetry, the Japanese survivor data seemed anomalously low (Figure 3.8). The distance of interest in the dosimetry data is between 1 and 2 km radius. Under 1 km, most died from prompt effects (blast and burns), and beyond 2 km long-term effects were difficult to ascertain.

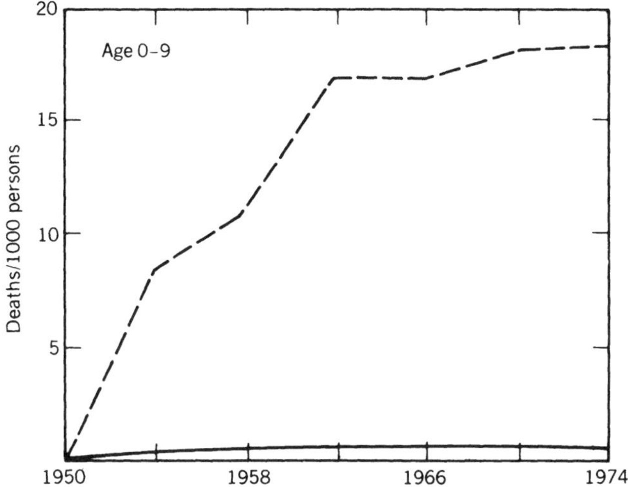

Figure 3.6. The timing of the appearance of excess cancer varies with the type of tumor as well as with the age at exposure. Cumulative leukemia deaths from 1950 to 1974 per 1000 A-bomb survivors alive on 1 October 1950 are shown here by age at exposure. The excess, the difference between the curves for exposure to less than 10 rads (solid lines) and to 100+ rads (dashed lines), appears early in each age group but tapers off sooner in the youngest groups; the greatest excess is seen in the youngest and oldest groups. [From Beebe et al., *American Scientist* **70,** 35 (1982).]

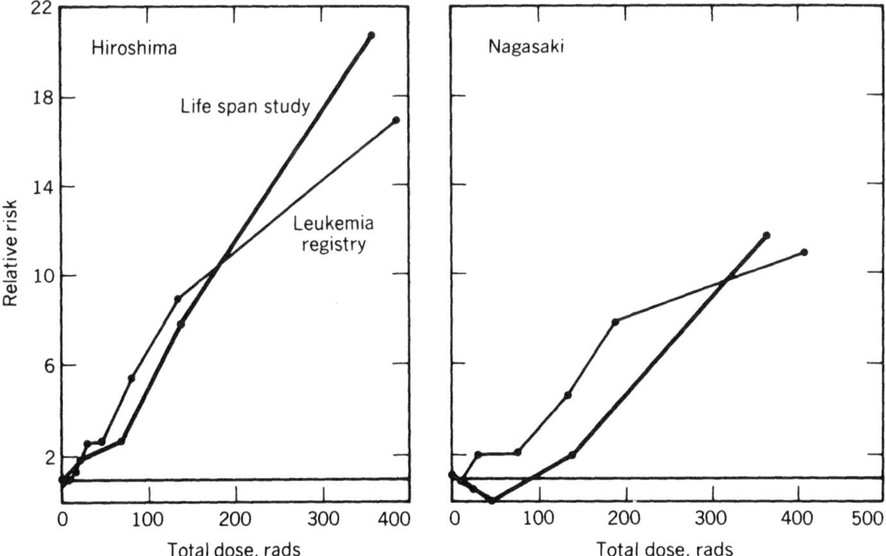

Figure 3.7. The data on leukemia among the Life Span Study sample of A-bomb survivors are too limited to discriminate among the dose-response models. From 1950 to 1974, the Life Span Study of 62,000 people in Hiroshima and 20,300 in Nagasaki includes only 110 leukemia deaths in the former city and 34 in the latter. The dose-response curve in Nagasaki is markedly nonlinear. [From Beebe et al., *American Scientist* **70,** 35 (1982).]

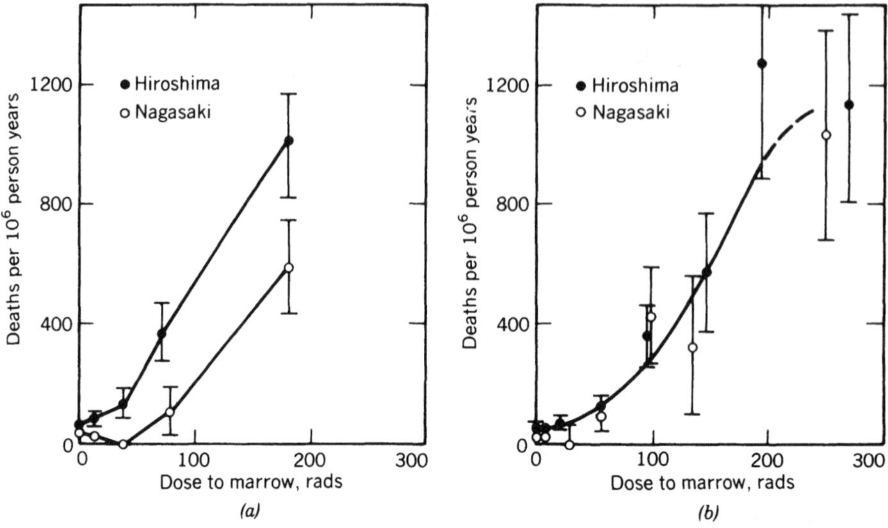

Figure 3.8. Leukemia mortality dose-response curves for Hiroshima and Nagasaki, (*a*) using the old T-65 dose estimates and (*b*) using the new Livermore dosimetry. Striking difference between cities in (*a*) had been attributed to the higher neutron component at Hiroshima and the very high relative biological effectiveness of neutrons. With the lower neutron dose estimates in (*b*), the difference between cities appears to go away. Both fit well to a single linear–quadratic function out to 200 rads. (From *Physics Today,* Sept., 1981.)

There is evidence that leukemia may be of viral origin.† For such a cancer, it is *plausible* that the combination of the virus and a single particle (i.e., either neutron or gamma ray) might initiate the malignancy. On the other hand, single gamma rays are unlikely to break chromosomes, although neutrons can.‡ (Both DNA strands must be cut.) Therefore, resolution of the neutron and gamma doses in the atom bomb survivors is important in our understanding of the relative biological consequences of these types of radiation.

The epidemiological studies of radiation's carcinogenicity are derived from high-dose exposures where the importance of dosimetry is well recognized. To relate radiation's observed effects to exposures outside the studied dose ranges requires additional assumptions. This is especially true at the low exposure levels. There is no complete agreement regarding possible health effects where low levels of ionizing radiation are delivered at low dose rates to the general public. The existing data on carcinogenic effects of radiation to humans have come from cases where (a) high-energy neutrons were important, (b) the total doses were greater by factors of 10^3, and (c) the dose rates were greater by factors of 10^6. To extrapolate across these large factors requires a model. An assumption that has nearly universal agreement as an upper bound is the "linear hypothesis."

This linear extrapolation of effects produces zero effect at zero dose, and is accepted by nearly all experts as a safe upper limit for predicting health effects. However, while data on neutron exposure often closely follow such a relationship, gamma radiation (the most likely source of public exposure from nuclear power) produces much fewer effects at low doses. A quadratic relationship seems to give a better fit of the data in this case. If a quadratic model were adopted, there would be many fewer effects at low dose.

The BEIR committee of the National Academy of Sciences has issued three reports on the subject. In 1972, BEIR-I adopted a linear hypothesis for low-level exposure effects. The BEIR-II report (1979), using the same model, was criticized for overestimating low-level radiation effects. This lead to a BEIR-III report (1980) which adopted a linear/quadratic model which presented a range of risks. The risk from radiation was assessed as follows:

1. A full rad/yr would increase the cancer rate in the general population 3–8%, that is, 5000–13,000 deaths/million.

†The data suggests this, but it is still only a hypothesis.

‡Neutrons can also cause transmutation of the atoms in gene molecules, affecting their chemical bonding. Chromosomes broken by gamma ionization can be reunited; this is not the case if neutron transmutation occurs.

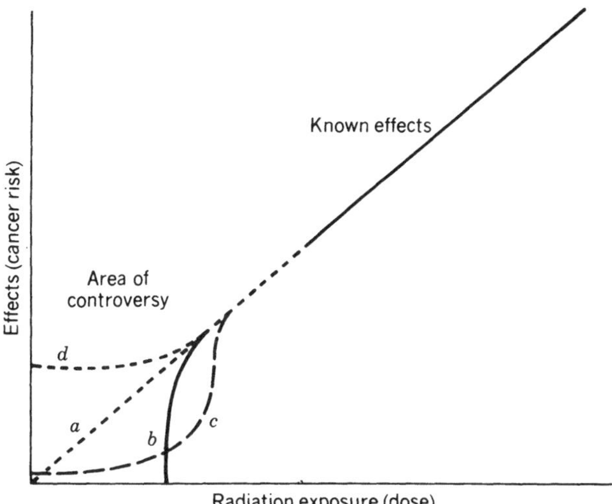

Figure 3.9. The risk of low-level radiation exposure to human health is not precisely known; it must be inferred (extrapolated) from the well-charted effects at high-level exposures that were developed through studies of the Japanese survivors of the atomic bombings, uranium miners, radium-dial painters, and radiotherapy patients. The prevailing view among radiobiologists has been that the risk of cancer is directly proportional to the dose, even at low levels (*a*). Yet this assumption has been recently questioned and the risk of low-level radiation has flared into controversy. Some researchers postulate a threshold below which the risk is effectively zero (*b*); others contend that the risks are disproportionately lower than expected by linearity (*c*) or higher than expected by linearity (*d*). Each of these theories is consistent with the available data. Distinguishing among them is frustrated by the fact that the effects predicted by each theory are small, and therefore it has been impossible to verify which is correct. [From L. Sagan, *EPRI Journal* **4,** 6 (1979).]

2. A 10-rad exposure once per lifetime would result in a 0.5 to 1.4% increase in the rate, that is, 750–2300 deaths/million.
3. These increases are detectable only by statistical means.

These estimates are about half that estimated in the BEIR-I report. The latest findings are similar to the 1977 UNSCEAR results. There is disagreement on both sides of the BEIR-III report. Some people think a linear mode is correct (and therefore the BEIR-III results are too low), while others think a pure quadratic model is correct (and BEIR-III is too high).

It appears that the controversy is unsolvable. Low-dose effects cannot be observed by purely statistical means, nor extrapolated from high-dose data, since the high-dose data sets available often can be fit by more than one of the possible functional forms (Figure 3.9). Moreover, if a curve gives an acceptable fit to the data, this does not mean that the curve is the right one. At most, statistical tests on radiation epidemiological data can show some dose-response curves are wrong. It is unlikely that sufficient data on a uniform population of sufficient size will ever exist that can show which curve is right.

Assuming the more conservative linear hypothesis, the radiation effects due to a large nuclear power economy would be small. Even among occupationally exposed workers, who routinely receive much larger doses than the public, the incremental cancer risk appears small. One study in England of 7000 radiation workers at Central Electricity Generating Board nuclear sites, with mean annual dose of 240 mrems, concluded that the additional cancer risk does not exceed a few tenths of one percent over natural incidence (Figure 3.10).

Recent Controversial Studies†

The preceding describes what has generally been accepted as consensus concerning radiological health. There are some experts and studies which suggest different conclusions. Public fears about nuclear power are often increased by disagreement among experts on questions of radiation

†The authors wish to thank L. Sagan for his contribution to this section.

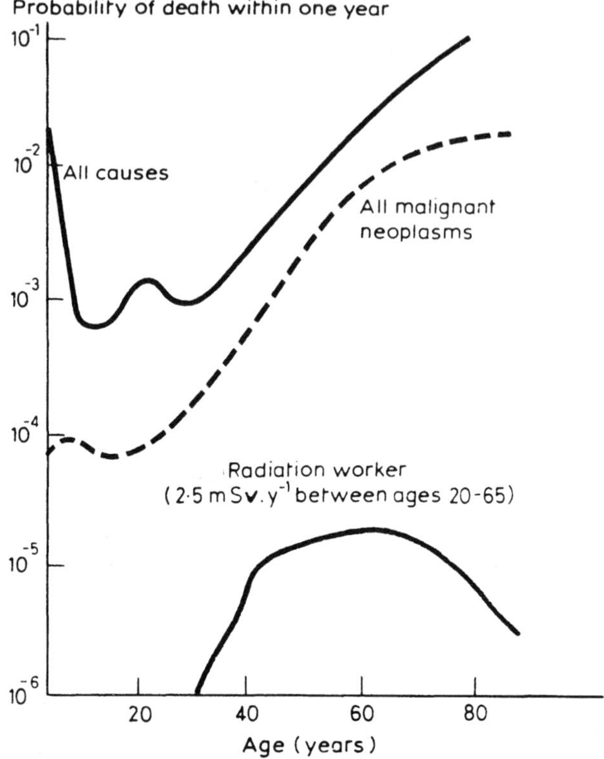

Figure 3.10. The annual probability of death for males in England and Wales varies dramatically throughout life, passing through a minimum at about age 10 and a small peak at age 20 when the number of fatal accidents is most significant. The large natural incidence of cancer, particularly in old age, is obvious. Bearing in mind that the probability scale is logarithmic, the increment of risk to nuclear workers (lower curve) never exceeds a few tenths of 1% of the risk due to natural causes. (From W. Mayneord and B. Wheatley, *CEGB Research,* January 1981.)

hazards. It is essential that the reasons for this disagreement be understood when attempting to form a judgment on the radiological safety of nuclear installations.

A point to be emphasized is that the expert groups that study radiation effects (ICRP, NCRP, UNSCEAR, etc.) have all arrived at essentially the same conclusions, and contrary to what is believed by the public, relatively little disagreement among experts exists. This does not mean, however, that a normal spectrum of opinion does not exist in the scientific community on some important points or that there are not some qualified individuals who are not in agreement with the consensus view of the expert bodies. The commissions do, however, reflect the majority and usually almost unanimous opinions of diverse groups of medical scientists.

There are many reasons for the differing expert opinions. Radiological health is a complex field; no individual can be expert in all the associated issues. Often a controversy is about specific details of an investigation of interest to specialists, for example, the interpretation of experimental data. On the larger issues, such as, "Are radioactivity levels around nuclear plants safe?" there is usually consensus on the basic biological processes and the significance of the results. It is in those cases when experimental data are inconclusive, or consistent with different interpretations, that controversy arises. The public does not always realize that controversy is often useful in resolving the issue, and a necessary ingredient in the scientific process. It certainly is not unique to questions of radiological health; it does and should occur in many areas related to environmental concerns and public well-being. Some of the factors leading to controversy on radiation health are summarized in Table 3.10.

A number of such controversial studies have been published within the last few years. These have received wide attention in the press and have thrown doubt in some quarters on the validity of the commonly accepted risk estimates. Each deserves some comment.

The most notable of these controversial studies was performed by Thomas Mancuso, Alice

Table 3.10. Factors Leading to Disagreement in the Area of Radiation Health

Complex Nature of Issues

Requires multidisciplinary approach including specialists in radiation generation, dosimetry, environmental science, epidemiology, and radiobiological response at the cellular, organ, and organismal level
Involves subjective factors of risk evaluation, often requiring extrapolation from animals to humans
Includes questions of carcinogenesis, teratogenesis, and mutagenesis

Paucity of Data on Humans

Only isolated experience exists from accidental, occupational, and medical exposure as well as the atomic bomb survivor data
Large population studies often confounded by other known or suspected causes of cancer
Statistical fluctuations often greater than the suspected result
Radiation effects data often equivocable, and open to various interpretations

Source: After J. T. Bushberg et al., *Radiological Health Risks; Reasonable Answers to Naive Questions,* Yale University School of Medicine, New Haven, Connecticut, 1983.

Stewart, and George Kneale (MSK). In 1964, Mancuso was commissioned to study the mortality rate among employees at Atomic Energy Commission laboratories. The first journal publication of data from the study appeared 13 years later in *Health Physics,* which reported an increase in cancer frequency among radiation-exposed employees of the Hanford, Washington nuclear facility.

This report created an unusual amount of interest and contention. Its unusual methodology depended on a technique called proportional mortality, which ignores the population at risk; that is, it compares relative frequency of causes of death rather than rates of disease in an exposed population. This technique is not often used because of the difficulty of interpreting such data. The MSK study has also been criticized for its practice of assigning average radiation dose values to persons with various causes of death. The problem with this technique is that a single high exposure to an individual can give a high average value for the entire group, most of whom were not exposed.

There were other reasons for skepticism of a radiation effect in the MSK observations, namely that leukemia, the disease most sensitive to radiation exposure, was not found to be increased in this population. Yet other cancers not usually found to be increased by radiation were among those cited for the excess mortality rate: multiple myeloma (a rare bone marrow tumor) and carcinoma of the pancreas. Several scientists have now published critiques, raising serious questions about the validity of the MSK conclusions. These include analyses from the U.S. Nuclear Regulatory Commission and the National Academy of Sciences.

The MSK report, nevertheless, created some concern about the accuracy of the generally accepted estimates of risk and the occupational exposure standards that are based on them. If the contested MSK findings were correct, then those risk estimates are low by a factor of 10. It was in this climate that three other studies appeared that seemingly lent weight to such a contention—those of Irwin Bross, T. Najarian, and Joseph Lyon.

Bross drew on the work of Saxon Graham, who in 1963 published the "Tri-State Leukemia Study." This study concluded that radiation exposures to adults at medical diagnostic levels (less than 1 rem) could induce leukemia in their children even when the parents' exposure preceded conception by as much as 10 years. In several subsequent papers, Bross reanalyzed those data, using an unusual statistical technique, and developed a dose-response relationship that indicated (as did the MSK study) a much higher radiation risk estimate than generally accepted. Several critiques of Bross' technique have now appeared, including commentary by the National Academy of Sciences' BEIR committee. A critique by John Boice and Charles Land of the National Cancer Institute, published in the February 1979 issue of the *American Journal of Public Health,* commented, "Although the data base for the Tri-State survey was large, the 'new statistical methodology' introduced by Bross et al. depends on a model that is far too complex to be useful. Without the incorrect statistical manipulations employed by the authors, the analysis would produce estimates so imprecise as to be meaningless." Boice and Land concluded that "it is doubtful that the model is a reasonable representation of the relationship between radiation dose and leukemia risk."

The Najarian study bearing on low-level radiation exposure was published in the British medical journal, *Lancet,* in May 1979. This work used mortality data on former employees of the Portsmouth Naval Shipyard in New Hampshire. The authors, T. Najarian and T. Colton, surveyed the deceased workers' next of kin. The relative was asked whether the employee had worn a film badge or had worked with radiation. The deceased group was then compared with U.S. males of similar age who had died of leukemia or other cancers. Najarian concluded that leukemia was increased 7.6-fold among the shipyard workers, based on the observation of 6 leukemia cases within the employee exposure group. It subsequently has been learned that two of these six employees had not been radiation workers, one had less than 1.0 rem of occupational exposure, and the other three had an aggregate exposure of less than 25 person-rems. Because one would expect 1.1 cases of cancer in a nonexposed population of similar size, the significance of the increase (3 cases) is in some doubt. Moreover, Najarian's observation seemingly contradicts the MSK study, which found no increase in leukemia among an occupationally exposed group.

The recent study by Lyon et al. analyzed childhood leukemia and cancer among children living in southern Utah during the period of weapons-testing fallout (1951–1958). In comparing these children with those living in northern Utah and those in southern Utah before and after the weapons-testing period, a significant increase in leukemia was found. Although the authors are cautious in their interpretation of these data, there is a strong implication that radiation is responsible.

There are also certain reasons for having reservations about a verified radiation effect in the Lyon study.

1. Mortality from leukemia was unusually low both before and after the exposure period in the high-fallout counties; it is not clear why.
2. When all other childhood cancers were examined, it was found that there was an inverse relationship between exposure and other types of cancer; that is, exposure produced a decrease in other cancers almost identical in magnitude to the increase in leukemia.
3. We have very poor estimates of the dose from fallout and so cannot attempt a dose-response analysis for this population.

So, although the Lyon study is consistent with a low-level radiation effect, inconsistencies in the data suggest the need for caution in interpretation.

There have been a number of claims concerning the cancer incidence around nuclear power installations. For example, an apparent excess of leukemia, later disproved, was reported around the Lingen reactor in Germany. Similar claims appeared in the United Kingdom about the research facility at Dounreay and the BNFL reprocessing plant at Sellafield. Comprehensive analyses of these cases have since shown that the mortality rates in these areas were not significantly different than the national rates. The environmental radioactivity around the sites was negligible, as it is around most nuclear power plants. For example, an Electric Power Research Institute sponsored study measured radiation levels around two PWRs and two BWRs. For all practical purposes the contribution of these plants to background radiation levels was insignificant. The plants studied had about the same impact on environmental radiation as most coal plants. However, coal plants tend to release considerable amounts of alpha emitters and heavy metals to the environment in contrast to the radiation from nuclear plants which are mostly β-emitting noble gases that are mainly external hazards.

3.5. RADIATION PROTECTION LIMITS: HISTORICAL EVOLUTION

Radiation was recognized as being potentially dangerous soon after its discovery by Roentgen in 1895. Within six months, Thomas Edison reported eye injuries, resulting from exposure to X-rays. Soon afterward, medical scientists were using shielding to protect personnel and patients from this new hazard, although no organized standards were developed. Cancer was first attributed to excess radiation exposure in 1902. Table 3.11 presents some early historical milestones related to the discovery of radiation and its effects.

By 1915, the clearly evident hazards of large amounts of radiation prompted the British Roentgen Society to issue radiation protection proposals which were then first published in 1921. Their suggested limitations on exposure were not widely followed, and serious overexposures resulted. In the 1930s, the U.S. National Committee on Radiation Protection (NCRP) succeeded in establishing the concept of a tolerance dose (0.2 R/day at first,† reduced to 0.1 R/day in 1936)—a dose below which there were believed to be no harmful effects from radiation.

It was supposed that an occupational worker could receive continuously, or at repeated intervals, such a dose without suffering changes in the blood, or damage to the skin or reproductive organs.

This concept of a "tolerance dose" persisted until World War II (see Table 3.12). The large amount of handling of radioactive material during the war, however, led to concerns which resulted

†R is an abbreviation for roentgen.

Table 3.11. Historical Milestones in the Discovery of Radiation

1895	W. Roentgen discovers X-rays (November 8)
1896	Roentgen's first communication (January 3) dated December 26, 1895
	Roentgen's second communication (March 9)
	First therapeutic applications of X-rays
	First diagnostic X-ray by E. Frost (February 3)
	H. Becquerel announces discovery of radioactivity (March 3)
	First applications in dentistry (March) probably by C. Kells and W. Rollins
	T. Edison reports eye injuries from X-rays (March)
	N. Tesla cautions experimenters not to get too close to X-ray tubes (June)
1898	E. Thomson uses aluminum filter for X-ray protection
	Discovery of radioactivity of thorium by G. Schmidt (March)
	M. and P. Curie discover polonium and coin word "radioactivity" (July 13)
	Curies discover radium (December 26)
	P. Villard discovers gamma rays
1902	Rollins experimentally shows X-rays could kill higher life forms
1904	Calorimetric dosimetry systems devised by Saboroud and Noire
1905	Ionization unit proposed by M. Franklin
1911	International radium standard and Curie unit
1912	T. Christen puts forth concept of half value layer
1914	Curie unit proposed for radium by a Debrierne and C. Regaud
1915	X-ray protection recommendations adopted by Roentgen Society (June)

Source: Adapted from R. L. Kathren, *Handbook of Radiation Measurement and Protection,* CRC Press, Boca Raton, Fla., 1979.

in new monitoring techniques and protection guidelines. At the end of the war, radiation protection groups including the NCRP adopted a "no-threshold" hypothesis, stating that there is no completely safe dose of radiation. It was deemed *prudent to assume* that any amount of radiation had some possibility of harm, however small, especially to the reproductive organs.

By the late 1940s, it was also recognized that guidelines for permissible doses to the general public were also required. The concept of relative biological effectiveness (RBE) and the acceptance of the rem as the unit of measurement led to the following ICRP standards:

1. To reduce the permissible dose by 50%, to 50 mrems/day.
2. To take the blood-forming organs as the most critical tissue, and to apply the permissible limit of 300 mrems/week to these organs.
3. To recommend RBE values of 1 for X-rays, gamma rays, and beta rays; 5 for thermal neutrons; and 10 for fast neutrons and alpha rays.

Table 3.12. Historical Development of Radiation Protection Standards

Year	Organization	Protection Criteria and Recommendations
1902	Rollins	Photographic film not fogged in 7 min (10 R/day)
1915	Roentgen Society	X-ray protection recommendations (shield source, etc.)
1921	British Roentgen Society	First standard issued
1931	NCRP	Roentgen (R) unit adopted
1934	NCRP	0.1 R/day "tolerance unit"
1946	NCRP	Concept of "tolerance dose" rejected, any amount of radiation may produce effects
1949	NCRP	0.3 rem/week, "avoid unnecessary radiation"
1954	NCRP	Recommends "as low as practical"
1956	National Academy of Science-ICRP	5 rems/yr
1957	NCRP	12 rems/yr (3 rems/quarter) provided average not exceed 5 R/yr since age 18; 0.5 rem/yr for members of the public

Source: A. Brodsky, "Radiation Risks: An Historical Perspective," Radiation and Health Physics Conference, Hershey, Pennsylvania, September 1979.

Table 3.13. ICRP Guidelines for Radiation Protection

Organ or Tissue	Maximum Permissible Doses for Adults Exposed in the Course of Their Work	Dose Limits for Members of the Public
Gonads, red bone marrow	5 rems in 1 yr	0.5 rem in 1 yr
Skin, bone, thyroid	30 rems in 1 yr	3 rems in 1 yr[a]
Hands and forearms; feet and ankles	75 rems in 1 yr	7.5 rems in 1 yr
Other single organs	15 rems in 1 yr	1.5 rems in 1 yr

[a]For the thyroid of children the dose is 1.5 rems.

By 1958, further experimental data on low-level radiation caused the ICRP to reduce weekly dose limits even lower, to 100 mrems/week. For reasons of flexibility, a rule was formulated that allowed up to 3-rem exposure in any calendar quarter, provided that the annual accumulated dose did not exceed 5 rems. Since it was customary that no worker less than 18 years old handle radiation, the following formula for permitted dose at any age N was adopted:

$$\text{lifetime dose} = 5(N - 18) \text{ rems}$$

The ICRP has provided further guidelines for radiation exposure to occupational workers and members of the public. These limits are given in Table 3.13. While these exposures are maximum permissible doses, and are generally accepted as quite conservative, all scientists agree that any unnecessary doses to occupational workers or the public should be avoided. This principle is known by the acronym ALARA (As Low As Reasonably Achievable). The ALARA concept is emphasized in all standards and regulatory guides governing nuclear power facilities. As shown in Table 3.13, the dose limits for members of the public are set at one-tenth that for occupational workers, with the addition that the dose limit for the thyroid be 1.5 rems/yr for children.

Internal contamination may also result from contact with radioactive materials, through inhalation, ingestion, or direct absorbtion through the skin. When considering internal doses, nonuniform doses and the tendency of some radionuclides to concentrate in certain organs are important. Radioiodine migration to the thyroid is an example of the latter. Biological half-life (i.e., the time required for the body to eliminate half the ingested substance) is also an important consideration, as well as the internal biological damage of the alpha and low-energy beta rays, not normally particularly hazardous outside the body. The maximum permissible annual doses for these internal contaminants are calculated, and limits are then placed on the permissible concentration of these radionuclides in air or water. Typical values of the concentration limits are given in Table 3.14. As a comparison, radioactivity in some common liquids is shown in Table 3.15, which shows the liquid effluents from nuclear power plants are typically a small fraction of radioactivity levels normally contained in river water, and 10 to 1000 times lower than some liquids deemed safe for human consumption.

Table 3.14. Typical Maximum Permissible Concentrations in Air and Water Above Natural Background for Radionuclides Commonly Encountered in Nuclear Power Activities

	pCi/liter	
Isotope	Air	Water
^{14}C	4×10^{-3}	20
^{137}Cs	6×10^{-5}	0.4
^{131}I	9×10^{-6}	6×10^{-2}
^{85}Kr	10^{-2}	—
^{239}Pu	2×10^{-9}	0.1
^{238}U	7×10^{-8}	1

Source: 10CFR30.

Table 3.15. Liquid Radioactivity Levels

	pCi/liter
Typical nuclear power plant radioactive waste discharge	1–10
Domestic tap water	20
River water	10–100
4% beer	130
Ocean water	350
Whiskey	1200
Milk	1400
Salad oil	4900

Source: From J. M. Smith Jr, "Perspective on Radioactive Effluents from BWR Nuclear Plants," *Trans. Am. Nuclear Soc.*, February 1971.

Radiation Exposure Control and Regulation

In addition to the standards and guidelines laid down by scientific bodies such as the ICRP and the NCRP, federal and state authorities restrict the amount of exposure allowed to both workers and the public. This is often done by codifying the NCRP health recommendations. In the United States, this is done in Part 20 of the Code of Federal Regulations, Title 10.† In addition, the NCRP, the regulators, and operators of nuclear facilities embrace the ALARA philosophy. This is implemented in nuclear plants by various methods used to reduce exposures to workers and to control radioactive effluents from the plants. For example, portable shielding is used to protect workers in high radiation areas. Records are kept on individuals and on the plant discharges to assure that overexposure does not occur. The success of the regulations in protecting the public from radiation hazards is shown in Figure 3.11. This figure also compares the regulatory situation for nuclear power relative to possible health effects due to the combustion of fossil fuels. The actual radiation exposures relative to the radiation protection standards are quite low. These exposures relative to the applicable EPA and NRC standards are given in Figure 3.12.

Implementing various regulations requires formal administration in every facility for radiation protection. To protect workers, it is not sufficient that such an administration merely exist. The worker's attitude toward the radiation hazard is equally important. It is therefore the job of the radiation policy administrators (the health physics organization in American plants) to instill in each worker a responsible attitude, and to provide a safe environment in which to work. To accomplish the latter, four measures are put into effect:

1. *Hazards Evaluation.* An important part of meeting radiation exposure regulations is determining the nature and extent of the hazards associated with the plant and its operation. Upon this evaluation (which starts in the design phase of the reactor), access areas and operational procedures are set up to adhere to the ALARA concept.

2. *Radiation Monitors.* Radiation exposure control is aided by two methods:

a. The radiation monitoring of personnel.

b. Area and environmental monitoring. This is accomplished by radiation detection devices such as film badges, personal dosimeters, ionization chambers and Geiger counters, whole-body counters, and so on. The strategy is to assure that dose rates are within the expected ranges. These monitors are important in detecting off-normal situations, and in accident situations. Personnel monitoring assesses individual dose and possible contamination of the body or clothes.

3. *Operational Procedures.* Well-defined operational procedures are the key to the ALARA concept. Written copies of these procedures are required and are used for all operations. Any operation that results in higher-than-desired exposure is noted and revised procedures prepared. For tasks in high-radiation zones, the procedures are often practiced beforehand to familiarize the technicians, so that the job can be performed quickly and efficiently. Special procedures are available for accident situations to protect the workers and the public. In emergencies, the potential

†Usually abbreviated 10CFR20.

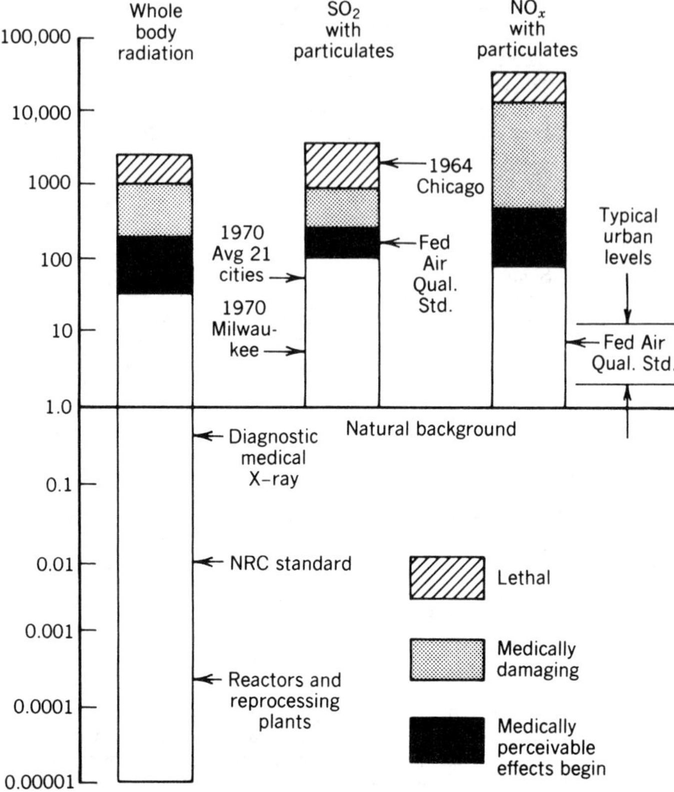

Figure 3.11. Comparison of standards and biological effects of radiation and pollutants. (Courtesy American Nuclear Society.)

hazard to operational personnel must be balanced with the necessity to safely shut down and secure the plant. Plans are established for off-site emergencies. This includes evacuation and warning procedures for the public. Liaison is established with the police, fire department, state public health authorities, and federal agencies (FEMA† and NRC). These plants are periodically tested and trial evacuations practiced.

4. *Recordkeeping and Discipline.* At each power plant lines of responsibility for safe operation are clearly drawn with each person cognizant of his responsibilities. A record of individual exposure is kept with many plants further breaking the record down to keep track of where, when, and for what reason the radiation exposure occurred. These records are permanent.

The handling of radioactive material, in particular waste disposal, is also controlled through federal and state regulations. This involves various licenses. Prior to issuance of such licenses, the authorities evaluate the environmental impact, including topographical, geological, meteorological, and hydrological aspects. In addition, the regulations require reports of any overexposure of personnel, excessive radiation levels, or concentrations. These incidents must be reported within 30 days of occurrence. More acute incidents, such as any worker receiving more than 25 rems of whole-body radiation, must be reported immediately.

For any serious reactor accident at a nuclear power plant, immediate notification of all the proper authorities is required. In the United States, 10CFR50 further requires that state/local officials have the capability to promptly notify the public in an emergency condition. This includes all people within the area likely to be endangered by a radioactive plume coming from a damaged plant—this area is called the emergency planning zone (EPZ). The planning basis for the state and local emergency response plans is the U.S. NRC document NUREG-0396 (1978). This document indicates that comprehensive emergency planning is advisable for an area having a radius of about

†U.S. Federal Emergency Management Agency.

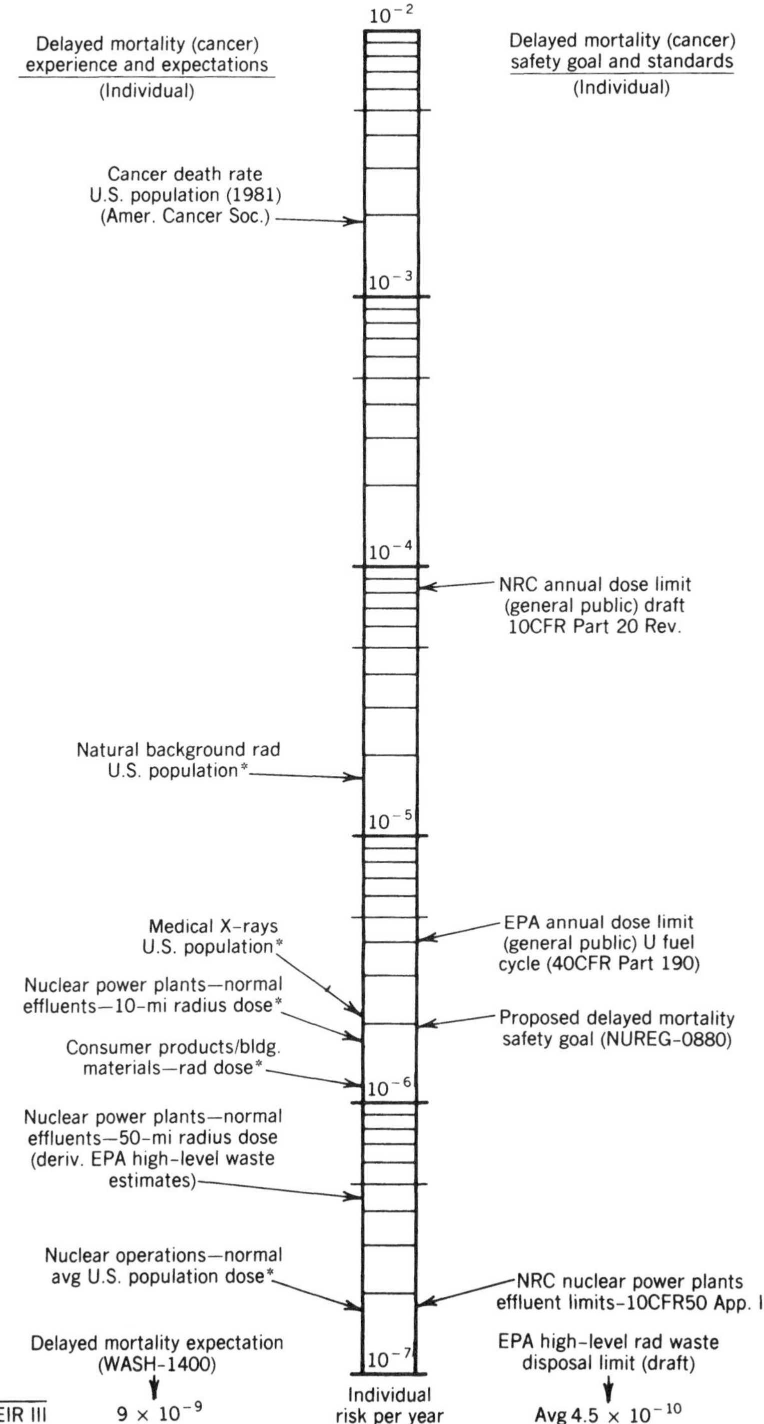

Figure 3.12. Ranges of individual risk per year related to radiation protection standards and actual exposure experience. (R. J. Catlin, private communication.)

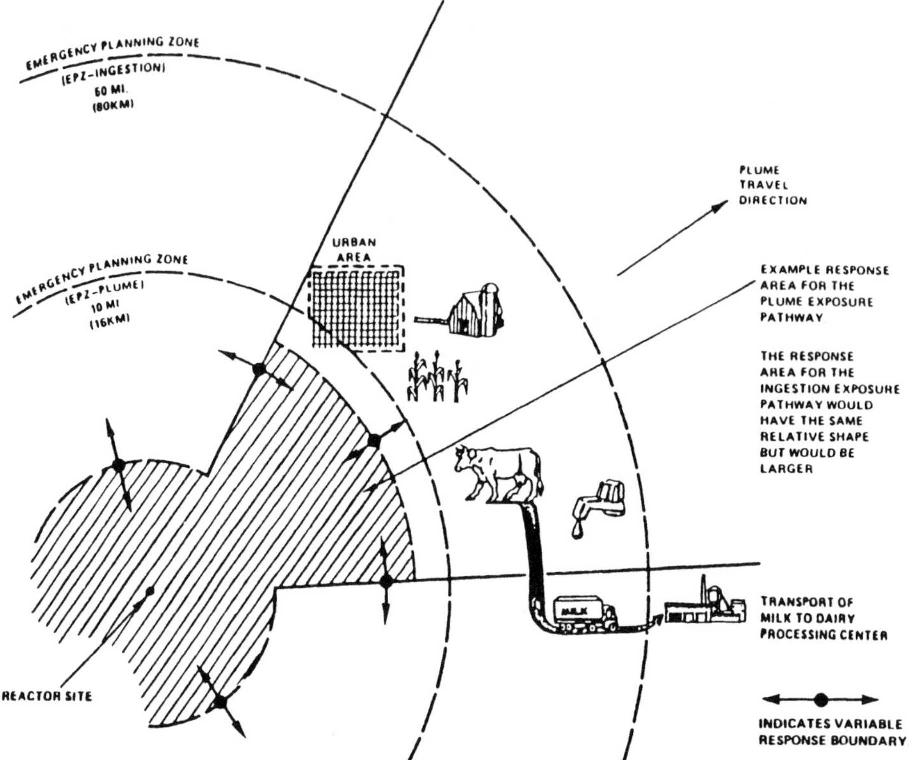

Figure 3.13. Concept of an emergency planning zone. [From NUREG-0396 (1978).]

10 miles surrounding a nuclear power station (Figure 3.13). The size of the actual EPZ is related to the assumed source term, (i.e., the magnitude, mix, and duration of any radioactivity leaking from a damaged plant), the weather conditions, and the off-site consequences. The EPZ radius is currently determined by the WASH-1400 Atmospheric Release Consequence studies and the Protective Action Guides (PAGs), established by the U.S. Environmental Protection Agency. The emphasis in the United States is on evacuation in the event of a radiological hazard to the public.

In Europe (particularly West Germany and Switzerland) and in Japan, the recommended initial protective action is sheltering. The population densities are much higher in these countries than in the United States. In West Germany, evacuation is envisioned only some hours after the passage of any radioactive plume during an accident, and then only for people exposed to more than 25 rems if they remained sheltered. Emergency response is planned only for a radius of 5–8 km, with actual implementation only when dose rate measurements indicate that more than 25 rems would be expected. The Swiss and Japanese emergency plans are similar.

Radiation Blocking Agents (KI)

Radioiodine is one of the radionuclides of concern in the event of an accident at a nuclear plant. If inhaled, radioiodine seeks the thyroid gland and collects there. The radiation dose to the gland carries a small risk that subsequent thyroid nodules or cancer could result. It is possible, however, to block the thyroid gland from taking up radioiodine by the use of potassium iodide (KI). This drug is advocated by the U.S. Food and Drug Administration for distribution to the general population living within several miles of a nuclear reactor, but its actual distribution in the United States has been limited to only one reactor because of various distribution problems, including that of storage.

The indiscriminate use of potassium iodide carries its own hazards, principally hyperthyroidism (overactive thyroid) and cardiac complications in older persons. The pros and cons of using KI revolve around three questions:

1. The amount of iodine released to the environment in the event of an accident (see Chapter 17).

Table 3.16. U.S. Occupational Exposures Estimates, 1975

Source	Person-rems/yr (in thousands)
Healing arts	40–80
Manufacturing and industrial	50
Nuclear energy	50
Research	12
Naval reactors	8
Nuclear weapons development and production	0.8
Other occupations	50

Source: HEW-1979.

2. The risk of thyroid cancer that will not respond to treatment.
3. The risk of the population due to complications from taking the blocking agent.

The risk trade-off in items (2) and (3) are complicated in that the FDA advocacy is based on the assumption that internal radiation doses from iodine produce cancer as effectively as X-rays for which most of the data exists. Apparently X-rays are more than 10 times as likely to cause cancer as radioiodine.

The situation concerning the relative risks in this area is rapidly evolving and is the subject of ongoing research. In the meanwhile, KI has been distributed at only a few reactor sites, mainly in Sweden and at the one U.S. plant, although several jurisdictions in the United States are considering stockpiling the drug in the case of a reactor accident.

Occupational Exposure and Dose Control in Nuclear Plants

Occupational radiation exposure is the result of people working in radiation fields. Most of the occupational exposure to ionizing radiation in the United States comes from medical, industrial, military-related, and research activities. This is summarized in Table 3.16, which shows that only a relatively small percentage (~20%) is related to nuclear power production. The radiation exposure associated with the various aspects of the nuclear fuel cycle is shown in Table 3.17. Most of the occupational exposure to radiation in nuclear power is associated with operating the plants, with only 2% of the total coming from the front and back ends of the fuel cycle (mining, enrichment, waste disposal, etc.). For the year 1979, the average radiation exposure to a worker in a U.S. nuclear plant was about 0.62 rem, well below the maximum permissible dose of 5.0 rems. Most of the workers involved received doses in the 0.2–0.3 rem range, with only a few workers exposed in excess of 1.0 rem (Figure 3.14). In some countries, occupational exposure levels have been held to considerably lower levels. In Sweden, for instance, workers averaged about half the U.S. rate.

The average annual individual dose to workers in the U.S. nuclear power industry has been fairly constant over the years 1973 to 1977, with a slight decrease in later years. In 1977, the average annual individual dose ranged from 0.46 to 0.74 rem, depending on whether all monitored workers (71,904) or just those with measurable doses (44,233) are included in the average. Therefore, it appears that the nuclear power industry is working within the recommended dose limits of the ICRP, the average dose being approximately one-eighth the annual 5-rem limitation.

It should be kept in mind that these statistics are industry-wide averages and include new plants as well as old. It is well documented that for boiling water reactors (BWRs), at least in the past,

Table 3.17. Occupational Exposure to Radiation, U.S. Nuclear Fuel Cycle 1979

Fuel Cycle Activity	Percent
Mining and milling	0.01
Enrichment	0.18
Fuel fabrication	1.7
Nuclear power production	98
Waste disposal	0.05

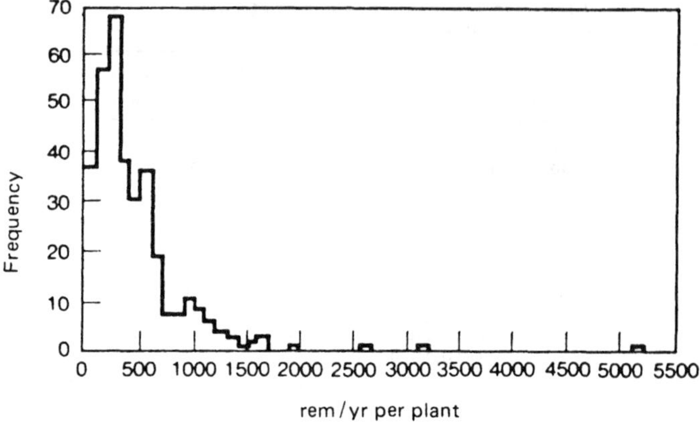

Figure 3.14. Annual radiation exposures per plant at United States LWRs for 1969–1978. [From R. A. Shaw, IAEA-SM-242/54 (1980).]

annual doses to workers increase with age of the plant. The main reason for the increase appears to be increased radiation levels due to the accumulation of corrosion product nuclides (e.g., ^{60}Co) in deposits on the inside of primary coolant pipes and valves. A similar, but less pronounced, increase in radiation levels at pressurized water reactors (PWRs) has also been noted. Therefore, provided all other factors contributing to dose are equal, as the industry matures, one would expect to observe higher annual doses to workers. Figure 3.15, which shows the geometric mean of plant collective exposures for the years 1969 to 1979, tends to support this.

It will probably require several more years of operating experience to establish definitive trends in occupational exposure rates. Early results seem to indicate a leveling off of exposure after a number of years of plant operation (Figure 3.16). From this figure, several fundamental conclusions can be drawn:

1. The annual collective dose equivalent rate in man-rems/megawatt-year increases with years of operation.
2. The increasing trend is better described by a leveling exponential model than by a linear model.
3. The equilibrium level reached after several years differs considerably between BWRs and PWRs.

The data also seem to indicate a considerably lower rate of occupational exposure per unit of electricity produced for the larger plants. However, since the larger plants tend to be the new ones, it remains to be seen if improved design, modern radiation control techniques, and optimized operation can be translated into long-term reductions in radiation exposure.

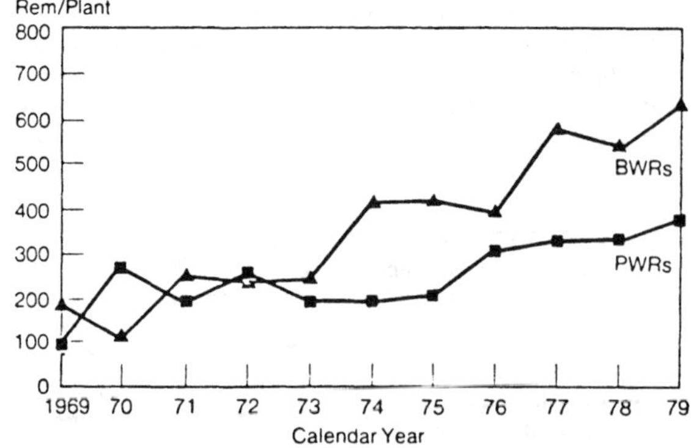

Figure 3.15. Geometric mean of U.S. plant exposures. [From F. J. Rahn et al., *Trans. Am. Nuclear Soc.* **38** (1981).]

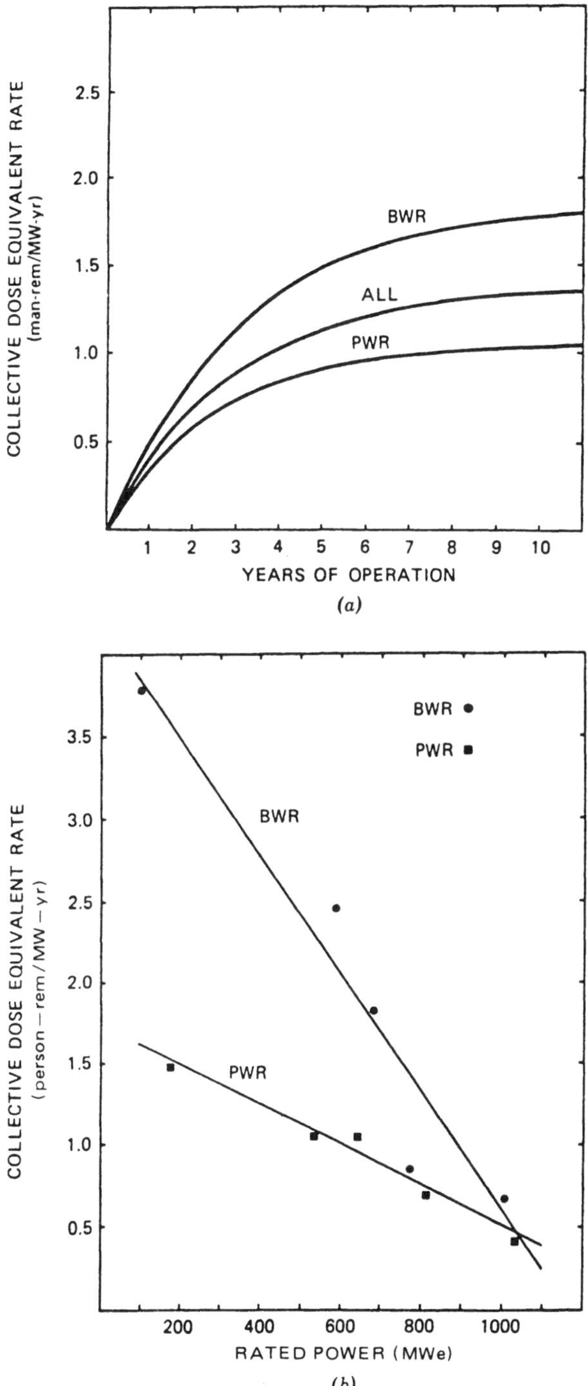

Figure 3.16. (*a*) Leveling exponential trends of radiation dose as a function of year of plant operation. [From L. A. Cross, *Trans. Am. Nuclear Soc.* **35,** 456 (1980).] (*b*) Collective dose equivalent rate upper limit values as a function of the rated power of a nuclear plant. (From L. A. Cross, ibid.)

Table 3.18. Career Doses for Radiation Workers Terminating During the Years 1969–1977. Nuclear Power Reactors

Total Length of Employment	Number of Monitored Individuals	Number of Individuals with Measurable Doses	Total Number of man-rems	Average Dose (rems) for the Period of Employment	High Individual Cumulative Dose (Includes Overexposures)
0–90 days	43,668	26,047	16,653	0.64	10
90 days–1 yr	18,663	13,363	14,209	1.06	—
1–2 yr	4,217	3,270	5,388	1.65	30
2–3 yr	1,510	1,197	2,862	2.39	31
3–4 yr	692	600	1,678	2.80	38
4–5 yr	269	221	900	4.07	25
5–10 yr	431	386	1,898	4.92	82
10–15 yr	131	113	669	5.92	60
15–20 yr	36	33	265	8.03	40
20 yr	54	37	237	6.41	37

Source: B. G. Brooks, "Occupational Radiational Exposures at NRC-Licensed Facilities," IAEA Symposium. Los Angeles, June, 1979.

In general, doses to radiation workers have been kept significantly below regulatory limits. As seen in Table 3.18, which shows lifetime dose versus length of employment, both yearly and cumulative doses tend to be low. Only in a few instances do individual exposures approach maximum permissible limits. This is one indication of the application of the ALARA principle, although continuing efforts are required to maintain, and lower, if possible, these exposures. In the United States, some consideration is being given by the Environmental Protection Agency to limit lifetime exposure to 100 rems. (Of the over 68,000 radiation records in Table 3.18, none to date has exceeded this level.) This presumably would reduce the maximum lifetime risk from radiation exposure to a level comparable with the average risks encountered in other occupations.

Because of the difficulty in maintaining records, transient workers require special steps to assure adequate radiation protection. A "transient worker" is typically an individual with special skills (e.g., welder, or refueling specialist) who travels from plant to plant performing special operations. The exposures accumulated by such individuals tend to be higher than for other radiation workers by a factor of about two (Table 3.19).

Since 1979 expedited recordkeeping is required for transient workers. This policy is set down in Parts 19 and 20 of the Code of Federal Regulations. Many plants throughout the world have installed "real time" computer readout dosimeters, both to improve their recordkeeping to meet government regulations, and to use such records in determining which operations lead to high worker exposure. In the latter instance, such records can be used to identify alternate procedures to reduce occupational doses.

A typical occupational exposure management system works in the following way: Each job requiring a work permit is defined by specifying plant, unit, job location, plant system, job category, major operation, component type, and component identification. There might be 72 plant systems from which to select, 32 job categories, 6 major operations, 29 component types, and up to 15 individual components within each component type. Additional information is recorded for further specification: power status, temporary shielding, system flushing, respirators, radiation

Table 3.19. Annual Doses of Transient Workers at Power Reactors

Year	No. of Workers Terminating with Two or More Employers Within One Year	Cumulative Dose, person-rems	Average Individual Dose, rems
1972	182	262.8	1.44
1973	362	552.7	1.53
1974	528	620.6	1.18
1975	1263	1459.2	1.16
1976	1996	2505.2	1.26

Source: B. G. Brooks, "Occupational Radiational Exposure at NRC-Licensed Facilities," IAEA Symposium, Los Angeles, June 1979.

Table 3.20. Estimated Annual Airborne Releases from a 1000-MWe BWR and a 1000-MWe PWR

Radionuclide	BWR, Ci/yr	PWR, Ci/yr
^{41}Ar	25	25
^{83m}Kr	[a]	1
^{85m}Kr	150	16
^{85}Kr	290	470
^{87}Kr	200	3
^{88}Kr	240	23
^{131m}Xe	18	82
^{133m}Xe	[a]	120
^{133}Xe	3200	12,000
^{135m}Xe	740	[a]
^{135}Xe	1100	86
^{138}Xe	1400	[a]
^{131}I	0.3	0.025
^{133}I	1.1	0.023
^{14}C	9.5	8
^{3}H	43	1100

Source: J. P. McBride, *Nuclear Safety* **19** (1978).
Note: Ar, Kr, and Xe are chemically inert noble gases.
[a]Annual release <1 Ci.

fields, and surface contamination. Each time a person is exposed to radiation, an entry is made of social security number, employee type, work group, time in the radiation field, and exposure.

Radiation work permit data are being sent to the Atomic Industrial Forum to form part of an industry-wide occupational exposure data base. Utilities, architect engineers, vendors, and the NRC will be able to search, sort, summarize, and otherwise analyze this information to form detailed profiles of activities contributing to exposures. The profiles will include dose rates, number of persons involved, the total exposure time, and how often a given activity is performed. These industry-wide profiles will be used together with utility-specific profiles to assist plant operation and utility management in substantiating their individual ALARA judgments.

3.6. RADIOACTIVE EMISSIONS AND HEALTH EFFECTS OF NUCLEAR PLANTS

It is impossible to have zero release of radioactive material from nuclear plants, just as it is impossible to have zero release of pollutants from any industrial enterprise. What is done is to ensure that such releases are as small as possible. Radioactive release from commercial nuclear power facilities is limited, by various regulations, to amounts that will not present hazards to the public and environment. In the United States, guidelines are specified in Appendix I in the Code of Federal Regulations, Title 10, Part 50.

Estimated airborne releases for nuclear reactors are given in Table 3.20. The majority of the radiation comes from noble gases (Ar, Kr, and Xe) which are chemically inert. They also decay fairly rapidly. The largest release, ^{133}Xe, has a half-life of 5.3 days. The combination of chemical inertness and short life considerably reduces the biological hazard. Thus, the release data in curies such as given in this table are not necessarily indicative of the hazard involved. For instance, radioiodine, which is only a tiny fraction of the total release, may dominate the risk. As a comparison, Table 3.21 presents typical radioactivity releases from coal plants. Note that most of the airborne radioactivity from a coal plant is from α-particle-emitting radionuclides which generally pose a high health risk per curie released. The question of relative hazard is taken up again in Chapter 17.

Radioactive Emissions: Fossil Versus Nuclear Plants

Coal contains up to 100 ppm of radioactive elements, such as U and Th. These are released to the environment when coal is burned. Although the number of curies released in burning coal is lower than for a nuclear plant, many of the radionuclides are long-lived alpha-particle emitters, and their biological hazard thus is correspondingly higher. The ash from burning coal contains such radio-

Table 3.21. Estimated Annual Airborne Radioactive Materials Released from a 1000-MWe Coal-Fired Power Plant

Isotope	Releases, Ci/yr	Isotope	Releases, Ci/yr
^{238}U Chain		*^{232}Th Chain*	
^{238}U	8×10^{-3}	^{232}Th	5×10^{-3}
^{234}Th	8×10^{-3}	^{228}Ra	5×10^{-3}
^{234m}Pa	8×10^{-3}	^{228}Ac	5×10^{-3}
^{234}U	8×10^{-3}	^{228}Th	5×10^{-3}
^{230}Th	8×10^{-3}	^{224}Ra	5×10^{-3}
^{226}Ra	8×10^{-3}	^{212}Pb	5×10^{-3}
^{218}Po	8×10^{-3}	^{212}Bi	5×10^{-3}
^{214}Pb	8×10^{-3}	^{208}Tl	1.8×10^{-3}
^{214}Bi	8×10^{-3}		
^{214}Po	8×10^{-3}	*Radon Releases*	
^{210}Pb	8×10^{-3}		
^{210}Bi	8×10^{-3}	^{220}Rn	0.4
^{210}Po	8×10^{-3}	^{222}Rn	0.8
^{235}U Chain			
^{235}U	3.5×10^{-4}		
^{231}Th	3.5×10^{-4}		
^{231}Pa	3.5×10^{-4}		
^{227}Ac	3.5×10^{-4}		
^{227}Th	3.5×10^{-4}		
^{223}Ra	3.5×10^{-4}		
^{219}Rn	3.5×10^{-4}		
^{211}Pb	3.5×10^{-4}		
^{211}Bi	3.5×10^{-4}		
^{207}Tl	3.5×10^{-4}		

Source: J. P. McBride, *Nuclear Safety* **19** (1978).

nuclides as radium-226.† Coal burning concentrates various nuclides, the most important being ^{210}Pb, ^{210}Po, and ^{231}Pa. In addition, coal ash contains large quantities of toxic metals (Table 3.22). These toxic metals may represent a long-term contamination problem not posed by nuclear plants.

In order to compare coal versus nuclear plants in their radioactive releases, individual dose commitment models have been developed. These models take into account various factors, such as meteorological conditions and topography. As shown in Table 3.23, the maximum individual dose commitments for a coal plant were greater than for a PWR (except thyroid dose) and less than for a BWR (except bone dose). In general, doses to individual members of the public for both coal and nuclear plants were about the same.

For doses to the entire population around a plant, the analysis shows that the releases from coal plants were generally higher than for nuclear plants (Table 3.24), in part because of the higher population densities which exist in the vicinity of coal plants. On the other hand, the ash release was assumed to be 1% for coal containing 1 ppm uranium and 2 ppm thorium, levels which are often exceeded. The major pathway for exposure for both types of plants was the ingestion of food, although many potential pathways exist. The total radiation dose equivalent for all pathways is approximately 0.1 person-rem/GW–year of electrical production.

A more complete analysis includes the entire fuel cycle for nuclear power generation, and the other phases of the coal fuel cycle (e.g., mining and waste management), and also includes the impact of other toxic substances and emissions. Such a comparison is given in Table 3.25, which gives a range of mortality estimates. This table reflects coal workers' black lung disease, accidents involving transportation of coal, and air pollution. Similarly, it also includes estimates of death and injury for uranium miners, and the effect of reactor accidents. Similar estimates for oil and natural gas are summarized in Table 3.26. In terms of mortality, a nuclear plant results in a slightly greater hazard than a gas-fired plant, and $\frac{1}{10}$ the hazard as a coal plant. In comparisons between nuclear and

†Radium-226 has approximately the same radiotoxicity as plutonium.

Table 3.22. The Quantities of Toxic Elements Discharged Annually from a 1000-MWe Coal-Fired Plant

Element	Approx. Annual Discharge, kg/yr
Arsenic	90,000
Barium	300,000
Chlorine	20,000
Manganese	70,000
Mercury	20,000
Nickel	70,000
Vanadium	70,000

Source: From "The Management of Canada's Nuclear Waste," *Atom* **257**, 74 (1978).

Table 3.23. Maximum Individual Dose Commitments from the Airborne Releases of 1000-MWe Power Plants, mrems/yr

Organ	Coal-Fired Plant	BWR	PWR	10 CFR 50, Appendix I Guides
Whole body	1.9	4.6	1.8	5
Bone	18.2	5.9	2.7	15
Lungs	1.9	4.0	1.2	15
Thyroid	1.9	36.9	3.8	15
Kidneys	3.4	3.4	1.3	15
Liver	2.4	3.7	1.3	15
Spleen	2.7	3.7	1.1	15

Source: From J. P. McBride, *Nuclear Safety* **19** (1978).

Table 3.24. Population Dose Commitments from the Airborne Releases of 1000-MWe Power Plants (Person-rems/yr; 88.5-km radius)

Organ	Coal-Fired Plant 100 m Stack Height	BWR	PWR
Whole body	21	13	13
Bone	225	21	20
Lungs	29	8	9
Thyroid	21	37	12
Kidneys	50	8	9
Liver	29	9	10
Spleen	34	8	8

Source: Adapted from J. P. McBride, *Nuclear Safety* **19** (1978).

Table 3.25. Estimates of Health Effects of Coal and Nuclear Fuel Cycles

Procedure	Occupational Deaths	Occupational Injuries and Disease	Nonoccupational Deaths
Coal fuel			
Extraction			
Accidents	0.45–1.24	22.0–80.0	—
Disease	0.00–4.8	0.6–48.0	—
Transport			
Accidents	0.055–1.9	0.33–23.0	0.55–1.3
Processing			
Accidents	0.02–0.05	2.6–3.1	1.0–10.0
Power generation			
Accidents	0.01–0.03	0.9–1.5	—
Air pollution	—	—	0.067–295.0
Total	0.54–8.0	26.0–156.0	1.62–306.0
Nuclear fuel			
Extraction			
Accidents	0.005–0.2	1.8–10.0	—
Disease	0.002–0.1	—	—
Transport			
Accidents	0.002–0.005	0.45–0.14	—
Processing			
Accidents	0.003–0.2	0.6–1.5	—
Disease	0.13–0.33	—	—
Power generation			
Accidents	0.01	1.3	0.01–0.16
Disease	0.00–0.1	—	—
Total[a]	0.035–0.945	3.7–13.0	0.01–0.16

Source: From *JAMA* **240,** 2193 (1978).

[a]Per 1000 MWe/yr.

alternate fuel cycles, it should be noted that, for the former, the data are sparse and difficult to interpret. Few people realize that natural gas and geothermal power plants emit radon gas, a radionuclide responsible for three alpha particles. For nuclear power, the radiation measurements are fairly precise, but the extrapolation of the resulting population dose effects to low levels is very controversial (and probably very conservative).

Effects of Lowering Maximum Permissible Limits

Maximum permissible radiation exposure limits have been trending downward ever since ionizing radiation was first discovered. In the past, exposure limits were large relative to what was needed for ordinary operations at nuclear facilities. Maximum dose reductions, therefore, had little impact on how these operations were carried out. The implementation of the ALARA philosophy tended to reduce radiation exposures over the years. At present, the average worker at a nuclear power

Table 3.26. Comparison of Health Effects for Alternative Fuel Cycles[a]

Effect	Coal	Oil	Natural Gas	Nuclear
Occupational deaths	0.54–8.0	0.14–1.3	0.06–0.28	0.035–0.945
Nonoccupational deaths	1.62–306.0	1.0–100.0	—	0.01–0.16
Total deaths	2.16–314.0	1.1–101.0	0.06–0.28	0.045–1.1
Occupational impairments	26.0–156.0	12.0–94.0	4.0–24.0	4.0–13.0

Source: From *JAMA* **240,** 2193 (1978).

[a]For electric power production per 1000 MWe.

Table 3.27. Projected Annual Impacts on an Operating Plant of Reducing Exposure Limits to 500 mrems/yr[a]

	BWR Case	PWR Case
Differential person-rem	85	84
Differential worker demand		
Permanent station	204	163
Outside	3,468	3,399
Total	3,672	3,562
Differential operating costs		
Personnel (permanent station)	$4,900,000	$3,900,000
Personnel (outside)	3,000,000	2,800,000
Outage extension	700,000	700,000
Total	$8,600,000	$7,400,000
Outage extension, hr	50	50

[a]1978 dollars (courtesy of J. Vance, AIF).

plant receives about one-eighth of the regulatory limit of 5 rems/yr.† The question sometimes arises about the impact of further radiation limit reductions on nuclear plants.

The results of lower exposure limits would be complicated, and would depend on the extent of plant and operational mode. However, it seems clear that reducing occupational exposure limits will result in increased cumulative worker doses and radiation worker demand (i.e., smaller doses distributed to more workers, with an increase in the total). This is because of what is termed "unproductive dose."

In a nuclear plant, there is a given amount of work in radiation fields with a given number of workers. If the limits are reduced, when a worker reaches this limit, another worker must take his place. In the changeover, a fraction of the new worker's dose is received while he is not actually accomplishing work (unproductive dose). This dose is received during his entering and leaving a work area, his orientation to the task, and his setting up of tools. The greater number of worker changes required to accomplish a given job, the greater will be the unproductive dose. In addition, the time required to complete a task (e.g., refueling outage) will be prolonged, as will the plant operating cost. Capital costs would also increase as design features are added to the plant to reduce radiation exposures.

Small changes in maximum permissible radiation exposures, say a factor of two reduction, would probably have a negligible impact on nuclear plants. This is because few workers today receive doses in this range. However, a factor of 10 reduction (to 500 mrems/yr) would have a severe impact on operations, as shown in Table 3.27. The largest impacts for a 500 mrem/yr limit are on worker demand and operating cost. More than a hundred additional permanent workers would be needed for the power plant staff, and several thousand additional outside workers would have to be brought in annually. A study by the Stone and Webster Engineering Company concluded that the amount of total radiation received by these workers would increase 85 person-rems.

The cumulative effect of a 500 mrem/year exposure limit is presented in Figure 3.17, which shows that about one-half a million additional person-rems would be incurred during the first 10 years that such a dose limitation would be in effect. The financial impact would also be quite severe. For example, the annual refueling and maintenance outage would have to be extended about four days. It currently costs about $750,000 in differential power costs for each day a nuclear power plant is not operating. Permissible dose reductions appear to be counterproductive unless they are imperative for worker safety.

Control of Plant Radiation Levels

Most utilities are concentrating on reducing total occupational exposures by controlling radiation levels in the plant. Such programs are typically coordinated with system vendors, architect/engineers, and service organizations. The objective is to increase plant availability through reduced radiation exposure while reducing worker doses in compliance with ALARA. Figure 3.18 shows various techniques used to accomplish this. Many of the radiation control programs in place emphasize the reduction of radiation sources by chemistry control, material use, and decontamination.

†The actual limit is 3 rems/quarter (12 rems/year) provided the maximum lifetime limit of $5(N - 18)$ rems holds. This is usually taken to be 5 rems/yr for simplicity.

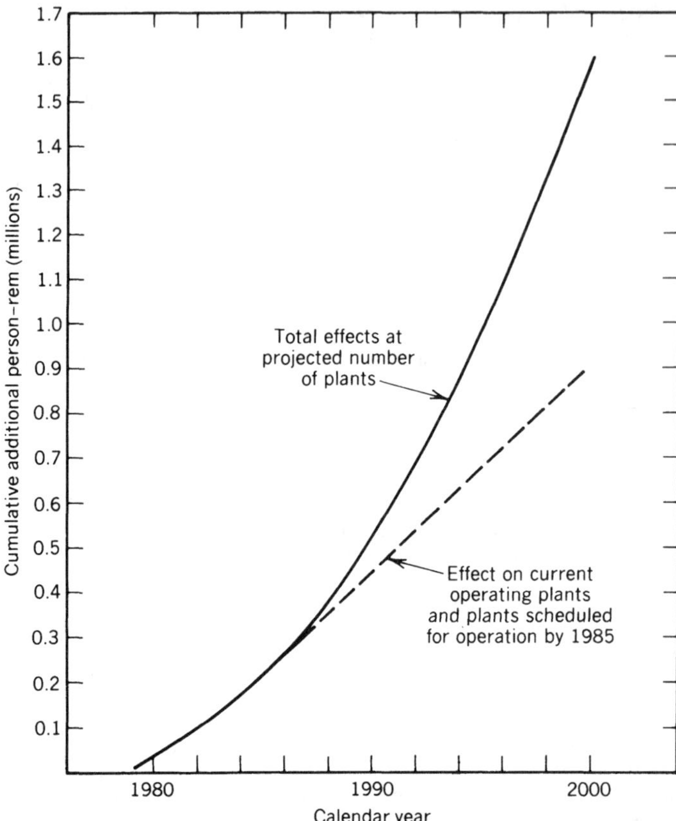

Figure 3.17. Cumulative additional person-rem for period 1979–2000. [From E. A. Warman, Stone & Webster Rept. RP-29 (1978).]

The largest radiation doses are received during maintenance and repair work. These doses are being reduced by the application of past experience to current problems. Most important among these steps is the assignment of specially trained personnel to work in high radiation areas, and the detailed preliminary planning of inspection and repair work.

Techniques used to reduce the time workers spend in radiation fields include:

1. Automatic nondestructive examination techniques.
2. Automatic welding techniques.
3. Remote steam generator inspection and tube plugging.
4. Mock-up training.
5. Semiautomatic reactor coolant pump seal maintenance.
6. Better design of equipment to increase maintainability.
7. Better design of equipment to decrease maintenance frequency.

These operational procedures are being combined with new design features and processes intended to further reduce radiation levels. Table 3.28 lists a few recent developments. Significant progress in the development of technology to reduce in-plant radiation fields has been made in the last few years. The principal improvements are:

1. Concentrated efforts are being made in many countries to develop and field test low-cobalt alloys for wear-resistant applications. This is important because these hard-facing, or wear-resistant, alloys are probably the source of a high proportion of the cobalt isotopes that are predominantly responsible for plant radiation fields.
2. The second principal source of cobalt is Inconel in PWR fuel assembly grids and steam

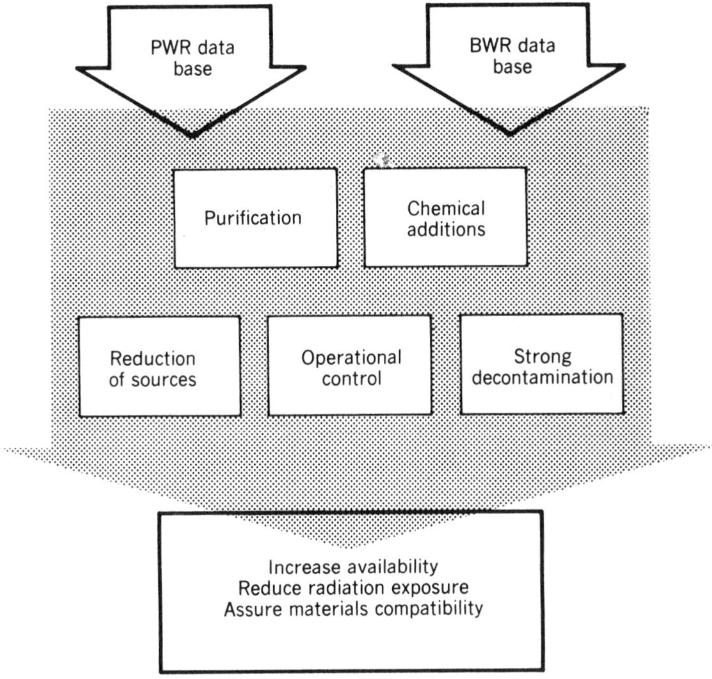

Figure 3.18. Radiation control program. [From R. A. Shaw, *Trans. Am. Nuclear Soc.* **27,** 765 (1977).]

generators. Two alternative materials, Zircaloy and low-cobalt Inconel, have been identified for these applications. Although the main incentive for changing from Inconel to Zircaloy grids is neutron economy, this change also provides the important benefit of reduced in-plant radiation. Low-cobalt Inconel is now being specified for steam generator tubing for most new plants worldwide, and is recommended for steam generator replacement or retubing applications.

3. Tests have shown that PWR coolant chemistry control, with constant high pH, reduces fuel crud thickness and radiation-field buildup on steam generators. Many utilities in France, Germany, Japan, and the United States are now using coordinated lithium–boron control to maintain a high constant pH throughout the fuel cycle. Chemistry control is especially effective for new plants if used consistently from initial plant start-up.
4. Routine draining and drying of BWR condenser and feedwater heater shells, with cold flushing of the feedwater system prior to buildup, reduces input to the core.
5. The use of dilute chemical decontamination techniques to reduce radiation fields. The LOMI process, developed by Britain's CEGB, and the Candecon system have both been used successfully to decontaminate portions of BWR circuits.

The fulfillment of the ALARA concept is a challenge, and an ongoing concern for all nuclear power plant operators.

Table 3.28. New Ways of Controlling Radiation Levels

Techniques now being used (or on the horizon) to reduce radiation levels in plants include:
1. Controlling the nature of the radiation field (particularly $Ni_xFe_{3-x}O_4$)
2. Operational (system) changes (pH control, etc.)
3. High flow rate filtration (development of magnetic filters)
4. Decontamination (use of EDTA, vanadium based reagents, etc.)
5. Better design to eliminate crud traps, allow easier maintenance, "human factors," etc.
6. Material changes (removal of Co alloys)

Source: R. A. Shaw, EPRI.

BIBLIOGRAPHY

A.P.S. Study Group, "Nuclear Fuel Cycles and Waste Management," *Rev. Mod. Phys.* **50** (1978).

Brodsky, A., "Radiation Risks: An Historical Perspective," Radiation and Health Physics Conference, Hershey, Pennsylvania, September 1979.

Bushberg, J. T., et al., *Radiological Health Risks; Reasonable Answers to Naive Questions,* Yale University School of Medicine, New Haven, Connecticut, 1983.

Cohen, B. L., "Perspective on Occupational Mortality Risks," *Health Physics* **40,** 703 (1981).

Cohen, J. J., et al., "Are Emergency Planning Requirements Justified," Workshop Proceedings, NSAC-50, 1982.

Goldstein, H., *Fundamental Aspects of Reactor Shielding,* Addison-Wesley, Reading, Massachusetts, 1959.

———, "Health Evaluation of Energy-Generating Sources," *J. Am. Med. Assoc.* **240,** 2193, 1978.

McBride, J. P., et al., "Radiological Impact of Airborne Effluents of Coal-Fired and Nuclear Power Plants," *Nuclear Safety* **19,** 497, 1978.

National Council on Radiation Protection and Measurements (NCRP), "Natural Background Radiation in the United States," NCRP Rep. No. 45, 1975.

———, "Problems in Assessing the Cancer Risk of Low Level Ionizing Radiation Exposure," Report to the Congress by the Comptroller General GAO Report EMD-81-1 (1981).

———, "Radiation Protection Procedures," Safety Series No. 38, International Atomic Energy Agency, Vienna, 1973.

Sagan, L., "Radiation and Human Health," *EPRI Journal* **4,** 6 (1979).

Tubiana, M., "Health Risks Due to the Use of Nuclear Energy for Electric Power Generation," *IAEA Bull.* **22,** 102 (1982).

Vance, J., et al., "Preliminary Assessment of the Potential Impacts on Operating Nuclear Plants of a 500 mRem/Year Occupational Exposure Limit," AIF, April 1978.

Webster, E. W., "Can We Resolve the Radiation Controversy," AIF Symposium, New Orleans (1982).

CHAPTER 4

RADIATION AND THE ENVIRONMENT: THE IMPACT OF NUCLEAR POWER FACILITIES

4.1. INTRODUCTION

Nuclear power facilities, like all power generating facilities, impact the environment in several ways. They require resources, such as uranium ore, in order to operate, and produce by-products, such as radioactive wastes, that must be properly disposed of. Land, water, and construction materials are also required.

A 1000-MWe light-water reactor (LWR) occupies 1000–3000 acres of land. The size of a power plant site varies considerably because it depends on a number of factors such as local meteorology and ecology, cost of land, and area population. Often the controlling factor is the radiological dose calculation to members of the public under normal and accident conditions. These calculations are greatly affected by the local population distribution and meteorology. It is worth noting that these dose calculations are highly stylized *licensing* analyses whose basis is prescribed in the United States by federal regulation, and are not necessarily indicative of *real* releases from nuclear plants.

10CFR100 requires a utility to control access to an exclusion area around a nuclear reactor. The size of this exclusion area is determined by the licensing analyses already mentioned. The utility generally owns the land in the exclusion area, which is typically 700–800 acres, plus as much additional land as suits its purposes. One possible use for this extra land is future plant expansion. Minimum land requirements, however, are determined by the licensing-based estimates of potential radiological releases.

How radioactivity behaves in the environment is important not only to plant siting but also to the radioactive waste disposal and long-term health effects of nuclear power. In this chapter the physical, chemical, and geologic processes that determine the migration patterns of radionuclides will be examined. Of particular importance will be any properties of the environment which hold up radioactivity dispersal or selectively concentrate it in any way. Understanding these processes will help answer the question of what impact does commercial nuclear power have on people or the environment.

This chapter deals with a number of wide-ranging topics: hydrology, ion exchange properties of rocks, toxicity of plutonium, and so on. These topics cut across a number of scientific disciplines: physical chemistry, mineralogy, geochemistry, human physiology. The common thread bringing them together is how a radionuclide finds its way into the geosphere as the result of the nuclear fuel cycle (from uranium mining to spent fuel disposal operations), and how it might be prevented from entering the biosphere. We first examine the amount of radioactivity and other plant releases involved.

4.2. NUCLEAR POWER FACILITY EFFLUENTS

The following discussion pertains to 1000-MWe pressurized water reactor (PWR) sited near a river with an overall plant efficiency of 33%. UO_2 fuel with approximately 3.3% ^{235}U enrichment is assumed. Resource utilization and environment impact are based on a 70% annual capacity factor. Although the effluents vary somewhat between nuclear power plants of different types, the data presented will be fairly typical.

The major elements of a PWR are shown in Figure 4.1. The points of environmental impact are identified in this figure by circles. These points are the principal sources of radioactive and nonradioactive releases and the inputs of fuel and water resources. Of particular interest are the radwaste building, which houses the gaseous, liquid, and solid radwaste processing systems; the makeup water treatment building, which contains the water purification system; and the natural

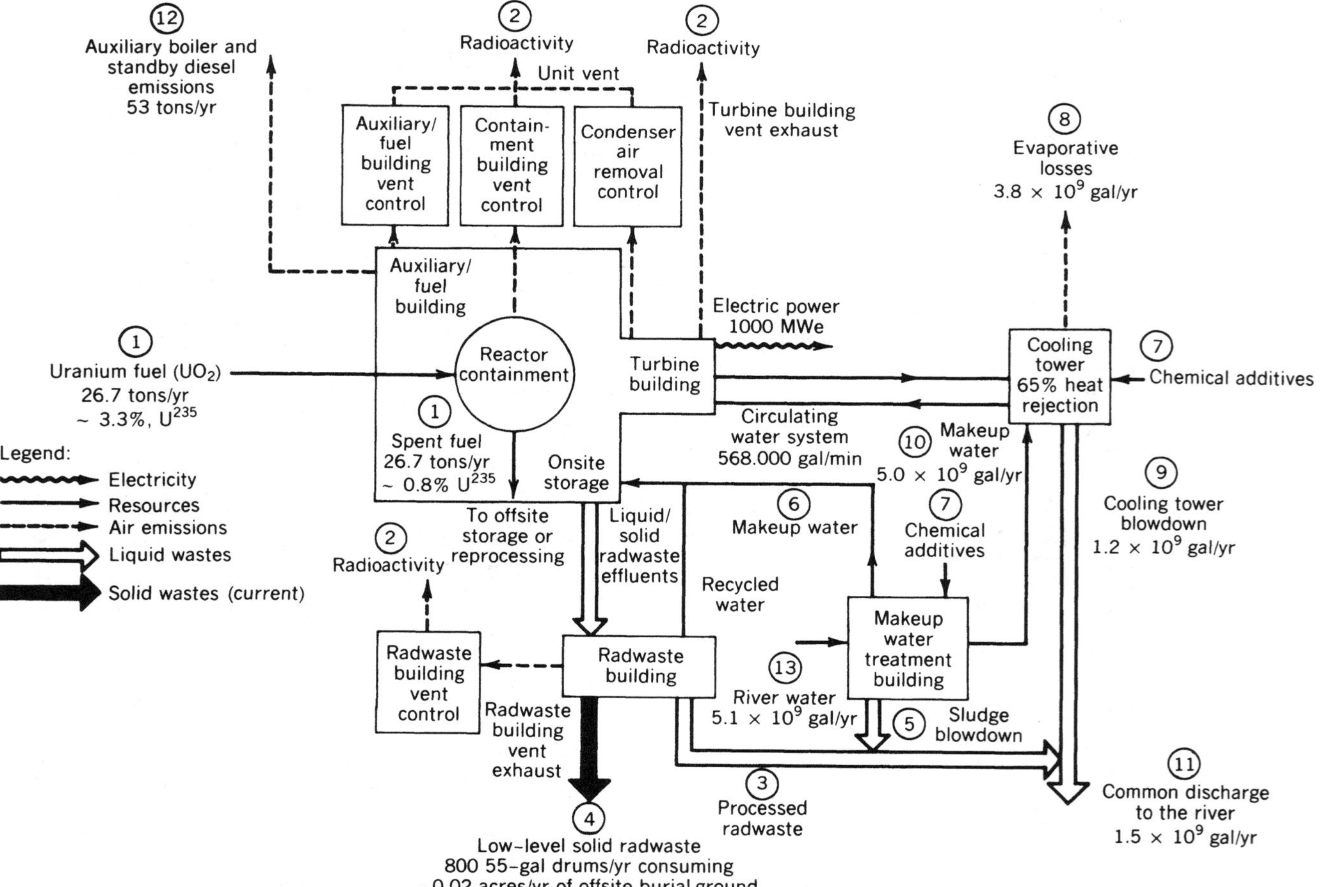

Figure 4.1. Environmental points of interest in a PWR. (From DOE/EP-0012.)

Table 4.1. Isotopic Transformation of New Fuel into Spent Fuel

	New Fuel, %	Spent Fuel After Operation, wt %
Uranium-235	3.3	0.80
Uranium-236	—	0.46
Uranium-238	96.7	94.30
Fission Products	—	3.50
Plutonium	—	0.89
Other Transuranic Isotopes[a]	—	0.05
Totals	100	100

Source: DOE/EP-0012.

[a]Transuranic isotopes are those having a greater atomic number than uranium, which are formed through the absorption of neutrons (without fissioning) in the uranium fuel (in particular uranium-238).

draft, hyperbolic cooling towers, which use local river water. Referring to this figure, the environmental impact points are:

Point 1. Uranium requirements and spent fuel disposition. The amount of UO_2 fuel required to load the core is 80 t. One-third of the core, 26.7 t, is replaced annually. This discharged fuel is then stored on site.† The characteristics of the spent fuel are summarized in Table 4.1 which shows that immediately after discharge the fuel contains about 10 billion Ci of radioactivity. After six months the shorter lived radionuclides have decayed to nonradioactive species, and the continuing decay is much slower. Because the remaining radionuclides have long half-lives and are potentially a biological hazard, the spent fuel, whether reprocessed or not, is of environmental concern, particularly after it leaves the reactor's spent fuel storage pool and is placed in a permanent waste repository.

Figure 4.2 shows the quantity of the radioactive isotopes present in nuclear fuel for various times after discharge from the reactor. Initially the radioactivity from fission products (particularly Cs and Sr) dominates but the radioactivity from actinides (plutonium, americium, etc.) is the major long-term concern. The relative mobility of these radioisotopes in the environment is determined by many factors—initial chemical form; properties of the ground, water, and soil; the nature of the geologic structures and the presence of any engineered barriers to prevent their release.

Point 2. Gaseous radioactive effluents from a PWR average 1800 Ci/yr for noble gases, 6.2 Ci/yr for ^{14}C, and 800 Ci/yr for ^{3}H. These gaseous releases come primarily from leaks in the fuel cladding that allow fission product gases to escape into the reactor coolant system. These gases are stripped from the coolant by the gaseous radwaste system, held for up to three months to allow short-lived isotopes to decay, and then are released through filters and a charcoal bed to remove radioactive particulates and radioiodine. The released radioisotopes dilute rapidly to much below allowable concentrations by the time they reach the site boundary.

Point 3. Liquid radioactive releases would average 0.12 Ci/yr from activated corrosion products and 302 Ci/yr from tritium if the plant operated with the following conditions:

(a) 0.12% fuel defects.

(b) 100 lb/day primary to secondary coolant leakage through the steam generator.

(c) Steam generator moisture carry-over of 0.25%.

Most reactors however achieve considerably lower releases because of fewer fuel defects and less primary to secondary leakage. Liquid effluents are kept small by processing and recycling the majority of liquid wastes generated.

Point 4. About 5300 Ci/yr of low-level solid radwastes (which include residual evaporated liquid wastes) can be expected. Chapter 15 describes the nature and composition of these wastes in detail.

Points 5, 6, 8–11, and 13. These identify various nonradioactive water inputs and discharges from the plant and can be summarized as:

†This has been the practice in the United States pending a national policy on fuel reprocessing and waste storage.

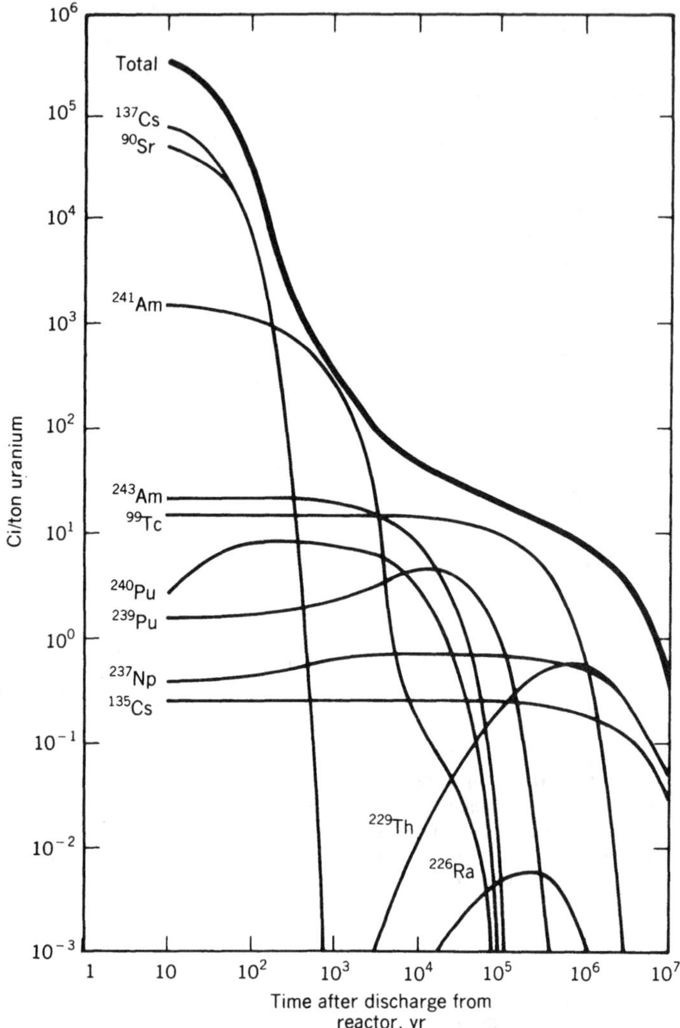

Figure 4.2. Radioactive isotopes in fuel discharge from a reactor, assuming reprocessing takes place shortly after discharge. (From Karnbranslesakerhet Report, 1978.)

(a) Blowdown from the makeup water treatment plant is returned to the river. This water contains nonradioactive sludge removed from river water prior to its use in the plant.

(b) Miscellaneous plant makeup water used in the plant amounts to 80 million gal/yr. Most of this water is used for laundries, showers, and in various plant systems.

(c) Cooling tower losses will approach 4 billion gal/yr to provide the required heat sink for the plant. This evaporated water may cause fogging or icing conditions to occur locally, a condition common to both fossil and nuclear plants that employ cooling towers.

(d) The blowdown from the cooling towers, about 1 billion gal/yr, is sent back to the river. In addition to concentrated dissolved solids, this water will contain chemicals added to prevent corrosion and fouling in the cooling tower. Sulfuric acid and chromate-based inhibitors are commonly added for this purpose.

(e) The water required for the cooling tower, the sum of (c) and (d), some 5 billion gal/yr, comes from the river directly.

Point 7. Various chemicals are added to the river water prior to its use in the plant. These chemicals, listed in Table 4.2, are needed to clarify, demineralize, stabilize, control pH, or chlori-

Table 4.2. Chemical Usage in Makeup Water Systems

Chemical	Use	Frequency of Use	Quantity Used		
			Average		Maximum, lb/day
			lb/day[a]	lb/yr[b]	
Polyelectrolyte (liquid cationic)	River water clarification	Continuous	100	25,500	1,175
Sodium hydroxide	Demineralizer regeneration	Once per train per day (2 hr/day)	2,450	626,000	3,700
Sulfuric acid	Demineralizer regeneration	Once per train per day (2 hr/day)	2,100	536,600	3,100
Sulfuric acid	Recirculating cooling water pH control	Continuous	12,600	3,219,300	15,500
Rock salt	Produce sodium hypochlorite (see below)	As needed (hypochlorite used on an intermittent basis)	4,200	1,073,100	8,750
Sodium hypochlorite	Biocide treatment of recirculating cooling water	Approximately 2 hr/day per cooling tower	1,200	306,600	2,500
Dispersant (organic phosphonate)	Scale inhibition in cooling water systems	Continuous	935	238,900	1,150

Source: DOE/EP-0012.
[a]100% capacity.
[b]70% capacity.

nate (i.e., as a biocide) the water. The quantities needed vary greatly from plant to plant depending on the local water quality.

Point 12. Fossil fuel combustion products are produced even at a nuclear power plant. Relatively small amounts of SO_2, NO_x, CO, and particulates will be produced by the standby diesel generators† and the auxiliary steam boiler used during plant start-up or the 6 to 8 weeks a year the plant is being refueled.

The parameters listed above were for a plant of 1000-MWe capacity. Older plants tend to have smaller capacity, while most modern nuclear units range from 1000 to 1300 MWe. To a first approximation, the plant inputs and effluents scale directly with capacity. For those few instances where a linear scaling is not strictly correct, the error would be no greater than about 20%.

Mines and Mills

The processes of mining and milling uranium ore can bring radioactive minerals previously sequestered deep in the earth to the surface where they can more readily enter the biosphere. The environment is impacted by these activities proportional to the amount of mill tailings generated. When ore is processed, most of the uranium is removed, but a small fraction remains behind, along with radium and radon, two elements naturally created in the uranium decay process. There are about 500 kg of mill tailings for every kilogram of uranium produced, although this amount varies considerably with the richness of the ore mined. On average, the tailings contain about 250 μCi of radium, and 200 nCi of radon per kilogram of uranium concentrate. Federal law requires the mill tailings to be stabilized and water runoff to be controlled. In some instances, moreover, the ore during processing is stripped of its radium content thereby removing the greater part of ore's hazard. Liquid effluents, which can leach radioactivity from the tailing piles, and gaseous radon are the main pathways leading to the environment. A summary of the radiological impact caused by atmospheric emissions of natural radioactive materials is shown in Table 4.3. A more detailed discussion of mill tailings is presented in Chapter 5.

†Operated only for emergency power when off-site power is lost, or while testing for about 2 hr/month.

Table 4.3. Summary of Radiological Impact Caused by Atmospheric Emissions of Natural Radioactive Materials

Source Category	Number of Sources	Principal Radionuclide Emissions, Ci/yr		Exposure levels: Maximum Individual, WL	Exposure levels: Regional Population, person-WL
Uranium mines					
Underground	251	^{222}Rn	6700	0.006	1.3
Open pit	36	^{222}Rn	2000	0.0008	0.4
Uranium mills	20	^{222}Rn	2700	0.005	0.5
		^{238}U + d	0.4		
Phosphate industry					
Mining and beneficiation	35	^{222}Rn	1300	0.0002	4.9
Drying and grinding facilities	20	^{222}Rn	20	0.00005	0.08
		^{238}U + d	0.03		
Phosphoric acid plant	35	^{222}Rn	480	0.0007	2.0
		^{238}U + d	0.1		
Elemental phosphorus plant	9	^{222}Rn	490	0.0004	2.0
		^{238}U + d	0.15		
		^{210}Po	7.4		
Coal-fired power stations					
New stations	145	^{222}Rn	1.9	<0.00001	<0.00001–0.024
		^{238}U + d	0.3		
		^{232}Th + d	0.07		
Existing stations	250	^{222}Rn	0.7	<0.00001	<0.00001–0.013
		^{238}U + d	0.8		
		^{232}Th + d	0.3		

Source: From EPA 520/7-79-006.

Reprocessing and Waste Handling

Fuel reprocessing plants are the major source of radioactive wastes in terms of radioactive content. The radioactive elements in the aqueous wastes from a reprocessing plant are highly concentrated, and hence are considered high-level wastes. They present, however, only a fraction of the volume produced in nuclear facilities because of their highly concentrated nature.

Figure 4.2 gives the quantity of radioactive elements in high-level wastes as a function of time after discharge from the reactor. Initially, the fission products ^{137}Cs and ^{90}Sr dominate in this figure; however, after several hundred years the actinide ^{241}Am and the fission product ^{99}Tc account for most of the radioactivity. Most direct health hazards from radioactive wastes arise from gamma radiation. However, if the wastes were ingested in some way, the biological effects would be more considerable, and of a different nature since alpha radiation would play a larger role. Figure 4.3 shows how the curves in Figure 4.2 would alter if they were weighted by maximum permissible concentrations to obtain a measure of the relative biological hazard. The effect of the actinides, especially at times longer than 1000 yr, is evident.

The figure assumes that reprocessing takes place after 10 yr. This time is of some importance for the activity of the high-level waste. ^{241}Pu, which is a beta emitter, decays with a half-life of 13.2 yr to ^{241}Am. The longer the wait for reprocessing, the more of this nuclide will be present in the waste. If the waste is only stored for 3 yr before reprocessing, the amount of ^{241}Am given will decrease to about 40%. If a much longer time passes before reprocessing, the amount of ^{241}Am will increase to roughly double the value given in the figure.

Reprocessing plants also have other liquid waste streams with much lower radioactivity levels. These streams generally do not contain any alpha-emitting radionuclides, but often are contaminated with beta and gamma emitters. Such streams may contain nitric acid used in reprocessing the fuel or chemical solutions used to decontaminate equipment.

Gaseous effluents are also produced during reprocessing. About 7000 Ci of radioactive ^{85}Kr and about 1 Ci of ^{129}I are generated in reprocessing a single metric ton of fuel. Tritium and some ^{14}C are also produced. In some plants, only the radioiodine is removed from the gaseous effluent by fixing

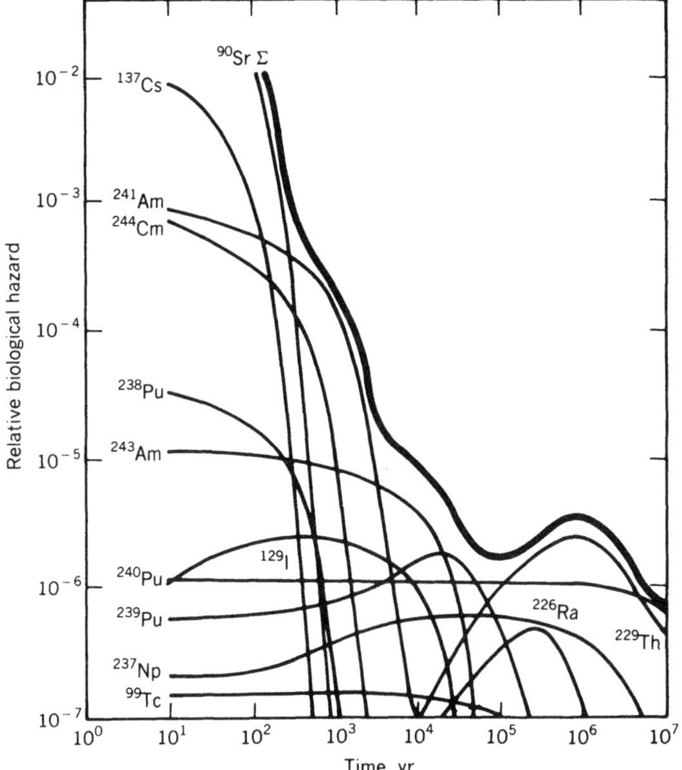

Figure 4.3. Relative biological hazard of radioisotopes in high-level nuclear wastes as a function of time. (From ORNL-79-10332.)

it on solid absorbers, while in others, most of the krypton is removed by a cryogenic process and stored, while tritium is collected as tritiated water.

Typically about 1 m^3/yr of high-level wastes, 3 m^3/yr of medium-level wastes, and 0.002 m^3/yr of gaseous waste can be expected for each metric ton of reprocessing capacity in a plant. Significantly large amounts of chemical wastes can also be expected. If a throwaway fuel cycle is adopted, and reprocessing not used, then the spent fuel itself would be considered high-level waste. The nature and handling of these wastes will be explored in Chapter 14 on reprocessing and Chapter 15 on waste disposal.

Other Facilities

Other nuclear fuel cycle facilities (fuel fabrication plants, uranium conversion, and enrichment plants) have considerably lower radioactive emissions than nuclear power or reprocessing plants. The radiological impact of these other sources are summarized in Table 4.4. As seen in this table, the off-site population exposures from nuclear power facilities are not significant compared to other sources of radiation.

4.3. HEALTH HAZARDS OF RADIOACTIVE MATERIALS

Chapter 3 examined the overall relationship between radiation and health. This section looks at some of the radioactive materials of particular concern in the nuclear fuel cycle: plutonium, other transuranics, radon, and fission products.

Plutonium

Plutonium is a silver, heavy metal, number 94 in the periodic table (in the actinide series). It was first produced in 1940 by E. McMillan, J. Kennedy, and A. Wahl, who were working with G. T.

Table 4.4. Summary of Radiological Impact Caused by Atmospheric Emissions from Licensed Sources

Source Category	Number of Sources	Principal Radionuclide Emissions, Ci/yr		Principal Dose Equivalent Rates: Maximum Individual, mrem/yr	Principal Dose Equivalent Rates: Regional Population, person-rem/yr
Uranium conversion facilities	2	^{238}U	0.08	Lung 88	120
		^{234}U	0.08	Bone 9	5
		^{234}Th	0.08		
Fuel fabrication facility	16	^{234}U	0.008	Lung 5	7
		^{235}U	0.0003	Bone 0.5	0.3
		^{236}U	0.0004		
		^{238}U	0.001		
		^{231}Th	0.0003		
		^{234}Th	0.001		
Light-water reactors	25				
Boiling water reactors		Noble gases	7,000	Thyroid 11	19
		Tritium	43	Whole body 2	8
		Halogens	1.4		
Pressurized water reactors	44	Noble gases	13,000	Thyroid 1	7
		Tritium	1,100	Whole body 0.8	5
		Halogens	0.05		
High-temperature gas cooled reactor	1	Noble gases	1,100	Whole body 0.5	6
(Fort St. Vrain)	1				
Radiopharmaceutical industry					
Producers	34	^{125}I	0.9	Thyroid 86	200
		^{131}I	0.9	Whole body 0.2	0.7
Oak Ridge Facilities	1	^{234}U	0.06	Lung 4.6	Total body 4.7
		^{131}I	1.4	Bone 5.5	
		^{85}Kr	8,600	Thyroid 1.5	
Portsmouth Gaseous Diffusion Plant	1	^{234}Th	0.05	Lung 1.1	Total body 0.19
		^{234}U	0.1	Bone 1.2	
		^{99}Tc	4.5	Kidney 1.1	
				G. I. tract 2.2	
Paducah Gaseous Diffusion Plant	1	^{234}U	0.2	Lung 6.3	NR
		^{238}U	0.2	Bone 0.9	

Source: From EPA 520/7-79-006.

Seaborg. Plutonium has 16 isotopes, the most important of which are plutonium-238 with a half-life of 86.4 yr, plutonium-239 with a half-life of 24,390 yr, plutonium-240 with a half life of 6580 yr, and plutonium-241 with a half-life of 13.2 yr. Extremely small traces of plutonium-244 have been found in cerium-rich minerals. This is all that remains of the natural plutonium present at the creation of the earth.

The biological effect of plutonium is based on predictions from:

(a) Known chemical, physical, or biological properties.

(b) The behavior of plutonium from weapons fallout and fabrication data.

(c) Observed effects in individuals exposed to plutonium through accidents.

In the nuclear fuel cycle, plutonium usually exists as an oxide, and as such is insoluble in water and body fluids. The sorption of plutonium onto rock particles causes it to migrate slowly in soil. When ingested into the body, plutonium oxide is mostly sorbed onto undigested food. This behavior and its insoluble nature cause plutonium to be poorly taken up by the gastrointestinal tract. The principal radiation hazard from plutonium is alpha rays which cause highly localized cell damage. However, plutonium is easily detectable so that unlike other carcinogens, protective action can be easily implemented. Because of the relatively long half-life of some of its isotopes, plutonium must be regarded as permanent in the environment.

Reactor grade plutonium normally consists of about 70% plutonium-239 and 30% plutonium-240. This is in contrast to weapons grade material which is almost all plutonium-239 with less than 5% plutonium-240. In a 1000-MWe LWR, there are approximately 600 kg of plutonium at the end of core life, while approximately 3000 kg are in the core inventory of a Liquid Metal Fast Breeder Reactor (LMFBR).

The physiochemical properties of plutonium determine its toxicity and hazard. The density of plutonium ranges from 16.0 to 19.9 g/cm^3. Plutonium is chemically active and dissolves in many acids, including hydrochloric acid. There are six chemical oxidation states ranging from 2 to 7. Oxidation state 4 is the most common and 2 and 7 are relatively rare. Plutonium forms salts with all elements in column VII of the periodic table. Most of these salts are highly insoluble in both acid and water. Most chemical processing of plutonium is done in a nitric acid solution where plutonium takes on a +4 oxidation state. It is the normal oxidation state (as PuO_2) in nuclear reactor fuel.

Plutonium ions hydrolyze and form chemical complexes as well as colloids and polymers of these species. These properties determine the behavior of plutonium in environmental situations that contain mineral sedimentations, such as clay. The extensive hydrolysis in aqueous solutions, especially in combination with basic chemical conditions (high pH), is significant in biological systems.

Hydrolysis is easiest for Pu^{4+}, and is also relatively easy for Pu^{6+}. Plutonium hydroxide $Pu(OH)_4$ precipitates; any soluble plutonium discharged to an aquatic environment also precipitates out locally. Plutonium in solution (even in trace quantities) is rapidly adsorbed (even in extremely pure water). It is released only in highly acidic solutions which rarely exist in biological systems or the environment. Colloids or polymers, however, may present a problem.

The risk from plutonium exposure is premature death due to latent cancers. Plutonium does not appear to concentrate in biological systems, and migrates only to an extremely small extent in the environment.

There are three basic ways in which humans can be contaminated with plutonium. These are ingestion via the food chain, inhalation from the air, or subcutaneous contamination in the blood stream. In the ingestion pathway, relatively little is absorbed by the body, because plutonium mostly mixes with the contents of the intestines (Figure 4.4). Relatively little tissue is irradiated because the range of alpha particles is not long enough to reach the inner lining of the intestines. The plutonium passes out of the body in due course. When considering plutonium inhaled through the lungs, approximately 40% of what enters is exhaled immediately (Figure 4.5). The remainder is removed by ciliary action in the gastrointestinal tract except for very fine particles. These particles, typically in the submicrometer range, tend to be lodged deep within the recesses of the lungs and are not easily removed. As a result, these fine particulates are the principal toxic hazard of plutonium. The localized radiation dose to the lung is about 2000 rems/μCi of deposited plutonium. Subcutaneous contamination is generally only a hazard for occupational exposure in plutonium fabricating facilities.

In the mid-1970s, a theory referred to as the "hot particle" theory was put forward by A. Tamplin and T. Cochran. It stated that the health hazards of plutonium were much larger than previously thought due to the effect of localized α-particle damage to the lung. The thesis was that a single particle of Pu, a so-called "hot particle," was capable of depositing sufficient localized energy to tissue that cancer would likely result in a high proportion of the individuals exposed. Some experimental data on animal populations existed, but was equivocable. Data on humans, including 25 individuals heavily exposed to plutonium during military programs at Los Alamos National Laboratory, did not confirm the "hot particle" hypothesis. Since no new data confirming this hypothesis have since appeared, it no longer appears to be an issue.

Recent results at Lawrence Berkeley Laboratory show that chelating agents can effectively treat plutonium poisoning, especially a new class of chelating agents called LICAM-C.† This agent has been effective in removing 70% of the plutonium injected into mice. Plutonium normally exists in the body in oxidation state +4 which is chemically similar to Fe^{3+}. Thus, the body concentrates it at iron sites such as the spleen, bone marrow, and the liver. Although other chemicals can remove plutonium from the body, they are less effective because they can also remove calcium, iron, and zinc. LICAM-C is a small enough molecule to be excreted through the kidney.

Other Transuranics

Americium, curium, and neptunium are the transuranic elements sometimes encountered in the nuclear fuel cycle in addition to plutonium. Americium has eleven isotopes with atomic masses between 236 and 247. The odd isotopes ^{241}Am and ^{243}Am are alpha-particle emitters with 458-yr and 7950-yr half-lives, while the even isotopes ^{242}Am and ^{244}Am emit beta-rays, and have half-lives of 16 and 10 hr, respectively. Because of their short half-lives, the even isotopes are not of particular environmental concern, but they decay to long-lived ^{238}Pu and ^{240}Pu.

†LICAM-C stands for Linear Catecholamide Carboxylate.

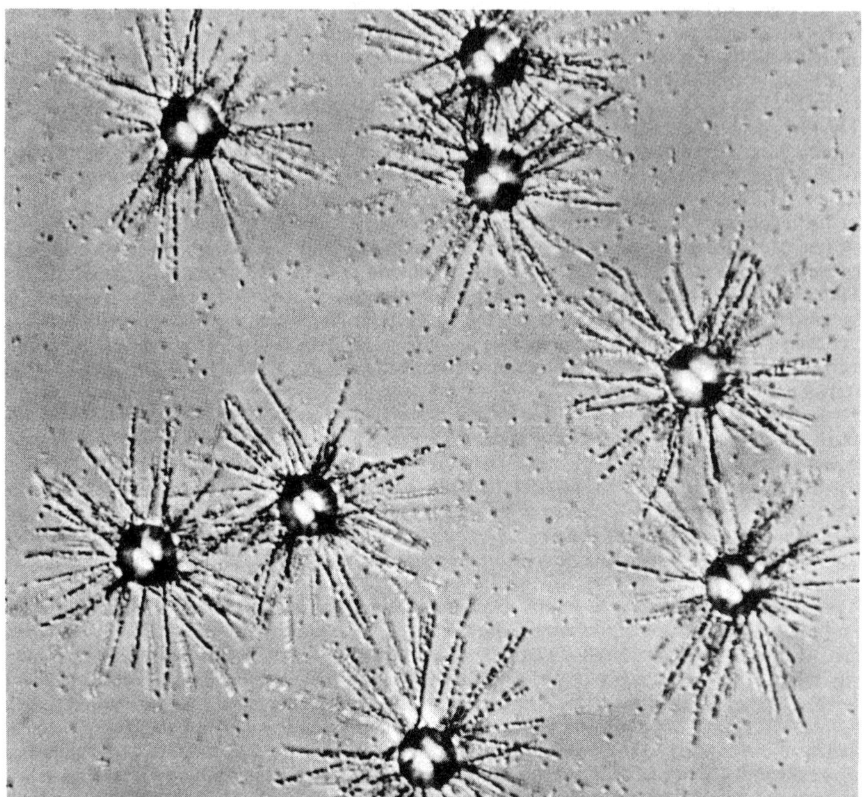

Figure 4.4. Ten-micrometer-diameter plutonium microspheres used in a continuing health research study involving the effects of plutonium. The Pu spheres are embedded in a gel-like material which simulates human tissue. The starlike patterns surrounding the spheres are due to alpha particles, the principal radiation hazard of concern for biological health effects. The range of alpha particles in such material is a few tens of micrometers. (From LANL.)

The isotope ^{241}Am is formed by the decay of ^{241}Pu which has a 13.2-yr half-life. When ^{241}Am decays, ^{237}Np is produced. ^{241}Am is present in the HLW† stream from a reprocessing plant, although its precursor ^{241}Am in HLW depends on when spent fuel is reprocessed. If the spent fuel is not reprocessed, all the ^{241}Pu it contains will eventually decay into ^{241}Am. If plutonium is to be recycled into reactors, the ^{241}Am contained in the fuel will grow with time and may require special shielding to protect personnel in a fuel fabrication plant from the gamma rays that accompany its alpha-particle decay.

The isotope ^{243}Am, on the other hand, arises mostly from neutron capture in ^{242}Pu, and since it is a higher mass actinide, has a much lower yield in reactor fuel. HLW usually contains 10 to 100 times less ^{243}Am than ^{241}Am. In aqueous solutions, americium exists in four valence states, although the hydrated forms Am^{3+}, AmO_2^{2+}, and AmO_2^{+} are usually formed. Like plutonium, complexes of americium are common.

Americium's hazard parallels plutonium's in many ways: being an alpha-particle emitter, ingestion into the body is of greatest concern. Americium tends to collect in the lungs, liver, and bones. In cases of radiation exposure, calcium DTPA, a chelating agent, has been used to bind heavy metals like americium and force them into the body's waste products. Large amounts of DTPA will, however, also deplete the body of zinc. Too great a loss of this essential element can lead to fatal intestinal bleeding and kidney damage. In cases of heavy contamination, an analogue compound, zinc DTPA, has been used with success without serious side effects.

Although curium has at least fourteen isotopes, ^{242}Cm is the most important in the nuclear fuel cycle. Although it is a large contributor to alpha activity in spent fuel and HLW, it decays rapidly

†High-Level Waste.

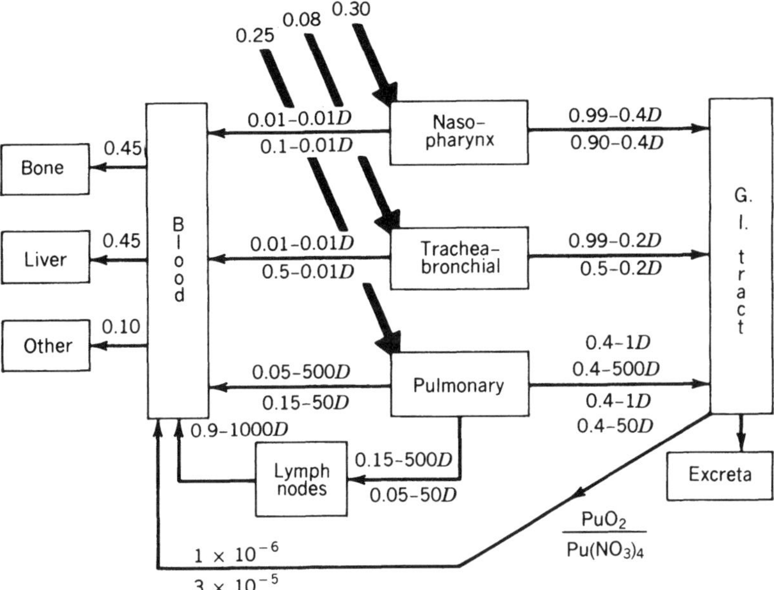

Figure 4.5. The disposition of inhaled Pu dust according to ICRP Publication 19. Heavy diagonal arrows from the top are the fractions of dust deposited in each part of the respiratory system. For other transfers the numbers above the lines refer to insoluble compounds like PuO_2, and the numbers below the lines refer to soluble compounds like $Pu(NO_3)_4$. The first figures are the fractional part undergoing transfer by this route, and second figures are the half-life in days (D) for the transfer. (Courtesy B. Cohen.)

with a 163-day half-life to ^{238}Pu. Because of its rapid decay, very little curium would find its way into the environment. However, if plutonium is recycled in nuclear reactors, ^{242}Cm and higher isotopes of curium will be more prevalent in the fuel and HLW.

Radon

Radon, element number 86 on the periodic chart, is a naturally occurring noble gas found in soil, uranium mines, and mill tailings. A daughter product of ^{238}U decay, its concentration around uranium deposits and ore is particularly high, although it is plentiful in some shales and mineral deposits.† It is colorless, liquefying at −61.8°C. Background atmospheric levels of ^{222}Rn come mostly from the decay of ^{226}Ra in the soil and rock of the earth's crust. A decay scheme for radon is given in Figure 4.6. Radon is quite soluble in cold water, although its solubility decreases rapidly with temperature. This characteristic is especially important for groundwater transport and subsequent radon release to the atmosphere. Typical groundwater contains 5–100,000 pCi/liter of ^{222}Rn.

The inhalation of radon, and its daughter products, is a principal health concern because of the alpha-particle radiation associated with radon decay. This radiation can damage the epithelial layer of the lung‡ and may lead to cancer. ^{222}Rn is a particularly potent alpha emitter because of its short 3.8-day half-life. Moreover, it decays into a series of very short-lived progeny§ including the alpha emitters ^{218}Po and ^{214}Po, so that each radon decay effectively results in three alpha particles.

Most of the lung cancers induced by radon exposure are readily identified because of their relatively uncommon type. It is not clear from the statistics whether these cancers can be caused at any level of exposure, or whether some minimum exposure is required. Excess fatal lung disease due to radon was first reported among miners in the Joachimstal region of Bavaria in 1546. This region has a relatively high radon level due to uranium deposits. The miners were exposed to high radon gas concentrations. The malignant nature of the disease was first noted in 1879. Lung cancer has been more recently observed in workers in unventilated uranium mines; however excess lung

†^{220}Rn can also result from the decay of ^{232}Th. ^{220}Rn subsequently decays to ^{216}Po and eventually to ^{208}Pb.

‡This is the tissue covering the inner surface of the lung.

§^{218}Po and ^{214}Po have half-lives of less than 3 min.

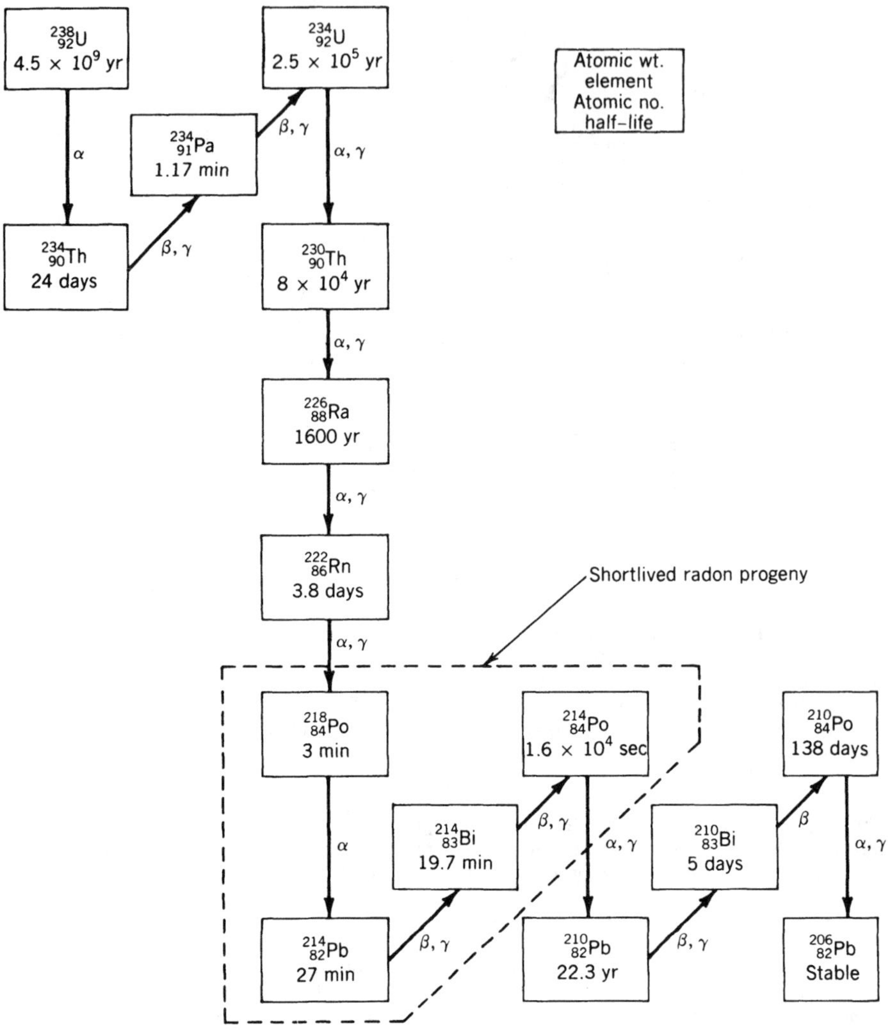

Figure 4.6. The ^{238}U decay series leading to radon. (From RPC 80-002.)

cancer also occurs in a variety of hard rock mines in which radon is present. The correlation seems to be between lung cancer and the radon daughter products, probably because radon itself does not directly deposit in the lung. The polonium daughter products become charged, however, due to the radioactive decay process. This electrostatic charge causes them to adhere to dust particles and remain in the respiratory tract.

The unit of radon exposure is the Working Level (WL). This rather cumbersome unit is defined as any combination of radon daughter products in 1 liter of air that will result in the emission of 1.3×10^5 MeV of alpha-particle energy. This is equal to the alpha energy released by the radon daughter products in equilibrium with 100 pCi/liter of radon gas. It was chosen because 1 WL per month (WLM) is the recommended maximum exposure limit set by the National Council on Radiation Protection (NCRP). In mines, the radon daughters are often present in much less than equilibrium concentration. In such cases, 1 WL may be equivalent to radon gas concentrations of 200–300 pCi/liter. Very roughly, 1 WL is thought to have the similar health consequences as about 5 rems of ionizing radiation.

The radon concentrations in the Schneeberg mines† were 30–150 WL. From health data on the miners, it has been estimated that the lung cancer rate is 3×10^{-6}/yr-WLM‡. Some more recent

†A uranium mining region in Germany.
‡The BEIR-III report uses 850×10^{-6}/WLM as the cancer risk.

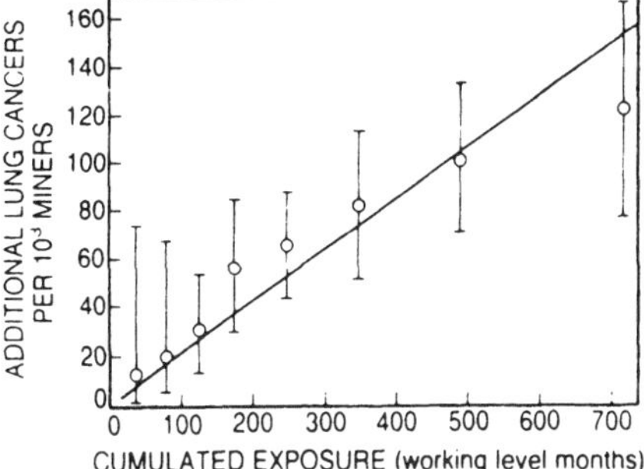

Figure 4.7. Increase in lung cancer for Czechoslovakian uranium miners as a function of dose from radon daughters. [From J. Sevc et al., *Health Physics* **30,** 433 (1976).]

radiological health data are shown in Figure 4.7. The usual concentration in U.S. uranium mines today is approximately ⅓ WL. In the post-World War II period, however, much higher levels were present. As a result of this past exposure, 250–600 uranium miners may eventually die due to radon exposure. This compares to the 5000 deaths/yr in the U.S. from environmental radon as predicted in the BEIR report. Studies on the lung cancer incidence data seem to show that if a threshold exposure is needed to cause cancer, it is quite low, apparently lower than 10 WLM.

Fission and Activation Products

Fission and activation products are the most common forms of radioactivity encountered in the nuclear industry. They are also the source of almost all of the radiation in terms of curies, with perhaps 99% of the occupational doses coming from the beta and gamma rays associated with them. Their health effects, determined by their beta and gamma radiation, were covered at length in Chapter 3, and so will not be repeated here.

4.4. BEHAVIOR OF RADIOACTIVE MATERIALS IN THE ENVIRONMENT

Radionuclides reaching the biological environment, either by transport through the geosphere, or by direct emission from a power plant, become a part of the natural cycle and thus may be transferred to plants, animals, and humans. Unless there is some substantial concentrating mechanism, it is doubtful whether normal radioactive releases from the nuclear fuel cycle would damage living organisms. If a major release of radioactivity from a damaged reactor were to occur, however, biological and ecological damage would be more severe. In particular, the concentration of ^{131}I in the human thyroid and the contamination of agricultural land by ^{137}Cs are major concerns addressed in accident consequence studies. Chapter 17 discusses the probability and magnitude of accident releases in detail.

After radioactivity has reached the biosphere, it can affect humans in different ways. The radioactivity can be ingested into the body either by food and water, or by inhalation. Knowledge of the transport and concentration of radioactivity in the food chain is therefore important.

In order to predict the behavior of radioactivity in the environment and the amount that could reach humans through food chains, and so on, the isotopes prevalent in each pathway must be monitored. The dominant isotopes for the most important pathways are given in Table 4.5. ^{129}I, ^{135}Cs, and ^{90}Sr are perhaps the most important radionuclides in this table which commonly appear in the nuclear fuel cycle. Indirect radioactive contamination may occur, for instance, if plants are growing on soils where radionuclides have migrated to the root zone. The uptake of radionuclides by plant roots is in general an inefficient mechanism of radiation exposure. At most, a few percent of the deposited radioactivity would be taken up by plants in one growing season. Radionuclides that deposit directly on plants, however, pose greater risk, because no dilution occurs. If the plants are then eaten, a direct pathway to man exists. The contamination of a plant depends on the particular species, which determines whether the radioactivity will accumulate on the leaves or pass through the plant to other parts. Likewise plants eaten by animals for fodder can result in radioactivity being passed on to man, either through milk products or meat. For some isotopes, such as ^{131}I, which has an 8-day half-life, the delay between the deposition on agricultural produce and its consumption may reduce the hazard (Table 4.6). Weathering (i.e., rainfall) is also a mechanism which tends to reduce the amount of radioactive material remaining on vegetation.

Direct contamination of vegetation is a transitory problem since it affects a single crop. Disposal of the contaminated vegetation, or not using it, would eliminate the problem. Incorporation of radioactivity into the top layer of the soil would affect crops over many growing seasons, but presents a much reduced hazard.

Table 4.5. Dominant Radioisotope in Important Environmental Pathways

Path of Exposure	Some Important Nuclides
Soil—grain	^{229}Th
Soil—green vegetables	^{237}Np, ^{229}Th, ^{93}Zr
Soil—root vegetables	^{229}Th
Soil—grass	^{129}I
Grass—milk	^{129}I, ^{226}Ra, ^{233}U, ^{90}Sr
Grass—meat	^{129}I, ^{229}Th, ^{233}U, ^{90}Sr
Grain—eggs	
Drinking water	^{237}Np, ^{226}Ra, ^{233}U, ^{99}Tc
Water—fish (fresh and salt water fish, respectively)	^{135}Cs, ^{129}I, ^{226}Ra
Land (external exposure)	^{229}Th
Beach activities (external exposure)	^{135}Cs, ^{229}Th, ^{99}Tc, ^{129}I
Bathing (external exposure)	
Fishing (external exposure)	^{99}Tc, ^{129}I, ^{135}Cs, ^{137}Cs, ^{229}Th

Source: Karnbranslesakerhet Report (1978).

Table 4.6. Delay Times Assumed Between Harvest (or Production) of Foodstuff and Consumption by Humans for the Estimation of Collective Doses via Ingestion

Food Product	Delay, days
Milk[a]	2
Milk products[a]	
Butter	28
Cheese	122
Beef	7
Mutton/lamb	7
Green vegetables[b]	
Fresh	5
Frozen/canned	90
Grain	365

Source: From NRPB-R137 (1982).
[a]57% of milk consumed as fresh liquid, 26% as butter and 17% as cheese.
[b]78% of green vegetables consumed fresh and the remainder frozen or canned.

Terrestrial Transport

Before radioactivity from spent fuel disposal can be harmful to humans, it must pass from the disposal site (geosphere) into the biosphere. Groundwater is the connecting medium between them; the main interface between the geosphere and the biosphere is where the groundwater comes in contact with human beings (Figure 4.8). As shown in part (*a*) of this figure, radioactive wastes buried in the earth can escape through various barriers (container, backfill, rock) and eventually reach the biosphere. Since any elements escaping would be dispersed by groundwater, the motion of and the dilution in groundwater are of prime importance. Part (*b*) of the figure shows how radioactive elements can be transferred between various reservoirs, such as water, sediment, biota, and so on. Backflows between these reservoirs can also be important. The models developed for radioactive element migration, of course, would apply also to chemical wastes and ore bodies. Thus, to determine the radioactivity release potential from buried waste, several interfacing areas need to be examined:

1. The point of groundwater outflow from the geosystem to the biosphere—Hydrology.
2. The area in the immediate region—Geochemistry.
3. The global structure of the surrounding area—Geology.
4. The packaging of the waste, covered in detail in Chapter 15.

The first important ground transport mechanism is the motion of the groundwater itself, so the topic of hydrology will be addressed first.

Hydrology

Two important parameters affect chemical mobility in geologic formations. These are the hydrogen ion concentration† (pH) and the oxidation reduction potential‡ (Eh). At room temperature, water (H_2O) dissociates into H^+ and OH^- ions. As shown in Figure 4.9, the amount of H^+ ions dis-

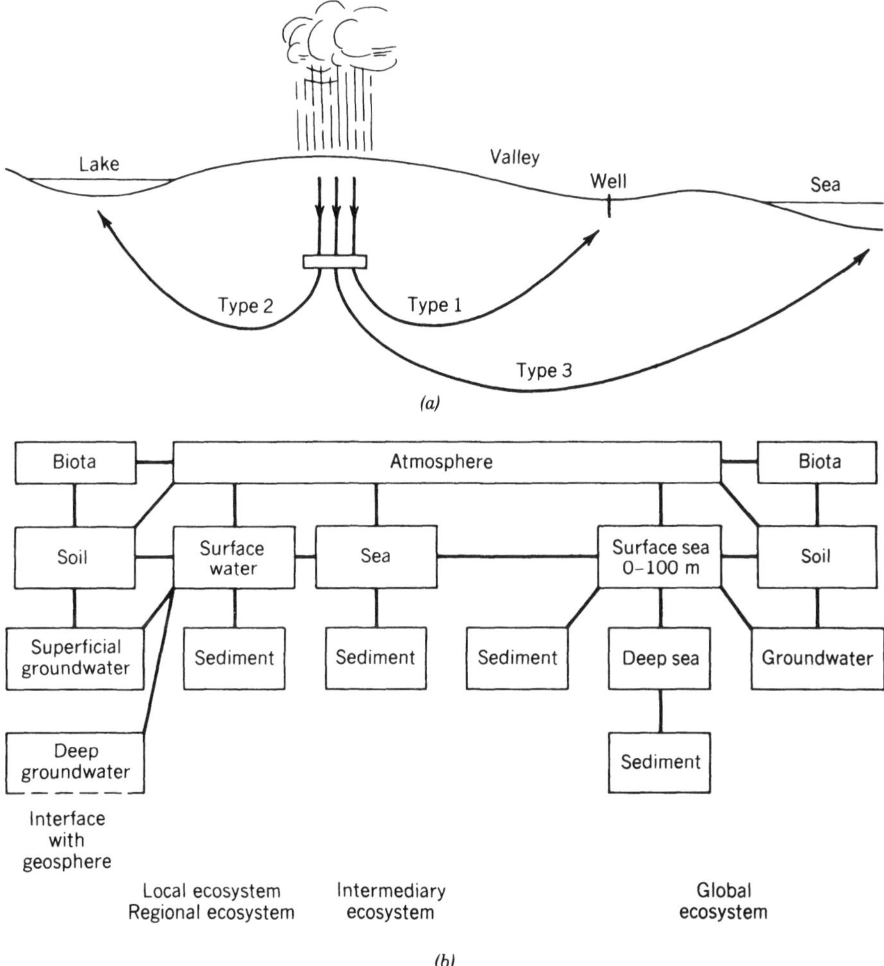

Figure 4.8. (*a*) The three main types of transport of radioactive elements to the biosphere: 1. outflow to a valley where a well or spring is located; 2. outflow to a lake of specified size; 3. outflow to the sea near the coast. (*b*) Reservoirs for the various ecosystems. (From Karnbranslesakerhet Report, 1978.)

†This is a measure of acidity, that is, the number of hydrogen ions in solution.
‡This is a measure of the ability of ions to change valence state, that is gain or lose electrons.

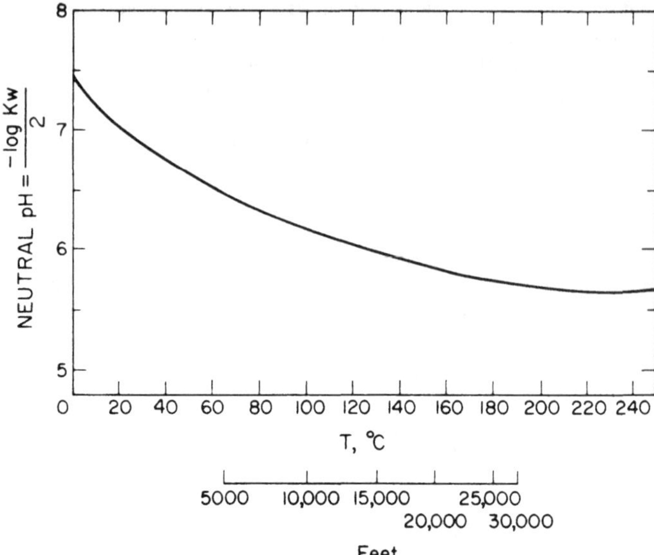

Figure 4.9. Variation in the dissociation constant of water as a function of temperature and depth in a geosyncline. (From Blatt et al., *Origin of Sedimentary Rocks,* Prentice-Hall, Englewood Cliffs, New Jersey, 1972.)

sociated varies with temperature. At room temperature, if the water is neutral—neither acidic nor basic—10^{-7} moles/liter of each ion is present, and the water has a pH of 7.0. The concentration of H^+ will be greater at 100°C than at 20°C. This is important because temperature usually increases with depth, and near thermal anomalies in the earth's crust. Radioactivity in a waste disposal site may also cause an increase in the surrounding temperature. Neutral pH is defined as the existence of equal numbers of H^+ and OH^+ ions, *not* as sometimes supposed as the condition when pH is 7.0. For example, at 100°C, the average temperature of the ground at 10,000-ft depth, neutral pH is 6.1 or $10^{-6.1}$ ion pairs/liter. Thus a pH reading of 7.0 at a depth of a few thousand feet indicates a hydrogen-poor or basic solution and this should be borne in mind in the discussion of pH in the transport of radionuclides.

In sedimentary geologic structures, the control of the oxidation reduction potential (Eh) is determined by the available gaseous oxygen in the environment and the competition for that oxygen by various processes, such as the decomposition of organic matter. The Eh of any system is relative to the active electrochemical species being created. It is usually arbitrarily defined relative to the hydrogen dissociation reaction

$$2H^+ + 2e^- \leftrightarrow H_2$$

which is defined as 0.0 V Eh potential, provided the temperature is 25°C and the pressure is 1 atmosphere.

In a ground system, both the pH and Eh of a solution are fixed by reactions with the surrounding mineralization. Typical values for various environments are shown in Figure 4.10. The control of pH and Eh involve three types of reactions:

(a) Reactions involving only electron transfer which are independent of pH such as

$$Fe^{2+} \leftrightarrow Fe^{3+} + e$$

(b) Reactions involving only hydrogen ion transfer which are independent of Eh such as

$$H_2CO_3 \leftrightarrow H^+ + HCO_3^-$$

or

$$Fe^{2+} + 2H_2O \leftrightarrow Fe(OH)_2 + 2H^+$$

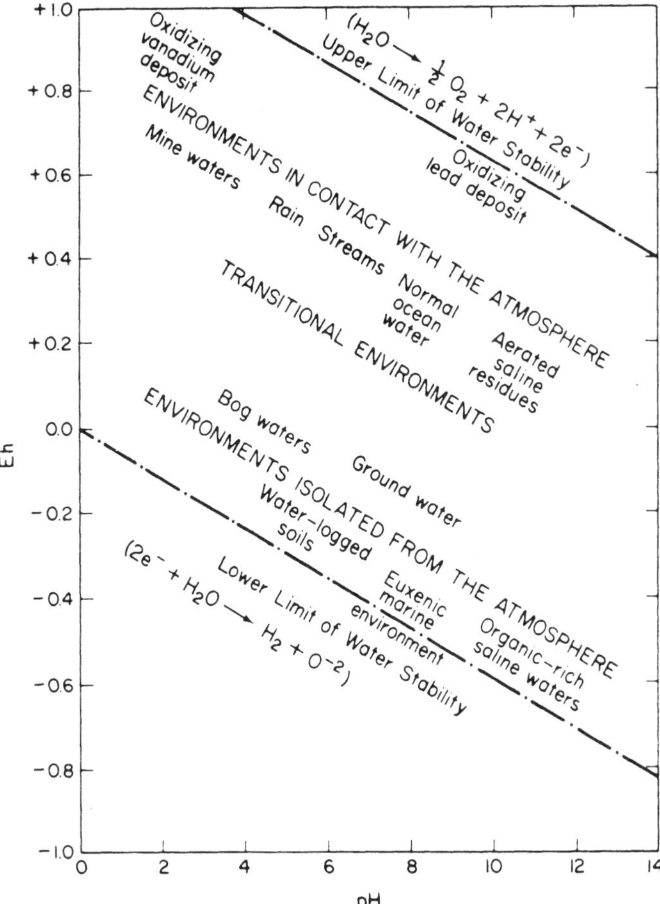

Figure 4.10. Ranges of Eh and pH for common environments. (From Blatt et al., *Origin of Sedimentary Rocks*, Prentice-Hall, Englewood Cliffs, New Jersey, 1972.)

(c) Reactions involving both electron and hydrogen ion transfer which involve both pH and Eh such as

$$Fe^{2+} + 3H_2O \leftrightarrow Fe(OH)_3 + 3H^+ + e$$

As seen in the figure, in the natural environment neither Eh or pH is an independent variable. Both are determined by reactions occurring in solution, such as the decomposition of organic matter or dissolution of rock. Nevertheless, it is often convenient and meaningful to consider the presence of various chemical species in terms of pH and Eh.

The competing reactions can be quite complicated. The conditions for individual chemical species can be estimated via Pourbaix diagrams,† such as shown in Figure 4.11 for groundwater in contact with iron. These types of diagrams, however, should be used with some care, since temperature and the presence of complexing ions can significantly affect their validity and the conditions under which ion mobility is low.

The key to radionuclide migration in the soil is the behavior of the only available solvent, groundwater. The H_2O molecule is peculiar in many ways that determine its solvent properties. It has the form of an isosceles triangle whose shape is determined by the electronic configuration of he hydrogen and oxygen atoms. Since oxygen is more electronegative than hydrogen, the electrons are attracted to the oxygen atom, creating a molecular dipole. The H—OH bond forms an

†Pourbaix diagrams show the dominant chemical species of an element for a given pH and Eh.

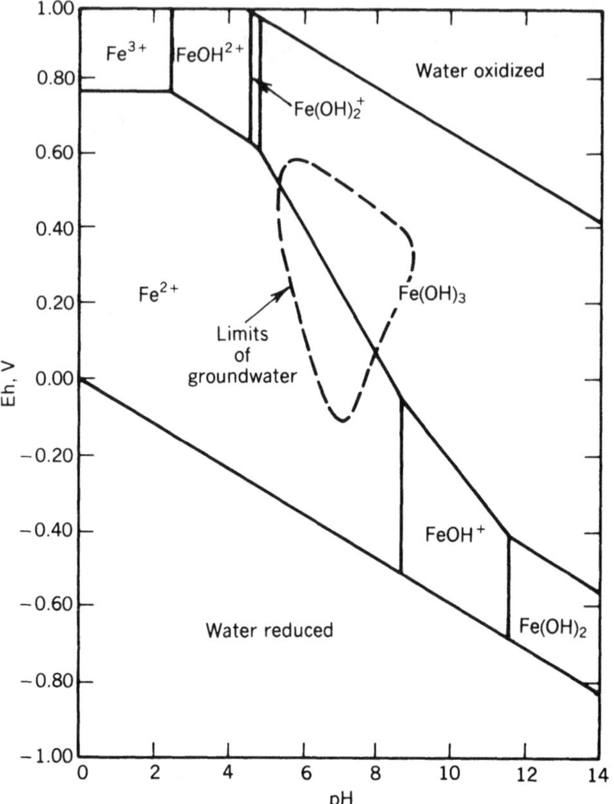

Figure 4.11. Pourbaix diagram for an aqueous ferric–ferrous system.

angle of 104.4°. Ordinarily, a 90° bond might be expected from the orientation of the electronic configurations, but residual charge on the H atoms causes repulsion and enlarges the bond angle (Figure 4.12*a*). This dipole nature is responsible for the solvent properties of the water molecule.

In the environment, the water dipole can interact with various minerals. When in contact with a crystal, the electric dipole attraction between the crystal surface and the water molecule causes the atoms of the crystal to go into solution (also called hydrolysis). The tendency of the H atom of one water molecule to be attracted to the oxygen atom of another molecule leads to several properties of water important to the mobility of radionuclide in groundwater environments. Particularly important are its high viscosity and high surface tension. The viscosity of water varies with temperature, decreasing from 1.8 centipoise at the freezing point to 0.3 centipoise at 100°C (Table 4.7). This decrease facilitates water movement through deep geologic formations. The high surface tension allows water to easily wet porous surfaces, and permits it to move through tight pores in rocks.

Migration Mechanisms for Radioactivity

Groundwater is the only significant medium for migration in the earth. Therefore, a correctly engineered radioactive waste repository will carefully consider the groundwater conditions and hydrology in its vicinity. Radionuclides moving through the soil environment as a result of groundwater motion are said to be transported by convective forces. Other physical and chemical processes tend to remove the radioactivity from this flow pattern. These are called dispersive forces. Ideally, in subsurface flow by conductive groundwater motion, the radionuclides and carrier fluid move in the same direction at the same rate. This is not always the case, since surface effects on the crystals comprising the medium can impede (or sometimes accelerate) the rate at which ions migrate. In many cases, porous media such as sandstone are present. Such formations can have a large effect on ion mobility.

Groundwater moves within the earth in response to various forces on it. These forces include

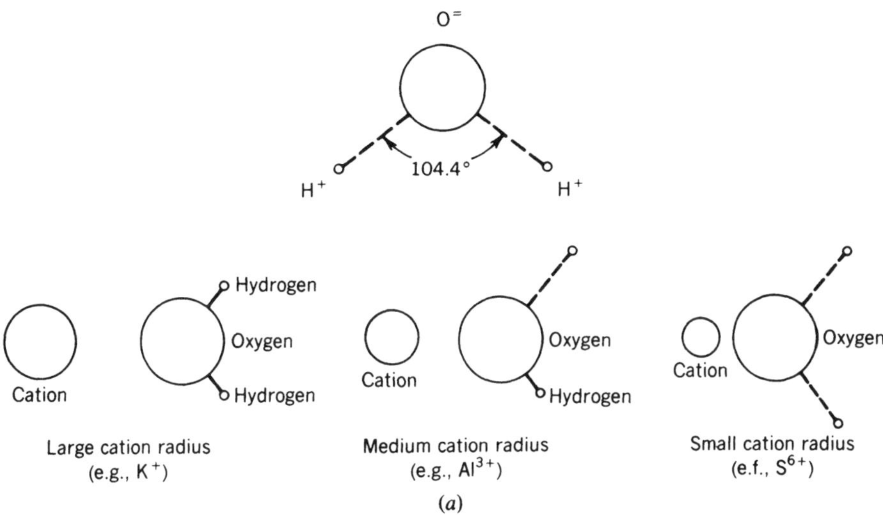

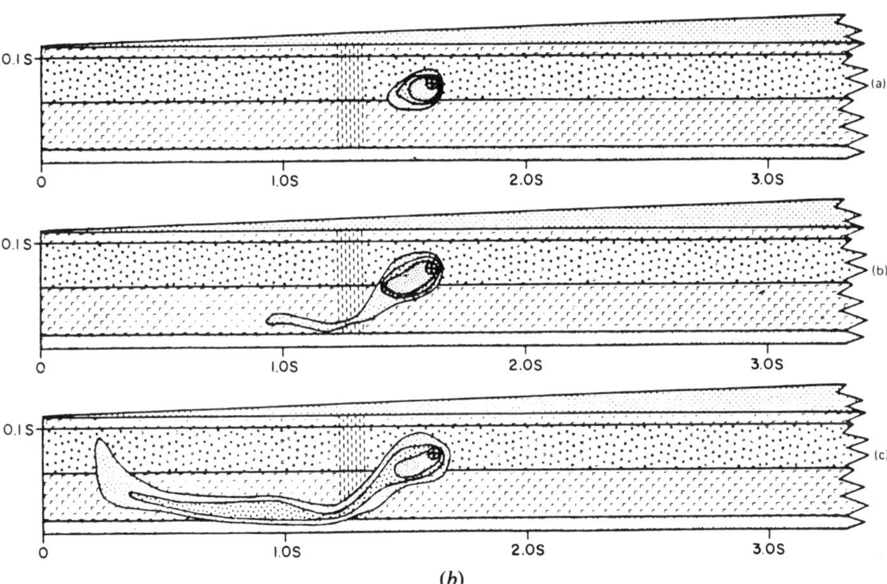

(*b*)

Figure 4.12. (*a*) Water molecules and ionic interactions. Top: Schematic of the water molecule. Note the angle of the bond between OH—H is 104.4°, not 90° expected from electronic configuration models. This deviation from 90° is responsible for the solvent properties of water. When water interacts with cations of various sizes, the distance between the H^+ and O^{2-} ions changes. Bottom: With decreasing radius of the cation, the electrons in the outer shell of the oxygen atom in the dipole are pulled nearer the cation. This weakens the bonding force between H and O in the molecule. In turn, this can put extra H^+ into solution, increasing the pH. (Developed from Blatt et al., *Origin of Sedimentary Rocks,* Prentice-Hall, Englewood Cliffs, New Jersey, 1972.) (*b*) Radioactive movement in the environment can be modeled. Such a model, specifically constructed to study migration around waste disposal sites (in rather carefully chosen geologic media), appears in this figure. For realistic soil permeabilities, such movement is slow. Figure shows one such model with five layers having relative hydraulic conductivities of 100, 10, 1, 10, and 100. The dash lines represent a high permeability vertical zone located between contaminant source and discharge area. The effect with time (a) after 200,000 yr, (b) after 400,000 yr and (c) after 800,000 yr. [From *Rev. Mod. Physics* **50** (1978).]

Table 4.7. The Viscosity of Water

°C	η, centipoise
0	1.787
20	0.978
40	0.653
60	0.466
80	0.355
100	0.282

Source: National Bureau of Standards.

In rock formations, particularly sediments, viscosity is a fundamental property determining migration of radioactivity. Experimentally, the rate at which fluid flows is inversely proportional to the fluid viscosity and directly proportional to the pressure gradient.

temperature, pressure, gravity, and chemical concentration gradients. In shallow environments, gravity is the primary force for groundwater motion. In deeper formations, thermal gradients and geostatic forces may be significant. The groundwater motion is further determined by geometry and the properties of the various rock that comprise the geologic medium. These factors also determine the flow velocities for the migration of radioactivity.

The region through which groundwater motion is possible in a particular locale is called the groundwater basin. This is not necessarily the same as a "structural" or topographic basin. The groundwater basin forms a closed system. Water moves into or out of the region only by the water table or on the surface of the earth. The water table configuration is the determining factor for groundwater flows in many instances, especially for regions close to the surface and where the thermal gradients do not exist. For example, a gently inclined water table and a relatively homogeneous medium result in a nearly horizontal flow field. On the other hand, a water table configuration with numerous pockets or undulations results in sub-basins; instead of moving horizontally, the groundwater will often move in an upward or downward direction. Thermal currents can greatly magnify such vertical flows.

In addition to the water table configuration, the geologic configuration also determines the flow fields. Just as for the water table configurations, the geological fields can be varied and complex. However, examining some simple situations can give us some insight into hydraulic behavior in various geologies:

(a) In layered structures, vertical flow through a low permeability layer is increased as the permeability of an underlying and overlying rock increases.

(b) In layered structures, the flow through a high-permeability layer is unaffected by the existence of an underlying low-permeability region.

(c) Partial aquifers recharging part of a basin can cause upward flows in other parts of the basin.

Typical hydraulic conductivities (the inverse of the resistance to groundwater motion) are given in Table 4.8. Extremely low conductivities mean that groundwater migration is slow enough to prevent radioactivity from reaching the biosphere. It should be noted from this table, however, that wide ranges of values occur for some materials. For instance, salt beds have a nominal value of 6×10^{-7} m/sec, but may occasionally be as high as 2×10^{-2} m/sec. Generally, a hydraulic conductivity below 10^{-6} m/sec would be a reasonable criterion for a radioactive waste site.† The results of some calculations using these conductivities, which illustrate the above observations, are shown in Figure 4.12*b*.

Countering the ability of groundwater to increase the mobility of radionuclides in the environment, certain physical and chemical processes have the opposite effect: they tend to reduce either the concentration or total amount of radionuclides that are mobile. The most significant of these processes are disperson, sorption,‡ and radioactive decay. Disperson and sorption reduce the

†Other criteria would also depend on sorptive properties of the media. In general, a systems analysis would be required; see Chapter 15.

‡Sorption includes absorption (into the volume of a crystal) and adsorption (onto the surface of the crystal).

Table 4.8. Hydraulic Conductivities of Geologic Media

Material	Hydraulic Conductivity
Slate	1.1×10^{-9} cm/sec
Clay, montmorillonite	4.7×10^{-9}
Salt, bedded[a]	6.3×10^{-9}
Shale[b]	$0.7–2.0 \times 10^{-7}$
Siltstone	1.2×10^{-7}
Limestone, argillaceous	0.9×10^{-7}
Sandstone, silty	2.2×10^{-6}
Limestone	6.6×10^{-6}
Silt	$1.0–7.8 \times 10^{-5}$
Sandstone, coarse	0.9×10^{-3}
Sand, river alluvial	1.7×10^{-2}

Source: Adapted from the *Rev. Mod. Phys.* **50** (1979).

[a]Measurements for some salts give values as high as 1.5×10^{-4}

[b]Measurements for some shales give values as low as 0.8×10^{-10}.

concentration flow velocity of radionuclides, either by mechanical effects which results in diluting the net concentration per unit volume, or by chemical ion exchange reactions with the soil or surfaces of rock. Radioactive decay is a mechanism that generally reduces the concentration of radionuclides. It is independent of groundwater flow and the physical and chemical states of the environment. It is especially effective in reducing the concentration of fission products, who half-lives are short compared to migration times in a geological formation. Groundwater moves through some geologic media with such low velocities that tens of thousands of years may elapse before it enters the biosphere. During this time, short-lived radionuclides, such as ^{90}Sr, ^{137}Cs, and ^{3}H with 28-yr, 30-yr, and 12-yr half-lives, will have decayed to insignificant levels. Actinides tend to be much longer lived than fission products so radioactive decay may be less important. The possibility also exists that the radioactive decay process will change one radioactive species into another with less chemical bonding to crystalline surfaces (and therefore with greater mobility) and vice versa.

Dispersion, a mixing phenomenon, causes radionuclides to spread out laterally. This results in dilution, that is, a reduction in concentration. Dispersion can be caused by (1) differences in flow velocity or concentrations between adjacent regions, (2) geometric expansion of the flow region, or (3) the porosity of the geologic medium itself. It is difficult in general to predict how much dispersion is likely to occur in a given formation. The complexity of the formation on the small, medium, and large scale affects the rate of dilution. Such variations are not easy to predict.

Ion exchange is another process that reduces radionuclide concentrations. It is dependent on (1) the coupling between the ions in solution and the unsatisfied chemical bonds on the solids; (2) the ion-exchange capacity of the solids; and (3) the ion valence. When the ionic coupling to the solid surface is high, strong bonding occurs. This requires a sufficiently dilute solution such that the ion-exchange sites are not close to saturation and flow velocity is not high.

The ion-exchange capacity is the total amount of an ion that can be absorbed. As already noted, clays have a particularly high ion-exchange capacity. The sorptive capacity of a groundwater basin reservoir is often proportional to the amount of clay materials it contains. This is true if the groundwater flow does not bypass these clay regions and fracture networks do not exist. The ion-exchange capacity usually varies considerably within a region.

The ion-exchange process is affected by ion size. Ion radii for some important actinides are given in Table 4.9. When clay minerals are involved, the degree of hydration and local pH are important parameters. The principal ions exchanged by clay are Na (0.95 Å), K (1.33 Å), and Ca (0.97 Å). As seen in the table, the ionic radii of these cations are close to those of many actinides. The valence of the bare actinide ions would not match the clay cations; however, in groundwater systems extensive complexing† occurs, especially with OH^-, to reduce the effective valence of the actinide.

†In this case a complex is the partial hydration of an actinide ion which reduces its effective charge and changes its effective radius. For example, Pu^{4+} is hydrated to $Pu(OH)_2^{2+}$ in the +2 valence state.

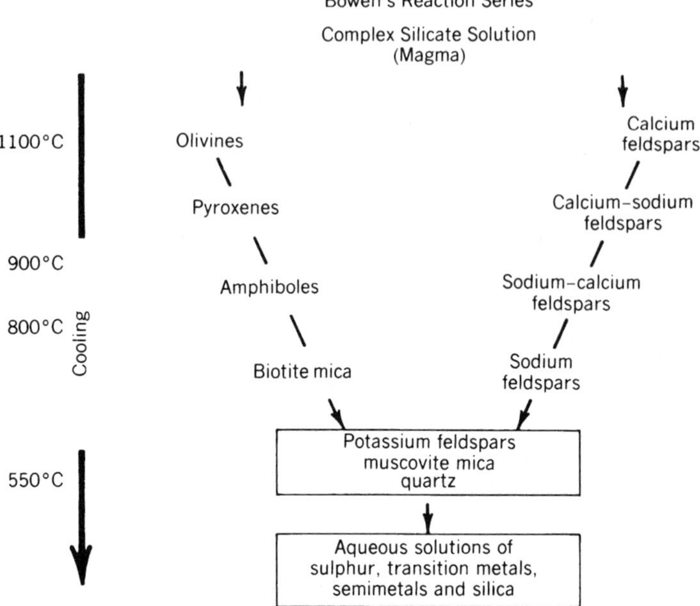

Figure 4.13. Many minerals are deposited from aqueous solutions in fracture zones of the crust, located in and near the large igneous bodies called batholiths. During crystallization of a batholith, its minerals form in a definite sequence indicated by Bowen's Reaction Series. Iron, magnesium, and calcium silicates (olivines and calcium feldspars) crystallize first. As the batholith cools, other ferromagnesian minerals and calcium–sodium feldspars crystallize, followed by potassium feldspar, muscovite mica, and quartz. These last three are the major minerals of granite, which makes up the bulk of the batholith we see, after it has been exposed by erosion, millions of years later. (Adapted from C. Sorrel, *Rocks and Minerals*, Golden Press, New York, 1973.)

The concept of a retention factor is sometimes used. The Retention Factor (RF) is the ratio of groundwater velocity to the radionuclide transport velocity. RFs of 30, 60, 450, and 1500 are typical of ^{90}Sr, ^{60}Co, ^{137}Cs, and ^{239}Pu in "ordinary" soil. Under conditions where groundwater migrates 300 m in 10 yr, ^{90}Sr would take 300 yr to move the same distance, plutonium 1500 yr. Almost all of the Sr would have decayed in this period, and about half of the plutonium. In contrast, ruthenium‡ disposed of at radioactive waste repositories has been a problem in the past. As a chloride, ruthenium is readily sorbed by most soils, but anionic ruthenium is not. In some experiments at Oak Ridge National Laboratory, ruthenium migrated through 100 m of soil around waste pits in a few years. However, the half-life of ^{106}Ru is approximately one year, greatly reducing the problem.

Adsorption of Radionuclides on Minerals

A large body of data exists concerning the adsorption of radionuclides on minerals. These data not only provide information on the terrestrial behavior of radioactivity, but aid in choosing materials for use in waste repositories and deciding whether the waste repositories themselves should be of salt, granite, or basalt.

Ion attraction to various minerals is, with few exceptions, correlated to the same order that the minerals crystallize from hot magma, as given by Bowen's reaction series shown in Figure 4.13. Again with few exceptions, the sequence in which minerals weather is the same order as they crystallize from magma. There are two general classifications of igneous rock: granitic types that are rich in silica and are therefore acidic due to the formation of H_4SiO_4, and basaltic types that are rich in magnesium and iron and are therefore basic due to the formation of $Mg(OH)_2$ and $Fe(OH)_2$.

The granite group includes such common minerals as feldspar and quartz. Ion attraction is great at the crystal surface and along cleavage planes where crystal bonding forces are weak and mineral alteration can be initiated. All crystals have high electrostatic forces at their surfaces. Hydrogen

‡Ruthenium is an important radionuclide since it is not as effectively removed from reprocessing wastes as most other fission products.

ions and dipole water molecules can easily attach to these sites. Basalts typically contain 12% total iron compared to about 4% in granite. The crystals in basalt are smaller than those in granite facilitating decomposition to clay minerals, aluminum oxides, or iron oxides. Clay and related minerals have large retention properties for many radionuclides.

In wet environments, ferrous iron† can be leached, then precipitate or migrate. It will then oxidize in dry, oxygen-rich regions. Electrostatic forces cause water to surround ions upon their release from silicate minerals. But when the water molecule is attracted more strongly to other water molecules than to the iron, precipitation occurs, usually as a hydrate. This was already seen in Figure 4.11 where the presence of iron in the soil will operate to set rather narrow limits of pH and Eh for groundwater that might be transporting radioactivity.

Several major mechanisms appear to dominate the sorption of radionuclides. They are hydrolysis, chemsorption, oxidation-reduction, complexation, and ion exchange. Surprisingly, however, the last mechanism, ion exchange, does not play an important role when actinides are involved. Why it does not operate in a significant way will be discussed.

The ion exchange properties of various elements are important when considering the mobility of fission products in the ground. The pH of solution is one of the properties that markedly affects the ion exchange capability of minerals. This is because of the activity of hydrogen atoms. A more important property when considering the migration potential of heavy metal cations,‡ such as the actinides, is the tendency for such cations to form complex ions in solution. When an actinide exists in a hexa- or pentavalent state, it tends to migrate right through a geologic medium, and not stick very well. The formation of complexes reduces the net charge of the actinide ion so that sorption may be more likely. The presence of iron minerals also helps reduce the valence of an actinide ion.

Ion-exchange effects are reversible when conditions change. Therefore immobilized radioactive ions may become resuspended in solution, free once again to migrate. In general, divalent ions are more strongly held by crystal surfaces than univalent ions. They tend also to be more hydrated and form bonds that are covalent in nature. When considering the mobility of fission products, ion radius is important, since the bond strength increases with this radius for ions of equal valence. Thus, the order of increasing ease of replacement in ion exchange processes is

Ba, Sr, Ca, Mg (divalent atoms)
Cs, Rb, K, Na, Li (univalent atoms)

The ionic radii of various fission product elements are given in Table 4.9 and Figure 4.14. The latter shows which elements are likely to become hydrated, form complexes, or become insoluble.

Univalent cations would have to have an ionic radius greater than 3.95 Å to equal the water–water attraction. Since from Figure 4.14, the cation with the greatest radius is Cs (1.67 Å), all univalent cations are hydrated. The critical radius for divalent elements is 5.17 Å. In general, larger ions are less hydrated.

Some actinides, such as uranium, neptunium, plutonium, and americium have such low solubilities in most groundwater that they cannot exist in high enough concentrations to be a health hazard. For instance, neptunium's solubility is about 2000 times less than its allowable concentration in drinking water. Only in waters with a high oxygen concentration does neptunium turn out to be a significant hazard.

Of particular importance is the behavior of radionuclides in clays, since they account for 40% of all mineral sedimentation and are often considered for backfill materials in radioactive waste disposal sites. Clays are a group of weathered minerals that are characterized by four features: a basic aluminosilicate structure, high stability, high chemical activity, and small size (about 2 mm). Diagrammatic sketches are given in Figure 4.15.

The structure of clay is comprised of alternating layers of sheet silicas. The first type is comprised of silicon–oxygen tetrahedra composed of Si_2O_5 units. Within this type, aluminum can substitute for up to 59% of the silica. The second type of sheet is comprised of octahedral coordination of Mg, Fe, or Al cations with oxygen and hydroxyl ions. These octahedral units share the anions in a sheet plane. Bonding within tetrahedral layers is mostly covalent,§ while it may be either ionic or covalent in the octahedral layers depending on the relative amounts of the +3 valence ions (Al) and the +2 valence ions (Mg and Fe). Between layers, largely covalent forces exist. This covalent bonding is important. Because of it, disaggregation of clay does not destroy its mineral structure.

†Ferrous iron is iron that has lost two electrons, and is therefore in the valence +2 state, sometimes written Fe^{2+}. Ferric iron is in the valence +3 state.

‡Cations are elements that form positively charged ions whereas anions are elements that form negatively charged ions.

§Covalent bonding of ions refers to sharing of electrons, while ionic bonding refers to the exchange of an electron between a cation and anion. Covalent bonding is usually weaker than ionic bonding.

Table 4.9. Ionic Radii of Important Fission Products and Geologic Elements

Element	Atomic Number	Valence	Radius, Å
Ba	56	+1	1.53
		+2	1.34
Ca	20	+1	1.18
		+2	0.99
Cs	55	+1	1.67
Fe	26	+2	0.74
		+1	0.64
I	53	−1	2.20
		+5	0.62
K	19	+1	1.33
Mg	12	+1	0.82
		+2	0.66
Na	11	+1	0.97
Ra	88	+2	1.43
Ru	44	+4	0.67
Si	14	−4	2.71
Sr	38	+2	1.12
	Ionic Radii of the Actinides		
Po	84	+6	0.67
Ra	88	+2	1.43
Ac	89	+3	1.17
Th	90	+4	1.02
U	92	+4	0.97
		+6	0.80
Pu	94	+3	1.08
		+4	0.93
Am	95	+3	1.07
		+4	0.92

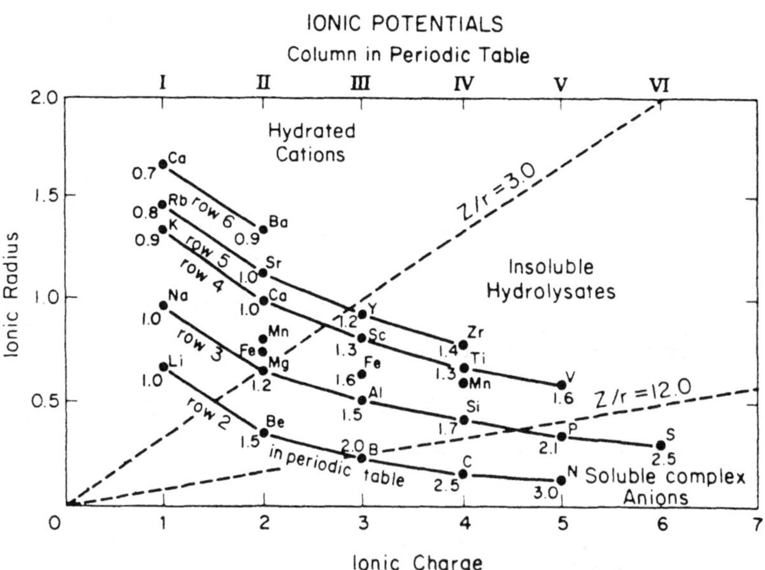

Figure 4.14. Ionic potentials and electronegativities of elements. The relative degree of hydration of ions can be expressed by Z/r; that is, the hydration is directly proportional to charge and inversely proportional to ionic radius. The parameter Z/r is called the ionic potential. (From Blatt et al., *Origin of Sedimentary Rocks*, Prentice-Hall, Englewood Cliffs, New Jersey, 1972.)

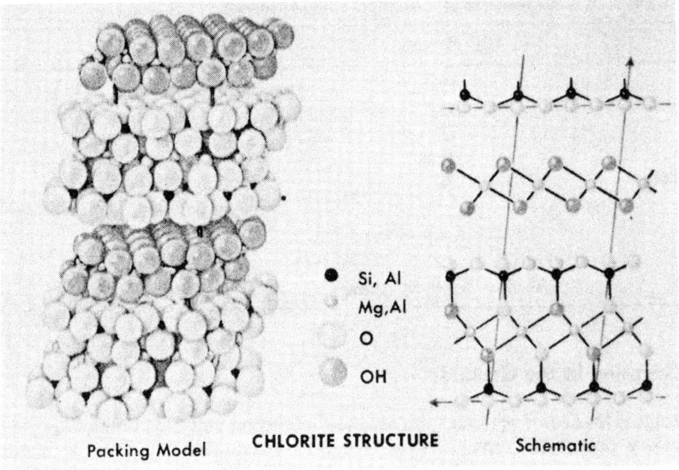

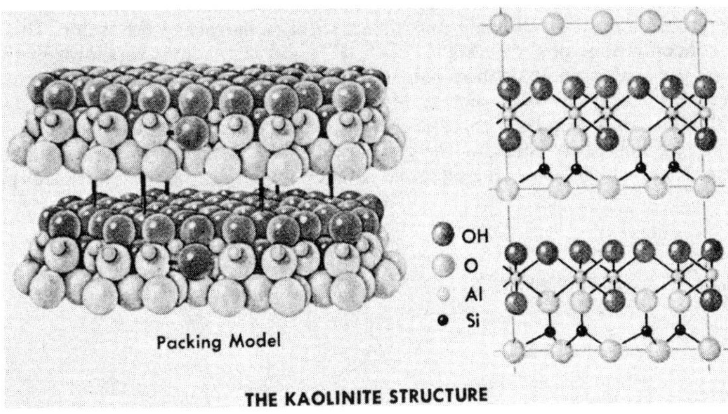

Figure 4.15. Clays are, in general, weathering products of preexisting rock. The chemical composition of a clay depends not only on the mineral from which it was formed, but also on the chemical environment of weathering, which in turn is largely the result of climate. Thus, in basic soils of warm-climate regions, weathering tends to remove alkalies and silica and leave aluminum and iron; the result is kaolinite formation and typical lateritic, or red, soils. In acid soils of temperate climates, weathering tends to remove all but the silica, lowering the clay mineral content. If incomplete weathering is the rule, as in arid climates, montmorillonites and chlorites may form and persist. (From C. Sorrel, *Rocks and Minerals*, Golden Press, New York, 1973.)

The compositions of the commonly occurring clay minerals are given in Table 4.10. The type of clay likely to be encountered by migrating radionuclides is determined by the prior geologic history of the formation. In particular, percolating water can cause "weathering" which causes selective leaching of K, Na, or Ca ions from certain clays. These ions are in interlayer positions, and are present because of electric charge deficiencies when Al^{3+} substitutes for Si^{4+} (or Mg^{2+} for Al^{3+}) in clay minerals. Illite has K in this position, while smectites typically have Na or Ca. The interlayer elements have relatively weak bonds to the layer structure of clay and the leaching of these elements leaves unsatisfied bonds that can fix migrating fission products and actinides. Fission product cations can then substitute for the leached cations, effectively preventing further migration of the fission product species. Although some clays are more selective than others in absorbing radionuclides, all are extremely good in fixing migrating ions. One type of clay, montmorillonite, is particularly good for use for engineered radioactive waste disposal purposes. The absorptive properties of clay exist over a wide range of geologic conditions. Only when the pH is greater than 10 or below 4 is the ion-exchange capability of clay destroyed. Such strongly acidic or basic conditions do not normally exist in ground environments.

Table 4.10. Chemical Composition of Common Clay Minerals

	(Fe, Mg) Oxides	(Na, Ca) Oxides	(K) Oxides
Chlorite	41%	0.2%	0.1%
Biotite	30	1.2	9
Muscovite	2	1.2	10
Illite	0.8	7	
Montmorillonite	6	2.3	5
Kaolinite		0.4	0.3
	(Balance aluminum)		
Alumina	Al_2O_3		
Bauxite	$Al_2O_3 \cdot 2H_2O$ hydrous		

Actinide Adsorption in the Ground

The high biological hazard of actinides makes their migration and fixation an important question. We have already noted the sensitivity of retention mechanisms to valence states, whereby uranium, neptunium, plutonium, and americium will greatly vary their adsorption characteristics. The various mineral constituents of the ground will also greatly affect these characteristics.

Dissolved bicarbonate ions (HCO_3^-) are especially important when considering the chemical state of the groundwater. Bicarbonate ions directly buffer the pH of the water. This indirectly affects the concentrations of Ca^{2+}, Mg^{2+}, Na^+, F^-, and PO_4^{3-} ions as shown in Figure 4.16. Nevertheless, the acidity and oxidation potential (pH–Eh) can vary considerably because reductants, such as Fe^{2+} and oxidants, such as Mn^{4+}, exist in the groundwater. For instance, Pu^{4+} migrates 250 times faster than Pu^{6+} through certain mineral formations. A similar change in migration rate can be obtained by changing the groundwater pH. A high pH induces more OH^- and CO_3^{2-} complexing, which lowers the effective actinide ion charge, as well as the sorption.

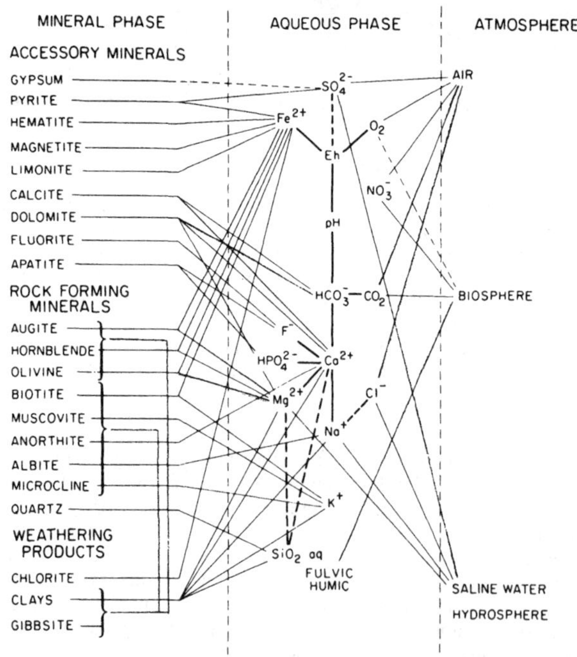

Figure 4.16. Equilibria and chemical exchange in the igneous rock/groundwater system. Figure illustrates the complexity and interdependence of these factors in the environment. Of special importance in natural waters are bicarbonate–carbonate ions, which directly determine and buffer the pH of the water and indirectly affect the concentrations of calcium, magnesium, sodium, fluoride, and phosphate. [From G. Beall and B. Allard, *Trans. Am. Nuclear Soc.* **32,** 164 (1979).]

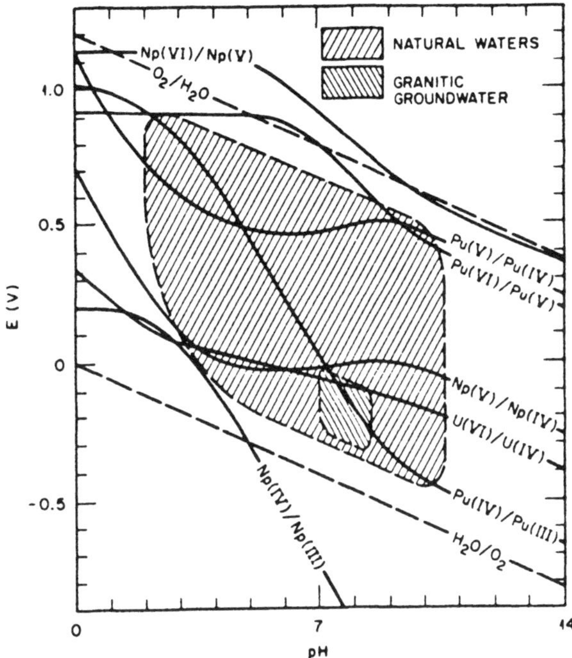

Figure 4.17. Potential Eh–pH diagram for soluble species of uranium, neptunium, and plutonium. [From G. Beall and B. Allard, *Trans. Am. Nuclear Soc.* **32,** 164 (1979).]

Other common actinide complexing agents are PO_4^{3-}, F^-, and natural organic acids. Humic acid materials are the major organic components of soils. These complex substances interact with clays and metal ions, which they bind into complexes. The ability of actinides such as Pu to complex with proteins, macromolecules, and amino acids is important for the study of actinide migration in humans and animals.

The chemical properties of actinides, and therefore their absorption characteristics, vary according to their valence states as shown in Figure 4.17. As we saw above, the groundwater can affect these valences due to the presence of buffering agents or reducing agents. For example, U^{6+} in aerated groundwater could go to U^{4+} in a reducing environment. (The +6 valence state is much more soluble than the +4 state.) Neptunium could be likewise in either the +6, +5 or +4 state while plutonium could be in any of four different states: +3, +4, +5, or even +6.

The formation of complexes decreases the charge of the actinide species, for instance, from Pu^{4+} to $Pu(OH)_2^{2+}$. Moreover, dilute solutions of $Pu(OH)_2^{2+}$ can "stick" to free surfaces because of their colloidal nature. Continued complexing, for example, to $Pu(OH)_4$, leads to an insoluble form. In any case, as actinide complex forms, adsorption may be enhanced.

It is interesting to compare Figure 4.17 with Figure 4.11. The latter shows rather specific ranges of Eh and pH much narrower than given in Figure 4.17 and lies very close to the area labeled "granitic groundwater." This dramatically illustrates the role of reducing groundwaters (due to the presence of ferrous minerals). Thus, uranium would be tetravalent in such a situation as would be neptunium. Plutonium (and americium) could exist as either tetra- or trivalent species. All these species, however, would be highly fixed, with little tendency to migrate, under such soil conditions.

Zeolites

Zeolites are naturally occurring minerals that have especially good ion-exchange properties. They are especially useful for the purification of radioactive liquids such as contaminated water, or for the recovery or separation of radioactive metals by ion exchange. For instance, they were extensively used after the accident at Three Mile Island to purify the radioactive water that collected in the basement of the reactor containment building. Like clays, zeolites are hydrated aluminum silicates of the alkali and alkaline earths,† which exchange Na and Ca ions. Unlike clays, they are

†That is, elements in column 1 and 2 of the periodic table.

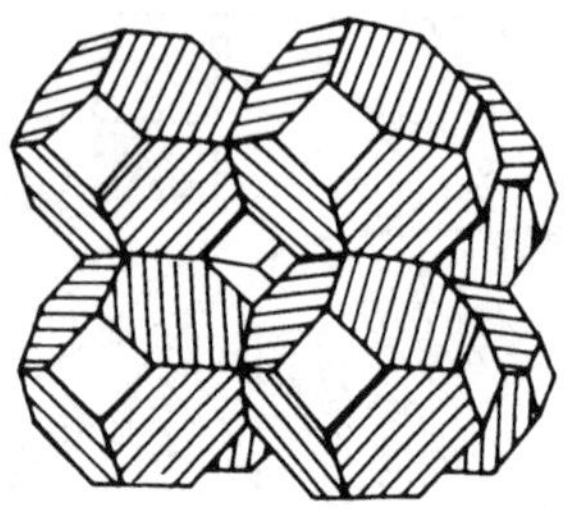

Figure 4.18. Zeolite structure. Basic building blocks of zeolite crystals are tetrahedra with a silicon atom at the center and an oxygen at each of its four apexes. The silicon may be replaced by aluminum and an additional metal ion. Zeolites are important for their sorptive properties of radionuclides, both in the natural environment and as engineering materials. Water and other liquids containing radioactive materials passing through zeolites will be purified by ion exchange. (From ORNL report TM-7782.)

not sheet silicates, but rather fall in the feldspathoid classification of minerals. They occur in silica-poor rocks which are rich in soda (Na_2CO_3) and potash (K_2CO_3). Natural zeolites are often found in the cavities of basaltic (low silica, high Mg and Fe) rock.

Zeolites were first recognized by Cronstedt in 1756. Forty naturally occurring forms have been found. They all have the structural formula

$$M_{x/y}[(AlO_2)_x(SiO_2)_z]\cdot wH_2O$$

where

$x + y$ = the number of tetrahedra in unit cell
$1 \leq z/x \leq 5$
y = the valence of the cation
w = the number of water molecules in the hydrated complex

Figure 4.18 shows the zeolite structure. An example would be the mineral chabazite, which has the chemical formula

$$Ca_4[(AlO_2)_8(SiO_2)_{16}]\cdot 26H_2O$$

Unlike clay, which swells or shrinks, zeolites have the ability to absorb and desorb large amounts of water without major alteration to the crystal structure. This is the property that makes them useful in many engineering applications, including use in radioactive waste processing and disposal. The cation-exchange behavior of zeolites is a function of (1) their structure, (2) size, concentration, and charge of the cation in solution, (3) solvent, usually water or aqueous gel, and (4) the temperature.

Synthetic zeolite crystals are often manufactured in a clay (kaolin) matrix which can be calcined into pellets having a high strength. They are sometimes hot pressed (without clay) to form 100% zeolite pellets. These crystals usually are much smaller than 100 μm.

It was the production of synthetic zeolites in the 1950s that renewed the interest in their use as ion exchangers in the management of radioactive wastes. Zeolites have been found to be stable when exposed to high doses (10^{11} rads) of radiation, which is a necessary criterion for their use in waste disposal. Another plus is their compatibility with glass vitrification, the leading process for long-term waste disposal.

Suitability of Geologic Sites for Radioactive Waste Burial

Disposing of radioactive wastes underground depends in part on the ability of natural formations to isolate radioactivity from the biosphere. Vast areas of the United States (see Figure 4.19) are covered by argillaceous ("clayey") formations. These include shale deposits, formed by the consolidation of clay minerals. These formations often have undergone changes in condition due to a thermal transformation under pressure called metamorphism. This metamorphism has recrystallized the minerals, flattening the microstructures and resulting in loss of much of the water they once contained. These metamorphized clays are referred to as the shale group and include slate. Argillaceous formations are potentially sites for radioactive waste disposal facilities, although these

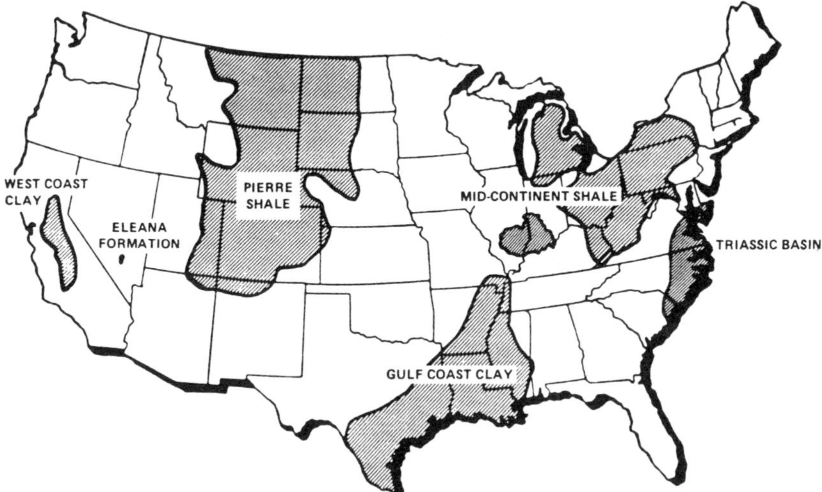

Figure 4.19. Clay formations in the United States. [From *Rev. Mod. Physics* **50** (1978).]

types of formations have not been as extensively studied as salt and crystalline formations for this use.

Crystalline formations potentially suitable for radioactive waste disposal also cover large parts of the United States (Figure 4.20). The main mineralization is tranite which is a medium grain mixture of quartz (SiO_2) and potassic feldspar [(K, Ca) $AlSi_3O_8$]. The rock is typically 30% quartz and 60% feldspar. Quartz is technically referred to as a framework silicate, where silica tetrahedra $(SiO_4)^{4-}$, forming covalent bonds, form the basic building blocks. All the tetrahedra share the O^{2-} ions with the adjacent tetrahedra in three dimensions. The feldspars are formed when K^+, Na^+, or Ca^{2+} ions enter the framework in large interstitial openings, with aluminum (Al^{3+}) ions substituting for silicon (Si^{4+}) ions. As with the clay minerals, there are many unsatisfied bonds on the crystal surfaces, where ions migrating in water may become bound. Also suitable for radioactive waste disposal is tuff, fragmental rock consisting of compressed volcanic debris covering large areas of the western United States.

The third of the formations under consideration for radioactive waste disposal are the rock salt deposits. These deposits are termed evaporites, because they were laid down by the evaporation of

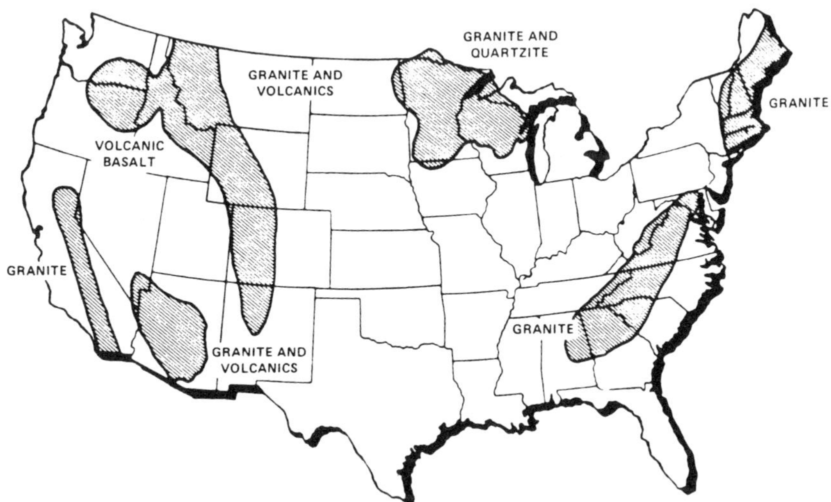

Figure 4.20. Crystalline formations in the United States. [From *Rev. Mod. Physics* **50** (1978).]

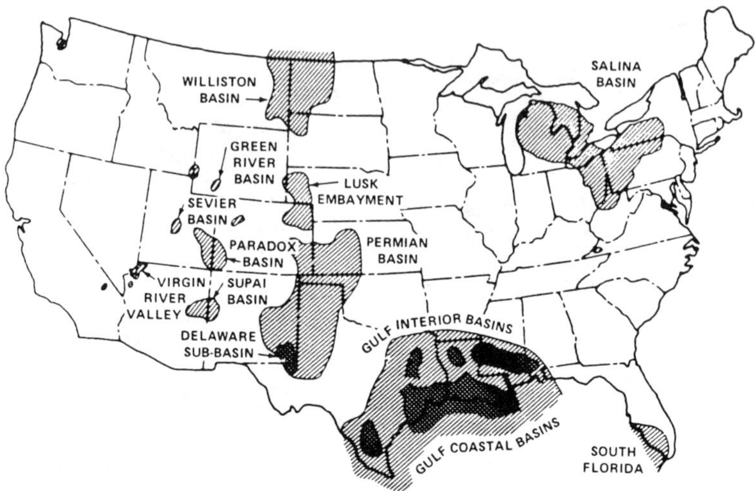

Figure 4.21. Rock salt deposits in the United States. [From *Rev. Mod. Physics* **50** (1978).]

large inland seas during past geologic periods. As seen in Figure 4.21, they are widespread, and consist mainly of halite† (NaCl). Other salts, especially those containing SO_4^{2-}, Ca^{2+}, Mg^{2+}, and K^+ ions, are usually also present. The attractiveness of salt deposits for radioactive waste disposal is threefold: (1) they are in geologic structures which have been stable for millions of years without the intrusion of groundwater; (2) they exist in regions of low seismic (and volcanic) activity; and (3) they have heat transfer properties that help in the dissipation of heat from radioactive wastes. While they appear to be adequate as radioactive waste repositories, salt formations also have several disadvantages, namely: (1) salt can leach due to chloride solubility, (2) chlorides are volatile and corrosive, (3) salt is not "self-healing" unlike clay minerals that swell when water is present, and (4) salt is not particularly absorptive of radioactive fission products or actinides. The acceptability of salt as a repository medium can be, however, considerably enhanced by site-specific engineering, such as cannister design and backfill provisions.

Actual Experience

The migration of radioactivity in the environment has been monitored for many years to evaluate its behavior. When plutonium, for instance, is released to the environment, its migration is controlled by the nature of the soil particles with which it came in contact.

Documented experience on the behavior of plutonium in the environment comes from several sites, including Oklo in West Africa; the low-level waste disposal areas at Hanford, Washington, and Maxey Flats, Tennessee; and the Rocky Flats‡ military installation in Colorado, Oak Ridge National Laboratory,§ and the Nevada Test Site.¶ All data bear out the observations that plutonium contamination is limited to small areas. At Maxey Flats a small amount of plutonium was observed in well water but was confined to regions some 200 m from surface trenches. At Rocky Flats, a large fire released a substantial amount of plutonium, 97% of which was found in the soil, 2% in plants, and only a very small amount on vegetation outside the site boundary. It is observed that plants take up very little plutonium from the soil, and that plutonium entering the aquatic environment rapidly ends up in sediments.

Plutonium from contaminated soils around Rocky Flats and Oak Ridge was associated with very fine silt and clay particles, as expected. The densities of these particles were 2.4–2.6 g/cm^3, similar to the aluminosilicates found in the soil giving evidence of sorption.

At the Nevada Test Site (Figure 4.22), plutonium released to the environment was again associated with silt-sized particles, but it was probably in the form PuO_2, due to the chemical environment at the time of the Pu release. The studies at the Nevada Test Site offer confidence that residual radioactivity produced by an underground nuclear explosion, below the water table, will

†Common table salt.
‡Site of plutonium facility for nuclear weapons.
§Site of uranium enrichment plants and a center for weapons research during World War II.
¶Site of nuclear weapons testing.

Figure 4.22. Subsidence craters left by deep underground nuclear tests at the Nevada Test Site. After a detonation takes place, the earth settles, forming these saucer-shaped craters. (Courtesy LANL.)

not migrate in dangerous amounts from the explosion cavity into the surrounding water supply. Plutonium released as a result of these underground weapons tests was incorporated in gravel-size particles (fused debris) very close to the detonation point, the particles decreasing to fine sand size within a short distance. It was found that most of the radioactivity was retained in the fused debris, while water that had been in contact with that debris for almost 10 yr contained only low concentrations of radioactive contaminants. The highest levels were determined to be in the region of the original explosion cavity and had not migrated from there. No activity was found 45 m (150 ft) below the cavity. Water with the highest radioactivity was found at the bottom of the original cavity and contained only two radioactive species, tritium and strontium-90, that were at levels higher than those recommended as acceptable concentrations in drinking water. Surface groundwater was not a factor at the Nevada site. As was case at Maxey Flats, Rocky Flats, and ORNL, no plutonium migration was observed, however, regardless of the local hydrology.

At Hanford, where high-level radioactive wastes also are stored, measurements were made of radioactivity leaking beneath liquid storage tanks. The radioactivity was retained to varying degrees by the soil. Figure 4.23 shows that the retention depended on the radionuclide involved. As seen in this figure, most important radionuclides were retained within a few tens of meters of the storage tanks. Cesium and strontium were reduced in concentration by a factor of 1 million within 20 m. Plutonium concentration was reduced 10^8 fold within 6 m. This attenuation was due to the sorptive quality of the ground, and the nature of the groundwater.

At Hanford, the liquid actinide wastes were discharged directly into the sediment. The actinide inventory was fairly high; for instance, one of the disposal areas received over a 20-yr period 57 kg of Pu and 1 kg of Am, contained in 6 million liters of aqueous waste. The pH of the liquid was quite low, approximately 2.5, a value that would tend to increase actinide migration. A subsequent examination of the site showed that

1. The distributions of Pu and Am were quite similar.
2. The concentration of Pu and Am decreased rapidly with depth, showing the sorptive properties of the soil.
3. Localized increases in actinides were associated with increases in the silt content of the sediment, confirming the importance of silt in actinide retention.

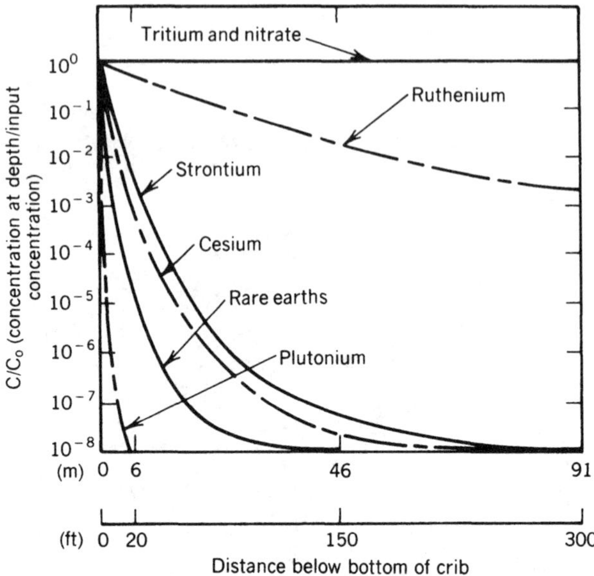

Figure 4.23. Approximate sorption patterns of radionuclides in the ground beneath a typical Hanford disposal crib. (From ERDA Report ERDA-1538.)

4. The spread of actinide contamination was more extensive along sediment interfaces, demonstrating the importance of flow paths in the migration of radionuclides.
5. The migration of Pu and Am was limited to a region of less than 30 m, with most of the contamination limited to 1 or 2 m of the discharge points.

Similar observations were made around earthen burial trenches at Savannah River,† where the migration of the plutonium wastes was also highly localized. It was retained within a 30-cm radius of the trenches, rather than widely distributed throughout the soil. Again most of the plutonium was associated with the clay fraction of the soil.

The importance of soil characteristics to actinide retention has also been demonstrated in other tests. Most soils strongly retain the actinides, but the soil's loam and sand content are important parameters. A certain soil with high sand and low loam content has the ability to effectively sorb uranium but not plutonium. This is a somewhat anomalous result, but nevertheless shows the importance of carefully assessing the physiochemical characteristics and geology of the soil in migration studies.

Oklo

Oklo is a uranium mining site in Gabon, a country near the equator in West Africa. A natural nuclear "reactor" operated there in prehistoric times. As a result, radioactivity from this "reactor" entered the environment, and traces of this radioactivity, primarily in the form of stable daughter products, remain today. These traces give experimental evidence as to how uncontained radioactive wastes would behave in the environment over long periods of time. In general, the migration of radionuclides was very small. The information obtained at Oklo is useful in evaluating the *long-term* effectiveness (over hundreds of thousands, even millions of years) of specific geologic sites in retaining wastes from nuclear reactors.

In May 1972, a batch of natural uranium being processed at the French enrichment plant at Pierrelatte was assayed. It was found to contain 0.7171% ^{235}U, compared to the normal assay of 0.7202%. This latter ratio is very precise, and constant in all uranium samples from throughout the world. It was first suspected that diversion of nuclear material, that is, the ^{235}U, was occurring. The anomaly, however, was eventually traced back to the ore's source, the Mounana uranium mill near Franceville in southeastern Gabon (see map, Figure 4.24). The discrepancy was further traced to

†Site of reactors for the military production of plutonium.

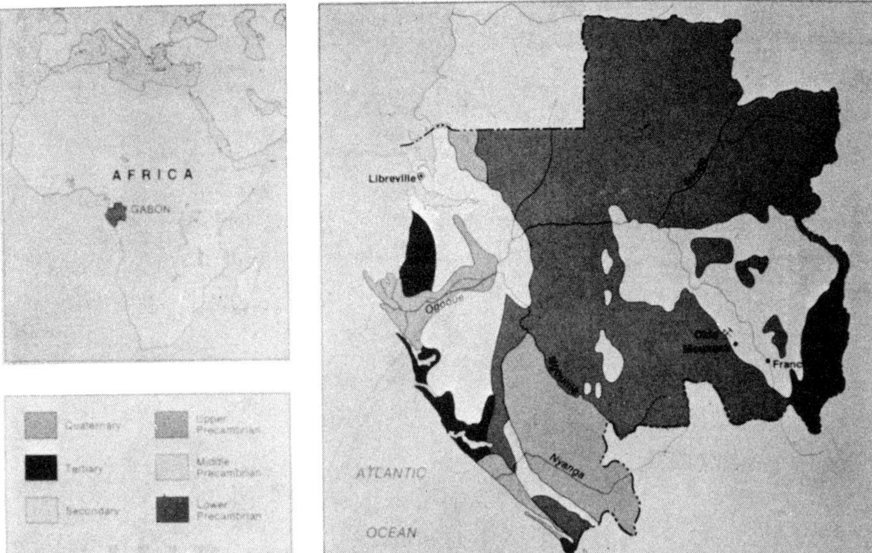

Figure 4.24. Location of the Oklo deposits. The Oklo mine rests in terrain predominantly of Precambrian age, that is, older than about 600 million yr. (Courtesy LANL.)

the Oklo mine operated by Mines d'Uranium de Franceville. There several samples were found to be below 0.44% in ^{235}U. Pictures of the site are shown in Figure 4.25 and 4.26.

The samples taken throughout the mine showed a regular depletion of ^{235}U across several veins. These ore veins were greater than 0.5 m thick. Calculations showed that if the groundwater in the seam was about 6% by weight, and the natural uranium was enriched to about 3% ^{235}U, conditions would be about right for a natural nuclear reactor.

Since the mine was in a tropical area, and fairly close to the surface, the existence of the correct amount of groundwater in the veins seemed probable, even likely. The ratio of the uranium isotopes was not normal since, as we have seen, the present natural abundance of ^{235}U is 0.72%. However, both ^{235}U and ^{238}U are radioactive, with different half-lives. ^{235}U decays with a half-life of 700 million yr, while ^{238}U decays much more slowly, with a half-life of 4500 million yr. As a result the isotopic ratio of ^{235}U is slowly changing. For instance, 400 million yr ago, ^{235}U would have been 1% in natural uranium, and the 3% ratio needed to make the vein "critical" would have occurred 1900 million yr ago. This then was when the Oklo reactor is believed to have operated. Six "reactor" zones have been identified, and indications of fission found in each of these zones. For instance, thorium (from ^{236}U decay) and bismuth (from ^{237}U decay) were found only in the reactor zones at the Oklo site. The actinide decay residues are consistent with the reactor operating at a slow simmer over many hundreds of thousands of years. The reactors were self-regulating since too much power would have boiled off the water, shutting down the reactor. Some 15,000-MW-yr of fission energy were produced, resulting in the formation of about 6 tons of fission products and 2.5 tons of plutonium. The energy production at Oklo was about 15 times the energy that would be released in a nuclear waste depository containing the entire 1980 U.S. inventory of spent fuel.

Most of the radioactive waste has been trapped inside the crystalline structure of the uraninite mineral found in the Oklo ore body. The elements that could not fit into the uraninite lattice (because of too large or too small an ionic radius) diffused or leached away. During the 1900 million yr since the Oklo reactors last operated at least half of the thirty-odd fission products were immobilized in the ore in spite of the abundance of groundwater at the site. These immobilized fission products include: La, Ce, Pr, Nd, Eu, Sm, Gd, Y, Zr, Ru, Rh, Pd, Ni, and Ag. Some of the Mo and I still remain in the lattice, along with traces of the noble gases Kr and Xe. The latter were expected to diffuse out of the vein. There appeared to be some partial migration of Pb, but the Pu migration was limited to less than 10 m. Only metals with valence of 1 or 2, that is, those with high solubility in water, have leached away. Hence, little or no Rb, Cs, Sr, Ba, or Cd were found at the site, nor were they expected. The isotopes of these elements have relatively short half-lives (tens of years or less), so they would decay to nonradioactive substances before they could migrate very far in the soil. The elements of concern from the standpoint of long-term environmental problems, particu-

Figure 4.25. Looking north into the Oklo mine at the base of an inclined sandstone wall on the left and immediately below some exposed uranium ore which is visible as an oxidized yellow uranate on the first vertical face. (Courtesy LANL.)

larly the plutonium, were retained in the geologic formation and effectively immobilized for nearly two billion years. Because plutonium has by now completely decayed to ^{235}U, the evidence for its stability is the absence of excess ^{235}U not only outside the reactor zone but also outside the grains of uraninite in which the plutonium was made during reactor operation. The radioactive inventory at Oklo roughly corresponded to about 15% of the uranium and 1.5% of the fission products contained in all the U.S. reactor wastes generated through 1980.

Actinide Mobility in the Biosphere

Most of our information on behavior of plutonium in the biosphere and its effects on people has come from the military program involving nuclear weapons. In excess of 200 t of plutonium have already been processed and about 5 t globally dispersed in the course of nuclear weapons tests. There have also been a few notable accidents involving plutonium. One of these was in Palomares, Spain in 1966 where two weapons were accidentally dropped. These weapons disintegrated on impact due to detonation of their high explosive triggers. As a result, plutonium was scattered over some 1200 acres. Another accident occurred in Thule, Greenland in 1968. In this accident, a bomber crashed and four weapons burned. Plutonium debris was left over a 700-m path. Levels of plutonium in the air near Thule and in the villagers near Palomares were always considerably below the permitted explosure levels.

There are certain similarities in the behavior of thorium and plutonium in the environment. The study of the mobility of thorium in the Morro do Ferro District in Brazil showed that the estimated annual mobility rate of thorium in the deposit has been less than 1 mm/yr. This is consistent with observations as to plutonium migration in the Oklo deposit in Gabon, West Africa. These data have relevance to the understanding of how slowly plutonium moves, for instance, in a nuclear waste repository breached by moving groundwater.

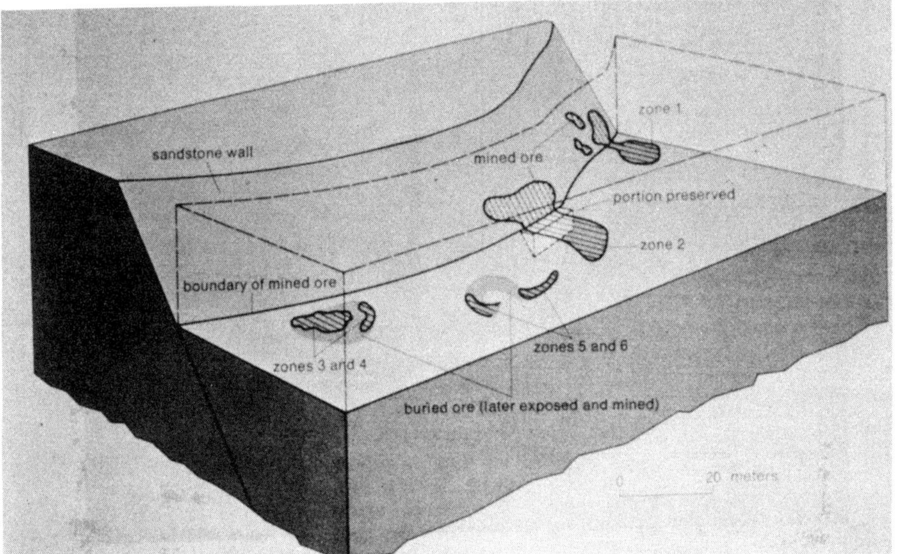

Figure 4.26. Of the six reactor zones initially detected at Oklo, portions of zones 1 and 2 had been mined when the reactor was discovered; their boundaries, therefore, are not known with certainty. Zones 3 through 6 had not yet been exposed, and their configurations were determined from core samples. Subsequent examination revealed that zones 3 and 4 were tortuously connected, as were zones 5 and 6, thus reducing the number of distinctly separate zones to four. (Courtesy LANL.)

Modeling of Radioactive Migration

Various models exist for the migration of actinides in the environment. A representative calculation is shown in Figure 4.27. These models tend to show only minimal radionuclide migration for sites with favorable geology and rainfall conditions. These calculations, along with the actual migration of radionuclides surveyed in this section, provide data important in assessing the safety of long-term storage of radioactive wastes.

4.5. AIRBORNE TRANSPORT OF RADIOACTIVITY

Radioactivity can also be transported in the atmosphere. Aerosol particles can be carried by the winds, forming a radioactive "cloud" that could pass from point to point. As it migrates the cloud would disperse as the weather changes, wind shifts, and turbulent regions are encountered. The behavior of the cloud is sensitive to the height and nature of its release, atmospheric conditions, and wind speed. Models exist that predict the dispersion and deposition of radioactivity from the cloud. Compared to the movement of radioactivity in the ground, atmospheric motion is very fast. It is determined by the wind speed, typically in the range of 10 km/hr.

As radioactivity is carried by the wind, atmospheric diffusion continually disperses it. This dispersion gradually reduces the radioactive concentration to a point where it eventually becomes so dilute that it ceases to be a problem. Average wind speed is the most important parameter in dispersion, since it determines both the direction of transport and the volume of air by which the radioactivity is diluted. Other important factors are precipitation, which can wash radioactivity out of a migrating cloud; storms or unstable weather patterns, which determine turbulent diffusion; and topography, which also influences turbulence.

For a radioactive cloud, the effluent concentration at any point downwind is a function of effluent (aerosols, curies, etc.) per unit volume released per unit time. Typical patterns are shown in Figure 4.28. As illustrated in this figure, radionuclide concentrations rapidly dissipate with both distance from the source and time after release. The dispersal of a radioactive cloud is often approximated mathematically by a Gaussian model, where each downwind location of the ratio of the ground-level radionuclide concentration in the air to the source strength is given by

$$\chi/Q = 2(3\sigma_y)^{-1}(\sqrt{2}\pi\sigma_z)^{-1}U^{-1} \tag{4.1}$$

where χ is the contaminant concentration in air (Ci/m^3), Q is the source strength (Ci/sec), $3\sigma_y$ is the

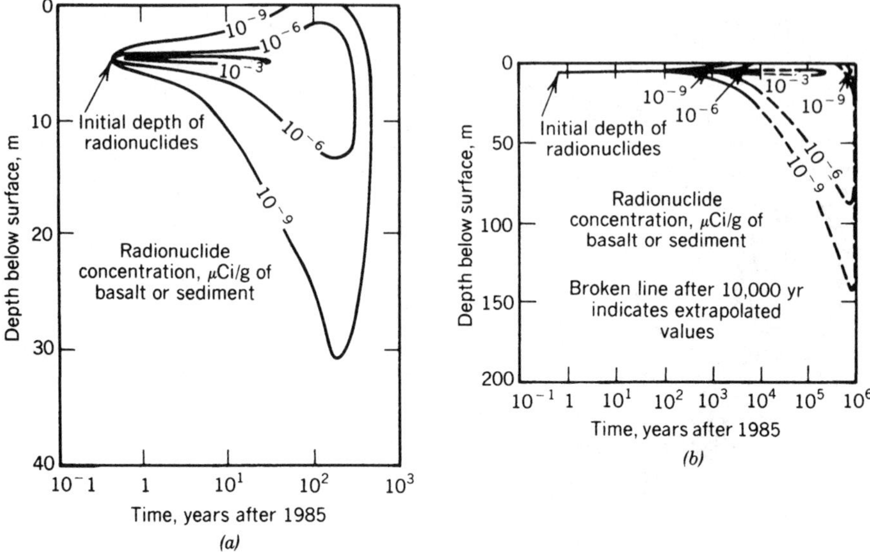

Figure 4.27. Projected migration of (*a*) ^{90}Sr and (*b*) ^{239}Pu. The figure shows a representative calculation of the behavior of ^{90}Sr and ^{239}Pu in a region above an aquifer. The calculation considers nuclide solubility in water and chemical retardation by the absorption of nuclides on soil particles. Precipitation and evaporation effects are also included. These scoping studies suggest that the ^{90}Sr migrates only 30 m, while ^{239}Pu migrates at extremely low concentrations to a depth of 140 m, after several hundred thousand years. [From T. G. Humphrey, *Nuclear Technology* **58,** 136 (1982).]

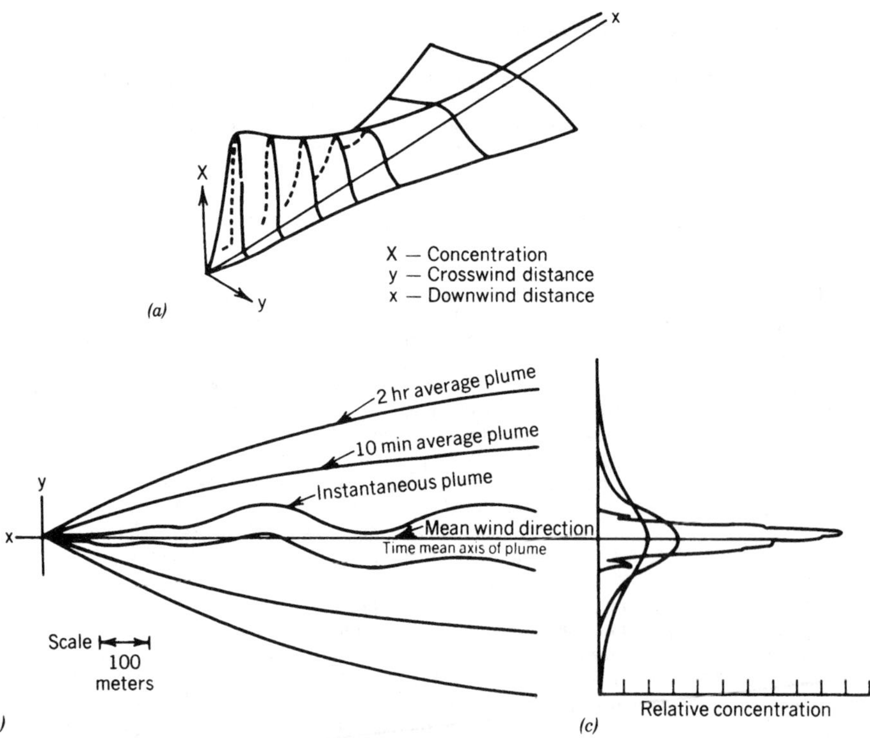

Figure 4.28. Plume dispersion models: (*a*) surface concentration pattern downwind from an elevated source; (*b*) approximate outlines of a smoke plume observed instantaneously and of plumes averaged over 10 min and 2 hr; (*c*) corresponding cross-plume distribution pattern. (From NUREG-75/1014.)

Table 4.11. Atmospheric Stability Classification

Description	Category	Change with Height (ΔK/100 m)		$\sigma_\theta{}^a$, rad
		Temperature	Potential Temperature	
Extremely unstable	A	< -1.9	< -0.9	0.436
Moderately unstable	B	-1.9 to -1.7	-0.9 to -0.7	0.349
Slightly unstable	C	-1.7 to -1.5	-0.7 to -0.5	0.262
Neutral	D	-1.5 to -0.5	-0.5 to $+0.5$	0.175
Slightly stable	E	-0.5 to $+1.5$	0.5 to $+2.5$	0.0873
Very stable	F	1.5 to $+4.0$	> 2.5	0.0436

Source: NUREG 75/014.

[a]Standard deviation of horizontal wind direction fluctuation over a period of 15 to 60 min. The values shown are averages for each category.

lateral width (m) of the assumed distribution, σ_z is the vertical standard deviation of the contaminant (m), and U is the mean transport wind speed (m/sec).

The distribution parameters σ_y and σ_z are each a function of downwind distance and thermal stability category. The stability categories are specified for each site according to the scheme of Regulatory Guide 1.23, as given in Table 4.11. The results are then corrected for building-wake effects, buoyant rise, differences in release duration, and depletion by deposition as well as radioactive decay.

As a radioactive cloud migrates through the atmosphere, deposition of aerosol particles occurs. Aerosols are removed by sedimentation (due to gravity), impaction on obstacles (such as trees), and rainout. Also important is radioactive decay. The period of time radioactive material might be airborne is only a few days, so only short-lived radionuclides will decay in this interval. Sometimes the decay product is also radioactive (e.g., ^{133}I decays to ^{133}Xe) so this also influences radionuclide migration.

Airborne Pathways to Humans

Once airborne, radioactivity might enter the biosphere several ways. Inhalation of gaseous and particulate matter by humans is the most direct way. The ingestion pathway is much less direct, since the radioactivity must first deposit of vegetation, be concentrated, and then be consumed. For particularly concentrated radioactivity, direct external exposure may occur but is not expected to be important except under severe accident situations.

Airborne releases of radioactivity from nuclear reactors, primarily fission products and tritium, were covered in Chapter 3 and Section 4.2 of this chapter. The depletion of reactor emissions is rapid and the health effects low due to negligible concentrations. More controversial, although still small, are the releases of radon to the environment around uranium mines and milling facilities. The pathways of radon from such facilities are given in Figure 4.29, which shows that the airborne pathway is the only significant means of radon entering the biosphere. The environmental impact of radon will be examined next.

Actual Experience—Environmental Releases of Radon

Radon in the environment comes from many different sources. Most of it is released from rocks in the earth's crust, often carried to the surface by flowing groundwater. The principal sources of radon released to the environment are given in Table 4.12. The most important natural source of ^{222}Rn is decay of ^{226}Ra in the soil and rocks in the earth's crust. Since exhalation of radon from soil is strongly influenced by local soil and atmosphere conditions, radon soil flux, and resulting atmospheric concentrations show considerable variation with respect to location and time of day. Sufficient data exist, however, to estimate a release of 1.2×10^8 Ci of ^{222}Rn/yr from this source. Relatively small amounts (less than 0.2%) come from activities of uranium mining and mill tailings associated with nuclear power production (see Chapter 5 for radon control techniques).

Naturally occurring ^{222}Rn concentrations in the interior of buildings is the major contributor in the United States to the general population dose from airborne radionuclides. This radon is primarily due to the materials of construction, such as concrete, or from deposits in the soil which infiltrate through the building's basement (Figure 4.30). The average population exposure in the United States to radon gas is 0.004 WL, approximately equivalent to 0.296 rem/yr of radiation exposure. Radon accounts for roughly 50% of the total background radiation exposure. In some homes, however, the radon decay product concentration exceeds 0.12 WL (approximately 8.8 rems/yr), especially in New England where radon concentrations in air range up to 25 pCi/liter.

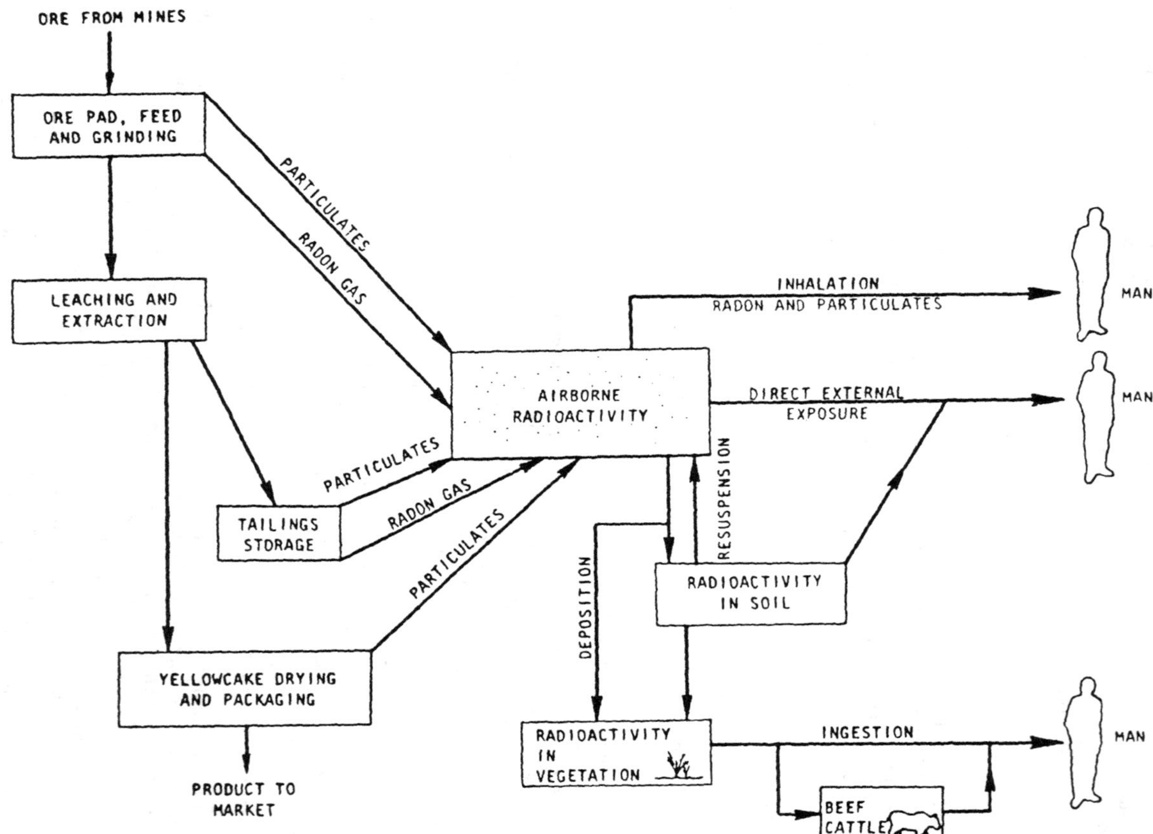

Figure 4.29. Sources of radioactive effluents from a uranium mill and exposure pathways to humans. (From NUREG-0556.)

Table 4.12. Estimated Release of ^{222}Rn in the United States in 1978 from Various Natural and Technologically Enhanced Sources

Source	Estimated Annual Release, Ci/yr
Building interiors	1.5E4
Natural soil	1.2E8
Evapotranspiration	8.8E6
Natural gas	
Domestic ranges	2.0E2
Domestic heaters	8.0E1
Industrial uses	1.1E4
Uranium industry	
Mining	2.0E5
Milling (active sites)	1.5E5
Milling (inactive sites)	5.1E4
Nonuranium Mines	
Phosphate	5.3E4
Coal	1.4E4
Phosphate fertilizer	4.8E4
Liquefied petroleum gas	
Domestic ranges	1.8
Domestic heaters	1.3
Geothermal power	5.8E2
Coal-fired power plants	5.0E2
Gas and oil wells	2.3E2

Source: From C. C. Travis, *Trans. Am. Nuclear Soc.* **33,** 144 (1979).

Concentrations are also quite high in some parts of Sweden, where houses have been constructed of concrete made from shale with high radium content. Measures taken to conserve energy may exacerbate these levels, because of the reduced ventilation usually associated with conservation techniques.

Tailings at active uranium mill sites have the potential for radon release to the environment. Numerous sites exist which contain ^{226}Rn residues in concentrations up to several thousand times that in the earth's crust. Such tailings piles are estimated to release about 2×10^5 Ci/yr of ^{222}Rn in the United States. The generation rate of mill tailings is given in Figure 4.31 which shows that almost a billion tons of such wastes will have accumulated by the year 2000. One of the concerns is the potential exposure to people living in the vicinity of these sites.

Three processes are required before radon from a mill tailings pile can pose an environmental problem: (1) the ^{222}Rn gas must escape from the soil matrix in which it is generated, (2) the gas must migrate to the surface of the pile, and (3) the gas must be transported from the site to the surrounding population. Only ^{222}Rn gas formed near the surface of the tailing granules (about 20% of the total) is likely to get into the porous spaces of the tailings pile, and diffuse to the surface. The rate of release to the environment can be estimated by various diffusion models.† The transport of Rn off site, determined by meteorological conditions, can be estimated using a Gaussian plume model. Table 4.13 contains results for such a calculation which show that for a typical site, whose population includes 55,000 people within a 50-mile radius, about 86 person-rems/yr of exposure would result. This is about one millionth of the average radon exposure in the United States from all sources.

Offsite concentrations for the Grand Junction, Colorado area (where many tailings piles exist) are generally in the 1 pCi/liter range, about four times as large as background levels, but comparable to the ambient air concentrations of radon gas in U.S. homes or at the Geysers geothermal power plants in California.

Health effects caused by airborne and waterborne contaminants from uranium mines are even smaller than from mill tailings. EPA estimates indicate that regional exposure of 0.07 person-WL

†The diffusion of radon gas through the pile could be considerably reduced by sealing the surface with a nonporous material.

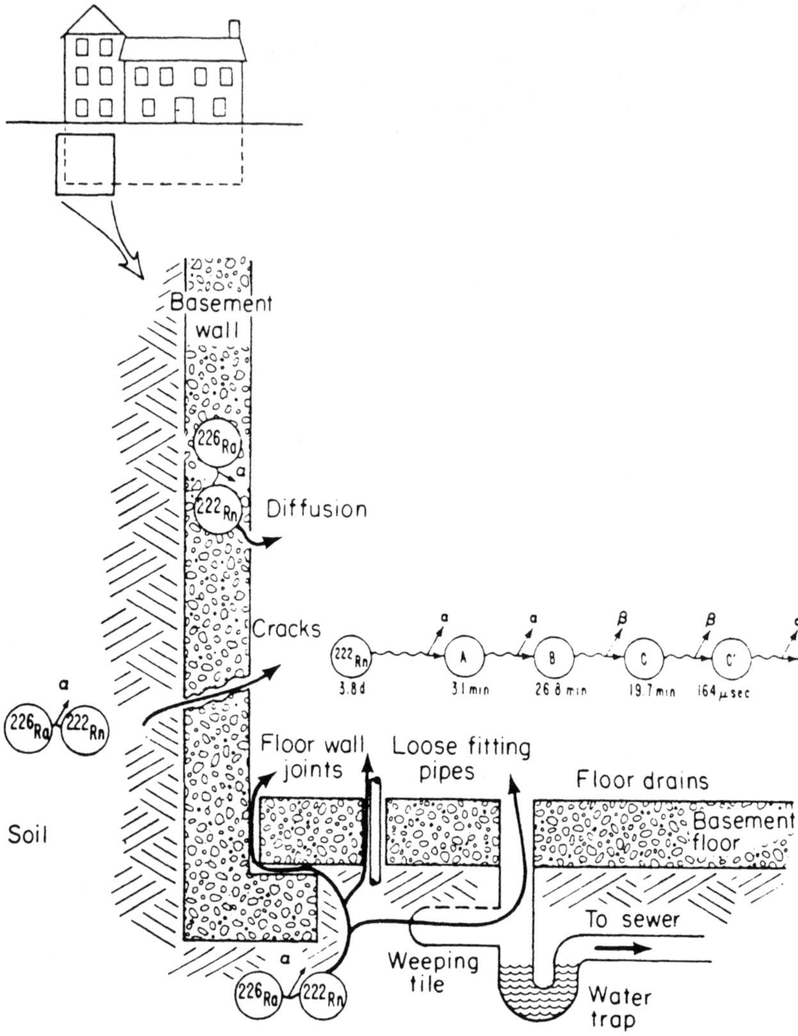

Figure 4.30. Primary pathways for radon entry in buildings. [From C. D. Holloway, *Trans. Am. Nuclear Soc.* **33,** 148 (1979).]

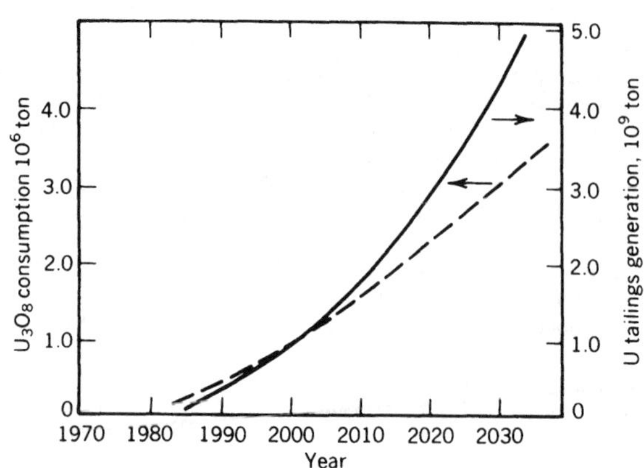

Figure 4.31. Uranium mill tailings generation rate. [From V. C. Rogers, *Trans. Am. Nuclear Soc.* **30,** 91 (1978).]

Table 4.13. Radon Distributions and Population Exposures from a Tailings Pile of Reference Size[a]

Distance from Pile Edge, miles	Population	Person-rem/yr	Health Effects/yr
0.5	30	16	5.9E-4
1	30	5	1.8E-4
2	200	10	3.8E-4
5	200	2	8.2E-5
10	2,500	11	3.8E-4
15	1,500	3	1.2E-4
20	4,000	6	2.1E-4
25	4,000	5	1.7E-4
30	4,000	4	1.4E-4
40	13,000	9	3.3E-4
50	25,600	15	5.4E-4
Total	55,060	86	3.1E-3

Source: From V. C. Rogers, *Trans. Am. Nuclear Soc.* **30,** 91 (1978).
[a]Average ^{226}Ra concentration is 256 pCi/g.

from the airborne ^{222}Rn release and 9.9 person-rem/yr from aquatic releases are to be expected from a "model" uranium mine. The maximum-exposed individual would incur a slight increase in cancer risk of 0.0002 (compared to the American Cancer Society's lifetime risk of fatal cancer of 0.15 from all causes).

4.6. SUMMARY

The hazards from terrestrial and airborne migration of radioactivity are far below those that might be expected from only considering its curie content. The amount of radioactivity reaching a particular individual would be greatly diminished by natural processes; in the case of terrestrial transport the time delay between release and entering the biosphere will be very long—long enough for the decay of soluble radionuclides such as ^{137}Cs and ^{90}Sr and tens-of-thousands of years for the more hazardous actinides. The way radionuclides might actually appear in the biosphere, given in Figure 4.31, is much different than either their curie content or hazard, given in parts (*a*) and (*b*) of Figure 4.3. Figure 4.32 shows that, for a repository 1000 m from the biosphere and 10 m/yr groundwater

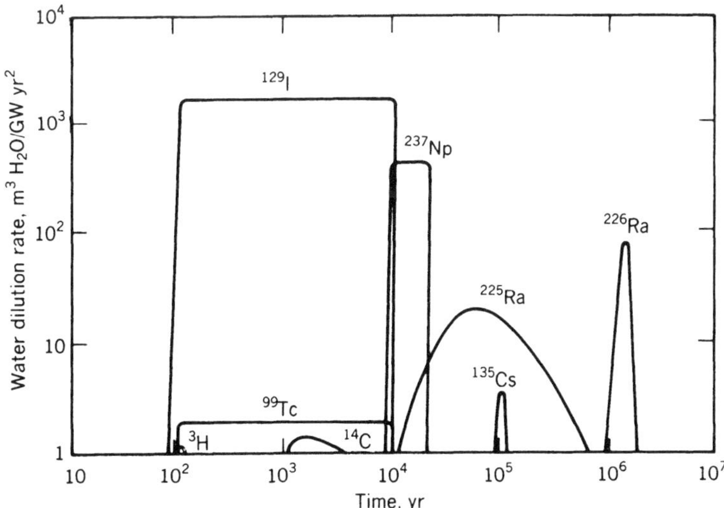

Figure 4.32. Water dilution rates. The water dilution rate of a radionuclide is its activity measured in curies divided by its maximum permissible concentration in drinking water. [From T. H. Pigford, *Chemical Engineering Progress*, March (1982).]

velocities corrected for holdup in the ground, ^{129}I becomes the nuclide of concern in the short time frame (less than 10^4 yr), while ^{237}Np and ^{226}Ra dominate further out. Strontium, plutonium, and americium isotopes that appeared dominant in Figure 4.3*b* are not prominent.

BIBLIOGRAPHY

Archer, V. E., "Effects of Exposure to Low Levels of Radon Daughters," *Trans. Am. Nuclear Soc.* **33,** 145 (1979).

Bass Becking, L. G., et al., "Limits of the Natural Environment in Terms of pH and Oxidation-Reduction Potentials," *J. Geol.* **68,** 243 (1964).

Beall, G., and B. Allard, "Chemical Factors Controlling Actinide Sorption in the Environment," *Trans. Am. Nuclear Soc.* **32,** 164 (1979).

Blanchard, R. L., et al., "Potential Health Effects of Radioactive Emissions from Active Surface and Underground Uranium Mines," *Nuclear Safety* **23,** 439 (1982).

Blatt, H., Middleton, G., and Murray, R., *Origin of Sedimentary Rocks,* Prentice-Hall, Englewood Cliffs, New Jersey, 1972.

Cohen, B. L., "The Hazards of Plutonium Dispersal," Institute For Energy Analysis Report, 1981.

Comar, C., "Plutonium: Facts and Inferences," EPRI Report EA-43-SR, August, 1976.

Ellett, W., "Exposure to Radon Daughters and the Incidence of Lung Cancer," *Trans. Am. Nuclear Soc.* **27,** 148 (1977).

Fleischer, R. L., et al., "Radon Levels in Homes in the Northeast U.S.A.," National Radiation Environment, Second Special Symposium, Bombay, India, January 1981.

Fowler, E. B., et al., "Radioactive Waste/Soil Interaction-Migration Potential of Four Soils," *Trans. Am. Nuclear Soc.* **33,** 164 (1979).

Geology, A Golden Guide, Golden Press, New York, 1973.

Goldsmith, W. A., and Clements, W. E., "Radon from Radium-Bearing Residues," *Trans. Am. Nuclear Soc.* **33,** 147 (1979).

———, Handling of Spent Nuclear Fuel and Final Storage of Vitrified High Level Reprocessing Wastes, Karnbranslesakerhet Report, Sweden, 1978.

Hebel, C., Ed., "Report to the American Physical Society by the Study Group on Nuclear Fuel Cycles and Waste Management," *Rev. Mod. Phys.* **50,** (1978).

Hess, P. C., "Phase Equilibria of Some Minerals in the K_2O–Na_2O–Al_2O_3–SiO_2–H_2O System," *Amer. Jour. Sci.* **264,** 289 (1966).

Hoffman, D. C., et al., "Radioactivity in the Underground Environment of the Cambric Nuclear Explosion at the Nevada Test Site," LASL-6877-MS, July 1977.

Holloway, C. D., et al., "Radon-222 in Energy Efficient Buildings," *Trans. Am. Nuclear Soc.* **33,** 148 (1979).

Humphrey, T. G., et al., "Projected Subsurface Migration of Radionuclides," *Nuclear Technology* **58,** 136 (1982).

Johnson, D., and E. Wilhite, "Migration of Transuranic Nuclides in Earthen Burial Trenches at the Savannah River Plant," *Trans. Am. Nuclear Soc.* **33,** 167 (1979).

Kasper, R. B., et al., "Transuranic Distribution Beneath a Retired Underground Disposal Facility at the Hanford Site," *Trans. Am. Nuclear Soc.* **33,** 165 (1979).

Pigford, T., "Geologic Disposal of Radioactive Waste," *Chem. Eng. Progress,* March 1982.

Pourbaix, M., *Atlas of Electrochemical Equilibria in Aqueous Solutions,* Pergamon Press, New York, 1966.

Prinz, M., et al., Eds., *Rocks and Minerals,* Simon & Schuster, New York, 1977.

Radiation Policy Council, "Report of the Task Force on Radon in Structures," RPC-80-002, August 1980.

Rogers, V. C., "The Environmental Impact of Uranium Mill Tailings Generated between 1975 and 2030," *Trans. Am. Nuclear Soc.* **30,** 91 (1978).

Sagan, L., Ed., *Human and Ecological Effects of Nuclear Power,* Thomas, Springfield, Illinois, 1974.

Sorrell, C., *Rocks and Minerals,* Golden Press, New York, 1973.

Tamuar, T., and Lee, S. Y., "Characteristics of Plutonium Significant in Migration Studies," *Trans. Am. Nuclear Soc.* **33,** 164 (1979).

Travis, C. C., "Environmental Sources of Radon," *Trans. Am. Nuclear Soc.* **33,** 144 (1979).

CHAPTER 5

MINING AND PRODUCTION OF REACTOR FUEL MATERIALS

5.1. INTRODUCTION

Nuclear reactors can be designed to use any of the fissile isotopes of uranium and plutonium as a fuel. These fissile materials are the odd atomic mass number isotopes ^{233}U, ^{235}U, ^{239}Pu, and ^{241}Pu. Other isotopes, however, can be converted to fissile material through the process of neutron capture and subsequent decay. These "fertile" isotopes are the even atomic mass isotopes of thorium, uranium, and plutonium. Because of nucleon-pairing effects, they do not readily fission and by themselves would not make a good reactor fuel. They can, however, easily absorb a stray neutron in a reactor core, thereby transmuting into an odd-A even-Z nucleus and a good reactor fuel. Important examples are ^{232}Th, ^{238}U, and ^{240}Pu, which by capturing a neutron (and in the first two cases emitting beta rays), turn into fissile ^{233}U, ^{239}Pu, and ^{241}Pu. The nuclear properties and relative advantage of each isotope for use in nuclear reactors are covered in Chapters 2 and 11.

Uranium and thorium are naturally occurring elements that can be obtained by mining the earth. Uranium is a common constituent of the earth's crust. It is about 800 times more abundant than gold, and far more common than, for example, mercury, cadmium, or silver. Thorium is even more readily available, being four times more abundant than uranium in the earth's crust. On the other hand, plutonium only comes from nuclear reactors, a by-product of the nuclear fuel cycle. Large inventories of all these elements now exist—the practical consideration is how to best produce them in the pure form needed. Their chemical (and mineral) properties are independent of isotope—for the production techniques described in this chapter only the chemical properties of the element count, although it should be recognized in the following discussion that chemical forms can change in some instances because of radioactive decay. This, however, is only of practical importance when considering ^{241}Pu which has a short 13.2-yr half-life.

^{235}U is the only fissile isotope available in nature. Even though it represents only a small fraction of natural uranium, ^{235}U forms the basis of the LWR fuel cycle, the production of military weapons materials, and the initial production of the fissile isotopes ^{239}Pu and ^{233}U—without ^{235}U, fuel cycles based on these isotopes could not be started easily. A bit like the chicken and egg situation, such fuel cycles are started by irradiating fertile materials in ^{235}U-fueled reactors to produce the ^{239}Pu and ^{233}U initially needed to get the cycle going.

There are three fuel cycle material combinations that are possible: (1) ^{235}U in various isotopic concentrations in uranium obtained from ore, the basis of the LWR and CANDU reactors; (2) ^{233}U fuel obtained from thorium transmutation, the basis of the HTGR; and (3) ^{239}Pu fuel obtained from transmutation of ^{238}U, the basis of the LMFBR. Plutonium recycle into LWRs is also possible, as are cycles based on various mixtures of thorium, uranium, and plutonium isotopes, but these are not currently in use. Chapter 11 describes these cycles in further detail.

5.2. URANIUM

Uranium is the principal fuel of nuclear reactors. The path followed by uranium in its various stages, from the mine to insertion into a reactor, is called the "front end of the fuel cycle." Figure 5.1 shows the steps involved in producing uranium fuel elements for an operating reactor. The source of the uranium is ore. The principal uranium-bearing mineral is pitchblende, although conglomerate and sandstone deposits are also economic to mine if their uranium concentration exceed 0.1%. Many deposits contain uranium in still lower concentration, but, in general, the cost of extraction increases as uranium concentration decreases. Processing these deposits is not economical as long as higher concentration ores exist, unless uranium can be obtained as a by-product, such as in phosphate production or gold mining. Uranium can also be obtained from reprocessing

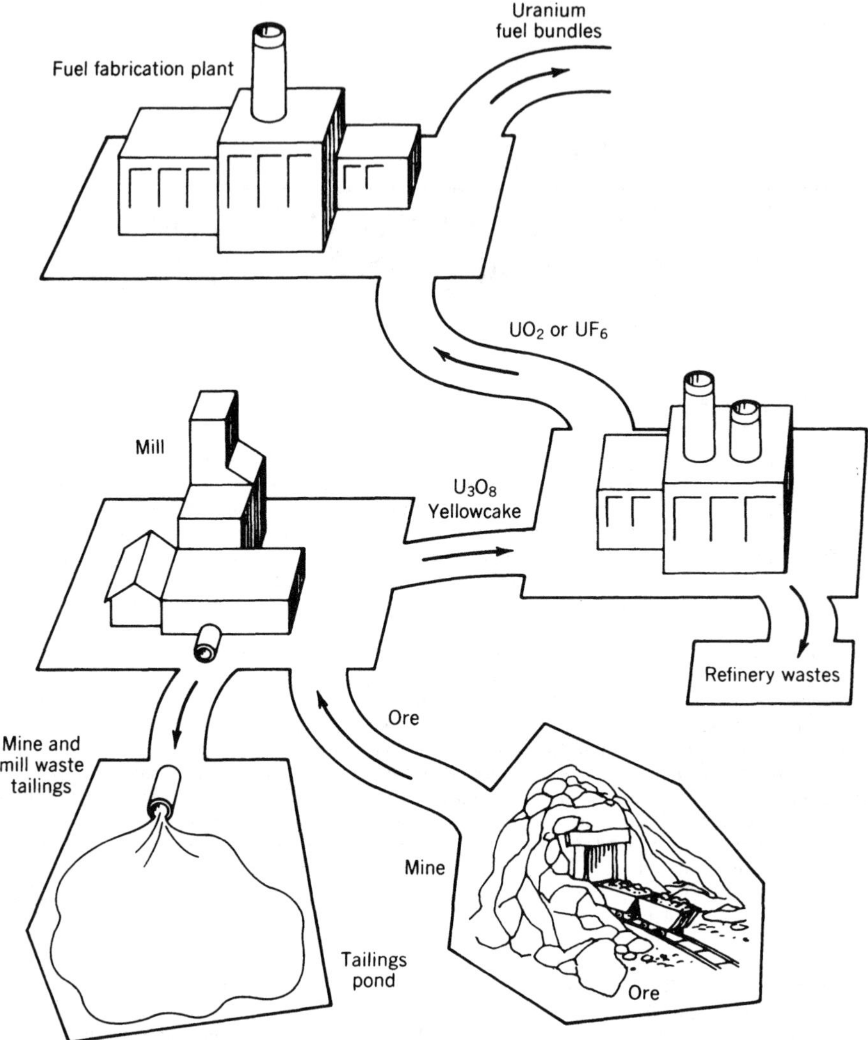

Figure 5.1. Path of uranium as it moves through the front end of the CANDU fuel cycle. The mill must be located close to the mine because the uranium concentration in ore is very low, and it would be uneconomical to ship the material any distance. Yellowcake from the mill is purified at the refinery and perhaps converted to UF_6. In an LWR fuel cycle, the uranium as UF_6 goes in an enrichment plant before fabrication.

spent fuel, since only a few percent of the uranium is burned in the reactor (although 60 to 80% of the fissile ^{235}U is normally used up).

After mining, the uranium in the ore is concentrated. Since the bulk of the ore is nonuranium, this step is carried out close to the mine location to minimize shipping costs. The ore is first crushed to a fine size, and usually dissolved in acid to extract a uranium salt concentrate. The concentrate is next shipped to another plant where it is refined. There the uranium is processed and purified, usually to the chemical form UF_6. Since some enrichment of the uranium in the isotope ^{235}U is usually required, the uranium is next processed in an isotope separation plant, before it is sent to be fabricated into fuel elements. Although many chemical forms of uranium (metal, alloy, oxide, or carbide) could be used for fuel in a nuclear reactor, the present LWRs use UO_2 enriched to about 3% in the isotope ^{235}U and clad with zirconium alloy (Zircaloy) as the standard fuel.

Table 5.1. Properties of Uranium Metal

Temperature	Allotrope	Structure	Density, gm/cm^3	Valence
Ambient –667°C	α Soft Ductile Anisotropic	Orthorhombic	19.04	Approximately 3.8 Covalent bonding
667–774°C	β Anisotropic Hard and brittle	Tetragonal	18.11	Approximately 5.0 Covalent bonding
774–1132°C m.p.	γ Soft	Body center cubic	18.06	Approximately 5.8 Mostly metallic

Uranium Properties

Uranium has 14 isotopes between mass numbers $227 \leq A \leq 240$. None are stable. Most have short half-lives, with the exception of ^{233}U (1.6×10^5 yr), ^{234}U (2.5×10^5 yr), ^{235}U (7.1×10^8 yr), ^{236}U (2.4×10^7) yr), and ^{238}U (4.5×10^9 yr). Since all the uranium isotopes are radioactive, their relative abundance has been changing slowly over the eons. Today, naturally occurring uranium deposits contain 99.3% ^{238}U and 0.7% ^{235}U, with trace amounts of the other isotopes. The isotope ^{235}U easily fissions, while ^{238}U only undergoes fission when bombarded with high-energy neutrons, so ^{235}U is the isotope used in current light-water-cooled commercial reactors.

As a metal uranium is not a very good reactor fuel. A dense, silvery-to-gray material, it has three allotropes (i.e., different crystal structures) given in Table 5.1. Uranium's three allotropes lead to thermal instability of the solid. The allotropic phase transitions are accompanied by large length and volume changes. Such volume changes are difficult to accommodate in solids without loss of physical integrity. Table 5.1 also lists the crystal structure and valence of the uranium phases. The cubic structure that is typical of most metals appears only at high temperature. The other crystal structures exhibit directional expansion and binding characteristics. The low symmetry and nearly covalent nature of the α and β phases greatly affect its mechanical properties, which more nearly resemble those of covalently bonded minerals than those of metals.

The existence of the three allotropes, and their anisotropic thermal expansion can distort any fuel made from uranium metal. Dimensional changes, such as swelling, also result from irradiation and the fission product buildup. Moreover, uranium metal is not very corrosion resistant, reacting with air, water, and hydrogen at low temperatures. Water attack of bare uranium metal can be severe. Hydrogen evolves and, without the presence of air, no protective film forms to slow down the reaction. For these reasons, uranium metal is not used in LWRs. Conversely, uranium dioxide (UO_2) has been found to be thermodynamically stable in a water environment, and does not exhibit the anisotropy and swelling of the metal. UO_2 therefore has been chosen as the preferred form for nuclear fuel.

Uranium dioxide is a blackish ceramic powder that can be sintered into solid fuel. Some properties of UO_2 are listed in Table 5.2. Notable in this table is the high melting point of UO_2 and its density which is much lower than that of the metal. Its cubic crystal structure gives it uniform expansion properties. Uranium dioxide must be kept from contact with air, especially before sintering. Otherwise it reacts with oxygen to form a higher oxide (U_3O_8). UO_2 is one of the four thermodynamically stable oxides of uranium proven to exist. The others are U_4O_9, U_3O_8, and UO_3. UO_2, however, is best thought of as not being a compound but as a mixture of uranium oxides whose oxide/uranium ratio "average" 2. Actually $UO_{2\pm x}$ is a more appropriate formula, where $0.0 \leq x \leq 0.1$. Phase diagrams of the U—O system are given in Figure 5.2. As seen in this figure,

Table 5.2. Properties of Uranium Dioxide (UO_2)

Melting point	2760°C
Crystal structure	Face centered cubic
Lattice parameter	5.47Å
Theoretical density	10.96 g/cm^3

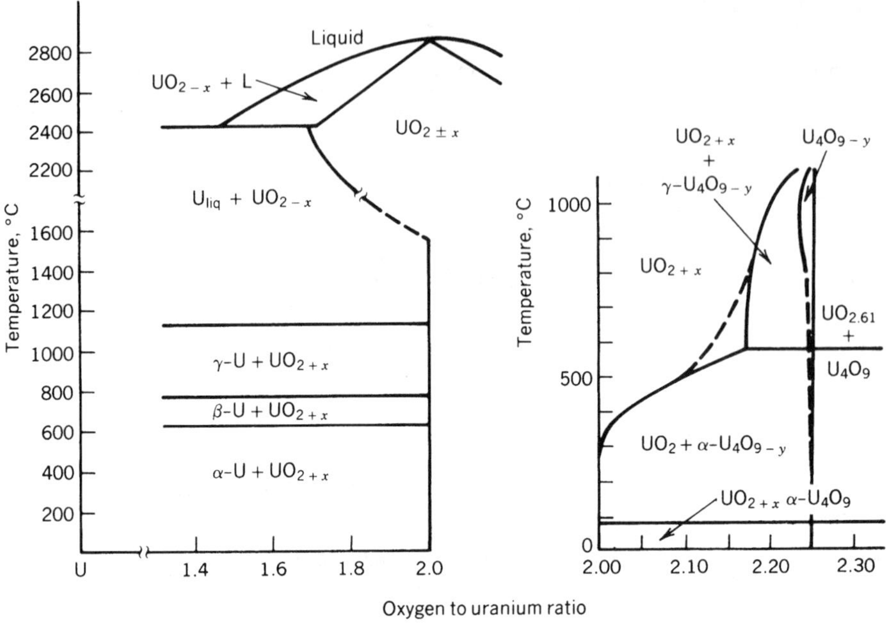

Figure 5.2. Uranium/oxygen phase diagram. (From SAND 74-0382.)

an extremely large change in oxygen potential occurs near stoichiometric composition (i.e., the *exact* oxygen-to-uranium ratio of 2). This keeps the *O/M* ratio very close to 2.00.

To prepare fuel pellets, the uranium dioxide is sintered to 94–96% of theoretical density. This allows gases and volative fission products to leave the matrix during irradiation in the reactor. It also lets the intermatrix void accommodate the metallic fission products. As a result, there is not very much fuel swelling with burnup. The methods of controlling UO_2 properties are discussed in Chapter 7 on fuel fabrication.

UO_2 has a low thermal conductivity. This is significant in reactor design, since it limits a fuel rod to a given size. The design criteria is some maximum temperature at the fuel rod center, which is determined by the thermal conductivity. Therefore, the amount of heat that can be transferred to the coolant is limited by this parameter. Thermal conductivity is also a function of the fuel's oxygen content. This is caused by compounds such as U_4O_9 precipitating at the grain boundaries of the UO_2 matrix. The temperature variation shown in Figure 5.3 is important since it affects the cracking of UO_2 fuel as a reactor's core goes through temperature transients. Such cracking is strongly dependent on temperature. Thermal conductivity is also dependent on fuel density for the temperatures of interest during normal reactor operation. This is also shown in Figure 5.3.

Figure 5.4 shows the heat capacity of UO_2. This figure shows that specific heat capacity increases as the oxygen-to-metal ratio becomes larger than 2. Very oxygen-rich materials, such as U_4O_9 and U_3O_8, have specific heat capacities considerably larger than UO_2, however, their incidence in reactor fuel is uncommon. Since under normal operating conditions, the temperature of the fuel rod's interior is much hotter than the surface, the energy stored is determined by the rod's heat capacity. After the reactor is shut down, this energy diffuses out into the coolant. Heat capacity is therefore an important parameter in analyzing hypothetical accidents.

High temperatures and thermal gradients because of low thermal conductivity can cause grain growth and cracking of the uranium, and possibly some melting of the matrix at the fuel centerline (see Figure 5.5). However, no large dimensional changes occur. Cracking is not significant, since the combination of the fuel column and cladding provides sufficient structural integrity. Cracking can have an indirect effect on the fuel, since it permits fission product gases to escape into the gap between fuel and cladding, raising the fuel temperature, releasing more fission product gas into the gap, and further lowering the thermal conductivity. This occurs because the overall thermal conductivity of the fuel is due to the conductivity of the fuel and the conductivity across the fuel-cladding gap. To ensure good gap conductivity, He gas is introduced into the fuel rod during manufacturing; the mixing of other gases with He reduces the efficiency of the heat transfer process.

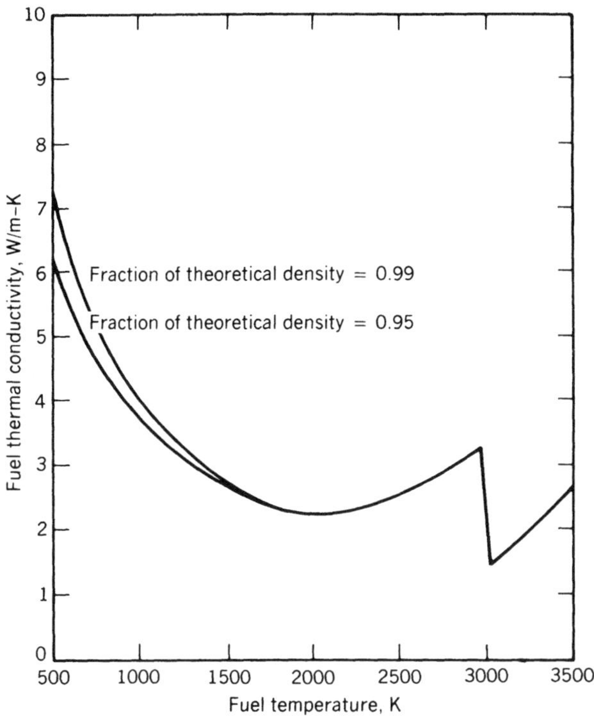

Figure 5.3. Thermal conductivity of UO_2. (From MATPRO.)

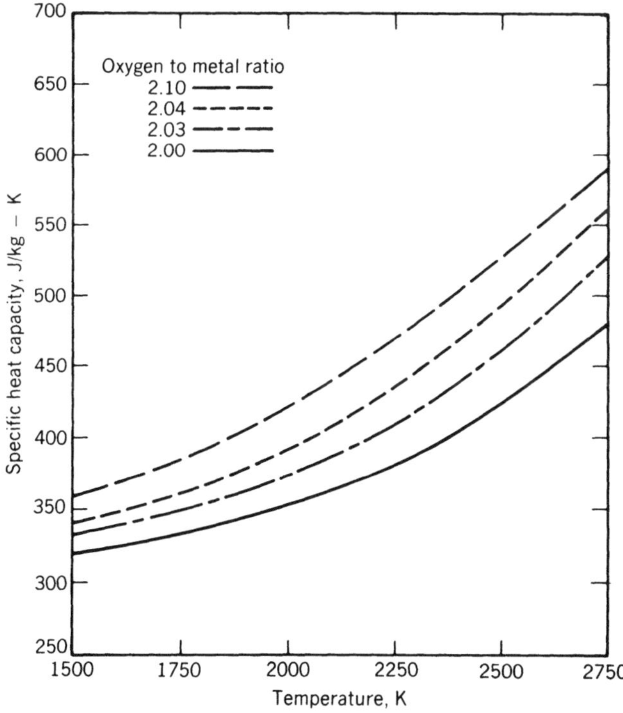

Figure 5.4. Specific heat as a function of temperature and oxygen to metal ratio for UO_2. (From MATPRO.)

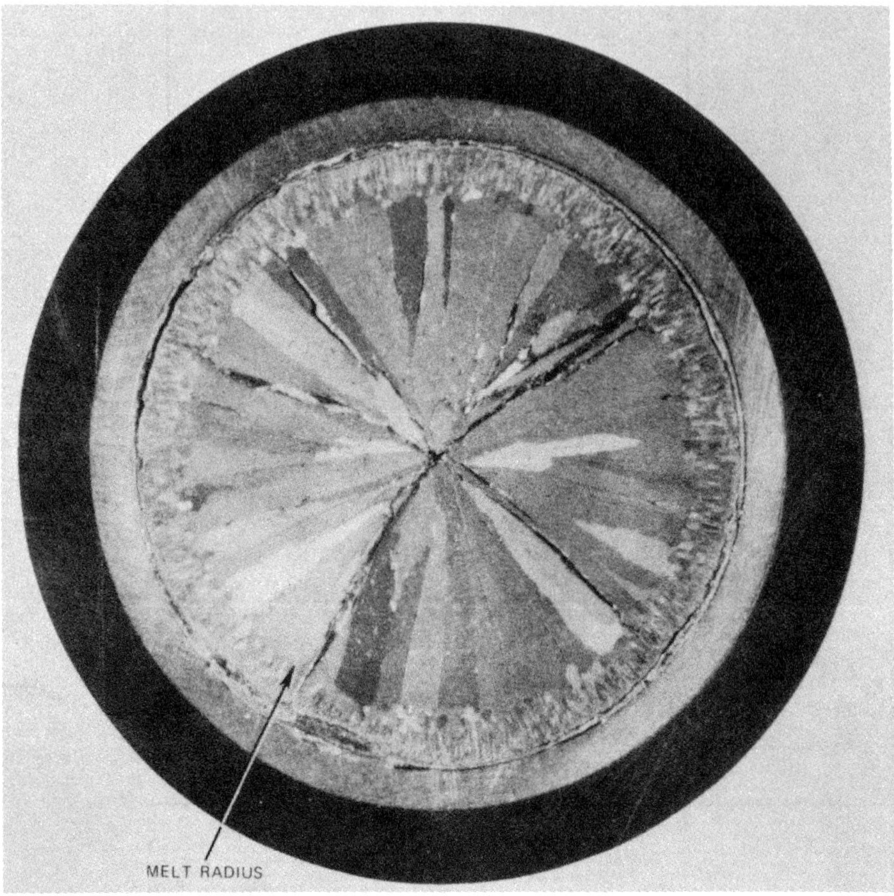

Figure 5.5. Cross section of a UO_2 fuel rod operated at a linear power high enough to cause extensive melting. [From M. F. Lyons et al., *Trans. Am. Nuclear Soc.* **8**, 376 (1965).]

Uranium Deposits

Uranium was discovered in 1789. Its earliest recovery was from pitchblende, an ore with a very high UO_2 content (up to 70%) which also contains radium, thorium, cerium, and lead. Table 5.3 lists the major uranium ores. These ores often contain uranium oxides of variable composition ranging from UO_2 to U_3O_8. Uranium is neither rare nor abundant in the earth. It is mostly found with deposits that contain phosphates, arsenates, and vanadates. For instance, uranium can be economically recovered from (calcium) phosphate rock, a common fertilizer, as a by-product. Marine phosphate often contains 400 ppm of uranium, which replaces some of the calcium. Uranium-bearing marine phosphorites in beds 5–10 ft thick are located under hundreds of square kilometers in Idaho, Montana, Utah, Wyoming, and Florida.

Richard Pearce found in 1871 the first pitchblende of economic interest in the United States. He discovered it in a dump of the abandoned Wood gold mine in Gilpin County, Colorado. From 1898 to 1910, small amounts of uranium were produced in the United States and sold to France as a source of radium, or used to color glass. Later, carnotite deposits on the Colorado Plateau were developed. These deposits were the world's major radium source from 1911 to 1923, and vanadium source from 1924 to 1945. Up through 1975, about 282,000 tons of uranium were produced in the United States out of a total world production of 579,000 tons. The principal worldwide deposits of uranium are listed in Table 5.4.

Uranium exists in nature in two valence states: U^{6+} and U^{4+}. This is the key to its behavior, since U^{6+} is soluble in water and U^{4+} is not. Many of the geologic mechanisms that concentrate uranium in ore deposits resulted from oxidation–reduction conditions, which changed the solubility

Table 5.3. Principal Uranium Ores and Compounds

U^{6+} (Uranus Ion)	
Uranphonane	$Ca(UO_2)_2(SiO_3OH)_2$
Autunite	$(Ca,Na_2H_2,K_2)(UO_2)_2(PO_4){\cdot}nH_2O$
Tyuyamunite	$Ca(UO_2)_2(VO_4)_2{\cdot}nH_2O$
Carnotite	$K_2(UO_2)_2(VO_4)_2{\cdot}nH_2O$
U^{4+} (Uranyl Ion)	
Coffinite	$USiO_4$
Uraninite	UO_2 component of pitchblende
Apatite	$Ca_5(PO_4)_3(OH,Cl,F)$ uranium often replaces Ca
Monazite	$(Ce,La,Th)PO_4$ often contains U
Gummite	Mixture of uranium, thorium, and lead ores

Uranium Oxides and Fluorides

U_3O_8 = yellow cake
UO_3 = orange oxide
UF_4 = green salt
UO_2 = brown oxide
UF_6 = hexafluoride

of uranium in water. The solubility of various uranium minerals is greatly increased as the water pH increases (see Figure 5.6). This affects its mobility. Uranium will also complex with carbonate and other ions to form complexes, such as uranyl carbonate $(UO_2(CO_3)_2)^{2-}$; this process affects its bonding to host rocks in geologic formations.

Uranium has a large ionic radius. That, and the heat from its radioactivity, are the dominant factors in its partitioning in geologic reservoirs. Like Na^+ and other large ions, uranium selectively enters partially molten rock and is thus carried out of the earth's mantle. It is carried to the earth's surface via granite, whose upward mobility is aided by the heat from radioactive elements (like uranium) it contains. The classification of uranium ore deposits in geologic media is given in Table 5.5.

Uranium minerals are easily oxidized. In the earliest geologic times (more than 2.8 billion yr ago), the earth's atmosphere lacked free oxygen. In that era uranium existed in the +4 valence state, and was largely insoluble. In recent eras, uranium has been soluble in the +6 state, as the oxygen partial pressure in the atmosphere increased (see Figure 5.7). Frequently in the past, uranium would dissolve from ore beds, and was carried by river waters. As the river entered delta regions, where dissolved oxygen in the water was taken up by vegetation, uranium was reduced to the +4 state, once again became insoluble, and precipitated. This mechanism often resulted in rich deposits. Figure 5.8 shows an example of uranium mineralization in the delta of a South African river. In this case, the uranium is found in conjunction with a rich gold deposit.

High-grade deposits occur in (1) ancient uranium placer deposits in quartz-pebble conglomerates of Precambrian age, (2) uranium-bearing veins localized in fractures of brittle rocks, and (3) in sandstone (especially in the United States). Lower grade deposits also exist in other types of formations. Placer deposits are the result of the weathering of igneous and metamorphic rock. The resultant minerals gradually move downslope and downstream. They collect around stream courses and beaches. Such deposits can be very large and average 0.1% U_3O_8. Conglomerate ores of this type exist in Blind River-Elliot Lake in Ontario, Canada. In South Africa, such conglomerate deposits, mined as a by-product of gold production, contain 0.05% U_3O_8. An example is the Witwatersrand, a reef in sedimentary rock in South Africa. Although less than 2 m thick, it extends for 250 km^2. The minute uranium grain size in this deposit (0.1 mm) means that the maximum uranium concentration is probably further downstream of the mined gold.

Uranium also occurs in metamorphic and igneous rock as sulfide vein deposits in rock fracture zones. These result from hydrothermal activity over long time periods. The concentration can be quite high in such deposits, up to 10% in some locations in Canada and Australia. France and Zaire also have significant deposits of this type. The ore body can be a few inches to hundreds of feet wide, and contain many different minerals besides uranium. The usual uranium mineral is uraninite (UO_2) which often hydrates to various colors, and is usually called pitchblende. Such deposits can be quite complex, but because of their richness account for 30% of the world's known reserves. Figure 5.9 depicts such a vein deposit, the Nabarel ore body formation in the Northern Territory of Australia. The deposit is relatively rich, with an average grade of 47 lb/ton. Like most uranium

Table 5.4. Tenor and Tonnage of Uranium Deposits

		Type	Tenor U_3O_8, %	Metric Tonnage of U_3O_8 in Largest Deposit	Largest Deposit	Other Products	Remarks
Primary Urinium Ores	Sandstone	Roll	≤0.15	33,000	Highland, Wyoming	None	Individual districts contain >45,000 tons. Average tenor of 1975 production—0.15%.
		Colorado plateau	≤0.18	50,000	Mt. Taylor, New Mexico	V	Individual districts contain >> 45,000 tons. Average tenor of 1975 production—0.185%.
	Skarn		0.12	12,700	Mary Kathleen, Australia	Rare earths	Only uranium producer in Australia up to 1978.
	Rossing		0.035	>143,000	Rossing, Namibia	UK	40% of teno—supergene. World's largest uranium mine in 1978.
	Jabiluka		0.38	228,000	Jabiluka, Australia	Au	World's 2nd largest uranium deposit.
	Roxby Downs		UK	1,200,000	Roxby Downs Australia	Cu, Au, Ag, REE	World's largest deposit.
	Athabasca		0.4–3.9	110,000	Ranger, Australia	Ni, Au	Now contains more reserves than any other type: most important area—N. Saskatchewan.
	Witwatersrand		0.8–0.14	>176,000	Can-Met, Ontario	Yt	Blind River district. Ontario is world's largest producer to 1978.
	Pegmatites		0.14	4,400	Faraday, Ontario	None	
	Midnite		≥0.135	≤11,000	Midnite, Washington	None	
	Lignite		0.008	UK	Southeast Mont. and Dakotas		Total amount of uranium in lignite in the three states probably <10,000 tons.
	Calcrete		0.15	50,700	Yeelirie, Australia	None	

By-Product Ores	Witwatersrand	0.012–0.030	≤11,000	Vaal Reefs, South Africa	Au	Largest gold producer in world's largest gold producing area.
	Phosphorite	<0.35	<22,000	Florida	P,F	Phosphorites in Florida <0.003% U_3O_8. Peak of phosphoria formation averages 0.004 and <0.035.
	Porphyry ores	UK	<11,000	Bingham, Utah	Cu, Mo, Ag, Au	
	Carbonatite	0.004	<3,300	Palabora, South Africa	Cu, Fe	
	Black shales	0.03	UK	Alum Shale Sweden	Base Metals	Gassaway member of Chatanooga shale—0.006% U_3O_8.

Source: Adapted from EPRI Report EA-1374.

UK = unknown.

REE = rare earth extracts.

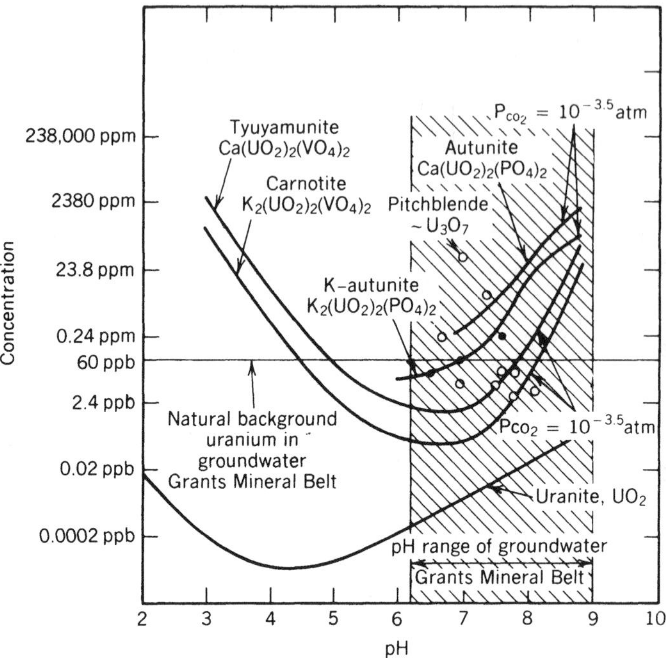

Figure 5.6. Solubility of uranium minerals at 25°C under air at atmospheric pressure. (From PNL-3540.)

deposits of this type, the area of highest mineralization is relatively small. The current theory of ore genesis is that uranium from the basement rock was precipitated in carbonate sediments. Some of it subsequently remobilized into other parts of the formation, and reprecipitated at physically and chemically favorable sites by hydrothermal solutions or circulating water.

Sandstone beds are the principal uranium source in the United States. Beds with high-grade uranium ore (usually carnotite) exist in Colorado, Utah, New Mexico, and Arizona. The carnotite exists as intergranular material in the sandstone. These deposits were laid down along ancient stream courses between 300 million and 1 million yr ago and can exist over extended areas. One such area is the Grants Mineral Belt, located in northwestern New Mexico, shown in Figure 5.10. The occurrence of uranium minerals in the Grants districts has been known for more than 50 yr; however, no mining was done until after 1950. The Grants uranium region consists of several contiguous mining districts almost 100 miles long. The main host rocks for the ore bodies are continental limestones and sandstones. The limestone deposits are replacements and disseminations in the form of tubular to elongate bodies ranging in size from a few hundred to hundreds of thousands of tons. The sandstone deposits are grain coatings, interstitial fillings, and replacements that form runs ranging in size from a few hundred to several million tons.

Two types of sandstone deposits exist: (1) roll bodies, and (2) tubular bodies. Roll bodies are elongated, crescent shaped, cross-sectional deposits scattered along the channels of former streams (Figure 5.11). Such formations can be many miles in length, and occur in the Tertiary and Cretaceous geologic age sediments in Wyoming, South Dakota, and Texas. The uranium minerals precipitated from oxidizing groundwater when they reached a chemically reducing environment. Such conditions existed on the convex sides of the crescent where the sandstone is unaltered (reduced) as shown in Figure 5.12. On the concave side of the crescent, the rock is altered (oxidized) sandstone. These roll-type deposits are caused by the influx and steady recharge of oxygenated groundwater. This lowers the pH when iron pyrite (FeS_2) associated with the deposit is oxidized to sulfite. The uranium, calcite, and pyrites go into solution and are carried (by gravity) below the ore roll where reducing conditions exist. The sulfite then disproportionates to sulfate and bisulfate ion. The bisulfate reduces the soluble U^{6+} to insoluble U^{4+} which precipitates. The uranium is confined to a narrow band, slowly moving downhill. Roll deposits on the Wyoming and Colorado Plateaus are in sandstone derived from Precambrian granite rock. These deposits are often covered with felsic (potassium rich-silicates) volcanic strata. The principal minerals are uraninite and coffinite. Average ore grades are 0.25% U_3O_8.

Tubular bodies are discrete pockets of uranium deposits (Figure 5.13). They occur in chiefly

Table 5.5. Classification of Uranium Ore Deposits

Ore-Forming Process: Relationship to Host Rock	Ore-Forming Process: Mode of Origin	Host Rock	Example	
SOURCE — SYNGENETIC	Sedimentary	CONGLOMERATES	*Elliot Lake* (Canada)	1
			Witwatersrand (S.A)	2
		Blackshales	Randstad (Sweden)	1
		Phosphates	Florida (USA)	1/2
			Cabino (Angola)	1/2
		Acid Tuffs	Wyoming (USA)	1
			Cotaje (Bolivia)	1
	Magmatic (Intramagmatic)	Peralkaline Syenites	Ilimaussaq (Greenland)	1/2
		Carbonatites	*Phalaborwa* (S.A.)	2
		ALASKITES	Rössing (SW Africa)	1
		Pegmatitic	Ross Adams (USA)	1
		Alkali-Granites		
		Granites	*Bingham* (USA) (Cu–Porphyry)	2
	Metamorphic	Phyllites	Forstau (Austria)	1
		Schists	Portugal	1
SOURCE — EPIGENETIC	Contact-Metasomatic	Calc-Silicates	Mary Kathleen (Australia)	1
	Magmatic	Pegmatites	Bancroft (Canada)	1
		HYDROTHERMAL VEINS	*Schwarzwalder* (USA)	1
	Supergene	VEIN-TYPES	*Rabbit Lake* (Canada)	1
		SANDSTONES	*Western USA*	1
		CALCRETE	Yeelirie (Australia)	1
		Lignites	N-S Dakota (USA)	1
		Phosphates/Karst	Bakouma (Zar.)	1/2

Source: From EPRI report EA-1374.

Italics indicate 1975 in production; 1—main, 2—by-product; capital letters indicate economic deposits; upper and lower case letters indicate subeconomic deposits.

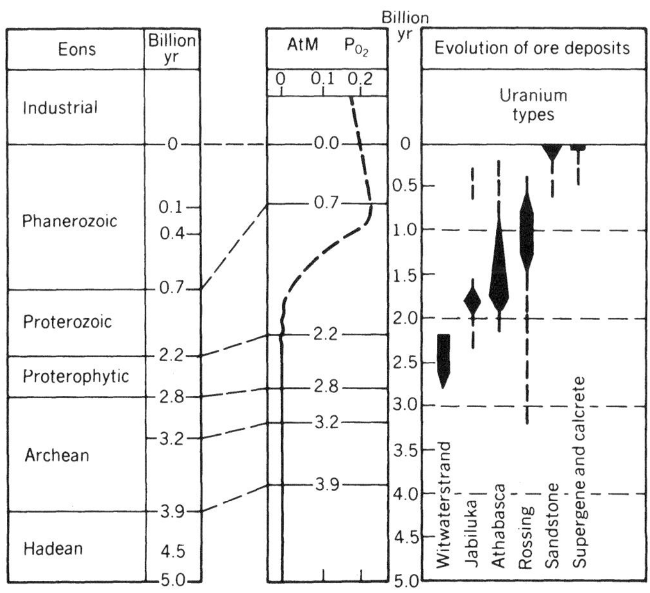

Figure 5.7. Evolution of the earth's atmosphere, crustal lithologies, and uranium ore deposits. (Adapted from EPRI Report EA-1374.)

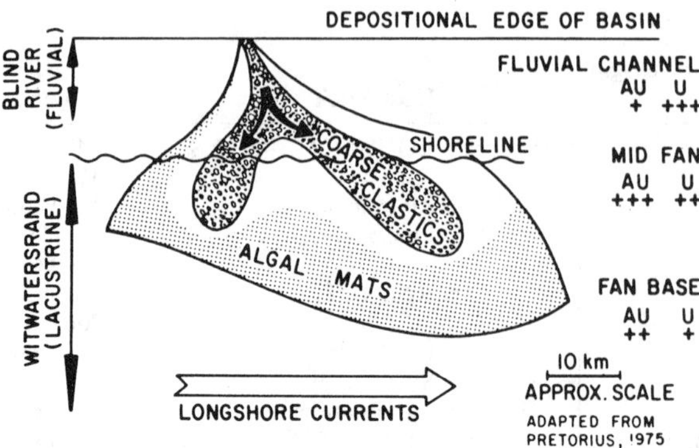

Figure 5.8. Geologic relationships of South African quartz-pebble conglomerates and algal mats. (From EPRI Report EA-1374.)

Jurassic and Triassic formations. The pockets are in sandstone of a completely reducing environment, and sit in a sea of unaltered (oxidizing) sandstone. It is thought that eons ago, groundwater carrying uranium in solution encountered areas of decaying organic plant matter or algae and this resulted in the reducing conditions, which caused the uranium to precipitate.

Uranium Resources

The costs (not prices) for the estimates of uranium resources are called forward costs. They comprise operating and capital costs in constant dollars incurred in producing uranium. These

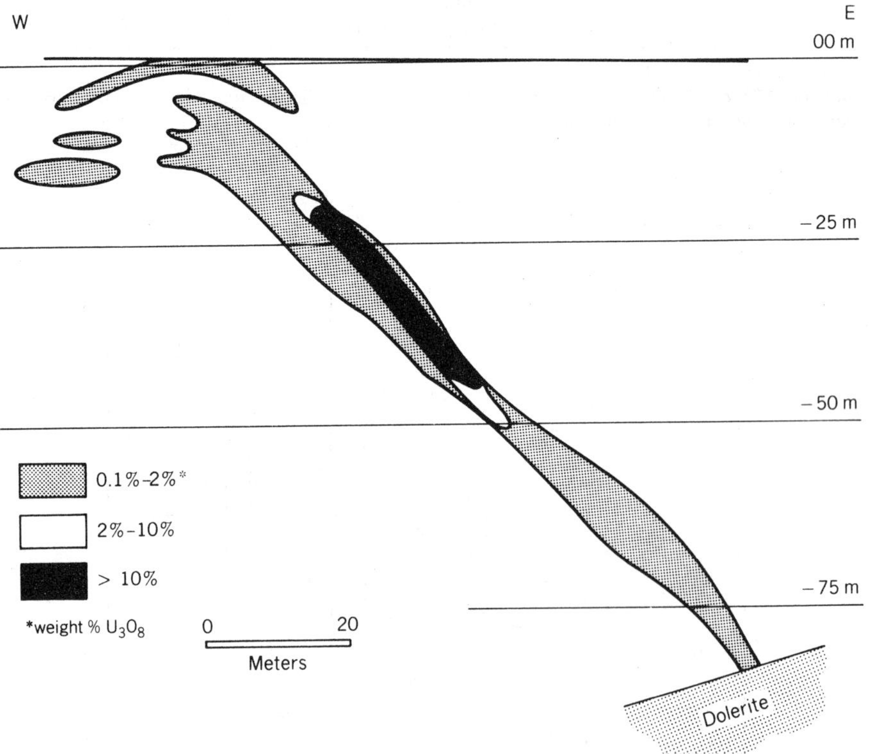

Figure 5.9. The Nabarel ore body formation in the Northern Territory of Australia. (From EPRI Report EA-725.)

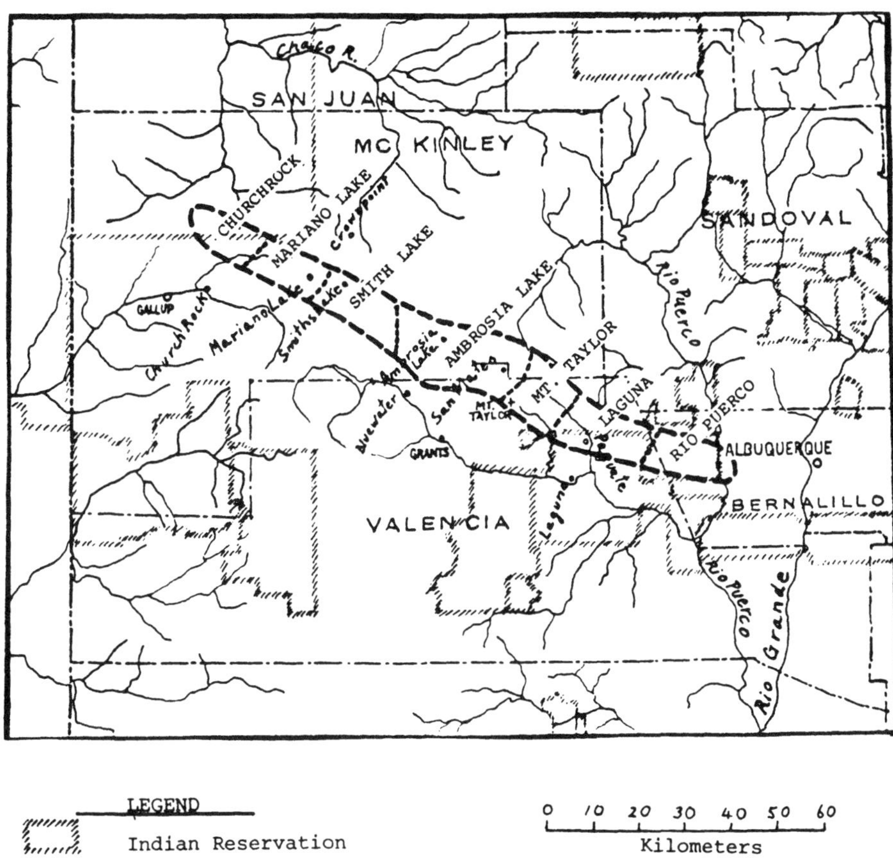

Figure 5.10. The Grants Mineral Belt area map. (Adapted from EPRI Report EA-401.)

include power, labor, materials, royalties, insurance, severance taxes, and G & A costs. Note that income taxes, interest, profit, and past costs (land expense, exploration) are not included.

A basic difference exists between uranium reserves and resources. Reserves are known uranium deposits, clearly delineated in specific mining properties, which can directly be converted to supplies at hand. Resources include inferences to uranium deposits, estimated at various degrees of certainty. The *probable* resources are an extension of known uranium deposits. The *possible* resources are estimates of uranium occurrences in formations similar to those where actual deposits were found; they are not based on direct evidence. Speculative resources are just such.

Of course, uranium reserves in the ground do not correspond to the availability of uranium supplies for power reactors. Lack of capital outlays, experienced miners or mining permits, and various restrictions and environmental regulations imposed on the uranium mining industry may inhibit the utilization of fuel resources. Changes in the price of uranium which do not materially affect the cost of nuclear-generated electricity can have a devastating impact on uranium mines and mills, and on plans for investment. During the period of low uranium prices in 1983, for instance, three major production centers closed in Canada, as did many of the high-cost production centers in the United States. In some cases, mines forced to close may never reopen, and their reserves are lost.

There exists a long controversy about the true and ultimate size of the U.S. uranium resource base. This issue has important consequences for the size of the supportable nuclear capacity, the closure of the nuclear fuel cycle, and the need for breeder reactors. On the professional side, there exists a conflict between the conservative resource estimates of uranium geologists and the more

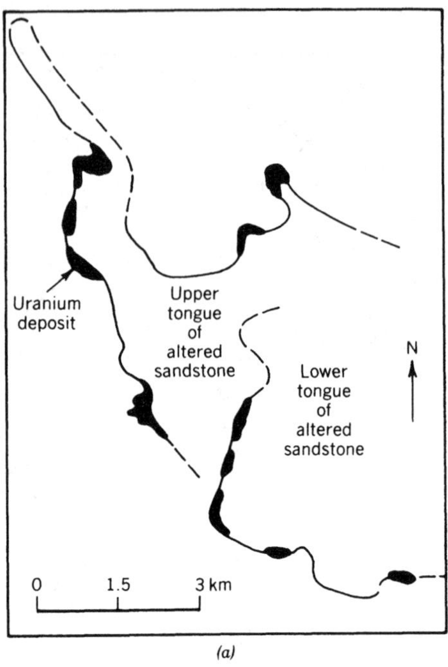

(a)

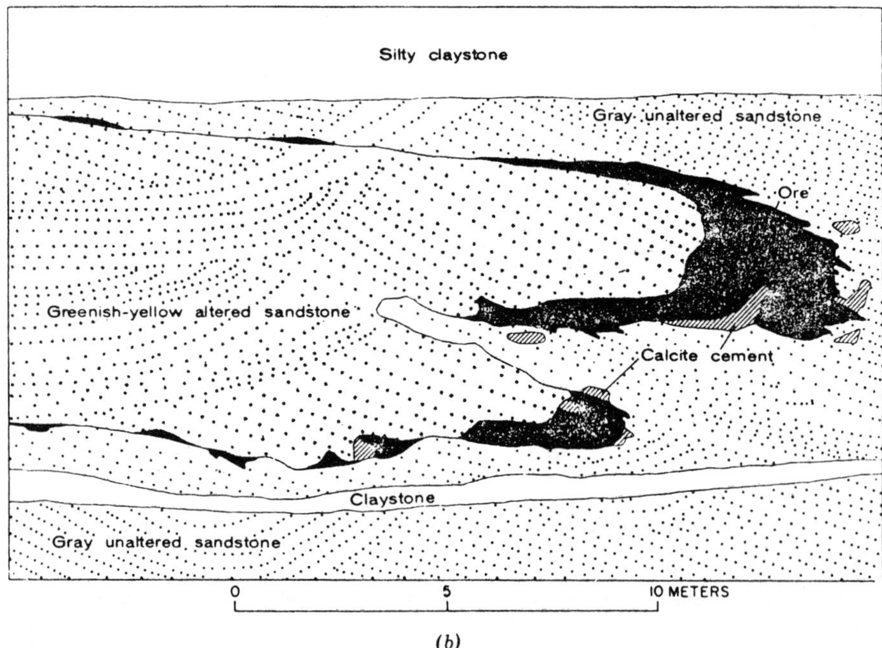

(b)

Figure 5.11. (*a*) Plan map showing outline of upper and lower altered sandstone tongues, Shirley Basin, Wyoming. Roll-type uranium deposits lie at the edges of large tongues of altered (oxidized) sandstone that vary widely in size, but typically are a few tens of meters thick, a few kilometers wide, and 10 km, more or less, long. The alteration was produced by the ore-bearing solutions. (From E. N. Harshman, USGS.) (*b*) Section of altered sandstone tongue showing distribution of ore. Ore bodies are in sharp contact with the altered tongues, extend a few centimeters to a few tens of meters outward from them, and grade gradually into unaltered (reduced) unmineralized sandstone. Some ore, in small tabular bodies, is found on the top and bottom surfaces of the altered tongues. The edge of a tongue is everywhere mineralized but it is not everywhere ore bearing. (From E. N. Harshman, USGS.)

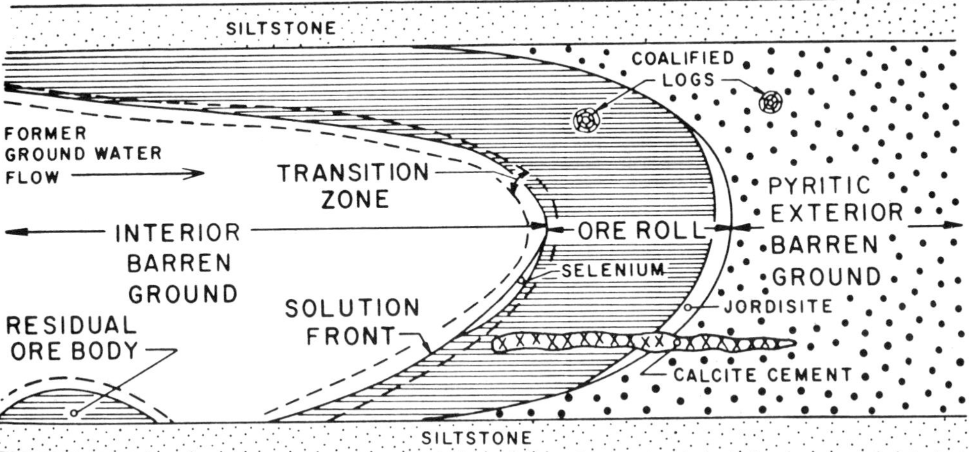

Figure 5.12. Schematic cross section of a Wyoming-type roll. (From EPRI Report EA-1374.)

optimistic estimates of the energy economists; the latter believe that with increased prices more resources will always be found. On the political side, the pro- and antinuclear groups have also taken opposite positions. These issues are discussed in the reports of the Committee on Nuclear and Alternative Energy Systems (CONAES)[1] and the FORD-MITRE study[2] on nuclear power issues and choices.

Uranium reserve estimates are usually derived from drill-hole data; direct radiometric and chemical sampling measurements are typically used. In the United States, the Department of Energy (DOE) prepares the domestic reserve reports from data made available by the uranium mining companies. These evaluations are made for uranium quantities in the United States for various cost categories. The cost categories are independent of the market price at which the uranium could be actually sold. Cost categories represent the maximum cost per pound U_3O_8 in a given category. Therefore actual production costs would be somewhat lower.

Collection of uranium resource data highly depends on economic conditions in the uranium industry. Most exploration is done in periods of high demand (and prices). Surface drilling methods for uranium exploration started seriously in the United States in about 1948 with about 210,000 ft of drilling data collected. It rose to 9.2 million ft in 1957, then quickly diminished to 2 million ft in the mid-1960s. It rose again to an all time high of 47 million ft in 1978, and recently has been at a much lower level. Over the years the drill holes have tended to get deeper, as deeper uranium deposits were explored (Figure 5.14).

Uranium resources versus forward cost in the United States are given in Table 5.6. As seen in this table, uranium reserves range between 470,000 tons at \$30/lb (U_3O_8) and 1,034,000 tons at \$100/lb. Other resource categories (probable, possible, speculative) are also given in part (b) of this

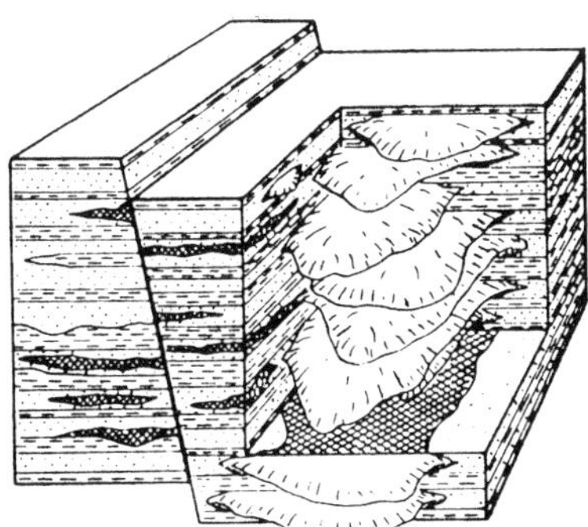

Figure 5.13. Tubular or "stack" compound uranium ore body. Reference: Ambrosia Lake, New Mexico. (Courtesy J. W. Gabelman, 1976.)

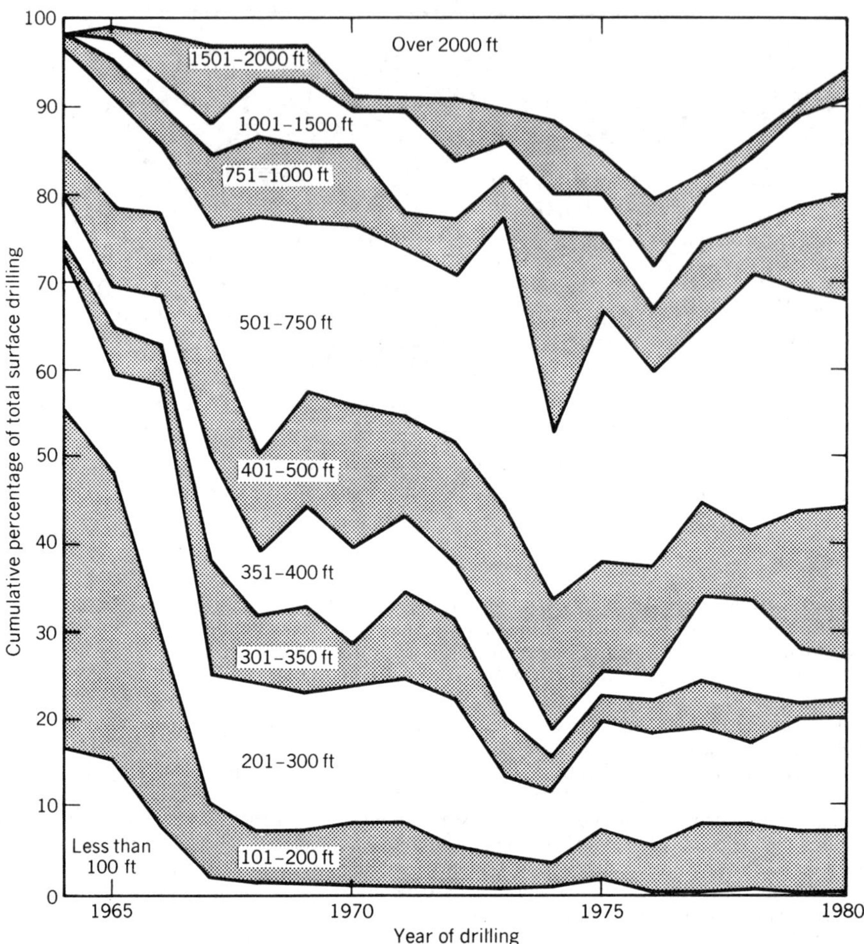

Figure 5.14. Percentage of surface drilling by selected depth ranges: 1964–1980. [From GJO-100 (81).]

table. The mean for all categories, both proven and potential, is the sum of parts (a) and (b): about 2.0 million tons at \$30/lb and 4.7 million tons for \$100/lb. This does not include secondary recovery of uranium through such activities as by-product of phosphate and copper milling. Secondary recovery could add another 150,000 tons/yr of production. Estimated resources in these selected cost categories cover wide economic conditions. By comparison, it takes approximately 6000 tons of uranium to satisfy the lifetime fuel requirements of a single 1000-MWe LWR.

Projected annual uranium requirements through the year 1990 are shown in Figure 5.15. The requirements forecast in this period are relatively insensitive to new orders or cancellations for nuclear plants; such changes in total nuclear capacity would only affect demand in the 1990s because of the long construction time for nuclear units. The uranium requirements and sales commitments in this figure are prepared by DOE for U.S. domestic users. After 1982, uranium procurement via an established contract price probably will decrease, and market price arrangements will grow significantly. This trend is labeled as "reported unfilled requirements" in the figure. Prior to 1975, contract pricing prevailed in the uranium market (market price procurement was less than 15%). As price rose rapidly, contract pricing terms did not cover cost escalation and remained far below market prices. As a result, such arrangements became unsatisfactory to uranium producers. Moreover, as prices rose, more uranium came from captive production, that is, utility-controlled operations. By the mid-1980s it is expected that contract price, market price, and captive operations will each have roughly equal shares of the uranium delivery to the utilities in the United States.

Table 5.6(a). Probability Distribution Values for Potential U.S. Uranium Resources, January 1, 1981[a]

Forward-Cost Category	Thousand Tons U_3O_8		
	Mean	Ninety-fifth Percentile	Fifth Percentile
$15/lb U_3O_8			
Probable	295	185	448
Possible	87	42	156
Speculative	74	30	162
Totals	456	280	704
$30/lb U_3O_8			
Probable	885	659	1161
Possible	346	194	530
Speculative	311	155	600
Totals	1542	1094	2097
$50/lb U_3O_8			
Probable	1426	1102	1802
Possible	641	346	973
Speculative	482	251	890
Totals	2549	1845	3369
$100/lb U_3O_8			
Probable	2080	1646	2573
Possible	1005	521	1526
Speculative	696	378	1225
Totals	3781	2766	4923

Source: Adapted from GJO-100(81).

[a]Estimated potential uranium resources include losses from mining; losses due to milling are not included and may range from 5 to 15%.

Table 5.6(b). Reported U.S. Uranium Reserves, January 1981

	Thousand Tons, U_3O_8
$30/lb	470
$50/lb	787
$100/lb	1034

Source: From GJO-100(81).

Large uranium reserves exist throughout the world, although the United States accounts for about one-fifth of the reserves below $80/kg. The seemingly large fraction is likely due to the United States having been more heavily explored than other areas in the world. The world uranium resources, shown in Table 5.7, are dominated by Australia, Canada, and South Africa in addition to the United States. Uranium production is high in these countries, although not necessarily proportional to their resources. Australia, for instance, tends to restrict production for political reasons. However, Australia recently decided to mine the world's biggest uranium deposit, the $1.5 billion Olympic Dam mine at Roxby Downs in South Australia. The deposit contains 1.2×10^6 t of uranium, as well as 32×10^6 t of copper, 38×10^6 oz of gold, some silver, and rare earths. The top five uranium-producing countries in 1981 were: the United States, Canada, South Africa, Niger, and Namibia (South West Africa). Their production figures are given in Table 5.8.

In the United States the areas of production are illustrated in Figure 5.16, which shows that nearly all U.S. production is in the West. Cumulative production has exceeded 10,000 tons U_3O_8 in eight different areas. Production in 1981 was about 13,500 t, mostly from traditional mining methods. A relatively recent type of uranium production is solution mining. The usual technique is in situ leaching (ISL), which uses chemicals to leach ore from geologic formations. As shown in Figure 5.17, solution mining of uranium, which accounted for virtually no production in 1975 is continuing to expand; ISL accounted for 3,000,000 lb of production in 1979. The low capital cost of

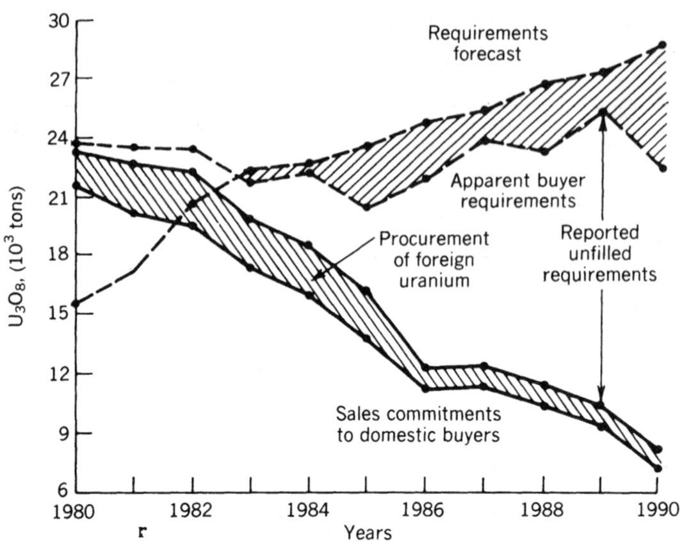

Figure 5.15. Uranium requirements and sales commitments in the United States. (Adapted from J. A. Patterson, "The Domestic Uranium Industry," March 1981.)

Table 5.7. Uranium Resource—1981 (Millions of Metric Tons)

	Assured Reserves		Estimated Reserves	
	$80/kg	$130/kg	$80/kg	$130/kg
Algeria	26	26	0	0
Argentina	25	30.3	3.8	13.4
Australia	294	317	264	285
Austria		0.3	0.7	1.7
Brazil	119.1	119.1	81.2	81.2
Canada	230	258	358	760
Central African Republic	18	18	0	0
Chile	0	0.02	0	6.7
Denmark	0	27	0	16
Egypt	0	0	0	5
Finland	0	3.4	0	0
France	59.3	74.9	28.4	46.5
Gabon	19.4	21.6	0	9.9
West Germany	1	5	1.5	8.5
Greece	1.4	5.4	2.0	7.3
India	32.0	32.0	0.9	25.1
Italy	0	2.4	0	2
Japan	7.7	7.7	0	0
Korea	0.04	11.04	n.d.	n.d.
Mexico	2.9	2.9	3.5	6.1
Namibia	119	135	30	53
Niger	160	160	53	53
Portugal	6.7	8.2	2.5	2.5
South Africa	247	356	84	175
Spain	12.5	16.4	8.5	8.5
Sweden	0	38	0	44
Turkey	2.5	4.6	0	0
United Kingdom	0	0	0	7.4
United States	362	605	681	1.097
Zaire	1.8	1.8	1.7	1.7
Total	1,747	2,293	1,605	2,720

Source: Courtesy of CNEN.

Table 5.8. Uranium Production, Metric Tons

	Before 1977	1977	1978	1979	1980	1981
Argentina	340	100	126	134	187	180
Australia	8,159	356	516	705	1,561	2,600
Brazil	—	—	—	—	—	100
Canada	112,080	5,790	6,800	6,820	7,150	8,400
Finland	30	—	—	—	—	—
France	23,133	2,097	2,183	2,362	2,634	2,824
Gabon	8,464	907	1,022	1,100	1,033	1,000
West Germany	151	15	35	25	35	—
Japan	38	3	2	2	5	3
Namibia	594	2,340	2,697	3,840	4,042	3,939
Niger	6,108	1,609	2,060	3,620	4,100	4,500
Portugal	1,932	95	98	114	82	107
South Africa	75,332	3,360	3,961	4,797	6,146	6,700
Spain	476	177	191	190	190	145
United States	209,800	11,500	14,200	14,400	16,800	13,500
Zaire	25,600	0	0	0	—	—
Total	472,237	28,349	33,891	38,109	43,965	43,998

Source: Courtesy of CNEN.

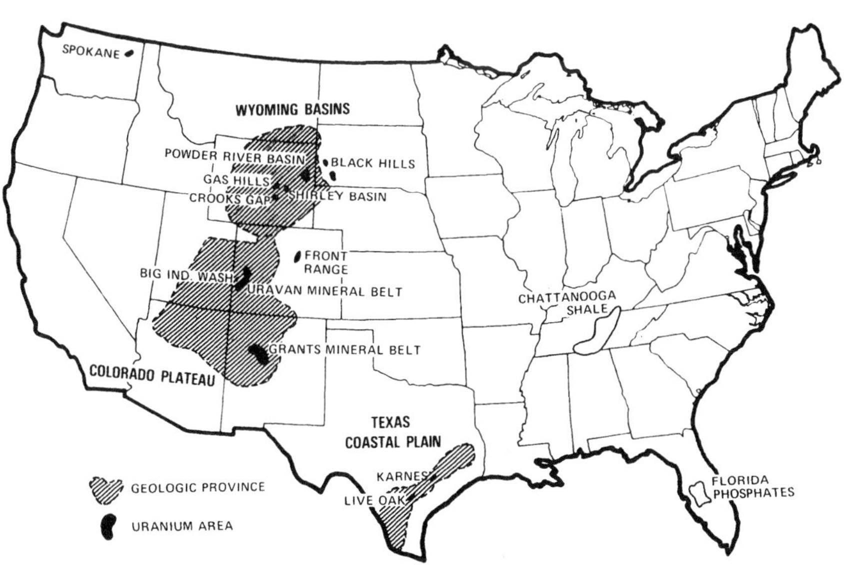

Figure 5.16. Areas of uranium ore production in the United States. [From GJO-100 (81).]

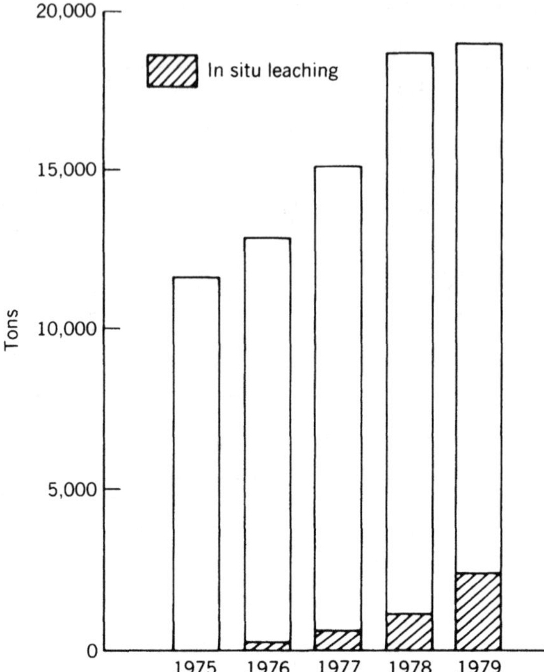

Figure 5.17. U_3O_8 production in the United States. (Courtesy NUEXCO Corporation, Monthly Report No. 151, March 1981.)

ISL is a distinct advantage. A second major advantage of ISL is modular expansion in small increments of ½ million lb of production a year. A large underground mine/mill facility would have to have 4 to 8 million lb of production to be economical. Such demand is not expected to materialize for at least a decade. A small open-pit mine/mill would need only 1 million lb/yr production to be economical, but would be inflexible in operating at various production levels. For these reasons, expansion in the solution mining of uranium is likely to continue.

Uranium Mining on Native Lands

In many parts of the world, uranium resources exist on land belonging to native or aborigine tribes. This is particularly true in the United States, and to some extent in Australia. For example, in the United States, Indian tribes own about one-half of the country's privately owned uranium. Three tribes, the Navajo, the Spokane, and the Laguna, accounted for 24% of the U.S. production in 1980 and about 12% of the total world production in that year. According to the U.S. Dept of the Interior, significant uranium amounts are believed to exist on several million acres of Indian lands.

By happenstance, Los Alamos National Laboratory, site of much early nuclear weapons research, was located in the middle of what is now one of the world's largest uranium deposits—the San Juan Basin and the Grants Mineral Belt—predominately Indian country. In 1950, a Navajo shepherd, who overheard geologists talking about uranium, walked backed to where he had seen similar deposits. These deposits were later identified as a major uranium find. The area has been responsible for up to half the U.S. uranium production in some years.

Uranium Mining

The geology of uranium does not restrict its occurrence to a small number of highly specific sites. Uranium is found in a wide range of geologic environments and in a large number of minerals. Each deposit presents its own unique extraction problems, and recent discoveries, including the large high-grade deposits, provide many new technical challenges.

There are three common methods of uranium mining: underground (hard rock) mining, open-air mining, and in situ (chemical) solution mining. The type used to recover any given deposit is determined by economics. Factors include the depth below the surface and deposit concentration,

Figure 5.18. Drilling to establish uranium deposits.

and whether the uranium is a by-product of other mining operations, such as for gold or phosphorus. Underground and open-air-type mining operations are the more conventional. Underground mining requires that the mine shafts be well ventilated to prevent radon gas buildup, which poses an occupational radiological hazard. Although radon gas is characteristic of uranium deposits, it is present in all hard rock mines, although usually in lower concentrations. Examples of typical mining operations are given in Figures 5.18 and 5.19.

Mine development begins with site acquisition, establishing an access road to the property, access to the levels, site preparations, installing gas and electricity at the site, personnel acquisition and training, and establishment of an overhead operation. When the initial shaft is in place, the venture will begin the mine development phase prior to production. The prime objective of a preproduction development program is to provide assurance that a continuous flow of production can be maintained with a minimum amount of development work.

After preproduction development has brought in the shaft and the main haulage drift, there will be a period of long-hole drilling to establish the working deposits. This in turn will lead to establishing the access raises to the deposits. When the main haulage drift and the raises are in place, the

Figure 5.19. An underground raise borer is used to drill a raise or hole upward to provide access to mining stopes. (Courtesy Kerr-McGee Corp.)

mine is considered ready to enter in the production phase, and is considered capable of producing at a constant grade and a constant output over an economic life of 15 yr. Within each deposit there is a repeating cycle of the hole drilling, development drifting, and setup through waste rock to reach the productive ore, then extraction of ore until exhaustion, then new drilling to find out in which direction the productive ore is going, followed by more development, then more extraction, and so on.

Over the years, the average grade of uranium ore mined in the United States has dropped as high-grade, easily accessible ore concentrations have been depleted. This is shown in Figure 5.20. In recent years, the concentration of ore processed has dropped to around 0.12%.

Uranium mining in sandstone deposits is one of two types: open-pit mining for surface deposits, and classical mining for deep deposits. The determining factor between the two is economics. Surface mines are limited to a 240-ft depth. Below this depth, the cost of removing overburden is excessive. Underground mines typically produce higher grade ore than surface mines; the added expense to go deeply underground is only offset by increased revenues from richer ores. A typical mine is shown in Figure 5.21.

Vein-type deposits can be mined by several methods; three commonly used methods are open stope, shrinkage stope, and cut and fill. The latter was designed to extract ore from vein-type deposits, using mill wastes to refill mined out areas; cut and fill is the common method used today for vein-type copper deposits.

An open stope is a cavity from which the ore has been extracted, and no fill added—the only rock support is an occasional post or pillar. The method is limited to narrow, nearly vertical ore bodies with good walls and ore strong enough to stand unsupported over the top of the stope. The stope is maintained by arching the back or roof. The ore is extracted in an overhand manner. As the ore is broken and drawn out, benches may be carved to provide a place for the miners to work. Generally, open stopes are less than 100 ft high. Within any one deposit, separate mining methods may be employed either in sequence or simultaneously. The mining method employed depends on the set of conditions at the ore face, the slope inclination upward from the horizontal, and the thickness of the seam as extraction progresses.

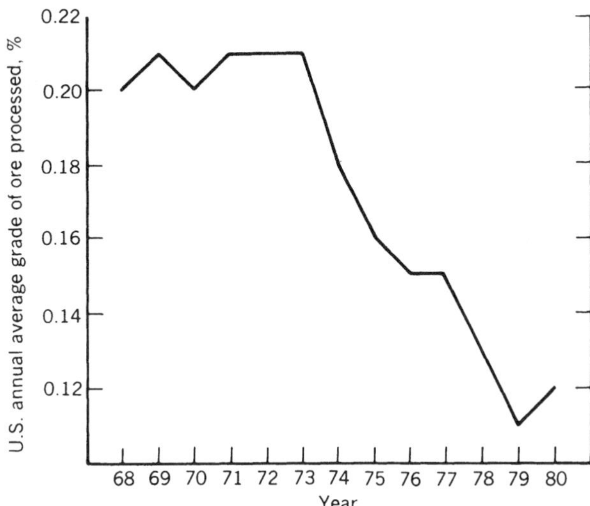

Figure 5.20. United States annual average grade of ore processed. (From NUEXCO Monthly Report on the Uranium Market, September 1980.)

Underground and surface mines are basically very different types of operations with differing unit production costs. Most high-grade deposits of uranium close enough to the surface to have been easily discovered have been worked out, leaving relatively low-grade ores for open-pit mining. At shallow depths, the mining method employed is open pit. One such mine is shown in Figure 5.22. This method employs dozers for stripping and mining, dozers and front-end loaders for loading, and mining-type dump trucks to haul the ore out of the pit. After the mine is played out, the pit is refilled with the overburden and reclamation is performed on the reconstructed surface.

A relative newcomer to uranium mining is the in situ method. This technique uses chemicals to dissolve the uranium in the ground, and pump it to the surface. Solution mining requires uranium mineralization in fairly porous formations underlain by impermeable strata. It was first applied in Shirley Basin, Wyoming, in 1960. The advantage of solution mining is that it does not require ore

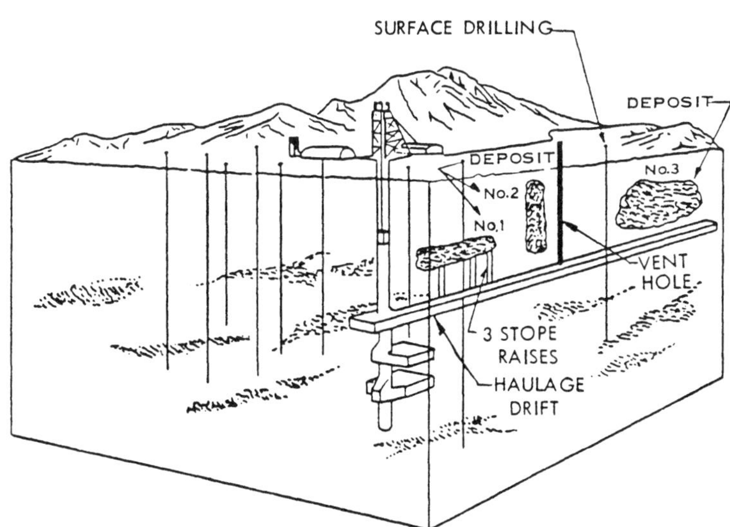

Figure 5.21. Typical underground mine in production. In the working mine configuration shown, the first deposit is being worked from three stope raises. (From EPRI Report EA-730.)

Figure 5.22. Open air mine in Haute-Vienna, France. (Courtesy COGEMA.)

handling, stockpiling, crushing, grinding, and mill tailings. The last item, mill tailings, is an environmental concern, as is the particulate emissions from the crushing and grinding of ore. The main disadvantages are the cost of chemicals used in production and low recovery from the ore body due to hydraulic short circuiting or solution losses. Currently 23 full or pilot plants have operated (Figure 5.23). These plants accounted for 6% of U.S. production in 1978. By 1987, this technique is expected to be responsible for approximately 13% of the U.S. total.

Solution mining uses a well field to recover the uranium. The wells are arranged in a regular geometric pattern, spaced every 10–20 m. A typical in situ operation is shown in Figure 5.24. The well field is an array of wells designed to permit controlled contact of the lixiviant with the uranium-bearing ore beneath the ground. The wells are either injection wells through which the lixiviant is introduced to the ore or production wells from which the uranium-bearing solution is recovered. The field is usually installed in a regular geometric pattern. The wells are cased and cemented so they are open only to the desired areas of ore.

In solution mining, the uranium is removed from the geologic formation by means of a lixiviant—a chemical solution that dissolves and mobilizes uranium in an ore body. It does this by reversing the natural conditions which led to the uranium deposit, in particular by changing the oxidation (valence) state of the uranium atoms from +4 to +6. The lixiviant is typically groundwater mixed with an oxidant and an anionic complexing agent. In a neutral or alkaline (basic) leach system, bicarbonate/carbonate is the complexing agent. In acidic leach systems, sulfate ions are used. However, acidic solutions also tend to dissolve other trace minerals associated with such an ore and, therefore, are less specific for uranium. As a result, basic (ammonium or sodium bicarbonate–carbonate) lixiviants with an oxidizing agent are now generally used in most in situ activities where carbonate minerals are known to be associated with the ores. A typical in situ process is given in Figure 5.25.

Microbes may interfere with in situ extraction of uranium. The bacteria are apparently introduced into the ore body by the drilling and injection process, and once there they thrive under the leaching conditions. The leach solution is usually a fairly neutral mix of carbonate–bicarbonate, with an oxidizing agent (often hydrogen peroxide) to convert the uranium's +4 valence to +6, so that it will form uranyl carbonate. However, the oxygen present also promotes bacterial growth.

A possible remedy may be to inject stronger concentrations of peroxide into the well to break down the organisms. Some companies have tried this with some success, but it has to be repeated periodically.

Loosely consolidated deposits such as many Wyoming sandstones can be hydraulically mined. In this process, a high-velocity water jet slurries ore particles from the uranium deposit and a slurry pump returns them to the surface. This process, however, has not been widely commercialized.

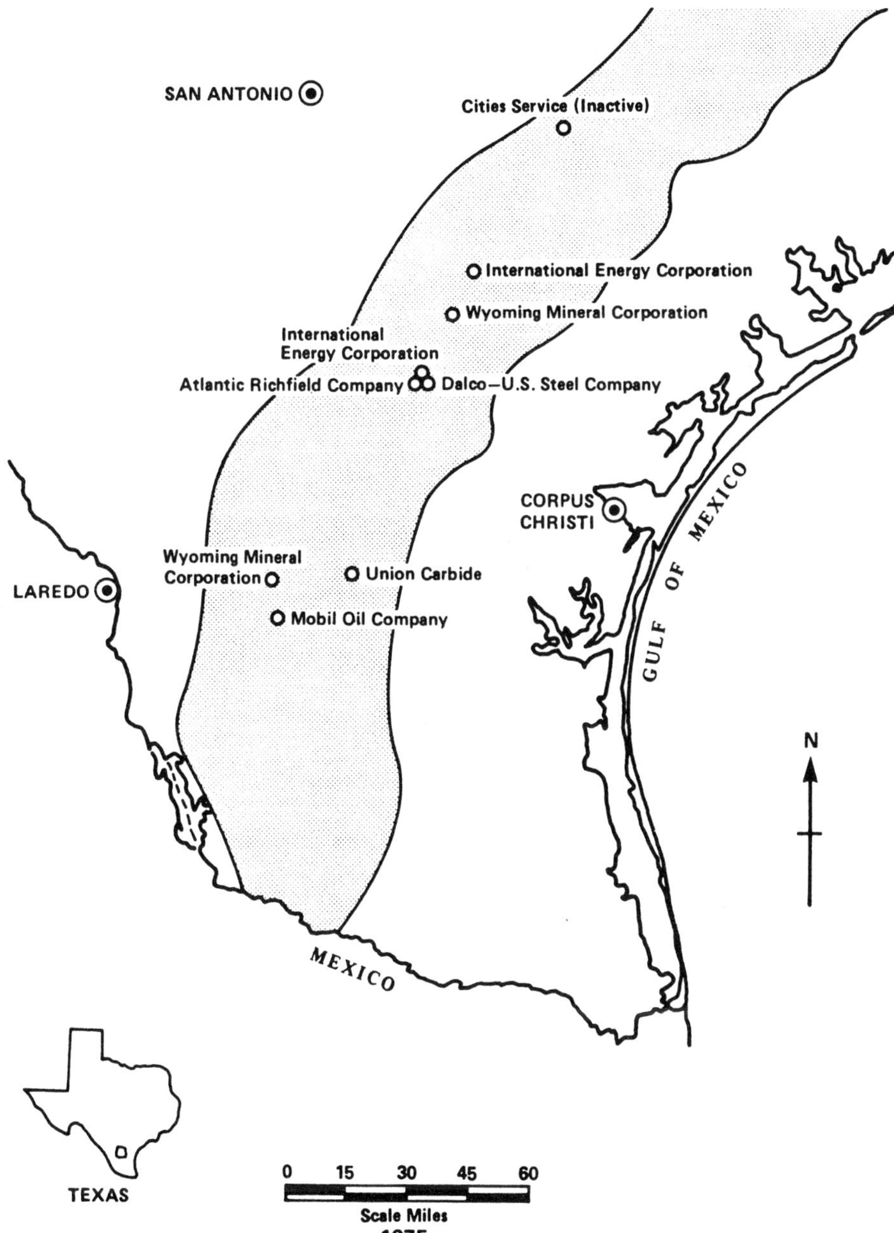

Figure 5.23. Recent uranium solution mining locations in Texas. (From EPRI Report EA-731.)

Uranium By-Product from Phosphates

Vast reserves of relatively low-concentration uranium deposits exist in the United States in the form of phosphates (Figure 5.26). Tens of billions of tons of such phosphate reserves contain U_3O_8 in the concentration range 0.004 to 0.04. These phosphates are a principal ingredient of fertilizer. When ore mined for fertilizer is processed, uranium can be obtained economically in a by-product process. When uranium is recovered from phosphate ore, a dihydrate process is usually used. A flow sheet for this method is shown in Figure 5.27. This type of extraction from a wet process phosphoric acid stream appears to be the only economical process available.

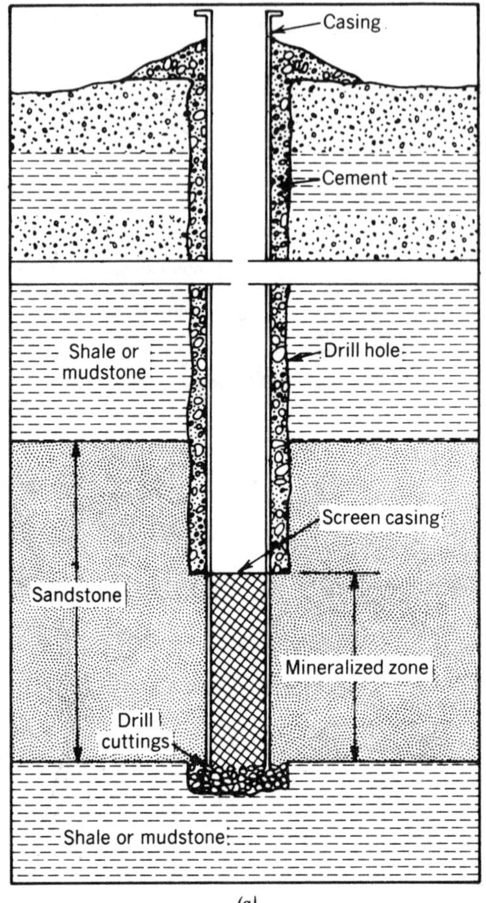

(a)

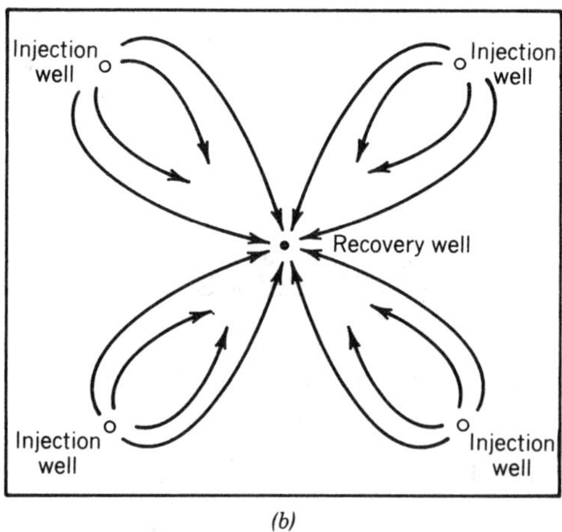

(b)

Figure 5.24. (*a*) Solution mining well construction. (*b*) Individual production cell flow pattern. [From *Nuclear Engineering International* **25** (1980).]

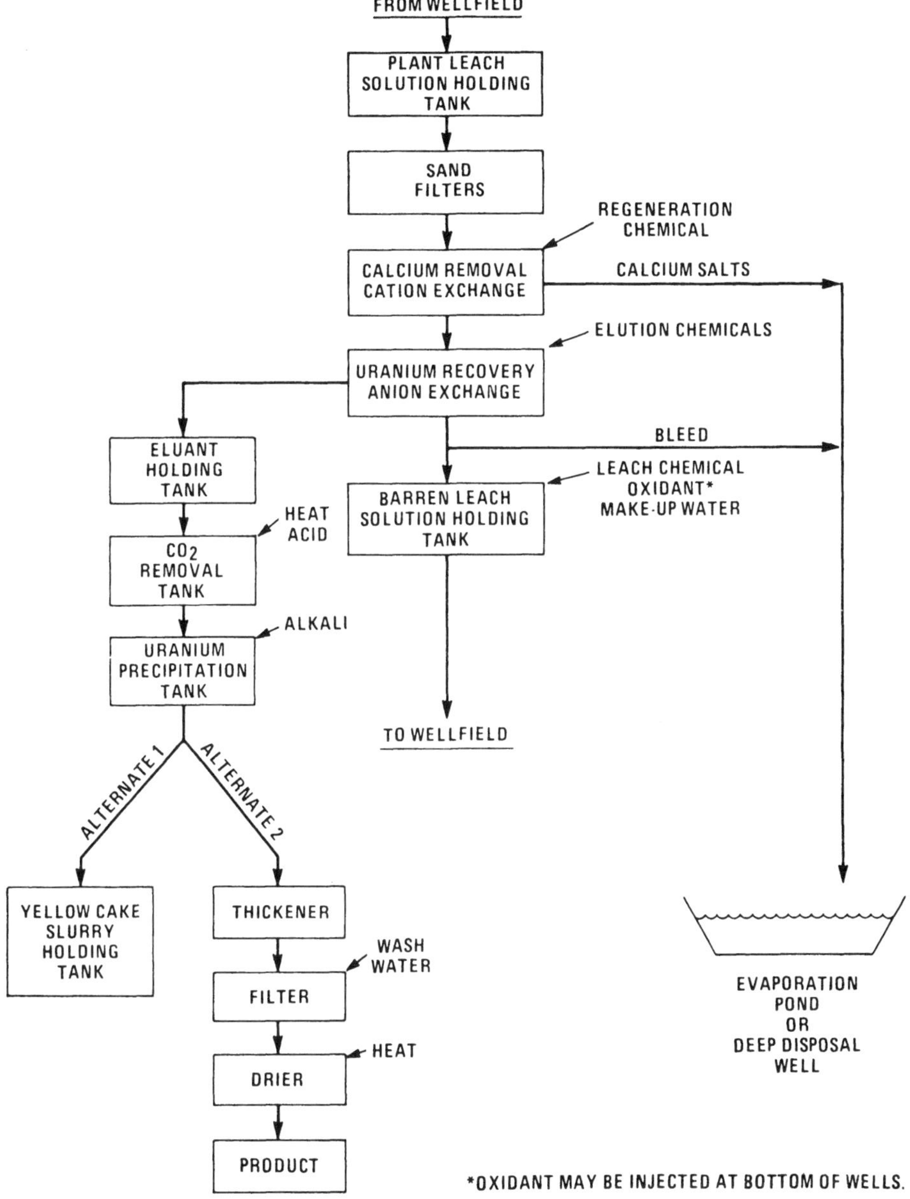

Figure 5.25. Typical alkaline in situ leach plant process. (From EPRI Report EA-731.)

The conventional dihydrate process of uranium from phosphoric acid requires a P_2O_5 concentration below 30%. The chemical bonds of uranium and $H_2PO_4^-$ are too strong for common solvents such as DEHPA-TOPO [di(2)-ethylhexyl phosphoric acid and tri-octyl-phosphine oxide] or OPPA (alkylpyrophosphate) to break. The TOPO enables uranium to be extracted from phosphoric acid, which contains on average 0.02% uranium. (It is estimated that the world's phosphate reserves contain at least 10 million tons of uranium.) The TOPO process uses liquid extraction, where uranium (in the +6 valence state) with the phosphoric acid is mixed with the organic solvent DEHPA-TOPO, usually diluted in kerosene. The solvent carries off the uranium, leaving behind the uranium-free phosphoric acid.

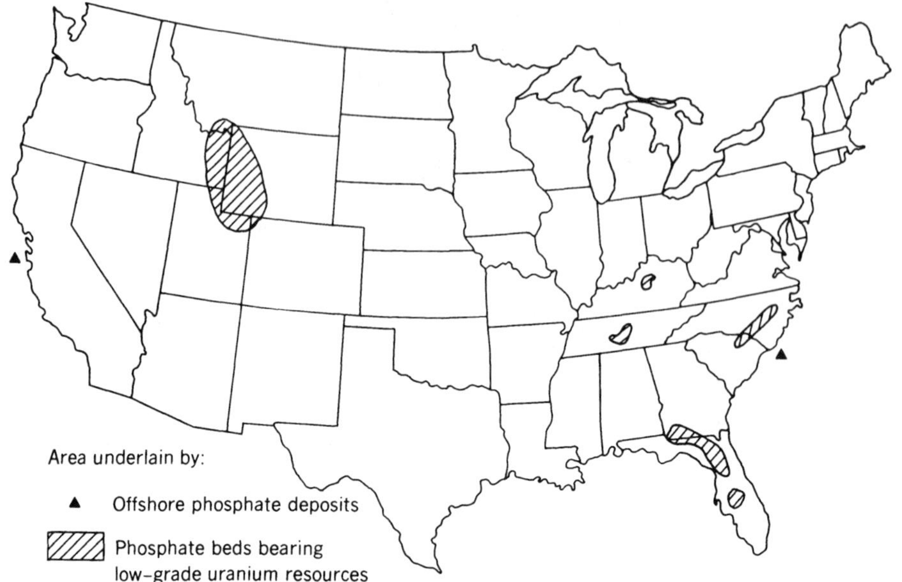

Figure 5.26. Location of known major phosphate deposits bearing low-grade uranium resources. (From EPRI Report EA-733.)

The newer hemihydrate phosphate plants produce superphosphoric acids of 40–50% P_2O_5. This requires a process that controls the uranium valence state. The +4 state remains in slurry solids of the phosphate digester, rather than dissolving in the acid. To accomplish this, a reducing gas such as SO_2 is bubbled through the digester bed. The uranium is then removed from the resulting gypsum ($CaSO_4$) by conventional means.

Uranium Ore Processing

A typical orebody will contain uranium in the form of one or more different minerals dispersed throughout a sterile matrix. The particles of ore are of considerably greater size than the particles of uranium contained. These ore particles must be reduced to a size about equal to the mineral size for effective subsequent processing of the ore. This is done at a uranium mill. Sometimes the individual ore particles can be sorted radiometrically to separate uranium-bearing rock from the barren gangue. This is done by monitoring the natural gamma radioactivity of each rock and using a mechanical means, such as an air blast, to remove the waste.

Figure 5.28 shows a typical uranium mill. The ore-milling procedure involves first crushing and rod and/or ball mill grinding. The finely ground ore is then subjected to acid or carbonate leaching, depending on the acid-consuming characteristics of the gangue rock. The leach solutions are then treated by solvent extraction or ion exchange techniques. The uranium is precipitated, dewatered, and dried.

Acid and carbonate leaching are fundamentally different processes. The former can be used to dissolve the uranium from the ore. The latter exploits the ability of uranium ions in solution to form stable carbonate complexes. Ammonium or sodium carbonate can be used. Carbonate leaching is generally more expensive than acid leaching. It is used, however, where ore composition such as high limestone content makes acid leaching impractical.

Sulfuric acid in the leaching step not only lixiviates the uranium content of the ore, but is also consumed in chemical reactions with carbonates and other constituents of the host rock. In fact, the loss of acid in chemical reaction far outshadows the uranium dissolution to the point where the economics of the acid leach process are governed by these secondary reactions. The acid consumption cutoff would be approximately 200 lb of acid per ton of ore. For acid consumption greater than this, the mill owner would have an economic incentive to employ the alternative carbonate leach process.

The last major technological change effected in the acid leach process was the introduction of solvent extraction to concentrate the pregnant liquor. Since then, technical gains have been limited to improving operations through better design.

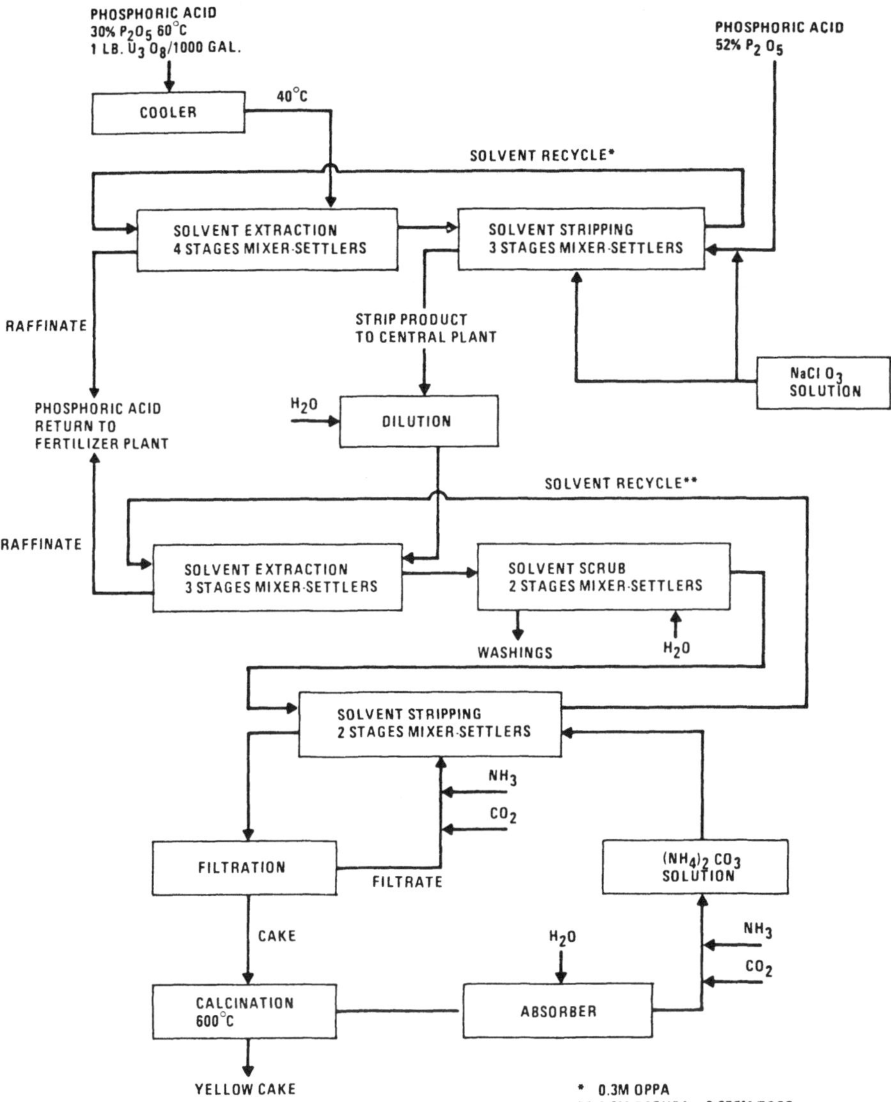

Figure 5.27. Process flow sheet for uranium recovery from phosphoric acid. (From EPRI Report EA-733.) The first necessary step is to cool the acid to about 40°C. In the subsequent solvent extraction operation, the coefficient of uranium extraction is increased with a decrease in temperature but phase separation in the solvent extraction circuit becomes slower as the temperature is lowered. The cooled acid is subjected to four stages of extraction with a 0.3 *M* solution of octylphenylphosphoric acid (OPRA) in a kerosene diluent. The uranium is taken up by the OPRA and the phosphoric acid is returned to the fertilizer plant for evaporation and sale. The loaded solvent is stripped in three stages with concentrated phosphoric acid (52–54% H_2PO_4) to which sodium chlorate has been added. The uranium is oxidized by the chlorate to the hexavalent state which is less extractable by the OPRA, and it, therefore, transfers to the strong acid solution. The acid solution containing about 15 g/liter U_3O_8 and amounting to only about 6000 gal/day can be transported to a central plant for further processing if so desired.

Figure 5.28. The Ambrosia Lake uranium mill near Grants, New Mexico, is currently the largest uranium processing mill in the United States and is wholly owned by Kerr-McGee. The Grants mill has successfully processed in excess of 7000 tons of ore per day. Uranium ores from other mining companies are also milled on a toll-milling contract basis. The Grants mill produces uranium oxide (U_3O_8) concentrate, commonly called yellowcake, from uranium-bearing ores using the acid leach-solvent extraction process. (Courtesy Kerr-McGee Corp.)

Nearly 80% of ore mined today is leached with an acid (usually H_2SO_4). A process flow sheet is given in Figure 5.29. The ground ore is usually leached for up to 24 hr as a 50 wt.% slurry at 35°C. MnO_2 is used as an oxidant.† The leached liquor is removed, using a multistage countercurrent decantation circuit, and clarified. It is subjected to solvent extraction with amine‡ and kerosene. The amine compound selectively absorbs dissolved uranyl ions from the aqueous leach solution. The uranium is stripped from the organic phase with sulfuric acid, precipitated as yellowcake using ammonia, filtered, centrifuged, and dried. Uranium extraction in such a process is high, about 95%. Another method less often used is an alkaline leach. The steps required for both these leaching methods are outlined in Table 5.9. The leach process produces uranium in the form $Na_2U_2O_7$ (yellowcake) which precipitates when the leach stream is treated with sodium hydroxide (NaOH). This final product is concentrated 70–80% yellowcake, and next passes to a purification stage.

The tailings from the leach process contain nearly all the ore's radium (^{226}Ra), since none of it is dissolved in leaching. This radium, and its daughter products, especially ^{222}Rn, could lead to an environmental hazard. Containing the mill tailings is required to prevent wind erosion, groundwater leaching, and the escape of radon gas. Mill-tailing slurries can be dewatered into a relatively dry solid. This is then put into a retention area to safely impound the tailings. A dam is constructed, as shown in Figure 5.30, which uses imported fill material and a seepage-reducing "impermeable" layer. ^{226}Ra can also be removed from the ore in the leaching stage. Radium leaches in hydrochloric acid (HCl); however, HCl is much more expensive than H_2SO_4, and less uranium extraction occurs. Sodium chloride (NaCl) (1–5M) releases the radium, which can be precipitated§ with $BaCl_2$ (Figure 5.31). $BaCl_2$ treatment will remove most of the radium from the ore if added to clear sulfuric acid solutions containing radium ions. $BaCl_2$ is also often used to treat uranium mine waters.

A process was recently developed in Japan, however, which bypasses the yellowcake stage, the intermediary process required in conventional uranium-processing methods, and makes UF_6, the feed for the enrichment plants, directly from ore. This process, it is thought, will play a significant role in the milling, refining, and conversion from ore to UF_6 in the future. The main innovations in

†$NaClO_3$ can also be used. Concentrations of 1 to 5 kg/t are common.

‡Alamine-336, a mixture of trioctyl- and tridecylamine, is commonly used.

§In this form the radium is effectively nonemanating since the precipitated substance is crystallographically "tight."

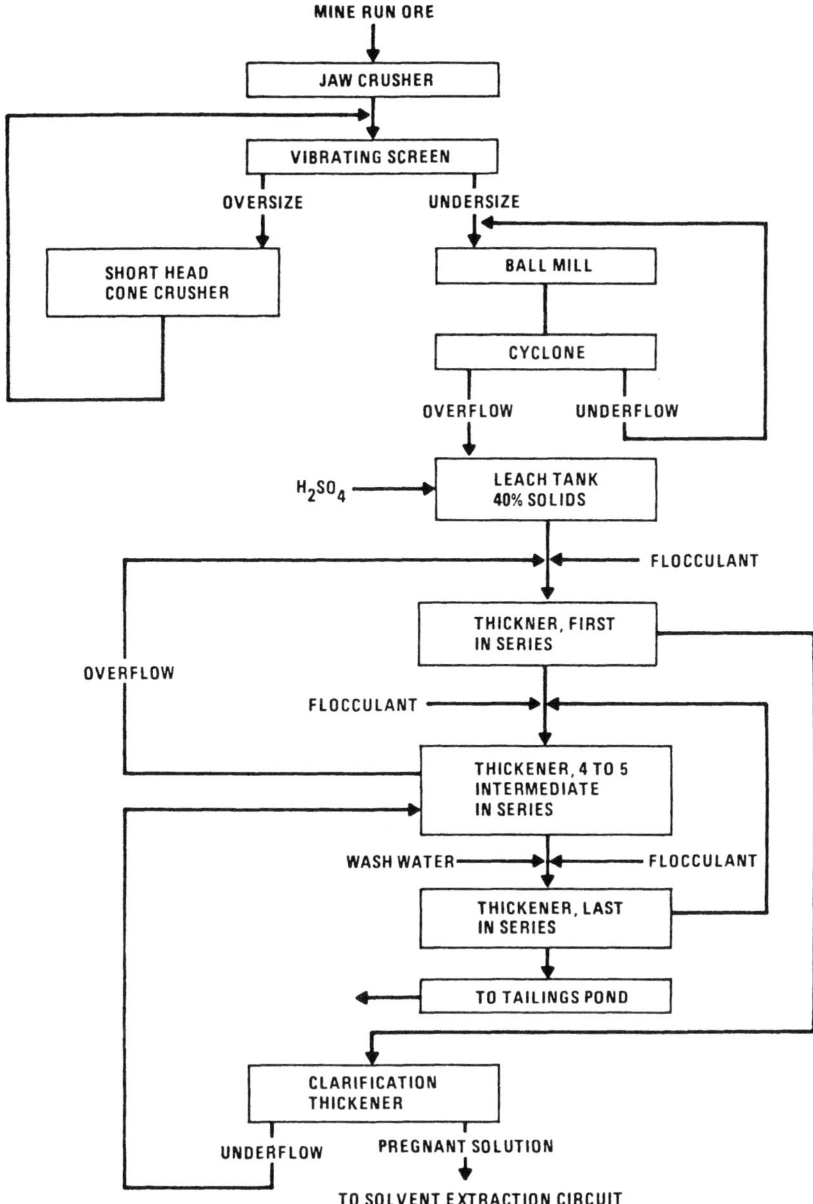

Figure 5.29. Process flow sheet for uranium recovery from vein deposits. (From EPRI Report EA-733.)

this process are the use of solvent extraction of the leached ore to produce UO_2Cl_2, followed by electrolytic reduction to UCl_4, which can then be directly fluorinated to UF_6. The process is shown in Figure 5.32. A third process was developed by Rio Tinto Zinc Company for use at the Rossing mine in South West Africa (Namibia). It (Table 5.10) utilizes ion-exchange techniques to isolate the uranium, and produces UO_2 as the final product. Uranium in sulfuric-acid leach solutions forms a mixture of species UO_2^{2+}, UO_2SO_4, $UO_2(SO_4)_2^{2-}$, and so on. Few metals other than uranium form anions in sulfuric acid, so that the concentration of the usual contaminating ions, such as those of iron, vanadium, and molybdenum, can be minimized. This process is also effective in extracting uranium from a carbonate leach solution.

Table 5.9. Extraction of Uranium from Ore

Acid Leach (Approximately 80% of Production)

1. Crush ore.
2. Wet grind to less than 28 mesh size.
3. Bathe several hours in a strong acid and oxidizer (H_2SO_4 and sodium chlorate).
4. Leach out uranium.
5. Wash residual solids (approximately 70%) and slimes (approximately 30%) into tailings ponds.
6. Extract uranium by solvent extraction or ion exchange.
7. Pump residual liquids also into tailing ponds.
8. Strip uranium from organic solvent or elute (wash) from ion-exchange column.

Alkaline Leach (Approximately 20% of Production)

1. Finely grind ore to 200 mesh size.
2. Leach with $Na_2CO_3/NaHCO_3$ solution at elevated temperature (250°F) and pressure (50 psi) with air as oxidizer.
3. Wash residual solids (approximately 50%) and slime (approximately 50%) into tailing pond.
4. Precipitate uranium as sodium diuranate ($Na_2U_2O_7$) using NaOH.
5. Recover sodium. Na may be redissolved with H_2SO_4 and reprecipitated with H_2O_2 or NH_3. The leaching solution can be recarbonated with CO_2 gas. Only a small fraction ends up in the tailing pond.

Environmental Protection and Safety

Uranium mining and milling do not pose the same potential safety hazards as nuclear power plants or reprocessing facilities. Table 5.11 shows the occupational incident rates for the fuel cycle's front end activities. In addition to the usual safety precautions needed for any mining activity, uranium production has added precautions because of the ore's radioactivity. Two principal areas of concern are (1) radon exposure to the miners (see the discussion in Chapter 4), and (2) protection of the public and environment from the potential risk posed by the mill tailings. Tailing piles must be properly managed.

One health hazard associated with uranium mining is lung disease: cancer related to radon exposure and pulmonary fibrosis due to silica dust. The latter is a problem in all rock mining in sandstone deposits. Uranium mining in the United States has probably resulted in about 100 excess cancer deaths through the mid-1970s. Other malignancies are still likely from this early period due to a long latency period of up to 25 yr for the disease. Increased ventilation of the underground mines subsequently has markedly reduced the risk of lung disease. It has never been prevalent in the open-pit mines where ventilation is not a problem.

The mass of the mill tailings roughly corresponds to the amount of ore processed, or about 500 kg of tailings for every kilogram of uranium produced. Tailings usually contain most of the ore's radioactivity, which is mostly due to radium, unless the ore has been specially treated during processing. About 250 μCi (250 μg) of radium and 200 nCi of radon are present in the tailings for each kilogram of uranium processed. Although these are very small quantities, if released to the

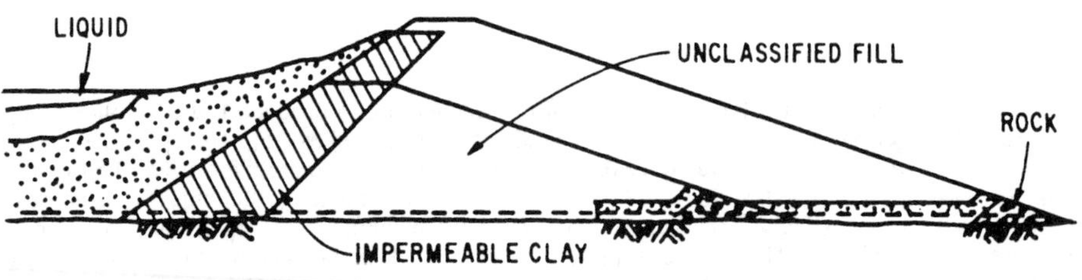

Figure 5.30. Basic method of embankment construction. (From NUREG-0511.)

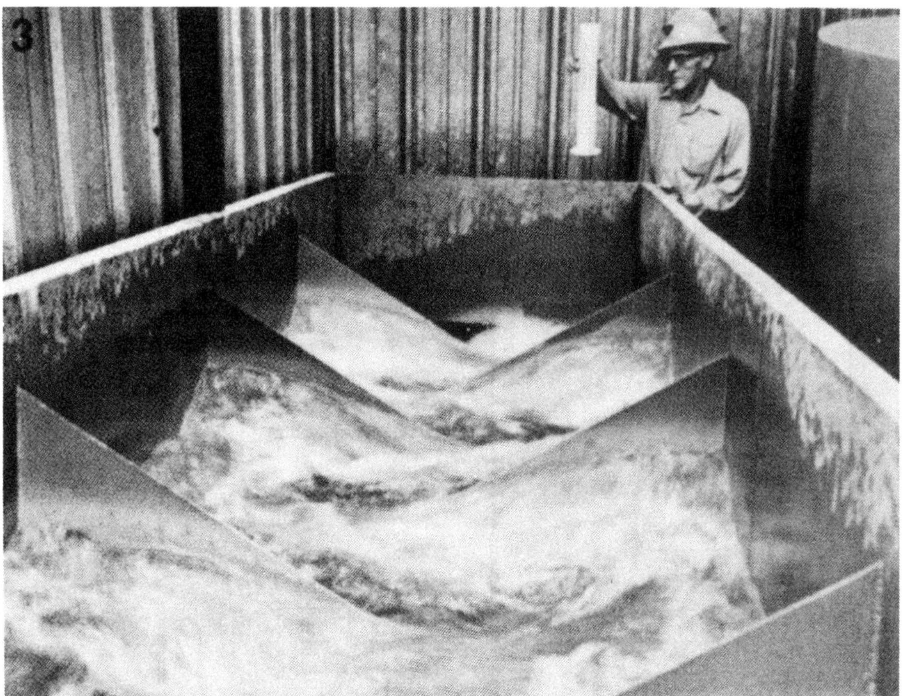

Figure 5.31. Barium chloride water treatment plant for removal of radium from mine water at the Bill Smith Mine in Wyoming. (Courtesy Kerr-McGee Corp.)

environment, they would raise the local background radiation levels. The main hazard to be controlled is radon gas release. Control of liquid effluents and mill tail leaching is also important.

For the above reasons, care is required to design and build mill-tailing facilities and to stabilize them. Particular attention is required in the construction of mill-tailing dams, which sometimes failed in the past. Although these past failures have at times involved large quantities of material, the radiological consequences have been relatively small. Nevertheless, standards (NRC Regulatory Guide 3.11 and the Generic Environmental Impact Statement on Uranium Production) are now strictly enforced for these facilities. The management of today's active tailing sites has been improved. Following the cessation of milling operations, tailings management provides for adequate stabilization of the tailings against long-term erosion and minimizes the leaching of radioactive solids and the diffusion of ^{222}Rn gas. Stabilization costs about \$10.30/kg of U_3O_8 produced, which translates to about 0.1 mil/kWh in the price of electricity.

Airborne Emission Control

Radioactive emissions during operations are effectively limited by the EPA's Uranium Fuel Cycle Standard (40CFR190) which limits annual dose commitments to offsite individuals, excluding contributions from radon and its daughters, to 25 mrems. Since NRC has responsibility for implementing this standard, emphasis is on identifying steps to control particulate emissions so this standard is met.

The major airborne control options available are:

1. Water cover, sprinkling, and chemical sprays to control diffuse sources of dust such as the tailings, roads, and ore storage areas.
2. Devices for wind shielding and dust collecting hoods such as may be applied in ore storage, handling, and crushing areas.
3. Stack controls including wet scrubbers and dry filters.
4. Process modifications such as wet grinding of ore which can eliminate dry crushing of ore, and elimination of yellowcake-drying operations by shipping product as a moist cake or slurry.

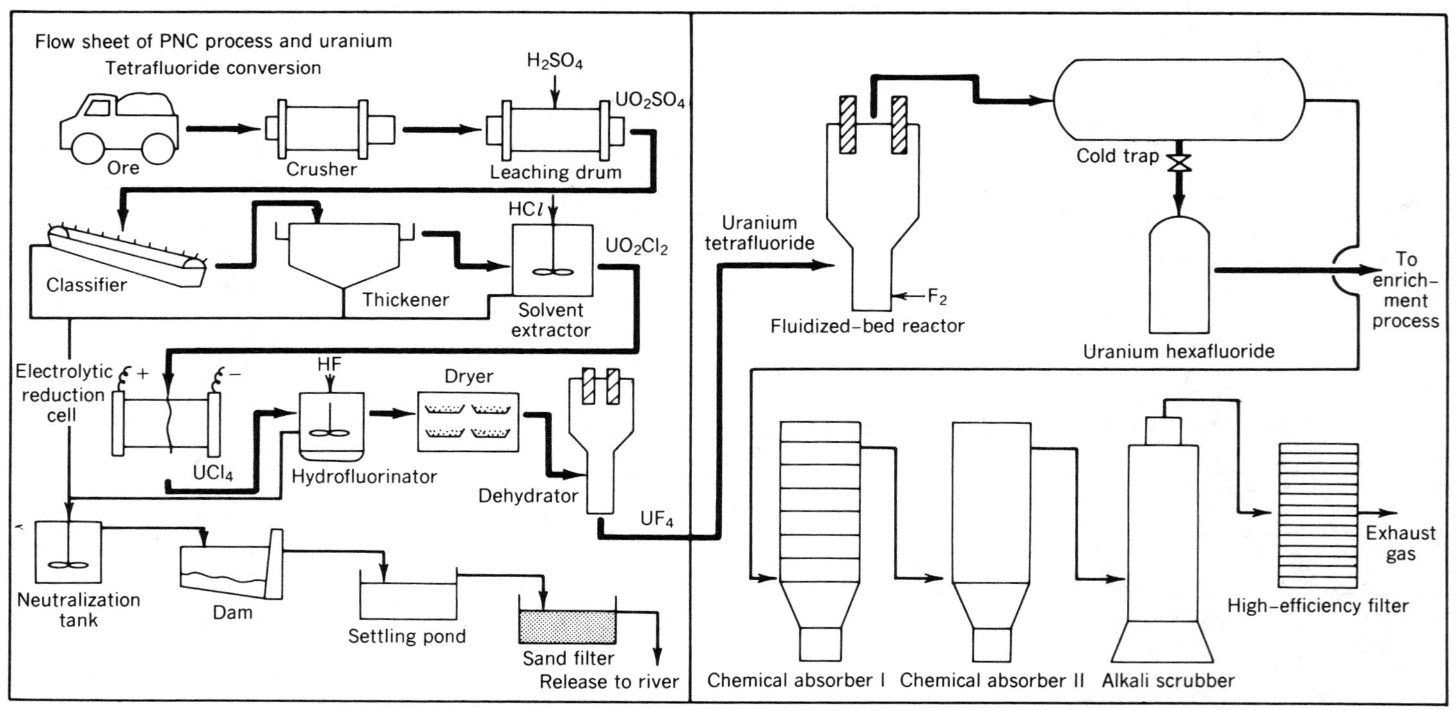

Figure 5.32. The Power Reactor and Nuclear Fuel Development Corporation (PNC) of Japan has a pilot plant for uranium processing and conversion to UF_6 at the Ningyo Toge Mine. The integrated uranium processing developed by PNC is more advantageous than other processes: uranium hexafluoride (UF_6) can be obtained directly from the ore. (From PNC.)

Table 5.10. Rio Tinto Zinc Extraction Process for Uranium Ore

1. Crush ore to less than 14-mm diameter.
2. Crush ore to a fine sand suspended in water.
3. Place mixture in leaching/oxidizing tanks where it is oxidized with MnO_2 and dissolved by H_2SO_4.
4. Separate sand/slime in cyclones, sand goes to tailing pond.
5. Pass pregnant solution through ion-exchange resin.
6. Remove resin for treatment in elution columns, where a strong acid will remove uranium from resin beads.
7. Mix acid elute with organic solvent, which takes up uranium component.
8. Mix with neutral aqueous ammonium sulfate solution $(NH_4)_2SO_4$, releasing acid for return to elution column.
9. Pass the resulting uranium solution to precipitation stage where it is mixed with NH_3 gas to produce ammonium diuranate $(NH_4)_2U_2O_7$.
10. Recover ammonium diuranate on a rotating drum filter.
11. Calcine to drive off ammonium, leaving UO_2.

In general, methods used to suppress surface dusting during operation will suppress radon emissions. Saturation of the pile with tailings solution will be most effective in radon control. The effect of superficial wetting or chemical stabilization on radon release is less certain.

Uranium Purification

After ore processing, the concentrate is purified prior to being enriched; very pure feed is required for the enrichment plants. Two commercial processes are available; one is based on solvent extraction of uranyl nitrate ("wet route"), the other on fluoride volatility ("dry route"). Either can be used to produce uranium pure enough to meet the enrichment feed specifications. The wet route is today more economical for the production of UF_6 needed for reactors. The sequence of operations follows some or all of the steps shown in Figure 5.33, in which uranium ore concentrates are first purified by solvent extraction and then converted to the materials of principal practical importance, uranium dioxide or uranium hexafluoride. In the dry route, currently used only in Allied Chemical's uranium refinery, the sequence of process operations is reversed, with conversion to UF_6 preceding purification, and with UF_6 as the sole purified product. The dry route's main advantage is that any accidental chemical contamination occurring in the production cycle can be removed in the final production stage by distillation. A listing of uranium refineries is given in Table 5.12. Many of these refineries are located within a few miles of the uranium enrichment plants.

The solvent extraction method works on uranyl nitrate $[UO_2(NO_3)_2]$ in aqueous and organic solutions. It is quite similar to the Purex process used in reprocessing used fuel (see Chapter 14 for a more detailed description of the process). For complete purification, countercurrent extraction of the immiscible aqueous and organic streams is required. The solvent extraction process steps are given in Figure 5.34 and Table 5.13. As received by the refinery, uranium ore concentrates usually consist of uranium oxide, or sodium or ammonium diuranate. These concentrates still contain appreciable amounts of elements other than uranium and some of uranium's radioactive decay products present in the original uranium ore, such as radium and radon. The organic solvent chosen

Table 5.11. Summary of Fatality, Serious Case, and Lost Work-Day Rates for Operation and Maintenance for Production of Electricity from Uranium

	Per 100 Person-yr		
	Fatalities	Serious Cases	Lost Work Days
Mining—Underground	0.11	5.8	350
Open pit	0.06	2.0	140
Milling	0.013	1.8	48
Conversion	0.014	2.4	21
Enrichment—Gaseous diffusion	0.0023	0.13	25
Gas centrifugation	0.0023	0.13	25
Fuel fabrication	0.0034	0.55	13

Source: From H. Hoy et al., *Trans. Am. Nuclear Society* **41**, 46 (1982).

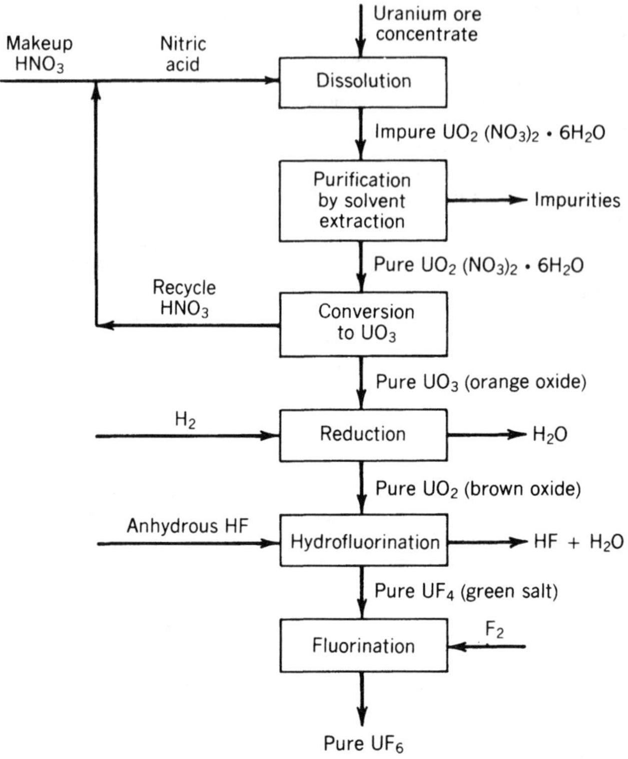

Figure 5.33. Steps in conventional uranium refining processing. (Adapted from M. Benedict et al., *Nuclear Chemical Engineering*, 2nd ed., McGraw-Hill, New York, 1981.)

is tributyl phosphate (TBP). Uranium ions are carried from the aqueous solution to the organic one, according to the formula

$$UO_2^{2+} + 2NO_3^- + 2TBP \leftrightarrow UO_2(NO_3)_2\,(TBP)_2$$

while impurities remain behind in the aqueous nitric acid solution. The TBP is relatively viscous; therefore, it is usually diluted to 30–40% concentration with an inert hydrocarbon, such as kerosene or dodecane. Other organic solutions such as butex or hexone could be used, but TBP is more stable than butex, and cheaper than hexone, while giving better separation than either. The impurities are "scrubbed" out of the extraction column bottom in the aqueous stream; the uranium, carried in the organic solution, goes to a stripping column, where uranium is removed

Table 5.12. Worldwide Uranium Refineries

Plant Owner	Location	Product[a]
Kerr-McGee	Gore, OK	UF_4, UF_6, UO_2
Allied Chemical	Metropolis, IL	UF_6
DOE	Fernald, OH; Paducah, OH [b]	UF_6
DOE	Portsmouth, OH	UF_6
Eldorado Nuclear	Port Hope, Canada	UF_4, UF_6, UO_2
British Nuclear Fuels	Springfields, United Kingdom	UF_6, metal
Comurhex	Malvesi, France; Pierrelatte, France [b]	UF_6, metal

[a]Principal feed for most plants is ore concentrate.
[b]Plants work in tandem.

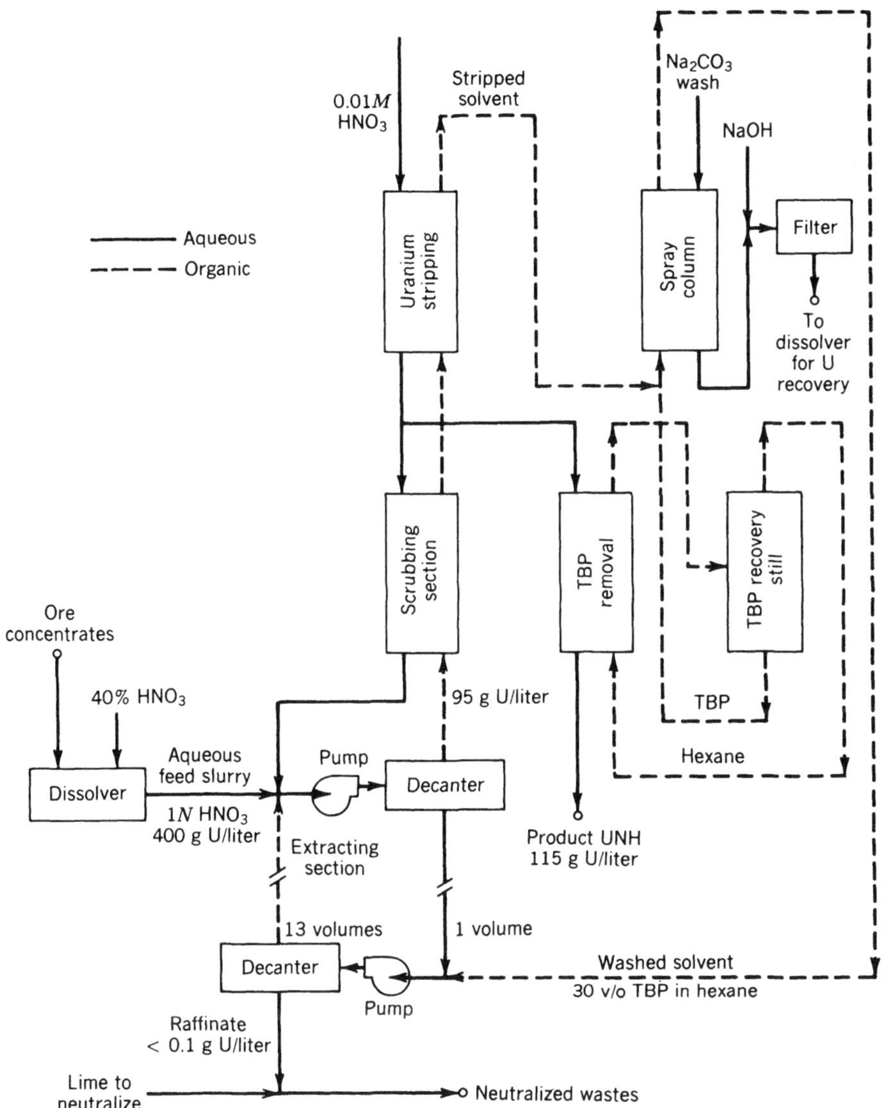

Figure 5.34. Purification of uranium ore concentrates by solvent extraction with TBP. (From M. Benedict et al., *Nuclear Chemical Engineering*, 2nd ed., McGraw-Hill, New York, 1981.)

Table 5.13. Solvent Extraction Process for the Purification of Uranium Concentrate

1. Grind finely the uranium concentrate.
2. Digest the concentrate with nitric acid (HNO_3), in which the uranium passes into aqueous solution in the form of nitrate.
3. Feed resulting slurry (unfiltered) to top of extraction column, where TBP (tributyl phosphate) flows in opposite direction (upward).
4. Scrub solution with dilute nitric acid to reduce impurities.
5. Feed solution to a "stripping column" where water is used to back extract U^{2+} into aqueous solution.
6. Evaporate solution until it roughly corresponds to uranyl nitrate hexahydrate, $UO_2(NO_3)_2{\cdot}6H_2O$, known as UNH.

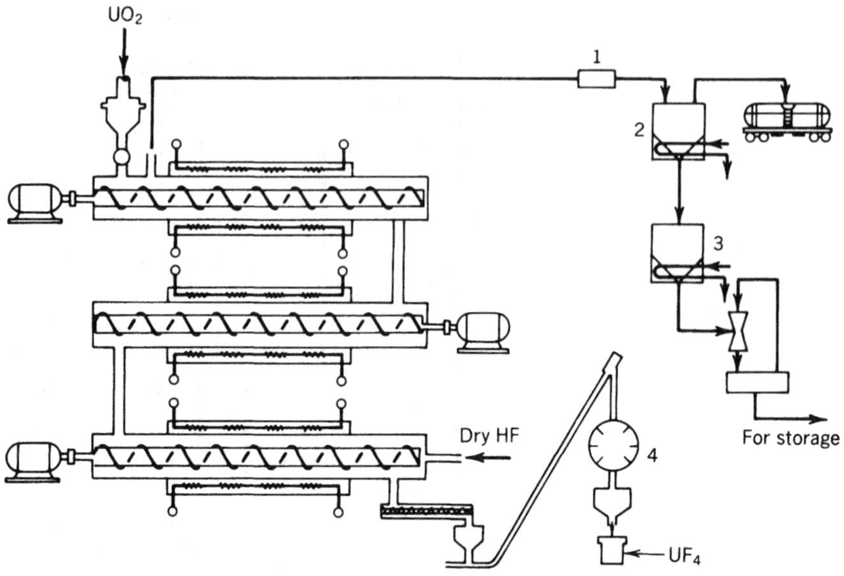

Figure 5.35. Diagram of hydrofluorination unit. UO_2 for fluorination enters the reactor in a horizontal worm feeder from an intermediate bin. The reactor consists of horizontal tubes of cast Inconel, whereby the reaction tubes are placed on top of one another. The reactors are heated by electrical resistance furnaces. The top reactor has four temperature zones each being of a lower temperature than the zone following it. A temperature gradient at the beginning and end of the fluorination is necessary to prevent sintering of the product and adhesion to the walls of the reactor which can lead to disturbance of the transport mechanism. 1—filter; 2—condenser for 70% hydrofluoric acid; 3—condenser for dry HF; 4—mixer. (From V. S. Yemel'Yanov and A. I. Yevstyukhin, *The Metallurgy of Nuclear Fuel,* Pergamon Press, New York, 1969.)

from the organic solvent by dilute nitric acid. This is then evaporated until a compound, uranyl nitrate hexahydrate (also called UNH), is formed. This compound is the intermediate product from which UO_2 (or sometimes uranium metal) is produced. It has the chemical form $UO_2(NO_3)_2{\cdot}6H_2O$.

When UO_2 is desired as the final product, the concentrated aqueous solution of uranyl nitrate is then heated to 540°C in a denitrator. This decomposes the nitrate and removes the excess water, forming uranic oxide, UO_3, also known as orange oxide because of its color.† The UO_3 is then reduced with H_2 gas in a fluidized bed at about 600°C. The product is pure UO_2, used for fabrication of (unenriched) fuel elements. The UO_2 is referred to as brown oxide, again because of its color.

When enriched fuel is required, the brown oxide is converted to UF_6, via the fluoride volatility process. In this process, UO_2 goes through two successive hydrofluorination fluidized-bed reactors where it is contacted with (anhydrous) hydrogen fluoride (HF).‡ The first bed operates at about 500°C, the second is somewhat higher at about 600°C. The reaction,

$$UO_2 + 4HF \rightarrow 2H_2O + UF_4$$

results in a nonvolatile solid, called green salt (Figure 5.35). This is further reacted with fluorine gas at about 400°C to produce uranium hexafluoride,§

†An alternate procedure is to treat the uranyl nitrate with ammonium to produce ADU, which is then dried and calcined to produce UO_3.

‡A new process used in France starts with UO_3. The reduction and hydrofluorination to UF_4 is carried out in the same "flowering bed" furnace. Improved fluidization is obtained by mixing UF_6 with CaF_2 and diluting the fluorine with nitrogen.

§UF_6 is a colorless crystalline solid under normal temperatures and pressures. Its density is 5.06 g/cm^3. It sublimes to a gas at 56.5°C, and has a triple point (i.e., where gas, liquid, and solid phase coexist) at 64.05°C and 1.5 bar. UF_6 is remarkable for its high chemical activity, due to the fact that it can decompose into UF_4 and F_2.

$$UF_4 + F_2 \rightarrow UF_6$$

which is condensed and collected as a solid at −15°C (Figure 5.36). UF_6 production always starts with UF_4 to cut down fluorine consumption. Uranium hexafluoride can be further purified by fractional distillation (b.p. 56.4°C) at pressures of 4–7 atm. This final step removes impurities, principally molybdenum and vanadium. The UF_6 product meets DOE's specifications for impurities allowable in uranium hexafluoride delivered for enrichment in the DOE's separation plants. The product is then ready for the enrichment process (see Chapter 6), and is usually stored in a solid form in cylinders holding 14 t each. These cylinders are usually made of monel, a high-nickel-based alloy, to resist the fluorine compound's corrosive effects.

About 15,000 t/yr of UF_6 is required by a gaseous diffusion enrichment plant with a 24,000,000 SWU/yr capacity.† This much UF_6 production calls for separate plants to produce the 7500 t/yr of HF and 2300 t/yr of fluorine used in the process. It is common for the UF_6 plants to be sited adjacent to the enrichment plants to cut down on transportation and improve the operation's safety. The UF_6 facility near Barnwell, South Carolina is pictured in Figure 5.37.

The projected need for UF_6 conversion is presented in Figure 5.38 for various growth scenarios. As seen from this figure, the need in 1990 will be between 30,000 and 40,000 t of UF_6 compared to 1985 requirements of about 20,000 t. The conversion value (1983) is about \$1.20/lb of U as UF_6. This is the market transaction price used among utilities for trading. The estimated cost is \$24 million/yr to construct and operate a new 10,000 t of U per year conversion facility. Capital and operating costs for such a facility are given in Table 5.14. Various other estimates range from \$1.90 to \$2.70/lb for uranium conversion costs for a new plant constructed in 1984.

Safety During the Conversion Process

The toxicity of natural uranium is not so much radiological as chemical. Its chemical toxicity is similar to lead. A quite different health hazard is presented by uranium hexafluoride.

UF_6 is a highly reactive substance. A UF_6 release to the environment is the main concern; it reacts with moisture in the air to form hydrofluoric acid (HF) and uranyl fluoride (UO_2F_2), both of which are toxic. The UF_6 gas density and likely high concentration levels make atmosphere dispersion estimates difficult but any release is likely to be highly localized. A few accidents have already occurred, including one in France where 7 tons of UF_6 were released in 12 min but with low off-site consequences. The principal risk seems to be to the employees at the conversion plant itself.

UF_6 facilities operate under negative pressure. This increases safety by virtually eliminating leakage of hexafluoride. Uranium and fluorine concentrations in the off-gases are constantly monitored, and are neutralized with a solution of potassium carbonate before release to the environment. To ensure safe UF_6 transportation to the enrichment plant, all shipping containers are checked for pressure tightness.

Reconversion of UF_6 to UO_2

After enrichment (covered in Chapter 6), the UF_6 is converted back to UO_2 to prepare it for fuel fabrication. There are three basic methods for doing this on an industrial scale:

1. AUC method (Ammonium Uranyl Carbonate).
2. ADU method (Ammonium DiUranate).
3. IDR method (Integrated Dry Route).

These processes are summarized in Table 5.15. Usually the UO_2 powder is stabilized and made chemically passive by slight oxidation to $UO_{2.1}$. Finally, the product UO_2 is pulverized. It is now ready for the fuel fabrication step.

5.3. PLUTONIUM

Plutonium, a man-made element, occurs only in trace amounts in nature. It was probably first produced in 1940, when University of California chemists irradiated uranium with deuterium. Others also claim its discovery, but its existence was certain by February 1941. Shortly, after its discovery, plutonium was found to undergo fission with thermal neutrons. This led to tremendous efforts to produce it in large quantities for military purposes. Plutonium, however, is central to the use of nuclear fission for producing electricity and has other uses in industry and medicine. All power reactors fueled by uranium create plutonium internally as an inevitable part of their energy

†SWU = Separative Work Unit.

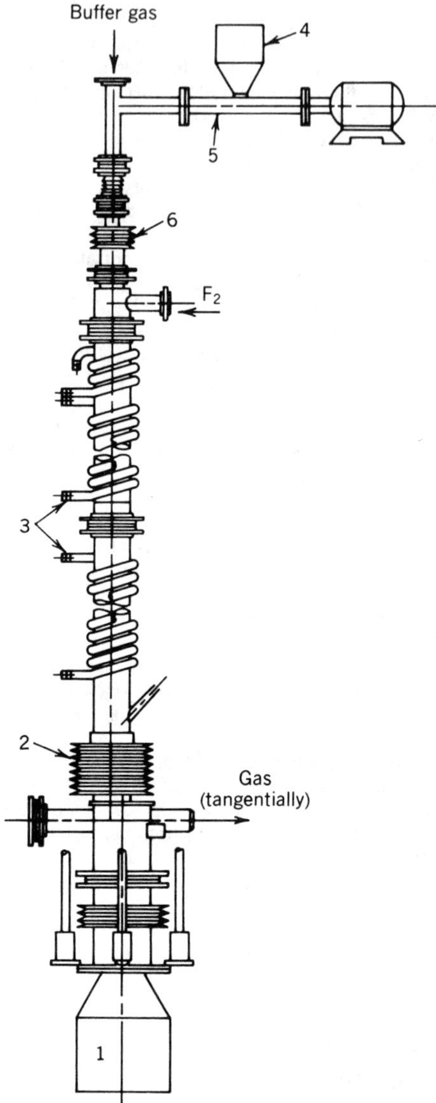

Figure 5.36. Diagram of the apparatus for fluorinating UF_4 to UF_6. The apparatus for fluorination is a Monel metal cylinder. Fluorine, carefully heated to 360–400°C, is fed into the reactor. The temperature of the walls of the apparatus is kept between 330 and 540°C by means of a cooler. The gaseous fluorination product, containing around 75% UF_6, is passed through water-cooled tubes and two cyclones, in which solid particles are collected. The gas is then fed into a condenser and cooled to −15°C. Here the gaseous UF_6 passes into the solid state. 1—ash residue receiver; 2—sylphon bellows; 3—cooling coils; 4—feed bin; 5—feeder worms; 6—vibration absorber. (From V. S. Yemel'Yanov and A. I. Yevstyukhin, *The Metallurgy of Nuclear Fuel*, Pergamon Press, New York, 1969.)

Figure 5.37. (*a*) UF_6 facility near Barnwell, South Carolina. (Courtesy Allied Chemical Corp.) (*b*) Gaseous fluorine generation. (Courtesy Allied Chemical Corp.)

(a)

(b)

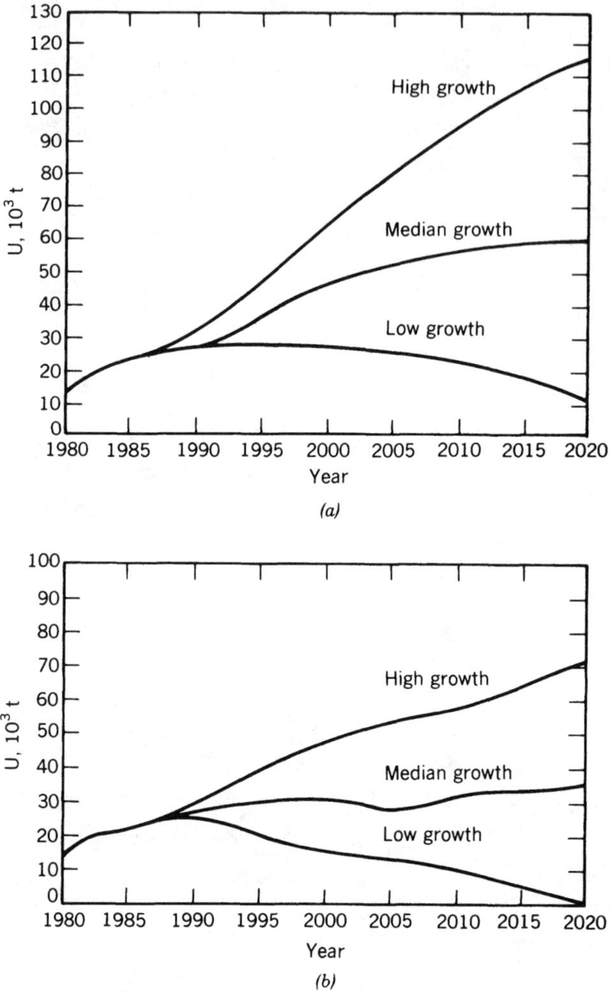

Figure 5.38. Projected need for UF_6 conversion for various growth scenarios. (*a*) For the once-through cycle. (*b*) For thermal recycle. (From NUREG/CR-1041.)

Table 5.14. Capital and Operating Costs for a 10,000 t of Uranium per Year Conversion Plant[a]

Expenditures	10^6 1979 Dollars
Capital cost	85.9
Operating costs	
Labor	6.9/yr
Supplies	14.5/yr
G&A	0.8/yr
Sampling and shipping	1.9/yr
Total operating costs	24.1/yr

Source: Courtesy of the U.S. Nuclear Regulatory Commission (Report No. NUREG/CR-1041, Dec. 1979).

[a]Basis: 10,000 t of uranium per year; capacity factor: 70%; lead time: 5 yr.

Table 5.15. Processes for the Conversion of UF_6 to UO_2

AUC Process (Ammonium Uranyl Carbonate)[a]

1. Evaporate UF_6 with steam.
2. Precipitate AUC by injecting UF_6, CO_2, and NH_3 as gas into demineralized water.
3. Adjust temperature and pH so that AUC forms as yellow crystals.
4. Filter and remove water.
5. Wash with ammonium carbonate and methyl alcohol.
6. Calcine and reduce to UO_2 in a carrier gas atmosphere of H_2 and superheated steam.

ADU Process (Ammonium Diuranate)[b]

1. Hydrolyze UF_6 with steam to UO_2F_2.
2. Further hydrolyze with a dilute solution of NH_3 to form a precipitate of ammonium diuranate.
3. Calcine to U_3O_8.
4. Filter, dry, and heat in a gas atmosphere of H_2 and steam to form UO_2.

IDR Process (Integrated Dry Route)

1. Process developed by British Nuclear Fuels, Ltd. (BNFL).
2. Roast UF_6 in a 40-cm diameter kiln in presence of steam and H_2.
3. Produces continuous stream of UO_2.

[a]Ammonium uranylcarbonate = $(NH_4)_4\,[UO_2(CO_3)_3]$.
[b]Ammonium diuranate = $(NH_4)U_2O_7$.

production. Some of the plutonium produced in the reactor is fissioned in place, producing about one-third of the heat generated, and to this extent we are already using plutonium as a fuel. However, about half of the plutonium remains in the spent fuel.

Subsequent to its discovery, 16 plutonium isotopes have been produced, all radioactive. The most important plutonium isotope as a nuclear fuel is ^{239}Pu, although ^{240}Pu, ^{241}Pu, and ^{242}Pu are usually present. The properties of these isotopes are given in Table 5.16.

The property of primary interest for ^{239}Pu in reactor engineering is its neutron production during fission. As seen in Table 5.16, for ^{239}Pu it is around 2, a value high enough so that breeding of nuclear fuel is practical. In a so-called breeder reactor, zones of fissile plutonium are interspersed with zones of fertile ^{238}U. In such an arrangement, neutrons leaking from the fissile zones are used to breed more plutonium in the fertile one. To a lesser extent, this happens in a LWR fuel element: by the end of a normal fuel cycle, enough ^{238}U has been converted to ^{239}Pu that roughly 50% of the fissions (i.e., power) are occurring in the plutonium. The method by which the plutonium isotopes are produced in a reactor is shown in Figure 5.39. Thus, the main way of producing plutonium is by the chemical reprocessing of ^{238}U that has been irradiated in a reactor.

Table 5.16. Nuclear Properties of Plutonium Isotopes

		Thermal Neutron Data[a]					
Isotope	Half-Life Period	σ_a	σ_f	σ_c	α	η	ν
^{238}Pu	90 yr	—	—	—	—	—	—
^{239}Pu	24,300 yr	1.022	731	291	0.399	2.070	2.9
^{240}Pu	6,600 yr	350	4	346	86.5	0.034	3
^{241}Pu	13 yr	1.336	971	365	0.376	2.200	3
^{242}Pu	9×10^5 yr	22.9	—	22.9	—	—	—
^{243}Pu	5 hr	100	—	—	—	—	—

Source: Adapted from V. S. Yemel'Yanov and A. I. Yevstyukhin, *The Metallurgy of Nuclear Fuel,* Pergamon Press, New York, 1969.

[a]σ_a, σ_f, and σ_c are the appropriate cross sections of absorption, fission, and capture without fission (barn); α = the ratio of the fission cross section to the capture cross section without fission; η = average numbers of neutrons formed by one disappearing atom of plutonium; ν = average number of neutrons liberated by one act of fission.

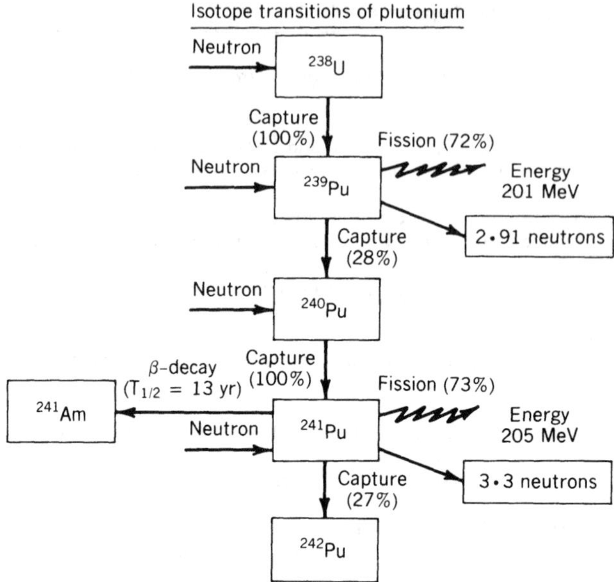

Figure 5.39. Diagram of the production and decay of ^{239}Pu.

An advantage of plutonium over ^{235}U is that it can be separated chemically to produce an acceptable reactor fuel. For most reactor purposes, isotopically pure ^{239}Pu is not required, as long as the fissile plutonium isotopes (^{239}Pu and ^{242}Pu) make up about 80% of the fuel. Therefore, unlike uranium, isotopic enrichment is not required. In fact, the presence of the isotopes ^{240}Pu and ^{242}Pu are advantageous because they render the material unfit for military purposes. Reactor-grade plutonium is roughly 70% ^{239}Pu and 20% ^{240}Pu, whereas weapons-grade plutonium is roughly 93% and 7%, respectively. Table 5.17 describes some typical isotopic mixtures. Generally speaking, the longer the fuel is utilized in the reactor, the higher the proportion of ^{240}Pu produced and the less suitable the plutonium for weapons purposes. Nuclear proliferation and diversion of plutonium by terrorist groups is therefore less of a concern for reactor-grade plutonium.

A disadvantage of plutonium fuel is its toxicity. Therefore, special handling procedures, such as glove boxes and remote fabrication, are required. For example, the maximum permissible air concentrations of uranium and beryllium are about the same, but plutonium's is about one million times lower. This toxicity concern would not be a particularly great handicap on a large production scale where automatic fabrication techniques would be used.

Table 5.17. Typical Isotopic Mixtures of Plutonium (%)

Plutonium Isotope	LWR Spent Fuel[a]	Pu Recycle Spent LWR Fuel[b]	LMFBR Fuel[b]	Weapons
238	2	3.4	1.07	—
239	61	43.6	70.4	93
240	24	26.0	23.4	7
241	10	15.9	5.1	—
242	3	11.1	—	—
g/Ci α	2.25	1.4	3.5	13.7

Source: Adapted from EPRI Report EA-43-SR.

[a]WASH-1327: *Generic Environmental Statement on Mixed-Oxide Fuel,* USAEC, Washington, D. C., November 1974.

[b]WASH-1535, Vol. 11, Section 4.3.: *LMFBR Program Environmental Statement,* USAEC, Washington, D. C.

Table 5.18. Structure of Plutonium Modifications

Modification	Temperature Interval, °C	Density, g/cm^3	Type of Lattice
α	From − 186 to + 119	19.816 (25°C)	Simple monoclinic
β	119–218	17.82 (133°C)	Body centred monoclinic
γ	218–310	17.14 (235°C)	Face centred orthorhombic
δ	310–450	15.92 (320°C)	Face centred cubic
η	450–472	16.0	Face centred tetragonal
ε	472–640	16.48	Body centred cubic

Source: Adapted from V. S. Yemel'Yanov and A. I. Yevstyukhin, *The Metallurgy of Nuclear Fuel,* Pergamon Press, New York, 1969.

Plutonium Properties

Plutonium is a silvery-white metal, atomic number 94 in the actinide series. It has a melting point of 640°C and boiling point of 3227°C. It has six allotropes (Table 5.18) that complicate its metallurgical properties. From this table, it can be inferred that plutonium alloys are metastable and that microsegregation of alloying elements can lead to phase instabilities. Like uranium metal, the large number of anisotropic phases gives metallic plutonium dimensional problems. Therefore, the oxide form (PuO_2) is preferred for reactor fuel use because of its mechanical uniformity with temperature. In fact, the mechanical properties of PuO_2 are quite compatible with UO_2, as seen in Figure 5.40. As a result, reactor fuels can easily use mixtures of uranium and plutonium oxide. Such fuels are referred to as Mixed Oxides (MOX).

The metallurgical properties of plutonium were also found to be incredibly sensitive to impurities. It differs considerably from uranium in many respects, including its chemical activity and its affinity for hydrogen at room temperature. Like uranium, it is self-heating, and also pyrophoric, igniting readily in air to form PuO_2, a yellowish substance. Perhaps the most important compound

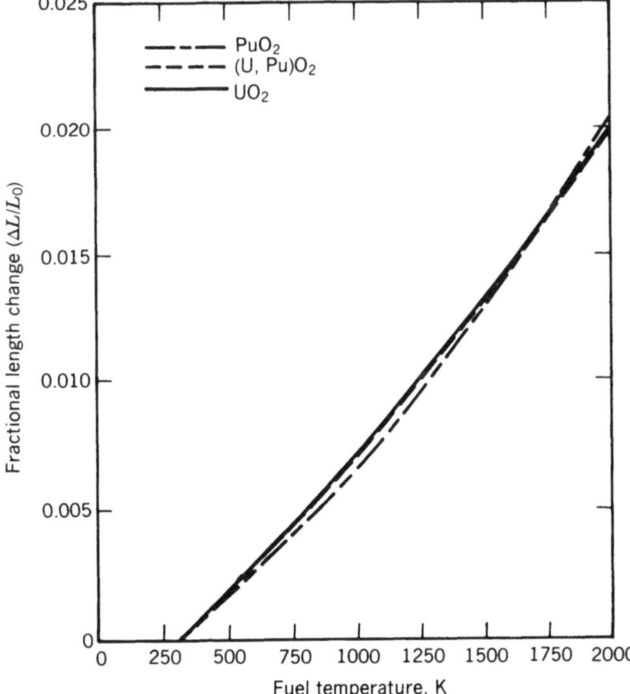

Figure 5.40. Comparison of changes in length versus temperature for PuO_2, MOX, and UO_2. (From MATPRO.)

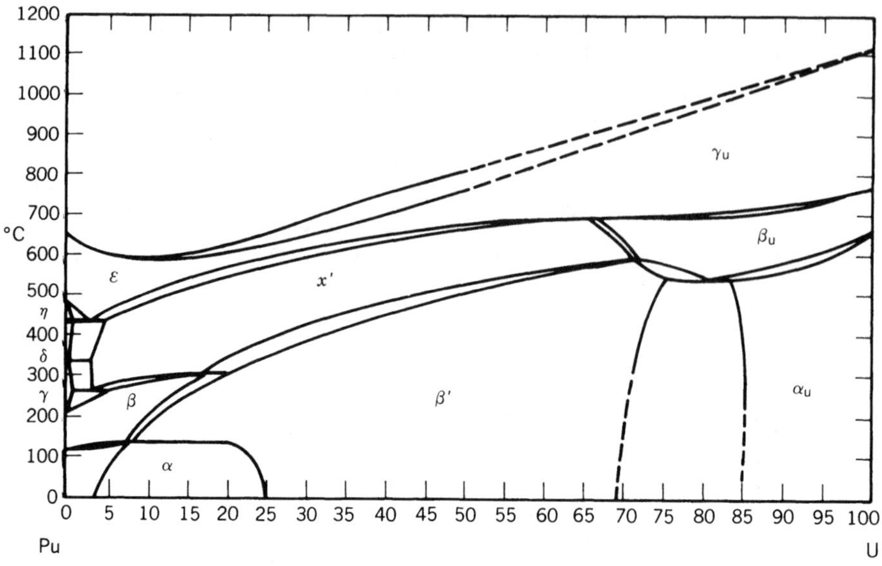

Figure 5.41. Uranium concentration (at.%).

is plutonium dioxide (PuO_2), which is formed when plutonium metal is burned or when plutonium oxalate or peroxide is heated in a vacuum. PuO_2 has a green color and melts at about 2300°C. It can be dissolved in hot (200°C) concentrated phosphoric acid. Plutonium oxide is usually produced by calcining the oxalate at high temperatures (300 to 700°C), which causes much of the mass to be in particles about 1 μm in diameter. Larger particles may be separated out conveniently by allowing them to settle out in water and then skimming the fine particles from the top.

Another important chemical property is the precipitation of $Pu(OH)_4$, a bright-green hydroxide, when an aqueous solution of plutonium is contacted with ammonia. Plutonium forms compounds with all halides, the best known being PuF_3 and PuF_4, both highly insoluble in water and in acids. Most chemical processing is done in nitric acid solution, where the plutonium ion rapidly takes on valence 4. $Pu(NO_3)_4 \cdot 5H_2O$ is the best-known crystalline nitrate. The high α activity of the plutonium isotopes can lead to technical problems. For instance, alpha radiation will decompose PuF_6, evolving fluorine which can corrode process equipment.

Plutonium as a Fuel Material

For a number of reasons discussed in Chapter 7, metallic fuel is no longer used in commercial reactors, although such fuels have been tested in the past. Alloys of plutonium with various elements have been found to form stable intermetallic compounds. One such important compound is Pu-U, whose phase diagram is shown in Figure 5.41. As we have already seen, two particular problems with plutonium alloys are dimensional instability due to allotropic changes and swelling from the volumetric expansion needed to accommodate fission products. One alloy tried with some success is a "fissium" alloy. It consists of about 70 at.% plutonium, 10 at.% of an equilibrium concentration of fission products, and the balance a third element such as molybdenum to stabilize the mixture against phase transitions.

Plutonium oxide has greater commercial importance as a reactor fuel material than plutonium metal. Three stable oxides exist as shown in Table 5.19. Of these, PuO_2 is of most interest, because it forms a continuous series of solid solutions with UO_2, and tends to stabilize its atomic structure.

Table 5.19. Plutonium Oxides

Composition	Crystal Structure	Theoretical Density, g/cm^3
PuO_2	Face-centered cubic	11.46
α-Pu_2O_3	Body-centered cubic	10.2
β-Pu_2O_3	Tetragonal	11.47

Table 5.20. Dry Methods of Reprocessing Spent Fuel

Process	Method	Temperature. °C
Fractional distillation of fluorides	Distillation of UF_6 from irradiated fuel, dissolved in BrF_6	~100
Extraction by liquid metals	Extraction of Pu from liquid uranium by molten silver or magnesium	~1200
Extraction by fused salts	Extraction of Pu from liquid uranium by fused UF_4 with additives of alkali metal fluorides	~1225
Vacuum sublimation	Vacuum distillation of Pu from the molten metal	1500–1800
Oxidizing slag formation	Separation of fission products from uranium in the form of an oxide slag	~1200
Zone melting	Separation of fission products by zone melting at end of billet	1500–1200
Electrolytic refining	Anode of irradiated uranium, electrolyte melt $CaCl_2$-UF_4 (purified uranium deposited at cathode)	900–1050

Source: Adapted from V. S. Yemel'Yanov and A. I. Yevstyukhin, *The Metallurgy of Nuclear Fuel,* Pergamon Press, New York, 1969.

The other features that make PuO_2 useful for reactor fuel are high melting point (above 2300°C), irradiation stability, compatibility with water and other reactor coolants, and ease of preparation. The theoretical density of PuO_2 is 11.5 g/cm^3, although when fabricated for reactor use, a somewhat lower density is deliberately achieved in order to tailor the properties of the fuel. When used in reactors, PuO_2 is either mechanically mixed with UO_2 powder, or a uranium–plutonium compound is coprecipitated from a nitrate solution. This is then calcined to form an oxide powder. Chapter 7 further discusses the methods of fuel fabrication.

Recovery and Purification of Plutonium

Plutonium's only source is its recovery by reprocessing irradiated fuel. The technical description of the process is postponed to Chapter 14. For historical reference, we include here Table 5.20, which lists a number of dry processes studied for plutonium recovery. For various reasons, these "dry" methods are not as commercially attractive as the "wet" ones. Wet and dry refer to whether the process involves an aqueous solution. The almost universal way of recovering plutonium is by the aqueous Purex process.

The isotopic content of the plutonium recovered depends on the fuel's cumulative irradiation. Typical ratios of the isotopes for various irradiations in an LWR are shown in Figure 5.42. The amount of recoverable plutonium is given in Table 5.21. These illustrations show that (a) the ^{239}Pu concentration peaks around fuel exposures of 30,000 MWd/t, (b) the ^{240}Pu (and higher plutonium isotopes) continue to build up with exposure, and (c) the ratio of ^{239}Pu to ^{240}Pu is highest with low exposures. The last is important in understanding the proliferation issue: since weapons require plutonium with a low ^{240}Pu ratio military production reactors discharge fuel much earlier than a commercial reactor.

Complete purification of plutonium is quite important. This is not so much from fuel requirements, as it is for safety. Any radioactive fission products that remain in the plutonium after reprocessing become a handling hazard due to the radiation they give off. Hydrometallurgical processes in aqueous solutions (e.g., Purex process) are capable of producing the high purity needed.

Pu Safety

In fuel reprocessing plants, plutonium compounds recovered from spent uranium fuel are converted into plutonium oxide. During the conversion process, minute particles of plutonium oxide could be carried by the gases given off. All off-gases are therefore passed through several High-Efficiency Particulate Air (HEPA) filters in series.

In a mixed-oxide fuel fabrication plant, PuO_2 is ground into a fine powder with a ball mill and blended with UO_2 powder. The mixture is then granulated and pressed into a pellet, which is sintered, ground to accurate dimensions, inspected, and loaded into fuel rods. Considerable dusting occurs during some of these operations. Most operations are carried out in air-tight glove boxes.

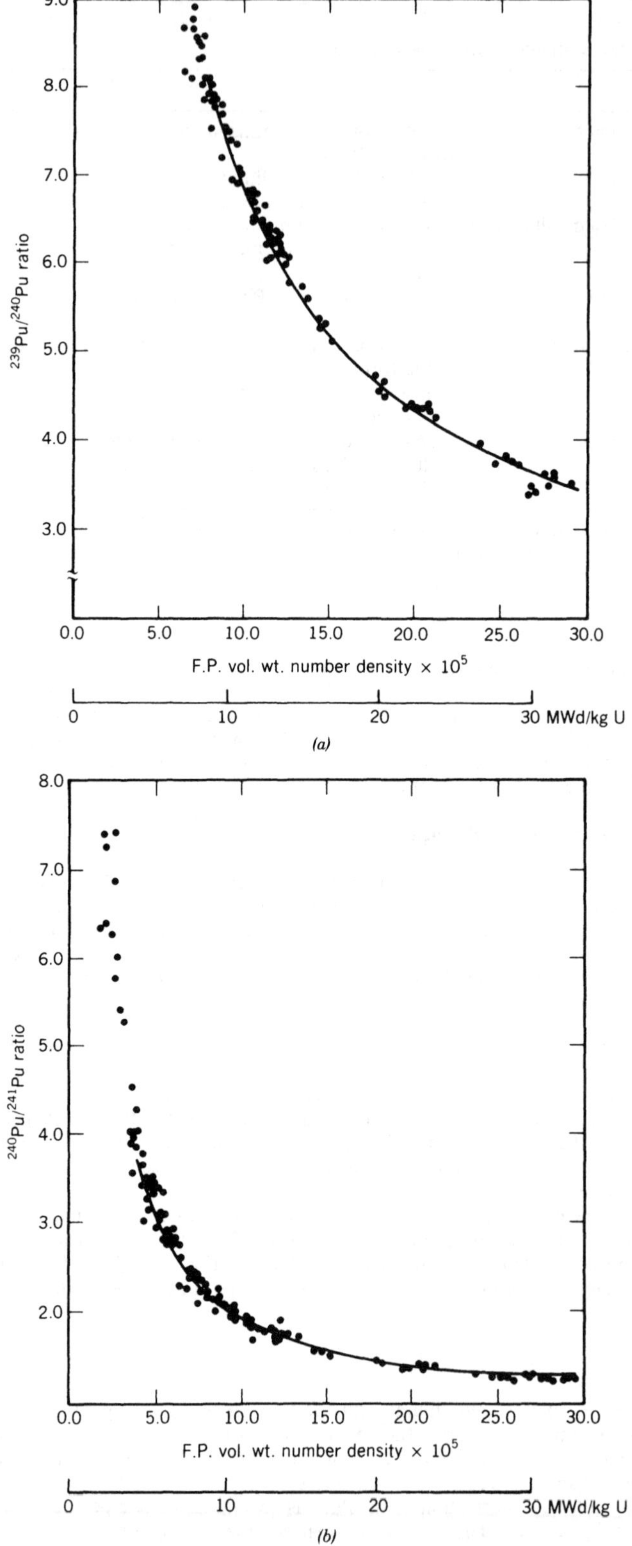

Figure 5.42. (*a*) The isotopic ratio $^{239}Pu/^{240}Pu$. (*b*) The isotopic ratio $^{240}Pu/^{241}Pu$.

Table 5.21. Plutonium Buildup in a PWR

	wt % Pu in Total Heavy Metal	
Fuel Exposure, MWd/T	^{239}Pu	^{240}Pu
100	0.0057	0.000013
1,000	0.054	0.0012
2,000	0.103	0.0044
3,000	0.147	0.0095
10,000	0.41	0.062
30,000	0.57	0.20
50,000	0.46	0.30

Air-cleaning systems, which usually include the HEPA filters, are designed to preclude the discharge of significant quantities of plutonium dust into the environment under both normal and accident conditions. Using coprecipitation to fabricate mixed uranium plutonium oxides considerably reduces the amount of dust involved in fuel fabrication.

Because of the high specific gravity, particles larger than 10 μm in diameter rapidly settle out by gravitation in air. However, gravitation has little effect on particles less than 5 μm in diameter—that is, those in the respirable range. HEPA filters effectively limit the size of plutonium particles to well below 1 μm in diameter. Partly because the efficiencies of HEPAs are highest for very large and very small particles, those particles that do penetrate tend to be about 0.3 μm in diameter.

Regulatory Standards for Plutonium

10CFR20 gives the basic standards for radiation protection involving plutonium isotopes. These are reproduced in Table 5.22. The actual discharges from nuclear power reactors have been very much below the limits stated in this table. Because of this experience, the NRC adopted the ALARA guidelines and extended them to cover effluents from reprocessing and fuel fabrication facilities.

In 1975, EPA issued regulations (40CFR190) to protect the general public from unnecessary radiation exposure. These regulations require that the total quantity of radioactive materials entering the general environment from the entire fuel cycle, per gigawatt-year of electrical energy produced, shall contain less than 0.5 mCi combined of ^{239}Pu and other alpha-emitting transuranic radionuclides with half-lives greater than 1 yr.

5.4. THORIUM

Thorium, discovered in Norway in 1828 by Berzelius, was named after Thor, the god of war. It is the first element in the actinide series. Thorium has only one abundant naturally occurring isotope, ^{232}Th, which is radioactive and has a half-life of 1.3×10^{10} yr. A total of eight isotopes exist, but these are mostly transient in nature since they derive from various radioactive decay series. ^{232}Th does not fission, but is a fertile material. Upon irradiation it is converted to ^{233}U, which is fissionable. ^{232}Th plus a neutron yields ^{233}Th, which then goes to ^{233}U by two beta decays. Thorium–^{233}U are a fertile-fissile pair, much the same as ^{238}U–^{239}Pu. Thorium is a primary fuel for the HTGR and GCFR systems. In thermal neutron reactors, ^{233}U has an important advantage in

Table 5.22. Guidelines for Concentrations of Plutonium Isotopes at Boundaries of Restricted Areas, μCi/mliter

	Air		Water	
Pu Isotope	Soluble	Insoluble	Soluble	Insoluble
238	7×10^{-14}	1×10^{-12}	5×10^{-6}	3×10^{-5}
239	6×10^{-14}	1×10^{-12}	5×10^{-6}	3×10^{-5}
240	6×10^{-14}	1×10^{-12}	5×10^{-6}	3×10^{-5}
241	3×10^{-12}	1×10^{-9}	2×10^{-4}	1×10^{-3}
242	6×10^{-14}	1×10^{-12}	5×10^{-6}	3×10^{-5}
243	6×10^{-8}	8×10^{-8}	3×10^{-4}	3×10^{-4}
244	6×10^{-14}	1×10^{-12}	4×10^{-6}	1×10^{-5}

Source: 10CFR20, Appendix B, Table 2.

Table 5.23. Common Thorium Ores

Mineral	Description	Properties	Deposit Locations
Monazite	Rare-earth phosphate (Ce,La, ..., Th) PO_4 with less than 10% ThO_2 and up to 1% UO_2	Density 4.9 to 5.5; pale-yellow to red-brown in color; paramagnetic	Widely distributed in alluvial and marine deposits
Thorite	$ThSiO_4$ with up to 77% ThO_2 and many other rare-earth minerals; often found with uranium and hematite	Density 4 to 6.7; orange-yellow to black in color	Found in vein deposits and alkaline igneous rocks
Thorianite	$(Th,U)O_2$ contains 45 to 90% ThO_2 and up to 50% UO_2	Density 8.9 to 9.9; dark-gray to black	Less abundant than monazite or thorite, it is often associated with granite and syenite

that the number of neutrons it produces per absorbed neutron (2.29) is about 10% higher than for ^{235}U and ^{239}Pu. The long-term advantage of thorium as a fuel is that it is several times more abundant than uranium in the earth's crust. As natural uranium becomes scarce, the production of ^{233}U from thorium should be of greater interest.

Thoria (ThO_2) is the chemical form of interest in commercial reactors. It is usually crystalline, although amorphous thoria exists. It forms solid solutions with UO_2 and PuO_2 over the entire range of compositions. ThO_2 is obtained by calcining thorium hydroxide, or by the thermal decomposition of thorium nitrate or oxalate. It has a fluorite crystal structure, and density of 10.0 g/cm^3. These last two properties are important because they are similar to those of UO_2, as are its chemical and thermal properties. Although a thoria ceramic can be prepared by sintering (a special atmosphere is not required), the usual fuel form is the TRISO particle, described in chapter seven.

Thorium Resources and Recovery

Like uranium, thorium concentrates in granite-type formations, and tends to accumulate in residual fixed rocks. In certain conditions thorium can migrate in hydrothermal deposits, but since it is predominately in the valence +4 state, it does not exhibit the same oxidation/reduction behavior as uranium. Therefore, sedimentary deposits are a much less common source of thorium ore. Thorium deposits are almost always associated with the rare earth minerals or uranium in its +4 valence state. The most important thorium ores are monazite, thorite, and thorianite (see Table 5.23).

The principal thorium ore is monazite,† found abundantly in India and Brazil, and in less-rich deposits in the western United States. The recovery of monazite from these alluvial deposits is a fairly straightforward mining operation. More difficult is thorium processing and purification. The problem comes from the many rare-earth and other elements present in the ore. These are difficult to separate chemically.

The first step in thorium production is the concentration of the monazite ore. This is done by washing the ore, and then using an electromagnetic separator to take advantage of monazite's paramagnetic properties. The resulting product is usually 95% monazite or greater.

When the monazite concentrates are processed, the thorium compounds are first separated, and then the by-product uranium, phosphorus and rare-earth elements are recovered from the thorium. This latter step improves the economics of the operation. The recovery process consists of:

1. Stripping the monazite concentrate of thorium using a mineral acid.
2. Entering of the thorium compounds into solution.
3. Recovery of the phosphate.
4. Separating the thorium from the rare earths and uranium.

Monazite is chemically very inert. Although several process are available to recover thorium from monazite, the alkali method is usually employed. It is shown in Figure 5.43. The alkali most

†Monazite is often found in beach sands. Vein deposits are less common, but account for significant resources in the United States.

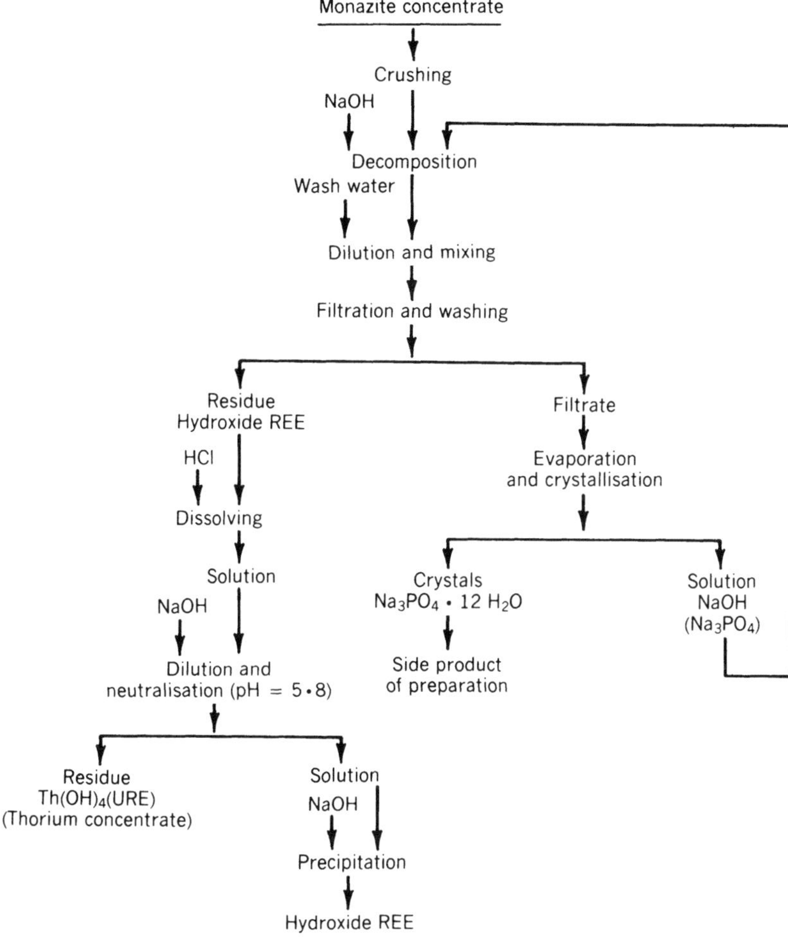

Figure 5.43. Flow sheet of the alkali method of treating monazite. (From V. S. Yemel'Yanov and A. I. Yevstyukhin, *The Metallurgy of Nuclear Fuel,* Pergamon Press, New York, 1969.)

used is sodium hydroxide, NaOH. The main advantage of the process is that sodium triphosphate, a valuable by-product, is obtained. The basic formula for this process is

$$Th_3(PO_4)_4 + 12\ NaOH \rightarrow 3\ Th(OH)_4 + 4\ Na_3PO_4$$

In addition, the resulting thorium and rare-earth hydroxides are highly soluble in HCl and other mineral acids, which facilitates production process and thorium separation from the other rare earths. When ammonium is used to neutralize the acid solution, thorium hydroxide precipitates out of solution at $3.5 \leq pH \leq 5.5$, while the rare-earth hydroxides do not start to precipitate until pH 6.2 The wet cake is reslurried in a water solution, filtered, and again reslurried to obtain a high degree of purity. The thorium concentrate is mostly $Th(OH)_4$, although some rare-earth elements usually still remain.

Thorium Purification

Several choices are also available for the final thorium purification, since the thorium concentrate is still too impure for reactor use. The rare-earth elements (Gd, Eu, etc.) that the concentrate usually contains are neutron absorbers that poison the chain reaction. Uranium in the concentrate is particularly objectionable since it would isotopically contaminate any ^{233}U produced during irradia-

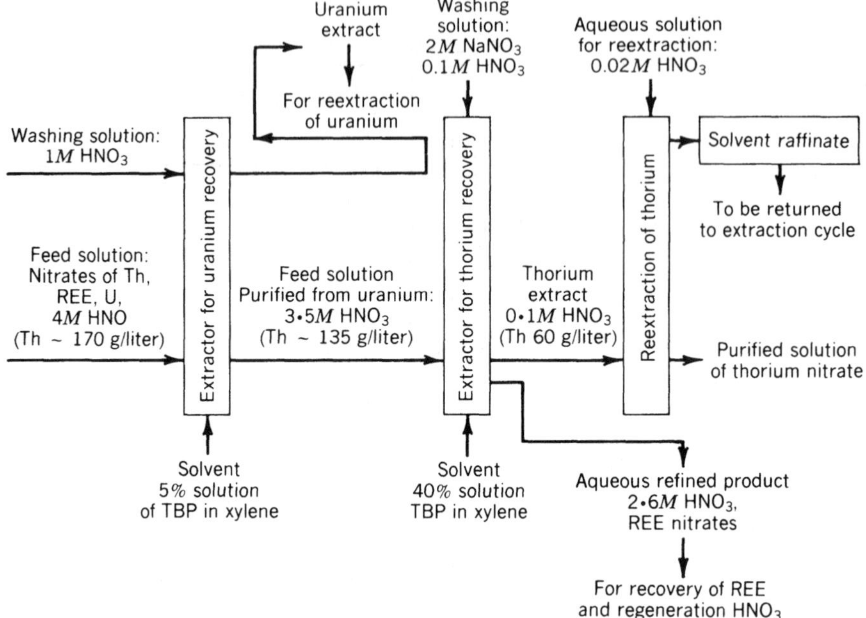

Figure 5.44. Basic scheme of extraction purification of a solution of thorium nitrate. REE = Rare Earth Element. (From V. S. Yemel'Yanov and A. I. Yevstyukhin, *The Metallurgy of Nuclear Fuel*, Pergamon Press, New York, 1969.)

tion. These elements must be reduced below a few ppm during the purification process. The usual technique is selective extraction by organic solvents. This method is similar in many respects to uranium processing and reprocessing of spent fuel. Nitric acid and tributyl phosphate (TBP) are used as the salting agent and organic solvent. The process is shown in Figure 5.44. Uranium is recovered in one of the extraction stages and the resulting thorium is of high purity.

The purified thorium is usually in an aqueous thorium nitrate solution. To convert thorium nitrate to ThO_2 one of two processes are used: (1) thermal decomposition which recovers nitric acid and water, or (2) precipitation of thorium oxalate followed by calcining. Precipitation of $Th(OH)_4$ by using NH_3 is also a successful process which results in a colloidal sol and forms the basis of the sol–gel process of fuel fabrication. This technique is further described in chapter seven.

REFERENCES

1. National Research Council Committee on Nuclear and Alternate Energy Systems, *Energy in Transition, 1985–2000,* National Academy of Sciences, Washington, D.C., 1979.
2. Nuclear Energy Policy Study Group, *Nuclear Power, Issues and Choices,* Ballinger, Cambridge, Massachusetts, 1977.

BIBLIOGRAPHY

Analysis of Uranium Program Data, EPRI Report EA-1374, March 1980.

Barnes, C. H., et al., *Uranium Data,* EPRI Report EA-400, June 1977.

Benedict, M., et al., *Nuclear Chemical Engineering,* 2nd ed., McGraw-Hill, New York, 1981.

Cheney, E. S., "The Hunt for Giant Uranium Deposits," *American Scientist* **69,** 37 (1981).

Cordfunke, E., *The Chemistry of Uranium,* Elsevier, New York, 1969.

Formation of Uranium Deposits, IAEA-SM 183/4, Proc. of IAEA, Vienna, 1974.

Gabelman, J. W., *Migration of Uranium and Thorium,* Am. Assos. of Petroleum Geologists, Tulsa, Arizona, 1977.

Hill, D. R., et al., *Uranium Exploration Activities in the U.S.,* EPRI Report EA-401, June 1977.

MATPRO, A Handbook of Material Properties, NUREG/CR-0497, August 1981.

McLeod, N. B., and J. J. Steyn, *Foreign Uranium Supply,* EPRI Report EA-725, April 1980.

Slack, A. V., Ed., *Phosphoric Acid,* Dekker, New York, 1968.

Sol-Gel Processes for Ceramic Nuclear Fuel, STI/PUB/207, IAEA, Vienna, 1968.

"Solution Mining in the United States," *Nuc. Eng. International* **25,** 29 (1980).

Toth, G., and C. K. Chase, *Uranium Solution Mining,* EPRI Report EA-731, December 1978.

Toth, G., et al. *U_3O_8 Production Analysis for Non-Sandstone Uranium Deposits,* EPRI Report EA-733, March 1980.

"Uranium Recovery," *Chemical Engineering* **88,** No. 24, 19 (1981).

Yemel'Yanov, V. S., and A. I. Yevstyukhin, *The Metallurgy of Nuclear Fuel,* Pergamon Press, New York, 1969.

CHAPTER 6

ENRICHMENT TECHNOLOGIES

6.1. INTRODUCTION

All light-water reactors (LWR) need enrichment services. The goal of enrichment is to increase the fissionable ^{235}U to around 3% from 0.7% occurring in natural uranium. The enrichment of other elements such as hydrogen to increase the deuterium content also can be important to the technology of nuclear reactors. Enrichment is the altering of isotope ratios in an element, and is usually done by way of isotope separation. Every enrichment process is rated by its single-stage separation factor—the weight or atom ratio in the entering (or head) stream divided by the corresponding ratio in the exiting (or tails) stream. Defined this way, the separation ratio is independent of composition. Enrichment processes can be made up of many stages, both in series and parallel, so it is usual to speak of separation factors per stage of the process. A value close to 1 means that separation is difficult; the greater the value, the easier the separation. Typical stage separation factors are 1.0043 for gaseous diffusion, 1.013 for chemical exchange, 1.25 and above for gas centrifuges, and over 2.0 for some of the experimental laser devices. Occasionally, the logarithm of a single-stage separation factor is used, and usually written as ϵ. A rule of thumb is that ϵ should be greater than 10^{-3} before any separation processes can be commercially feasible since any new process would have to compete with those already named whose ϵ all exceed this value.

When each process stage has only a small separation factor, many stages in series are needed to get the desired enrichment. Also, when each stage has only a limited throughput, many stages are needed in parallel to get the required production rate. Adequate throughput is a major requirement for any enrichment technology. Since it is difficult to achieve both high separation and high throughput in a stage, design compromises are often made.

To obtain the desired enrichment and quantity, an enrichment plant is designed as a series of cascades, each with multiple units. At each stage, the enriched product feeds a higher enrichment cascade, and the depleted product a lower one. The unit of measurement of enrichment is the Separative Work Unit (SWU). This is defined in mathematical terms (see Section 6.2), but is best thought of as related to the amount of energy required to take 1 kg of material from one enrichment to another. Sometimes another unit, the t-SWU which represents 1000 kg-SWU, is used when large quantities of enrichment are involved (100 kg = 1 t). SWU and kg-SWU mean the same thing, but there appears to be no standard usage in the literature, which is a confusing situation. We have adopted the most commonly used term, SWU, in this book.

A typical enrichment scheme is shown in Figure 6.1. The feed material is fed into the center of the cascade, and is continually enriched or depleted until the final product or tails go out the enrichment cascade. For LWRs, the final product is usually 3% enriched in ^{235}U. This ranges between 2 and 4%, depending on the specific fuel cycle requirements. The tails, or rejected material depleted in ^{235}U (i.e., enriched in ^{238}U), usually contain 0.2 to 0.3% ^{235}U. Natural uranium feed is supplied at the cascade center; the enriched product is drawn off one end of the cascade and the depleted product off the other. The desired percentage of enrichment and depletion depends on three economic factors: the number of stages in the cascade, energy per separative work unit, and cost of capital construction.

Most enrichment processes use UF_6 for feed, although elemental uranium can be used in others (e.g., some types of laser enrichment). In the United States, enrichment is provided by the Department of Energy (DOE) on a toll basis. The DOE has three enrichment plants. They all use gaseous diffusion and are located at Oak Ridge, Tennessee; Paducah, Kentucky; and Portsmouth, Ohio (see Table 6.1 and Figure 6.2). In addition, a Gas Centrifuge Enrichment Plant (GCEP) is under construction at Portsmouth, Ohio, at a cost of $10 billion. The material is sold to utilities. Two-thirds winds up in the United States; the rest goes to foreign customers. By law, all the government's costs must be recovered through uranium sales. These plants also supply enriched uranium for the

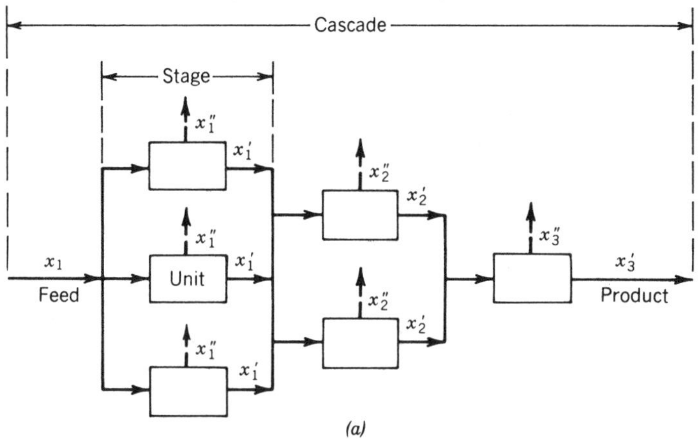

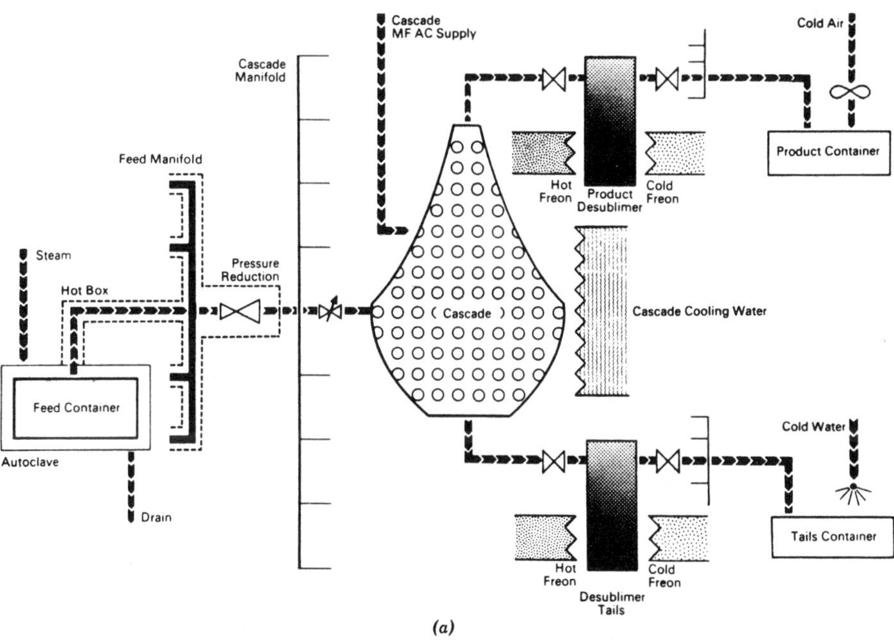

Figure 6.1. (*a*) A diagram illustrating the concept of unit, stage, and cascade. Each unit is an individual enrichment component, a stage is a bank of such components producing a given increment of enrichment, while a cascade is the arrangement of such stages to produce ^{235}U of given enrichment. The x' is the product stream of more enriched ^{235}U to the next stage, while x'' is the waste stream of less enriched ^{235}U usually fed to the previous stage. This allows a high recovery rate. If the feed material is valuable, as is the case for uranium, the cascade will have stages that are enriching material whose concentration is lower than that of the feed. This is called a stripping section. This would require that x'' be recycled to stages of below the feed, not shown in the diagram. (*b*) Process flow for a typical diffusion enrichment plant, showing the method of gasifying the UF_6 from the storage cylinders, and desublimating the product. Actual plants may have several additional stages on top of the cascade (not shown) for drawing off of light gaseous contaminants.

Table 6.1. Uranium Enrichment Capacity in the United States (1983)

Plant	Operator	Type	No. of Stages	Capacity, SWU/yr (millions)	Top Enrichment	Power Required, MWe
Oak Ridge	Union Carbide	Diffusion	1340	6.43	4%	1835
Paducah	Union Carbide	Diffusion	1760	9.81	2%	2870
Portsmouth	Goodyear	Diffusion	4020	7.29	97.65%	2165

Note: Although these plants could operate as separate facilities, they are actually operated as an integrated complex where feeds of various assays are transferred between plants.

U.S. military. Uranium used in research reactors and nuclear weapons is enriched to 93% ^{235}U compared to around 3% for commercial reactors.

The three operating DOE plants use about 3% of the total electricity produced in the United States last year. About 5% of the energy obtained from a nuclear reactor is required to enrich its uranium fuel using diffusion technology. The United States once had a free-world monopoly to enrich uranium for power reactors, but this no longer exists. Other countries now offer enrichment services on a routine basis (see Table 6.2 and Figure 6.3). They have a big advantage over the United States: cheap power and the more efficient gas centrifuge process already installed. By comparison, the diffusion plants run by the DOE are energy intensive. The bill for electricity alone at the three U.S. plants runs almost $1 billion a year, making it necessary for the United States to charge far more for enrichment services than its European competitors.

The work to separate ^{235}U from ^{238}U is used to base enrichment charges (currently about $100/SWU); this varies with the desired enrichment in ^{235}U, and is shown in Table 6.3. This table also shows the U_3O_8 to be purchased per kilogram of enriched uranium as a function of enrichment.

Figure 6.2. Background—The DOE gaseous diffusion enrichment plant at Paducah, Kentucky. This plant has 1760 stages requiring 2870 MW of electricity. It produces 9.8 million SWU's at a maximum enrichment of 2%. Center—The TVA Shawnee Steam Plant which burns fossil fuel and produces some of the electricity needed to run the gaseous diffusion plant at Paducah. Foreground—The Allied Chemical Corporation UF_6 conversion plant at Metropolis. This plant produced UF_6 from the fluoridization of UO_2 for use in the enrichment plants. Stacks of 14-ton cylinders containing UF_6 are arranged in the yard. (Courtesy Allied Chemical Corp.)

Table 6.2. World Enrichment Plants

Location	Type[a]	Owner	Status[b]	Capacity, million SWU/yr	Date of Operation
Argentina	D	CNEA	O	0.02	1985
Brazil					
No site yet	J–N	NUCLEBRAS	P	2	1989
China					
Lanchow	D	—	O	0.08	1963
France					
Pierrelatte	D	CEA	O	0.3	—
Tricastin	D	EURODIF	U	2–10.8	1979–1982
Federal Republic of Germany					
Jülich	C	—	E	na	1970
Karlsruhe	J–N	STEAG	E	0.5(?)	na
Gronau	C	URENCO/CENTEC	P	1.0	1985
Japan					
Ningyo-Toge	C	PNC	E	0.05	1981
—	C	PNC	P	0.7	1985
Netherlands					
Almelo	C	URENCO/CENTEC	E	0.025	—
Almelo	C	URENCO/CENTEC	E	0.025	—
Almelo	C	URENCO/CENTEC	E	0.2	1979
Almelo	C	URENCO/CENTEC	U	1.0[c]	1982
South Africa					
Valindaba	J–N	UCOR	E	0.006	1975
Valindaba	J–N	UCOR	P	0.25	1982
United Kingdom					
Capenhurst	D	BNFL	O	0.4	—
Capenhurst	C	URENCO/CENTEC	E	0.2	1979
Capenhurst	C	URENCO/CENTEC	E	1.0[d]	1984
United States					
Oak Ridge, TN	D	DOE	O	6.4	—
Paducah, KY	D	DOE	O	9.8	—
Portsmouth, OH	D	DOE	O	7.3	—
Portsmouth, OH	C	DOE	P	8.8–13.2	1988
USSR					
Siberia	D	—	O	7–10	—

[a]C = gas centrifuge. D = gaseous diffusion. J–N = jet nozzle or stationary walled centrifuge.
[b]E = pilot or laboratory facility. O = operating. P = planned. U = under construction.
[c]0.25 operating in 1983.
[d]0.1 operating in 1983.

6.2. ENRICHMENT REQUIREMENTS

For each MWd of thermal energy a reactor produces, 1.24 g of ^{235}U is consumed. Assuming a 70% capacity factor, a 1000-MWe LWR needs about 30 t of 3% enriched uranium per year. About 120,000 SWU/yr are needed to enrich this uranium, although more (up to 200,000 SWU/yr) are needed during the first few years of a reactor's operation.

This higher SWU requirement in the first few years is a result of the batch fuel management scheme used to refuel reactors. When a reactor is first started up, all fuel used in the core is new. At the first refueling outage, some 12 to 18 months later, up to one-third of the fuel is replaced even though a high burnup has not been achieved. In succeeding refueling outages, fuel with higher burnup is replaced until after four or five outages an "equilibrium cycle" is reached. However, the first few refuelings replace inefficiently burned up fuel; both the amount of uranium and enrichment required are therefore higher.

Like the purchase of uranium, it is common for utilities to contract for enrichment services many years in advance of their anticipated need. What those needs are, however, are sometimes difficult to estimate since a large fraction of the future demand will be from plants now under construction. The need for already operating plants is relatively easy to project: since nearly all

Figure 6.3. Headquarters of the EURODIF gaseous diffusion plant. Cascade Building No. 1 and 2 are in the background. The site is located in France next to the Tricastin Nuclear Plant on the Rhône River, north of Marcoule and adjacent (south) to the Pierrelatte enrichment plant. The average power required to run the EURODIF plant is 3100 MW. (Courtesy COGEMA.)

nuclear plants are operated as baseload units, their future enrichment requirements are directly proportional to the capacity factor the plants achieve. For plants under construction, however, future enrichment needs are determined by the date the plant first enters operation—which is difficult to predict because of licensing and construction delays, availability of money to finish the plant, and the system-wide need for power. The projected demand and cost of enrichment services is taken up again in Chapter 19.

Deuterium is mainly used as a moderator in CANDU reactors. It is not used as a gas, but rather in the form D_2O, heavy water. The source of deuterium is natural water, whose deuterium content is about 0.0150 at.%, which varies slightly because of a slight isotopic fractionation caused by evaporation and condensation of water vapor in the atmosphere. CANDU reactors require about 0.8 t of heavy water for each MWe capacity: for instance, each unit in the Bruce A station in Canada with a 745-MWe capacity has a 568-t heavy water inventory.

Of the approximately 3400 t/yr worldwide capacity for producing heavy water, about 75% is located in Canada, often sharing the same site with a CANDU reactor plant.

Inputs and Outputs of the Enrichment Process

The input to the enrichment process is uranium feed, electrical energy, and cooling water. In the gaseous diffusion and centrifuge methods, the feed is provided in the form of uranium hexafluoride. The output is a product of the desired composition and a waste stream, or tails, at a prefixed composition called "tails assay." Relations between the various input and output quantities and a simple method for determining the separate work required are presented in this section.

Engineers usually refer to:

P as the amount of product of composition x_P.

F as the amount of feed of composition x_F.

W as the amount of tails of composition x_W.

The ratio of tails to product is

$$\frac{W}{P} = \frac{x_P - x_F}{x_F - x_W} \tag{6.1}$$

Table 6.3. Enriched Uranium Data

Enrichment, wt % ^{235}U	Kilogram Natural U Feed Material to Diffusion Plant	U_3O_8 to be Purchased[a]	Equivalent Units of Separative Work[b]
	Per Kilogram of Enriched Uranium Product		
0.20	0		
0.30	0.196		−0.258
0.40	0.391		−0.198
0.50	0.587		−0.173
0.60	0.783		−0.107
0.70	0.978		−0.012
Nat. 0.711	1.000	2.613	0.000
0.8	1.174	3.068	0.104
0.9	1.370	3.580	0.236
1.0	1.566	4.092	0.380
1.2	1.957	5.114	0.698
1.4	2.348	6.136	1.045
1.6	2.740	7.160	1.413
1.8	3.131	8.182	1.797
2.0	3.523	9.206	2.194
2.1	3.718	9.716	2.397
2.2	3.914	10.228	2.602
2.3	4.110	10.740	2.809
2.4	4.305	11.250	3.018
2.5	4.501	11.762	3.229
2.6	4.697	12.274	3.441
2.7	4.892	12.784	3.656
2.8	5.088	13.296	3.871
2.9	5.284	13.808	4.088
3.0	5.479	14.318	4.306
3.1	5.675	14.830	4.526
3.2	5.871	15.342	4.746
3.3	6.067	15.854	4.968
3.4	6.262	16.364	5.191
3.5	6.458	16.876	5.414
3.6	6.654	17.388	5.638
3.7	6.849	17.898	5.864
3.8	7.045	18.410	6.090
3.9	7.241	18.922	6.316
4.0	7.436	19.432	6.544
5.0	9.393	24.544	8.851
10.0	19.178	50.112	20.863

[a]0.5% U_3O_8 to UF_6 conversion losses included.
[b]Tails assay at 0.2 wt. % ^{235}U.

while the ratio of feed to product is

$$\frac{F}{P} = \frac{x_P - x_W}{x_F - x_W} \tag{6.2}$$

An expression for separative work required per unit of product

$$\frac{S}{P} = (2x_P - 1)\ln\frac{x_P}{1 - x_P} + \frac{x_P - x_F}{x_F - x_W}(2x_W - 1)\ln\frac{x_W}{1 - x_W} - \frac{x_P - x_N}{x_F - x_W}(2x_F - 1)\ln\frac{x_F}{1 - x_F} \tag{6.3}$$

The equation shows that separative work, S, is proportional to the amount of product P and is measured in the same units, usually kilograms or metric tons. Its dependence on enrichment of product and on the amount of stripping (i.e., on tails assay x_W) is described by Eq. (6.3). The quantity S/P increases with the difference between the compositions of product and feed. It also increases with the difference between the compositions of feed and waste. The separative work requirement can be computed from the following simplified formula:

$$\frac{S}{P} = \left(\frac{S}{P}\right)_P + \frac{W}{P}\left(\frac{S}{P}\right)_W - \frac{F}{P}\left(\frac{S}{P}\right)_F \tag{6.4}$$

where the values of W/P and F/P are calculated from Eqs. (6.1) and (6.2) and the quantities $(S/P)_P$, $(S/P)_W$, and $(S/P)_F$ are obtained from the first column of Table 6.3 for the corresponding value of x_P, x_W, and x_F. The separative work corresponding to a value 0.2% is zero.

Case History

Suppose that a utility company needs 10,000 kg of uranium containing 3.2% ^{235}U for the next lot of fuel for its nuclear reactor. The company already owns 9000 kg of uranium in the form of UF_6, containing 0.9% ^{235}U. How many kilograms of natural uranium in the form of UF_6 should it supply to the government's enrichment plants, in addition to the 0.9% material it already owns, under a specification of 0.2% tails assay? How much would the charges be for separative work if the price is $100/kg-SWU?

First, the company must process 9000 kg (F) of recycle fuel at 0.9% (x_F), enriching it to 3.2% (x_P) at an enrichment plant operating at 0.2% tails (x_W). From Eq. (6.2), the ratio of feed to product turns out to be 0.23, so that 9000 kg can be processed into 2100 kg of 3.2% enriched fuel. To fulfill the 10,000-kg requirement, another 7900 of 3.2% uranium is needed.

To find out how much natural uranium to buy, the company applies Eq. (6.2) again, finding 5.87 as the feed-to-product ratio. This implies that 46,380 kg of natural uranium must be purchased. Actually about 1% more is required since there are slight losses of uranium during processing, such as in the conversion of uranium oxide to UF_6.

To determine the amount of separative work, the company would use Eq. (6.4) and Table 6.3. It finds that 7840 SWU are required to enrich the 9000 kg already on hand, and 37,490 SWU are required for the new 46,380 kg of natural uranium, a total of 45,330 SWU. At $100/SWU, this would cost $4,533,000.

Notice that the waste material (at 0.2%) is assigned a zero value. The natural uranium is also assigned a zero value when treated as feed. If depleted uranium is supplied to the process as feed, it is assigned a negative value. This means that the third term in Eq. (6.4) becomes a positive contribution, adding rather than subtracting to the total enrichment.

This analysis reveals, also, that there is a trade-off between the amount of uranium and the amount of separative work needed to produce enriched uranium. If uranium resources are perceived to be scarce, then, by using a lower tails assay, one could lower the requirements for uranium and pay a penalty in terms of separative work (when the number of lemons is limited, one squeezes more juice out of them by squeezing harder). On the other hand, if uranium resources do not seem to be a problem but the availability of electric energy is, the government could set a higher number for tails assay, for example, 0.25 or 0.3. Even higher numbers have been mentioned as a possibility for the future for reasons of energy conservation. As a rule of thumb, the increase of tails assay from 0.20 to 0.30% causes an increase in uranium yellowcake requirements by 20% and a simultaneous decrease in separative work requirements by 20%.

Given a price for uranium yellowcake, separative work, and conversion to UF_6, an optimum tails assay (i.e., for the lowest cost of enriched uranium) may be computed. These optimum values of tails composition are given in Table 6.4 as a function of the ratio of the cost of feed to cost of separative work. However, price variations over time and long-term contracts for enriching services may not allow the customer to choose the tails assay. Many contracts, however, allow for a variable tails assay option (VTAO). This allows a utility to select a tails assay between 0.16 and 0.30% (the standard transaction assay is 0.20%). This still may not allow an optimum mix of SWU and feed, however, if a utility must take a contracted-for amount of SWUs in a given year. In 1983, the optimum tails assay was about 0.32%.

6.3. ENRICHMENT TECHNOLOGIES

Several technologies can be used to enrich uranium. The differing enrichment technologies being pursued include gaseous diffusion, which is presently the production mainstay of the United States and France; the gaseous centrifuge, which is the production plant for URENCO and the technology for future United States enrichment expansion; the aerodynamic processes, which include the jet nozzle (also known as the Becker process) and the fixed-wall centrifuge (also known as the Helikon process); chemical processes; and the Laser Isotope Separation processes (also referred to in the

Table 6.4. Optimum Tails Compositions

Ratio of Feed Cost to Cost of Separative Work	Optimum Tails Composition, wt%	Ratio of Feed Cost to Cost of Separative Work	Optimum Tails Composition, wt%
0.0	0.71150	1.3	0.19971
0.2	0.40248	1.4	0.19229
0.4	0.32750	1.5	0.18549
0.6	0.28240	2.0	0.15840
0.8	0.25078	2.5	0.13892
0.9	0.23806	3.0	0.12410
1.0	0.22684	4.0	0.10283
1.1	0.21684	5.0	0.08816
1.2	0.20783	∞	0.0

literature as LIS). Of the many methods for enriching uranium, the only one that has achieved industrial and economic maturity is that of gaseous enrichment. In use for more than 40 yr, it has provided 98% of all the uranium enrichment to date. Today, all enrichment work in the United States for commercial reactors uses gaseous diffusion, but new additions to U.S. capacity will be of the gas centrifuge type, whose main advantage is the lower power consumption per SWU. Much research and development work is also being done on laser enrichment. This method may prove to be commercially feasible in the near future.

In Europe, URENCO, a multicountry consortium (Federal Republic of Germany, Netherlands, and United Kingdom) hopes to have over 3,000,000 SWU/yr capacity by 1985 using gas centrifuge technology. It has plants at Capenhurst (UK), Almelo (Holland), and Gronow (FRG). However, diffusion is still viable, especially when cheap electric power is available; another group, EURODIF (Belgium, France, Iran, Italy, and Spain), will have over 10,000,000 SWU/yr capacity by the mid-1980s using gaseous diffusion. Techsnabexport, the marketing organization for enrichment services of the Soviet Union, also primarily relies on gaseous diffusion technology. It has plants located in Siberia capable of producing 7–10,000,000 SWU/yr, and has stated that it would be willing to supply on long-term contracts 3–4,000,000 SWU/yr to the western world. Japan, however, will use gas centrifuges for its future enrichment needs and is now in the demonstration phase of its program. Their Power Reactor and Nuclear Fuel Company (PNC) will have some 75,000 SWU/yr capacity operating in 1985. Other technologies such as chemical enrichment and aerodynamic techniques are being worked on, and still are contenders for future enrichment commercialization.

Gas Diffusion Technology

Gaseous diffusion is a technically proven process based on the rate at which gases of different molecular weight pass through a porous wall. This wall contains billions of pores per square meter. The diameter of the pores, below 0.04 μm, must be of uniform size. Production of these porous walls is the most difficult part of the gaseous diffusion technology (and is classified). Early porous barriers were made by acid etching of thin sheets of aluminum (or silver zinc alloy). Barriers with pore sizes of 100 Å made by acid etching have been reported by the French. Sintering of fine aluminium or nickel powder has also been used. The barriers are about 50 μm thick.

The principle here is that a gas made up of different molecules will divide its energy equally among the molecules. Thus, to have equal energy, the lighter particles must have higher velocity (as seen from the formula $E = \frac{1}{2}mv^2$). The lighter particles will therefore impinge on the walls of the container more often, and if the wall is thin and porous, the lighter molecules will pass through the wall at a slightly higher rate than the heavier molecules. If the gas is UF_6, then more $^{235}UF_6$ molecules will pass through the wall than the heavier $^{238}UF_6$. Thus, on the other side of the wall the product will be richer in ^{235}U and the remaining gas will be correspondingly richer in ^{238}U.

The diffusion rate is inversely proportional to the molecular velocity, that is, the square root of the molecular weight. The theoretical separation factor per stage is the same ratio: for UF_6 it is 1.0043. This separation factor, however, is not fully achievable in practice because of various inefficiencies in the process. By repeating the stages many times, this small factor can be exploited to produce any desired enrichment.

UF_6 is the only gas suitable for diffusion. It has three main advantages: (1) it is a gas at low temperatures (56.4°C is its sublimation temperature at normal pressure); (2) fluorine has only one isotope, and (3) fluorine has a low atomic weight. Disadvantages of UF_6 are how it acts with moisture to form UO_2F_2 (uranyl fluoride) and its very corrosive attack of metals and organic materials, such as lubricating oil. The corrosiveness of UF_6 can be a problem for the porous barriers, which need to keep their shape and pore size for a long time. For this reason, structural materials inside the process vessels are usually of nickel coated steels or aluminum. Teflon, a fluoroethylene polymer, is stable to UF_6 decomposition products. It is a useful material for fabricating porous barriers and gaskets.

The choice of operating temperature and pressure are determined by the properties of UF_6. For a given pressure, the lowest temperature allowable in the system is the UF_6 gas liquefaction or crystallization point. At 300 torr, for example, UF_6 crystallizes at 40°C. High temperatures, however, increase the work required for compression, the rate of corrosion, and the rate of diffusion through the pores. The first two of these effects are considered negatives.

Figures 6.4 and 6.5 are a scheme of one stage of a gaseous diffusion plant. Each stage requires an axial-flow compressor (Figures 6.6 and 6.7) to supply the pressure to drive the UF_6 across the barrier. Adjustable blades allow for aerodynamic regulation of the flow. The coolers are needed to remove the compression heat. One of the advantages of the gaseous diffusion method is that it is essentially static mechanically, the only moving parts being the motor compressors. This leads to both long life and great reliability, with comparatively small needs for maintenance. The compressors are powered by large electrical motors; those in the United States are rated at 3300 horsepower. To illustrate the scale involved in these components, over 640,000 kg of UF_6 must be circulated to produce a single SWU. The large amount of UF_6 recirculating in a diffusion plant is a direct result of the low separation factor available in the process. From Table 6.3 we see that to produce 1 kg of 3% enriched uranium, 5.479 kg of feed material (i.e., 8.1 kg of UF_6) is required. This feed rate is independent of the plant inventory which is a characteristic of the process and plant design. Gaseous diffusion plants usually have about 0.1 kg of uranium in the system for each SWU/yr of capacity. The large circulation rate per SWU again illustrates the large amount of power required to enrich uranium using gaseous diffusion. The energy cost is about 5 MeV for each ^{235}U atom separated using gaseous diffusion. (Around 200 MeV is obtained when that atom is fissioned in a reactor.)

Since the separation factor is so low, the enrichment in any diffusion stage is small. The desired enrichment is won by connecting the diffusion stages into a cascade. The cascade is arranged so that at each stage the enriched product feeds a higher stage, and the depleted product a lower one. There are many ways, however, of connecting the feed of one stage to other stages. The optimum way is called the "ideal cascade," defined as one in which there is no mixing of streams of unequal concentration. Mixing a stream of concentrated ^{235}U with one of less concentrated ^{235}U would undo the separation process; obviously an inefficiency to be avoided. An ideal cascade has the minimum specific power consumption.

Although the separation factor differs from unity by only a small fraction, that fraction is very important. In an ideal plant both the number of stages and the interstage flow rate are inversely proportional to this difference. Consequently, the physical plant size goes as its square power.

Diffusion stages between the feed point and product end are called the "enriching section," those between the feed point and tails end, the "stripping section." The stripping section is used in the cascade because lightly depleted uranium is too valuable to discard. A typical process cell of 16 diffusion stages, and bypass piping for isolating the cell for maintenance, is shown in Figure 6.8. Figure 6.9 shows that to produce material even of low ^{235}U enrichment requires many hundred stages. For example, to obtain 4% enriched ^{235}U, with 0.25% tails assay, 1180 stages are necessary in a practical plant design. This compares to 658 stages, the minimum number of stages required for a simple cascade without reprocessing of tails but with perfect efficiency to produce the same enrichment assay.

Cascade Design

As enrichment of the UF_6 gas goes up or down within the cascade, the power requirements and equipment size should, in theory, vary accordingly. The equipment capacity would be largest at the feed point and decrease toward the product and tails exit points. To use these ideal design conditions, a plant is arranged by its "length" (number of stages) and "width" (size of stages). The ideal cascade shape has a gradual decrease in flow with each stage in the enriching or stripping section. To reduce the detrimental effects of mixing, real plants try to achieve this ideal shape (Figure 6.10). Since a great number of separating elements are used, the diffusion method can be tailored closely to the ideal shape and thus attain high cascade efficiencies.

Since the flow must be maximum near the feed point of the cascade, and decrease toward the product and tails ends, enrichment plants theoretically should adjust the size of each stage according to its cascade position. This is economically impossible; however, by using a large middle part, small extremities, and intermediate sizes between the two others, a square cascade results. This is a suitable compromise for the ideal cascade. An important aspect of every practical cascade is the recycling of the tails stream from each stage to a lower stage in the cascade. This allows a high recovery of enriched isotope.

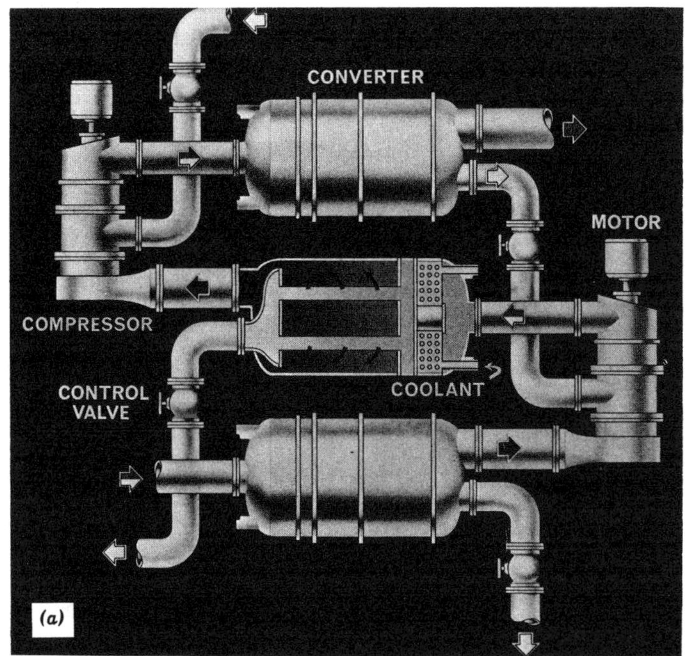

Figure 6.4. (*a*) Schematic arrangement of basic stage equipment in a gaseous diffusion cascade. The large drums are converters. Each contains a cooler and thousands of barrier tubes. The axial-flow compressor recompresses the UF_6 that has passed through the barriers. (Courtesy DOE.) (*b*) Cell of equipment (compressors, diffusers, and piping) at the Oak Ridge Gaseous Diffusion Plant, Oak Ridge, Tennessee. (Courtesy DOE.)

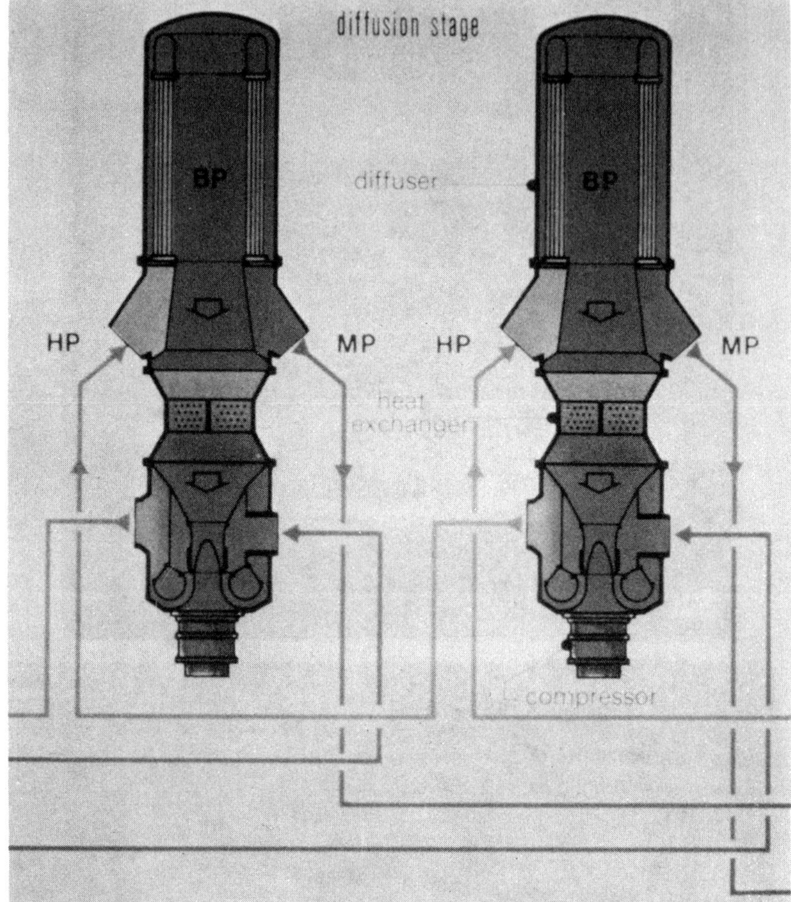

Figure 6.5. Schematic of a COREDIF gaseous diffusion stage. About 1200 stages in series are required to obtain 3% enrichment in ^{235}U with 0.25% tails assay. Each stage consists of a diffuser, compressor, and heat exchanger. The vertical arrangement shown in this figure greatly reduces the amount of interconnecting piping and the size of the building required to house the equipment. HP = High-pressure gas from the compressor of the previous stage. MP = Medium-pressure UF_6 gas of less enriched ^{235}U, which did not cross the diffusion boundary. BP = More enriched ^{235}U which is now at low pressure due to the pressure drop across the diffusion boundary. (Courtesy COGEMA.)

In this way it is possible to use a single equipment size that operates at close to maximum efficiency. An ideal cascade requires more stages than the simple cascade without tails feedback. For the conditions given in the last paragraph, 1169 stages would be needed. This is fairly close to the number (1180) quoted for the practical plant design. At the top end of the cascade equipment, several stages of small size are often used to purge contaminant gases (of low molecular weight) from the system.

After enrichment, the $^{235}UF_6$ product is removed by a compressor–condenser–accumulator to liquefy the gas, before it is put into 10-ton product storage cylinders. The $^{238}UF_6$ depleted tails are likewise removed by a compressor–condenser–accumulator from the bottom of the stripping section. These tails are drained into 14-ton storage cylinders, and put into long-term storage awaiting further use. There are over 250,000 t of these tails in the United States stored at sites such as Oak Ridge. The potential energy stored in these cylinders (see Figure 6.11) is an enormous energy resource, which can be used when Liquid-Metal Fast Breeder Reactors (LMFBR) enter commercial operation. Laser isotope separation techniques, when commercialized, could also be used to recover most of the 0.2% ^{235}U in these tails. This is discussed later in the chapter.

Figure 6.6. The diffuser of unit 120 at the Tricastin uranium gaseous diffusion plant (EURODIF). Scale is evident from workers in center of the picture and the ladder at left. Subassembly ducts connect one diffusion stage with another, as shown in Figure 6.5. (Courtesy COGEMA.)

Figure 6.7. Rotor compressor for a diffusion stage. The location of the rotor compressor is given in Figure 6.5, and its size can be inferred from the previous figure. The fins are shaped to compress the UF_6 gas with as much aerodynamic efficiency as possible. The rotor compressor, like a gas turbine, is surrounded by a stator assembly to reverse the tangential flow of the gas. (Courtesy COGEMA.)

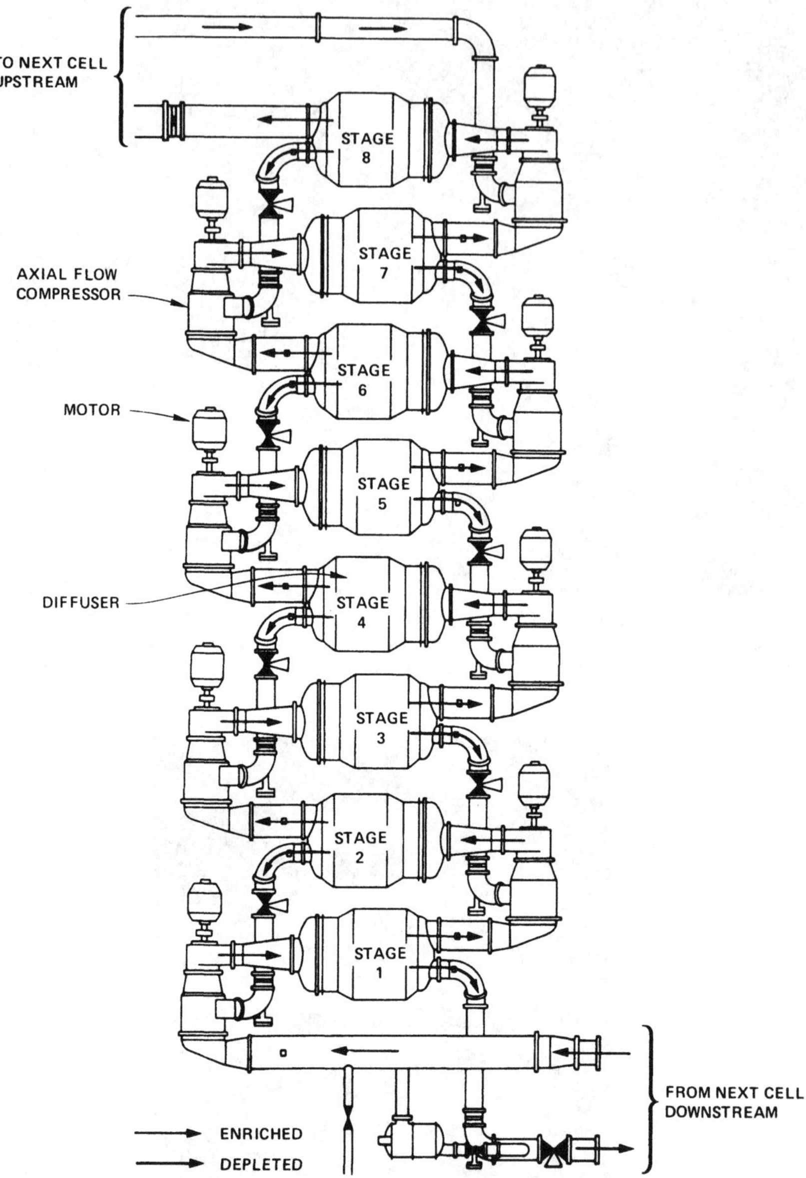

Figure 6.8. Diagram of the 8-stage process cell shown in Figure 6.4*b*. (Courtesy DOE.)

Operating Conditions for Gaseous Diffusion Plants.

The compressor power, the area of the barrier surface, and the volumetric flow rate are the three quantities that substantially determine the cost of the gaseous diffusion enrichment process. Most plants are designed to operate at temperatures between 110 and 65°C, at low pressures (260 torr† with a Δp across of the barrier of 225 torr) and a high compression ratio of about 8. At a given pressure, the temperature must be kept above where UF_6 gas changes state, or clogging of the barrier pores will occur. As already mentioned, UF_6 solidifies at 40°C when the pressure is 300 torr. Operating at increased temperature will reduce the amount of area required in the barriers, but

†torr is a unit of pressure, with 760 torr equal to 1 bar or 14.7 psi.

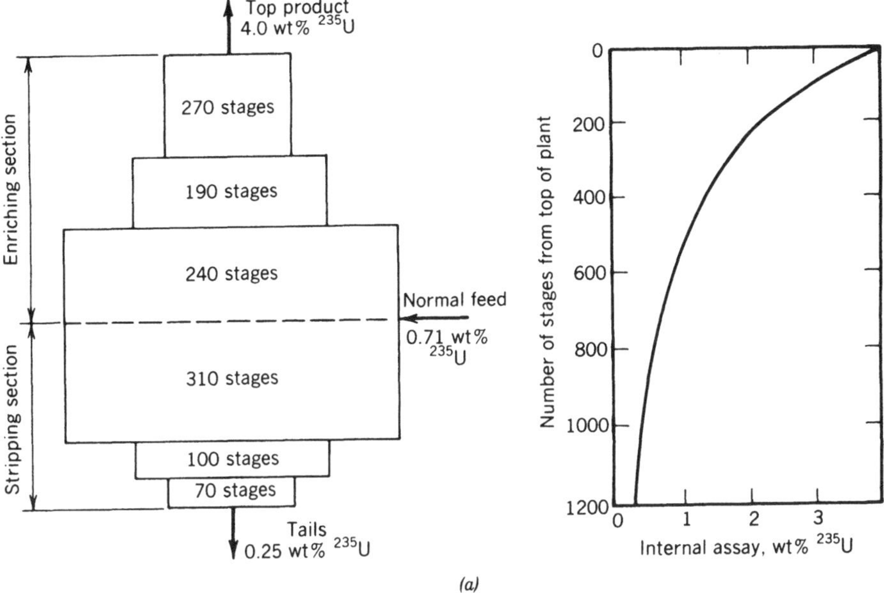

Figure 6.9. (*a*) Schematic diagram and internal assay gradient for an enrichment plant. (Courtesy DOE.) (*b*) Product and tails withdrawal facility. (Courtesy URENCO.)

requires more compressor work and higher pressures (to keep density constant). Since the UF_6 is normally cooled after compression, there is little advantage to using these higher process temperatures. Operating pressures higher than 760 torr are possible by using barriers with pore radii below 100 Å, but this would decrease the gas permeability.† Durability and mechanical strength of the barriers are also important. Small pore radii quickly clog, while thin barriers, which have high permeability, have low mechanical strength.

The principal technical problem setting up any enrichment plant is the elimination of the inleakage of air. The oxygen in air causes trouble, and any moisture in the air is a special problem because of its reaction with fluorine. Leak-tight specifications are typically 10^{-5} vol. %/hr. This allows a high vacuum (below 5 mtorr) to be achieved.

†Permeability is the ratio of the molecular velocity to the pressure differential.

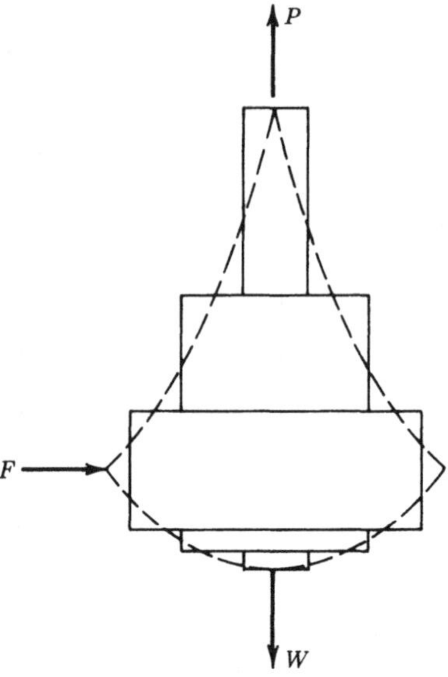

Figure 6.10. Ideal cascade approximation using square sections.

Figure 6.11. Storage of depleted uranium in the form of UF_6 as a solid in 14-ton cylinders at Oak Ridge, Tennessee. Corrosion of the outside of the cylinders is due to storage in the open. The energy contained in the first row of cylinders is roughly comparable to that of all the present oil reserves of Saudi Arabia. The scale can be inferred by the truck in the right center of the photograph. (Courtesy DOE.)

Figure 6.12. Cascade hall in the centrifuge enrichment plant at Capenhurst, U.K. (From URENCO.)

Gas Centrifuge

Most of the new enrichment capacity being built today employs gas centrifuge technology (Figures 6.11 through 6.13). The gas centrifuge process, which also uses UF_6, is based on the separation effect of a strong centrifugal field in a rotating cylinder. Gas centrifuge has two major advantages over gaseous diffusion: (1) it is more energy efficient by a factor of about 10; and (2) its plants have many fewer stages to a given enrichment. Although centrifuges have much smaller throughput than diffusion stages, this allows incremental capacity to be put on-line in smaller steps. The capital cost per unit capacity is about the same for both.

The first work on centrifuge enrichment was started by J. Beams at the University of Virginia in 1934. G. Zippe continued the work in the 1950s and 1960s, first at the University of Virginia and later at Oak Ridge National Laboratory (ORNL). Gas centrifuge technology, like gaseous diffusion, uses the mass difference between ^{235}U and ^{238}U to separate the isotopes, but the typical separation factor is much higher. It ranges from 1.25 in installed units to 2.0 for advanced units, compared to 1.0043 for gaseous diffusion. In addition to its use for commercial nuclear reactors, gas centrifuge technology has considerable military value, so that many of its critical details remain secret.

Schematic diagrams (Figures 6.14 through 6.16) of gas centrifuge operation show the complexity of the flow field in the units. The working fluid is the highly corrosive gas UF_6. If ^{232}U enters a centrifuge as $^{232}UF_6$, it becomes a problem since the daughter products (^{228}Th) would probably plate out, thorium fluoride being nonvolatile. When it rotates at high speed, pressure differences in the centrifuge cause the separation of the ^{235}U and ^{238}U isotopes. For rotor speeds of 400 m/sec, the local separation factor at the outer radius is 1.10, and the center-to-outer radius pressure ratio exceeds 10^5. By creating a countercurrent flow inside the centrifuge between the enriched stream nearest the axis and the stripped stream near the radius, the separation factor can be made much larger since the concentration difference between top and bottom can be made greater than what is achievable between the two streams at the same elevation. To set up the countercurrent flows, baffles, thermal gradients, and external pumps can be used.

The secret of success is the trick of changing the direction of enrichment from radial to vertical (axial); this increases the enrichment by inducing a weak axial (countercurrent) flow in the rotational motion of the gas. The result is that ^{238}U diffuses to the bottom of the centrifuge and ^{235}U to the top, where they are collected. Separation is due to a combination of centrifugal forces which drive the $^{238}UF_6$ to the outer wall and convection forces, established by a heat gradient, which

Figure 6.13. Enrichment plant in Almelo, Netherlands. The plant consumes about 133 kWh/SWU. 160,000 SWU/yr of separative work was on line by 1979. The plant is being expanded to a total capacity of 1.6 million SWU/yr in 1984. The centrifuge failure rate at this plant has been 0.1%/yr.

allow a vertically flowing inner stream to be enriched. Opposing separation are molecular diffusion effects that must be overcome by the centrifugal and convective forces.

The total throughput is limited by the condensation pressure of UF_6. This is about 125 torr at 20°C. Throughput typically might be 100 mg/sec for some first-generation commercial machines. The separative power of a centrifuge (in SWU) is the separative factor times the throughput (in kilograms of uranium per year, not UF_6). The separative work increases with the fourth power of the rotor speed, with the axial length of the rotor to the first power, and the difference of the molecular weight of the gases to the second power. For this reason, the rotors are designed as long as possible and to run at high angular velocities. The rotors are enclosed in a container under a vacuum which also acts as a missile shield in case the rotor disintegrates. The vacuum reduces friction of the tube with air, thereby lowering energy consumption, and acts as a thermal insulator to prevent heat transfer, thereby preventing temperature transients in the rotor.

Conflicting design requirements can lead to instabilities in the centrifuges. Long rotors have a tendency to bow, leading to mechanical stresses and nonuniform flow fields. The lower bearings are critical components which must support the total weight of the rotor. There is also a problem with potential structural resonances during start-up of the machines. Certain rotational speeds can cause a thin cylinder to vibrate. If a centrifuge operates for very long near one of these speeds, the induced vibration can destroy it. A centrifuge is referred to as a subcritical or supercritical machine, depending on whether it operates below or above the first flexural resonance. Most advanced designs are supercritical ones. They must operate at rotational speeds away from the resonances, and must have drives and breaks that allow them to pass through the resonant speeds quickly.

Angular velocity, and hence the separative power of the centrifuge, is limited by the ratio of strength to density of the rotor material. For current materials (aluminum or stainless steel), maximum peripheral rotor speeds are ~400 m/sec, although new composite materials permit design to hypersonic velocities around 700 m/sec. These hypersonic machines improve separation considerably. The most advanced prototypes made by the U.S. DOE, which are roughly 1 ft in diameter and 30 ft high, are reported to produce 280 SWU/yr. Machines with up to 600 SWU/yr capacity are under design.

Centrifuges being built in Europe (Urenco design) typically have separative power of between 2 and 20 SWU/yr. Therefore a plant with a 1 million SWU capacity might require over 50,000 centrifuges. The capital cost for centrifuge capacity is approximately $1500/SWU (in 1984 dollars). The Urenco plants have achieved high availability, above 99%. This is due to the high integrity of the vacuum systems and the optimized redundancy of vital systems. Moreover, since failure rates are high during centrifuge start-up, plant operators try to keep the machines running continuously. Centrifuge failure rates have been consistently 10 times better than the design failure rate of 1% per year.

Photo Excitation (LASER) Separation

Photo-excitation enrichment processes rely on the slight shift of electron energy levels in ^{238}U compared to ^{235}U. This shift in energy levels is due to second-order effects caused in the electron configuration of the ^{238}U atom due to three extra neutrons in the nucleus. This effect can be taken advantage of by high-tuned, monochromatic light produced by lasers at the same wavelengths as the electronic transition. This resonance leads to enhanced ionization, molecular dissociation, or chemical reaction of the excited atom. Since the principal means of producing highly tuned monochromatic radiation is with a laser, enrichment by photoexcitation techniques is usually called Laser Isotope Separation (LIS).

There are four conditions for laser enrichment:

1. An isotopically shifted line must exist in the atomic or molecular spectrum, and must be sufficiently separated from the other isotopes and other lines in the spectrum.
2. A laser must be developed and tuned to the appropriate frequency.
3. The atoms or molecules to be enriched must be kept from excessively colliding with the walls of the equipment or other molecules.
4. Physical or chemical processes must be developed to affect the final separation of the enriched species.

For example, mercury isotopes can be easily separated because of the cleanly spaced lines of their atomic spectra. It is not so easy for uranium, because of the high temperature to which uranium must be heated to produce an atomic gas, and the complexity of its spectrum and that of the low-temperature uranium molecule UF_6. The most technically intriguing aspect of the laser separation technique is that large, single-step isolation factors of 2 or more are possible for even the rare isotopes of any element.

The laser separation schemes used today are based on variations of the following processes:

1. An atomic or molecular beam is irradiated transversely. Photons, absorbed at particular resonance energies in a selected isotope, impart a transverse velocity to those components. Atoms can be repeatedly excited to remove them from the beam, but this requires many high-energy laser photons.
2. A laser is used to break various chemical bonds of a molecule in a stable ground state. The molecule decomposes when irradiated, and the chemical bond energy imparts recoil energy to the molecular radicals, removing them from the beam.
3. The atom is ionized by a laser beam and the ionized particles are removed by means of an electric field.

Atomic Vapor Laser Isotope Separation (AVLIS)

The Lawrence Livermore Laboratory (LLL) process is an example of an atomic uranium laser separation scheme. It has been selected by the U.S. DOE for development and demonstration of the laser process. An oven at 2600 K produces a uranium vapor, with 45% of the atoms in the lowest possible energy state, and 27% in a very slightly higher metastable state. This metastable state is not independent of the ground state and is not reachable by a radiation transition. Only ions in this metastable state are excited and collected. The process is referred to as the Atomic Vapor Laser Isotope Separation (AVLIS) process.

The absorption spectrum of metallic uranium is very complex; however, several sharp resonance lines are sufficiently resolved and displaced from the other uranium isotopes so that selective excitation is possible. A xenon laser operating in the ultraviolet region at 3781 Å will only excite atoms of ^{235}U. These atoms are then ionized by a krypton laser producing radiation at 3507 and 3564 Å. For this second irradiation, any laser with a wavelength less than 4400 Å would suffice, since all that is required is to overcome the ionization potential of the excited atom. The krypton laser is not isotopically selective. It must, however, almost immediately hit the excited ^{235}U atom, whose half-life in the excited state is only 235 nsec. This is usually done by triggering the two lasers together and arranging their beams on a common axis. The ionized ^{235}U atoms are then collected on a plate in an electric field. To reduce the corrosion caused by hot uranium on the process equipment, an alloy of uranium and rhenium can be used as the uranium vapor source.

An alternate scheme, and the one currently used at LLL, excites ground state ^{235}U atoms by visible photons from a sequence of three tunable dye lasers. These photons produce autoionizing uranium atoms. A high-repetition copper-vapor laser drives the dye laser and the uranium ions are collected from the vapor as a liquid metal.

The yield is invariably reduced, as some ^{238}U atoms are ionized (usually in the oven) or

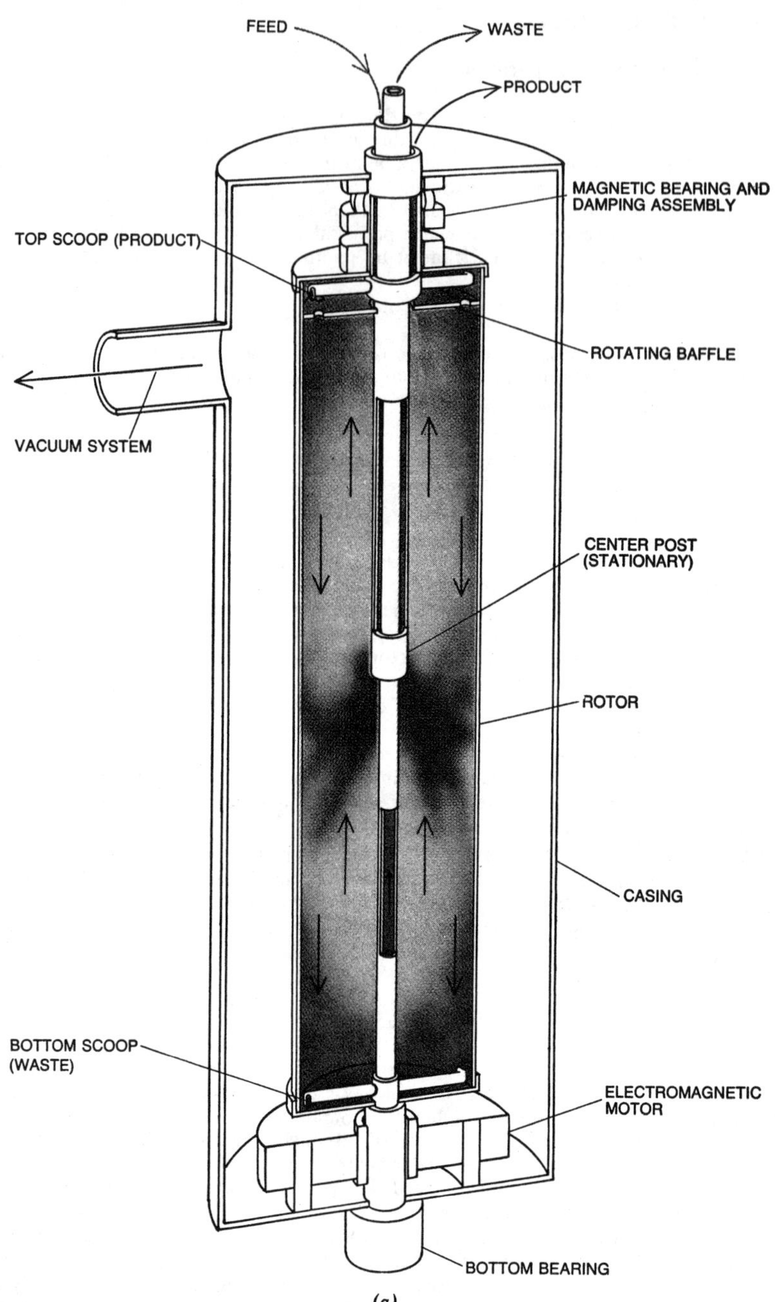

(a)

Figure 6.14. (*a*) Interior of a centrifuge is shown in this cutaway drawing. The thin-walled rotor is driven by a small electromagnetic motor attached to the bottom of the casing. The top end of the rotor is held in a vertical position by a magnetic bearing and does not touch stationary components. Gas is fed into and withdrawn from the rotor through the stationary center post, which holds three concentric tubes for the feed, the product, and the waste. The stationary bottom scoop protrudes into the spinning gas and provides a mechanical means for driving the vertical flow of gas. The top scoop, which serves to remove the enriched product, is protected from direct interaction with the rotating gas by the baffle, which has holes allowing the enriched gas to be bled into the area near the scoop. The baffle is needed to keep the top scoop from imposing a vertical flow that would counteract the crucial one generated by the bottom scoop. [From D. Olander, *Scientific American* **239,** 37 (1978).] (*b*) High-capacity gas centrifuges in the Advanced Equipment Test Facility, Oak Ridge, Tennessee. (Courtesy DOE.)

Figure 6.14 *(Continued)*

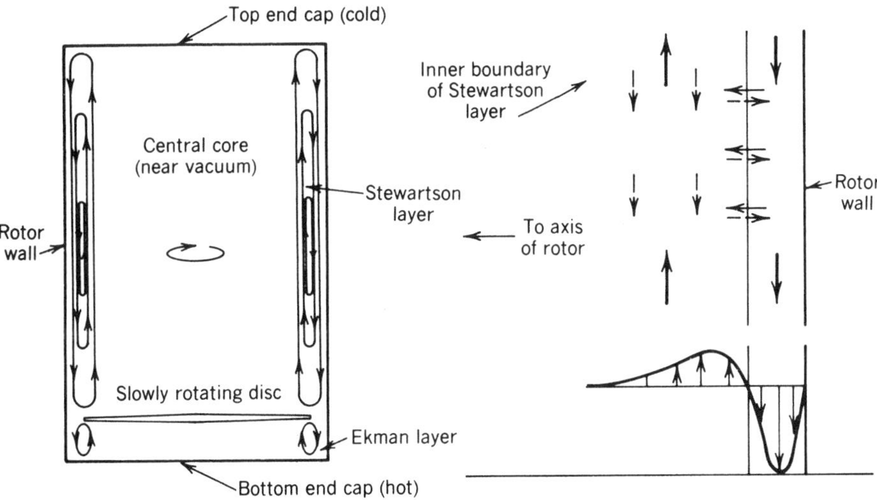

Figure 6.15. Gas movement in a centrifuge begins with the effect of rotation (left), which drives the gas against the rotor wall in a region known as the Stewartson layer, where the isotope separation takes place. As a result of temperature differences at the top and bottom caps and the effect of the bottom scoop (an effect stimulated mathematically by a disc rotating slightly slower than the rotor), a weak vertical circulation is set up (arrows). In addition, thin gas-containing zones known as Ekman layers, each only a fraction of a millimeter thick, are formed at the extremities of the Stewartson layer, where the circulatory flow changes directions. Countercurrent circulation and molecular transport in the Stewartson layer (right) result in the enrichment of the gas. The thin solid arrows indicate the direction of movement of uranium-235 molecules induced by the pressure-diffusion effect arising from the centrifugal force. The broken-line arrows show the directions of transport of uranium 235 by molecular diffusion. Convective motion of the gas as a whole is represented by the thick arrows. Lighter shading indicates areas that have the higher concentrations of uranium 235. The lower curve shows a typical mass-velocity profile (the units of mass velocity being g/cm^2-sec) that characterizes the countercurrent circulation in the Stewartson layer. [From D. Olander, *Scientific American* **239,** 37 (1978).]

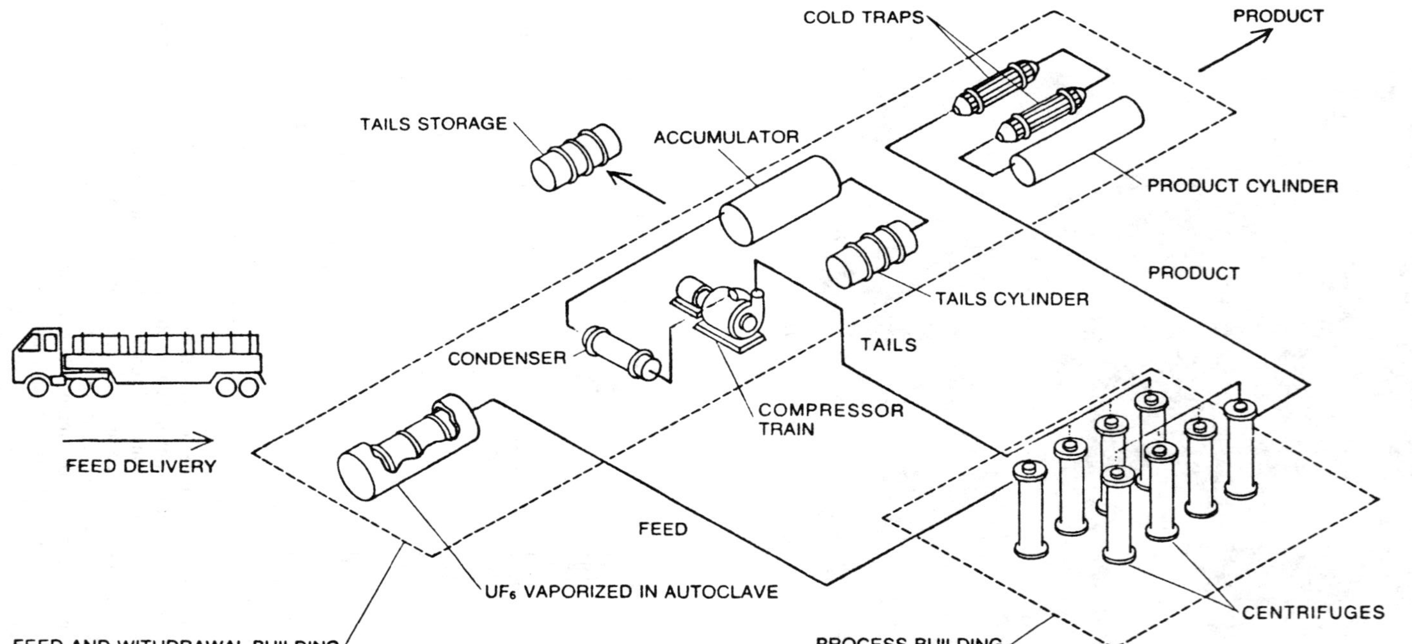

Figure 6.16. Flow diagram indicates how a gas-centrifuge plant might operate. Uranium hexafluoride (UF_6) is received at the plant in 14-ton cylinders. They are heated to vaporize the compound, which is then piped to the centrifuge cascade. The product streams, consisting of uranium hexafluoride enriched in uranium 235, are removed from the cascade for final processing and put into $2\frac{1}{2}$-ton cylinders for shipment to a plant that makes the enriched compound into fuel for nuclear reactors. The stream of depleted uranium hexafluoride is then condensed into 14-ton cylinders, which are put in an outside storage yard. A gas-centrifuge enrichment plant that is now under construction at Portsmouth, Ohio, is scheduled to include eight process buildings (each the size of four football fields) and several other buildings. (Courtesy DOE.)

collected on the plate. The ^{238}U atoms can also collect on the plate if they collide with the ionized ^{235}U atoms transfering an electron from one to the other. Nevertheless, enrichments of 3% ^{235}U are routinely achieved in a single pass.

The LLL process has a major limiting factor: the density of uranium atoms in the beam, which limits throughput. Other problems that are troublesome, but not limiting, are the corrosiveness of the high-temperature uranium in the beam and problems with the laser itself: energy density, pulse rate, tuning precision, stability, and reliability. Heat transfer poses an engineering problem. There is a need to get heat into the system to vaporize the uranium, but for engineering considerations, it is better to keep the system cool.

Lawrence Livermore Laboratory is also working on a method to separate the isotopes of plutonium. Pu melts at 1187°C, about 500°C below uranium. But a problem is the small mass differences between the isotopes of Pu. With uranium, for example, there are 3 AMU (Atomic Mass Units) between ^{235}U and ^{238}U; but in the case of plutonium, there is only 1 AMU between the isotopes. Moreover, it is desirable to collect ^{239}Pu and ^{241}Pu, the fissionable isotopes, and reject ^{238}Pu and ^{240}Pu, which are nonfissionable. This form of "hopscotching" the isotopes presents many technical problems. The molecular enrichment technique using PuF_6 has the problems of PuF_6 stability (it is much less stable than UF_6). PuF_6 becomes more thermodynamically stable with temperature, but an F_2 overpressure is usually required to keep it from dissociating. Fluorine gas is corrosive, though, and presents a difficult engineering problem of its own.

Separation factors for laser enrichment are large, but the throughput must be increased if it is to compete with the other enrichment technologies, such as centrifuge or diffusion processes. Laser enrichment has potentially a large energy advantage. Assuming a 0.2% efficiency for converting power into monochromatic light via a laser, from 500 to 5000 eV is required per atom of ^{235}U. This compares to 5 MeV already mentioned for diffusion methods. Recently the Department of Energy has decided to build an AVLIS uranium enrichment pilot plant at LLL. Oak Ridge, Tennessee had been in the running for the $100 million facility, but DOE opted for the California site instead, primarily because of cost and time considerations. The K-25 site at Oak Ridge is still being considered as the location for the full-scale plant. The pilot plant is scheduled for 1986 operation.

Jersey Nuclear Avco Isotopes (JNAI) Company, formerly a joint venture between Avco and Exxon Nuclear, developed another atomic vapor laser isotope separation process that uses an electron beam/copper crucible to vaporize uranium atoms.† At 1000 gauss and 1000 K, the isotope shift is approximately 0.1 Å (the level is 5027.29 Å for ^{235}U and 5027.40 Å for ^{238}U). The process is also complicated by fine structure in the spectra. A tuned light beam, precisely kept at one part in 10^5 wavelength units (about 0.02 Å), is required. This is done by a multiple-reflected tunable-dye laser beam through which the uranium vapor passes. It is basically a once-through process, since the process tails are not recycled, and requires batch processing.

One technical problem encountered with AVLIS is due to the large temperature range between melting (1150°C) and boiling (4200°C) for uranium. Uranium is difficult to vaporize from a solid, even at high vacuums and heat fluxes. An electron-beam melting process has been found to be satisfactory. At 2270°C, the pressure at the vaporizing surface is only 10^{-4} torr. For sufficient vapor flow, high temperature and vacuum are required. But at high temperatures, the uranium atoms no longer populate only the ground state. To overcome this problem, the JNAI process used four laser wavelengths to selectively excite atoms from the ground state and thermally excited states. Because DOE has chosen the LLL process for further development, the JNAI process is no longer being actively pursued.

Laser Technology

The enrichment factor for the AVLIS process is somewhere between 3 and 15. This is higher than the per stage enrichment factors of a gas centrifuge and much higher than those for diffusion. The high separation factor makes possible a "tail-stripping" strategy where the tails from the diffusion plants (0.2% ^{235}U) could be enriched in one step to reactor grade (~3% ^{235}U).

Two lasers have been considered for pump lasers, copper-vapor, and xenon chloride lasers. The copper-vapor laser is more highly developed, although the xenon chloride laser is potentially cheaper. The pump lasers generate the process light which energizes a second laser, which finally produces the light used in the separation process. This separates the requirements for efficiency and wave-length precision. The second system consists of dye lasers (Figure 6.17) which converts the pump laser light to process light. It is tunable and reliable. The dye lasers are efficient converters of green and yellow light to precisely tuned red light that matches the absorbtion lines of atomic uranium.

The tunable-dye lasers, which use conventional organic dye in a liquid solvent, are inefficient

†The JNAI process, invented in 1969 by Levy and Sargent at the AVCO-Everett Research Laboratory, is the basis for the subsequent LLL process.

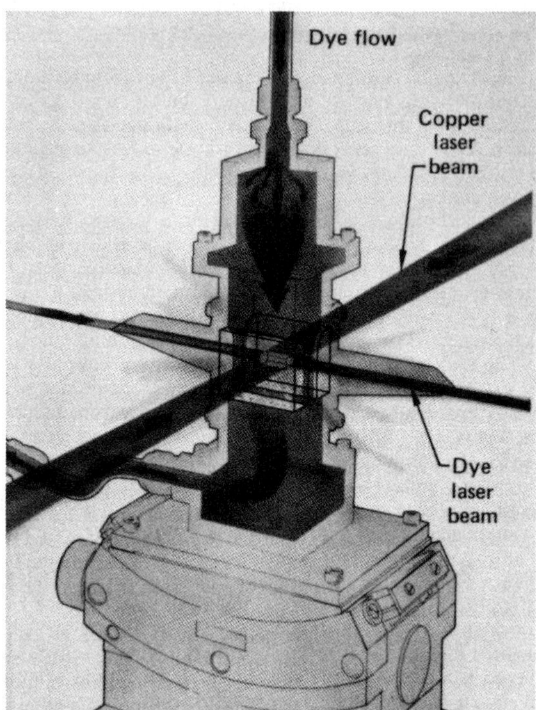

Figure 6.17. Dye lasers. The dye laser units used in uranium enrichment are compact triaxial units in which pump laser light, the flowing dye stream, and the dye laser beam intersect in a small flow channel. The pump laser light is converted to dye laser light, thus amplifying the dye laser beam. These units are simple and reliable. (Courtesy DOE.)

(~0.2%) and operate at low repetition rate (~100 ppm). Dye solutions are commercially available, but must be purified for laser use. These solutions decompose and, therefore, must be continually replenished. The dye concentration is small, but the solvent flow rate is high. This presents a formidable problem. The pulse rate (~10,000 ppm) is determined by the uranium vapor velocity, so that many laser amplifiers operating in sequence are required.

Commercialization of the AVLIS Process

The ^{235}U is extracted by electric or magnetic fields and collected on plates. The enrichment factor is determined by the number of ^{238}U atoms that also end up on the collection plates. These ^{238}U atoms can be due to (1) diffusion directly onto the plates, (2) charged particle extraction due to the electron beam, or (3) collisions with laser-extracted ^{235}U resulting in charge transfer. Commercial realization of the atomic vapor process faces severe obstacles due to the aggressivity of the uranium vapor and the low working pressure. It is, however, the only laser process that has yielded considerable enrichment factors.

Initial estimates indicate that AVLIS consumes 100–200 kWh/SWU of energy. This is comparable to advanced gas centrifuge energy consumption and about one-tenth that of gaseous diffusion (Table 6.5). The capital cost of the AVLIS technique is $20–80/SWU (1979 dollars) compared to $120/SWU for either diffusion or centrifuge enrichment (Table 6.5 and Figure 6.18). A large fraction of the plant cost is in the laser and mirror system. The high cost of laser energy is the crucial issue

Table 6.5. Relative Parameters of Gaseous Diffusion (GD), Gas Centrifuge (GC), and LIS

	GD	GC	LIS
Capital cost ($/SWU)	388	233	195
Energy requirement (kWh/SWU)	2100	210	170
Economic plant size (t/yr)	9000	3000	3000

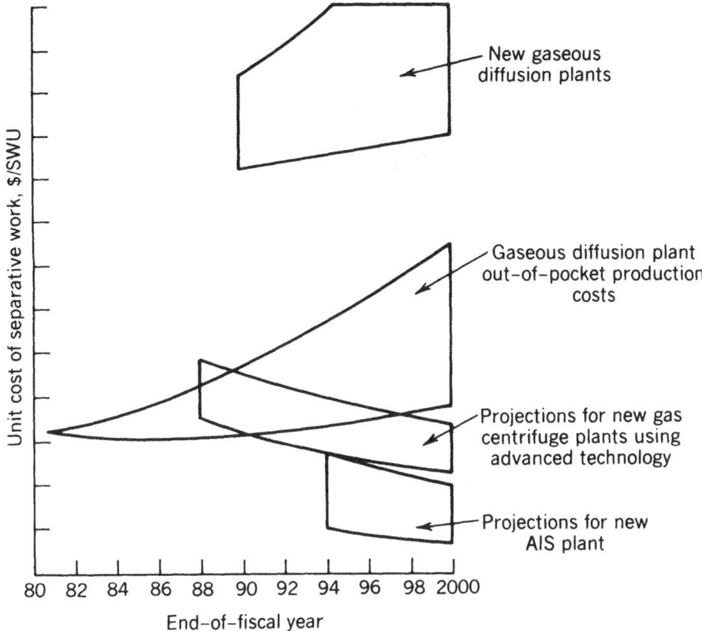

Figure 6.18. Relative cost comparisons of enrichment alternatives. [From W. R. Voigt, Jr., *Nuclear Europe* **2,** 14 (1982).]

in the laser isotope separation process. The power consumption is determined largely by the quality of the mirrors. With 99.6% reflection quality and over 300 reflections per laser pulse, over 70% of the energy is lost in the mirrors alone. When this is factored into the absorption cross section and the 6.2 eV required to ionize each uranium atom, a laser system requiring several kilowatts and operating at 0.2% efficiency would need several megawatts of electrical input energy.

Molecular Laser Isotope Separation (MLIS)

As an alternate to the atomic laser enrichment work at LLL, Stanford University and Los Alamos National Laborabory (LANL) are focusing on vibrational modes that utilize the motion of a uranium atom in a UF_6 molecule. This is referred to as the Molecular Laser Isotope Separation (MLIS) process. It involves a two-stage process with multiple-photon absorption: the first photon selectively excites the molecules of a particular isotope (^{235}U) and then the second photon dissociates the excited molecule. The first step uses infrared radiation (IR) at 16 μm to excite the $^{235}UF_6$ molecule. This causes a transition between vibrational states of the molecule. The absorption spectrum of UF_6 is even more complicated than that of atomic uranium because of the vibrational and rotational frequencies of the molecule. To aid in the selective excitation of $^{235}UF_6$, the absorption spectrum is simplified by expanding the gas in hydrogen through a hypersonic nozzle. This causes $^{235}UF_6$ to cool, but not to condense. The net effect of this expansion is to convert most of the random kinetic energy of the UF_6 gas into translational motion in the nozzle. Energy stored in vibrational and rotational modes is reduced by intermolecular collisions downstream of the nozzle. This reduces the number of molecules in higher vibrational and rotational states, thereby simplifying the absorption spectrum around 16 μm (Figure 6.19). The UF_6-hydrogen gas is cooled to about 30 K, at which temperature nearly all the molecules are in the lowest vibrational ground state.

The second step is the decomposing and collecting of the excited molecule. Radiation in the ultraviolet part of the spectrum (0.308 μm) is used, and the dissociation products are $^{235}UF_5$ and F_2. The UF_5 subsequently precipitates from the gas as a fine powder, called "laser snow," and is collected (Figure 6.20). The gas is then recompressed through a diffuser.

Like the LLL atomic-laser process, the LANL technique will benefit as laser technology improves, particularly in the areas of energy density, pulse rates and reliability. The LANL "laser snow" process has further opportunity to improve by controlling the exchange of energy between $^{235}UF_6$ and $^{238}UF_6$ molecules and the recombination of UF_5 and F_2 gas. Once these problems are reduced and throughput increased, laser isotope separation may become a viable technology.

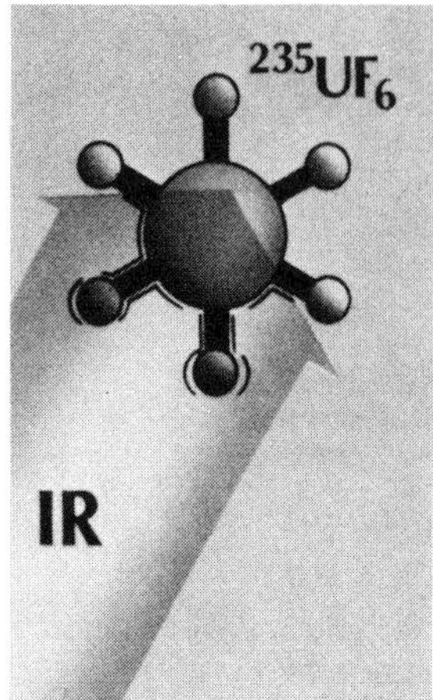

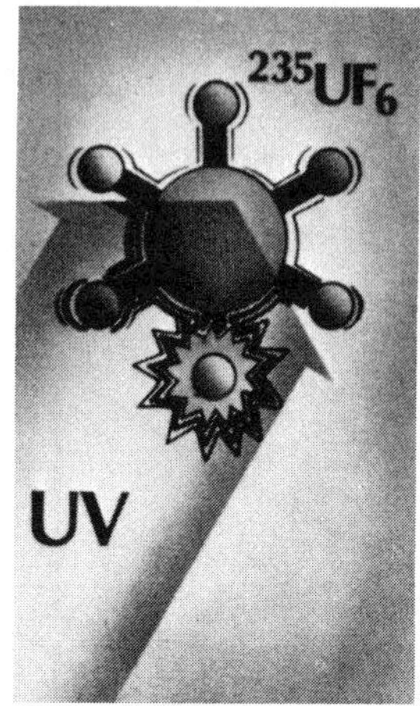

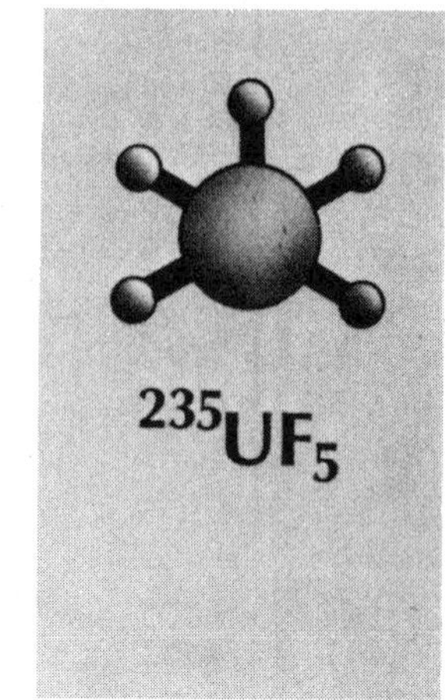

Figure 6.19. Schematic of the laser enrichment process. A near simultaneous irradiation of a $^{235}UF_6$ molecule with infrared (IR) laser and ultraviolet (UV) laser light produces UF_5, termed "white snow." (Courtesy ORNL.)

Chemical Separation Using Lasers

Some work has been done on chemical reactions, but this is not as advanced as other methods. The technique is to mix a chemical scavenger with the laser feedstock to react only with the excited states (Figure 6.21). Such a chemical scavenger has been used to separate chlorine isotopes. The combination of ICl and bromobenzene has been used as feedstock and scavenger according to the reaction:

$$I^{37}Cl + 6050\text{ Å} \rightarrow I^{37}Cl^* + C_6H_5Br \rightarrow I + Br + C_6H_5{}^{37}Cl$$

$$I^{35}Cl + 6050\text{ Å} \rightarrow \text{No reaction}$$

The ^{37}Cl is collected by chemical processing of the resulting chlorobenzene molecule.

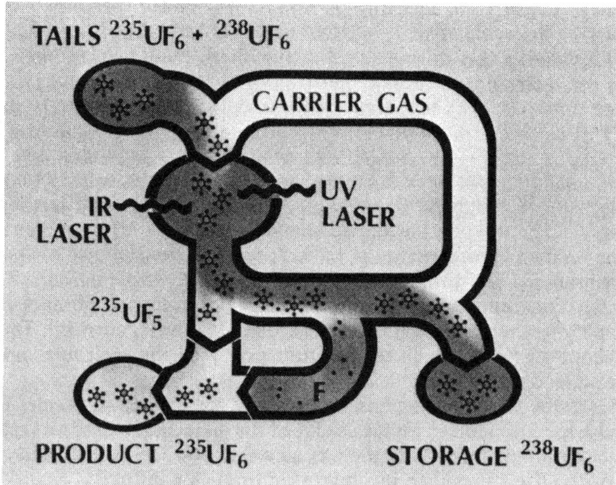

Figure 6.20. Schematic of the laser enrichment process. The IR and UV lasers act on a flowing gas stream. The depleted $^{238}UF_6$ is stored. The product $^{235}UF_5$ is sent to a refluorination tank to produce UF_6 gas. (Courtesy ORNL.)

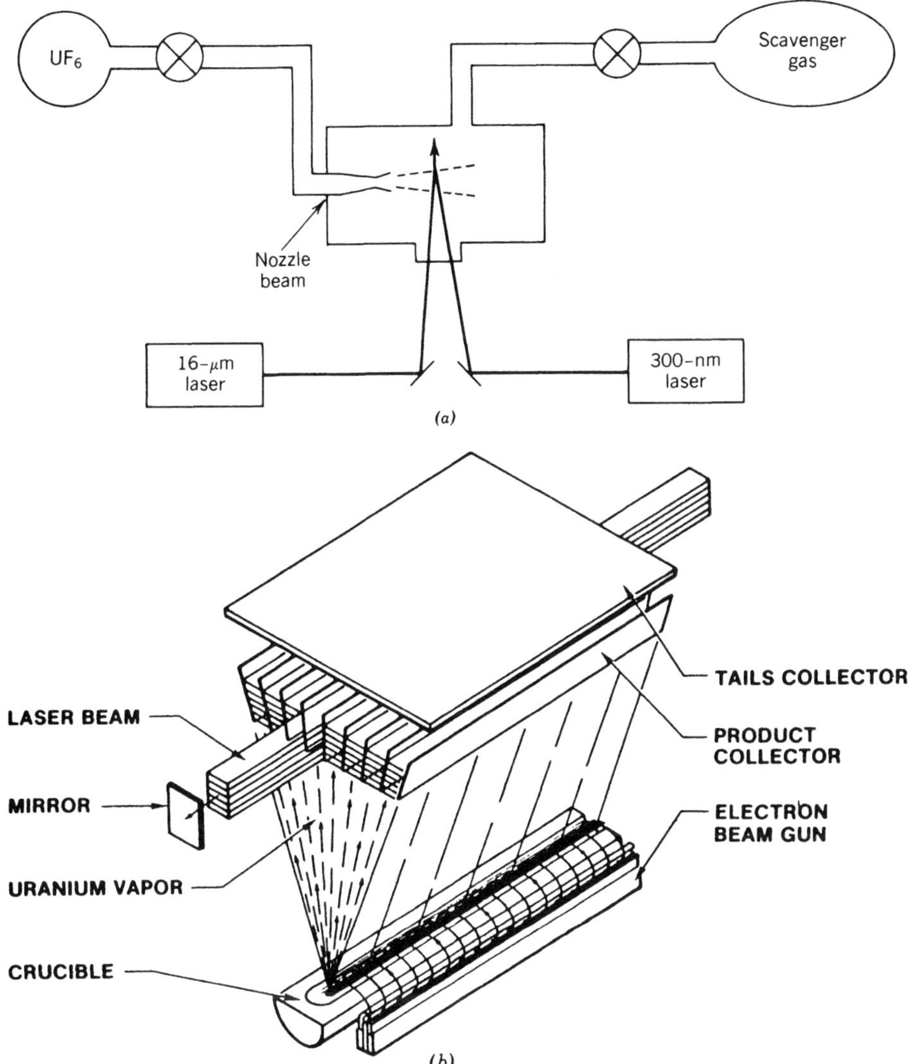

Figure 6.21. (*a*) A Molecular Laser Isotope Separation (MLIS) configuration. (From EPRI Report NP-334.) (*b*) JNAI-LIS process, vapor generation, and ion extraction. Uranium atoms, vaporized by an electron beam in a vacuum, pass between collector plates where they are illuminated by laser light. The ^{235}U atoms are selectively ionized and are attracted to the collection plates by means of an electric field. (From XJA-EL-P-001.)

Recent work has emphasized organic uranium compounds, especially the metallo-organic group uranyl-dihexafluoroacetylacetonate, referred to as UO_2L_2B. Asymmetric stretch vibrations of the central uranyl group, induced by a CO_2 laser, are important for uranium separation. Separation factors around 2 appear possible. A critical requirement is that any compound used must have a sufficiently high vapor pressure, as well as chemical stability. Another prerequisite is to use compounds that undergo permanent changes by IR absorption while showing isotopic selectivity. Much more work is required before this method is useful for the separation of uranium isotopes.

Cascade Design

The cascade design for gaseous diffusion, centrifuge, and nozzle enrichment technologies is not necessarily optimum for advanced separation methods such as laser enrichment. This is because

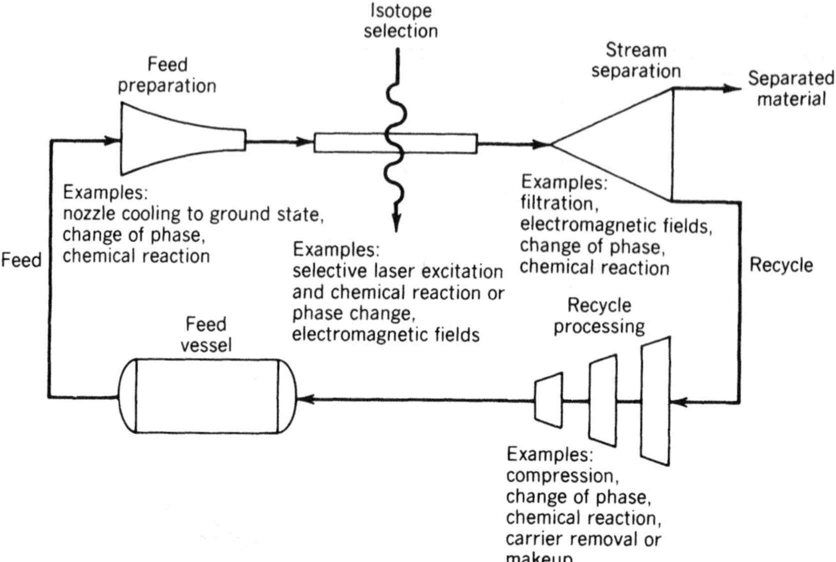

Figure 6.22. Schematic diagram of batch recycle system. [From J. H. Pendergrass, *Trans. Am. Nuclear Soc.* **41,** 140 (1982).]

laser methods can involve (1) large separation values, (2) a limit on the selection of cuts for economic performance, (3) chemical and/or phase changes with a need to regenerate the feed materials, and (4) an energy-efficient process with a high capital cost. For the low separation processes, such as gaseous diffusion, ideal cascade design implies no mixing of streams of different enrichment within the cascade. Such a mixing would increase the entropy of the feed stream and increase the energy required for separation. Low separation processes can come fairly close to an ideal cascade by accommodating feed and product/waste streams. For advanced, high-separation methods, nonideal cascades may be necessary to achieve lowest production cost, especially when more than two isotopes are involved. Hazardous isotopic mixtures can be separated in small batches to lower risks. If (a) the separation system preparation time for each batch is substantial and/or (b) the single-pass cut (fraction of isotopic mixture feed diverted by separation equipment) is small, multipassing of unseparated isotopic mixture through the separation equipment can be cost effective. Figure 6.22 shows a schematic diagram of how a laser system would operate in a batch mode.

For laser systems, economically optimum designs will match product/waste stream purity with the number of stages, feed preparation, and laser light requirements. Partial recycle may be cost effective when only a small fraction of the separation power of an additional stage is required to meet the enrichment goal. Stream splitting may be considered when a large fraction of a stage's separating power is required. This will reduce feed and laser parameters, but will also reduce final enrichment. Unusual numbers of enrichment and stripping stages, with bunching of the feed streams at the cascade feed stage, may be effective in reducing the total number of stages needed to meet the desired final enrichment.

Phase Equilibrium Processes

Separation of isotopes by phase equilibrium depends on small volatility differences of the isotopes between their solid, liquid, and gas phases. Several processes have been investigated. These include fractional distillation, gas–liquid absorption, and fractional sublimation. Fractional distillation, once used for the production of heavy water (D_2O), is a relatively simple process, but costly compared to chemical exchange processes except for the final concentration of deuterium (see next section). For uranium enrichment only fractional distillation of UF_6 has been considered, since UF_6 is the only liquid with sufficient vapor pressure at room temperature. $^{238}UF_6$ is more volatile than $^{235}UF_6$, with an ϵ of -4×10^{-5}.

Gas-liquid absorption has also proved to be technically possible. This process makes the use of fluorocarbons, which are the only known solvents for UF_6. The estimated ϵ of 6×10^{-6} is lower than for fractional distillation. Fractional sublimation is another phase equilibrium process that can be used to enrich uranium. It is similar to distillation, except that a slight enrichment takes place when a solid, such as UF_6, sublimes to the gas phase at low pressures. Because UF_6 has a negative ϵ, theory suggests that ϵ will not change significantly on freezing. This alone would eliminate fractional sublimation as a practical uranium enrichment technique.

Other processes—such as liquid–liquid extraction and fractional crystallization—have been investigated, but no useful separation factors were obtained. In general, studies of phase equilibrium show that although enrichment of uranium is possible with these processes, the separation factors are not large enough to make them commercially attractive. The highest separation factors have been achieved with fractional distillation, which is used for the distillation enrichment of liquid hydrogen, but it is still at least 20 times lower than what is required for uranium.

Chemical Exchange

Another class of enrichment processes depends on the preferential stability of certain isotopes in various chemical compounds that lead to chemical exchange enrichment. This process depends on two chemical compounds exchanging isotopes rapidly with a useful net separation factor. Three basic requirements are: (1) the compounds must be stable together, (2) they must be separable by simple means, and (3) they can be contacted by means of simple countercurrent flow. In theory, if compounds exist in separate liquid and gas phases, then distillation can form the basis of an enrichment procedure. The cost of chemical enrichment depends on being able to reuse the chemicals (reflux) at the end of each stage. An inexpensive method of converting the compounds into each other is therefore desirable.

Chemical exchange is used for many kinds of enrichment processes important to nuclear power generation, including the enrichment of ^2H (deuterium for use in heavy water) and ^{10}B. In general, the chemical exchange techniques have values of ϵ, the logarithm of a single-stage factor, 10 to 100 times larger than phase equilibrium methods. Typical values of ϵ are 1 for hydrogen and 10^{-2} for uranium. These high values for the light elements make their enrichment by chemical means a commercial attraction. As mentioned, D_2O and ^{10}B are today separated by chemical means on a large scale.

Production of ^{10}B

An example of the technique is the exchange distillation process used to obtain ^{10}B. The chemicals used are boron trifluoride (BF_3) and boron trifluoride etherate [$BF_3O(CH_3)_2$]. The latter is undissociated in liquid form, but in the vapor partially dissociates into BF_3 and $O(CH_3)_2$. The etherate and dissociation products are distilled by a conventional technique. The reaction is given by the following equation:

$$^{10}BF_3 + {}^{11}BF_3 \cdot O(CH_3)_2 \leftrightarrow {}^{11}BF_3 + {}^{10}BF_3 \cdot O(CH_3)_2$$

This method is typical of similar schemes to obtain ^{10}B.

Production of Heavy Water

There are several commercial methods for producing heavy water. The most common way is the dual-temperature, water–hydrogen sulfide exchange process, which is used 90% of the time. The final step in the production of heavy water, however, usually uses a second process, often a water distillation method. The water–hydrogen sulfide exchange works as follows.

The concentrating of deuterium uses a reflux step in which the part leaving an exchange column as an enriched liquid is returned to the column as a vapor. The dual-temperature system provides reflux by purely physical means. Two towers are used, one at 32°C, the other 138°C, hence the name of the process. Hydrogen sulfide circulates between the towers, carrying deuterium (as D_2S). The cold tower has a dissociation factor of 2.3, and the hot has one of 1.8, for the deuterium exchange reaction

$$H_2O + HDS \leftrightarrow HDO + H_2S$$

The process is illustrated in Figure 6.23.

With the proper flow ratios of hydrogen sulfide to water, the lower dissociation factor in the hot tower causes deuterium to transfer from the water to the H_2S, creating D_2S for recirculating to the cold tower. There deuterium is transferred from the D_2S to natural water in the feed, producing enriched water. The towers can be divided into stages to optimize feed, product, and waste streams. The production rate of enriched water is sensitive to the gas-to-liquid flow ratio.

A plant might typically produce water enriched to 15% in deuterium. Although the actual flow diagram to produce this enrichment is complex, the process is efficient. To complete the production

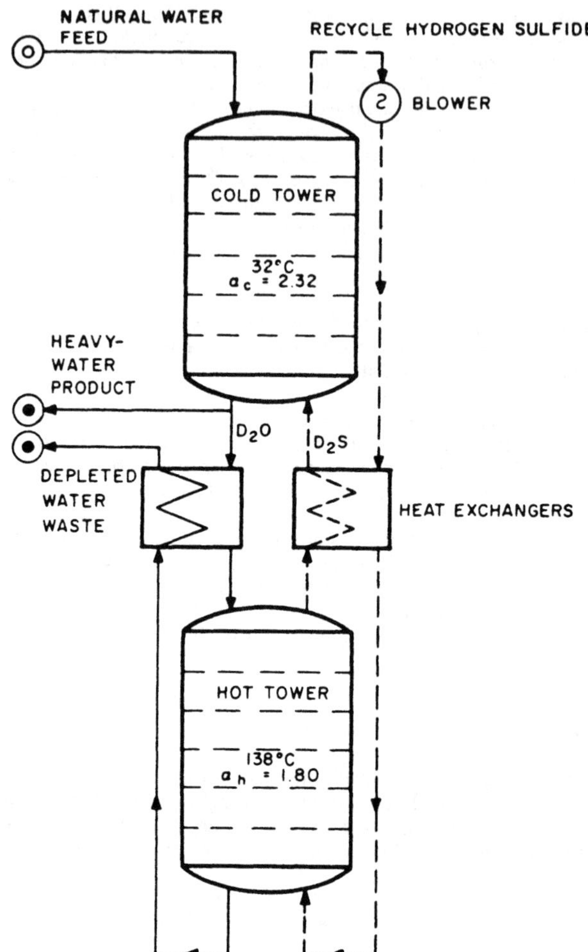

Figure 6.23. Dual-temperature reflux for water-hydrogen sulfide process. (From M. Benedict et al., *Nuclear Chemical Engineering*, McGraw-Hill, New York, 1981.)

of heavy water, the enriched water from the water–hydrogen sulfide process is distilled. The boiling points of H_2O and HDO differ by 0.7°C. By continual reboiling of the feed, a final heavy water concentration of 99.8% deuterium can be reached. The energy consumption is high for this final step.

Production of ^{235}U

For uranium, the low value of ϵ (approaching 10^{-3}) makes enrichment by chemical exchange more difficult. Early experiments at Columbia University looked for a system that had one uranium compound in a solvent, and a second solvent immiscible with the first. Ideally, the solubility of uranium compounds would be high in one solvent and low in the other. Research focused on equilibrating UO_2^{2+} and U^{4+} dissolved in a strong mineral acid with pH around 2. The ^{238}U was found to concentrate in the U^{4+} oxidation state, but no useful process could be developed.

Further research at Goodyear Corporation examined various oxides of nitrogen (NO, NO_2, NOF, and NO_2F) for chemical exchange with uranium hexafluoride (UF_6) at room temperatures. Useful separation factors were found for $NOUF_6$ dissolved in HF against UF_6 dissolved in fluorocarbons. However, the development of the reflux chemistry for the reuse of feed chemicals moved unsatisfactorily, and the process was abandoned.

But in Japan, chemical enrichment by a similar process is being commercialized. Asahi Chemical Company is testing a $21 million model plant of 500 kg/yr capacity that will be used as the basis

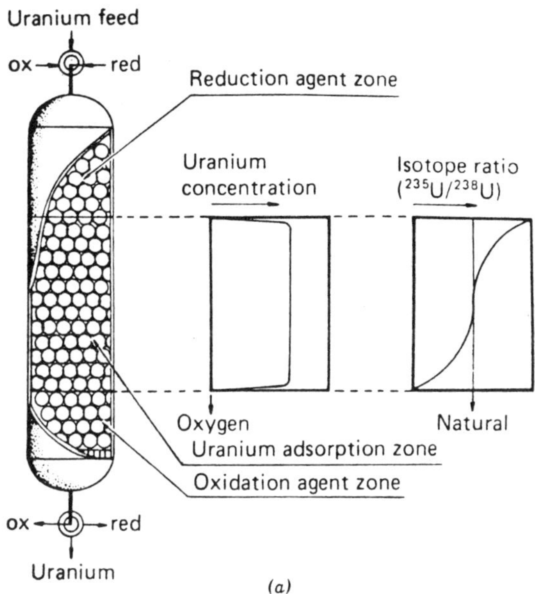

(*a*)

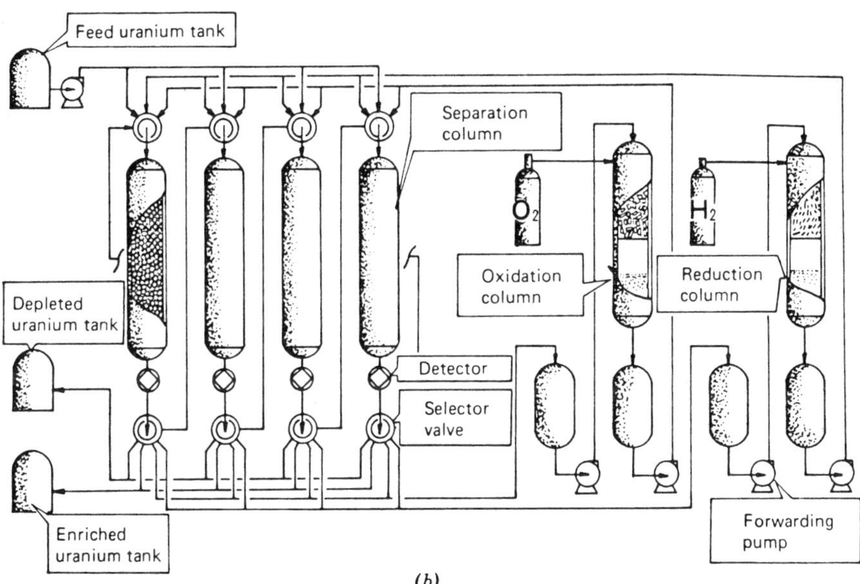

(*b*)

Figure 6.24. (*a*) Schematic view of redox chromatography. (*b*) Flow diagram of Asahi separation unit. [From M. Seko et al., *Nuclear Technology* **50,** 178 (1980).]

for a 1.5 million SWU/yr plant whose construction started in 1982. The process relies on redox chromatography, where uranium ions are kept in solution by a low pH. As in the Goodyear process, UF_6 and $NOUF_6$ are the chemical compounds used. The reaction is repeated in a solid–liquid exchange column (see Figure 6.24). By alternating oxidizing and reducing agents (such as O_2, and H_2 gas), UO_2^{2+} absorbs into packing surfaces in the exchange column, where simultaneous separation into enriched and depleted uranium occurs. In the Asahi process, the working separation factor is about 1.08. One characteristic of the process is the absence of an actual cascade, allowing the recovery of 3% enriched ^{235}U and 0.1% tails. Because the process is basically reversible, the claimed energy consumption is modest, about 150 kWh/SWU.

The French CEA now claims a chemical enrichment process (CHEMIX) based on the equilib-

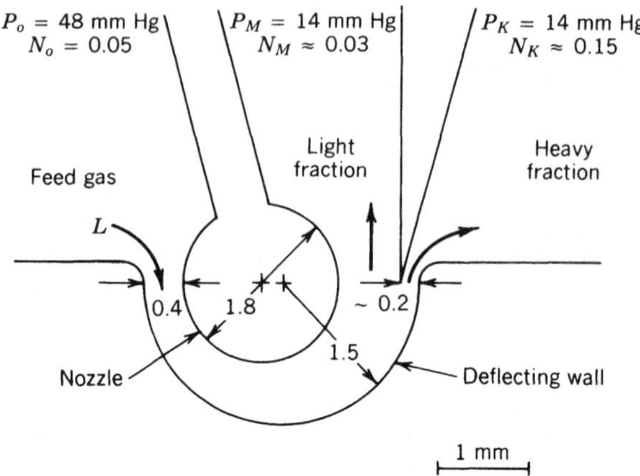

Figure 6.25. Cross section of the separation nozzle system of the Becker Process. (Courtesy Karlsruhe Nuclear Research Center.) P = total pressure; N = mole fraction of UF_6 in the UF_6/He mixture. Subscripts o, M, and K refer to feed gas, light and heavy fractions, respectively.

rium difference between nonmiscible aqueous and organic liquid phases, each one of which withholds preferentially one of the uranium extracting compounds. The process uses approximately 600 kWh/SWU. Pulsed counterflow exchange columns with reflux are used in an iterative flow sheet. To produce 3.5% enriched ^{235}U with 0.2% tails, two cascades are used. Up to 20 columns are arranged in series in each cascade. The enrichment principal can be based on either distillation mass transfer, or even better, liquid–liquid extraction using pulsed columns and a high reflux ratio. The isotope gradient, as well as the separative power of the columns, depends on the contracting efficiency of the phases and the height and diameter of the columns. Details of this process are not available, but the claimed system resident time of 15 months to obtain 3% enriched ^{235}U implies a large uranium inventory is needed.

Also of commercial possibility is the Redox ion–exchange process. In this, uranyl ions are traded between aqueous salts and cation exchange resins. U^{4+}, sorbed on columnar cation-exchange resin bed, are eluted downward by flow of an oxidizing agent such as an aqueous ferric chloride solution. The sorbed U^{4+} is oxidized to U^{6+} and is immediately liberated into the aqueous phase. The aqueous phase in turn percolates downward, along with the ferrous ions, through resin particles occupied by U^{6+} ions. This allows ^{235}U and ^{238}U to distribute between U^{6+} in the aqueous phase and U^{4+} in the resin phase. A depletion of the ^{235}U isotope in successive fractions of the U^{6+} solution occurs, as the last of the U^{4+} on the resin bed is converted to U^{6+} and displaced.

Aerodynamic Processes

Many aerodynamic processes have been investigated for the enrichment of uranium. All are based on a pressure gradient between the isotopes which divide the working fluid into a light fractionate slightly enriched in ^{235}U, and a heavy fractionate slightly depleted in ^{235}U. The fluid flow fields are complex and difficult to analyze. So far, three types of aerodynamic system have been investigated: nozzles, vortex tubes, and shock fronts.

Becker Nozzle

Perhaps the most advanced of the aerodynamic processes is the Becker Separation Nozzle developed at Karlsruhe, West Germany. Details are shown in Figures 6.25 through 6.27. The Becker Separation Nozzle uses UF_6 as the uranium carrier, and a light gas like H_2 or He to increase the jet velocity. Higher velocities considerably improve the separation of the uranium isotopes. Feed compositions range from 5 to 15% UF_6 mixed in hydrogen. Using helium increases the specific energy consumption 25%, but presents fewer safety problems than hydrogen. The cost of helium plays only a small role in the economics of the process since the carrier gas is recirculated. The nozzle operates at subatmospheric pressures of about 20 torr downstream and 80 torr upstream of the nozzle.

The feed gases pass through the nozzle and deflect off a curved wall. A knife edge carefully positioned at the nozzle outlet "cuts" the gas stream into a light and heavy fraction. The hydrogen helps prolong the transient time during the centrifugal acceleration phase of the process when the

Figure 6.26. The Becker Nozzle Process at Karlsruhe, Germany. The separation tubes are being loaded into a separation nozzle stage. This is an experimental facility for the development of the process. The first commercial plant is scheduled for Brazil. This stage is positioned over a gas compressor and cooler (not shown) which produce the required UF_6 pressures and temperatures. (Courtesy Karlsruhe Nuclear Research Center.)

^{235}U concentration is maximum, thereby facilitating the partitioning of the streams. Separation values of 1.025 are achievable. The nozzle requires high precision fabrication; the normal spacing between knife edge and wall is about 0.2 mm. The process seems to be optimized when the flow partition between the light and heavy streams is 1/4. For such a flow split, the separation factor is about 1.015. However, a 1/4 split requires a modification to the cascade design such that the product of a single stage feeds three stages ahead, and the tails feed the stage just below in concentration. The optimum pressures are somewhat higher than before: around 140 and 300 torr downstream and upstream of the nozzle. A main drawback to the Becker nozzle concept is its high specific energy consumption (3000 kWh/SWU), greater than the gaseous diffusion process. This is due to the power required to recompress the light carrier gases. A demonstration plant is being built at Resende, Brazil with a full production capacity of about 300,000 SWU/yr expected by 1988.

The most economical way of increasing the production capacity of the Becker process is to raise the operating pressure. This in turn, requires a reduction in the size of the nozzle systems. Since the UF_6 is highly diluted (by H_2 or He), operating pressures up to 1.5 bar are possible without condensation of the UF_6. For such relatively high pressures, the optimal radius of the deflection groove inlet is 17 μm. Such small dimensions can be obtained by a lithographic process called the LIGA method which produces the grooves by photoetching of metal foils. A double deflection system is now used. The depleted heavy fraction of the nozzle is close coupled to a second section which repeats the process. In this manner, three fractions are produced. The intermediate fraction is recycled within the separation stage to the suction side of the compressor. This improves the separation effect, and the optimum cut of the stage, reducing the total number of stages required for a given enrichment by 40%. The separative capacity of the stages range up to 22,000 SWU/yr when the LIGA style separation elements are used. Product assay of 3.2% requires about 250 stages.

Vortex Tube

A second aerodynamic process is the vortex tube. In this, a tangential velocity is set up in a gas flowing axially in a tube. This is done by tangential injecting of a gas at the tube wall. High experimental separation factors (1.02 to 1.07) have been achieved for the separation of argon

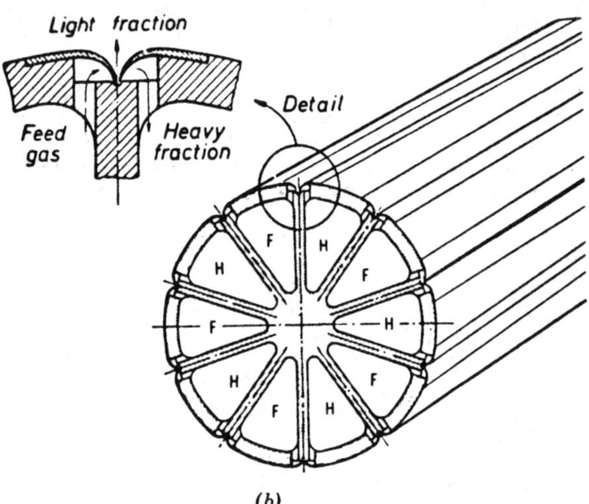

(b)

Figure 6.27. (*a*) Separation tubes for enriching of uranium isotopes by the Becker nozzle separation method. One of these tubes is shown being loaded in the previous figure. They are made of aluminum and are 2 m long. (Courtesy Karlsruhe Nuclear Research Center.) (*b*) Becker separating element with 10 slits. (Courtesy Karlsruhe Nuclear Research Center.)

isotopes $^{36}Ar/^{40}Ar$ using H_2 or CF_3Cl as injection gases. Little published data are available for the separation of the uranium isotopes.

Helikon Process

A related process, a "stationary wall centrifuge," was developed in South Africa. This is the Helikon process using UF_6 in H_2 as the process fluid. It is also referred to as the UCOR process. Operation at a pressure of 6 bars and temperature of 75°C yields a separation factor of about 1.03. The Helikon process is based on transmitting streams of different isotopic concentrations without mixing by an axial-flow compressor. Since the Helikon process has a UF_6 cut fraction of about 0.05, many stages are needed in spite of its relatively high separation fraction. Many stages, however, can be combined into a single unit. An advantage of the Helikon process is its low material inventory and short cascade equilibrium time of about 16 hr. Around 85 SWU/yr per

Table 6.6. Technical Comparison of ^{235}U Enrichment Processes

Characteristic	Gaseous Diffusion	Gas Centrifuge	Laser Enrichment	Aerodynamic Processes	Chemical Exchange
Stage enrichment	Low	High	Very high	Medium	Medium
Throughput	High	Low	Very low	Medium	High
Process pressures	Moderate	Low	Very low	Moderate	Low
Inventory	High	Low	Low	Low	High
Power usage	Very large	Small	Very small	Large	Small

separation stage has been achieved at a power consumption of about 300 kWh/SWU in the separation element, although a much higher specific power consumption is required when the various plant inefficiencies are factored in.

Fenn Shock Process

The last of the aerodynamic isotope separation schemes is the Fenn shock process. It is based on UF_6 gas at high pressure being converted to a shock flow at high Mach number. This is accomplished by passing the gas through a convergent–divergent nozzle. The stream impinges on a group of slots in a duct. At the nozzle exit, a detached shock front forms. The gas is collected through the slots in the duct, enriched in heavy isotopes. The Fenn shock process is still speculative concerning its commercial application. Little experimental or theoretical data are available for the separation factors that can be obtained.

6.4. TECHNOLOGY COMPARISON

The major considerations in assessing the relative merits of an isotope separation process can be grouped into technical and economic factors. There are four important technical factors:

1. Separation factor is perhaps the most important aspect of any enrichment process. For most enrichment processes, however, the separation factor is inversely proportional to the throughput rate. It also varies with the product withdrawal rate from each stage. The latter determines how the stages in a cascade should be connected.
2. Throughput is important—the greater the better. It is often limited by the nature of the process used. A process with a lower separation factor and high throughput may be better than one with a high separation factor and low throughput. The purpose of an enrichment plant is to produce the maximum amount of separative work, which means the greatest throughput at the highest concentration desired.
3. In-process inventory should not be too high for the process equilibrium time to be acceptable. The processes that use a gaseous form of uranium generally have a lower inventory than those that use a liquid.
4. Specific power requirements range between 100 and 10,000 kWh/SWU. Obviously large amounts of power are required for some of the commercial processes. The availability of power and the power supply infrastructure can therefore be a problem.

The last two of these technical factors also have economic implications. They will be taken up again when the economic factors affecting enrichment are discussed in Chapter 19.

A technical evaluation of the various uranium enrichment processes are summarized in Table 6.6. One very striking result is the trade-off between stage enrichment and throughput. Some technologies have special features not reflected in this table. Gaseous diffusion, for example, is relatively simple and flexible. It runs continuously with little attention. The gaseous diffusion plants can also be run under a very wide range of operating conditions without much loss in efficiency. Centrifuge plants, on the other hand, are highly energy efficient, as are the laser processes. Large improvements in technical performance are likely in both the centrifuge and laser isotope separation methods. The time may soon come when it may be more economical to replace existing diffusion plants with advanced isotope separation processes than pay for their large power requirements.

6.5. SAFETY CONSIDERATIONS

The primary safety problems in enrichment plants are handling of UF_6 gas and criticality accidents, although chemical explosions are always to be considered because of the aggressive chemicals

Table 6.7. Total Energy Release Predicted in Past Criticality Accidents

	Characteristics of Fissile Material System				Number of Fissions (10^{17}), Actual Excursion	
Location	Form	Mass, kg fissile	Volume, liter	Duration of Excursion, min	Initial Burst	Total
Y12	$UO_2(NO_3)_2$[a]	2.5	56	13	~0.1	13.0
LASL	Pu/organic	3.3	168	<1	1.5	1.5
IF	$UO_2(NO_3)_2$[a]	34.5	800	20	1.0	400.0
IF	$UO_2(NO_3)_2$[a]	8.0	40	<1	~0.6	6.0
Hanford	Pu complex	1.5	~ 60	2220	~0.1	8.0
Wood River	$UO_2(NO_3)_2$[a]	2.6	~ 70	<1	1.1	1.3
Windscale	Pu/organic	2.5	~100	<1	0.01	0.01
ORNL	$Pu(NO_3)_4$	1.15	64	<1	~0.8	0.8
ORNL	UO_2F_2	18.3	55	<1	0.5	0.5
ORNL	$^{233}UO_2(NO_3)_2$	~ 1.0	5.8	<1	0.11	0.11

Source: From R. L. Hooper et al., *Trans. Am. Nuclear Soc.* **19,** 189 (1974).
[a]Uranium enrichment ~93 wt% ^{235}U.

involved. An important feature of an isotope separations plant is that UF_6 does not change chemical form. The separations plant has other features which lessen the concerns about safety:

1. Most of the pressure in the equipment piping is around or below atmospheric pressure.
2. The equipment is fully air-tight, or it will not function properly. Small leaks are immediately noticeable due to degraded plant operation.
3. UF_6 gas does not present a criticality problem at any moderating level. For solid UF_6 at the modest enrichments used in commercial reactors, hydrogen/uranium ratios below 0.38 avoid all criticality situations.

The prevention of criticality accidents requires the control of hydrogeneous materials around enriched uranium. When hydrogeneous materials are necessary to the operation of an enrichment plant, neutron poisons (e.g., boron) are mixed in with them, and safe-geometry vessels are also employed. However, not using any hydrogeneous materials is preferred.

At least one criticality accident occurred at a uranium recovery operation in an enrichment plant. In 1958, the Y-12 plant at Oak Ridge suffered a plant excursion which was the result of an aqueous solution leaking into a vessel being cleaned. Five persons received radiation doses above 200 rems, although no fatalities occurred. As in other criticality accidents, a flash of radiation followed by disassembly of the critical mass occurred. The accident, not typical of commercial enrichment plant operation, led to improved safety techniques. About 10 criticality accidents have occurred to date, mostly in reprocessing plants for military operations. Total energy released in these incidents, shown in Table 6.7, were in the range 10^{16}–10^{19} fissions. As a comparison, 10^{17} fissions release about the same amount of energy as burning ¼ lb of gasoline. Radiological consequences were limited to the sites involved. The chemical hazards associated with handling UF_6 were considered in Chapter 5 when the uranium conversion process was described.

6.6. SAFEGUARDS CONSIDERATIONS

Material accountability is the basic strategy for safeguarding an uranium enrichment plant against diversion of material. Accountability is required for the feed, product, tails, and waste streams of the facility. This includes recording the ^{235}U weight fraction of these streams, preferably measuring on a continuous basis the enrichment of the flowing UF_6. A number of nondestructive devices exist that do enrichment monitoring. A common technique is to use gamma-ray measurements to determine both enrichment and total uranium concentration while the UF_6 is in the gas phase. The ^{235}U concentration is determined by measuring a gamma ray particular to this isotope (e.g., 185.7 keV line from ^{235}U decay), while the total uranium concentration is determined by the transmission of gamma rays from an external source (e.g., 60 keV gamma rays from ^{241}Am could be used). The ratio of the two concentrations gives the enrichment. The verification of materials accountability is a responsibility of the International Atomic Energy Agency (IAEA) for uranium enrichment facilities under its jurisdiction.

BIBLIOGRAPHY

Benedict, M., "Developments in Uranium Enrichment," *AICHE Symposium Series* **169** (1977).

Benedict, M., "Report of the Uranium Isotope Separation Review Committee," ORO-694, June 1972.

Benedict, M., T. Pigford, and H. W. Levi, *Nuclear Chemical Engineering,* 2nd ed., McGraw-Hill, New York, 1981.

Becker, F. S., and K. L. Kompa, "Uranium Isotope Separation with Lasers," *Nuclear Technology* **58,** 329 (1982).

Gallagher, P., et al., "Field Ionization for Laser Isotope Separation," EPRI Report NP-334 (1976).

Lawrence Livermore Laboratory, Atomic Vapor Laser Isotope Separation, LLL-TB-035 (1981).

Mihalka, M., "International Arrangements for Uranium Enrichment," R-2427-DOE, September 1979.

Olander, D. "The Gas Centrifuge," *Scientific American* **239,** 37 (1978).

Pendergrass, J. H., "Advanced Isotope Separation Cascade Design Considerations," *Trans. Am. Nuclear Soc.* **39,** 201 (1981).

Seko, M., et al., "Uranium Isotope Enrichment by Chemical Method," *Nuclear Technology* **50,** 178 (1980).

U. S. Dept. of Energy, Uranium Enrichment, 1983 Annual Report, ORO-773 (1984).

U. S. Dept. of Energy, "Uranium Enrichment Strategy Study," October, 1980.

Villani, S., *Isotope Separation,* American Nuclear Society, 1976.

———, "Report of the Energy Research Advisory Board Study Group," L. Roddes, Chairman, November 1980.

———, "Technology Demonstration Program for Laser Isotope Separation," XJA-EL-P-001, Jersey Nuclear-Avco Isotopes Inc. (1979).

Zare, R. N., "Laser Separation of the Isotopes," *Scientific American* **237,** 86 (1977).

———, Atomic Vapor Laser Isotope Separation, Lawrence Livermore Report 1-587-055 (1982).

———, U. S. Gas Centrifuge Program, DOE Report UCC-ND (1981).

———, Uranium Enrichment, DOE Report ORO-825 (1982).

CHAPTER 7

NUCLEAR FUEL: ITS PROPERTIES, DESIGN, FABRICATION, AND PERFORMANCE

7.1. INTRODUCTION

The steps in fuel manufacture are determined by the type of fuel required for each reactor type. Historically, three types of fuel have been used in nuclear reactors: metallic fuels, oxide or carbide fuels, and particle fuels in metal or graphite matrixes. Liquid fuels have also been tried but never used in a commercial nuclear reactor. Because oxide fuels are used in light-water reactors (LWRs), the discussion of process steps will focus on these fuels.

A fuel fabricator has three goals: a high-quality, dependable fuel element; economy of manufacture; and, if possible, an ultimate capability to handle radioactive materials through recycle of the isotopes ^{239}Pu or ^{233}U, which are produced by neutron irradiation in the reactor. Today, the emphasis is on high-quality, high-capacity production through the fabrication of UO_2 fuel elements. An LWR uses about 30 t of fuel per year. The fuel is arranged in the core in a lattice containing 30,000 to 40,000 fuel rods. When fuel rods fail, they allow radioactive fission products to leak from the fuel into the coolant. This is undesirable for two reasons: (1) the radioactivity would be deposited throughout the system, increasing the radiation levels and making maintenance more difficult, and (2) fuel clad integrity is one of the major barriers to the release of radioactivity to the environment in the event of an accident. If more than a few fuel rods fail during an operating cycle (i.e., the time between refueling), the reactor then must be shut down and the leaking fuel assemblies removed. In practice, failure rates† less than five fuel rods per cycle have been routinely achieved in LWR reactors.

7.2. FUEL MATERIALS

Uranium metal fuels were the first to be developed for reactor use but were found to have unacceptable dimensional stability under irradiation. Alloys and compounds of uranium were also investigated for fuel use, with fairly extensive consideration given to uranium carbide (UC) and uranium oxide (UO_2), both of which are ceramic materials. Today oxide fuels are universally used. First developed in the 1950s, they have several advantages over metallic and carbide fuels. These include (1) a high melting point and low-vapor pressure, (2) mechanical stability due to the absence of metallic phase transitions, and (3) less swelling and chemical incompatibility than carbide (see Table 7.1). The microstructure of oxide fuel can also be controlled in a way to minimize fission product gas release.

Another type of fuel that has been developed is the particle fuel. These are submillimeter spheres of fuel which are coated with such materials as carbon or silicon carbide. Particle fuels typically release more gas than pellets, but some features related to proliferation resistance may make them attractive in the future. Uranium carbides or the particle fuels might eventually prove technically superior, but oxides are technically entrenched and, indeed, are economic and perform adequately. As a result, manufacturing capability and fuel utilization almost uniquely favor oxide fuels.

Variations of oxide fuels have been also developed which contain "burnable poisons."‡ These

†The design and licensing failure rate, however, is much higher (1%).

‡A burnable poison is a control material fabricated in the fuel matrix to compensate for excess reactivity at the start of a fuel cycle.

Table 7.1. Metal versus Ceramic versus Particle Fuel for LWRs

Metal Fuel

1. Low melting and high vapor pressure a disadvantage in reactor accidents that can damage the core.
2. Phase expansions at low temperatures lead to swelling and mechanical instability. To overcome these tendencies requires an alloy (e.g., 10% molybdenum–90% uranium) to stabilize the fuel.

Ceramic Fuel

1. Carbide (UC)
   a. There is a chemical reaction with stainless steel cladding.
   b. Swelling and cracking can be a problem.
   c. Carbide is an extremely hard material, which can gouge the cladding.

2. Oxide (UO_2)
   a. The fuel pellet cracks during normal operation due to thermal stress, although swelling is not so much a problem.
   b. The microstructure can be controlled, which helps lower fission gas release.
   c. High melting point is an additional safety margin.

Particle Fuel

1. Achieving high density of the microspheres had previously been a problem.
2. Tends to release more fission product gases than oxide fuel.
3. May have certain proliferation advantages.

materials, such as gadolinia (Gd_2O_3) or europia (Eu_2O_3), do not alter the basic ceramic nature of the UO_2 fuel, but are interspersed in the fuel matrix. In some applications, uranium oxide can be mixed together with plutonium oxide to produce what is referred to as a mixed-oxide fuel. A breakdown of the fuels used in the various reactor types is given in Table 7.2. Only the HTGR uses a nonoxide fuel (UC_2) as its primary choice.

7.3. OXIDE FUELS

The fuel now used in LWRs is essentially pure UO_2, although sometimes burnable poisons† are added. For the proposed "plutonium recycle" fuels, 3–7 wt% plutonium dioxide (PuO_2) is added to the UO_2. The plutonium content is increased to about 20 wt% for the prototype LMFBR fuel.

The older metallic fuels were fabricated at maximum physical density, that is, without porosity, but this proved to be a problem because of the fission product yield. For every uranium atom that fissions, two fission products result. Of this 200% fission product yield, approximately 100% are metallic, 40% are gases at high pressure, and 60% are cesium and other volatile elements (see Table 7.3). These gases and volatiles caused swelling in the fuel. This swelling, combined with anisotropic thermal growth due to the crystal nature of the uranium matrix, led to early fuel failure at about 20,000 MWd/t.

The problem was solved by developing oxide fuels at 90–94% theoretical density and by widening the gap between the fuel and its cladding. In this manner, the internal voids allow the high-pressure gases to escape the fuel matrix, and the larger fuel-clad gap allowed some swelling before the fuel matrix could reach, and fracture, the clad. Some experimental fuel, such as that used in the LMFBR EBR-II, has attained burnups to 120,000 MWd/t.

The fuels in current use have the following characteristics:

1. 94–96% theoretical density.
2. Gases and volatiles leave matrix.
3. Matrix swells minimally.
4. Intermatrix void handles fission products.

†Especially to those fuels used in BWRs.

Table 7.2. Major Power Reactors and Their Ceramic Components

Reactor Type	Coolant	Fuel		Control	
		Primary	Alternates	Primary	Alternates
Light water					
BWR	H_2O	UO_2[a]	UO_2[b], $(U—Pu)O_2$[a,b]	B_4C, $UO_2—Gd_2O_3$	
PWR	H_2O	UO_2[a]	UO_2,[b] $(U—Pu)O_2$[a,b] $(U—Th)O_2$[a,b]	$Al_2O_3—B_4C$	$UO_2—Gd_2O_3$
Heavy water					
HWR	D_2O	UO_2[a]	$(U—Pu)O_2$[a] $(U—Th)O_2$[a]	B_4C	
Graphite moderated					
AGR	CO_2	UO_2[a]	$(U—Pu)O_2$[a]	—	
HTGR	He	UC_2[c] (ThO_2)[c] (UO_2)	$(U—Pu)O_2$[c], $(U—ThO_2)$[c]	B_4C	$Gd_2O_3—Al_2O_3$, Eu_2O_3
Breeder reactors					
GCFR	He	$(U—Pu)O_2$[a]	$(U—Pu)C$,[a,c] $(U—Pu)N$[a,c]	B_4C	Eu_2O_3
LMFBR	Na	$(U—Pu)O_2$[a]	$(U—Pu)C$,[a,b] $(U—Pu)N$[a] $(U—Pu)O_2$[b]	B_4C	Eu_2O_3
LWBR	H_2O	$(U—Th)O_2$[a]	—	—	

Source: Adapted from J. T. A. Roberts, *Powder Metallurgy International* **11** (1979).

[a]Pellets.

[b]Sphere-pac.

[c]Coated particles.

Abbreviations key:

BWR	Boiling Water Reactor	HWR	Heavy-Water Reactor	HTGR	High-Temperature Gas Reactor	LMFBR	Liquid-Metal Fast Breeder Reactor
PWR	Pressurized Water Reactor	AGR	Advanced Gas Reactor	GCFR	Gas-Cooled Fast Reactor	LWBR	Light-Water Breeder Reactor

Table 7.3. Elemental Fission-Product Yields in a Fast-Neutron Spectrum

Chemical group	Elemental yield	
	^{235}U*	^{239}Pu
Zr + Nb	0.298	0.204
Y + rare earths[a]	0.534	0.471
Ba + Sr	0.149	0.096
Mo	0.240	0.203
Ru + Tc + Rh + Pd	0.263	0.516
Cs + Rb	0.226	0.189
I + Te	0.012	0.070
Xe + Kr	0.251	0.248

Source: J. H. Davies and F. T. Ewart, *J. Nucl. Mater.* **41,** 143 (1971).
[a]Lanthanum, cerium, praseodymium, neodymium, promethium, samarium, europium, and gadolinium.

The most important structural effect is pellet cracking as the fuel is burned. This is increasingly important at high power levels. If a pellet is operated above 40 kW/m, extensive cracking can be expected. These cracks form during reactor start-up and cooldown, where peak thermal stresses are encountered. For fast reactor fuels, even more extensive fuel pellet cracking can be expected because of the high power (up to 60 kW/m) and high burnup.

Grain growth is also pronounced in LMFBR fuels; in fact, it is not uncommon to observe a central void in irradiated LMFBR pellets (the result of porosity migration). For the LMFBR mixed-oxide fuels, this grain growth can also be accompanied by radial segregation of the uranium and plutonium in the pellet.

Oxide fuels are now successful to the point that swelling, once the leading contributor to fuel failure, is no longer a major problem. Some other causes of failure are pellet-cladding interaction and corrosion of the fuel cladding. These all affect fuel performance, and the availability and capacity of nuclear plants to produce power. The impact of fuel problems on overall plant performance is shown in Figure 7.1. How fuel problems are overcome is the subject of this section.

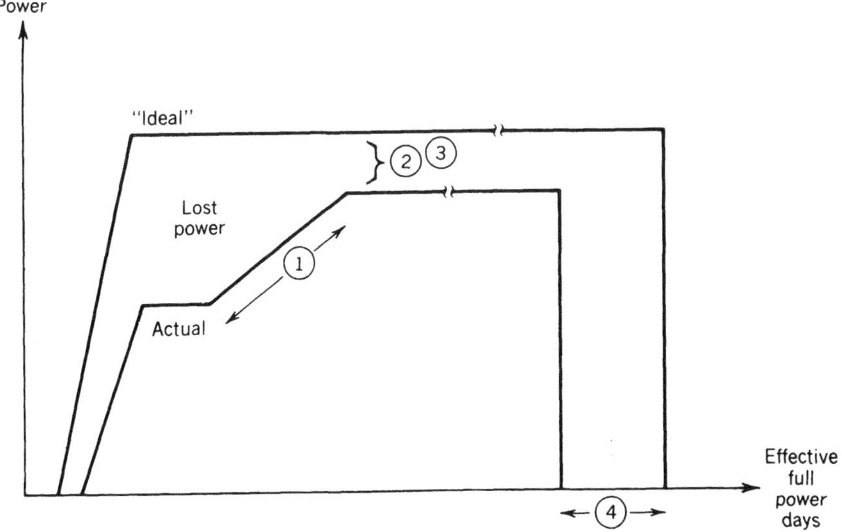

Figure 7.1. Capacity loss caused by fuel performance uncertainties. ① Minimize pellet-cladding interaction failures. ② Uncertainties in safety analyses. ③ Fission product release/spiking. ④ Clad corrosion/crud effects.

Table 7.4. Summary of GE Fuel Designs for BWRs

	7×7		$7 \times 7R$	8×8	$8 \times 8R$
Introduction date	1966	1968	1972	1973	1977
Fuel rod O.D. (in.)	0.563	0.570	0.563	0.493	0.483
Fuel rod I.D. (in.)	0.499		0.489	0.425	0.419
Nominal clad thickness (mils)	32	35.5	37	34	32
Nominal pellet/clad gap (mils)	11	12	12	9	9
Pellet type	Long, sharp corners			Short, chamfered	
Getter	No		Yes	Yes	Yes
Number of water rods	0		0	1	2
Linear power (peak kW/ft)	18.5		18.5	13.4	13.4
Prepressurized (3 atm)	No		No	No	Yes

Source: From W. E. Baily et al., "BWR Fuel Performance," ANS Topical Meeting, April, 1979.

LWR Fuel Design

During the midsixties, the prevailing BWR design was the 7×7 rod configuration (refer to Figure 2.13). With the onset of the various fuel-related problems discussed above, an evolution of fuel design occurred. Factoring in all aspects known at the time, such as the effect of temperature on fission gas release, and so on, it was found that an 8×8 fuel rod design was more advantageous. Since that time, fuel design has evolved slowly. The latest designs incorporate the following features: 8×8 configuration with a low linear heat rate, fully annealed Zircaloy-2 cladding to reduce corrosion; all Inconel low-pressure-drop spacers; and burnable poisons to reduce power peaking in the core. The evolution of BWR fuel since 1966 is shown in Table 7.4.

A similar evolution occurred for PWRs. The initial 14×14 and 15×15 designs have been replaced by 16×16 and 17×17 configurations. The cladding material used is Zircaloy-4 which performs better than Zircaloy-2 in the slightly reducing chemical conditions of the coolant in a PWR. The use of burnable poisons in PWR has been more slowly introduced than for BWRs because of the presence of the control rods in the core during normal operation. Moreover, PWRs use boron dissolved in the coolant water to help control reactivity, which is not the case for BWRs. The concentration of the boron is adjusted as the core burns up (see Chapter 12) giving, in part, the time-varying reactivity control burnable poisons provide, although without the fine spatial distribution that is possible with gadolinia. However, the use of burnable poisons in PWRs is increasing with the use of more advanced refueling schemes and operational practices. Lower fuel cycle costs result when the burnable poisons are used because of better fuel utilization (see Chapter 11).

Fuel Chemistry—Oxygen

UO_2 is not a compound, but a mixture of uranium oxides whose oxide ratio "averages" 2. The actual formula is UO_x, where $1.9 \leq x \leq 2.1$ in practical fuels. As the uranium burns out, the oxygen in the fuel can accommodate the change. Fission products, however, have in general less affinity for oxygen than for uranium (or plutonium). The accommodation of oxygen in the fuel lattice is important, because if it is not chemically bound up it is free to migrate through the lattice and can cause corrosive attack at other locations of the fuel or cladding. For UO_x, there is an extremely large change in oxygen potential near stoichiometric† composition (see Figure 7.2). The oxygen potential shown in Figure 7.2 cannot be extrapolated to $x = 2.00$ and below because of the rapid change in the free energy as stoichimetry is approached. The effect of this discontinuity is to maintain the oxygen/uranium ratio at 2.00. Slight excesses of oxygen cause U_4O_9 to precipitate at the grain boundaries of UO_2. Moreover, the oxygen potential of the fuel determines whether the fission product elements in the fuel can oxidize the metallic cladding. This is shown in Figure 7.3 where the stable regions for the various fission product elements is shown. The physiochemical properties determined from this figure are important for normal operating fuel performance and during potential accident situations. The situation also favors low cladding corrosion because of the accommodation of the oxygen by the UO_2 fuel matrix. Therefore, thin cladding is possible. This reduces reactor core size and improves neutron economy.

On the other hand, PuO_2 (Figure 7.4) is really PuO_2, not a mixture of oxides. As the plutonium burns, the oxygen, which is very reactive, has nowhere to go except to "attack" the fuel cladding.‡

†Stoichiometric composition is the exact ratio of metal atoms to oxygen atoms where the compounds form, in the case of uranium dioxide, 2.00.

‡The oxygen potential determines the "state" of the fission products that actually attack the cladding. Oxygen, per se, does not bother the cladding.

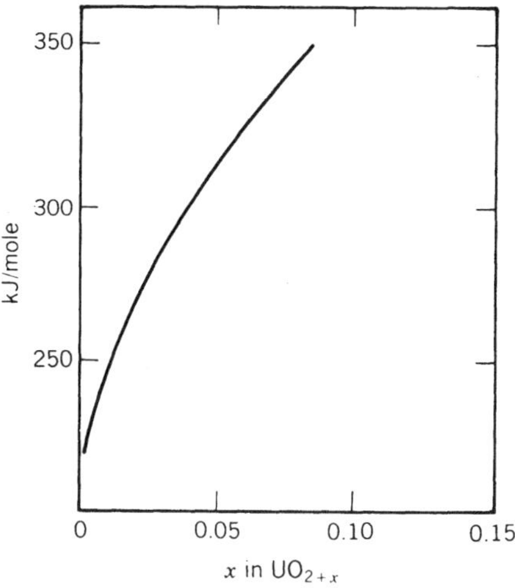

Figure 7.2. Free energy of oxygen in UO_{2+x}.

To overcome this, when plutonium is to be used as a reactor fuel, it is mixed with uranium oxide. Such mixing mitigates the effects of oxygen on plutonium fuel performance and fuel pin lifetime. The oxygen ratio in mixed plutonium–uranium oxide fuels increases during operation; if the initial oxygen/metal ratio was not adjusted to hypostoichiometric ratios (1.93–1.97), then excess oxygen once again could cause cladding problems. Low stoichiometric ratios are achieved by adjusting the plutonium concentration in the fuel and, as described in Section 7.4, controlling conditions during fuel manufacturing to reduce oxygen concentrations. Low oxygen levels are needed also to mitigate fuel migration—the tendency of plutonium to migrate toward higher temperature regions. Pu redistribution is not a problem when the oxygen levels are kept low. Otherwise, hot spots in the fuel could develop as the plutonium migrated to the center of the fuel rod.

Fuel Chemistry—Fission Products

Most fission fragments, initially traveling at high speed following fission, are stopped by the fuel matrix, and are accommodated by the fluorite† structure of UO_2. The fission fragments, however, do not remain fixed, but can migrate through the lattice. Upon encountering a free surface, they can be released from the fuel matrix. The effects of fission products on the chemistry of oxide fuels are summarized in Table 7.5. Of these effects, three are noted below:

1. *Iodine Attack of Cladding Materials.* Iodine will attack zirconium to form ZrI_4, or attack the principal components of stainless steel to form FeI_2, CrI_2, and NiI_2. This attack is favored at the cladding where the temperature is cooler, after iodine has diffused across the gap between the fuel and clad. The clad corrodes and eventually fails. The corrosion may be particularly acute at the grain boundaries. When mechanical stress is also present, clad failure might be rapid. Under adverse circumstances FeI_2, for example, can be transported back to the fuel, releasing the iodine to attack the clad anew. Thus, a rather small amount of iodine can cause considerable clad damage. This effect is partially mitigated by the tendency of cesium, which is 10 times as abundant as iodine in the fuel, to form the compound CsI.

2. *Swelling due to Fission Gases.* The noble-gas fission products xenon and krypton are nearly insoluble in the fuel matrix. As a result, these fission products are either (a) released from the fuel and retained in the fuel-clad gap, or (b) form small gas pockets within the fuel matrix (Figure 7.5). The former leads to greater cladding stress, while the latter implies that low-density bubbles have formed in the fuel matrix. Swelling of the fuel, lower thermal conductivity, and fuel-clad contact can result. Gas bubbles often nucleate along the tracks of fission fragments. These bubbles, 20 Å in diameter, migrate through the fuel matrix until pinned by a lattice dislocation. They remain there until reaching a critical size, and then drag the dislocation to a grain boundary.

Noble gas behavior is determined by a number of factors. These include temperature and temperature gradient, fuel matrix stress, and fission rate. In modern fuels, swelling of about 1% per

†UO_2 crystallizes in a cubic system forming cubes or octahedra. Because eight oxygen ions are required to shield the positive metal (U) from other metal ions, the fluorite structure, with each U surrounded by eight O, and each O surrounded by four U, is assumed.

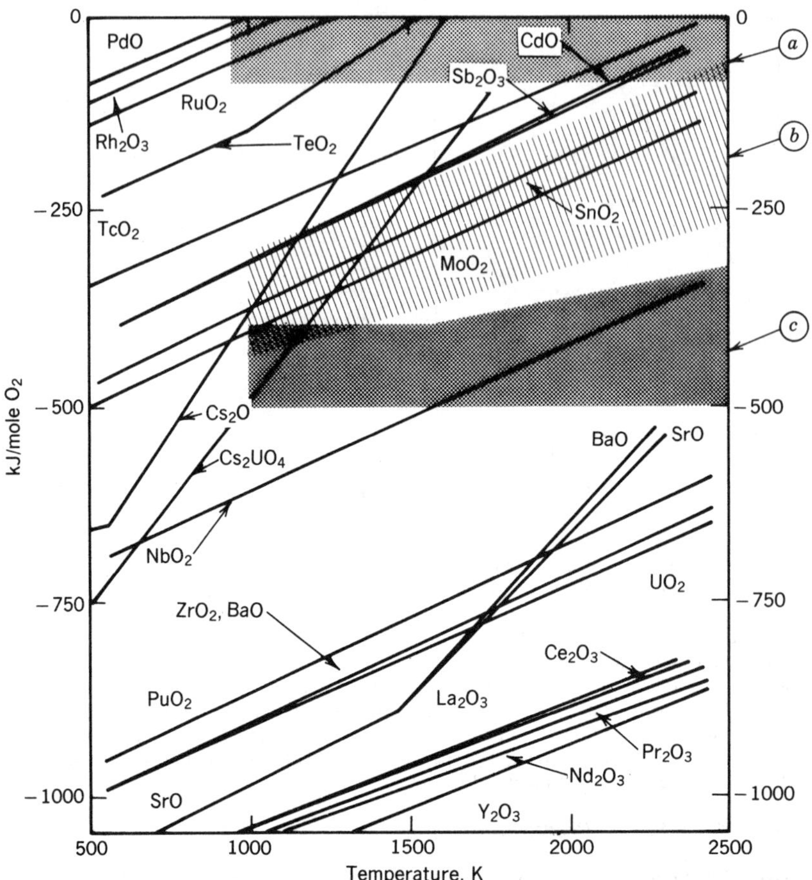

Figure 7.3. Oxygen potential of UO_2 fuel. In this figure, the area above the line is a stable region for an oxide. There are three regions of interest: (*a*) normal operating region for an intact fuel rod; (*b*) failed fuel rod in the presence of steam and H_2; (*c*) failed fuel rod in air. From this figure several conclusions can be drawn: 1. Zr and the rare earths form more stable oxides than UO_2. This group includes Ba and Sr which form compounds such as BaZrO. 2. Many other elements (Ru, Rh, Ag, etc.) form less stable compounds than UO_2, are reduced to their metallic state, and appear to precipitate out as metallic inclusions. 3. Cesium forms stable uranates (Cs_2UO_4) and molybdates (Cs_2MoO_4). It has also been found that Cs, I, and Mo migrate from hot to cooler regions of the fuel, while Ru goes counter to the thermal gradient. (Courtesy D. Cubicciotti.)

10,000 MWd/t can be expected.† Gas behavior is controlled by regulating various fuel properties, including fuel microstructure, grain size, and dislocation density.

3. *Formation of Compounds for the Elements Posing the Largest Radiological Risk in the Event of an Accident.* Risk assessment models (Chapter 17) predict relatively large off-site concentrations (and thus health consequences) for cesium, iodine, and tellurium in the event of a major reactor accident. Therefore, their behavior in the fuel matrix is an important question. The alkali-metal cesium is a strongly charged cation that combines with the anions I^- and Te^{2-} to form CsI and Cs_2Te untill all the iodine and tellurium are consumed. (There is roughly 10 times as much cesium as iodine and tellurium produced in LWR fuel, and about twice as much in fuel made up of 100% PuO_2.) These elements tend to migrate from the hot interior of fuel pellets to the cooler regions at the surface. Crystals of CsI have been observed, for instance, on the surface of the cladding. The remaining cesium is likely to exist as either a uranate (Cs_2UO_4) or molybdate (Cs_2MoO_4).

†This corresponds to about 0.5% per 10^{20} fissions/cm^3.

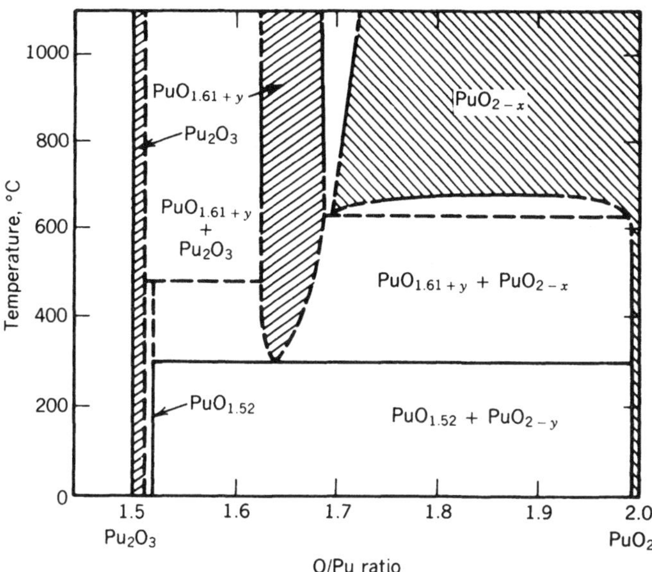

Figure 7.4. Phase diagram of the plutonium–oxygen system. Below about 2000°C, no oxide of higher oxidation state than PuO_2 is found. [From H. M. Mattys, *Actinides Rev.* **1,** 165 (1968).]

Table 7.5. Effect of Fission Products on the Chemistry of Oxide Fuel

Phenomena	Result
1. Large number of fission products produced	1. The tendency to form or not form oxides controls oxygen level in fuel. High oxygen levels lead to cladding defects. Some chemical species such as iodine, can attack cladding directly.
2. One uranium atom replaced by two fission products	2. In LWR fuels, typical burnup is 3%, so end-of-life fuel will contain about 6 at.% fission products. For LMFBRs, these numbers are 3–4 times as high. Swelling in fuel can produce internal stresses and mechanical contact with cladding.
3. A large fraction of fission products are noble gases (xenon and krypton).	3. Noble gases are not retained in the fuel matrix, but escape into the internal space within the cladding. This increases the internal pressure of the cladding. These gases also are poorer thermal conductors than He (the gas filled in the plenum during fuel fabrication), so that the fuel operates at a higher temperature.
4. Nonvolatile fission products have different physical properties than UO_2.	4. Thermal conductivity of fuel decreases, internal temperatures increase. Melting point of fuel changes. Metallic inclusions form, sometimes leading to cracking. Fission products migrate up or down the temperature gradient existing during normal operation. Changes in grain size occur.

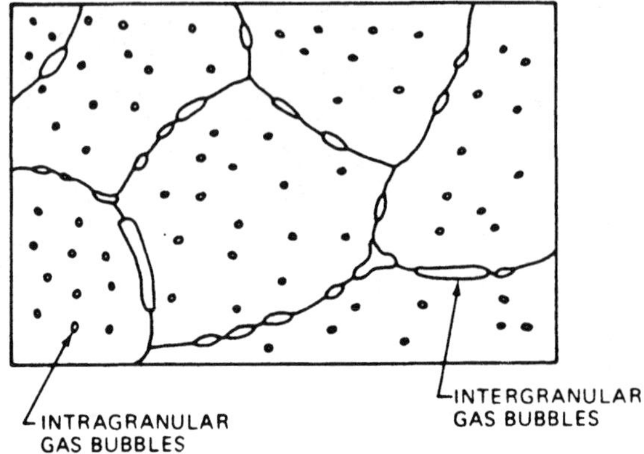

Figure 7.5. Gas bubbles in grains and on grain boundaries.

Fuel rod chemistry is controlled by careful engineering of the fuel, its matrix, and its composition in order to achieve maximum performance. Because it is impossible to change a parameter once irradiation has started, careful fuel fabrication is key in prolonging fuel life.

7.4. FUEL CLADDING

All commercial reactor fuel is contained in metal cladding tubes. The term "cladding" in this case does not imply the deposition of one metal on another, but simply refers to the outer jacket of the fuel. This cladding is used to prevent pellet corrosion and serve as a barrier to the release of radioactive fission products. Most operating reactors use an alloy of zirconium for the cladding material. A few LWRs have used stainless steel. The advanced gas-cooled reactors in the United Kingdom and the LMFBR fuels also use stainless steel.

The cladding material must have the following characteristics:

1. Mechanical and chemical compatibility with the fuel, and with the coolant of the reactor. When UO_2 is used as the fuel, and water as the coolant, the cladding is necessary to prevent corrosion, and to support the UO_2 which lacks structural strength.
2. Ability to withstand high heat loads without melting or losing mechanical integrity. The electrical capacity of a nuclear reactor is directly proportional to the temperature attained by the fuel; the inability of the cladding to handle high heat loads would penalize the efficiency of the plant.
3. Ability to accommodate radiation damage. This permits high fuel utilization and long operating cycles.

The cladding material of choice in LWRs is an alloy of zirconium because of neutron economy. Zirconium has a low neutron capture cross section. The other important properties of zirconium are given in Table 7.6. Of particular note is its crystal structure, which is hexagonal close pack arrangement of the atoms. In spite of its hexagonal (i.e., anisotropic) form, zirconium can be

Table 7.6. Properties of Zirconium Metal

	Phase		
	α-Zr	β-Zr	ZrO_2
Density (g/cm^3)	6.49	6.44	5.82
Specific heat (J/kg-K)	375	650	604
Thermal conductivity (w/m^2-K)	19.6	28.5	2.2
Crystal structure	HCC[a]	BCC[b]	
Melting point	862°C	1865°C	

[a]HCC = Hexagonal Close Pack.

[b]BCC = Body Center Cubic.

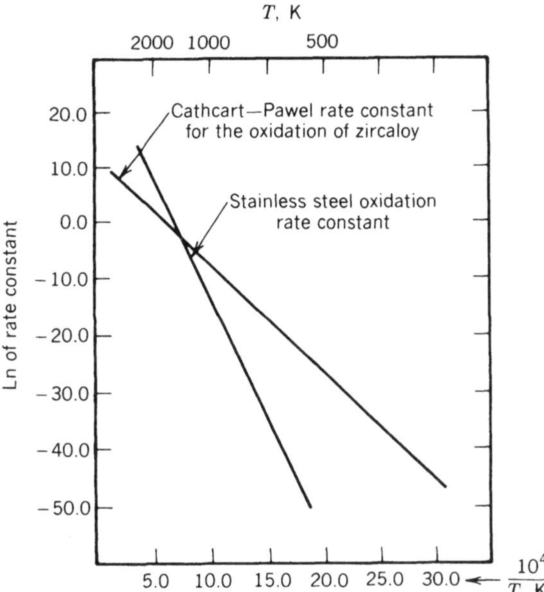

Figure 7.6. Comparison of reaction rates for steam oxidation of Ziracaloy and stainless steel as a function of temperature. Stainless steel has a much lower rate of corrosion at normal operating conditions than Zircaloy. At about 1500 K, however, the rate constants cross over and stainless steel corrosion is higher. Such high temperatures would only be reached in a severe core damage accident. The rate difference probably would not be significant in such an event because other phenomena (e.g., hydrogen blanketing) may control the reaction, which would be very rapid at these temperatures.

prepared in ductile form, and has mechanical properties similar to carbon steel. Zirconium does not offer as much oxidation protection as stainless steel (Figure 7.6), a reason why stainless steel was chosen in some LWR cores in the past.

A phase diagram for zirconium–oxygen is given in Figure 7.7. Zirconium's oxidation rate is important in predicting its corrosion potential and mechanical integrity at high temperature. Zirconium normally forms an adherent oxide film that protects it from corrosion. When oxidized as ZrO_2, the volume expands about 50%, reducing its mechanical strength. Oxygen, however, can be used to stabilize the alpha phase. When the temperature increases, oxidation can become very rapid. For instance, about 17% of a typical fuel cladding will oxidize within 1 hr at a temperature of 1100°C, and film boiling on the surface of a fuel rod can cause oxygen embrittlement of Zircaloy-4 in the temperature range of 800–1100°C. Therefore, the usual design goal is to keep the cladding temperature below 550°C. The "safe equivalent" temperatures allowable so that no cladding failure occur via oxidation are shown in Figure 7.8. The amount of oxidation that is allowable is also an important parameter for safety purposes. The safety criteria associated with the use of zirconium alloys are designed to protect its strength as a fuel cladding. As a result, licensing criteria (in the United States) require that in the event of a loss-of-coolant accident, the cladding temperature must remain below 1477 K and that less than 17% of the wall thickness of the cladding be oxidized. To ensure cladding integrity during emergency cooling of the fuel, the 17% oxidation limit is required in the U.S. NRC regulations.† Recent experimental results (Figure 7.9) show that this is a conservative requirement with respect to both thermal shock and impact loads. Less conservative regulations would lead to better thermal margins for LWRs.

Zirconium must be highly purified for use as a fuel-cladding material. Zirconium ore normally contains between 0.5 and 3.0% of the element hafnium. The neutronic properties of hafnium are just the opposite of zirconium; hafnium has a high neutron capture cross section. For this reason, hafnium is sometimes used as a control rod material, but under normal operating conditions it should not be introduced in the core. The chemical properties of zirconium and hafnium are very

†Since zirconium at high temperature reacts with water to produce hydrogen, there are also limits (1%) on the amount of hydrogen allowed.

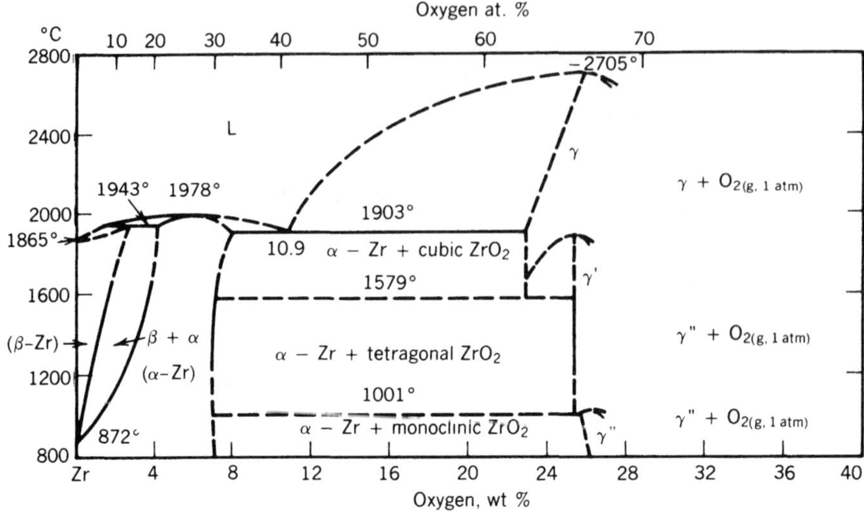

Figure 7.7. Zirconium–oxygen phase diagram.

similar. As a result, the processing and purification of zirconium is difficult. Several processes exist. They are summarized in Table 7.7.

To improve the structural and corrosion properties of the pure element, alloys of zirconium have been developed (Table 7.8). These usually contain greater than 98% zirconium, with tin being the principal alloying ingredient. The material currently used for PWR cladding is Zircaloy-4; the main advantage of this particular alloy is increased resistance to hydrogen embrittlement. In BWRs where oxygen is present in the coolant, Zircaloy-2 is used. The fabrication of Zircaloy into tubing is fairly conventional. However, during fabrication care must be taken in the following areas:

1. Oxygen, nitrogen, and carbon content of the alloy must be controlled; otherwise, embrittlement and increased corrosion rate become problems.

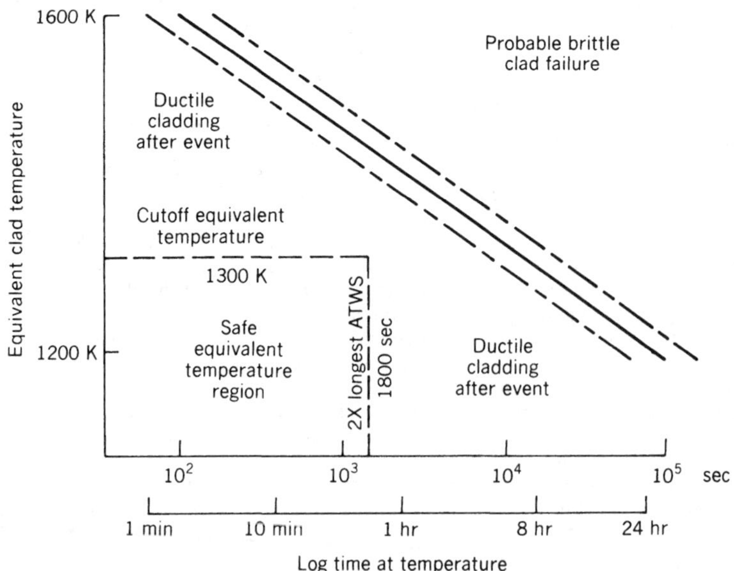

Figure 7.8. "Safe" equivalent clad temperature(s). (No clad failure by oxidation.)

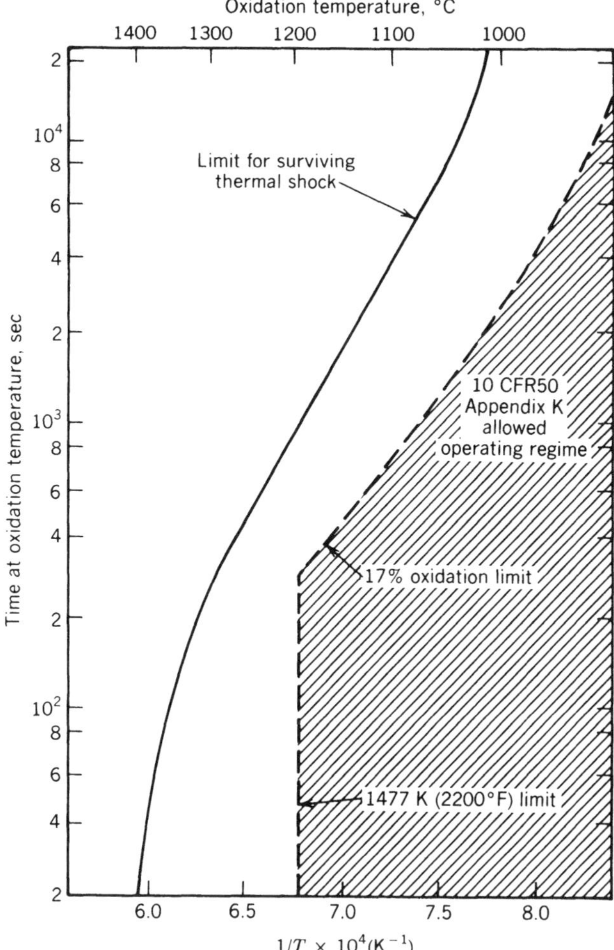

Figure 7.9. Zircaloy embrittlement data compared to LOCA Appendix K criteria. (From R. R. Biederman, EPRI Report NP-734.)

2. Hydrogen levels during manufacturing levels should also be controlled; otherwise, zirconium hydrides (ZrH_2) can precipitate at grain boundaries.
3. The alloying elements must be finely dispersed in the material in order to avoid corrosion on the side of the cladding tubes contacted by the water coolant.

The fabrication of Zircaloy tubes, per se, is straightforward. It welds easily, although an inert gas atmosphere is required.

Cladding for Fast Reactors

An LMFBR is not as affected as LWRs by neutron capture in the fuel cladding and core structural materials. This is because the amount of these cladding and core materials per unit of fuel is smaller, as is their capture cross section at high neutron energies. LMFBR materials, therefore, are chosen for mechanical strength, chemical compatibility and cost (Zircaloy is quite expensive). Most LMFBR designs call for cladding made of stainless steel, or one of the other advanced Fe-Ni-Cr alloys (Table 7.9). If stainless steel is used, a Type 316 (an austenitic variety) is usually selected. The newer alloys (such as D-9) with 30–50% nickel content seem to give good performance as a cladding material due to less creep at high temperature. D-9 has a higher nickel content than the 13% contained in SS-316.

Table 7.7. Zirconium Processing

Conventional Process

1. $ZrCl_4$ and $HfCl_4$ is extracted from the mineral matrix via solvents, acid and thiocyanate complexing; this then precipitates.
2. Calcining reduces the zirconium complex to $ZrCl_3$ (but not the hafnium).
3. Distillation removes the more volatile $HfCl_4$.
4. The zirconium compound is rechlorinated to $ZrCl_4$ and processed into sponge.

New Process (Ishizuka Research Institute)

1. Extraction, precipitation, calcination, and chlorination steps similar to conventional process.
2. $ZrCl_4$ separated from $HfCl_4$ (and other minerals) by fractional distillation at 400–500°C and 20–25 bars.

Solvent-Free Process (Pechiney–Ugine–Kuhlman)

1. Conventional recovery uses a solvent (methyl isobutyl ketone) which causes problems with corrosion, dangerous fumes, and effluent disposal.
2. P–U–K process involves mixing molten chlorinated zirconium and hafnium ore with molten aluminium and potassium chlorides at 350–400°C.
3. Distillation at 1 bar results in less than 50 ppm hafnium. The aluminium and potassium chlorides allow distillation at 1 bar, otherwise 20 bars are required.

Table 7.8. Zirconium Alloys

Alloy	Composition	Comments
Zircaloy-2	1.5% Sn; 0.12% Fe; 0.09% Cr 0.05% Ni; balance zirconium	1. Thermal conductivity 30% less than pure zirconium 2. Used in BWRs because of oxygen level in the coolant
Zircaloy-4	Eliminate Ni and replace with 0.2% Fe	1. Better resistance to hydrogen embrittlement than Zircaloy-2 2. Used in PWR fuel because of the coolant chemistry.

LMFBR cladding and core structural materials must perform in a difficult environment. Typical conditions are:

1. Temperatures in Excess of 800°C. Such high temperature can cause creep† and rapid corrosion (Figure 7.10). There is an effect of irradiation on the creep rupture life of solution-treated material. There is also a loss of material life, probably due in a large part to a loss of ductility.
2. High Fast-Neutron Fluences‡. High fluences (above 10^{23} neutrons/cm^2) can produce radiation damage, swelling, and embrittlement due to the formation of helium bubbles (Figure 7.11). As a result of the *n*, alpha reactions in a (thermal or) fast reactor, there will be helium formation, helium being an alpha particle. This helium is essentially insoluble in the metallic lattice. The helium atoms want to coalesce and leave the metal lattice. They will eventually find their way to the grain boundaries where they coalesce into bubbles. Under conditions of strain by grain boundary motion these bubbles result in cracks which make the metal fail at a relatively low ductility.
3. The two above effects can lead to mechanical problems of bowing and bulging (Figure 7.12). Diametrical strains can exceed 3%. These distortions can interfere with neighboring fuel assemblies, and affect the thermal performance of the fuel.

†Creep refers to elongation of a material specimen (resulting in mechanical distortion) due to realigning of the atoms or grains.
‡Fluence refers to the total number of neutrons which strike a unit area of material over the entire exposure time.

Table 7.9. Advanced LMFBR Cladding and Duct Development Alloys

Alloy Class	Potential Application	Commercially Available Alloys	New Developmental Alloys	Expected Characteristics
Ferritics	Duct only	HT-9[a] (12 Cr–Bal Fe)	D57[a] (10 Cr–6 Mo–Bal Fe)	Very low swelling: strength too low for cladding
Solid-solution-strengthened austenitic	Duct and cladding	310 CW 330 CW (20,35 Ni–25,16 Cr)	D9[a,c] D11 (14,20 Ni–14,7 Cr)	Moderate swelling: strength marginal for cladding
Precipitation-strengthened austenitic	Cladding and duct	A286 M813 Inconel 706 PE-16[b] (25–43 Ni–15–18 Cr)	D21[a] D25 D32 D66, D68[a] (25–45 Ni–9–12 Cr)	Low to very low swelling: high strength acceptable for cladding
High-nickel austenitic	Control assembly	Inconel 718 (52 Ni–19 Cr)	D42 (60 Ni–15 Cr)	Very low swelling and high strength: nickel too high for fuel assembly

Source: From J.T.A. Roberts, *Powder Metallurgy International* **11** (1979).

[a]Selected for advanced stage of U.S. program.

[b]In U.K. PFR.

[c]Similar to alloy chosen for Super Phenix.

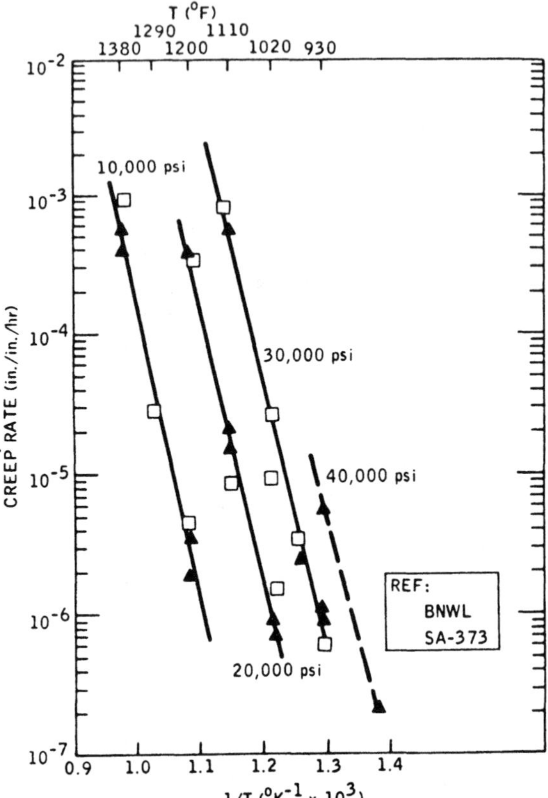

Figure 7.10. Plot of creep rates for annealed 304 stainless steel.

The development of advanced cladding materials for LMFBRs has emphasized alloys with low void swelling and irradiation creep strains, while keeping the cost, fabricability, mechanical properties, and corrosion resistance acceptable. High-nickel alloys suffer from the greater production of radioactive corrosion products and high neutron absorption. For these reasons, 316-type stainless steel, modified with Ti and/or Si and cold-worked, is often chosen for LMFBR fuel assemblies.

7.5. FUEL FABRICATION

LWR fuel is fabricated in the form of pellets, roughly the size and shape of the last digit of most people's little finger. These pellets are 0.82 cm in diameter, 1.34-cm long for PWRs, and slightly larger (1.23-cm diameter, 1.90-cm long) for BWRs. Since these pellets are to be stacked in columns and operated at high temperature, the ends of the pellets are dished out during manufacturing to accommodate thermal expansion (see Figure 7.13). In the first step of uranium oxide fuel manufacture, the UO_2 powder is sized, ground to a fine powder, and mixed, if necessary, to incorporate burnable poisons, such as gadolinia oxide. The UO_2 powder is then compacted, shaped into pellets, and sintered in an inert atmosphere of nitrogen, argon, and hydrogen to ensure that the stoichiometry of the UO_2 pellets is properly controlled. These steps are summarized as follows:

Powder Preparation. Important characteristics of powders used for nuclear fuel are density, shape, and size distribution of the grains; all are affected by the method by which the powder is produced. Uranium oxide powder can be produced in many ways, although most commonly it results from a calcining operation for reduction of U_3O_8 by hydrogen and steam (see Chapter 5). The size of powder used is controlled by screening it through a sieve of the proper mesh. The powder is then prepared for use by mixing and blending to produce a uniform mixture.

Compaction. Powders are formed into desired shapes by compression in dies. The pressure applied must force the particles into enough contact to hold the pellet together until it is sintered. The pressure also is adjusted to produce the required density. The pressing operation and dies are

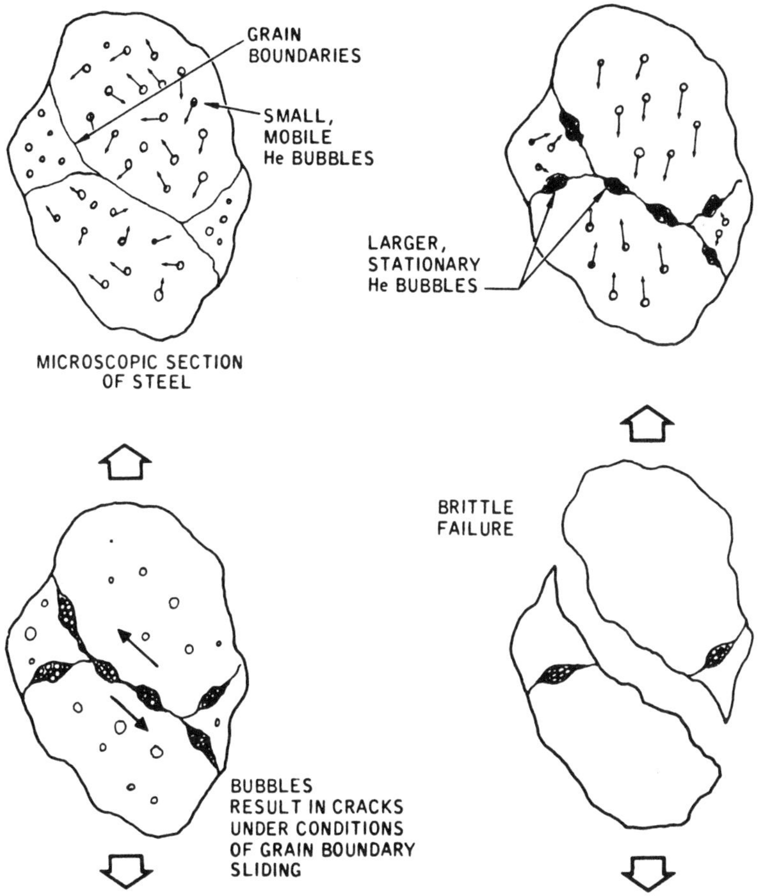

GRAIN
BOUNDARIES
SMALL,
MOBILE
He BUBBLES
LARGER,
STATIONARY
He BUBBLES
MICROSCOPIC SECTION
OF STEEL
BRITTLE
FAILURE
BUBBLES
RESULT IN CRACKS
UNDER CONDITIONS
OF GRAIN BOUNDARY
SLIDING

Figure 7.11. Brittle failure due to helium bubbles.

B
A
or
OPPOSITE DUCT BOWING CONFIGURATIONS
(a)
(b)

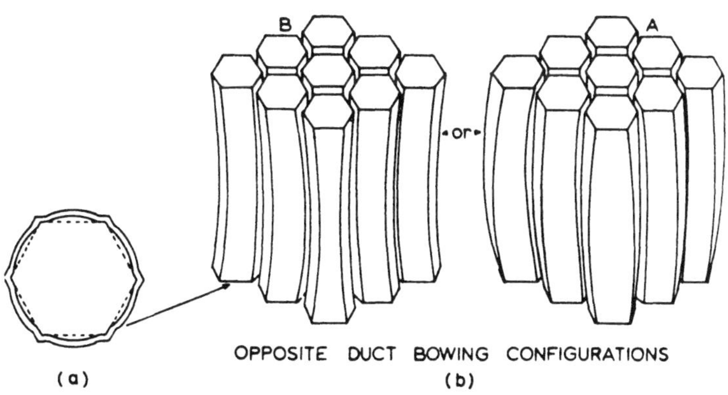

Figure 7.12. Schematic representations of (*a*) duct bulging and (*b*) core restraint loads from differential swelling of ducts. [From E. R. Gilbert et al., *J. Nucl. Mater.* **65**, 266 (1977).]

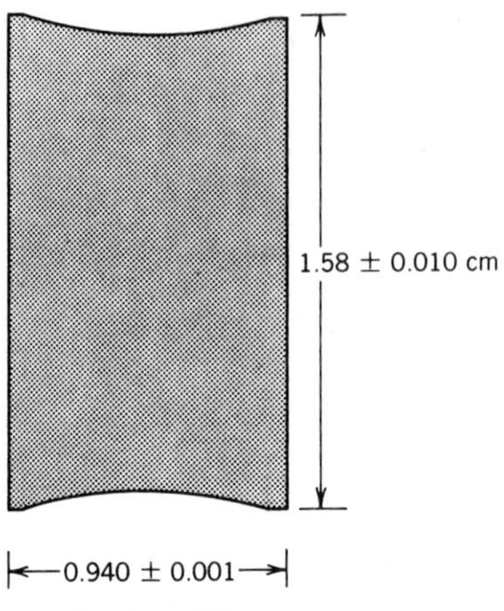

Figure 7.13. Sketch of conventional fuel pellets. The pellets, which are cylindrical, are dished on either end to accommodate thermal expansion during normal operation. Note the close tolerances to which the fuel is fabricated.

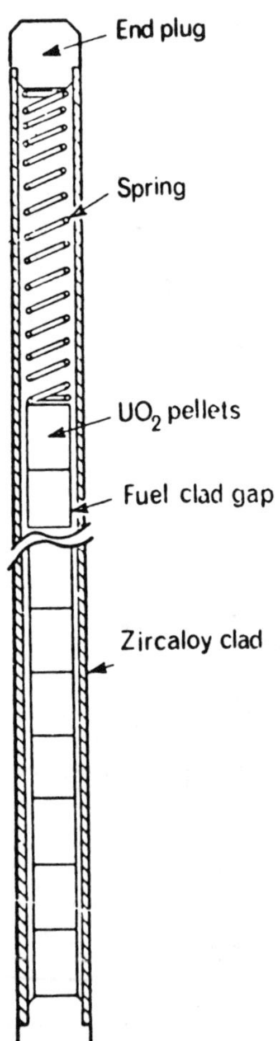

Figure 7.14. A typical modern LWR fuel rod with UO_2 pellets sealed in a Zircaloy sheath. Clad o.d. = 0.422 in.; Clad i.d. = 0.374 in.; Pellet o.d. = 0.367 in.; Pellet clad diameter gap = 0.007 in.; Pellet length = 0.600 in.; Fuel rod overall length = 152 in.; Active UO_2 length = 144 in.; Gas plenum length = 7 in.

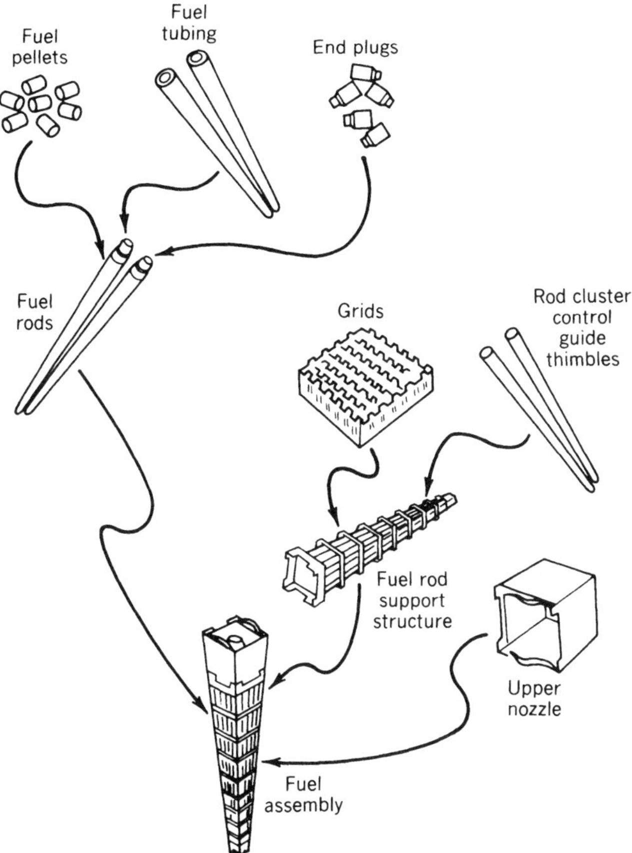

Figure 7.15. Process flow—fuel fabrication. (Courtesy Westinghouse Electric Corp.)

designed to achieve maximum uniformity. Pressing is done at 280–420 MPa, using binders and lubricants to control density and gradients.

Sintering. The green pellets produced by compaction are sintered to cause recrystallization and grain growth. The sintering furnace can be of the continuous type and contains a carefully controlled nitrogen atmosphere to adjust the oxygen content of the fuel as required; about 6% H_2 is added to the atmosphere to control grain size. Initial grain sizes larger than 10 μm seem to lower the release of radioactive fission products during operation. The temperatures in the furnace (1650°C) are well below the melting point of the uranium oxide. Since the pellets must be kept to close dimensional tolerances, they are brought to exact size after sintering by either a re-pressing operation, or more commonly, by centerless grinding.

The centerless grinding assures the control of pellet dimension. Pellets are next loaded in Zircaloy tubes, referred to as cladding (Figure 7.14). The Zircaloy casing maintains pellet position, and also acts as a barrier to the release of radioactive fission products. Plenum fittings, springs, and other structural materials are also inserted. In most cases, inert helium gas is added before the fuel rod is sealed to partially balance the rod's internal pressure against that of the coolant. This helps prevent the cladding from collapsing onto the fuel pellets during operation, a condition that has sometimes led to early fuel failure. Finally, the fuel rods are assembled into fuel assemblies by insertion in grid structures and, in some cases, fuel channels (Figure 7.15).

Some problems with the fuel encountered over the last three decades have made it necessary to control various parameters during the fabrication process. Many fuel problems were caused by high operating temperatures: 900°C at the surface of the pellet, and 1100–1500°C at the center. These temperatures lead to thermal shock, grain growth, pore migration, and the release of fission

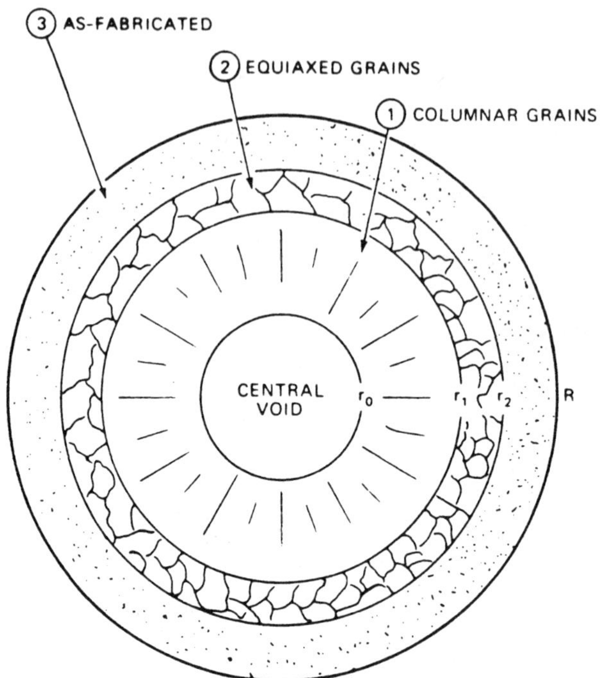

Figure 7.16. Regions of a restructed LMFBR fuel rod. LWR fuel rods, because of lower initial porosity, usually do not develop a central void. (From TID-2674.)

products from the fuel matrix. Figure 7.16 shows possible restructuring of a fuel rod as a result of normal operation. Although the fuel was originally solid, a void can form when pores migrate to the center where the temperature is hottest. This central void, however, is not as common in LWR fuels as for LMFBR ones. If the fuel were fabricated at 100% density, the cladding would be expanded before the void formed.

The other fuel regions seen in Figure 7.16 are:

1. A region made up of large columnar grains where the temperature gradient is important.
2. A region made up of large equiaxed grains where the temperature is the significant parameter.
3. A region where the grains of the as-fabricated fuel have grown to many times their original size.

It is not uncommon for the pellets to be severely cracked. The grain growth shown in the figure is not unique to reactor fuel, but occurs in many ceramics held at high temperatures for long times. Problems have also been caused by contamination of the fuel during fabrication. Careful fabrication procedures and quality methods have overcome these problems.

The flow sheet for the actual fuel fabrication is summarized in Figure 7.17 and Table 7.10. The fuel is assembled in an array which can be easily and quickly inserted into a nuclear reactor (Figure 7.18). Since a completed nuclear fuel assembly incorporates over 66,000 parts—most of them critically exact in chemical, physical, or dimensional specifications—the manufacturing process is necessarily complex and precise in its execution. A modern fuel fabrication facility is highly automated. The fuel tubing is extruded, heat-treated, and ultrasonically inspected. End plugs and other hardware are machined to precision tolerances from materials produced to exacting specifications. The welding of the top and bottom end plugs is best performed by electric beam welding which produces a very deep penetration and facilitates ultrasonic testing. The spring clip grids are assembled with the guide thimbles to create the structure of the assembly (Figure 7.19). Fuel rods now containing the pellets are inserted into this structure after exhaustive quality control checks. The final assembly is also inspected (Figure 7.20) and then packaged for shipment to the reactor site in special shipping containers.

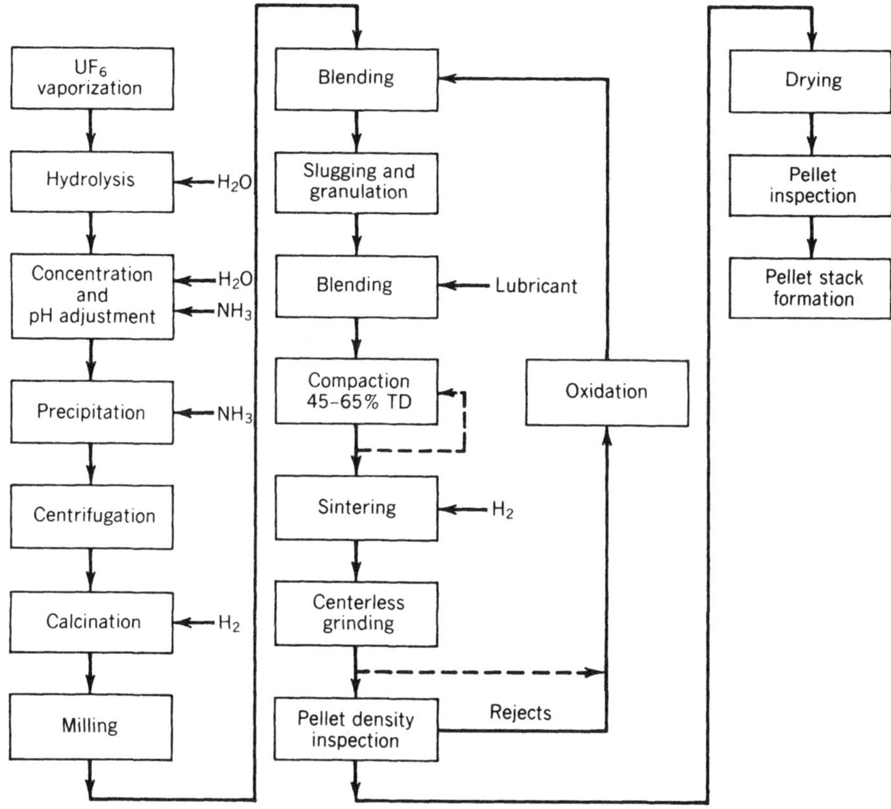

Figure 7.17. Flow sheet of UO_2 pellet fabrication.

Fabrication of Mixed Oxide Fuel

The mixed-oxide (MOX) fuel used for commercial power production is generally of two types: fuel with PuO_2 concentrations below 6 wt% that is intended for thermal reactors (LWR or HTGR); and fuel with PuO_2 concentrations of about 20% intended for fast reactors (LMFBR). The fuel fabrication processes are essentially the same for both. The MOX fuels are formed into pellets and clad similarly to UO_2 fuel pins used in LWRs. Indeed there is no visual difference between a normal UO_2 LWR fuel assembly and a MOX LWR fuel assembly.

For use in LMFBRs, the pellet diameters are somewhat smaller (about 6 mm) for better heat transfer, and are clad in stainless steel for economy and strength. The fuel pins themselves usually are wire wrapped to separate them and also to improve the heat transfer from the fuel to the coolant as it flows past. Figure 7.21 shows a typical fuel pin for a fast reactor. Suitable operating parame-

Table 7.10. Flow Sheet for the Fabrication of LWR Fuel

1. UF_6 from the enrichment plant is changed from solid to a gas in a steam chest.
2. Convert UF_6 to UO_2.
3. Compact UO_2 into approximate final form, called "green pellets."
4. Sinter "green pellets" in a hydrogen atmosphere in a high-temperature furnace to produce a ceramic.
5. Check for moisture content.
6. Load pellets into Zircaloy fuel cladding.
7. Weld end fittings to fuel cladding.
8. Perform QA testing.
9. Assemble fuel rods with mixing vane/grid spacers, and nozzle components.
10. Complete QA and envelope check.

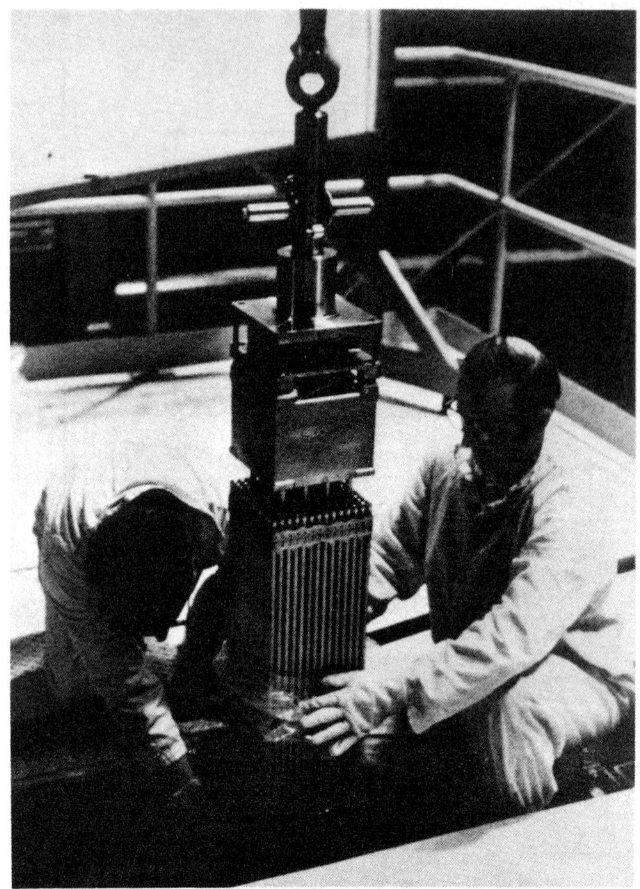

Figure 7.18. Completed fuel assembly being loaded into a PWR. Note that new fuel assemblies are not highly radioactive, as evidenced by the hands-on operation. Such operations are not possible once the fuel has been burned. (Courtesy Rochester Gas and Electric.)

Figure 7.19. Typical grid spacer. The purpose of the grid spacer is to provide mechanical support for the fuel rods. They are designed to minimize pressure drop and to give good thermal hydraulic mixing. They are usually made of Inconel. The trend is to fabricate these elements with zirconium alloys to improve fuel economy.

Figure 7.20. Inspection of a nuclear fuel assembly during fabrication. (Courtesy Combustion Engineering.)

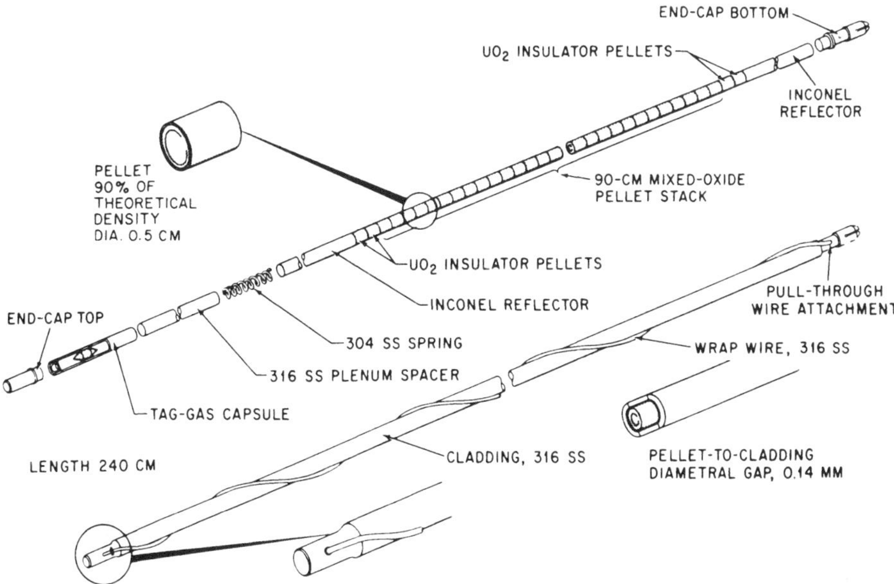

Figure 7.21. Fuel pin of the Fast Flux Test Reactor. (Courtesy HEDL.)

Table 7.11. Typical Operating Parameters for LMFBR Fuel

Power density (average)	200 kW/liter
Fuel material	PuO_2–UO_2
Fuel contents	
$PuO_2/(PuO_2 + UO_2)$	17.7 wt. %
$^{235}U/U$	23.0 wt. %
Burnup (average)	75,000 MWd/t
Maximum neutron flux	2.2×10^{15} neutrons/cm^2-sec
Fuel elements	
Cladding material	Stainless steel
Number per subassembly	91
Diameter (outside/inside)	6.3/5.6 mm
Maximum clad temperature	540°C

Source: Courtesy of PNC.

ters, given in Table 7.11, reflect the high neutron fluxes (up to 10^{15} n/cm^2-sec) and power densities (200 kW/liter) such fuel assemblies are exposed to.

The actual fabrication of MOX fuel assemblies is similar to that for LWR UO_2 fuel; the main differences are the blending of the UO_2-PuO_2 powders (Figure 7.22). The fuel fabrication process typically is a dry process where PuO_2 are mechanically blended to achieve fuel pellet homogeneity.

The PuO_2 in air, ball-milled as 2.5-kg sublots, is screened, V-blended, and sampled. The PuO_2 is combined with the required amount of UO_2 and dry recycle PuO_2-UO_2, V-blended, jet-milled, and screened.

An organic is added as a pore former to produce a low density pellet of nominal 90.5% theoretical density. The PuO_2-UO_2 with organic is slugged to 45–50% TD, granulated, and screened. A die lubricant of 0.3% sterotex is V-blended with the granules for press feed. Pellets are pressed using a hydraulic press.

The green pellets are loaded into molybdenum boats, presintered at 700 to 800°C for 2 hr in Ar + 8% H_2. The product is sintered at 1675°C for 4 hr, also using argon plus 8% hydrogen gas.

Additional precautions are needed because of the toxicity and proliferation problems associated with plutonium (Figure 7.23). Because of the latter problems, material accounting procedures are much stricter for any fuels containing plutonium. In spite of these additional procedures, MOX fuel fabrication is quite routine.

The preparation of mixed UO_2-PuO_2 ceramic compounds is complicated by the tendencies of UO_2 to oxidize, and PuO_2 to reduce. This means that the fuel materials must be carefully sintered. Three factors must be controlled to achieve the proper density:

1. The Starting Powder. UO_2 uranate powders and PuO_2 oxalate powders produce the required fluorite cubic phase. The fineness of the powder controls the surface area and the grain size.
2. The Sintering Temperature. Around 1600°C is the usual temperature to achieve reciprocal cation diffusion.
3. The Atmosphere. Hydrogen or carbon dioxide atmospheres are used to control the oxidation/reduction of the mixtures.

Urania–plutonia mixtures can be also prepared by the coprecipitation of uranium and plutonium from nitrate solutions. These form a solid solution of the oxides upon calcining (see Chapter 14).

Fabrication of Thoria and Thoria–Uranium Fuels

Thoria (ThO_2) fuels have been developed mainly for the HTGR and the Light-Water Breeder Reactor (LWBR). Fuels of interest primarily consist of thoria–urania (ThO_2-UO_2) or thoria–uranium carbide (ThO_2-UC) mixtures with relatively low uranium loadings (less than 10%). The urania itself consists of 93% highly enriched ^{235}U, although newer designs have considered 20% medium enriched ^{235}U to allay proliferation concerns. The thorium (100% abundant in the isotope ^{232}Th) serves as a fertile material which is converted to fissile ^{233}U in the reactor. The spent fuel contains valuable fissile materials, including the ^{233}U bred from thorium during power plant operation.

HTGR fuel is made of coated fuel particles, blended with graphic pitch and molded into finger-sized rods which are inserted into graphite blocks (see Figure 7.24). The graphite block is the basic fuel element. Graphite functions also as moderator and core structural material. The graphite fuel

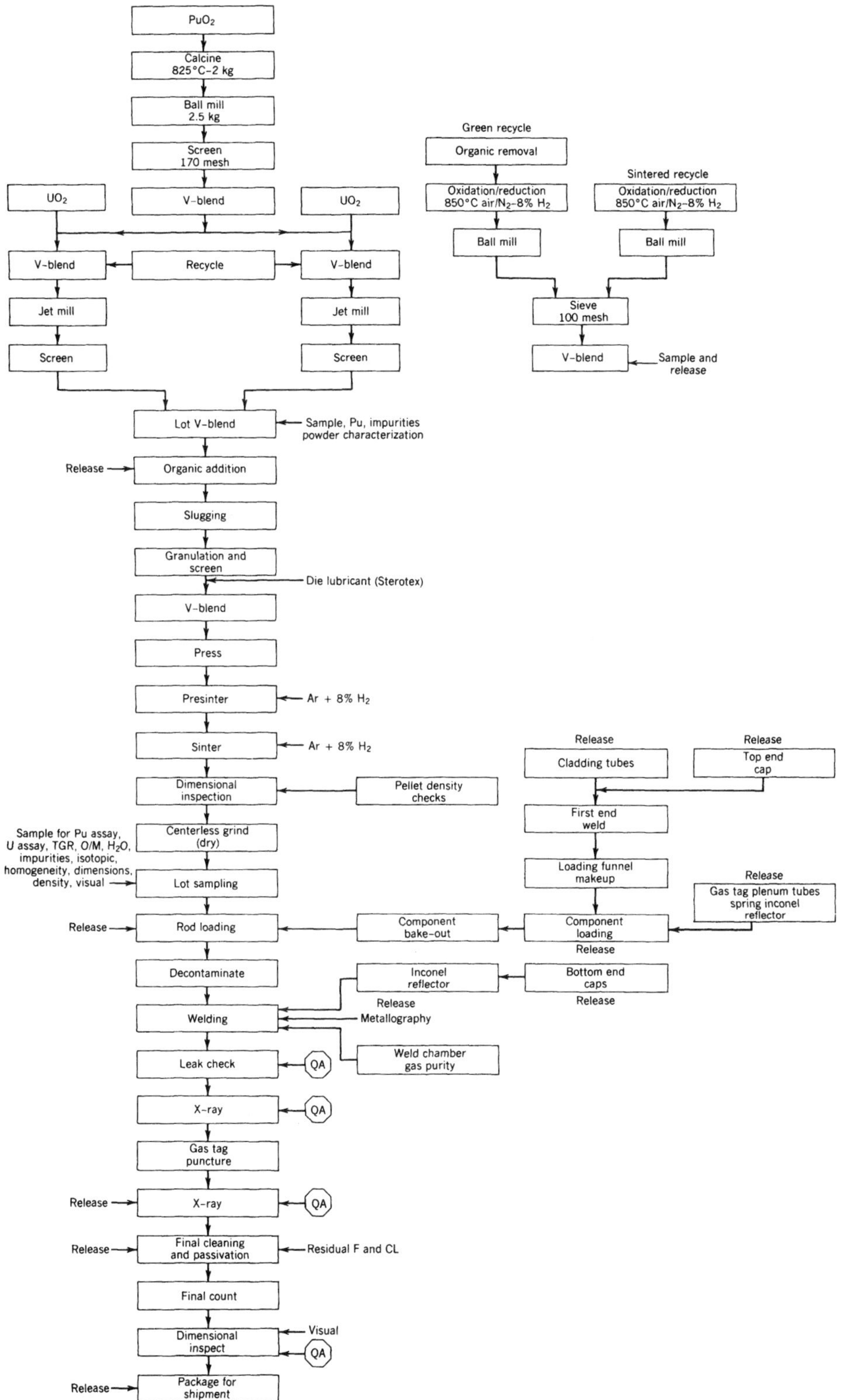

Figure 7.22. Flow diagram for MOX fuel fabrication. [From W. J. Ross, *Trans. Am. Nuclear Soc.* **21,** 248 (1975).]

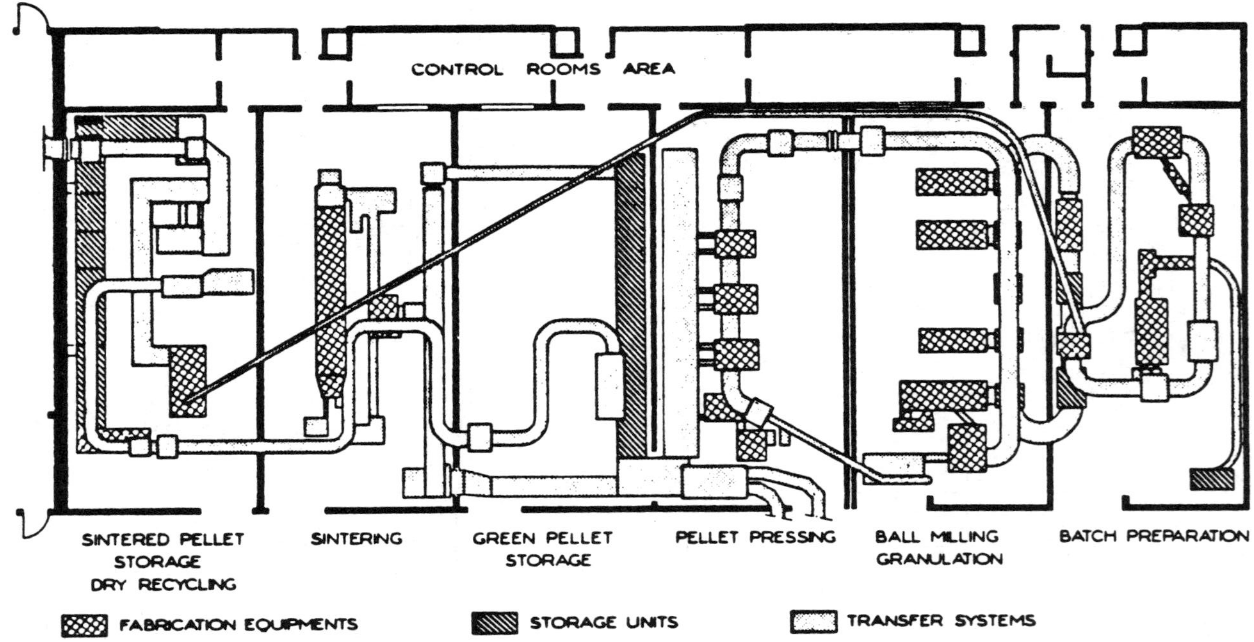

Figure 7.23. SuperPhenix 1 pellet line. The building comprises a large number of cells which constitute secondary containment zones around the primary glove-box containment. Except for operating incidents, the cells are kept contamination free, and are thus accessible to personnel wearing standard operational clothing. Powder operations are all mechanized and almost fully automated, and can thus be directed from control rooms adjacent to the cells and monitored by closed-circuit TV. The operators enter the powder cells mainly for adjustment and maintenance work. [From H. Bailly et al., *Trans. Am. Nuclear Soc.* **32,** 228 (1979).]

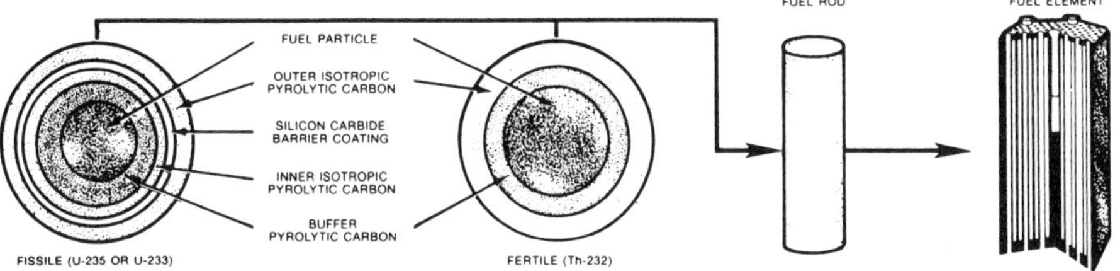

Figure 7.24. HTGR fuel components. (Courtesy General Atomic Co.)

element is 79.3-cm (31.4-in.) high with a hexagonal cross section 35.9 cm (14.2 in.) across the flats. It is drilled lengthwise with two sets of holes—one set to contain fuel rods, the other to allow the passage of helium coolant.

Fuel particles are of two types, identified as BISO and TRISO according to the coatings that have been applied to them. BISO particles, initially loaded only with fertile thorium oxide, are coated with a relatively porous buffer layer of pyrolitic carbon and then with a dense outer layer of isotropic pyrolitic carbon. TRISO particles, loaded with uranium, have an added inner layer of isotropic pyrolitic carbon plus a layer of silicon carbide inside the dense outer layer.

The fabrication of HTGR fuel is summarized in Figure 7.25. The BISO particles are thoria

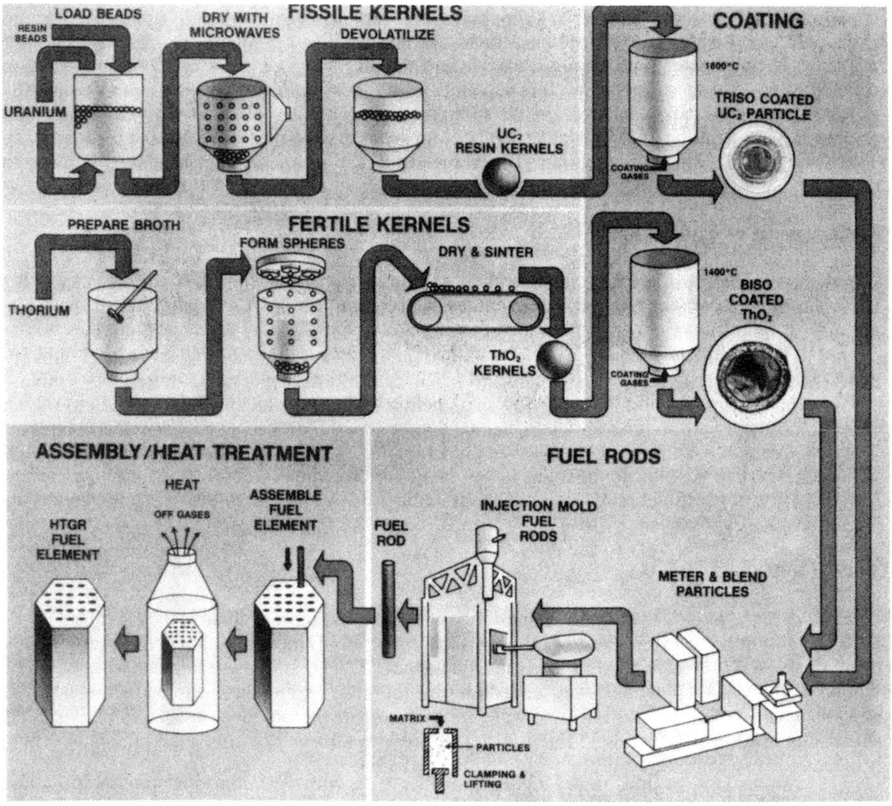

Figure 7.25. Manufacturing process for HTGR fuel. The fabrication of HTGR fuel is a highly automated process that increases its diversion resistance. The processes that produce the fertile and fissile particles start with an aqueous solution of thorium nitrate or uranium absorbed on ion-exchange resin beads. Spheres of thorium hydroxide are formed as the thorium nitrate droplets fall into an ammonia bath. Both the uranium and thoria particles are dried, sintered, and coated. Commercial production produces about 0.4 kg/hr of uranium and 10 kg/hr of thorium. (Courtesy General Atomic Co.)

Table 7.12. LWBR Thoria Based Fuel

High density	97% of theoretical density
High integrity	
Grain size porosity	ASTM 4-10.5
a. Granule segregation	No indication of granule outline.
b. Pore size	<0.025 in equivalent diameter (seed)[a]
	<0.030 in equivalent diameter (blanket)[a]
c. Pore orientation	Orientation angle between pore axis and pellet radius <70
d. Pore distribution	Uniform distribution.
Internal cracks	0.0004 in.^{2} max crack area (seed)[a]
	0.0008 in.^{2} max crack area (blanket)[a]
	cracks cannot intersect opposite pellet surfaces.

Source: From W. A. Weinreich et al., *Trans. Am. Nuclear Soc.* **27**,305 (1977).

[a]Seed pellets are ~0.250-in. diameter.

Blanket pellets are ~0.500-in. diameter.

microspheres produced by the Gel-Supported Precipitation (GSP) process. An aqueous solution of thorium nitrate (usually with additives to stabilize the shape of the droplet) is formed into spheres, and de-nitrated in a steam (ammonia) process which yields thorium hydroxide. Drying and sintering results in thoria particles which are then coated with pyrolitic carbon by high-temperature vapor deposition (pyrolysis).

The TRISO uranium carbide microspheres are produced using uranium absorbed on ion-exchange resin beads. These beads are dried and devolatilized, resulting in UC_2 resin kernels, which are in turn coated with pyrolytic carbon and silicon carbide. Sophisticated equipment inventories the fuel in process and accurately accounts for all the uranium to assure proper safeguarding of nuclear material. The small size of the fuel particles simplifies satistical sampling for material accounting and quality control purposes. HTGR fuel rods are then formed from the blended BISO/TRISO pellets by injection molding. These fuel rods are placed in the pre-cured carbon fuel elements.

Performance of Thoria Fuels

Experience on thoria-based fuel pellets is limited, but it appears that the fuel performs as well as UO_2. Thoria fuel swelling may be somewhat less a problem than in UO_2. Additional verification is probably required for the compatibility of thoria pellets with Zircaloy cladding materials.

For the BISO/TRISO fuel particles used in the HTGR, fuel performance also has been relatively good. The initial purpose of the coatings—to retain fission products—has not been a complete success. The coatings become permeable and sometimes rupture. The anisotropy of the pyrolytic carbon, if not kept below a critical value, can lead to coating failures. Control of process temperatures and coating rate considerably improves this problem. The release of fission products, through the increasingly permeable coatings, has been related to the redistribution of the pyrolytic carbon at higher reactor operating temperatures. Operating below this critical temperature mitigates coating failures and fission gas release.

Thoria Fuels in LWBRs

For light water breeder reactor (LWBR) fuels, the product is quite similar to LWR fuels. High-density, high-integrity, thoria-based fuel pellets are required. The definition of these properties is given in Table 7.12. Of particular note is the high density (97%) required of the pellets compared to that for LWRs (92%). High density is needed for high thermal conductivity, stable fuel dimensions, and enhanced breeding. Fine grain size was found necessary to minimize creep, gas release, and densification problems. It is found that fine grains are accompanied by the small pores necessary for mechanical strength and resistance to defect corrosion.

The uranium isotope utilized to fuel the LWBR is ^{233}U, with ^{232}U impurities limited to 10 ppm. ^{233}U inevitably contains some ^{232}U (Figure 7.26) which, because of its radioactive decay, poses a material-handling problem. Although the ^{232}U level is quite low, total containment is utilized to minimize personnel handling exposure.†

†The gamma activity and external gamma dose rate due to ^{232}U daughters grows rapidly after thorium fuel reprocessing. After 100 days, uranium as small as 1 kg and containing 100 ppm ^{232}U will produce a gamma dose rate as large as 0.1 rem/hr at 1 m. Recycled uranium in a uranium cycle may contain about 200–1000 ppm of ^{232}U.

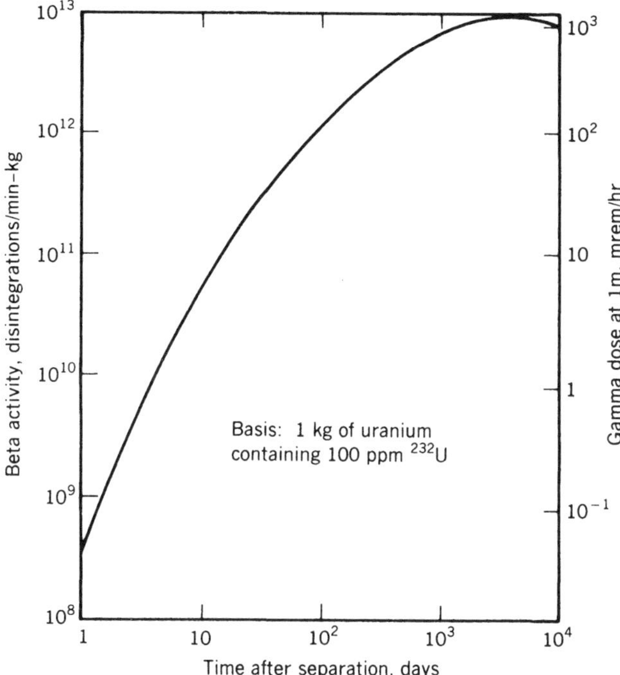

Figure 7.26. Growth of beta activity and gamma dose rate due to ^{232}U in uranium from irradiated thorium. [From *Rev. Mod. Physics* **50** (1978).]

The main steps in producing LWBR pellets are given in Table 7.13. A key to producing fuel pellets with consistent properties is starting with thoria and urania powders with compatible characteristics, such as grain size. In addition, a close control of intermediate product properties, such as intermediate density and impurity content, is necessary to produce a consistent high density, high-integrity fuel pellet.

7.6. QUALITY ASSURANCE (QA) OF NUCLEAR FUEL‡

Nuclear fuel elements are expensive pieces of hardware whose reliability is important to plant operations, safety, and economics. Quality assurance (QA) is thus important and actively pursued during the manufacturing process. In addition, QA is mandated by government regulation for all nuclear fuel. In the United States, guidance for acceptable QA procedures is contained in various NRC documents (see Table 7.14). In addition, each fuel vendor has his own program in order to produce fuel that will perform to specification and warranty.

The U.S. rules and regulations pertaining to QA is contained in Title 10, Code of Federal Regulations, Part 50 (10CFR50). The code is fairly detailed in prescribing what elements of QA are required (Table 7.15). These criteria are implemented by the NRC, and by voluntary industry compliance and standards. Figure 7.27 shows the interrelationship of the various codes, NRC regulations, and industry standard in the United States.

Various NSSS vendors have structured their organizations and the resultant QA programs differently. The two variations are as follows. In the first type of organizational setup, nuclear fuel design and manufacturing activities are performed by the same organization and are covered by the same standardized QA programs (standard safety analysis report or QA topical report). In the second situation, the QA program covers only fuel design and procurement. Any subcontractor is subject to quality controls via procurement requirements, audits, and routine surveillance. The NRC oversees these vendor programs by performing licensing reviews, QA audits, and inspection of nuclear fuel fabrication facilities to verify industry compliance. Similar programs are in place in other countries.

‡Note to the reader: QA is covered in some depth at this point as an example of how it is treated by the nuclear industry in the fabrication of various components. The discussion is not repeated in other sections.

Table 7.13. LWBR Thoria/Urania Fuel Pellet Process

1. *Power Blending (Dry mixing of thoria and urania)*

2. *Micronization (Powder activation)*
   Powder surface area 7.5 m^2/g-min

3. *Agglomeratin (Binder addition)*
   Binder: 1.25% carbowax 6000

4. *Lubricant Addition*
   Lubricant: 0.15 wt% of 200 mesh Sterotex

5. *Compaction*
   Green density of 61–63% of theoretical density

6. *Pretreatment (Binder and lubricant removal)*
   a. Co_2 is controlled in pretreating furnace.
   b. Product is evaluated for carbon and O/U ratio.

7. *Sinter*
   a. H_2 and N_2 flow in atmosphere is controlled.
   b. Minimum density 96%.
   c. Grain size evaluated.

Table 7.14. Regulatory Guidance of Applicability to Nuclear Fuel Quality Assurance

Regulatory Guide 1.28—Quality Assurance Requirements (Design and Construction (6/7/72)
Regulatory Guide 1.58—Qualification of Nuclear Power Plant Inspection, Examination and Testing Personnel
Regulatory Guide 1.64—Quality Assurance Requirements for the Design of Nuclear Power Plants (Rev. 1, 2/75)
Regulatory Guide 1.74—Quality Assurance Terms and Definitions
Regulatory Guide 1.88 (Rev. 1, 12/75)—Collection, Storage and Maintenance of Nuclear Power Plant Quality Assurance Records
WASH 1283 (Rev. 1, 5/74)—Guidance on Quality Assurance Requirements During Design and Procurement Phase of Nuclear Power Plants

Table 7.15. Quality Assurance Criteria of 10CFR 50, Appendix B

I. Organization
II. Quality assurance program
III. Design control
IV. Procurement document control
V. Instructions, procedures, and drawings
VI. Document control
VII. Controls of purchased material, equipment, and services
VIII. Identification and control of materials, parts, and components
IX. Control of special processes
X. Inspection
XI. Test control
XII. Control of measuring and test equipment
XIII. Handling, storage, and shipping
XIV. Inspection, test, and operating status
XV. Nonconforming materials, parts, or components
XVI. Corrective action
XVII. Quality assurance records
XVIII. Audits

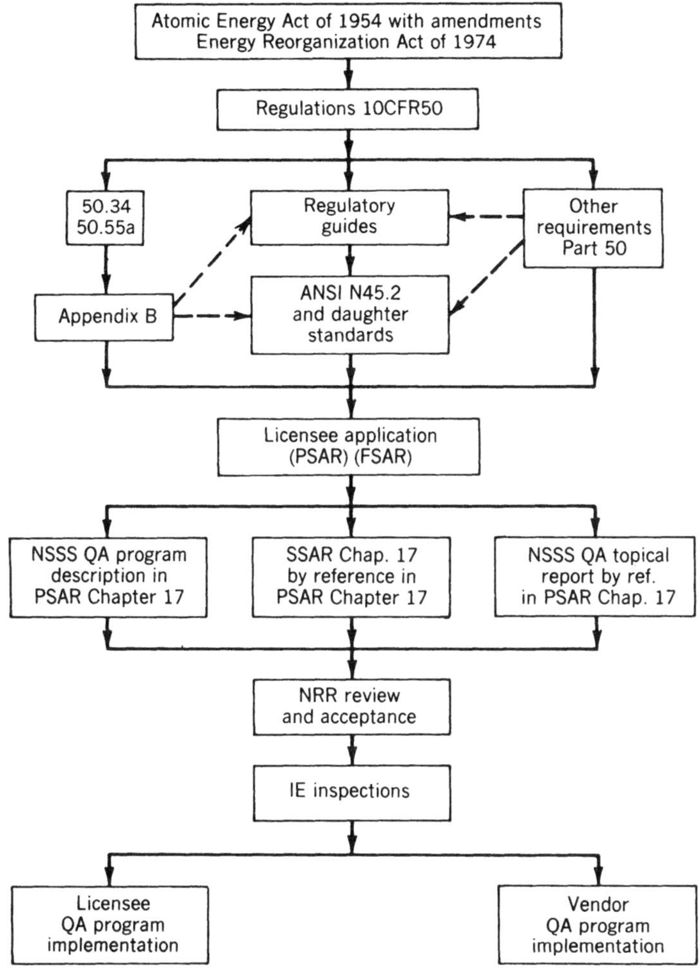

Figure 7.27. QA requirements in the United States. An interrelated set of codes, regulations, and industry standards exist to ensure that various safety-related criteria are met. The NRC has the responsibility to verify that a fuel vendor's QA program is being followed. NRC inspectors perform various audits to fulfill this duty.

Quality assurance requires the following four aspects:

1. The formulation of the fuel manufacturer's policies and procedures, including the preparation of a QA manual, and the qualification of test procedures.
2. The enforcement of QA on component and material procurement, including all manufacturing at subcontractors to ensure compliance with drawings and specifications, and the proper raw material properties.
3. Inspection procedures to verify that all manufacturing is done to specification. Typical inspection points during the assembly of a fuel element are shown in Figure 7.28. Complete documentation of the QA for each component is required.
4. Systematic audits are necessary to ensure that all procedures are strictly followed.

As important as the formal QA program outlined above is the ability to engineer quality into components. This is done by integrating "technical know-how" into a consistent manufacturing

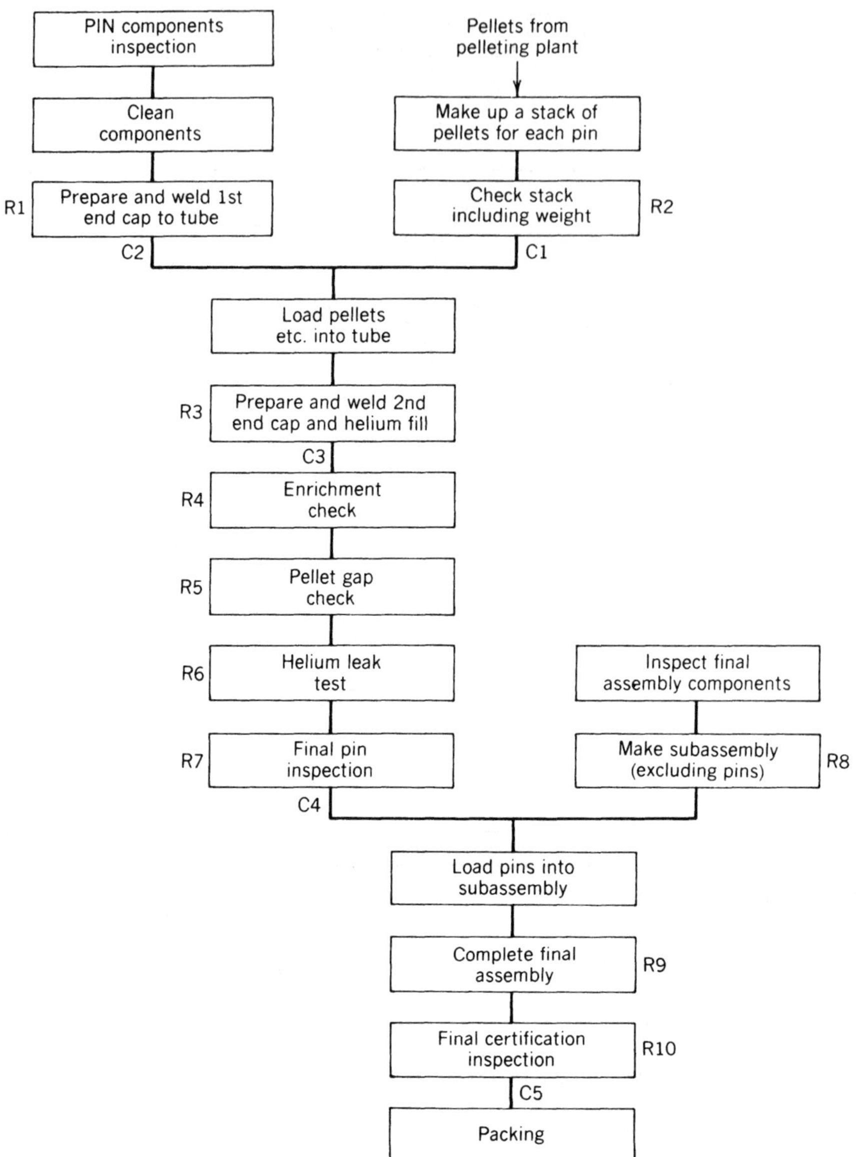

Figure 7.28. Inspection points for QA in the manufacture of full elements. R1 to R10 are release points. C1 to C5 are quality control checks.

system, and includes feedback from the performance of fuel in-reactor. The aspects of quality engineering are embodied as follows:

1. *Uniform Design Principles.* The mechanical and thermal operating conditions for LWR fuel elements overlap, such that the same mechanical requirements such as strength, ductility, and creep resistance can be used. Thus, the dimensional criteria and tolerances can be uniformly applied, even if the dimensions, per se, are different.

2. *Optimization of Design Requirements.* Table 7.16 illustrates the use of design targets (in this case for the cladding) in establishing mechanical criteria. The three criteria on ductility, strength, and material creep necessitate producing Zircaloy in a stress-relieved condition (Figure 7.29). From the optimization of the design requirements a material condition results which is very

Table 7.16. Design Targets for Mechanical Properties of Zircaloy Cladding

Criteria	Requirement	Technical Target
Ductility	High *uniform* circumferential *elongation* at elevated temperatures	High potential for deformation to get an optimum for: long-term circumferential elongation; local pellet-clad interaction
Strength	High *yield strength* at elevated temperatures	To minimize: permanent strain, i.e., pellet cladding interaction
Creep	Low *circumferential creep rate* at elevated temperatures	To minimize: cladding creepdown and ovalization; low-cycle fatigue

Source: From G. Dressler and W. G. Weidinger, Kraftwerk Union AG.

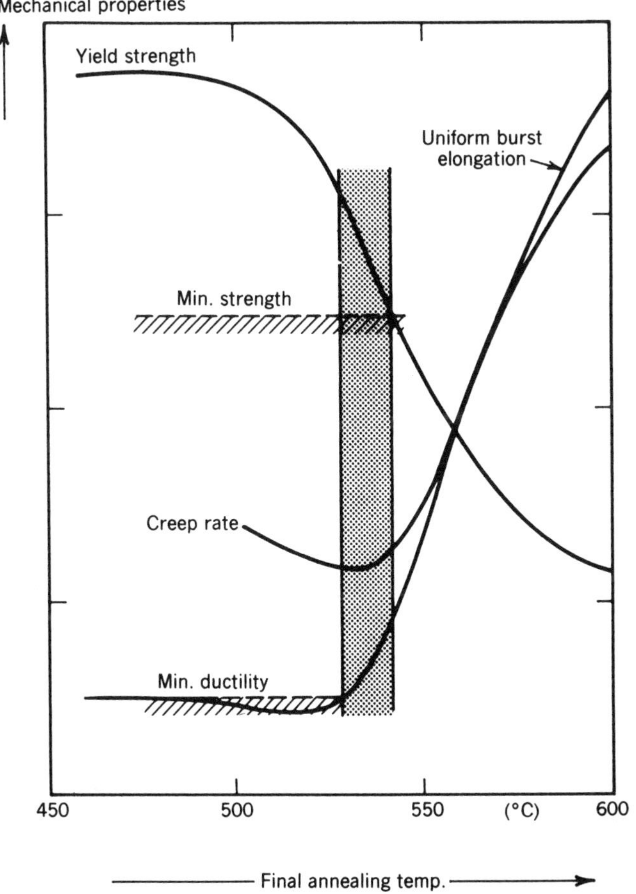

Figure 7.29. The stress-relieved condition of Zircaloy cladding tubes characterized by mechanical properties. (From G. Dressler and W. G. Weidinger, Kraftwerk Union A.G.)

sensitive to deviation in the material treatment, such as cold-work or heat treatment parameters. Since strength and ductility depend in the opposite way on such process parameters, a narrow "window" can be defined, which the manufacturer has to "shoot at."

3. *Uniformity of Product Properties such as Impurity Content or Yield Strength.* The usual way to achieve this is through specification. However, specifications lead to testing and the ultimate success then relies on testing requirements and frequency. The total reliance of product uniformity on testing can be overcome by the use of approved processes and fabrication parameters. A proper combination of the manufacturing parameters, such as the annealing temperature, is allowed. If this is done, it helps ensure that all the mechanical properties will fall with narrow-prescribed limits.

To achieve a high degree of quality assurance, the important aspect is a commitment to a high-quality product. To implement a successful QA program requires an in-depth understanding of the technology involved. The fabrication of nuclear fuel elements relies on both of the above to achieve the quality necessary for regulatory and warranty requirements.

7.7. FUEL PLANT ECONOMICS

Commercial fuel fabrication facilities typically have a daily capacity of 2 t of heavy metal (t-HM). A plant fabricating PWR fuel has an annual capacity about 500 t-HM/yr. Such a plant might cost about \$32M, plus an additional \$34M for equipment, and have annual operating expenses of \$36.5M (1979 dollars). The levelized cost of production would be \$138 per kilogram of heavy metal (or about \$63,600 per fuel assembly). Several price projections predict that the fabrication costs will vary little over the next 25 yr when measured in constant dollars. These projections estimated 1980 costs between \$120 and \$148/kg-HM for direct-contact fabrication of nonradioactive, slightly enriched uranium. Fabrication of radioactive recycled fuel for LWRs will require remote operation, which may double the unit costs.

7.8. CURRENT FUEL PERFORMANCE EXPERIENCE

With the advent of higher power reactor cores starting in the late 1960s, a succession of phenomena appeared which threatened the lifetime of LWR fuel. These problems included internal cladding hydriding (1970) and pellet-clad interaction (1971). As various design changes were made to overcome these problems, LWR fuel evolved into the highly reliable form available today. Whereas a typical fuel rod failure rate was about 1% in the 1960s, the failure rate in today's designs is well below 0.03%.

Current LWR fuel experience is characterized by high burnup levels and a low, essentially acceptable, failure rate. Research and development is continuing to assure that pellet-clad interaction and water-side corrosion do not become a life-limiting or operations-limiting factor in the fuel design. The main factors that have limited fuel performance in LWRs in the past (and their remedies) are listed in Table 7.17.

One particular problem has been the hydriding of the Zircaloy cladding caused by moisture and/or oil left in the fuel during manufacturing. This historically has led to fuel failures. At high temperature hydrogen from the moisture attacks the zirconium, the main constituent of the Zircaloy, to form zirconium hydride (ZrH_2), a powdery substance. Cracks in the cladding result. The problem's solution has been to develop fuel pellets with low surface area, and to load the fuel pellets into the cladding while hot, with a vacuum to remove the moisture.

Another problem stems from the actual fuel pellet itself, which is not "solid" UO_2, but rather, a material comprised of UO_2 which is sintered to 90–94% of theoretical density. The voids are necessary for various reasons, including the accommodation of the fission product gases that form during irradiation. However, the high temperatures present in the fuel during reactor operation can lead to further sintering of the fuel, giving higher density than desired (Figure 7.30). This has been found to result in fuel consolidation and occasionally gaps in fuel length. This, in turn, leads to local power peaks, increase in the fuel temperature, and the collapse of the clad into the gaps. These are potentially serious problems, serious enough that significant numbers of fuel assemblies have had to be discharged early and the thermal limits of some plants reduced.

The probable cause of the densification problem is the initial presence of fine porosity in the fuel pellets. It is thought that densification is the result of the elimination of fine porosity by radiation damage. Another key to stable fuel is increased grain size (see Figure 7.31). To overcome the densification problem, the final pellet density is carefully controlled. Large grain size and controlled large porosity of the pellet is obtained by using pore former material† and sintering at higher temperatures. These techniques produce a densification resistant pellet. Densification is no longer a problem in current LWR fuel.

†Ni_2O_5 is sometimes used.

Table 7.17. Main Factors That Have Limited Fuel Performance and Remedies

Factors	PWR	BWR	Remedies
Hydriding of Zr	X	X	Elimination of moisture in fabrication; addition of getters
Scale deposition		X	Elimination of copper tubing from feedwater heaters
Enrichment errors	X	X	Gamma scanning all rods prior to shipment
Clad collapse	X		Prepressurized cladding, stable pellets
Pettet densification	X	X	Stable pellet microstructure
Other manufacturing and handling defects (e.g., faulty welds)	X	X	Improved quality control (now constitute <5% of defects found in reactor)
Clad corrosion or fretting		X	Rare; control of clad quality and cleaning; spacers
Fuel rod growth and bowing	X		Control of texture; axial clearances; spacer design
Channel bulging		X	Use of thicker wall channels and control of residual stress
Pettet-clad interaction (PCI) on power increases	X	X	1. Slow power rise (PWR). 2. Plus local power shape control (BWR). 3. Plus fuel "preconditioning" phases (BWR and PWR). 4. Plus fuel pellet design changes (BWR and PWR)

Source: From M. Levenson et al., *Annual Review of Energy* **1,** 645 (1976).

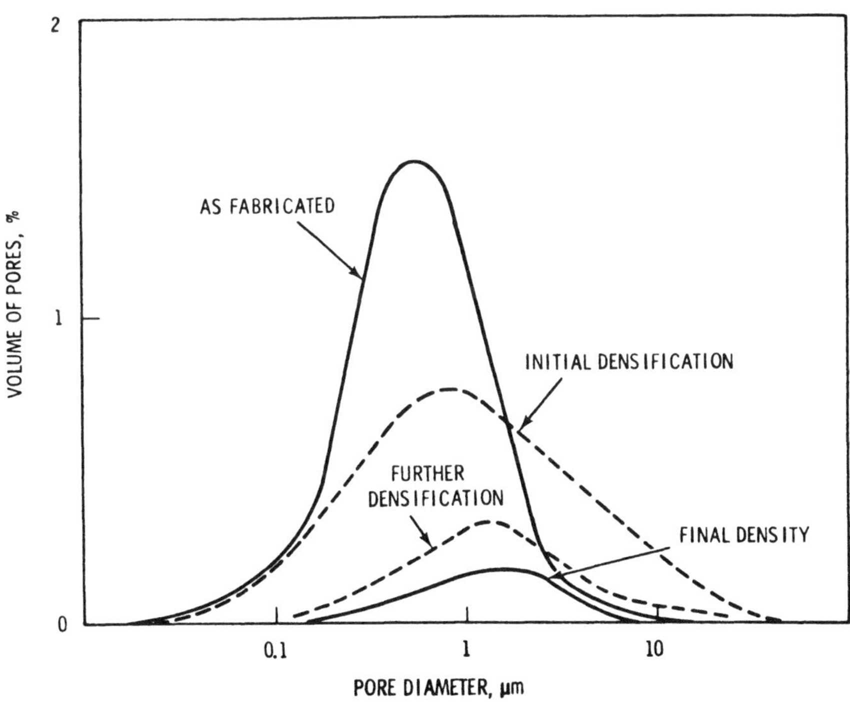

Figure 7.30. Typical porosity distribution for unstable UO_2 fuel. The volume fraction of porosity less than 1-μm diameter contributed significantly to densification of fuel, since density increases are accompanied by a significant decrease in the volume fraction of pores in this size range. The porosity distribution in unstable UO_2 fuel shifts during irradiation. (From EPRI Report 131.)

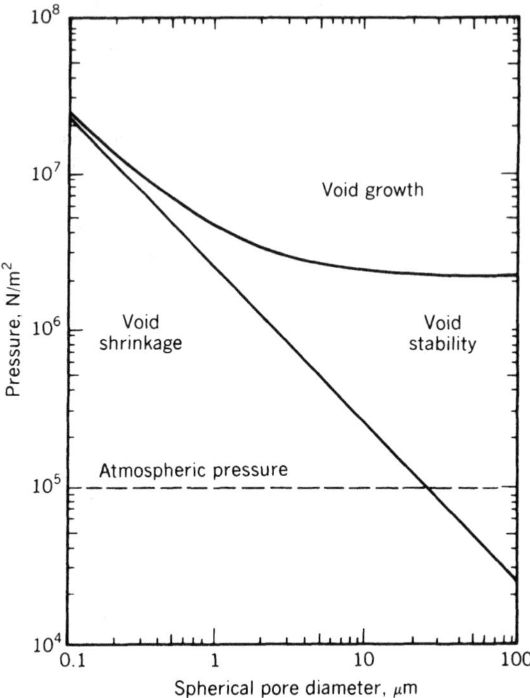

Figure 7.31. Criteria for void stability in sintered UO_2 pellets at 1650°C. In order to produce a uranium dioxide fuel pellet whose porosity is stable both to thermal and radiation treatment, it is necessary to minimize the amount of porosity below about 5 μm and have the majority of the pores 20 μm or greater. [From T. J. Heal et al., "Development of Stable Density UO_2 Fuel," *Int. Conf. on Nuclear Fuel Performance*, London (1973).]

A third but related problem has been Pellet-Clad Interaction (PCI). This is a stress corrosion cracking phenomena caused by the fission product iodine (also cadmium and cesium) attacking the cladding (Figure 7.32). The principal mechanisms for fuel-clad interactions are shown in Figure 7.33. An important aspect of PCI is that the cladding alloy is a strong getter† for iodine. The problem is exacerbated if the pellet and cladding make contact, producing local stress (Figure 7.34). Stress-corrosion cracking of this type is serious, causing the cladding to lose its ability to retain the radioactive fission products. Thus, fuel design and operating changes were introduced. They included shorter chamfered pellets to reduce local clad stress. Fuel assemblies were rearranged to contain more fuel rods of smaller diameter, which lowered the power levels and peak temperatures per rod. Special start-up procedures were instituted to minimize mechanical interaction of the pellet and its cladding.

Several other remedies are available for pellet-clad interaction. One is the so-called "barrier fuel," where the inside of the cladding is coated with copper or pure zirconium to prevent attack of the Zircaloy itself (Figure 7.35). Another remedy is to control temperature transients in the fuel during operation to limit stress produced when the fuel contacts the cladding. This is done by limiting the heat generation rate during operation and the rate of power increase during reactor start-up in PWRs. Still another remedy for the PCI phenomena is to pressurize the fuel rods during fabrication. Helium gas at 20–50 atm is often used in PWRs. This extends the time before the cladding creeps down into contact with the fuel, thus minimizing PCI. By reducing the amount of possible fuel-clad interaction, the stresses and strains to which the cladding will be subjected are reduced and reliability is improved. The improvement arises from two sources: delayed fuel-clad contact and reduced cyclic stresses and strains after contact. Even a moderate level of internal pressure (such as 250 psig) results in a severalfold increase in the time to contact. Prepressurizing of the fuel also improves the thermal conductivity of the fuel, resulting in lower operating tempera-

† A "getter" is an element that strongly interacts chemically with another element, attracting it to a specific place.

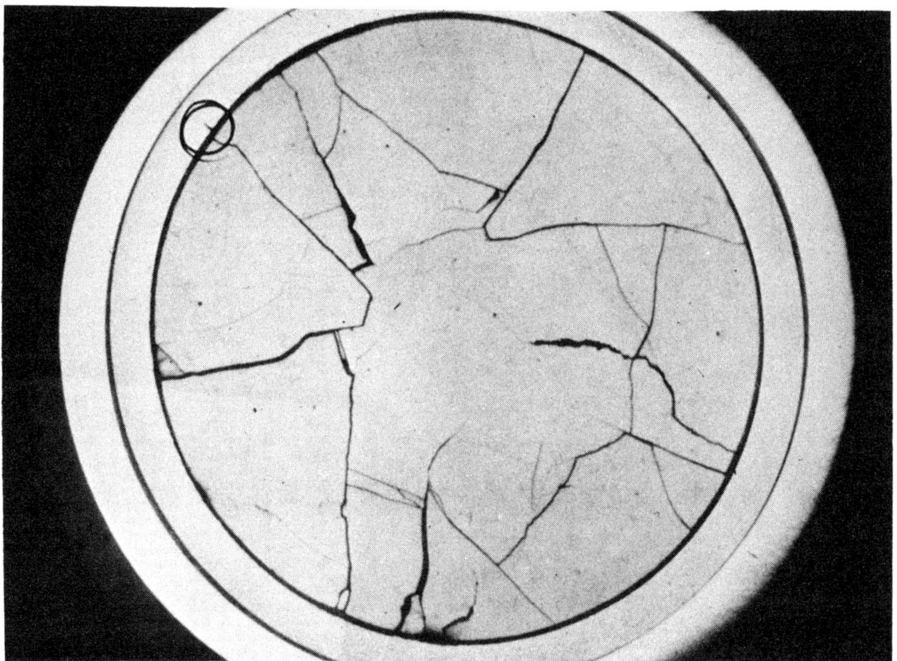

Figure 7.32. Fuel-cladding chemical interaction and an incipient cladding crack. Note crack in upper left quadrant of the cladding.

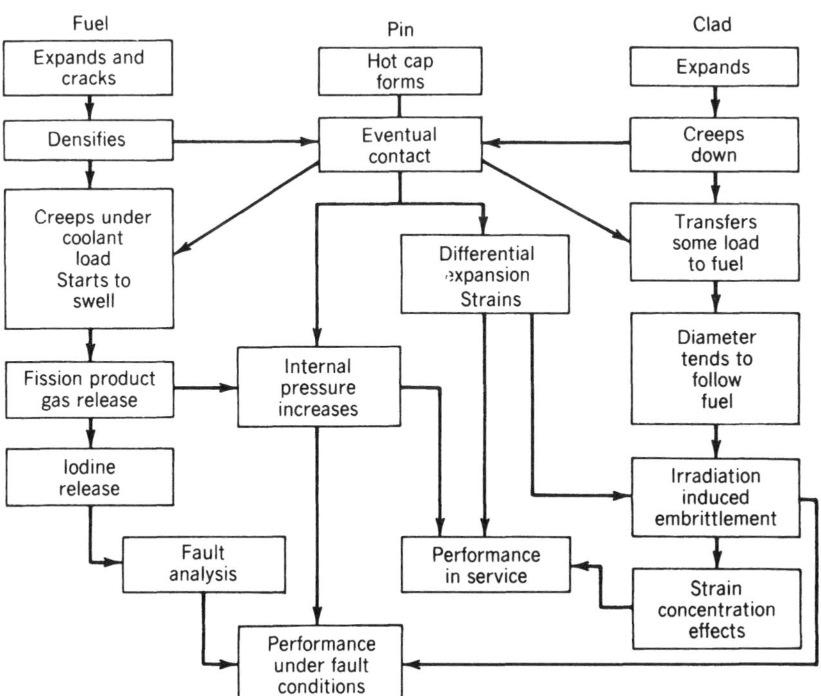

Figure 7.33. Diagrammatic representation of the major fuel pin interactions.

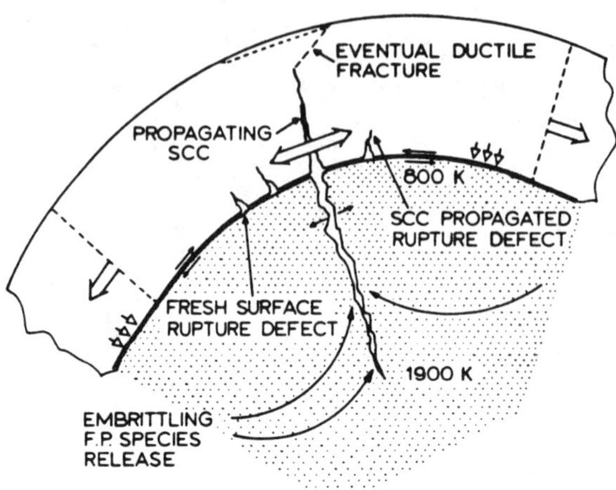

Figure 7.34. Schematic of PCI Zircaloy fuel rod failure mechanism. (Courtesy J. T. A. Roberts.)

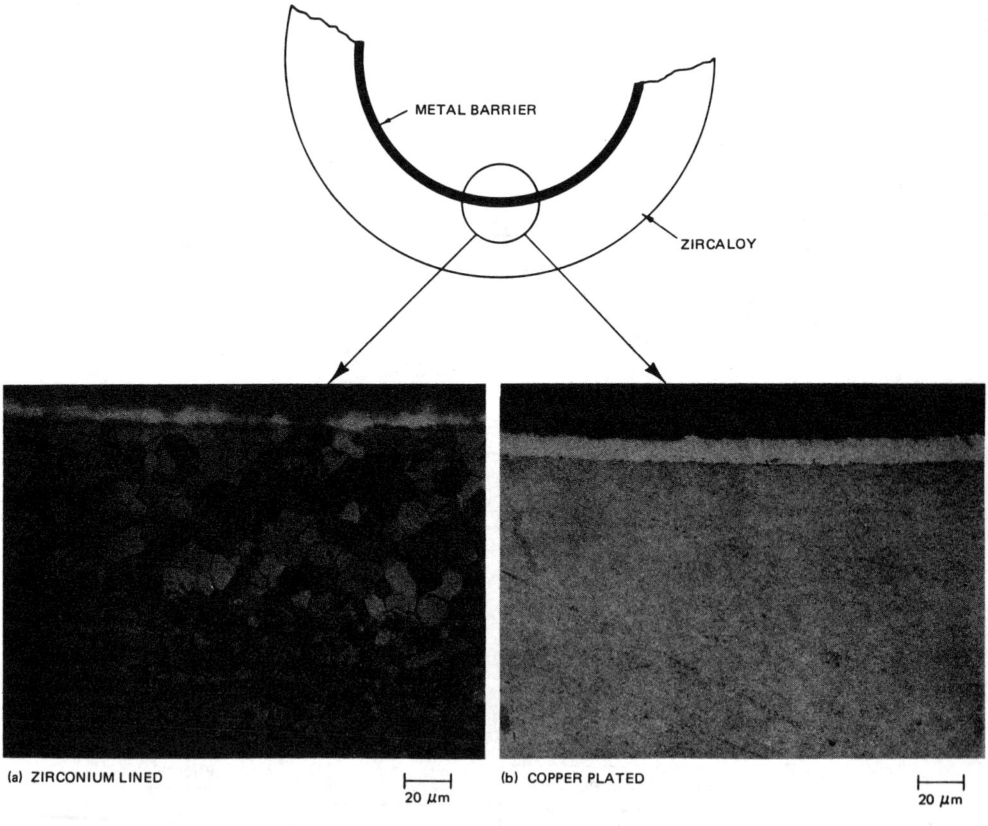

METAL BARRIER

ZIRCALOY

(a) ZIRCONIUM LINED 20 μm

(b) COPPER PLATED 20 μm

Figure 7.35. Photomicrographs of barrier cladding. [From J. H. Davis et al., *Trans. Am. Nuclear Soc.* **35,** 203 (1980).

Table 7.18. Techniques for "Sipping" Nuclear Fuel[a]

Sipping Method	Advantages	Comments
Wet	Can be done in-core if fuel channels exist (as in a BWR); otherwise the fuel assemblies are removed	Should be done about 3 weeks after shutdown.
Dry	10 to 100 times as sensitive as the wet method	Decay heat of the fuel may result in cladding damage
Vacuum	Relies on differential pressure technique to allow off-gas of radioisotopes	GE innovation which minimizes the time required to transport the fuel elements to and from the fuel sipping containers

[a]Sipping is a procedure performed by utilities to identify and locate fuel elements that have developed defects during operation. It is normally performed during a refueling outage, or during an extraordinary plant shutdown when major fuel failure is suspected. It consists of sampling the vicinity of the fuel to detect any radioactive gases that would leak through a defect.

tures and less fuel swelling. BWR fuel, on the other hand, is not as subject to creep because of the lower system pressures. Only about 3 atm of helium are required inside the fuel rod to counteract the system pressure and to prevent creepdown of the cladding onto the pellet.

Recently, interest has been shown in the development of annular or duplex fuel pellets.† Design advantages include reductions of centerline temperatures, fission product transport, and mechanical stress. Such designs have the potential for reducing many fuel problems.

Fuel Performance Monitoring and Operational Improvements

Fuel performance in an LWR is typically monitored by measuring fission products in the coolant or in off-gas stream. This monitoring can provide the plant operator with a fairly accurate idea of the fuel's integrity in the core. The isotopes of Xe and Kr are monitored as well as the iodine isotopes. These isotopes originate in the fuel and are released to the coolant via fuel rod defects. Of secondary importance are the isotopes such as ^{60}Co and activated corrosion products. By measuring the ratio of the long-lived to short-lived Xe, Kr, and I isotopes, and their magnitude, the number of defected fuel pins in a reactor's core can be estimated. For example, many BWRs monitor the radioactivity of the gas at the exit of the steam-jet air ejector. Incremental activity levels of about 3000 μCi/sec above background is usually indicative of a leaky fuel bundle. After the reactor is shut down, the leaking fuel bundle can be identified by a technique called fuel sipping, which is sampling for radioactive gases around a fuel assembly. If a failure is present, the fission products escaping the fuel will identify the failure's location. Sipping has been found a useful technique for locating defected fuel bundles. Table 7.18 and Figure 7.36 illustrate the procedure.

Along with the design changes came several changes in operating procedures which helped fuel performance. Two of the more important operational changes are:

1. *Fuel Preconditioning.* If the fuel is operated at higher power levels for sufficient time, the cladding is mechanically deformed. The procedure is to raise the power gradually to the planned steady-state power level beforehand and slightly deform the clad, taking care to stay below the threshold for stress corrosion cracking. If subsequently the core is again operated at a high-power ramp rate, but remains at or below the preconditioned power level, then the mechanical loading on the preconditioned cladding is not as it would have otherwise been, and fuel failure is much less likely. Figure 7.37 shows the more rapid start-up possible with preconditioned fuel.
2. *Maneuvering‡ Guidelines.* Based on the results of analysis and operating experience (e.g., sipping results for defected fuel), various maneuvering guidelines have been formulated by fuel vendors. These operating recommendations prevent rapid power increases above a "preconditioned power level." A typical restriction would limit the power ramp rate to 0.25 kW/m-hr above the preconditioned power level of 27 kW/m. Other restrictions might limit the rate of withdrawal for a control rod.

†Fuel pellets with hollows or a lower enrichment in their centers.

‡Maneuvering of a core refers to the operational sequence of raising and lowering power levels by various ways of inserting or removing reactivity.

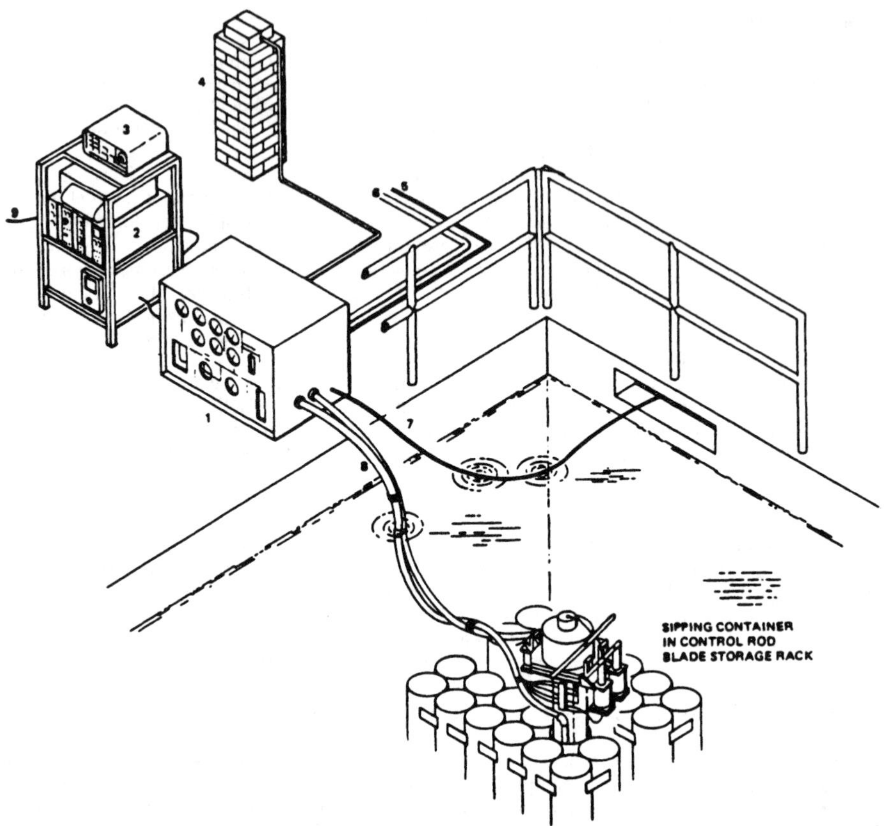

Figure 7.36. General Electric vacuum sipping equipment. [From T. A. Green, *Trans. Am. Nuclear Soc.* **30,** 333 (1978).] 1—hydraulic console; 2—electronic console; 3—solid-state electronic controller; 4—lead cave containing beta scintillation detector; 5—service air; 6—demineralized or reclaimed (condensate) water; 7—drain harness to fuel pool cleanup system; 8—hydraulic console to sipping container harness; 9—110-V, 60-Hz power supply.

7.9. FUTURE TRENDS

The evolution of fuel fabrication technology is influenced by three factors: (1) possible plutonium recovery for the manufacture of breeder reactor fuel, (2) the desire to achieve higher burnup levels which would reduce fuel consumption, and (3) the desire to produce fuels which will give nuclear plants load-following† capability.

Present developments include alternative methods to produce powder for oxide fuels for use in MOX fuel fabrication. What is sought is a mixture of uranium and plutonium oxide that will permit better accountability of plutonium and potentially better fuel performance. To accomplish this, three alternative approaches are being considered at the laboratory scale.

A new fuel under development, but not yet used commercially, is the sol–gel process. This process produces microspheres of uranium or mixed oxide. It is similar to the process for producing HTGR fuel. Droplets of mixed uranium and plutonium nitrates are injected into an appropriate environment (i.e, the basic environment to prepare microspheres by jelling). A UO_2 filter cake is formed by precipitation from a UNO_3 solution. The filter cake is then broken up into what is termed a UO_2 sol (small green particles of the cake) by ultrasonic waves in the solution. The gel is used to support the UNO_3 during precipitation. The cake is fired at typically 1150°C in a reducing (H_2) atmosphere. A flow diagram of the process is shown in Figure 7.38. This "wet" route of producing

†Demand for electricity varies with time of day, season, and so on. Utilities usually run some of their plants at constant full power (baseload) while other plants attempt to follow the demand curve (load follow).

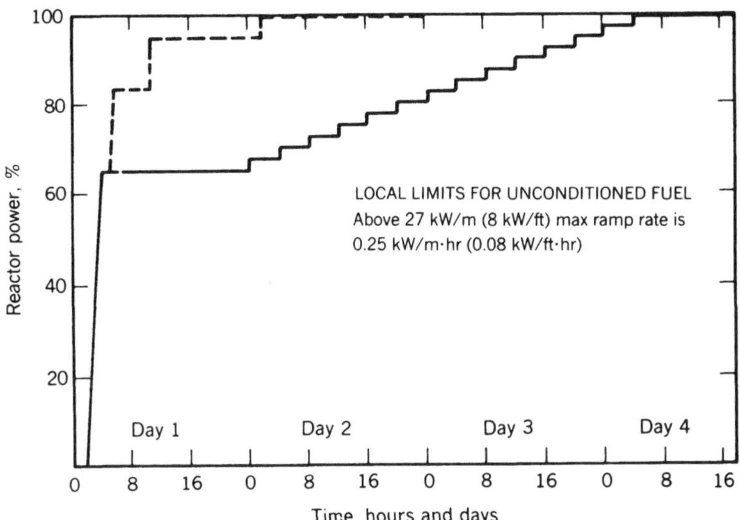

Figure 7.37. A typical start-up after a refuelling or a control rod sequence exchange (———) and a cold start with preconditioned fuel (– – –). Note the more rapid ascent to operating power with preconditioned fuel. This can save over $500,000 in replacement power costs. (Courtesy B. Norman, Synkraft.)

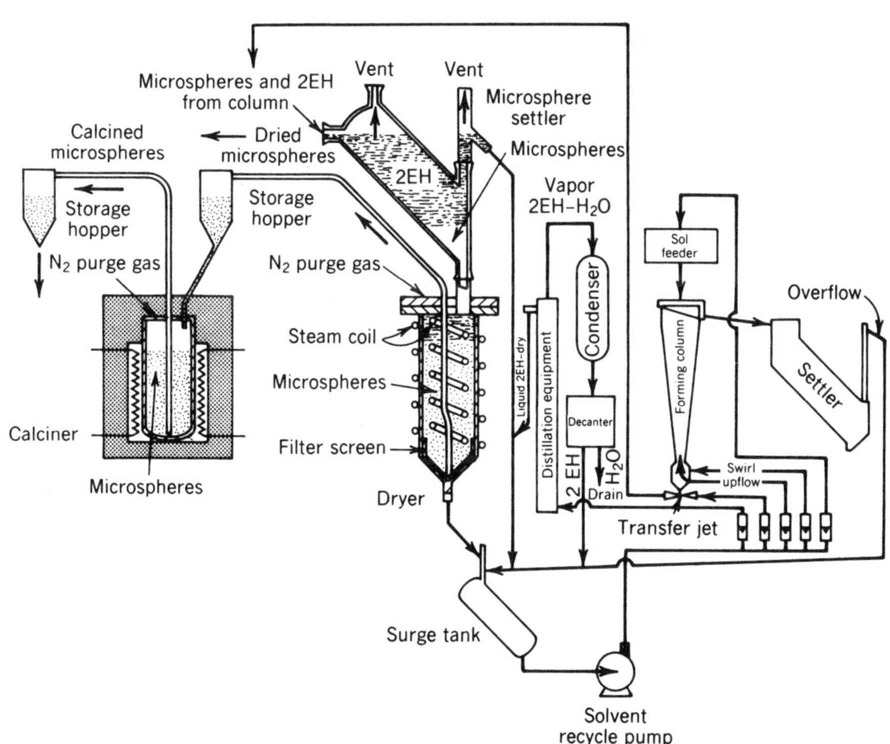

Figure 7.38. Sol–gel process flow sheet showing the process equipment. The working fluid is 2-ethyl-1-hexanol (2EH). (From IAEA-STI/PUB/207.)

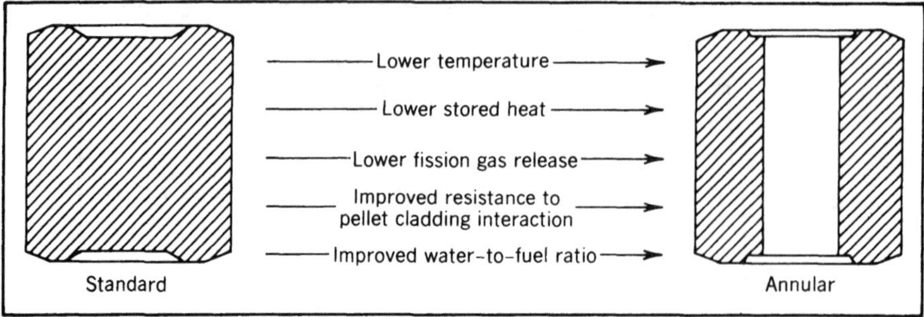

Figure 7.39. Comparison between standard and annular fuel pellets. Annular fuel pellets have advantages over standard fuel, and do not require design changes to the reactor or fuel assembly. [From C. K. Anderson and M. G. Andrews, *Nuclear Engineering International*, **26**, 25 (1981).]

fuel results in less dust production and fewer process steps. It is therefore more suitable for remote fabrication. This would be an advantage if mixed oxide $(Pu,U)O_2$ fuels were to be used in LWRs in a plutonium recycle fuel cycle. A process such as sol–gel would be easily adaptable to denaturing or spiking (i.e., deliberate adding of radioactivity to reduce the diversion possibilities) if plutonium recycle were to be adopted (see Chapter 14).

The sol–gel process produces small microspheres, typically in the 40–60 μm range. The microspheres are fabricated into a dense fuel rod either by compaction of different-sized microspheres or by pressing the spheres into ceramic pellets. In the former process, microspheres are loaded into cladding by vibration. The loading process goes by various names, such as sphere-pac, or VIPAC. Loading the microspheres directly into the fuel rod avoids dusting associated with pellet production and grinding. This has advantages both in automation and in quality control. To obtain a high geometrical packing ratio, spheres of two or three different radii are used. In this manner fuel densities close to sintered pellets can be obtained.

The two other process alternatives being developed to produce MOX fuels are (a) coprecipitation of uranium and plutonium from nitrate solutions, which produces a mixture of uranium and plutonium hydroxide which can be denitrated to a mixed oxide powder, and (b) direct denitration of uranium and plutonium solutions which can be used to produce a mixed uranium–plutonium oxide powder. These are not described here in detail because they are still very far from being commercial processes.

New fuels under development emphasize pellet designs that reduce fission product release. The two chief ways of achieving this are by lower fuel temperatures (since high temperature promotes fission product diffusion) and by larger grain sizes (which tend to trap fission products). Several possibilities exist:

1. Annular Fuel Pellets. The central portion of the fuel pellet is hollow (see Figure 7.39). As a result of no power production in this void, the peak temperature reached in the pellet is greatly reduced. The central void may also be able to reduce stresses in the fuel by providing room for the pellet to "expand." Early testing results show encouraging results, with no extra cracking or filling of the central void with fragments.
2. Graded Enrichment Pellets. The concept relies on a decreasing concentration of ^{235}U across the radius of the fuel pellet. Some designs employ two enrichment zones: a relatively highly enriched outer zone, a lesser enriched inner zone. Most of the power in such an arrangement would come from the outer part of the pellet, and the central (peak) temperature would be considerably lower. This should reduce mechanical stress and improve fission product retention, especially if accompanied by large grain size (which can be produced by seeding with Nb_2O_5).

The evolution of new fuel designs is leading to increased fuel performance. As a measure of fuel performance, the burnup obtained during reactor operation is often used. As of 1982, burnups of 35,000 MWd/t were commonly achievable. By 1985, burnups of 40–45,000 MWd/t are predicted. This is expected to reach around 50,000 MWd/t by the end of the decade.

BIBLIOGRAPHY

Davis, J. H., et al., "Barrier Fuel Ramp Tests," *Trans. Am. Nuclear Soc.* **35,** 203 (1980).

Dressler, G., and H. G. Weidenger, "KWU Fuel Cladding Technology and Quality Assurance," IAEA-SR-7/7, May 1976.

Ferrari, H. M., "Pressurization Improves Fuel Rod Reliability," *Nuclear Engineering International*, July 1970.

Lawrence, L. A., and J. W. Host, "Fuel-Cladding Chemical Interaction," *Trans. Am. Nuclear Soc.* **35,** 211 (1980).

Olander, D. R., *Fundamental Aspects of Nuclear Reactor Fuel Elements*, TID-26711, 1976.

Roberts, J. T. A., "Ceramic Utilization in the Nuclear Industry," *Powder Metal International* **11** (1979).

Roberts, J. T. A., *Structural Materials in Nuclear Power Systems*, Plenum Press, New York, 1981.

Yemel'Yanov, V. S. and A. I. Yevstyukhin, *The Metallurgy of Nuclear Fuel,* Pergamon Press, New York, 1969.

———, "Sol-Gel Processes for Ceramic Nuclear Fuel," STI/PUB/207, IAEA, Vienna, 1968.

———, "Proceedings on International Conference on Nuclear Fuel Performance," London, October 1973.

———, "Proceedings of a Seminar on Nuclear Fuel Quality Assurance," Oslo, May 1976.

———, "Proceedings of the ANS Topical Meeting on Light Water Reactor Fuel Performance," Portland, Oregon, April 1979.

CHAPTER 8
LIGHT-WATER REACTOR SYSTEMS

8.1. PLANT HEAT BALANCE AND THE STEAM CYCLE

The nuclear chain reaction in the reactor core produces energy in the form of heat, as the fission fragments slow down and dissipate their kinetic energy in the fuel. This heat must be removed efficiently and at the same rate it is being generated in order (a) to prevent overheating of the core and (b) to transport the energy outside the core where it can be converted to a convenient form for further utilization. A fluid is used for this purpose. In the light-water reactor (LWR) case, water is used as both moderator and coolant. The energy transferred to the coolant, as it flows past the fuel elements, is stored in it in the form of temperature and pressure, and is called the "enthalpy" of the fluid. In an electric power plant the energy stored in the fluid is further converted into kinetic energy through a device called "a prime mover" which, in the case of nuclear reactors, is, predominantly, a steam turbine. (In high-temperature gas-cooled reactors (HTGR), the enthalpy of the coolant gas could be converted into kinetic energy, in one of the proposed schemes, through direct expansion in a gas turbine, as further explained in Chapter 13.) Another conversion takes place in the electric generator where kinetic energy is converted into electric power as the final energy form to be distributed to the consumers through the power grid and distribution system.

The transport of thermal energy from the core to the turbine takes place either through one circuit or loop as in the BWR, or through two separated but interlocking loops, connected through a steam generator. These two different configurations of a LWR plant are shown schematically in Figure 8.1.

After the steam expands in the turbine, it exits into the condenser where the remaining amount of heat is removed to produce condensate water which is then fed back either to the core or to the steam generator, and the cycle is repeated. The condenser is a very large and important part of the plant. Roughly, twice the amount of heat that has been converted in the turbine for the production of electric power is removed in the condenser for further rejection to the environment due to the second law of thermodynamics which limits the fraction of useful energy that can be attained by a thermal engine. Large amounts of water circulate through the condenser to carry the waste heat to its ultimate sink, which may be the sea, a river, a lake, or the atmosphere itself through cooling towers (see Section 8.2, Ultimate Heat Sink).

The energy conversion part of the power plant (i.e., excluding the reactor itself with its main components and system) is often called Balance of Plant (BOP). It incorporates a large number of components and systems which will be described in detail in this and the following chapters. It represents the largest portion of the plant's total cost, and its importance for the efficient and safe operation of the plant is great.

In the following sections, we will focus on a description of plant systems in the two dominant reactor types, the pressurized and the boiling water reactors (PWR and BWR). About 70% of the total number of reactors operating worldwide belong to the class of LWR. Present construction and future plans are based almost exclusively on this type of reactor.

8.2. PRESSURIZED WATER REACTORS (PWR)

PWR Primary and Secondary Loops

The name of the PWR derives from the fact that the primary circuit is kept at a very high pressure, typically around 2200 psi (equivalent to about 15 MPa), such that at the maximum prevailing temperature in the system, no boiling can occur. At 2200 psi, the boiling temperature of water is about 650°F (343°C), well above the maximum temperature of 629°F (332°C) allowed in the primary

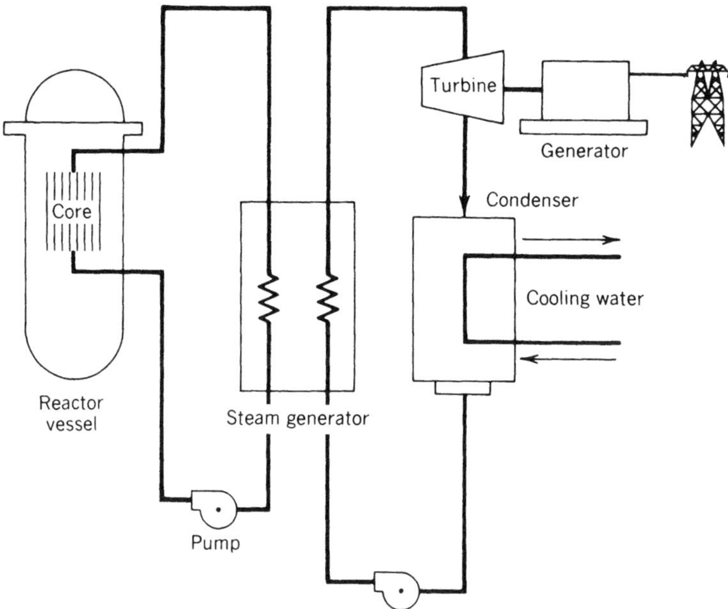

Pressurized water reactor

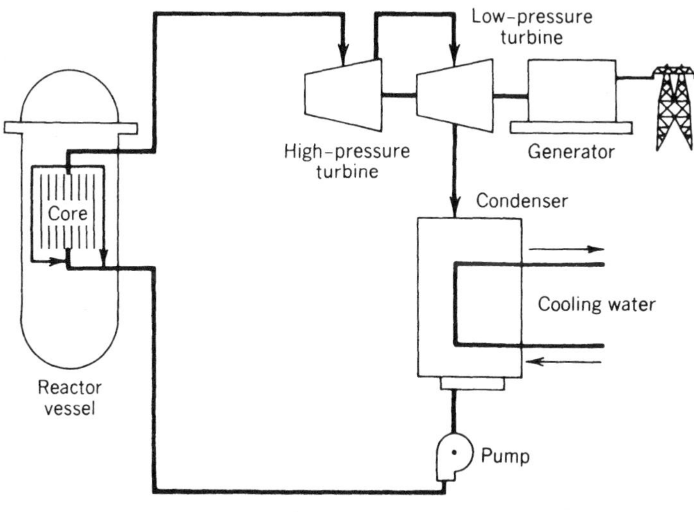

Boiling water reactor

Figure 8.1. Schematic of LWR plants. Two distinct methods of heat removal and energy conversion were developed in LWR plants. In the PWR (and also in the heavy water pressurized water reactor), the primary loop is pressurized (~2200 psi) to prevent boiling. Heat is transferred through a heat exchanger to a secondary loop where steam is produced, which in turn moves the turbine. In the BWR, steam is produced in the reactor vessel, since pressure is maintained at about half the pressure of a PWR. This steam goes directly to the turbine and returns to the core through the steam condenser.

Table 8.1. 3600-MWt Standard NSS Design Data

Number of fuel assemblies	205
Core power, MWt	3,600
NSS power, MWt	3,618
Linear power, kW/ft	5.43
Steam pressure, psia	1,060
Superheat, °F	50
Net plant output, MWe[a]	1,244
Net plant heat rate, Btu/kWh[a]	9,909
Active fuel length, in.	143
No. of control rod drives	
U core	72
Pu core	77
maximum	89
Reactor coolant system flow, 10^6 lb/hr	150.5
Reactor vessel inlet temperature, °F	572.3
Reactor vessel outlet temperature, °F	628.8
Reactor vessel I.D., in.	182
Reactor coolant hot leg I.D., in.	38
Reactor coolant cold leg I.D., in.	28
Pump suction I.D., in.	32
Number of steam generator tubes	16,000
Steam generator height, ft	75.4
Reactor vessel–steam generator spacing, ft	34.0
Core flooding tanks, number/volume, unit ft^3	2/1,800
Low-pressure injection pumps, number/flow, unit gal/min	2/5,000
High-pressure injection pumps, number/flow, unit gal/min	3/700

Source: Courtesy Babcock & Wilcox.

[a]Estimated at 2 in. Hg backpressure, seven FW heaters.

water. A list of characteristic quantities in a PWR is given in Table 8.1. The basic circuits and components of a PWR plant are shown in Figure 8.2. They include mainly:

1. The reactor pressure vessel, which contains the core.
2. The primary coolant circuit. These constitute the primary pressure boundary which contains water circulating at high pressure to remove fission-produced heat from the core.
3. A heat exchanger or steam generator, in which heat is transferred to a secondary loop, also containing circulating water, where steam is generated.
4. The energy conversion system where steam is used to make electricity.

A more detailed description of the components in a PWR plant is given in Chapter 9.

The primary system with all its piping and components, along with the steam generators, is enclosed in a specially designed structure called the containment. It is provided to isolate from the environment any radioactivity that may escape from the fuel into the primary water and from the primary water into the surroundings via a potential leak. Primary system water, at about a pressure of 2200 psi (15 MPa) and a temperature of about 572°F (300°C) enters the reactor vessel through the inlet nozzles near the top. It then travels downward in the annular space (called the downcomer) between the vessel and the core barrel and enters the reactor, it picks up heat, and its temperature reaches about 629°F (332°C) as it exits into the upper plenum of the reactor vessel. In a typical PWR producing an electrical output of 1244 MWe (which requires the production of about 3600 MW of thermal power), a water flow on the order of 150 million lb/hr (18.8 Mg/sec) carries away the heat released in the core and holds the cladding temperature below a comfortable 700°F (370°C).

The hot primary fluid exchanges its heat with the secondary fluid in the steam generator and then returns to the core through the primary coolant pumps. Two, three, or four such primary loops have been used in various designs. Figure 8.3 shows the primary system of a Babcock & Wilcox Company design utilizing two loops; Figure 8.4 depicts a four-loop plant such as those manufactured by Westinghouse. In each of these figures, an additional vessel, called the "pressurizer," is also shown connected to the primary system. Its function is to maintain control of primary system pressure, and it is further described in Chapter 9. Some current PWR designs are equipped with primary loop isolation valves. These enable continued operation of the plant in the case of a fault in one of the loops.

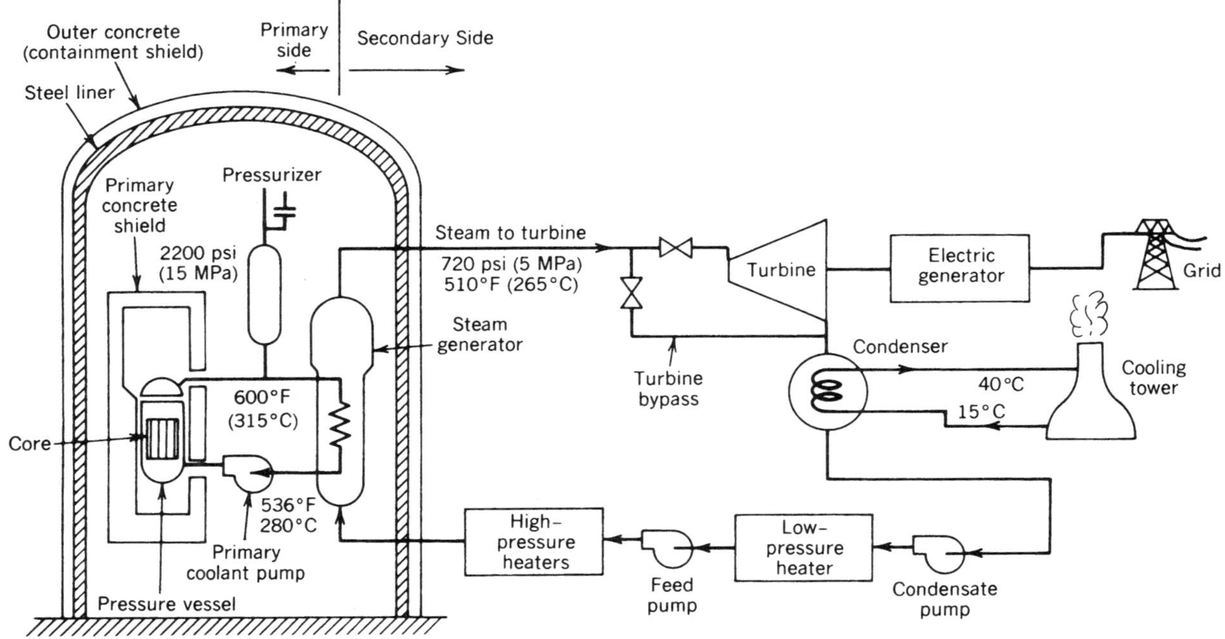

Figure 8.2. Schematic PWR power plant. The primary reactor system is enclosed in a steel-lined concrete containment building. Steam generated within the building flows to the turbine–generator system (outside the building), after which it is condensed and returned to the steam generators.

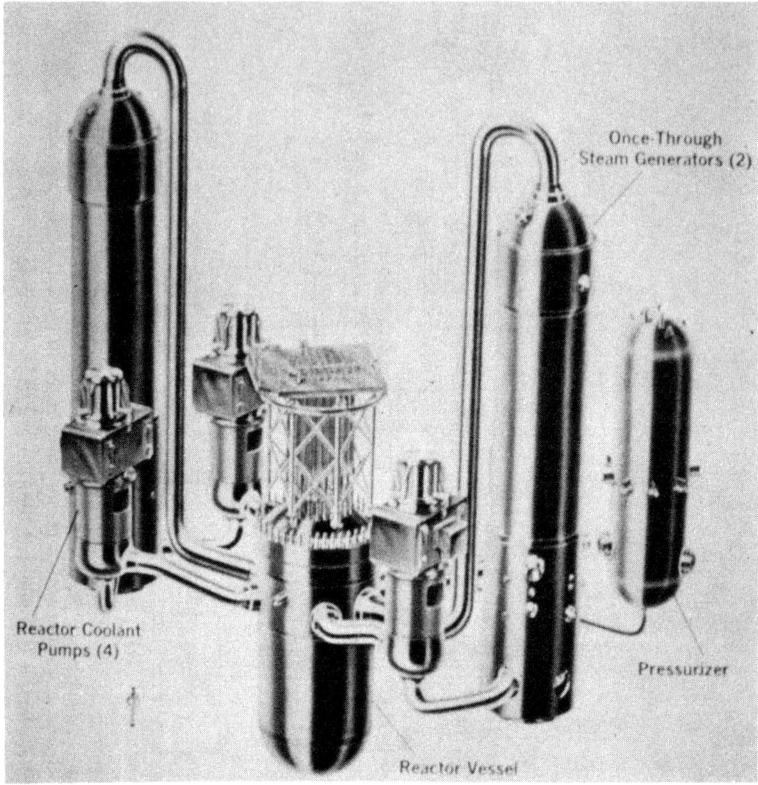

Figure 8.3. Babcock & Wilcox Oconee type nuclear steam supply system. The reactor is shown at the center, and it supplies energy for the two once-through steam generators, each of which has a pair of circulating pumps. (Courtesy Babcock & Wilcox Co.)

The secondary system is maintained at considerably lower pressure, typically 720 lb/in.^{2} (5 MPa) and a temperature of 510°F (265°C). Figure 8.2 also shows a turbine bypass line. This pipe has the capacity to take steam from the main steamline directly to the condenser. It is used to minimize transient effects on the reactor coolant system during events such as start-up, hot shutdown, and cooldown and abrupt reductions or total shedding of the generator load. It consists of pipes, headers, and valves. The bypass line, combined with the ability of the reactor coolant system to accept a 10% abrupt load change, enables the plant to accept up to 50% load shedding of the turbine-generator rated load, without reactor trip and actuation of the relief and safety valves. These, however, could not be avoided for a load rejection of more than 50%.

Also shown in Figure 8.2, in the secondary loop, are high- and low-pressure heaters. These are heat exchangers used to gradually heat the condensed water as it makes its way back to the steam generator by drawing (extracting) small amounts of steam from various stages of the turbine. Thermodynamic theory indicates that by this process the thermodynamic efficiency of the cycle is improved by a few percentage points.

Temperature limitations, imposed by the requirements for the safe operation of the plant, have considerable effect on plant efficiency. Total plant thermal efficiency is the product of the theoretical thermal efficiency, also called Carnot efficiency and the conversion (or engine) efficiency;

$$\eta_{overall} = \eta_c \cdot \eta_{conversion}$$

The Carnot efficiency is given by the simple formula

$$\eta_c = \frac{T_1 - T_2}{T_1}$$

where T_1 is the temperature of the hot reservoir, and T_2 is the temperature of the cold reservoir,

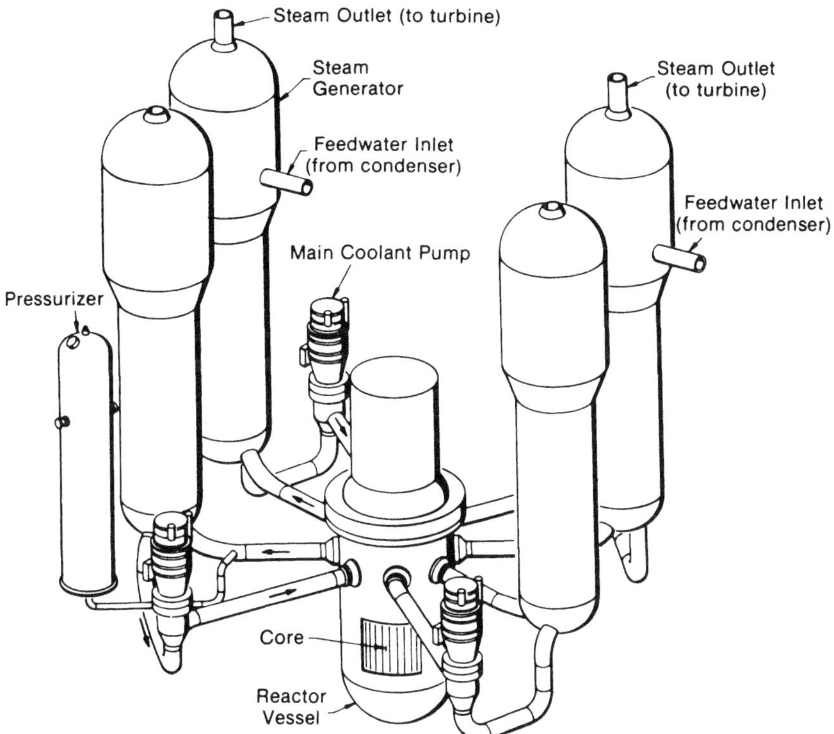

Figure 8.4. PWR primary system with four loops. Each of the four loops in this arrangement has its own steam generator and coolant pump. A pressurizer, for pressure control, is connected to one of the loops. This design, used by Westinghouse, utilizes U-shaped tubes in the steam generator (see Chapter 9), and hence both the inlet and outlet of the steam generator are at the bottom. (Courtesy Westinghouse Electric Corp.)

both in absolute degrees Kelvin. The conversion efficiency relates to the various losses during heat transfer and transport losses from friction and other similar processes; it can be improved, but not much beyond a certain point. It is obvious that in order to increase the plant's overall thermal efficiency it is desirable to increase the temperature T_1 to as high a point as possible. The limitations in T_1 originate from the capacity of various materials to perform under conditions of stress. This capacity is normally reduced at high temperatures.

Because the primary coolant must be kept below a certain temperature limit, dictated by primary system pressure and materials behavior, the secondary fluid temperature must necessarily be kept at a still lower temperature. Thus, the overall thermal efficiency of PWRs is a modest 32–33%, which is considerably lower than the thermal efficiency achievable in modern fossil-burning power stations (about 40%), where higher temperature steam can be used.

The Chemistry and Volume Control System (CVCS)

Each nuclear reactor plant is equipped with many auxiliary systems to support the main function of the plant and to provide the means for compliance with safety and environmental regulations. The main and auxiliary systems of a PWR are shown in the highly simplified diagram in Figure 8.5. We shall first describe the chemistry and volume control system.

Through wear and corrosion, and possibly through leaks in some fuel pins, impurities are produced in the primary coolant. If allowed to accumulate, these impurities would cause progressive surface fouling, and accumulation of crud† in certain parts of the primary system with resultant problems for plant operation and maintenance, and unfavorable impact on plant availability. To

†Crud: term used to denote radioactive corrosion products, primarily cobalt-60, which accumulate on surfaces of the primary coolant system. The presence of this active material makes maintenance more difficult.

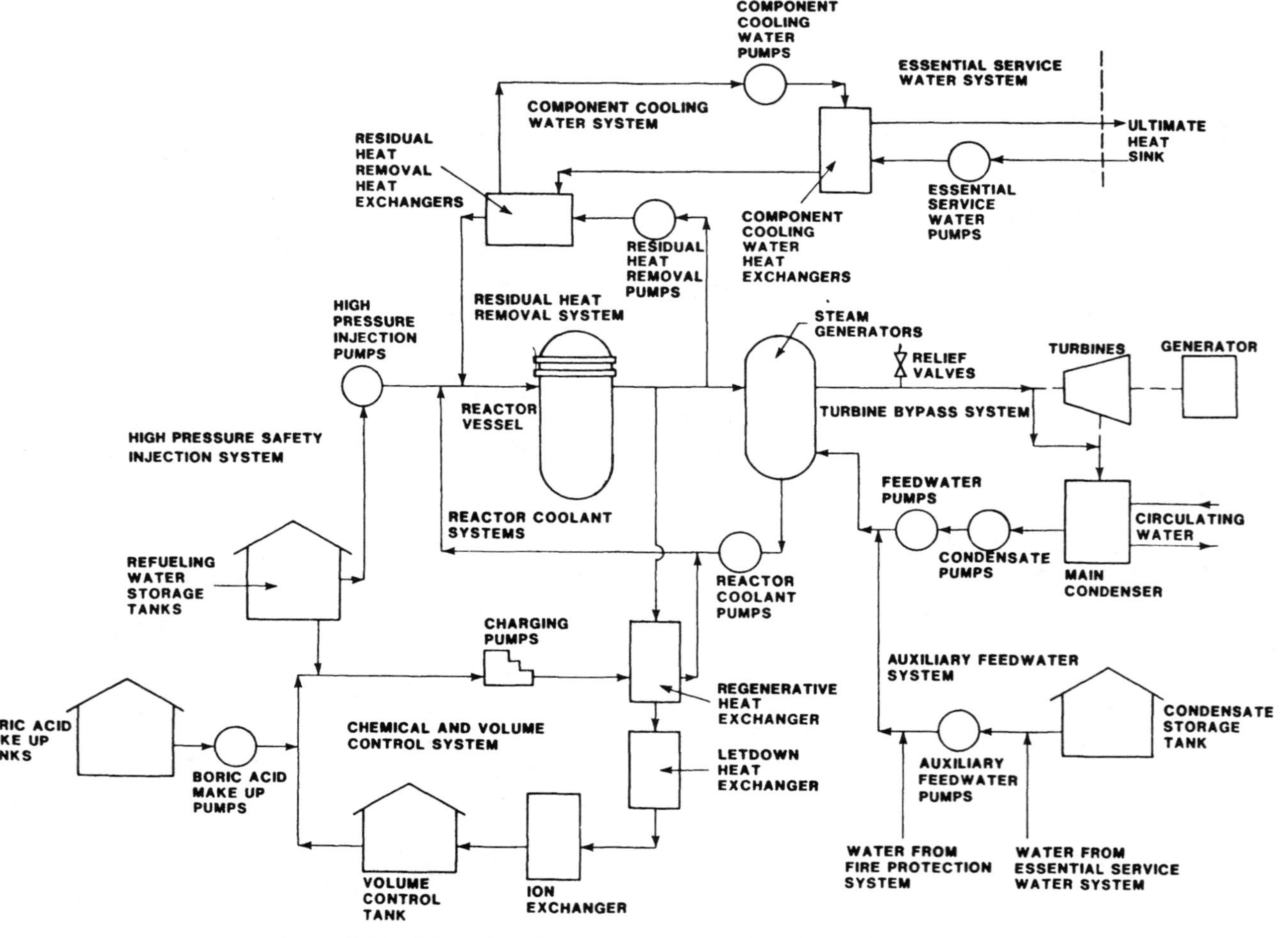

Figure 8.5. PWR main and auxiliary systems. (From NUREG/CR-1556.)

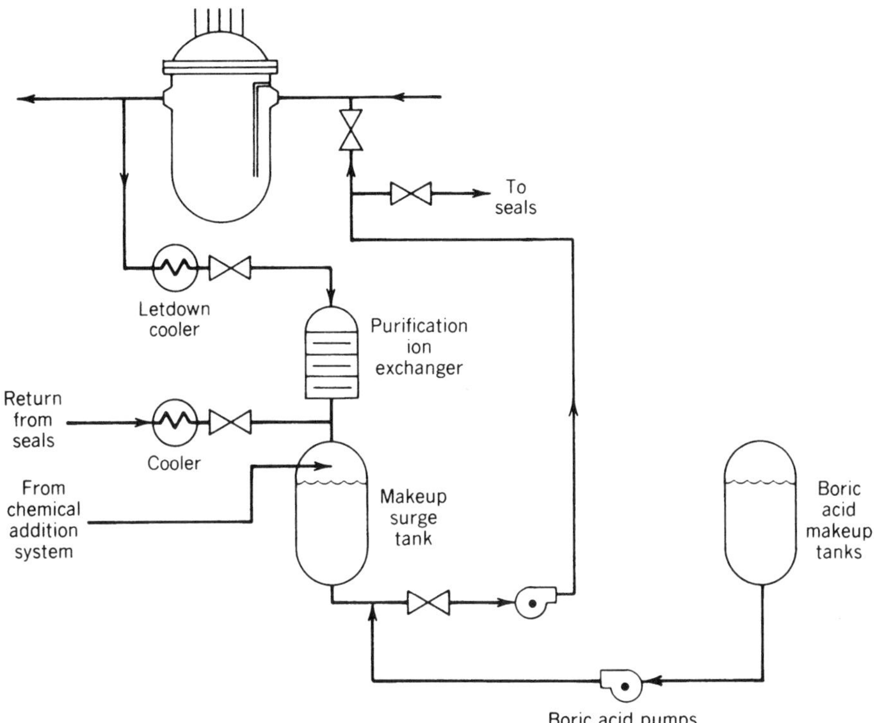

Figure 8.6. PWR chemical and volume control system (CVCS). (Adapted from Babcock & Wilcox, *Steam, Its Generation and Use*, 1978.)

combat this problem, the Chemistry and Volume Control System (CVCS) is provided. As shown in Figure 8.6, it consists of piping, valves, pumps, tanks, and other components and performs mainly three functions: (1) removes fission and corrosion products in the water and keeps their concentration to acceptably low levels; (2) provides a constant supply of water for the primary system and makes up for losses; and (3) maintains the boron concentration at prespecified levels, which change slowly with time for reasons which will be explained below. The system is also called "makeup and purification system." As the primary coolant circulates, a certain fraction of it is continuously removed (bled) from the primary loop through a letdown cooler, then is passed through a demineralizer (or ion exchanger) where impurities (other than boron) are removed, and is then introduced to a makeup surge tank from which it is pumped back to the reactor coolant system as required. The control is effected through maintenance of the pressurizer water level. The makeup tank is designed to be large enough to accommodate anticipated changes in the total primary fluid volume without any discharge of the primary (and radioactive) coolant. Connected to the CVCS is also the water to and from the various pump and other seals of the primary system. Low-temperature water is continuously fed to the seals to prevent the leakage of primary coolant. The portion of this water that leaks outward at the seals is returned to the CVCS through separate coolers.

The *demineralizers* used in the CVCS and in several other applications in power plants, are special components designed to remove dissolved materials from the reactor coolant water and various other liquid wastes. A typical unit is shown in Figure 8.7. They are steel tanks filled with a bed of resins, organic substances with the consistency and appearance of sand. Through a process of chemical ion exchange, the resins can absorb and retain materials dissolved in the water, whether radioactive or nonradioactive. A typical chemical reaction is $2HCl + RCO_3 = RCl_2 + H_2CO_3$. The carbonic acid is removed by aeration. When the resin bed is fresh, its retention ability for dissolved material is very high, but as the resins are saturated, this ability is gradually reduced.

The resins can be regenerated and reused. A typical reaction for regenerating the anion exchanger is $RCl_2 + Na_2CO_3 = RCO_3 + 2NaCl$. In the case where nonradioactive water is fed to the demineralizers for purification, such as fresh water from a river or lake, the ions removed from the purified water can be purged from the resins and returned to their original source, together with the small amounts of chemicals (neutralized acid and alkali) that were used in the resin bed

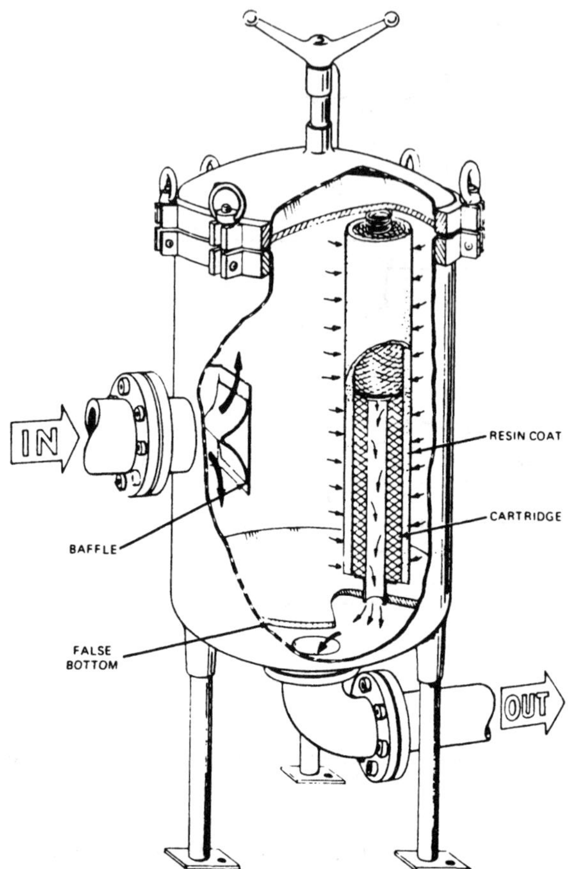

Figure 8.7. Cutaway drawing of a typical ground resin filter/demineralizer unit. (Courtesy Graver Water Conditioning Co.)

regeneration. If, however, the demineralizers were used to remove radioactive substances, they are used only once. When saturated, they are replaced with fresh demineralizers and are treated as solid waste from the plant. The radioactivity level of such used resins is such that they are characterized as intermediate level wastes. Often, demineralizers function in sets connected in parallel (Figure 8.8). This allows for a continuous and a more reliable operation.

The same system is used to perform another important function at the plant: chemical sampling operations and chemical addition. The chemical sampling provides a means for monitoring the concentration of various chemicals in the reactor coolant and auxiliary systems. Two parameters are of particular importance: the pH level, which measures the degree of acidity or alkalinity of a solution (a value of 7.0 indicates a neutral solution), and the oxygen level and conductivity of the coolant (a high value indicates dissolved salts). These two parameters have the potential of promoting corrosion in the plant if not carefully controlled.

Corrosion

Corrosion is always a serious threat to the integrity and to the efficient operation of power plants. It eats away the material of the walls and can produce cracks, pits, or grooves and potentially ultimate failure of the component. For this reason, the phenomena of corrosion are under intensive investigation for a more complete basic understanding and for the discovery of effective remedies. It appears that dissolved gases are the dominant factor in corrosion although the simultaneous occurrence of other conditions, such as composition and sensitization of the material, and the level of stresses play an important role. The most deleterious gas is oxygen although other gases such as carbon dioxide (CO_2), hydrogen sulfide (H_2S), and ammonium (NH_4) are also detrimental. Oxygen may enter the feedwater system either in solution in the makeup water or through leaks in the low-

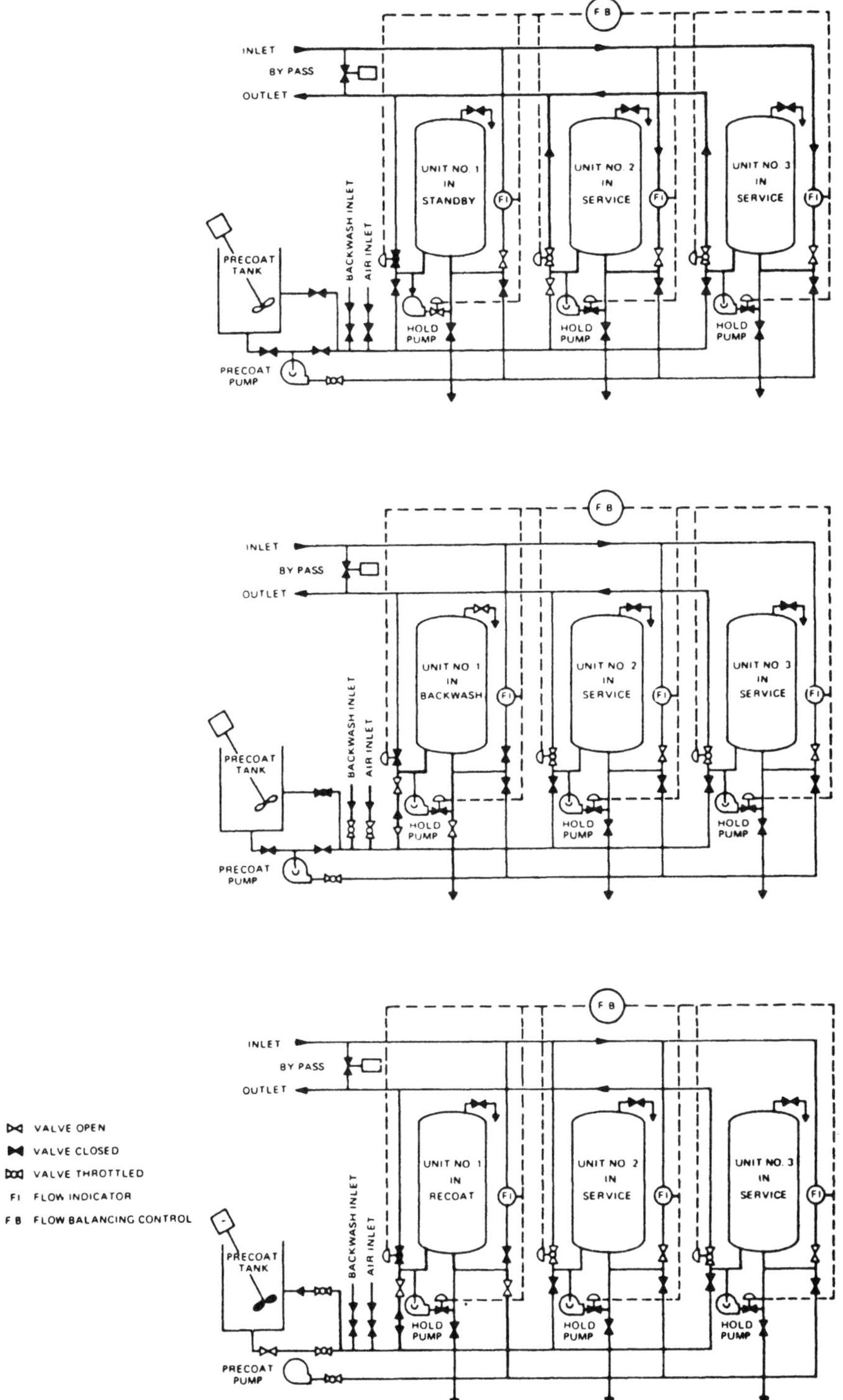

Figure 8.8. Unit nos. 2 and 3 of this ground bed demineralizer plant are in service, while the holding pump keeps unit no. 1 on standby (top) until needed; unit no. 1 being backwashed (center); and unit no. 1 being precoated with resin (bottom).

pressure points of the condensate system, such as the hotwell of the condenser and the low-pressure heaters. The chemical processes can be outlined as follows. A number of water molecules are split inside the metal pipe to give positive and negative ions (see also Figure 8.8).

$$H_2O \rightarrow H^+ + OH^-$$

When this occurs in contact with iron, positive iron ions tend to replace the hydrogen in water as follows:

$$Fe^{2+} + 2\ OH^- \rightarrow Fe(OH)_2$$

Although a film of hydrogen is formed at the iron surface, this hydrogen tends to recombine with the existing oxygen to reform water, thus exposing continuously the iron surface. Oxygen also reacts with the ferrous hydroxide already formed as follows:

$$2Fe(OH)_2 + O_2 + 2H_2O \rightarrow 2Fe(OH)_4$$

The material formed is ferric hydroxide, otherwise known as common rust. It is also possible for ferric oxide ($Fe_2O_3 \cdot 3H_2O$) to form. The corrosion effect caused by dissolved gases is particularly pronounced in high-temperature regions of the plant in the form of pits or depressions which have a hard crust with an underlayer of black magnetic iron oxide (Fe_3O_4) or red ferric oxide (Fe_2O_3). To reduce this corrosion to a minimum, nuclear power plant vendors and operators have established strict guidelines regarding the monitoring and control of oxygen levels. Mechanical and chemical treatment is used for this purpose. Deaerators in several points of the system allow gases to escape from the coolant, but the process does not allow oxygen levels to drop to the very low levels required. Chemical treatment is used to supplement the process of oxygen removal. Through the chemical addition system, which is part of the CVCS, chemical substances can be injected into the system for oxygen control. Hydrogen injection can be used to reduce the existing traces of oxygen by direct chemical recombination to produce water. Hydrazine (N_2H_4) is widely used for oxygen control through the reaction

$$N_2H_4 + O_2 \rightarrow 2H_2O + N_2$$

Hydrazine solution, a clear, waterlike, alkaline liquid which smells like ammonia, introduces alkalinity to the water and produces no solids. The nitrogen gas can be removed through the gaseous effluent control system.

The pH factor is another important parameter because it indicates the acidity of the primary water. An acidic water tends to be corrosive since the process of corrosion occurs as metal ions replace hydrogen ions. Lithium hydroxide is used to keep the water alkaline well above the 7.0 pH level. The degree of corrosion is, of course, also dependent on the type of materials used. All inner surfaces of the primary pressure boundary in a PWR, where high-temperature and high-pressure water circulates, are covered with a stainless steel layer which is highly resistant to corrosion.

The addition of chemicals is usually done through the makeup surge tank shown in Figure 8.6. The same system of chemical addition may also be designed to add chemicals to the steam generator feedwater and condensate systems which also require careful chemical control (see Chapter 9).

One of the important chemical additions in PWRs is that of boric acid (H_3BO_3).† Since boron is a strong absorber of neutrons, boric acid dissolved in the primary coolant is used in conjunction with the absorber rods to control the chain reaction. This form of control is called "chemical shim" (see also Chapter 12). In fact, as reactors are designed today, control rods alone are not sufficient to keep the reactor from going critical at the beginning of core life. Whereas control rods are used to respond quickly to operational requirements, such as load following, reactor shutdown and start-up, chemical shim (using boric acid) is used to keep the reactor critical during xenon transients and to compensate for the depletion of fuel and the buildup of fission products of the life of the core.

There are many reasons to use chemical shim. The number of control rods required in a reactor, along with the associated mechanical and electrical systems, are reduced; this results in cost savings. The boric acid is uniformly distributed in the core, and therefore, the power distribution in the core is not disturbed as the concentration of boron is changed. This also enhances the productivity of the plant. The boron concentration changes over time to match the condition of the core. This is done remotely and automatically at the command of the reactor operator (Figure 8.9) but cannot be performed at a speed required for quick response. The concentration over time is shown in Figure 8.10 which is also known as the "boron letdown curve."

†The solubility of boric acid in water is 63.5 g/liter at room temperature, 267 g/liter at 100°C. Maximum boron concentration is about 14% in hot water. In a PWR, the boron charging system feeds hydrogen-saturated water containing 4–12% boric acid into the primary coolant system.

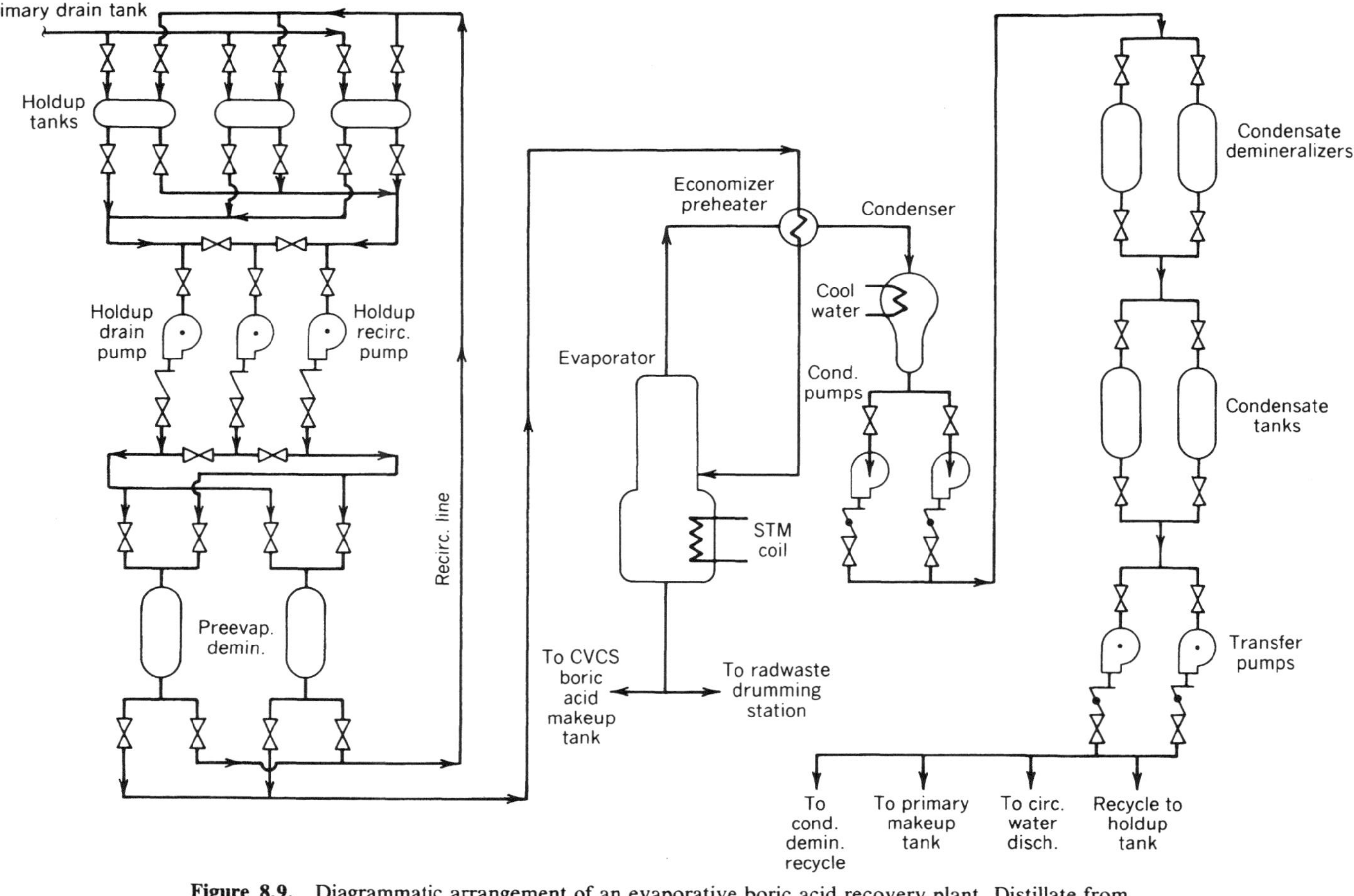

Figure 8.9. Diagrammatic arrangement of an evaporative boric acid recovery plant. Distillate from this plant is recycled as primary system makeup; concentrate is recycled to the concentrated boric acid storage tank. This system will be required for any "near zero release" PWR plant. (See Chapter 12.)

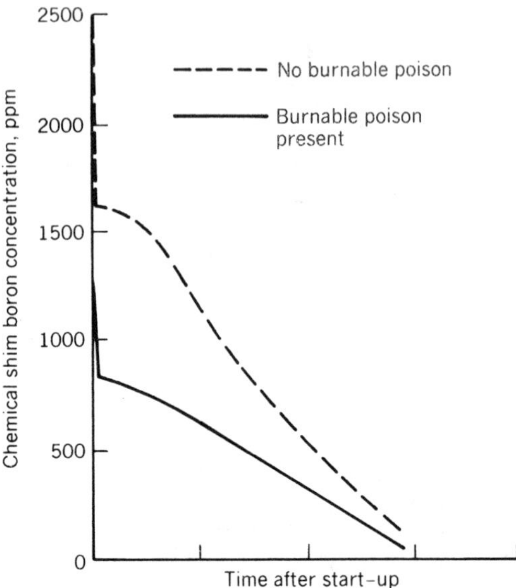

Figure 8.10. Boron shim with and without burnable poison. (Courtesy Westinghouse Electric Corp.)

The concentration of H_3BO_3 is usually measured in parts per million (ppm) of water. One ppm means that 1 g of boron is dissolved in 10^6 g of water. This can easily be converted into grams of boric acid dissolved into water, knowing that the molecular weight of H_3BO_3 is 61.8 and the atomic weight of boron 10.8. Using as an example the initial concentration value of $C = 2500$ ppm shown in Figure 8.6, we can calculate that the chemical shim must contain $(61.8/10.8) \times 2500$ ppm = 14,306 g of boric acid per 10^6 g of water (= 1 t of water). The initial concentration of 2500 ppm boron provides a shutdown margin of about 9% with the control rods fully inserted. As the xenon and samarium accumulate over the first few days of operation, the concentration is dropped to about 1600 ppm to balance this loss of reactivity. Following the initial sharp drop, the letdown curve follows a smooth path down to practically zero at the end of core life.

The various operations applied to vary the concentration of dissolved boron are collectively known as "boron management." To increase the concentration, highly concentrated boron solution is injected into the system through the charging pumps. In order to reduce the concentration, one can utilize either a bleed and feed system (bleeding the existing primary coolant and feeding in pure water) for rapid changes, or a deborating demineralizer which works slowly.

In the system described so far, the boron removed from the solution resides in the demineralizer. Because economic reasons do not allow its recovery, this boron is lost as waste. An alternative solution with higher capital but lower operating costs is based on an evaporative system through which both the boric acid and pure water are recovered for reuse. Such an evaporative system, shown in Figure 8.9, is favored for the future because it minimizes the amount of radioactive wastes to be handled and fits within a scheme of operations based on the concept of "zero release" from power plants.

The soluble poison in PWR, despite its advantages, has the potential of causing some problems in the moderator temperature coefficient and in the case of accidental boiling in the core. Although a fractional loss of moderator (e.g., through thermal expansion during a power transient) reduces the reactivity in the core, the simultaneous fractional loss of soluble poison tends to counteract this effect. As a result, the negative moderator temperature coefficient† may not be as negative as desired. To reduce this concern, the use of burnable poisons in solid form, mixed with fuel in a number of fuel rods, was introduced. This development allowed a reduction in the boron concentration as shown in the lower boron letdown curve shown in Figure 8.10. The maintenance of proper chemical control of the primary system is very important and plant operation must adhere to the standards set by the vendor. These are summarized in Table 8.2.

†This coefficient measures the reduction in reactivity as the moderator heats up. A negative coefficient provides a built-in factor of safety against rapid increases of power level.

Table 8.2. Primary Water Chemistry Specifications

Specific conditions vary from vendor to vendor, but typical conditions are:	
pH	4.5 to 10.5
Conductivity	1 to 30 micromhos/ cm at 25°C
Oxygen, ppm, max	0.1
Chloride ion, ppm, max.	0.15
Fluoride ion, ppm, max	0.1
Hydrogen cm^3 (STP)/kg H_2O	25–35
Total suspended solids, ppm, max.	1.0
Boric acid, as ppm B	0 to 4000–4500
Makeup water must be similarly treated to the following specifications:	
pH	6.0–8.0
Conductivity	< 2.0 micromhos at 25°C
Oxygen, ppm	< 0.1
Chloride ion, ppm	< 0.15
Fluoride ion, ppm	< 0.1
Total dissolved solids, ppm	< 0.5
Co_2, ppm	< 2.0
Solids filtration	< 25 μm

Source: K. C. Lish, *Nuclear Power Plant Systems and Equipment,* Industrial Press, Inc., New York, 1972.

Condensate and Main Feedwater System

This system, consisting of a number of pipes, tanks, valves, and related instrumentation, handles the condensed water as it exits from the main condenser to the feedwater nozzles of the steam generators. In a typical four-loop plant (Figure 8.11), the system consists of four condensate pumps, four condensate booster pumps, and three feedwater pumps, each with a capacity of 50% of total feedwater flow. There can be five stages of low-pressure feedwater heaters and one stage of high-pressure heater. The condensate pumps take suction from the condenser hot well, and pump the condensate through a series of other equipment (such as the polisher, the air ejector, and gland steam condensers) to the suction of the condensate booster pumps. The booster pumps take the condensate through the five stages of low-pressure feedwater heaters to the feedwater pumps. The water discharge from the feedwater pump flows through one high-pressure heater and into the steam generators.

Normally, three pairs of condensate and condensate booster pumps are in operation. The fourth pair is on standby and starts automatically on a signal of low pressure at the feedwater pump suction to ensure adequate flow at that point of the loop. The three feedwater pumps have common suction and discharge headers. Two of them are turbine driven and the third is motor driven, for diversity of power supply. Since each pump has a capacity of 50% of total flow, two of them are adequate, at any time, to provide the necessary feedwater flow to the steam generators. The motor-driven pump is used for start-up (since steam is not yet available) and as a reserve or standby. The feedwater leaving the discharge header is then distributed to the four lines, one for each steam generator. The flow is controlled by a feedwater regulator in each feedwater line.

The polisher, mentioned above, is provided after the condensate pumps to maintain the feedwater to an appropriate level of purity. Impurities may enter the secondary system through various paths, notably through leaks in the condenser (see also Chapter 9). Usually strong-base anion-exchange materials are used to absorb weak acids (silica types) as well as strong acids. For the removal of chlorides, sulfates, and nitrates, weak-base anion-exchange materials are most efficiently used. The "polish" demineralizers are mixed-bed anion exchangers used to remove small amounts of remaining anions (such as cloride originating from seawater intrusion) from already demineralized water.

Auxiliary Feedwater System (AFWS)

This system, consisting of redundant pipes, valves, pumps, tanks, and control devices is an appendage to the main feedwater system. The purpose of this system is to provide a continuous supply of water to the secondary side of the steam generator in case the main feedwater system becomes

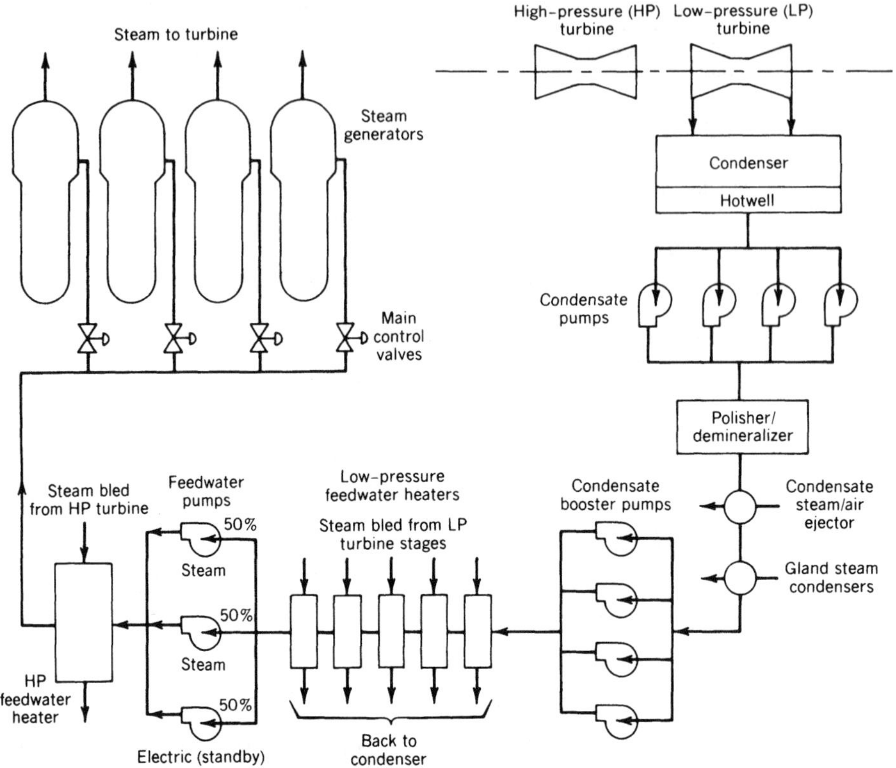

Figure 8.11. Main feedwater system of a four-loop plant.

unavailable. In this way, a heat sink is always provided for the removal of heat from the primary system. It can also be used as an alternate to the main feedwater system during start-up, hot standby, and cooldown. There is a great variety of configurations of AFWS, depending on the vendor and the specific plant. A relatively simple schematic of an AFWS is shown in Figure 8.12*a* for a two-loop PWR. It is a system with two pumps and two delivery trains. Two important characteristics of the system are redundancy and diversity. Thus two pumps are provided, each with a capacity of 200%, namely, with the ability to provide water supply to both steam generators simultaneously. The two pumps discharge water to each steam generator through a cross connection in the main feedwater line. This arrangement ensures a supply of feedwater to both steam generators even in the case of a rupture of the main feedwater line upstream of the pump discharge check valve. The diversity is provided by having one pump driven by a steam turbine, whereas the second is driven by an electric motor. Notice also that one group of valves is operated by dc motors while the other functions with ac. The ac-driven pump and the associated ac-motor-operated valves can receive power from both on-site and off-site power sources. The trains are started either automatically or manually from the main control room. The primary source of auxiliary feedwater is the condensate storage tank. A secondary or backup source of auxiliary feedwater is also provided.

The figure also shows a number of manually operated check valves. These valves must normally be left open to allow the flow of auxiliary water when needed, and can only be closed for short periods of time for purposes of maintenance. It was these valves, left closed at the TMI-2 plant contrary to proper procedure, which caused the auxiliary feedwater to be unavailable, following a trip of the main feedwater (caused by the clogging of air-control valves). It was this series of events, coupled with a number of other failures of equipment (stuck-open valve) and operator action, which caused the most severe accident in the history of civilian nuclear power.

Since that accident, the need for a high availability AFWS has been highlighted. Proposals to increase the availability of the system by providing more redundancy and diversity have been made. One of the proposed modifications is shown in Figure 8.12*b* where three pumps and two trains are provided. It has been calculated that in the event of a total loss of main feedwater (assumed to have a frequency of three events per year), the modification shown in Figure 8.12*b*

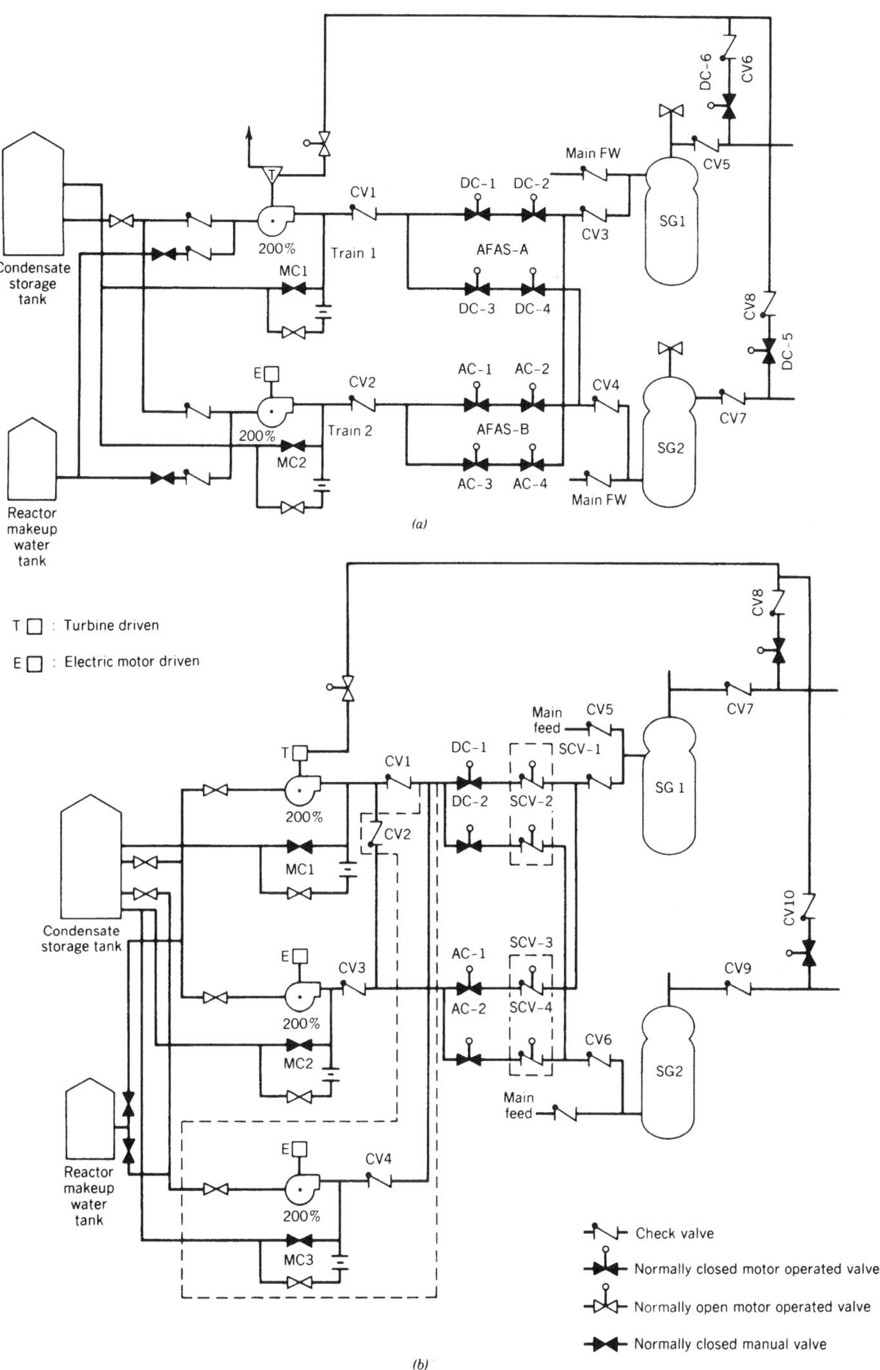

Figure 8.12. PWR auxiliary feedwater systems.

brings about a reduction in the failure probability from 1.8×10^{-2}/yr to 1.4×10^{-3}/yr, a reduction by a factor of 13. It must be noted that any decision regarding modifications to increase system diversity and redundancy must be made in the overall context of reduction of risk and of the costs associated with both the construction and installation of the upgraded system.

To ensure the availability of the system, periodic inspection, surveillance, and testing are required. The pumps can be tested while the plant is in normal operation. A recirculation and full flow test line to the condensate tank enables operational testing of the system up to the steam generator isolation valves. Discharge pressure and flow indicators are provided locally and in the control room. Periodic testing (once a month) verifies the discharge pressure and flow rate of the turbine and motor-driven pumps. It also identifies any "plugged" valve failures. At least once in every 18 months, the operator verifies that each automatic valve in the flow path is actuated to its correct position [upon receipt of an engineered safety feature (ESF) test signal].

Variations exist in the details of the AFWS in various designs. Figure 8.13 shows a comparison between two-, three-, and four-loop designs used in the United States and their counterparts used overseas.

Auxiliary feedwater systems are closely related to additional safety systems such as the Residual Heat Removal (RHR) system and the High-Pressure Injection System (HPIS). These systems are described in detail in Chapter 18 which is devoted to the safety aspects of nuclear plants.

Gaseous and Liquid Wastes Handling

Since radioactivity is produced in the fission process and through neutron activation, small quantities of radioactive materials are formed in the primary coolant system. These constitute radioactive and nonradioactive gases, soluble materials, and insoluble solids. They are mainly the product of corrosion of structural materials which have been activated through neutron activation. Leaks that may occur in some fuel elements due to cladding failure also allow fission products to escape into the coolant. Leakage from failed fuel can also occur during refueling operations or while spent fuel is stored under water in the spent fuel tanks.

All plants must be equipped to handle the gaseous and liquid wastes in conformity with regulatory requirements. These are outlined in the Code of Federal Regulations (CFR) Part 10, Chapter 20. The regulations specify the limits imposed on both instantaneous releases as well as on the releases integrated over time (usually 1 yr). Limits exist on the release of individual isotopes as well as on collective discharges. Radiation monitors are required at potential exit points of the plant as well as at critical points inside the system. For the proper design of the waste-handling systems, design objectives are given in Appendix I of CFR Part 10, Chapter 50. As a basis for the design, the assumption is made that 1% of the fuel rods have failed, and, therefore, have released the fission gases to the coolant. Gaseous wastes originate also (and primarily) from gases dissolved in the coolant, radiolytic decomposition of water into hydrogen and oxygen, and added gases such as hydrogen and nitrogen. The gaseous waste system is connected to the chemistry and volume control system and provides holdup tanks in which radioactive gases are retained for a certain time period to allow radioactive substances with short half-lives to decay. If, for example, three half-lives of waiting time is allowed, the activity is reduced by a factor of $(\frac{1}{2})^3 = \frac{1}{8}$. Among the radioactive gases, most predominant are xenon-135, a noble gas produced in fission, with a half-life of 9.23 hr and krypton-85, with a rather long half-life of 10.3 yr. A holdup of several days causes a reduction of xenon-135 by orders of magnitude, but it cannot affect appreciably the radioactivity of krypton-85.

Figures 8.14 and 8.15 are schematic representations of a PWR and BWR gaseous waste system. The details of each design can differ considerably according to each manufacturer, but the main features are common. At the top of the diagram, the primary coolant off-gas systems is shown. Among the isotopes in that system, iodine, krypton, and xenon constitute the major radiation hazards. Only iodine is chemically reactive and can, therefore, be retained by chemical means. For the noble gases xenon and krypton, physical methods must be used. A time delay, as mentioned earlier, allows the shorter lived radioactive elements to decay to very low levels. In PWRs where the gas volumes are rather small because the primary system is sealed, the gases are compressed and stored in the decay tanks for 30 to 45 days before they are released in a controlled manner to the environment through roof vents. The release of any gas is done through three stage filters, as described below. Typical quantities of radioactivity released annually from a 1000-MWe PWR are shown in Table 8.3. Most of the activity of the treated gases (~300 Ci) is ^{85}Kr.

In the case of a BWR, released gas volume is much larger because the feedwater is continuously deaerated and the gas produced at the deaerator must be treated as radioactive since it was in direct contact with the fuel. BWR gases contain also oxygen and hydrogen formed by the radiolysis of water as well as nitrogen-13, nitrogen-16, and oxygen-19. Whereas the off-gases in a PWR are treated in batches, in a BWR they are treated and released continuously, because of the quantities involved, with a minimum of holdup time of 30 min in large holdup pipes. Radioactive gases can also be absorbed on large charcoal beds for more prolonged holdup times. Holding periods of 16 hr

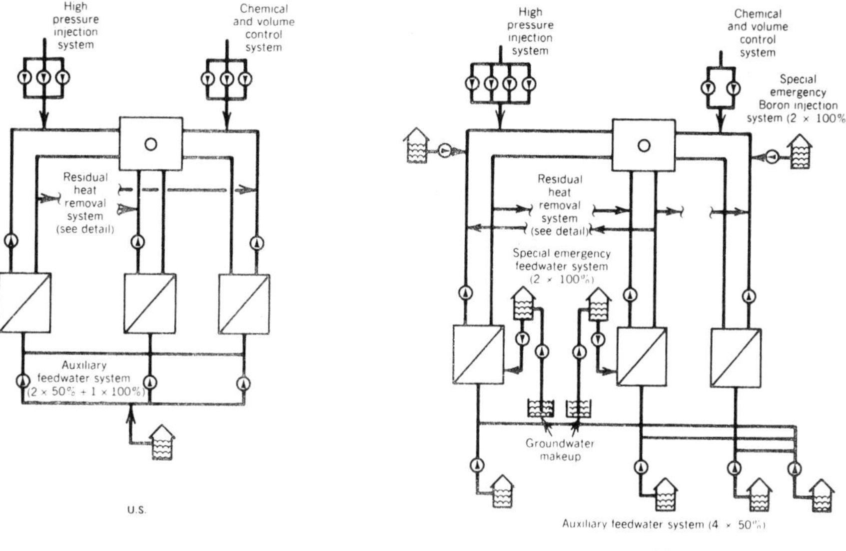

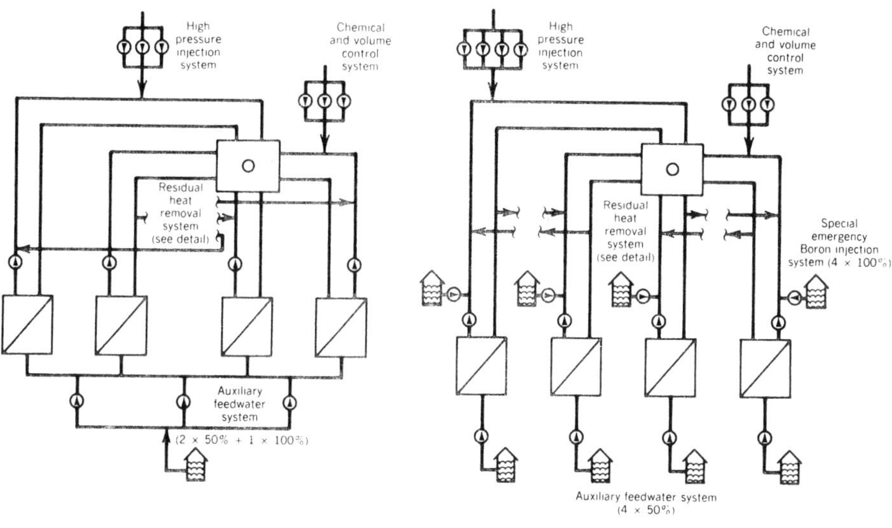

Figure 8.13. Comparison between international types of AFWS. (From NUREG/CR-1556.)

are used for the short lived radioactive krypton and 9 days for radioactive xenon. When BWR gases are held up for the short time of 30 min, they are directed to a tall stack (about 100 m or 300 ft), diluted with other air, and released to the atmosphere. Dilution and dispersion reduces the concentration of the radioactive gases in the atmosphere in the plant vicinity to very low, acceptable levels (see Chapter 3). Typical quantities of radioactive gases from a 1000-MWe BWR are shown in Table 8.4.

If it becomes necessary to isolate specific radioactive gases from the environment for very long periods of time, new, highly efficient (and probably very costly) separation methods will have to be devised and incorporated in the waste gas system. The simplest method would be to compress the gases and store them for the life of the plant. Another scheme would be to separate the noble gases for long-term storage and release the remaining gases. For separation, two methods have been

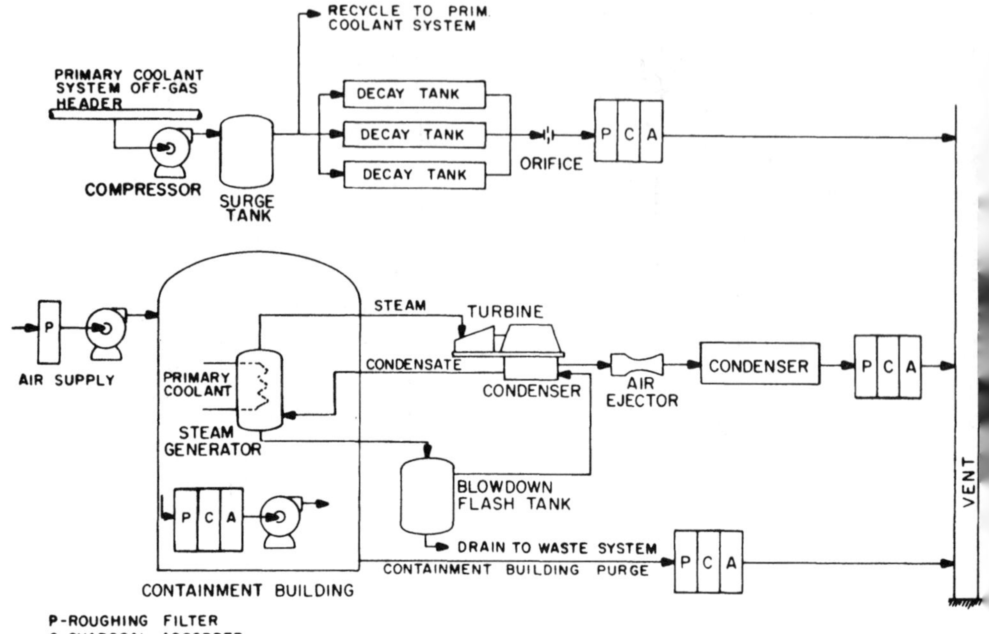

Figure 8.14. PWR gaseous waste system. (From WASH-1250.)

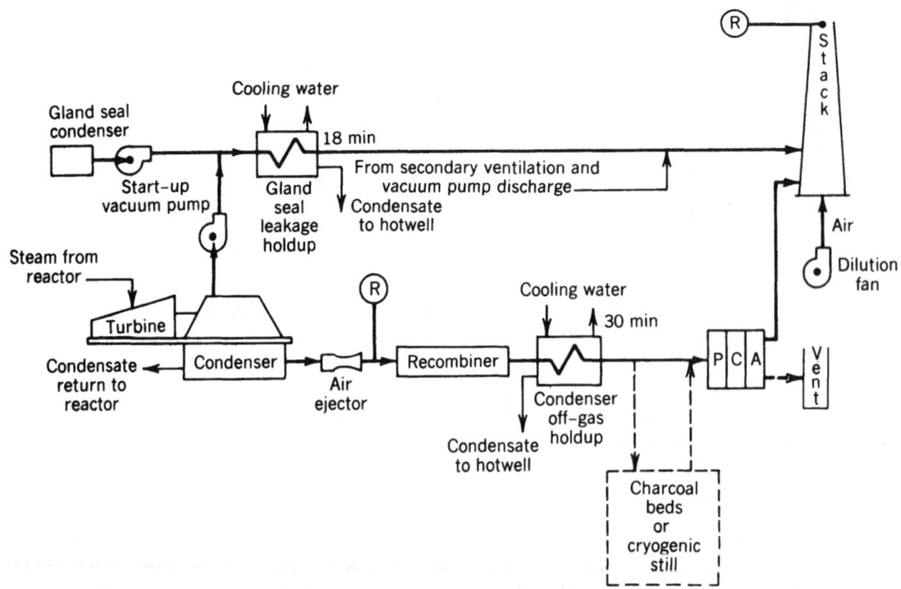

Figure 8.15. BWR gaseous waste system. (Adapted from WASH-1250.) P—roughing filter; C—charcoal adsorber; A—HEPA filter; R—radiation monitor.

Table 8.3. Effectiveness of Various Waste Gas Treatment Systems for Noble Gases in 100-MWe PWRs

Source of Release	Annual Release, Ci
Waste gas treatment systems	
Untreated	316 000[a]
Charcoal delay (72-day delay for xenon; 4-day delay for krypton)	329[a]
Pressurized storage	
60 days	412[a]
90 days	306[a]
Estimated from other sources[b]	
Containment building	88[b]
Auxiliary building	10[b]

Source: D. T. Pence, *Nuclear Safety,* **22,** No. 6, November–December (1981).

[a]Of this amount, ~300 Ci is ^{85}Kr.

[b]Based on full letdown of 0.00473 m^3/sec (75 gal/min).

proposed: cryogenic distillation and absorption with refrigerant-12, separated by distillation. Both techniques are performed under very low temperature conditions.

In the BWR waste gas system, a catalytic recombiner (see discussion below) to combine hydrogen and oxygen into water is included. After a 30-min delay, moisture is removed by condensation at a few degrees above the water freezing point. A charcoal absorption system follows which further delays the release from the plant. With this processing, the continuous gaseous discharges from a BWR are 1% of the limits specified in 10CFR20. High-level discharges are thus converted into solids which are either held on the plant site or shipped in shielded containers to authorized storage sites.

The atmosphere inside the containment building (for both PWR and BWR), as well as in fuel storage areas, may contain small amounts of radioactive gases. Under certain accident conditions, the radioactivity level may reach high levels. Careful monitoring is done at selected points in the containment and the air is pumped through filters for purification prior to controlled release of the gases to the environment. The air in other large spaces of the plant, such as the turbine building air, is monitored for radioactivity and the air discharged directly from the roof.

Recombiners, seen in the BWR diagram in Figure 8.15, are devices in which hydrogen and

Table 8.4. Effectiveness of Waste Gas Treatment Systems for Noble Gases in 1000-MWe BWRs

Source of release	Annual Release, Ci
Waste gas treatment systems	
With 30-min delay	1,260,000[a]
With recombiner with subambient charcoal-adsorption delay system[b] (80-day delay for xenon; 2.7-day delay for krypton)	282
Estimated from other sources	
Containment building	125
Auxiliary building	373
Turbine building	3,637
Radwaste building	1,144
Gland seal exhaust	5,652
Mechanical vacuum pump	1,800

Source: D. T. Pence, op. cit.

[a]Of this amount, 240 Ci is ^{85} Kr.

[b]Based on a 21,800-kg (24-ton) system operating at −18°C (0°F), −29°C (−20°F) dew point, and 36 m^3/hr (21 ft^3/min) air inleakage.

oxygen combine to produce water. In a BWR, the hydrogen and oxygen produced by the radiolytic decomposition of water in the core are mixed with the radioactive gases from leaky fuel rods and enter the gaseous waste treatment system. The recombiners reverse the process by producing steam which is removed by condensation, thereby reducing considerably the amount of gaseous wastes to be further treated. In PWRs, the primary system is under pressure of hydrogen and nitrogen which causes the continuous recombination of radiolytic oxygen and hydrogen into water. However, hydrogen can also be produced through the oxidation of the zirconium cladding in the fuel rods, if the temperature rises to unacceptably high levels. Such a massive oxidation of fuel cladding occurred at the TMI-2 station when the core became uncovered for several hours. Hydrogen was released in the primary system and through the stuck-open valve to the containment, causing a hydrogen explosion (evidenced by a pressure spike). A certain concentration of hydrogen in air, of the order of 7%, can form an explosive mixture, with lower concentrations causing lesser phenomena called deflagration or burn. The need for effective management of hydrogen in a containment building was highlighted. Recombiners were used at TMI-2 to process the air from the containment building and to reduce hydrogen concentration.

A typical recombiner is a steel tank containing a replaceable cartridge or bed made of a chemical catalyst. Metallic strips or ceramic materials, like alumina pellets, are coated with fine particles of platinum or palladium which performs the chemical catalytic function. The most effective performance of a recombiner is observed at temperatures between 250 to 900°F, depending on the specific flow sheet. Higher temperatures shorten the life of the catalyst, whereas at lower ones the effectiveness of the process drops off. Therefore, appropriate heating and cooling of the bed is necessary for optimum performance. To avoid the dangers of uncontrolled combustion of hydrogen upstream of the recombiner, the composition of the feed gas in hydrogen must be controlled to below about 4% in volume. The diluent gases are made up of oxygen, and other inert gases like steam and nitrogen. If iodine and other radioactive materials are contained in the feed gas, the recombiner could gradually lose its effectiveness; it becomes chemically "poisoned." In practice, multiple recombiners are used in parallel to provide redundancy and the ability to replace periodically the catalyst cartridge without interruption in the plant operation.

Filtration is widely used in the gaseous waste system to capture particulates before any gases are released to the atmosphere. Three filters are used in tandem; a roughing filter or prefilter made of fiberglass; a charcoal absorber, mainly to capture halogens, especially radioiodine, and a High-Efficiency Particulate Air (HEPA) filter. A standard HEPA filter is made of flat modules of a pleated mat of fiberglass with typical dimensions of $24 \times 24 \times 11\frac{1}{2}$ in. Each module has a nominal capacity of 30 m^3/min (1000 ft^3/min). The performance specifications for the HEPA filters require that they remove 99.97% of the entering particles that are larger than 0.3 μm in diameter.

The roughing filter, usually placed as a first-stage filter, is provided to prolong the useful life of the HEPA filter. Since iodine is one of the fission products of concern because of its high short-term activity and the potential of uptake and retention by living organisms, protection against radioactive release is provided by a third kind of specially designed filters. These contain charcoal absorbers and are placed either before or after the HEPA filters. The activated charcoal absorbs iodine, normally in the form of gas absorbed by small solid particles. Filtration is all that is needed, normally, to process large volumes of air from reactor containment and auxiliary buildings.

Liquid wastes originate from a variety of sources like equipment drains, steam generator blowdown, demineralizers, floor drain collection tanks, laboratory processes, "hot" shower and laundry drains, and equipment washdown and decontamination operations. In a PWR, the boron management and primary system volume control system may produce additional liquid wastes. Although specific designs vary, the basic engineering principles are the same. Figures 8.16 and 8.17 present simplified schematic diagrams of the liquid waste treatment system of a typical PWR and BWR, respectively. The designs have grown in size and complexity over time together with reactor size and regulatory requirements. The principle concerning the treatment of liquid wastes (as for gaseous and solid wastes) is that each product of effluent treatment must be carefully monitored for radioactivity and then disposed of in a specified manner in consonance with existing regulations. Sampling and monitoring equipment is installed throughout the system. The function of the system is to collect, concentrate and contain the radioactive materials in the waste and separate them from pure water which can then be reused or discharged.

Wastes are classified in various ways, depending on the level of radioactivity, the origin, and the chemical contaminants contained in them. Liquid wastes are, therefore, collected in a number of separate holdup tanks for batch treatment. This allows for identification and proper treatment of individual batches, which may differ from batch to batch. We often distinguish between "clean" and "dirty" wastes, according to their content in chemical contaminants. Wastes originating in the primary or any other system with pure water are called "clean," whereas those originating in the "hot" showers, laundry, or chemistry laboratories are called "dirty." They often require different treatment. Wastes from clean systems can be treated with maximum recovery of condensate which can be returned to the system for reuse. The treatment consists of batch evaporation and demineralization. This has the effect of drastically reducing the final volume of the active waste

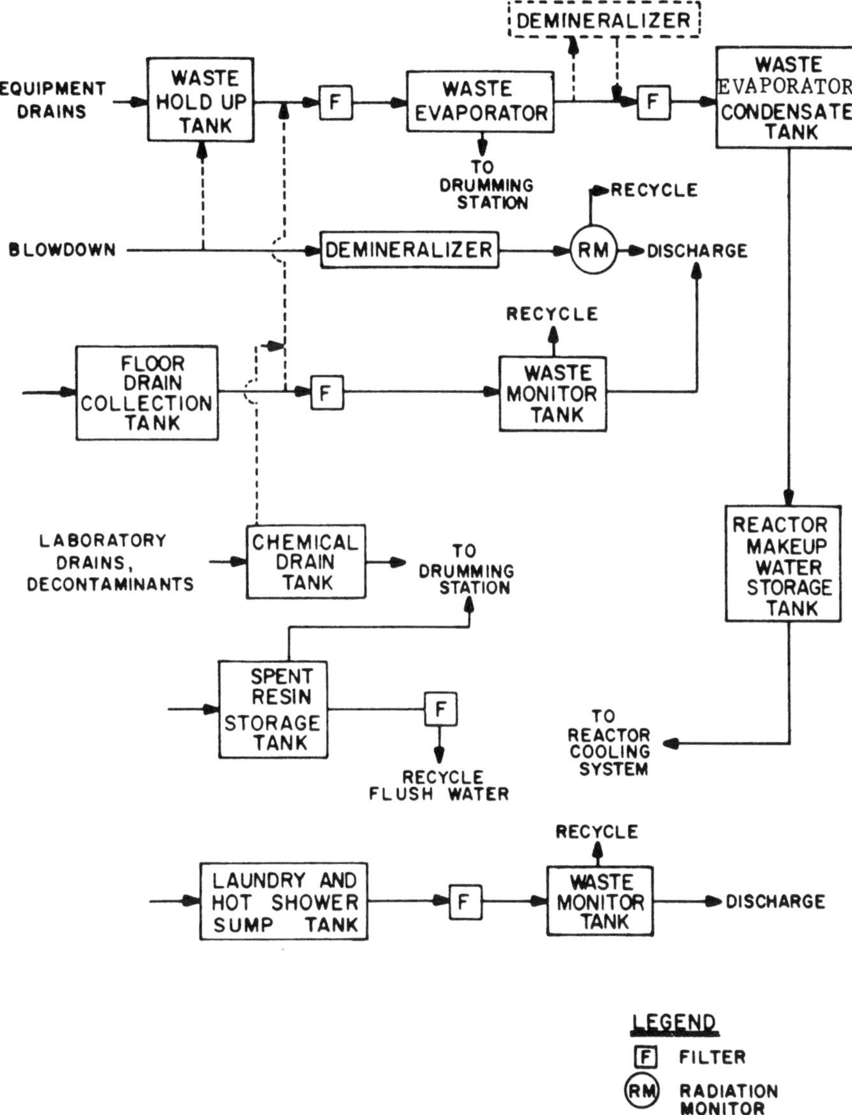

Figure 8.16. PWR liquid waste system. (From WASH-1250.)

concentrate. This latter is finally mixed with inert materials and converted into a solid concrete cylinder, inside a metal drum for final burial.

Demineralizers, filters, and evaporators are widely utilized in the waste treatment system. *Evaporators* concentrate the radioactive substances by boiling off the water in the solution. A simple evaporator consists of a simple vessel with coils of heating pipes inside through which steam is circulated. A more elaborate device, called vapor compression evaporator, consists of pumps and pipes to circulate the waste through outside heaters and of compressors for the produced vapors, for a higher heat efficiency. The performance of an evaporator is measured in terms of the volume reduction achieved and of the purification factor reached in the condensate. Depending on the amount of dissolved solids, a reduction in the radioactive waste volume of 10 to 50 is possible. The distillate produced from the vapors can have a radioactivity level reduced as much as 10,000 times compared to the original waste. Dirty wastes, containing detergents or other chemicals, are not usually subjected to evaporation because the foaming and entrainment which is caused by them reduces the degree of separation achievable.

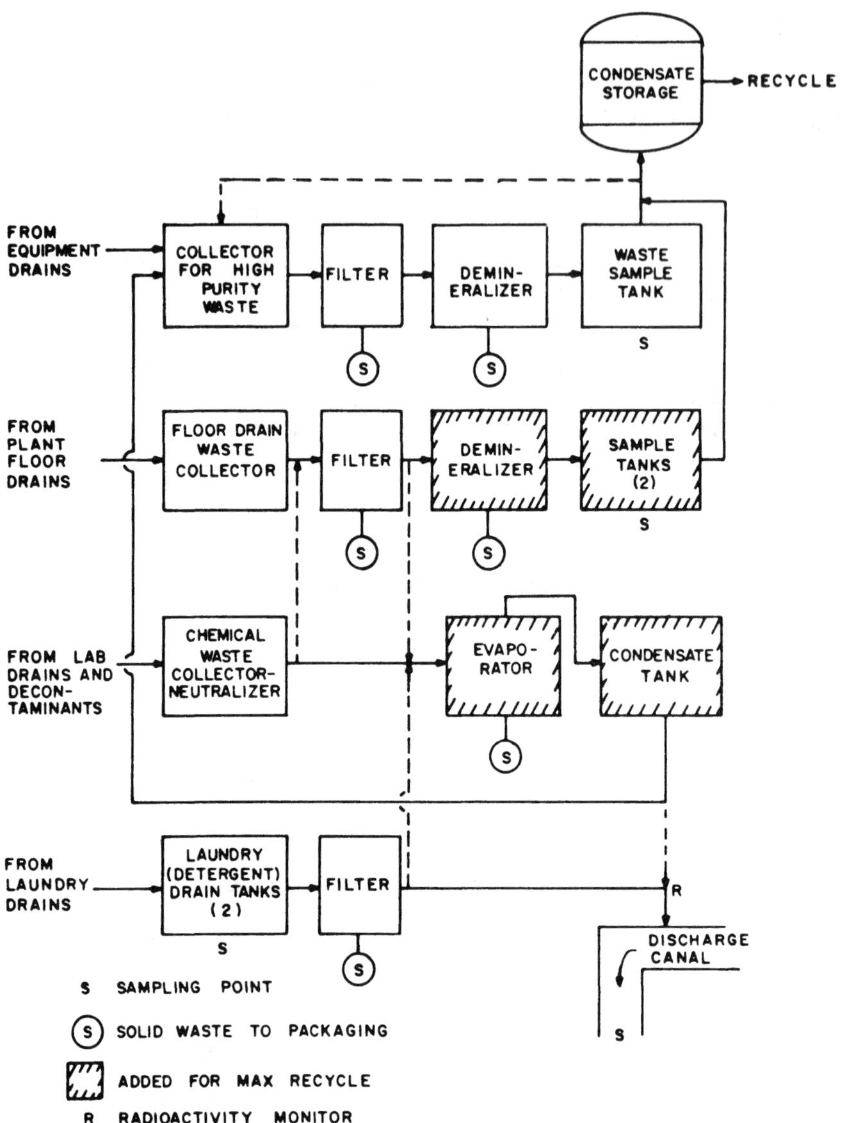

Figure 8.17. BWR liquid waste system. (From WASH-1250.)

Filters are shown on all trains in Figures 8.16 and 8.17. The purpose is to remove solids suspended in the liquid waste. They are of the cartridge type so that a change can be readily done when either of the following two conditions occur: the pressure drop across the filter is too high, indicating heavy accumulation of particulate matter and plugging, or when the radioactivity level reaches a certain high reading.

Filters that treat low-level wastes, such as from laundry, can be charged manually without any undue hazard to personnel. The cartridges used in these filters are changed when the pressure drop becomes high. High-level waste filters are not handled manually to avoid exposure of personnel. These filters can be cleaned by a backwash cycle that reverses the flow and breaks the accumulated cake or sludge loose from the filter matrix. The buildup of pressure across a filter can, when excessive, cause a deformation of the filter elements. When the pressure drop reaches a fraction of an atmosphere (several pounds per square inch) above normal levels, the operation of the filter is interrupted, and the backwashing cycle is activated, often aided by the introduction of bubbling steam into the tank to facilitate the breakup and removal of the solid deposits on the filter surface.

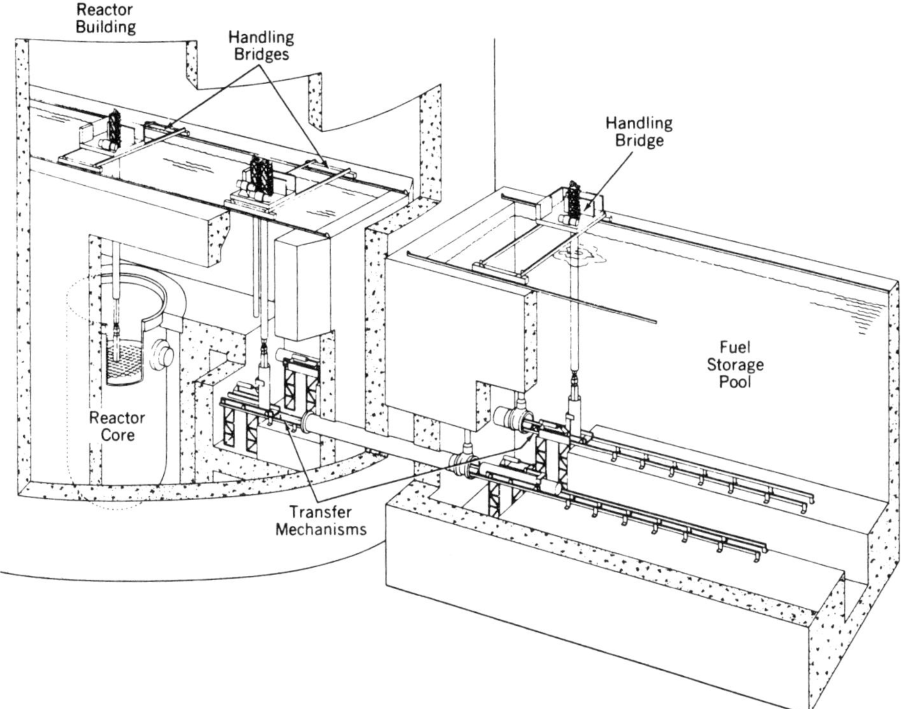

Figure 8.18. Fuel-handling system for a nuclear steam supply system. (From Babcock & Wilcox, *Steam, Its Generation and Use*, 1978.)

The backwashing fluids constitute concentrated wastes and must be processed properly at the facility.

Separation of solids from liquids is also possible through centrifugation in a cylindrical vessel rotated at high speed. Solids separate at the walls while the clear liquid overflows and is collected in a surge tank. The centrifugation method is commonly used to dewater sludges produced in the filtration and evaporation processes of the waste treatment system. The concentrated liquid wastes and the spent resins from the demineralizers are, subsequently, solidified for long-term physical and chemical stability. This is usually done by mixing the wastes with cement and allowing the mixture to harden inside suitable metal containers, such as 55-gal drums, for further off-site disposal (see also Chapter 16).

Refueling and Fuel Storage Pool

In order to replenish the fuel that is gradually depleted of fissile material as it burns up in the reactor core and to build up the reactivity of the reactor, the reactor is shut down periodically and a refueling operation takes place. An additional reason could be the need to remove fuel that has developed leaks due to the accumulation of fission products, unfavorable irradiation effects, and corrosion. The frequency of refueling is normally once a year, but several utilities are examining the feasibility and economics of 18-month refueling. During the refueling operation, a fraction of the fuel assemblies (between one-third and one-quarter) is removed and new fuel assemblies are placed in the core. Each year, a large power reactor discharges 25–40 tons of spent fuel in 60–200 fuel assemblies. There are several schemes to perform this operation which are explained in detail under the Fuel Management section in Chapter 11.

The removed spent fuel is highly radioactive and, consequently, also a source of heat. It needs to be handled and stored carefully under prescribed procedures. A dedicated system consisting mainly of a transfer device and of a separate building housing a spent fuel water pool is provided in each reactor. Figure 8.18 shows a typical arrangement of such a fuel-handling and storage facility. A transfer canal and specially designed equipment serves for the transfer of fresh and spent fuel between the two buildings. The fuel pool is deep enough to accommodate the length of the fuel assemblies and provide an additional 4 m (12 ft) of water for effective shielding.

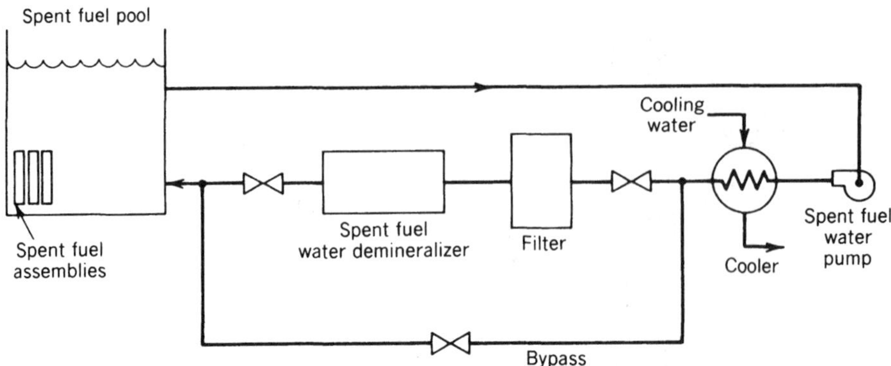

Figure 8.19. Spent fuel cooling system schematic.

The steps in the refueling operation can be summarized as follows: Following reactor shutdown, cooldown, and depressurization, designated personnel enter the containment building to remove the reactor vessel head with all its attachments and to drain the reactor below the top head flange. The refueling canal is filled with water to provide shielding and cooling during the transfer while certain pressure vessel internals are being removed. A number of predefined fuel assemblies are removed and the others are repositioned if a reshuffling scheme is called for. The fresh fuel assemblies are then installed in the open assembly positions and the spent fuel assemblies are transferred to the fuel storage pool. The reactor internals (like upper support plate and instrumentation) are returned to the core, the vessel head is replaced, and the canal is drained. The pressure vessel is then refilled, vented, and tested at pressure. Following a number of tests to ensure that systems that have been disturbed function properly, the reactor system is brought back up to temperature and pressure and is readied to produce power.

The fuel pool is equipped with a dedicated cooling system, as shown in Figure 8.19. The system includes a cooler, a filter, and a demineralizer for the removal of all radioactive and nonradioactive particulate and soluble materials. Leaks, in some discharged fuel elements, may also cause the release of radioactive gases which will bubble up to the surface of the pool, through the approximately 4 m (10–12 ft) of pool water. These gases are sucked by the fuel pool ventilation system, become diluted with large volumes of air, are purified by filtration, and discharged from the plant stack or roof vent.

Tritium in Nuclear Reactor Plants

Tritium is a radioactive substance produced in nuclear power reactors but none of the radwaste systems described so far is designed to remove it from the water. Thus, tritium either remains in the plant or is slowly released to the environment with other liquid effluents.

Tritium (^{3}H) is an isotope of hydrogen, containing one proton, like ordinary hydrogen, plus two neutrons. It is radioactive, emitting only a soft beta ray, with a half-life of 12.3 yr. It is not concentrated by living organisms and passes quickly through the human body. The sources of tritium in a reactor are: (1) the fission process and (2) activation of substances diluted in the coolant, primarily boron. In a 1000-MWe plant (PWR or BWR), the annual production of tritium through fission is in the range 15,000–25,000 Ci (or about 1.5 to 2.5 g of tritium). Most of this amount (99.9%) remains locked in the fuel rods. Some tritium may enter the coolant through cladding leaks or through diffusion. The diffusion process is much more pronounced in stainless steel cladding rods than in zirconium clad rods. Since zirconium has replaced stainless steel in new plants, the tritium source through diffusion has been decreased. Leaks of tritium may occur in the primary loop itself or in the fuel storage tank.

Additional amounts of tritium may be produced through activation of boron or lithium elements found in compound form in control rods of both PWRs and BWRs. The largest source of tritium is, however, encountered in PWRs through the activation of boron dissolved as boric acid in the PWR coolant as an additional means of control (chemical shim), as described earlier in this chapter. The nuclear reaction is

$$^{10}\mathrm{B} + {}^{1}n \rightarrow {}^{3}\mathrm{H} + 2\,{}^{4}\mathrm{He}$$

A similar reaction occurs with lithium to produce tritium. Small amounts of lithium compound are

Table 8.5. Tritium Disposition in 1000-MWe LWRs

Tritium Source	Maximum Expected Releases to the Coolant, Ci/yr PWR	BWR
Ternary fission (assuming 0.1% enters coolant)	40	40
Soluble boron	560	—
Lithium reactions	17	—
Deuterium reaction	10	10
Total	627	50

Note: Tritium is released to the coolant of nuclear reactors from the fission process and from neutron activation of various substances. The dominant source of tritium is found in PWR and originates in the boron poison, dissolved in the coolant as boric acid, to provide additional long-term reactivity control. Tritium, a mild beta-ray emitter, is either retained in the coolant or discharged slowly with other innocuous wastes.

introduced in the coolant to control its acidity. A summary of the amounts of tritium released is given in Table 8.5.

The difficulty in treating tritium comes from the fact that as soon as it is released, in the form of gas either as T_2 or HT, it quickly exchanges its position with an ordinary hydrogen atom and becomes an integral part of the water, through the reaction

$$HT + H_2O \rightarrow HTO + H_2$$

There exist no economical ways today to separate tritiated water from ordinary water. It remains, therefore, mostly inside the primary system. Since some liquid waste leaks or is withdrawn from the system, tritium is also discharged at a controlled rate along with these waste waters to the environment. Under a potential zero-release concept for both gaseous and liquid wastes, these wastes would have to be continuously recycled and perhaps later disposed of. This still leaves open the question of tritium loss as water vapor in ventilation air and of the form and method of final disposition of tritiated water.

The Intermediate Cooling System

There are several additional systems in a nuclear plant, which perform secondary functions.

The intermediate cooling system shown diagrammatically in Figure 8.20 provides a closed circuit of cooling water for a number of components, namely: shielding surrounding the reactor vessel, housings of the reactor coolant pumps, reactor pump seal cooling, quench tank cooling coils, and letdown coolers and other components. Because of the proximity of all these systems to the reactor (they are all located inside the reactor building), and for safety reasons, a closed system has been prescribed for their cooling, which provides isolation from the environment in case radioactivity leaks into the system. The heat removed from those components is in turn transferred through a heat exchanger to the service water which can be released to the environment.

Ultimate Heat Sink

The *circulating water system*, consisting of several pumps, piping, seal tanks, and associated instrumentation serves to carry the rejected heat from the main condenser and other heat exchangers to the ultimate heat sink. A great variety of schemes exist to perform this function both in terms of the kinds of heat sink and of the technology utilized. *Open* (or "once-through") systems take cooling water from the sea, a river, or a lake and reject the heat in same.

Closed systems, of which there exists a great variety, recirculate more or less the same mass of water through the plant and the heat sink. Wet closed systems use the evaporation method to reject heat to the atmosphere through a cooling pond or a cooling tower. The latter is a large structure with striking lines which has been used in the power industry for quite a few years and is often used as a succinct symbol of a power plant (Figure 8.21). The dry closed systems keep the circulating water isolated from the atmosphere and remove heat through circulation of air. These latter are obviously more suitable in dry regions.

The heat rejection to the ultimate heat sink has brought into focus the question of "thermal

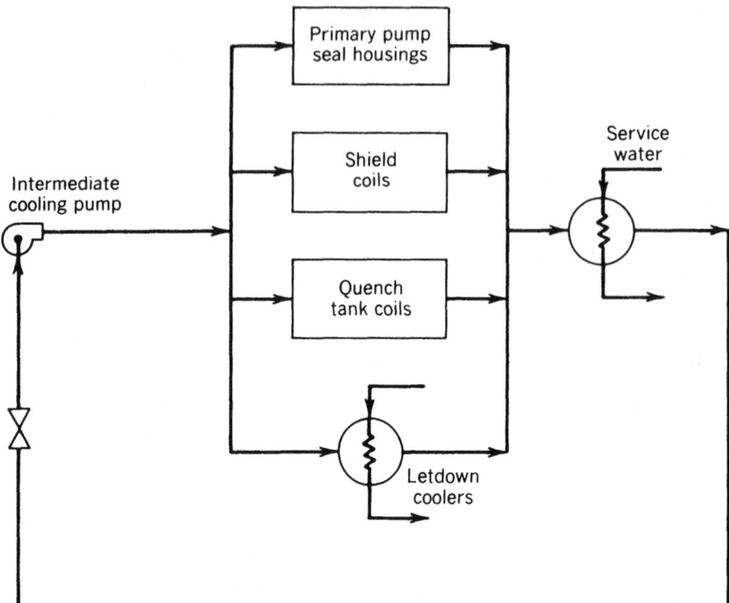

Figure 8.20. Intermediate cooling system schematic.

pollution.'' The problem is somewhat more acute for nuclear plants as compared to conventional thermal plants because of the nuclear plants' lower thermal efficiency. For the same electrical power output, a nuclear plant rejects almost 50% more heat to the environment than a high-efficiency modern fossil fuel plant. If the temperature of a certain mass of water in a river, an estuary, or a lake is allowed to rise by more than a few degrees, a disturbance of the aquatic life may result with potential adverse ecologic consequences. Because of these concerns in many countries installing nuclear power plants, the regulations require that, except for reactors built on the ocean, all new power plants must use cooling towers for ultimate heat rejection. Thus, instead of heating up the water bodies, heat is rejected to the atmosphere. It must be noted, however, that warm water could have a beneficial effect in many applications like agriculture and seafood. Installations have been tested in Japan, France, and the United States where warm water releases from thermal plants have been successfully used in hothouses for the production of fruits and vegetables. Warm waters have also been found to accelerate the growth of seashells, lobster, shrimp, and other fish life, with potential economic benefit.

Example: Heat Rejected to the Environment. It must be recognized that the amounts of cooling water needed for heat rejection is enormous in a large power plant. A 1000-MW electric plant may require up to a million metric tons of cooling water per day for heat rejection to the environment. To calculate the water flow needed for heat removal from the condenser, the following basic heat balance equation is used (see also Figure 8.22).

$$\dot{m} \times \Delta h = \dot{M} \times \Delta H$$

The equation states that heat removed per unit time from the steam as it passes through the condenser is equal to the heat carried away (also per unit time) by the circulating water. The meaning of the quantities involved in the equation is as follows:

$\dot{m}$ = the steam flow rate in kg/sec or lb/min. Instead of total flow rate, the ''steam rate,'' namely steam flow per kWh produced can be used.

h = the enthalpy difference between the exiting condensate and the entering exhaust steam. This value depends on the specific thermodynamic characteristics of these phases of water. A typical value is 2 MJ/kg (1000 Btu/lb).

$\dot{M}$ = the mass flow rate of the circulating water (in kg/sec or in lb/min). This again can be equivalently expressed in kg or lb/kWh produced.

Figure 8.21. The scene at the Saint-Laurent-des-Eaux plant of Electricité de France is dominated by the two cooling towers. The Saint-Laurent-des-Eaux B plant includes two 880-MWe PWR units. Commercial operation began in June, 1981. Although the plant is located on the Loire River, cooling towers have been installed to minimize temperature rise in the river.

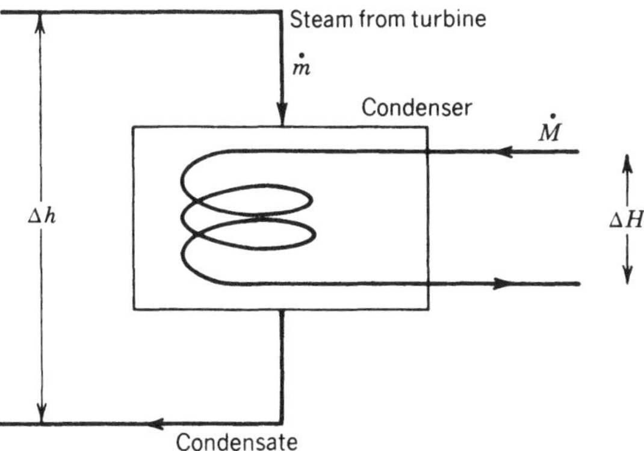

Figure 8.22. Schematic for heat balance between the condenser and the cooling system.

H = the increase in enthalpy of the circulating water. This quantity can be obtained through the formula

$$\Delta H = C_p \cdot \Delta T$$

where C_p is the specific heat at constant pressure for water. For the temperatures of interest C_p = 4.18 kJ/K-kg (~ 1 Btu/°F-lb). The temperature difference between inlet and outlet water varies depending on specific installation design, weather, and so on. A typical value would be 28–30 K (50–55°F). In this case, typical ΔH would be

$$\Delta H = 4.18 \text{ kJ/K-kg} \cdot 30 \text{ K} = 125.4 \text{ kJ/kg}$$

Therefore, the mass flow ratio would be

$$\frac{\dot{M}}{\dot{m}} = \frac{\Delta h}{\Delta H} = \frac{2 \times 10^6 \text{ J/kg}}{0.1254 \times 10^6 \text{ J/kg}} = 16$$

To complete the example, let us assume that the plant has a capacity of 1000 MWe and a steam rate of 3.6 kg/kWh (8 lb/kWh). Total steam flow would then be, at full load,

$$\dot{M} = \dot{m}\left(\frac{\Delta h}{\Delta H}\right) = 3.6 \times 10^6 \text{ kg/hr} \times 16 = 57.4 \times 10^6 \text{ kg/hr}$$

In an evaporative cycle (cooling tower, pond), the heat is rejected to the environment through the lost vapor. A few percent of the cooling water (typically 2%) must be continuously made up to maintain the constant flow to the condenser.

8.3. BOILING WATER REACTORS (BWR)

Although the civilian applications of nuclear power began with the highly pressurized type of reactor, specifically the Shippingport reactor in Pennsylvania, it was also found that it was feasible to generate steam right inside the reactor core by boiling. In fact, the feasibility of boiling in the core was established at the BORAX experiment in Idaho, many years before Shippingport. Thus, the second major type of light-water reactor, the BWR, came into being. Like the PWR, it also utilizes ordinary water as coolant and moderator, but the design pressure is much lower, about one-half of that in PWRs. This allows for a considerably smaller vessel thickness, although the size of the vessel is much larger in a BWR than in a PWR of the same power output. The first commercial BWRs were designed with a dual cycle quite similar to the arrangement of a PWR, with the use of steam generators. Such plants are the Dresden 1 plant (180-MW) which is still in operation in Illinois, and the KWU† plant (640 MWe) at Wuergassen, Federal Republic of Germany. With study and experience, it became evident that full economic advantage of boiling in the core could be taken by using a single cycle which was feasible from both a technical and safety point of view. Progress in the design of BWRs is shown in the comparative Table 8.6. The sole vendor of BWRs in the United States is General Electric Company. Boiling water reactors have been built also by manufacturers in Japan, Germany, and Sweden.

The boiling principle has been used in several varieties of reactors other than the dominant BWR. The Canadian reactor, using natural uranium and heavy water moderator, can be designed to use boiling light water as its coolant. The Gentilly 1 reactor, a 250-MWe reactor, called a Boiling Light-Water Reactor (BLWR) but with D_2O moderator, is owned by Hydro Québec and has been in operation near Bécancour, Québec since 1972. It has not, however, found any imitators. The Soviet Union has built a large number of units using a boiling water pressure tube design with graphite as moderator, known as the Light-Water Graphite Moderated Reactor (LWGR). However, the future plans for nuclear expansion in that country are based on the PWR technology and on liquid-metal fast breeders.

BWRs are based on the direct cycle philosophy which eliminates steam generators and simplifies the energy conversion loop. There are two other fundamental differences between the two systems which will become more apparent in the discussion that follows. Since the working fluid, which removes heat from the core enters the turbine directly, radioactivity is no longer securely enclosed in a tightly sealed primary system. In fact, through the deaeration of the condenser, gases that may contain radioactivity are continuously removed from the system and discharge from the stack becomes more critical. Also, shielding of the turbine and associated piping becomes necessary for the protection of personnel. Thus, the problem of handling radioactivity and

†KWU: Kraftwerk Union, a Division of Siemens, is a major European reactor supplier.

Table 8.6. Evolution of the General Electric BWR

Product Line Number	Year of Introduction	Characteristic Plants
BWR/1	1955	Dresden 1, Big Rock Point, Humboldt Bay, KRB Initial Commercial BWRs First internal steam separation
BWR/2	1963	Oyster Creek Plants purchased solely on economics Large direct cycle
BWR/3	1965	Dresden 2 First jet pump application Improved ECCS: spray and flood
BWR/4	1966	Browns Ferry Increased power density (20%)
BWR/5	1969	Zimmer Improved ECCS systems Valve flow control
BWR/6	1972	BWR/6 8 × 8 fuel bundle Improved jet pumps and steam separators Added fuel bundles, increased output Reduced fuel duty: 13.4 kW/ft (44 kW/m) Improved ECCS performance Improved licensability Solid-state nuclear system protection system Compacted control room

Source: General Electric Co.

protecting personnel in a BWR is a more cumbersome and demanding task than in other type plants.

A second important difference lies in the control system which is described in detail elsewhere. Control rods in a BWR are inserted in the core from the bottom, to allow room at the top of the core for the steam formation process, and for the installation of equipment such as steam separators and dryers. Therefore, gravity force cannot be used for scramming and other, very reliable systems must be devised and installed which, however, may not have the same degree of reliability as gravity.

Also complicating the operational control of a BWR is the continuous formation and distribution of steam bubbles in the core. The creation of a bubble removes moderator from the core and tends to decrease the reactivity and thus tends to reduce the rate of fissions taking place. This, in turn, affects the rate of power production. As the load on the turbine changes, the pressure in the reactor vessel tends to change, which changes the density of steam bubbles per unit volume, which tends to affect the rate of power generation. Although there are ways to control the processes effectively, the fact remains that the coupling between the thermal hydraulics and the neutronics in a BWR are strongly coupled and that the operational control of BWRs is a much more sensitive matter than in PWRs.

BWR Steam Cycle

With these basic, conceptual characteristics of the BWR in mind, we proceed to a more detailed description of the BWR thermal cycle. A simplified schematic of the cycle is shown in Figure 8.23, while a more descriptive picture of the reactor vessel and of the flow paths in it is shown in Figure 8.24. Additional characteristic data for a typical BWR with a nominal output of 1220 MWe are given in Table 8.7. Description of components may be found in Chapter 9. The basic feature of the loop is that the pressure is maintained at about 7 MPa (1040 psi) which allows the water to boil as it passes through the core. Feedwater enters between the middle and top of the reactor vessel. Flow is induced downward in an annular space between the core "shroud" and the vessel wall by a set of jet pumps internal to the vessel as shown in Figure 8.24. The coolant then turns into an upward flow in the lower plenum, passes through orifices at the bottom of the fuel assemblies, and flows through the channels or cans that contain each fuel assembly (see also Chapter 9).

As the water flows through the core, it is gradually heated to a boil and bubbles begin to form at an increasing rate as the coolant moves upward. At the core exit, the coolant is a mixture of steam

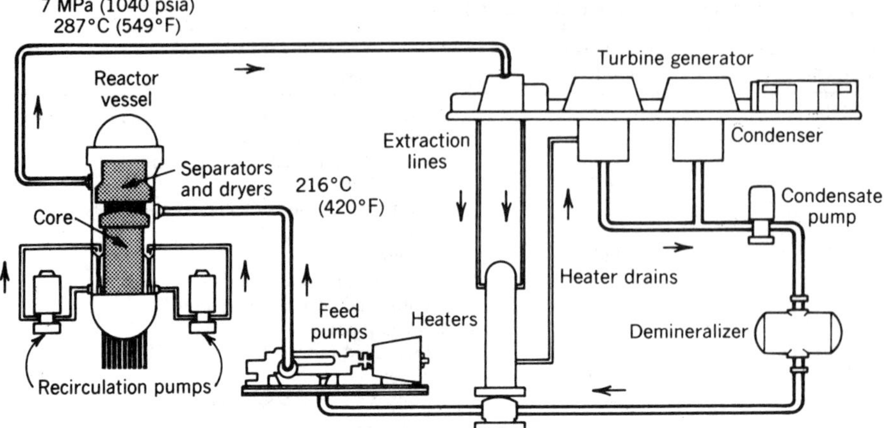

Figure 8.23. BWR single-cycle power loop. (Courtesy General Electric Co.)

and water to a proportion of steam ranging from 9 to 15% by weight. The water fraction is recirculated downward by the force of the jet pumps, while the steam keeps its upward movement. Banks of steam separators and dryers are placed above the core to provide a further separation of moisture and to provide a constant flow of dry steam to the turbine.

About one-third of the total cycle flow goes through the recirculating pumps. This flow is, of course, variable and plays an important role in controlling the level of power generation in the core, according to demand. The recirculating pumps are capable of controlling the load between 75 and 100% level without the need for any control rod movement. (Even without the recirculating pumps, up to 30% of power generation can be accommodated by natural circulation alone.) To raise power levels, the recirculation flow rate is increased, thus reducing the void traction in the core. This, in turn, provides more neutron moderation, shifts the neutron spectrum toward a lower temperature, and increases reactivity. The power level will then rise, stabilizing when the increased boiling reduces the reactivity back to zero. An increase to a higher power level will thus have been

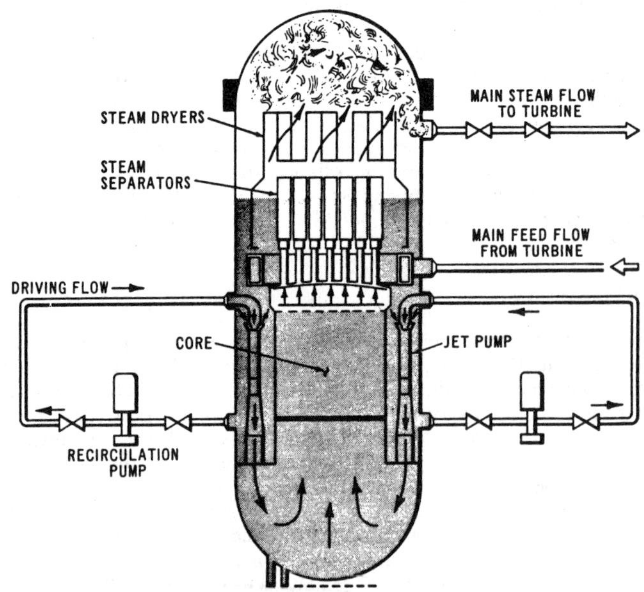

Figure 8.24. BWR jet pump system. (Courtesy General Electric Co.)

Table 8.7. Typical System Characteristics of a Current BWR Design

Rated core power (thermal)	3579 MWt
Electric output	1252 MWe
Efficiency	33.6%
Steam flow rate	1.94×10^3 kg/sec (15.396×10^6 lb/hr)
System pressure, nominal	7 MPa (1040 psia)
Average power density	56 kW/liter
Core coolant flow rate	13.24×10^3 kg/sec (105×10^6 lb/hr)
Reactor feedwater rate	1.94×10^3 kg/sec (15.358×10^6 lb/hr)
Feedwater temperature	216°C (420°F)
Core inlet temperature	277°C (532°F)
Core outlet temperature	288°C (550°F)
Steam quality at core outlet (design)	14.88% steam by weight
Number of recirculation loops	2 (pipe material: carbon steel)
Number of jet pumps	20
Number of steam lines	4

Sources: General Electric Co. See also *Nuclear Engineering International*, August Supplement, 1983.

achieved. The opposite occurs when a reduction in the recirculation rate causes a reduction in the power level.

Steam exiting from the vessel dome is typically at a pressure of about 7 MPa (1040 psi) at which pressure water boils when heated to a temperature of 287°C (549°F). These conditions characterize saturated steam. This limits the enthalpy available for conversion into mechanical energy through expansion in the turbine, and for this reason, the thermal efficiency of BWR cycle is, as with PWRs, a modest 32–33%.

BWR Systems

A great deal of the discussion given under Section 8.2 on PWRs is applicable to PWRs, or incorporates a discussion of pertinent BWR aspects. In the following paragraphs, we concentrate on those BWR systems that are different and important enough to warrant a separate presentation. A schematic diagram of the BWR systems is shown in Figure 8.25. Several of these systems are related to safety functions and are discussed separately in Chapter 17, such as the Residual Heat Removal (RHR) system, safety coolant injection, containment spray, and so on. Boiling water reactors have a turbine bypass similar to that of PWR, by which steam can be dumped directly to the condenser.

Control Rod Drive System

Control rods, in the form of cruciform blades (see Chapter 9), enter the core from the bottom, since the top of the core is occupied by bulky equipment for steam separation and drying. Consequently, a high-reliability hydraulic system is provided for the movement of control rods in and out of the core through control rod drives at the bottom of the vessel. Two basic functions are performed: the regulation of power generation level according to demand (a relatively slow operation), and the rapid insertion for emergency shutdown, called reactor "scram." Figure 8.26 is a simplified diagram of the BWR scram hydraulic system showing the accumulator, operating valves, and interconnecting pipes. The lines and valves provided to affect the slow insertion and withdrawal of rods were omitted for simplicity. The hardware for each drive package (contained in the broken line in Figure 8.26) is preassembled, as shown in Figure 8.27, and tested at the factory. The assemblies shipped to the plant site need only pipe and electrical connections.

Water derived from the condensate storage is pumped to a pressure thimble outside the reactor vessel. Two centrifugal pumps, each with a 100% capacity, are provided. The control rod drives are also provided with a circuit of cooling water with a pressure slightly higher than vessel pressure (by about 0.15 MPa or 20 psi) which results in a slow leakage through the seals and into the reactor vessel. To insert a rod into the core, the operator allows the pressure from the charging system to build at the bottom of the control rod drive piston which is connected to the control rod via the index tube (see Figure 8.26). This is accomplished at a controlled rate via a speed-control valve. After reaching the desired position, the control rod is locked in place both hydraulically and mechanically. The withdrawal of a rod is similar, but a little more complicated and the sequence is automatically programmed.

The "scram" function of the system is one of the most important features of the system, from a

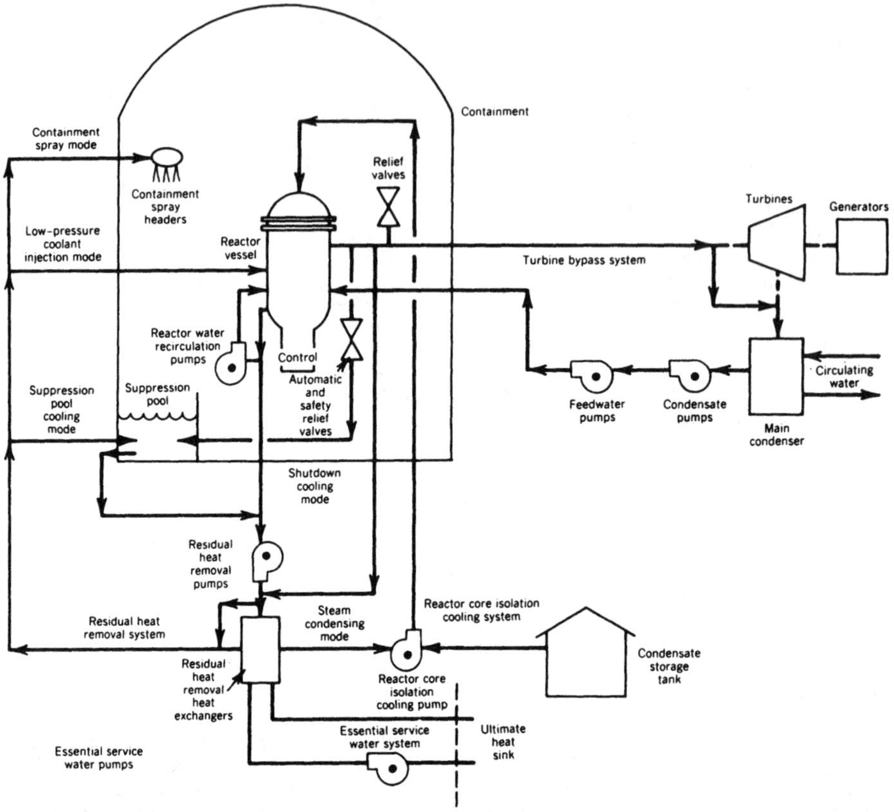

Figure 8.25. Boiling water reactor decay heat removal systems. (Modified from NUREG/CR-1556.)

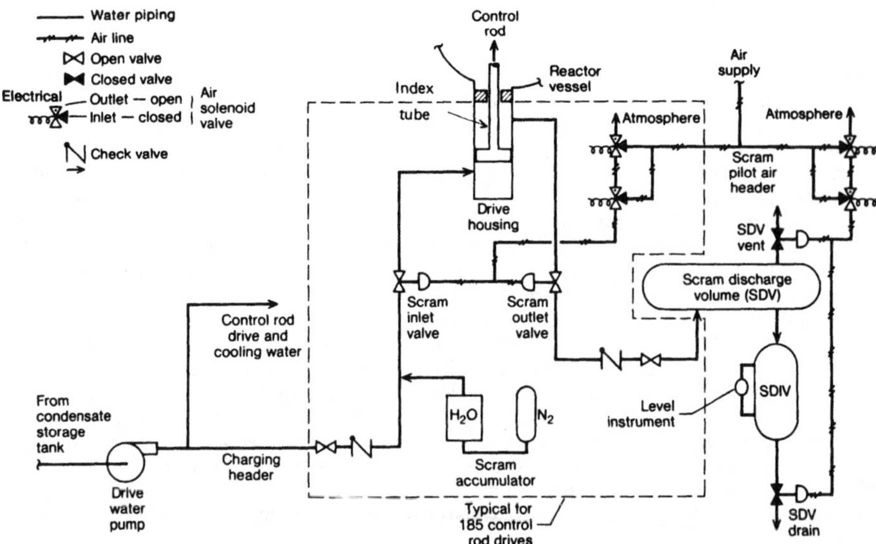

Figure 8.26. BWR scram hydraulic system (scrammed valve lineup). (From NSAC-20/INPO-3.)

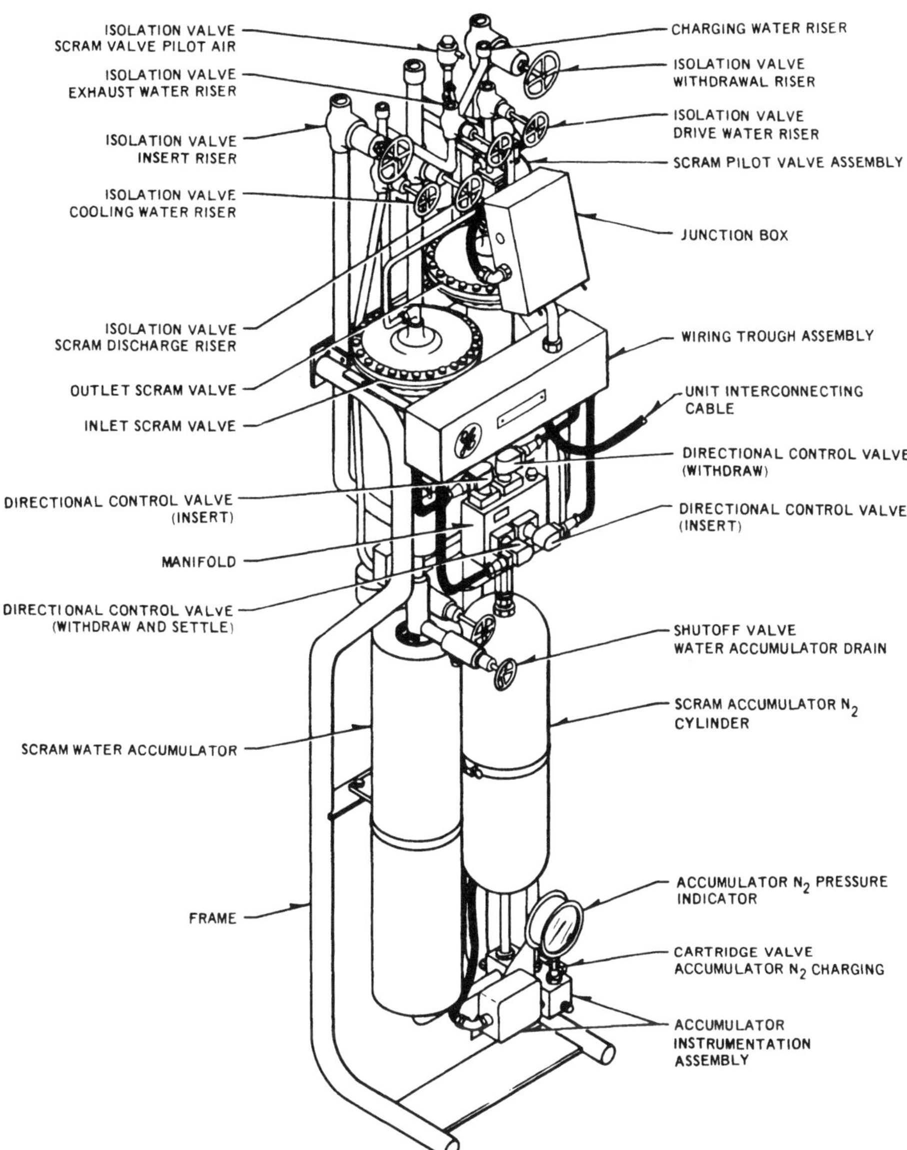

Figure 8.27. Control rod drive hydraulic control unit (component assembly).

plant protection point of view. This operation was designed to be passive, namely, independent of outside power for maximum reliability. When a scram signal is generated by the reactor protection system, the inlet and outlet scram valves open through a change in the air line. High pressure, provided by a scram accumulator under nitrogen pressure (of about 10 MPa or 1500 psig), pushes water below the drive piston while the top side of the piston is vented into the scram discharge headers which are normally kept at atmospheric pressure. The large pressure difference across the piston provides a large enough force (up to eight times the force of gravity) to give the control drive a high initial acceleration and to overcome possible friction or binding in the drive line. Under this acceleration, the control rod drive quickly reaches a velocity of 1.5 m/sec (5 ft/sec). However, as the index tube closes off ports in the cylinder wall, the water above the piston encounters increasing resistance to outflow and the piston speed is reduced. The number, size, and spacing of the

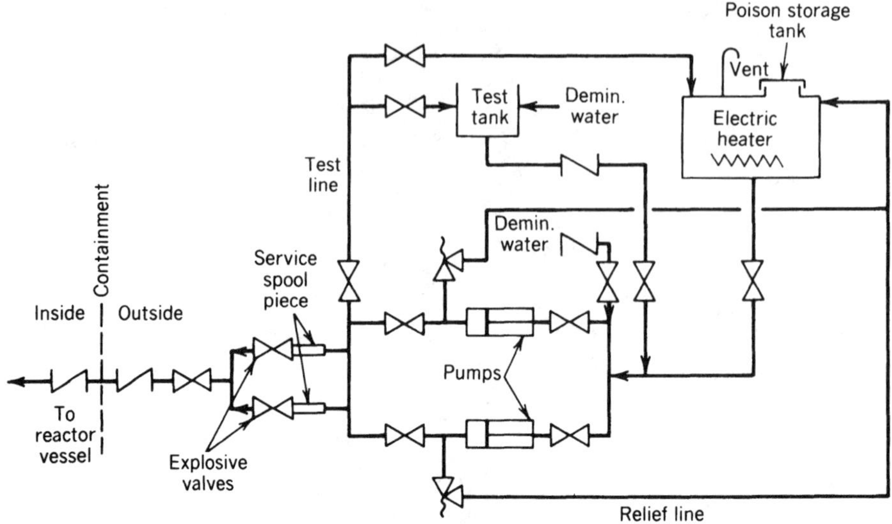

Figure 8.28. Schematic arrangement of the standby liquid control system.

holes in the control rod drive piston tube, which are gradually closed with the upward movement, are chosen to provide a gradual deceleration of index tube movement.

At low reactor pressures, the accumulator alone is capable of supplying all the force needed to complete the scram. At high reactor pressures, the gradually dropping accumulator pressure is unable to complete the operation. Water is admitted from the main vessel through a check valve in the underpiston water port to supply the force required to complete the full insertion of the control rods.

The only known instance when a malfunction in the system was experienced occurred on June 28, 1980, when a manual scram of the Browns Ferry 3 BWR (a 1067-MWe reactor built by General Electric and owned by the Tennessee Valley Authority) was attempted. This was done in conjunction with a planned shutdown to repair a feedwater line in the turbine building, but otherwise all plant conditions were normal. Scram signals were initiated at a level of 36% power, but complete control insertion did not occur. Of a total of 185 control rods, 10 were already fully inserted, but 76 rods failed to insert completely upon scram, ranging from 95 to 5% insertion. Repeated manual scrams (four in all) managed to cause complete insertion of all rods. There is no indication and no reason to believe that any damage occurred because of the delayed control rod insertion. However, because of the crucial importance of the ability to shut the reactor down quickly and reliably, an intensive study of the incident was done. The study concluded that the reason for the malfunction was that the scram discharge volume (see Figure 8.26), serving one-half of the core control rod drives, was for some reason almost filled with water prior to scram. Because there was no adequate volume to accommodate the additional water discharged from the top of the rod drive pistons, insertion was impeded. The origin of the water in the scram discharge volume has not been firmly established, but there were several possible explanations.

Corrective measures have been proposed to ensure that there is always room available for the water discharged from the rod drive mechanism, but specifics will vary from plant to plant because of design variations and differences in procedures.

Standby Liquid Control System

Boiling water reactors are also equipped with a liquid control system to inject liquid poison in the core in sufficient quantities to shut the reactor down in an emergency. Poison is in the form of sodium pentaborate solution (this form is much more soluble than boric acid). This is an emergency system, designed to be used in extreme circumstances since boron poison is not normally present in the BWR coolant system, unlike the situation in PWRs. Boron injection would, therefore, cause quite a perturbation in the system's operation, necessitating flushing of the system and thorough cleanup (via demineralizers). It must be added that to date there have been no known cases where the system had to be activated in any commercial installation, except during routine tests. A schematic diagram is shown in Figure 8.28.

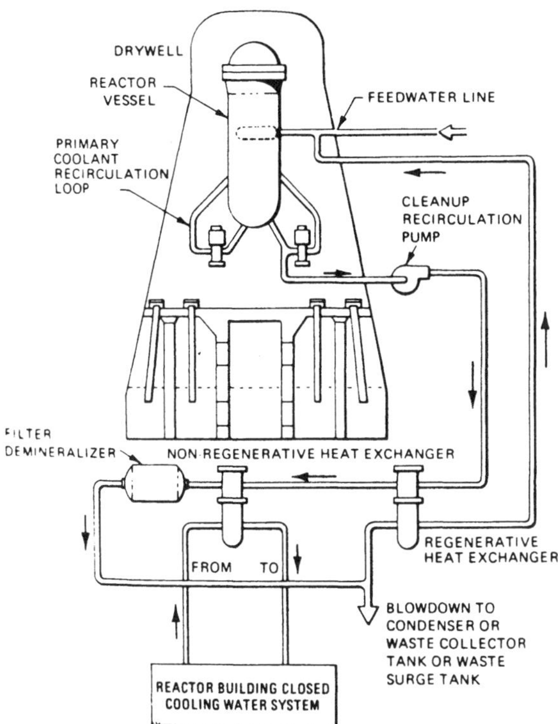

Figure 8.29. Reactor water cleanup system. (Courtesy General Electric Co.)

Reactor Water Cleanup System

The full flow of the working fluid passing through the turbine and the condenser is treated in a condensate demineralizer, connected at the condenser outlet, prior to returning to the reactor vessel. However, a large fraction of primary water (up to 80%) circulates between reactor vessel and recirculation loops and never goes to the turbine. Provision is, therefore, made to clean the reactor coolant through a system connected to a recirculation loop and to the feedwater line as shown in Figure 8.29. The system removes fission products, corrosion products, and other impurities before and during reactor refueling. Its capacity is such as to handle a full reactor water inventory in about $4\frac{1}{2}$ hr at reactor pressure. It is made of stainless steel and comprises pumps, pipes, heat exchangers, and filter/demineralizers. Heat exchangers are provided to cool the fluid and prevent damage to the demineralizer resins. Remotely controlled isolation valves are provided to enable the operator to remove the system from the loop during reactor operation.

It is important to note that, since the system is not connected with the reactor during normal operation, it does not constitute a safety system even though it handles primary coolant. Therefore, all its components are built to less exacting standards (Class 3, Section III of the ASME code) than systems and components vital to plant safety. Strict specifications are prescribed for the BWR chemistry as shown in Table 8.8. The system also performs volume control by removing excess water volume from the reactor because of thermal expansion or other reasons.

Table 8.8. BWR Water Chemistry Specifications

Water conductivity	1.0 micromho/cm
pH	5.6–8.6
Chloride ions	0.1 ppm

Source: General Electric Co.

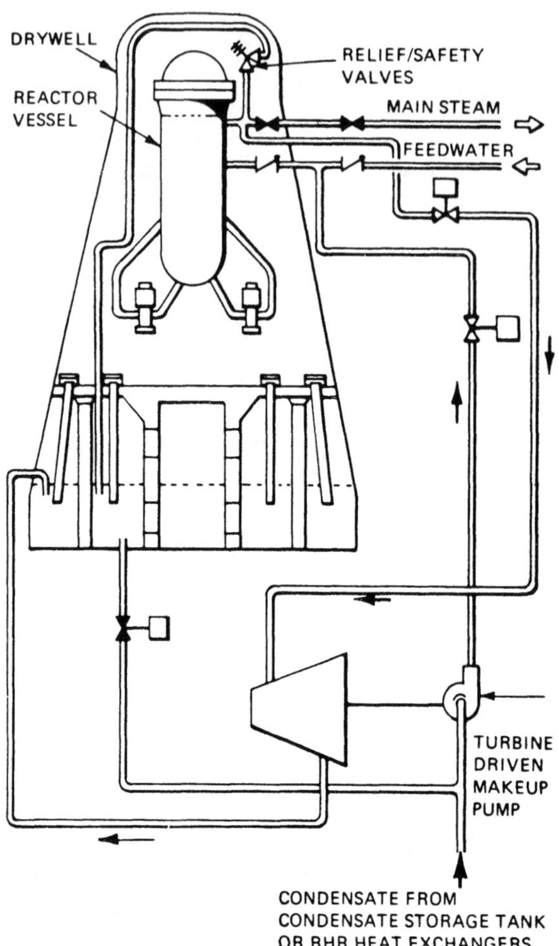

Figure 8.30. Reactor core isolation cooling system. Steam generated from decay heat is used to drive the turbine. (Courtesy General Electric Co.)

Reactor Core Isolation Cooling System (RCIC)

This system might be viewed, for BWRs, as the equivalent to the auxiliary feedwater system provided for PWRs. It is not necessarily associated with any accidents. Rather, it is designed to provide adequate water inventory in the core in case the reactor becomes isolated from the turbine. This may happen when, for a variety of reasons, the main steam isolation valve, turbine throttle valve, or turbine stop valve are closed. A schematic diagram of the RCIC is shown in Figure 8.30. A pump, with a 100% capacity of total need, takes suction from the condensate storage tank and discharges into the reactor vessel via the feedwater line as shown. A backup source of water is provided through a connection to the pressure suppression pool which contains very large amounts of water (as described in Chapter 9).

The sequence of events that would actuate the RCIC system is as follows. Upon closure of the isolation valves, the reactor scrams in order to terminate the neutron chain reaction. However, fission products accumulated in the fuel rods continue to release decay heat which produces additional amounts of steam. Excessive steam production lifts the relief valves located inside the drywell and is discharged to the pressure suppression pool. When the water level inside the vessel drops below a certain preset point, the RCIC is activated. The system pumps water into the vessel to maintain inventory and prevents the automatic initiation of the high-pressure safety injection system. This latter system would take over in case the RCIC failed to operate. But while the high-pressure safety injection is a safety system, the RCIC is classified in a somewhat lesser category (Class 2 of Section III of the ASME code). The pump of the RCIC is driven by a small dedicated

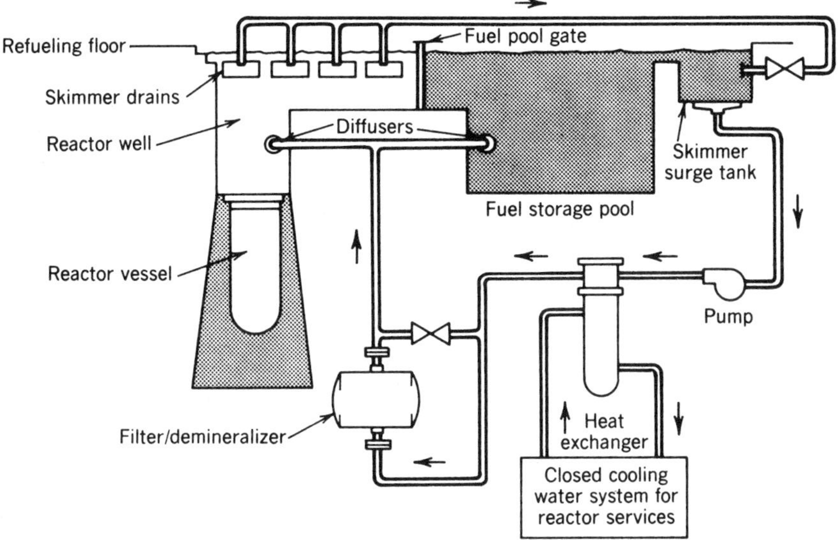

Figure 8.31. Fuel pool cleanup and cooling system. (Courtesy General Electric Co.)

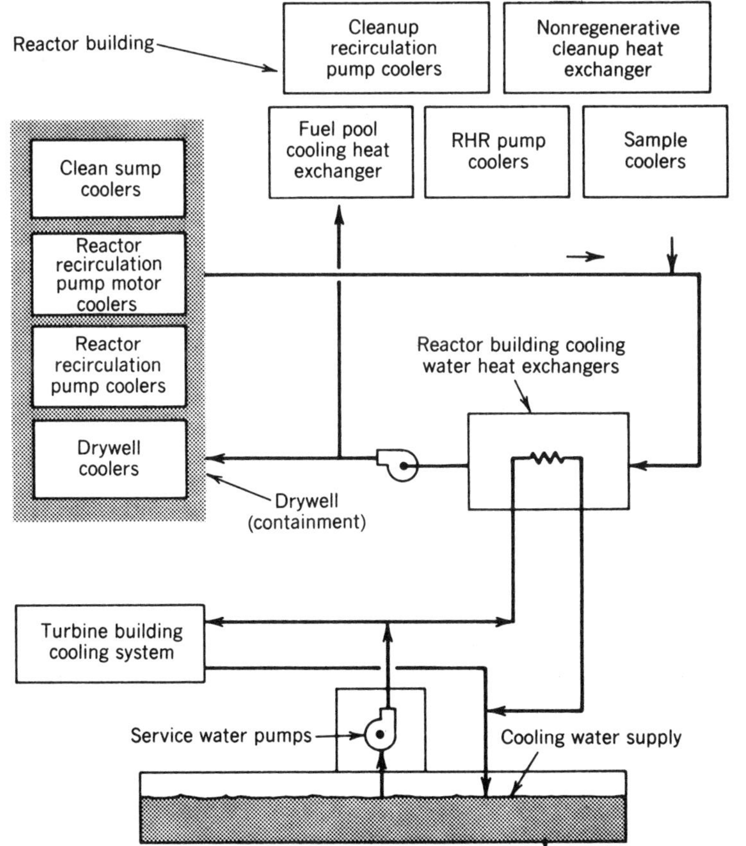

Figure 8.32. Auxiliary closed loop and service-water cooling systems. (Courtesy General Electric Co.)

turbine which draws steam from the steam line very close to the reactor steam outlet nozzle. Power for the control of the system is drawn from the station batteries. Thus, no external power source is needed for the operation of the system.

Fuel Storage Pool System

Refueling in a BWR takes place, normally, once a year, as in a PWR, and takes 2 to 3 weeks to complete. Most of the information given on PWRs in Section 8.2 is valid for BWRs also. A fuel pool is neccessary for the storage of spent fuel under water to allow the radioactivity to decrease while decay heat is dissipated. Fuel pools in BWRs are also used to perform remote assembly operations on new fuel bundles under water since the irradiated channels (see Chapter 9) can be reused. Special equipment, remotely operated from the control room, is provided for this purpose. The fuel pool is equipped with a cleanup and cooling system, shown in Figure 8.31. The functions it performs are similar to those described in Section 8.2. A typical installation has two pumps (each with 50% capacity of total needed), two heat exchangers, and two filter demineralizers for filtration and purification of the pool water. In the diagram, the pumps supply water to both the reactor well and the fuel pool. The capacity of the pumps allows them to circulate one full pool volume in 24 hr. The system is cross connected with the residual heat removal system (RHR) described in Chapter 18, to provide a backup for heat removal if needed. In general, the various auxiliary systems of the BWR are strongly interconnected and synergistic as can be seen in Figure 8.25.

Closed Loop Cooling System and Service Water

A large number of pieces of equipment, spaces, and water pools require continuous cooling. To provide an additional barrier of radioactivity to the environment, an intermediate, closed, and demineralized cooling system is provided. A schematic of a typical system is shown in Figure 8.32. Two categories of equipment and coolers obtain cooling from the system, those inside the containment (drywell) and those in the reactor building. The heat removed is in turn transferred to the service water which is the ultimate sink for all heat loads generated at the plant except the main condenser.

The system, under normal conditions, contains no radioactivity. To release radioactivity in the open loop of the service water and hence into the environment, two failures in series must occur. Continuous monitoring is performed, however, for any sign of activity in the system. If this happens, it would be an indication of radioactive leakage in some of the components served and corrective measures would be needed.

BIBLIOGRAPHY

Babcock & Wilcox, Co., *Steam, Its Generation and Use,* 39th ed., 1978.

Berry, D. L., and P. R. Bennet, "Study of Alternate Decay Heat Removal Concepts for LWRs," NUREG/CR-1556, SAND80-0929, RA, April 1981.

Commonwealth Edison Co., "Zion Station Final Safety Analysis Report," Docket 50295-16 to 50295-21, December 1970, and May 1972.

General Electric Co., *BWR/6, General Description of a Boiling Reactor,* September 1980.

Godfriaux, B. L., and C. A. Stephens-Labrie, "Aquaculture Program Indicates Possible Profitability," *Power Engineering,* October (1982).

Kramer, A. W., *Boiling Water Reactors,* Addison-Wesley, Reading, Massachusetts, 1958.

Lahey, R. T., Jr. and F. J. Moody, "The Thermal Hydraulics of a Boiling Water Nuclear Reactor," American Nuclear Society Monograph, 1977.

Lamarsh, J. R. *Introduction to Nuclear Engineering and Economy,* Addison-Wesley, Reading Massachusetts, 1975.

Lish, K. C., *Nuclear Power Plant Systems and Equipment,* Industrial Press, New York, 1972.

Nawaz, A., "Use of Charcoal Absorbers in Nuclear Plants," *Power Engineering,* October (1982).

Nero, A. V., Jr., *A Guidebook to Nuclear Reactors,* University of California Press, Berkeley, 1979.

Nuclear Safety Analysis Center, and Institute for Nuclear Power Operations, "Analysis of Incomplete Control Rod Insertion at Browns Ferry 3," NSAC-20/INPO-3, December 1980.

Pence, D. T., "Critical Review of Noble Gas Recovery and Treatment Systems," *Nuclear Safety* **22,** No. 6, November–December (1981).

Skrotzki, B. G. A., and W. A. Vopat, *Power Station Engineering and Economy,* McGraw-Hill, New York, 1960.

USAEC, "The Safety of Nuclear Power Reactors and Related Facilities," WASH-1250, July 1973.

CHAPTER 9
LWR COMPONENTS

9.1. GENERAL

Nuclear power plants are, with some exceptions, large installations made up of a great number and variety of components. Since several manufacturers are in the business of supplying nuclear reactors internationally and since an even larger number of architect/engineer organizations collaborate with the vendor in the design, procurement, and construction of the plant, it is not surprising that a great deal of variation exists in the details of plant layout, component selection, and general engineering approaches. Compounding these differences was the rapid development of nuclear power plant design from one generation to the next, by the same manufacturer. These changes were dictated, to some extent, by necessary improvements in plant performance and the need to conform to environmental and safety regulations. Another powerful motivation was to increase the size of the plant in order to achieve economies of scale. This rapid evolution was difficult for the utility industry to absorb comfortably, and the economies of scale reached a point of diminishing returns in the 1970s. The tendency in recent years has been toward stabilization to a certain model by each vendor, and a need for standardization.†

Despite the great variability in plant layout, systems, and components, the basic features of the plants remain essentially the same. Even between PWRs and BWRs, with their differences in the energy transport loops, there exists a great deal of similarity: A large pressure vessel containing a nuclear core of fuel bundles made up of similar fuel rods, occupies the heart of the nuclear plant. Control rods are provided to control the nuclear reaction, to change power level, and to shut the reactor down. Piping provides a path for the coolant to carry away the heat produced and is complemented by valves and pumps. Turbines, feedwater heaters, condensers, and other items are used in the energy conversion cycle. All plants are provided with multiple barriers to prevent the escape of radioactivity under normal or abnormal conditions. Redundant and diverse components are installed to fulfill safety functions and to provide comfortable margins with respect to imposed requirements. Containment structures are required now in all countries (this was not true in the USSR until a few years ago) to contain potential release of radioactivity from the plant and to protect against external natural or man-made forces such as earthquakes, floods, tornadoes, tsunamis, explosions, fires, and even airplane crashes.

The major components encountered in nuclear plants will be described in the following paragraphs. While all the varieties cannot possibly be covered in a book of reasonable length, an effort will be made to review the most commonly used types with an emphasis on the current designs. PWR and BWR components, common in many respects, are described in parallel rather than consecutively for easier comparison.

It is useful to review briefly the various conditions under which the components must be made and tested. In the United States these standards were set in the codes written by the American Society of Mechanical Engineers (ASME code) and, separately, by Committee N-18 of the American Nuclear Society. (Similar codes exist in Europe and Japan.) The categorization into safety classes done by these organizations is very similar. This categorization defines component and system classes as follows:

Safety Class 1. This is the most vital category and applies to all components of the primary coolant system whose failure could cause a loss of reactor coolant, in operating conditions III or IV.‡ The criteria are, therefore, most stringent. This terminology means that coolant is lost from the system faster than the plant can make up for the loss.

†This approach is most advanced in France, where a single vendor (Framatome) with essentially two different designs (900 and 1300 MWe) supplies all the country's needs.
‡Abnormal operating conditions of the plant, see Chapter 18.

Safety Class 2. This applies to structures and components that are required to fulfill a safety function (for example, to shut down the reactor; to provide cooling for the core or the containment; to cool another safety system; to contain and control radioactivity that may be released in an accident, etc.).

Safety Class 3. This applies to systems whose failure would allow release to the environment of gaseous radioactivity that would normally be held for decay within the plant.

In the following sections occasional reference to these classes will be made.

9.2. REACTOR VESSEL AND INTERNALS

PWR Vessels

The reactor vessel is one of the most important components of the plant in terms of size, weight, cost, and safety significance. It is a massive structure, cylindrical in shape, containing the reactor core and other related components. Its size, for a large PWR plant, could be over 12 m (around 40 ft) in height by 4.7 m (around 15 ft) in diameter with a wall thickness in excess of 0.20 m (around 8 in.). It is designed to withstand a pressure of approximately 17 MPa (2500 psi) and a temperature of 340°C (650°F). A measure of its size can be gleaned from Figure 9.1, which shows the reactor vessel of a large plant being placed in position inside the reactor building. Figure 9.2 gives another perspective, showing a vessel being transported on site with the reactor containment building in the background. The total weight of a large reactor vessel could approach 450 tons.† Transportation of the component from the fabrication shop to the site is a major undertaking and could take many weeks.

A cutaway view of a PWR pressure vessel is shown in Figure 9.3. The vessel has a removable top head which, when in operation, is held in place by a large number (up to 60) of studs, each about 6½ in. in diameter, and made of high-tensile-strength alloy steel. The top is removable to allow refueling operations to take place (typically once a year, as described in Chapter 12) and for other maintenance of core infernals. The vessel head has a number of fittings for the mechanisms that move control rods in and out of the core (control rods in a PWR are inserted from the top whereas in a BWR they are inserted from the bottom as explained below). Other fittings are needed for the insertion of instruments to monitor the core, although most instrumentation thimbles are placed at the bottom of vessel. Slightly above the midplane (waist) of the vessel, a number of nozzles protrude from the vessel to provide connection to the piping of the primary coolant system. The number of nozzles depends on the capacity of the plant; the number of loops is either two, three, or four. A vessel for a four-loop plant (shown in Figure 9.3) will have a total of four inlet and four outlet nozzles. Another example is shown in Figure 9.4 where a total of six nozzles (four outlet and two inlet) are used. To support the nuclear core, which could weigh more than 100 t, a cylindrical core barrel with a lower core plate is provided. The core barrel hangs inside the pressure vessel from a support ledge near the top head flange (Figure 9.3). The fuel assemblies are lowered into the core and sit in holes drilled in the thick lower core plate. Radial supports are placed between the bottom of the core barrel and the vessel to minimize horizontal movement inside the vessel. Other items worth noting are an upper support plate with openings for the control rod mechanisms, and a fairly thick thermal shield which, together with the core barrel, cut down the intensive radiation that originates in the core and could damage the vessel.‡ Newer PWR designs do not have separate 360° shields but use abbreviated pads instead.

The importance of the Reactor Pressure Vessel (RPV) and the safety implications of its failure mean that a high degree of reliability is paramount. This is guaranteed only through careful attention to design, materials, fabrication, quality assurance, testing, inspection, and so on. Accordingly, the manufacture of RPVs is performed under conservative methods and codes specified by national engineering societies in various countries (Class 1, Section III of the ASME code in the United States). The vessels are welded together from several segments which start either as plates or forgings. The base material is either carbon steel or low-alloy steels with high "toughness," that is, with a high resistance to the extension of an existing crack. Typical materials contain 1% manganese, 0.6–0.8% nickel, and 0.5% molybdenum. All internal surfaces that come in contact with primary coolant are clad with a layer of stainless steel (or sometimes inconel) to minimize corrosion. Various physical and chemical processes during operation could affect the properties of

†"Tons" refers always to metric tons = 1000 kg and is abbreviated t. Others call the unit "tonne" and abbreviate as te or Te.

‡Gamma radiation could produce thermal stress in the vessel, whereas neutrons cause embrittlement of the metal.

Figure 9.1. Reactor vessel being placed in position inside the reactor building.

Figure 9.2. Reactor pressure vessel arriving at the plant site.

the material. Thermal aging (due to high temperature), strain aging,† and embrittlement from neutron irradiation must not cause undue deterioration of the vessel's toughness over time. Materials that contain relatively high levels of impurities, such as copper, sulfur, and phosphorus are particularly susceptible to neutron embrittlement, therefore, control of the amount of these impurities became important. Certain areas of the vessel are particularly sensitive to property deterioration, mainly due to changes in operating conditions.

Particularly sensitive locations are the cylindrical region adjacent to the reactor core (where neutron irradiation is at its maximum), and the region around the nozzles (because of the concentration of stresses at these points). To assure the necessary high reliability of the reactor vessel, a combination of measures are taken: conservative methods of design; choice of appropriate materials; carefully specified fabrication methods; repeated inspection during fabrication; use of surveillance capsules‡, and, finally, operation of the reactor so that temperature and pressure transients do not exceed safe limits. One concern raised in the past few years is related with the possibility of lowering the temperature of the coolant (and by inference also of the vessel wall) too rapidly while the reactor is still under high pressure and while the vessel material has lost much of its ductility due to prolonged neutron irradiation. More on this issue and on the answers developed under a variety of research efforts is to be found in Chapter 10.

BWR Vessels

Boiling water reactors need even larger pressure vessels than PWRs. A typical vessel for a 1000-MWe plant is over 22 m (72 ft) in height, and about 6.5 m (21 ft) in diameter. The wall thickness

†"Aging" results in embrittlement of steel due to changes in its microstructure.

‡Placed in the space between reactor vessel and core barrel, which can be retrieved and used as monitors of the condition of the vessel material.

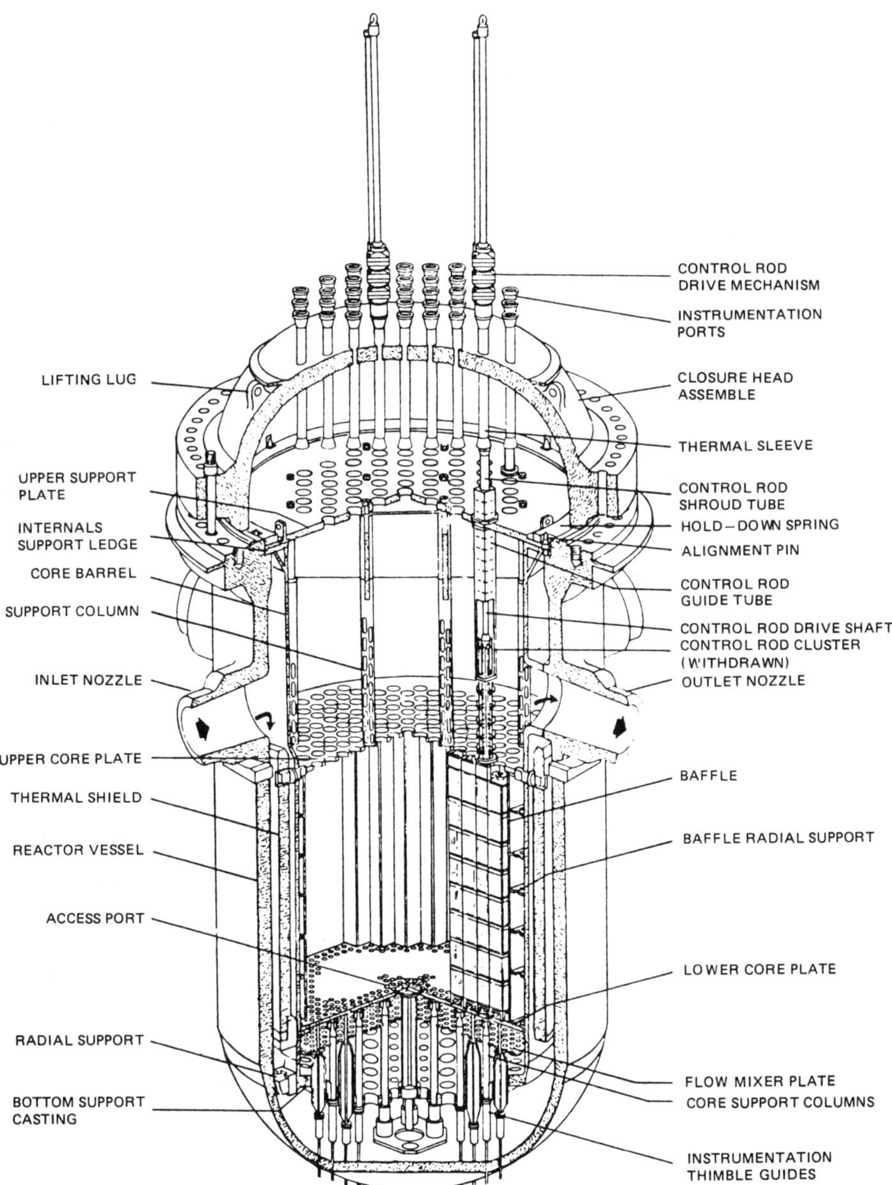

Figure 9.3. PWR reactor vessels and internals. A PWR vessel is a large component, several inches thick. Water enters the vessel through the inlet nozzle, and travels downward between the core barrel and the vessel wall. From the lower plenum, it moves upward through the core, removes heat, and exits at the outlet nozzle to the steam generators. At the top of the core, the control rods and their drive mechanisms can be seen. (Courtesy Westinghouse Electric Corp.)

Figure 9.4. The figure shows a plan view of the main components and their connections in the primary loop of a PWR built by Babcock & Wilcox. This plant has two coolant loops, four inlet nozzles connected to four primary coolant pumps, and two outlet nozzles connected to two steam generators. The pressurizer can also be seen connected to one of the hot legs near the outlet nozzle. (Courtesy Babcock & Wilcox Co.)

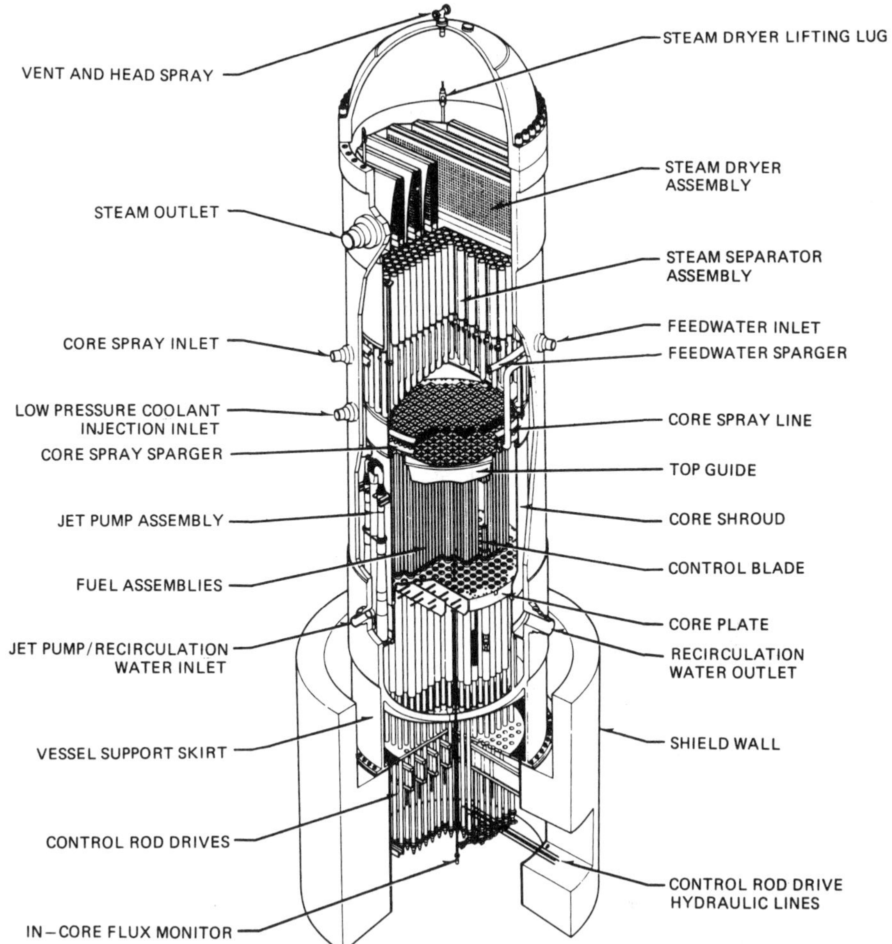

Figure 9.5. BWR reactor vessel and internals. A number of assemblies have been removed in this figure to better show the different components. Above the core, the separator and steam dryer assemblies can be seen. Control rod drives insert control rods from the bottom. Jet pump assemblies internally recirculate the reactor coolant. (Courtesy General Electric Co.)

between 15 and 18 cm (6 and 7 in.) is somewhat smaller than in a PWR vessel since the pressure it is called to withstand is about half that of a PWR.

A BWR reactor vessel with its internals is shown in Figure 9.5. The BWR vessel is much larger than its PWR counterpart because it must accommodate a larger core and other large additional pieces of equipment (such as jet pump assemblies, steam separators, and dryers). The head is removable to allow refueling. Steam outlet connections are welded to the vessel body in order to eliminate the need to break flanged joints in the steam lines when opening the vessel for refueling. A high-pressure seal is provided by two concentric metal O-rings, and a detection system is installed to detect any leaks. The material of the vessel is low-alloy steel clad in the interior with a layer of stainless steel to provide resistance to corrosion. The vessel head interior surface, however, is not clad since it is always exposed to an environment of saturated steam.† The vessel in a BWR is not as critical a component as in the PWR: the pressure is lower and the irradiation of the material from neutrons coming from the core much lower, hence, the degree of embrittlement is much reduced. One reason is the thick layer of water contained in the annular space between the core shroud and the vessel wall. Nevertheless, the same care must be paid to the selection of materials, the fabrication methods, and the inspection methods to ensure the integrity of the vessel. Surveillance sam-

†The oxygen concentration in the steam is much lower than in the liquid, hence corrosion is lower.

ples are placed within the vessel to provide periodic monitoring of changes in the material properties. Other supports and attachments, including a thick core plate on which the fuel assemblies rest, are shown in Figure 9.5. Externally the vessel is mounted on a supporting skirt which is attached with bolts onto a cylindrical concrete pedestal, an integral part of the reactor building foundation.

Some variations exist in the designs of other manufacturers of BWRs (only one exists in the United States). Figure 9.6 shows the somewhat more compact design of a reactor vessel by a European vendor.

Other BWR Internals

The core is surrounded by a cylindrical, stainless steel structure, the shroud, which separates the coolant's downward flow in the annulus from its upward flow through the core. The shroud mates at its upper part with the top guide, a circular metal belt that embraces the upper part of the core. The top guide, in turn, mates with the steam separator assembly to form a space above the fuel into which coolant from the core is discharged. The bottom of the shroud, through an annular ring, called the peripheral shelf, is welded to the vessel. Penetrating the shelf are the discharge diffusers of the jet pumps which introduce the coolant into the core inlet plenum. Thus a closed chamber is formed around the core. This allows the core to be completely covered in the event of a loss-of-coolant accident which might occur through a break in the recirculation loop.

Two ring spargers, circular pipes located at the top of the core and below the steam separators, are provided as safety systems. They provide emergency core cooling in the event of an accident. They do not interfere with the movement of fuel in and out of the core.

The core is capped with a dome, which forms the core discharge plenum. The steam–water mixture from the core of a BWR contains 86% or more water by weight. It flows from the core into the core discharge plenum where some mixing occurs. The mixing, which tends to equalize the wide distribution of steam qualities coming from the core, optimizes steam separator performance. Welded into holes on the dome are a number of steam separators. Each consists of a standpipe and a three-stage separator attached at the top of each standpipe. The steam separator assembly with the dome are bolted to the top flange of the core shroud by long holddown bolts. These bolts extend above the top of the steam separators to facilitate removal during refueling operations. The fixed, axial-flow steam separator is shown schematically in Figure 9.7. The assembly of steam separators is a large component of the BWR (Figure 9.8). In order to further dry the steam, a bank of steam dryers is installed at the top of the steam separators. This assembly is held in place by the vessel head and forms the top and sides of the wet steam plenum. The steam dryers are made of several panels, one of which is shown in Figure 9.9. Steam from the separators flows upward and then sideways through the stationary vanes. Passing through them in a sinuous path, the wet steam deposits moisture on the vane surfaces. Water is collected in the trough below and is led into the water pool surrounding the separators and from there to the downcomer annulus surrounding the core for recirculation. The separated water discharging downward from the separators flows around the standpipes and returns to the recirculation pumps. Normally, the water surface is maintained about mid-separator. This optimizes the system by minimizing both the carryover of water into the steam, and carryunder of steam into the water. The separators discharge steam containing no more than about 5% water by weight and water containing no more than 0.2% steam by weight. The steam dryers discharge steam with no more than 0.1% water by weight. Water from the dryers merges with that from the separators and the returning feedwater, then it flows to the jet pumps to be recirculated through the nuclear core.

Water Recirculation and Jet Pumps

A unique feature of the BWR is the recirculation system which was described in some detail in Chapter 8. It consists of two external loops each of which has an outlet from the reactor, an external centrifugal pump, and the necessary valves. Each loop feeds four to six pairs of jet pumps internal to the reactor shown in Figure 9.10. The total number of jet pumps ranges from 16 to 24, depending on the size of the reactor. These are installed in the annular space between the core shroud and the vessel wall as shown in more detail in Figure 9.11; the size of this component is shown in Figure 9.12. A single riser pipe provides the driving flow for each pair of jet pumps. Each jet pump, 5.8 m (19 ft) in length, consists of an inlet mixer, a nozzle assembly with five discharge ports, and a diffuser. The diffuser, which has a conical section, terminates with a straight cylindrical section at the lower end, which is welded onto the shroud support. The submersion of the core up to the level of the inlet to the jet pumps is illustrated in Figure 9.13, while the principle of operation of the jet pump is shown in Figure 9.14. The flow rate through the jet pumps is controllable to cover a wide range. This is important because one of the principal ways of adjusting the power of a BWR is by controlling the flow of coolant through the core (see Chapter 12).

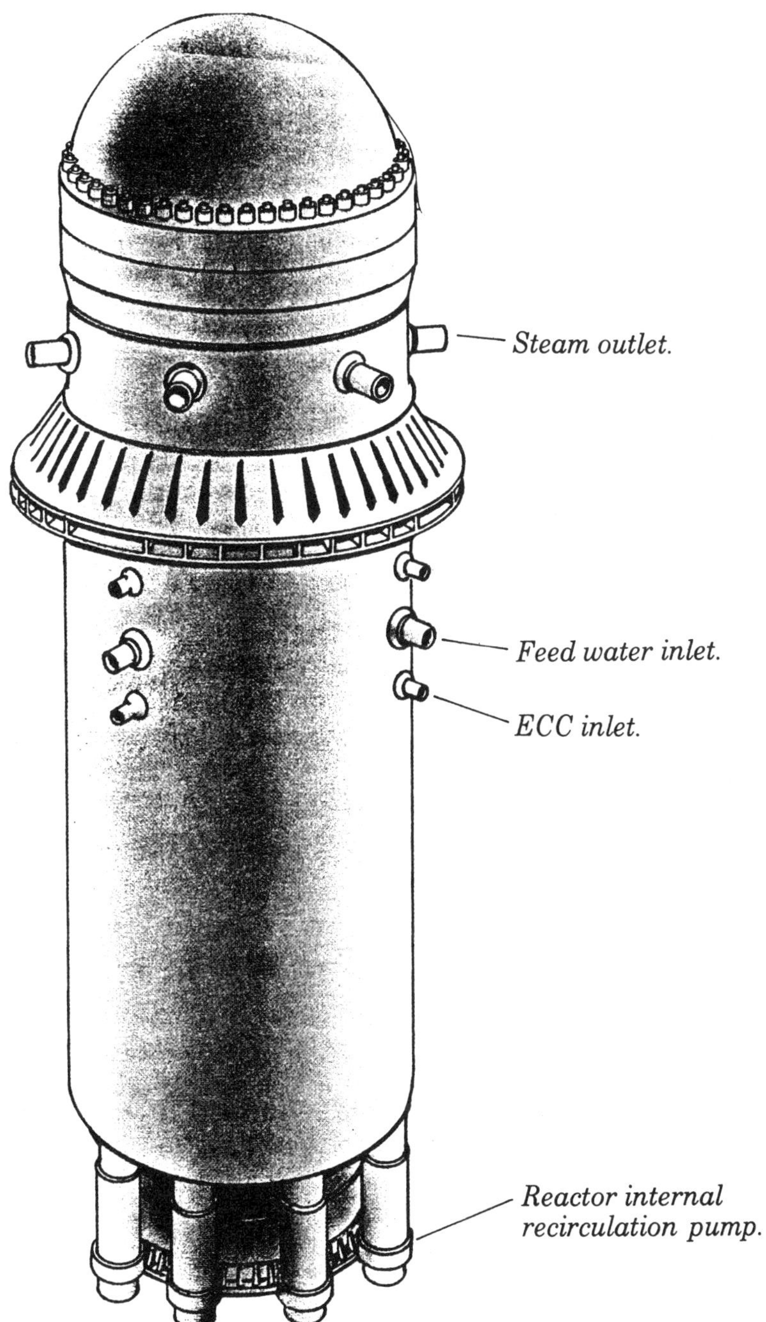

Figure 9.6. ASEA-Atom, a Swedish manufacturer produces BWRs of a somewhat different design from that of General Electric. This figure shows the ASEA-Atom BWR pressure vessel with its internal recirculation pump. The grid around the upper portion of the vessel is for support of the vessel on its concrete base. (Courtesy ASEA-Atom.)

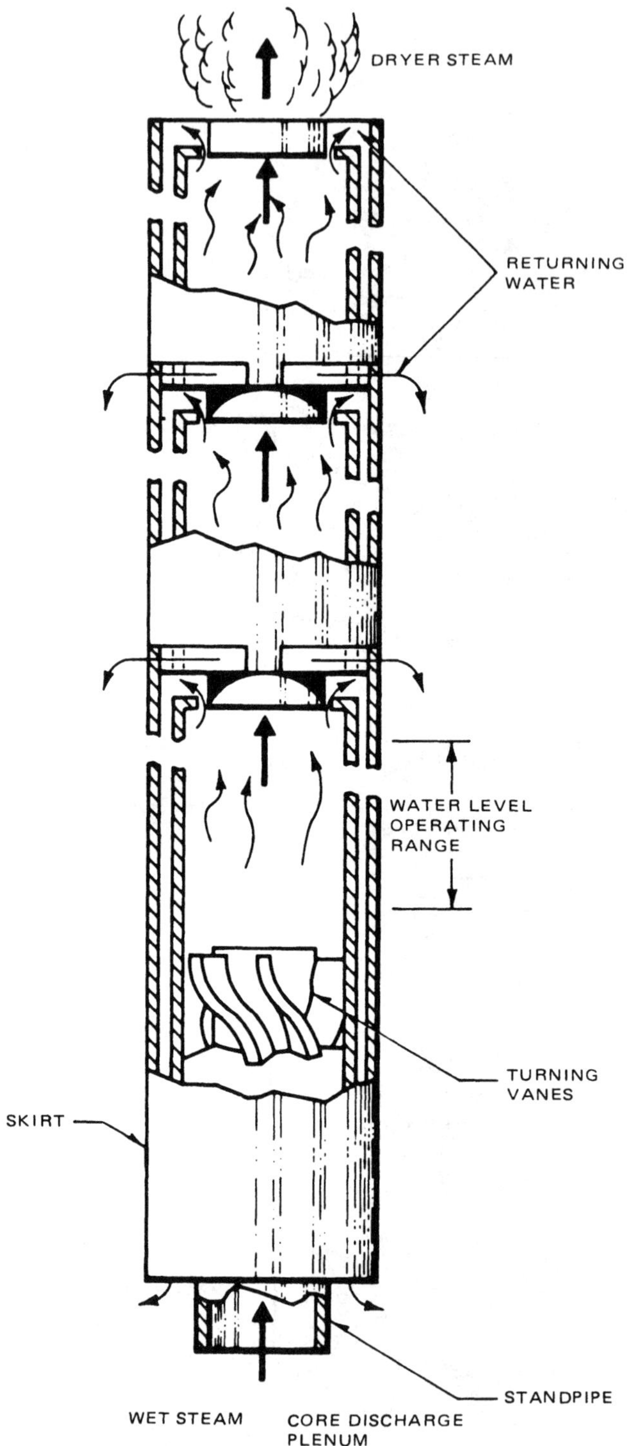

Figure 9.7. Internal steam separator for a BWR. The component is made of stainless steel, has no moving parts, and comprises three stages. Wet steam enters from the bottom through the standpipe and impinges on turning vanes. The mixture swirls and the centrifugal force separates water (which flows to the edges) from steam (which continues upward). The steam at the exit is dryer than the wet steam from the standpipe. (Courtesy General Electric Co.)

Figure 9.8. BWR steam separator assembly. (Courtesy ASEA-Atom.)

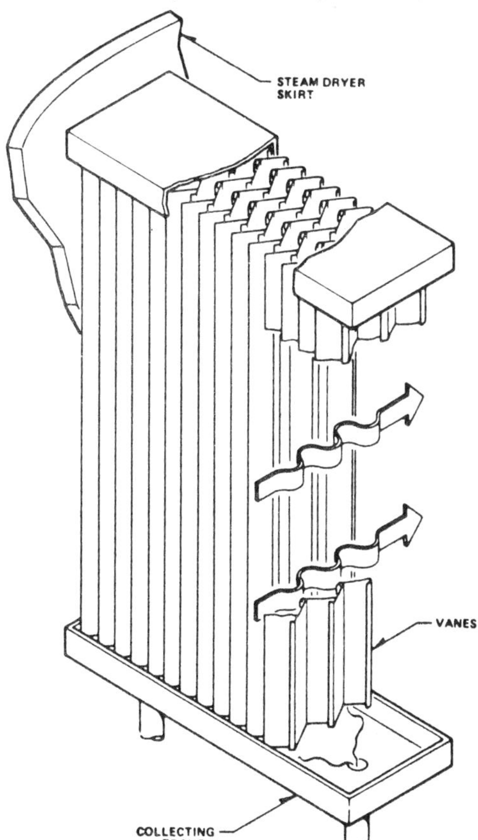

Figure 9.9. A panel of a steam dryer. The device consists of stationary vanes that force the mixture into a sinuous path. Water is collected on the vanes and falls into the collecting trough.

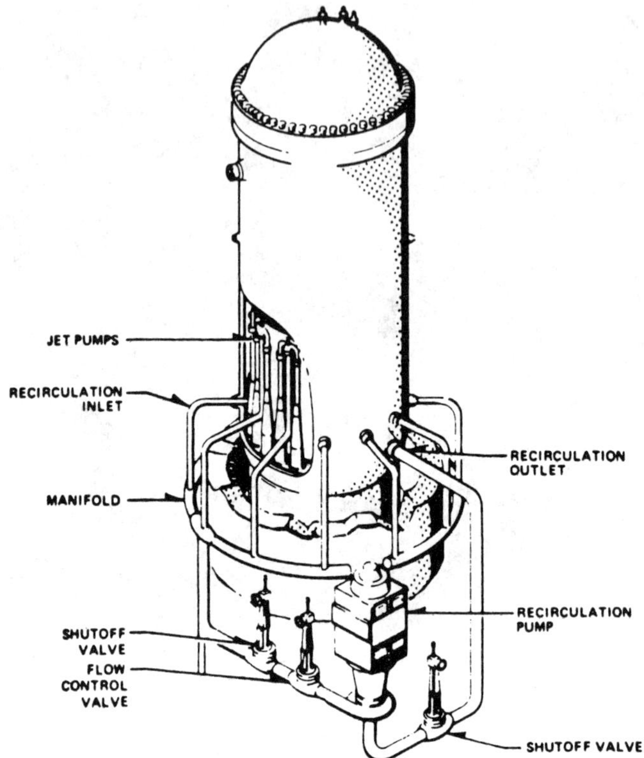

Figure 9.10. Jet pump recirculation system in a BWR. The diagram shows one of the two systems provided. Water is drawn from the vessel through the recirculation outlet. The centrifugal pump discharges into a circular manifold surrounding the vessel. Six inlet nozzles correspond to each pump (for a total of 12) to provide water to the jet pumps inside the vessel to drive the coolant.

9.3. FUEL AND CONTROL RODS

General Fuel Description

The basic fuel component in a LWR is the fuel rod. It is roughly the same in all LWR reactors. A fuel rod consists of a large number of uranium dioxide pellets stacked inside a tube (cladding) made of stainless steel or zirconium alloy as shown in Figure 9.15. The fuel pellets are right cylinders with a diameter of 8–10 mm and length of 10–15 mm, depending on the reactor design. The pellets are sintered (that is, heated to a high temperature), machined to the exact desired dimensions, and inserted in the cladding tube in an atmosphere of helium, under varying pressure. Helium is used because it is chemically inert and because it has good heat transfer properties. After placing an insulator wafer and an expansion spring, the rods are capped with an end cap which is hermetically welded on the tube. The springs holds the fuel pellets together while at the same time allowing them to expand axially due to temperature and irradiation. The space formed at the top of the pellet stack is called the fuel rod plenum. It provides a volume for the collection of gases (mostly krypton and xenon) formed in the fissioning process. The total active length of the fuel pin is about 12 ft (3.65 m) and about 10 mm in diameter.

The pins are then clustered together to form fuel "assemblies" or "bundles." These are held together with top and bottom fittings. Several spacer grids maintain the proper distance among the rods along the length of the assembly. The assemblies for PWRs and BWRs are somewhat different despite the similarity of the fuel rods.

PWR Fuel Bundles

A PWR fuel bundle is shown schematically in Figure 9.16. It is an open bundle design, allowing cross flow, unlike the BWR bundle as we shall see later. In earlier designs, 14 × 14 or 15 × 15 rod

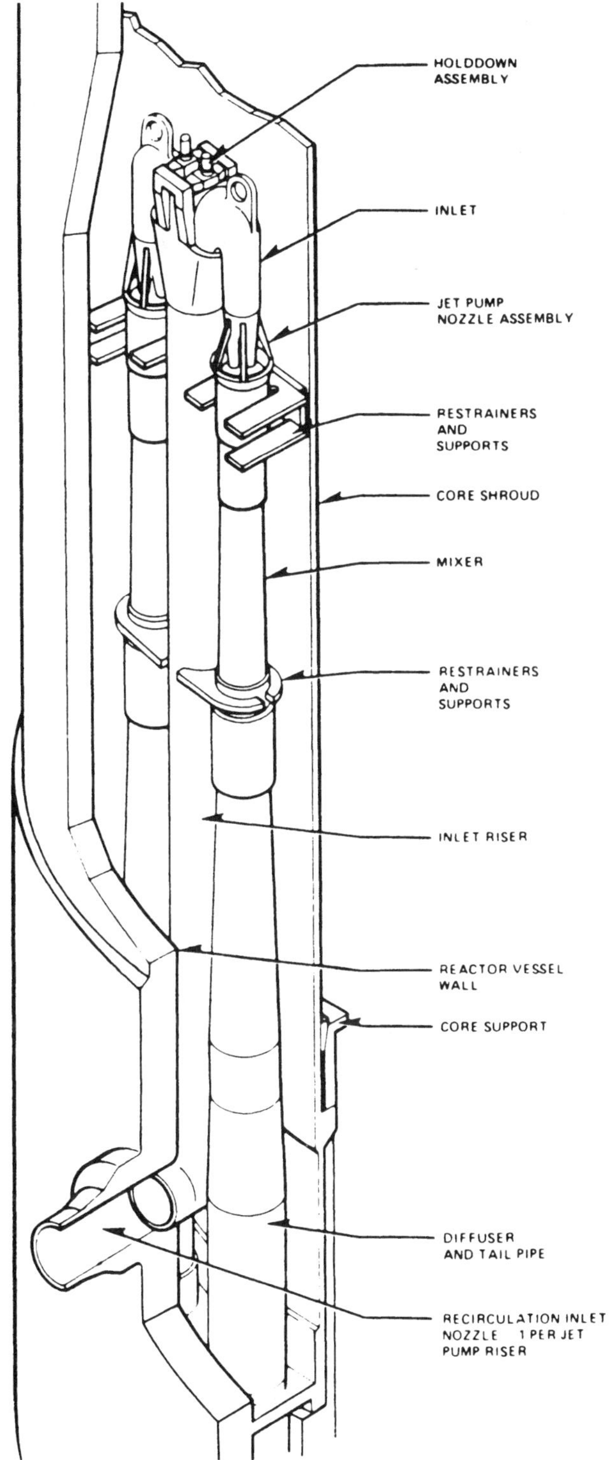

Figure 9.11. Jet pumps are assembled into pairs deriving their driving flow from a common inlet riser. Recirculation water enters through the inlet, moves up through the common riser, is split into two streams, and proceeds downward through the two jet pumps. The suction flow is taken from the fluid in the annular space between shroud and reactor vessel; it enters the jet pump at the jet pump nozzle. (Courtesy General Electric Co.)

Figure 9.12. Assembly of the jet pumps in the reactor pressure vessel of the 940-MWe BWR at Leibstadt. (Courtesy Sulzer Co.)

arrays were used. Beginning in the mid-1970s new designs of fuel assemblies were introduced with thinner and more numerous rods. (It is obvious that it is easier to cool a thinner rod than a thicker one with a given amount of flow.) Two of the PWR vendors have adopted a 17 × 17 rod array design and one has introduced 16 × 16 assemblies. Additional data pertaining to current designs of fuel and plant are given in Table 9.1. In some, but not all the fuel assemblies, positions are provided for the insertion of control rods, as seen in the assembly cross section in Figure 9.16. An actual picture of PWR fuel assemblies stored and ready for shipment is shown in Figure 9.17. The fuel assembly, more than 12 ft (3.65 m) in length and $8\frac{1}{2} \times 8\frac{1}{2}$ in. (21.6 × 21.6 cm) in cross section is the operational fuel unit and represents a very large amount of energy.† A large number of assemblies (200 or more for a large 1000-MWe plant), containing between 40,000 and 50,000 fuel pins, form the core of the reactor. A cross section of such a core is shown in Figure 9.18. The total fuel loading of a 1000 PWR is 100–110 t of uranium dioxide. Core diameter ranges from 2.8 to 3.5 m (9 to 11.5 ft), depending on plant size. The uranium used is LWRs is enriched to between 2 and 4% in ^{235}U. The enrichment varies across the core in order to flatten the power generation which could

†At a burnup of 35 MWd/kg, the amount of energy extracted from a fuel assembly is approximately equivalent to the energy of a quarter million barrels of oil or 51,000 t of coal.

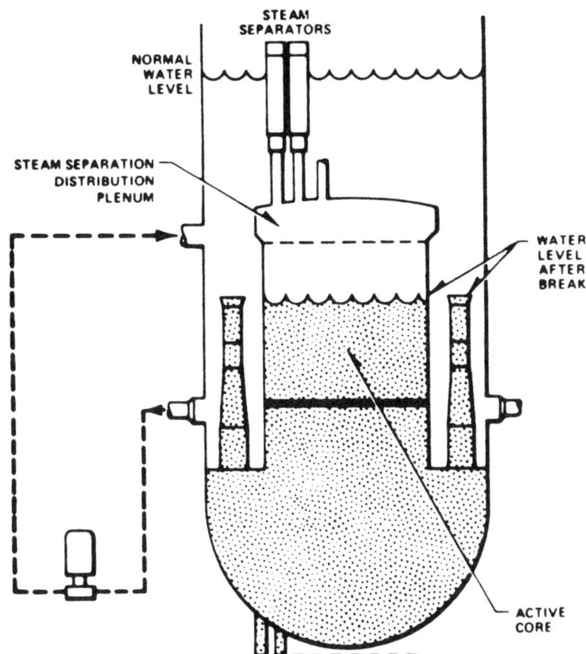

Figure 9.13. BWR schematic showing that the design of the jet pumps and the welding of the diffuser end to the shroud shelf ensures submersion of at least two-thirds of the core through reflooding in the case of a break in the recirculation piping (loss-of-coolant accident). (Courtesy General Electric Co.)

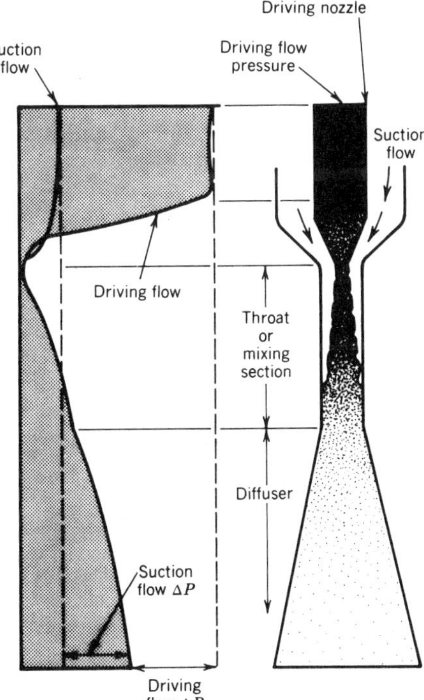

Figure 9.14. Principle of Operation of Jet Pump. The flow in the driving channel converts high pressure into high velocity as the fluid goes through the nozzle. The high-velocity stream entrains the fluid in the surrounding annulus and gives it a downward velocity. As the two fluids mix and proceed to the diffuser, the velocity is converted back into pressure. Thus the suction flow has gained pressure, shown in the diagram as "Suction flow Δp."

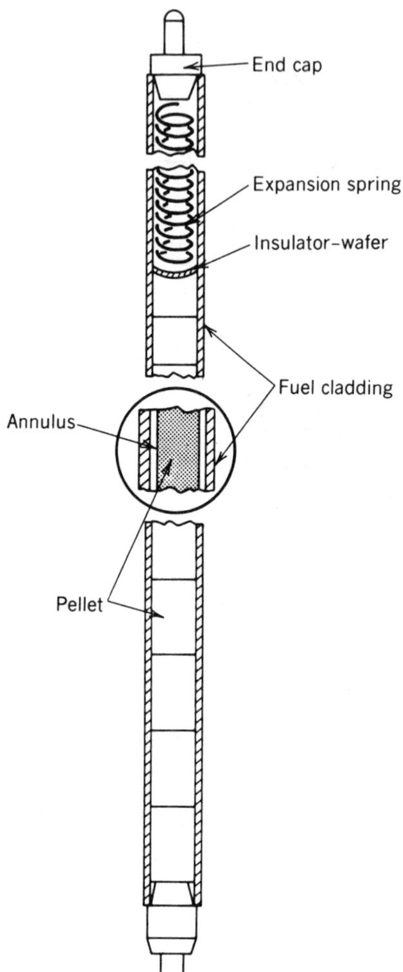

Figure 9.15. Cutaway of oxide fuel for commercial LWR power plant.

otherwise tend to be maximum in the center of the core, and falling off somewhat toward the edges. For this reason it would be desirable to have the highest enrichment (a little over 3% in the periphery and the lowest toward the center region).† This provides a fairly uniform distribution of power density with an average value of about 100 kW of thermal power per liter of core. As the burning of the fuel proceeds, some new fuel is generated through conversion of the fertile isotope ^{238}U into the fissile ^{239}Pu. Some of this plutonium is burned in the core before the removal of the bundle but most of it remains unburned in the fuel when it is removed from the core.

PWR Control Rods and Drives

A number of assemblies in a core contain control rods. In these "rodded" assemblies, open spaces marked by an ⊗ in Figure 9.18 are provided for the insertion of the control rods. Depending on the design, 16 to 25 such positions are used. The center position is reserved for an instrumentation thimble. A 16 control rod assembly is shown in Figure 9.19. An isometric view of the fuel bundle and control rod assembly of another manufacturer is shown in Figure 9.20. Each control rod contains a neutron-absorbing material [boron carbide or an alloy of silver (80%)–indium (15%)–cadmium (5%)] clad in cold-worked stainless steel (type 304) tubing, with stainless steel end pieces

†As will be seen in Chapter 11, the fuel-loading pattern can be quite complicated. For other reasons, the highest enrichment may not necessarily be found in the periphery.

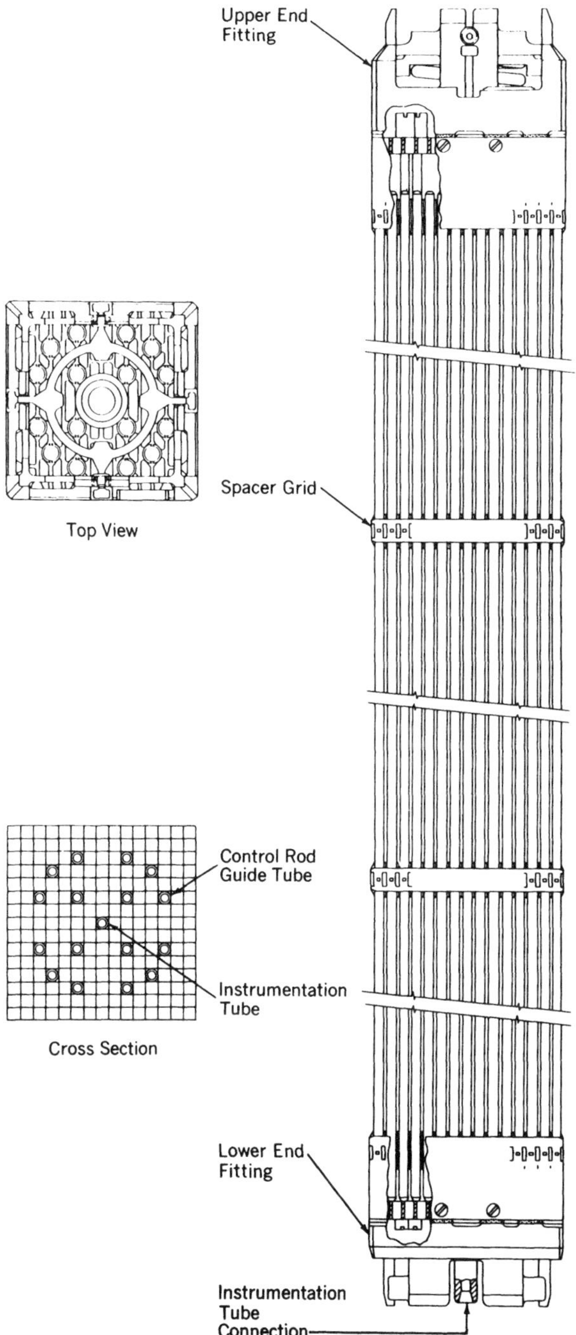

Figure 9.16. A typical fuel assembly of one vendor is shown in side and top view. It is made of a 15 × 15 rod array held together with upper and lower tie plates and seven spacer grids evenly spaced along its length. This assembly (but not all the assemblies in the core) has open channels for the insertion of control rods from the top, and for the insertion of an instrument thimble from the bottom. (Courtesy Babcock & Wilcox Co.)

Table 9.1. Typical Characteristics of a Current PWR Design

	Plant
Thermal power	3425 MWt
Electric output (gross/net)	1150/1100 MWe
Efficiency	33%
	Core
Active core (or fuel rod) height	3.7 m (144.0 in.)
Core diameter (equivalent)	3.4 m (132.7 in.)
Fuel inventory	101-t UO_2 (222,740 lb)
Number of fuel assemblies	193
Assembly pitch	30.4 cm (12 in.)
Rod pitch	1.26 cm (0.496 in.)
Average core power density	104.5 kW/liter
	Fuel
Fuel material	UO_2
Enrichment	Three regions with 2.1, 2.6, 3.1%
Pellet dimensions (diameter and length)	0.82 × 1.35 cm (0.3225 × 0.530 in.)
Assembly array	17 × 17 (open type)
Total number of fuel rods	50,952
Cladding material	Zircaloy-4
Cladding outer diameter	0.95 cm (0.374 in.)
Cladding thickness	0.6 mm (0.0225 in.)
	Control
Number of control clusters	53
Number of control rods per cluster	20
Absorber material	Ag—In—Cd
Absorber rod cladding	304 stainless steel
Control rod type	Cylindrical rods assembled into clusters inserted from above
Other control systems (first core)	Burnable poison rods, borosilicate glass
	Vessel
Material	SA533, Mg–Mo–Ni steel with inner cladding
Wall thickness	21.9 cm (8.6 in.)
Vessel dimensions (diameter and height)	4.4 × 12.6m (14.4 × 41.3 ft)
	Coolant
Material	Ordinary water (H_2O)–liquid phase
System pressure	15.5 MPa (2250 psia)
Number of loops/steam generators	4
Mass flow	15.9 Mg/sec (126 × 10^6 lb/hr)
Core inlet temperature	298°C (568°F)
Core outlet temperature	326°C (618°F)
	Fueling
Type	Off-load, radial shuffling
Refueling sequence	⅓ of core every 12 months
Shutdown period	30 days
Annual spent fuel discharge	30.4 t
Design fuel burnup	33000 MWd/t

Sources: Westinghouse Electric Corp. See also *Nuclear Engineering International,* August Supplement, 1983.

Figure 9.17. Nuclear fuel assemblies for a PWR. (Courtesy Babcock & Wilcox Co.)

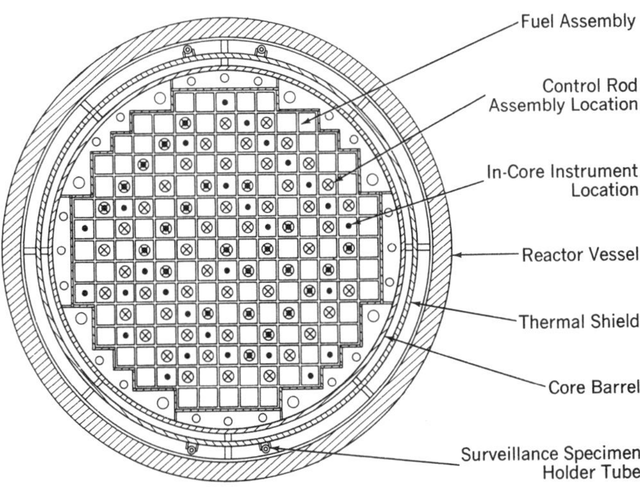

Figure 9.18. Cross section of reactor vessel and internals.

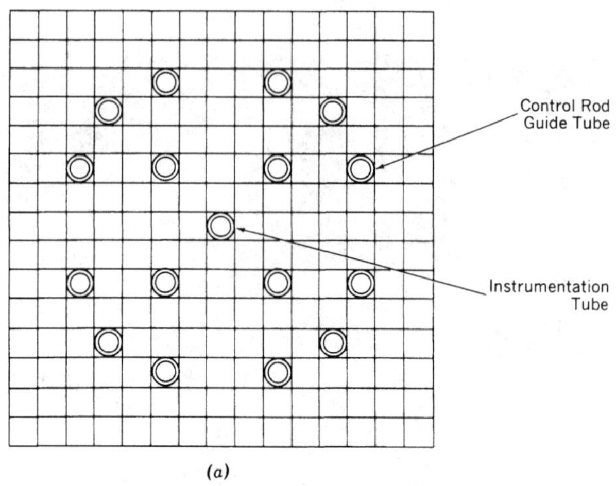

(a)

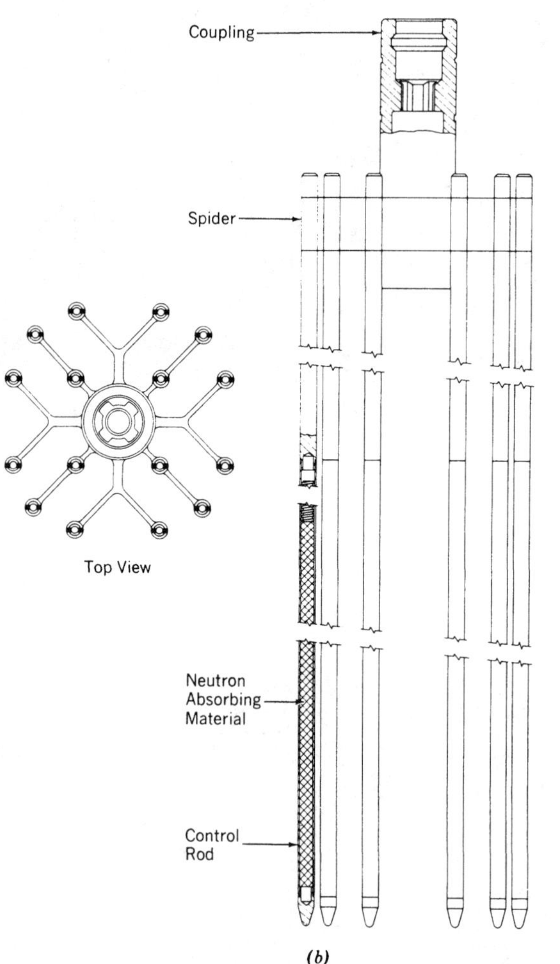

(b)

Figure 9.19. (*a*) Diagrammatic cross section of fuel assembly showing instrumentation-tube and control-rod-guide-tube locations. (*b*) The control rod assembly of this design consists of 16 rods each containing a silver–indium–cadmium alloy as absorbing material encased in a stainless steel tube. The rods are held together through a spiderlike piece at the top which also carries a coupling for connecting to the control rod drives. (Courtesy Babcock & Wilcox Co.)

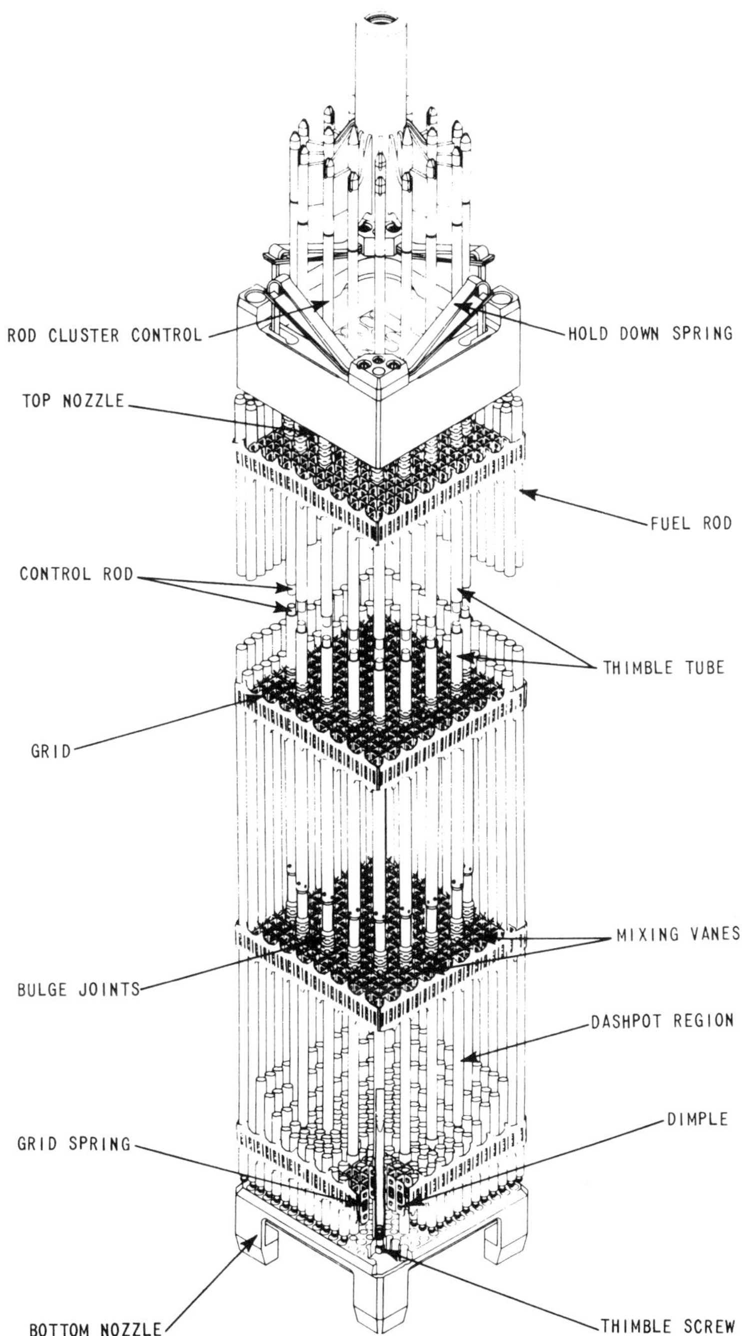

Figure 9.20. A fuel assembly, with a 17 × 17 rod array used in some recent PWR plants. The control rod cluster is inserted in corresponding thimbles which are an integral part of the assembly. The spiderlike holding piece is visible at the top. (Courtesy Westinghouse Electric Corp.)

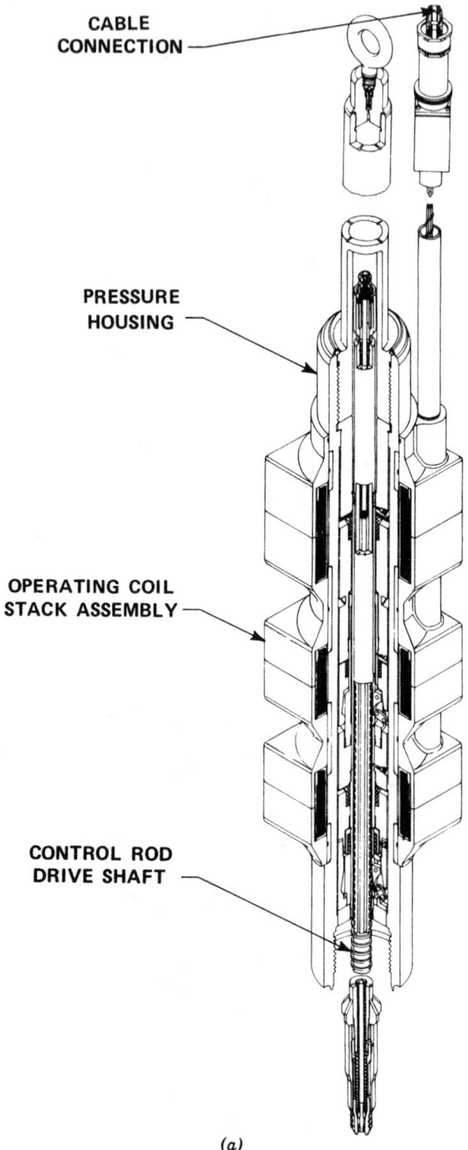

Figure 9.21. (*a*) Full-length control rod drive mechanism (isometric view). (Courtesy Westinghouse Electric Corp.)

welded to the upper and lower ends. The rods are attached, at the top, to a metal piece with spiderlike arms, which is, in turn, connected to control rod drives that penetrate the vessel head. A "loose" connection to the spider allows better conformity of the rods to the guide tubes provided in the channels. Guide tubes are also placed above the core, in the upper plenum. so that the control rods have full-length guidance throughout their stroke.

Most of the control rods are used to regulate the reactor power level or bring the reactor to a quick shutdown (scram). They are called "shim" safety control rods. A small fraction (8 out of 69 shown in Figure 9.18) contain poison only at the lower one-fourth of their length and are used to improve (that is, to even out) the axial profile of the power distribution. In addition to the control rods, a boron solution in the coolant assists in controlling reactivity. It is called "chemical shim" and will be further described in Chapter 12.

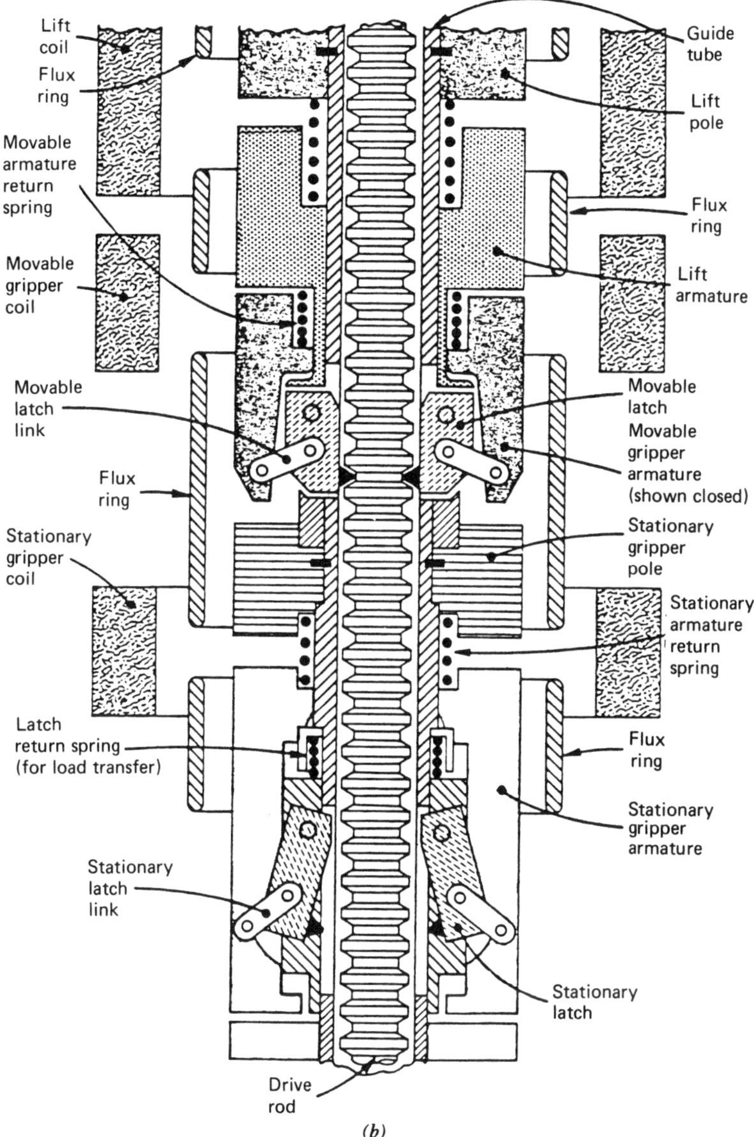

Figure 9.21. (*b*) Schematic section showing the operation of latches and their coupling with the drive rod. (Courtesy Westinghouse Electric Corp.)

About 30% of the assemblies in the core do contain control rods. In the rest of the assemblies the corresponding channels are filled with one of the following: (1) burnable poison rods which are used to compensate for initial excess reactivity; (2) neutron sources necessary for start-up; (3) dummy, orificed rods, through which no coolant flow takes place that equilizes coolant flow between the assemblies.

To move the control rods in and out of the core, specially designed control rod drives are provided. They are attached to the top of the control rod cluster and extend upward above the reactor head through guide tubes. A schematic of one design of control rod drive is shown in Figure 9.21. Other designs may differ but their general features and function are the same. In PWRs control rods are withdrawn from the core upward and drop into the core downward. A magnetic device keeps the drive mechanism engaged to the control rod. When current is cut off from the magnet, the device is de-energized and the control rods drop into the core by the force of gravity. This quick shutdown of the reactor is called scram. Rods can be positionable either in a continuous fashion or by discrete steps. The control rod drives have indicators to inform the operator of the exact position of each control rod. Each reactor has a large number of such control drive mechanisms, 40 to 70, depending on plant size and vendor.

BWR Fuel Bundles

Although the fuel rods used in both PWRs and BWRs are quite similar, the fuel assemblies are somewhat different. In the United States, the fuel assembly and control rod design has changed little since the first commercial unit, Dresden 1, was built. A BWR fuel assembly shown in Figure 9.22 is composed of fuel rods somewhat thicker than those in PWRs, with an outer diameter of 12.3 mm (0.483 in.), a length of 4.07 m ($160\frac{1}{4}$ in.), and cladding thickness of 0.81 mm (0.032 in.). Of the total rod length 3.8 m (150 in.) is active fuel and 241 mm (9.5 in.) at the top of the rod forms the rod plenum for the collection of fission gases. A diametral gap of 0.23 mm (0.009 in.) exists between pellets and Zircaloy cladding to accommodate different degrees of expansion of these two components. The fuel is uranium oxide (UO_2) of varying enrichment, averaging about 2.8% and the cladding is Zircaloy-2.

Early fuel assemblies contained a square 7 × 7 rod array but the current BWR/6 design by General Electric Co. is made of an 8 × 8 rod array, supported by lower and upper tie plates and spaced by seven fuel rod spacers. The latter are equipped with metal springs to prevent the bowing of individual rods and to keep the coolant channels open at all times. The lower tie plate is shaped as a nosepiece through which the assembly rests on the core support plate and through which coolant enters in the assembly. The upper tie plate has a handle for the transfer of fuel bundles. Both tie plates are of stainless steel.

Unlike PWR fuel assemblies, which are open at the sides, BWR assemblies are enclosed in a metal sheath, called the fuel channel. It serves two purposes: to contain the coolant flow in the assembly, and to provide a guide for the control blade assemblies. For the BWR/6 design the channel is made of Zircaloy-4 with approximate dimensions of 14 × 14 cm (5.5 × 5.5 in.) and 4.2 m (167 in.) in length. The channels are reusable after the discharge of spent fuel by inserting fresh uncanned rod assemblies at the reactor site (see also Chapter 8). The channel provides operational flexibility by the following two features. First, the orifice of each channel, that is, the size of the entrance to the channel, can be individually adjusted. Thus the flow of coolant to each channel and the design of reload fuel can be changed as desired to meet changing requirements and technology. Second, a sampling of each bundle is made possible for the detection of possible leaking fuel rods.

Four bundles are clustered together into a module with a cruciform control blade between them as shown in Figures 9.23 and 9.24. Mechanically and structurally, the fuel assemblies are designed to minimize any external forces acting on the rods. For example, an expansion spring (made of Inconel-X†) is located over the pin of the top end plug of each fuel rod (see Figure 9.22). This spring keeps the fuel pin securely seated in the lower tie plate while allowing it to expand axially through the holes of the upper tie plate. This frees the rod of any stresses from differential thermal expansion. The design also allows the removal and replacement of individual fuel rods in the assembly without complete dismantling.

Each assembly contains three types of rods (see Figure 9.23). In addition to normal fuel rods there are eight tie rods in each assembly, two on each side. These fuel rods differ from the rest in that they are attached to the upper and lower tie plates to hold the assembly together during fuel-handling operation when the assembly hangs by the handle. Each assembly also contains two water rods at its center. These are made of Zircaloy-2 tubes and are filled with water rather than fuel. The water, which is allowed to circulate in the rods through small holes located at the lower and upper ends, is needed to provide extra moderating material in the center of the assembly. Thus, the inner fuel rods are equalized, in terms of moderator material, with the outer rods of the assembly which are close to the extra water in the interchannel spaces.

The enrichment in a BWR core is variable not only from region to region but also from the first core to subsequent reloads. The purpose of changing the enrichment from one location to another is to even out, as much as possible, the power generation density, in other words, to reduce the local power peaks. The power peaks lead to restrictions in the operation of the plant. Lower enrichment fuel is used in corner rods and in rods nearer water gaps; the enrichment is higher in the center of the assembly. In addition, small amounts of gadolinium, a neutron poison, are blended with the uranium fuel in selected rods. These gadolinium rods provide a burnable poison in the core and help the long-term control reactivity, much like the boron soluble poison performs the same function in PWRs (Section 8.2, subsection "The Chemistry and Volume Control System").

A typical large BWR of 1220 MWe (like the BWR/6 design of General Electric Co.) incorporates 748 fuel assemblies and 177 control rod assemblies forming a core in the shape of a right cylinder

†Inconel-X is an Ni, Fe, Cr alloy.

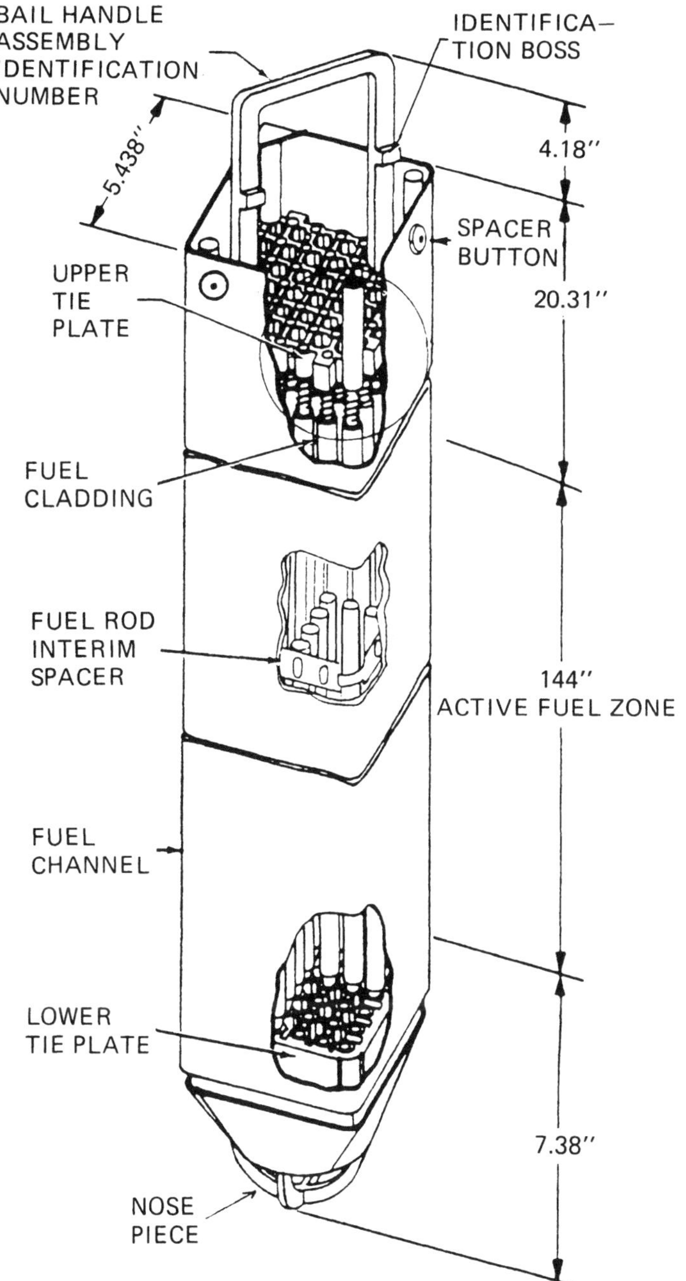

Figure 9.22. BWR fuel assembly. (Courtesy General Electric Co.)

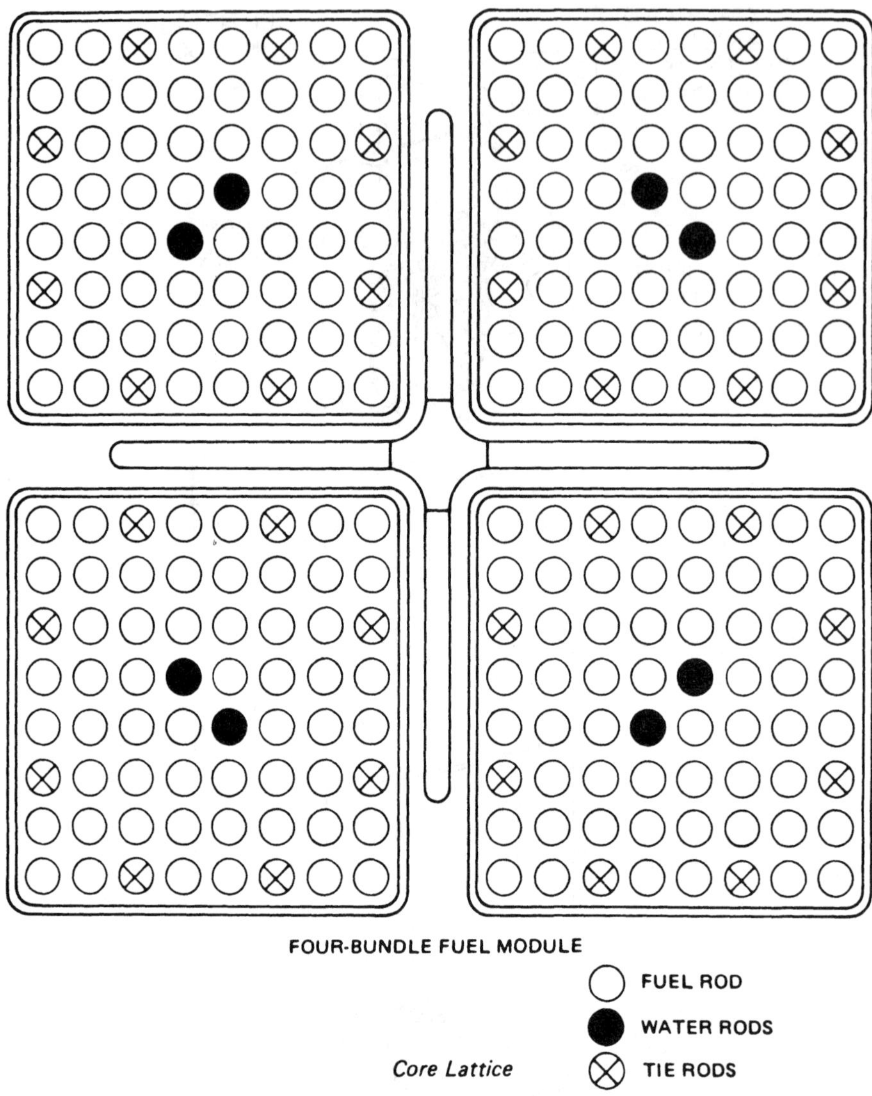

Figure 9.23. BWR bundle arrangement. Four fuel bundles, each with an 8 × 8 array, form a basic module with a cruciform control blade at the center. The figure also shows the channels (or can) surrounding each assembly, and the tie and water rods which are used to flatten the neutron flux, and, hence, to even out the power distribution across the module.

Figure 9.24. A BWR/6 fuel cluster containing four fuel assemblies and a cruciform control rod. (Courtesy General Electric Co.) 1—top fuel guide; 2—channel fastener; 3—upper tie plate; 4—expansion spring; 5—locking tab; 6—channel; 7—control rod; 8—fuel rod; 9—spacer; 10—core plate assembly; 11—lower tie plate; 12—fuel support piece; 13—fuel pellets; 14—end plug; 15—channel spacer; 16—plenum spring.

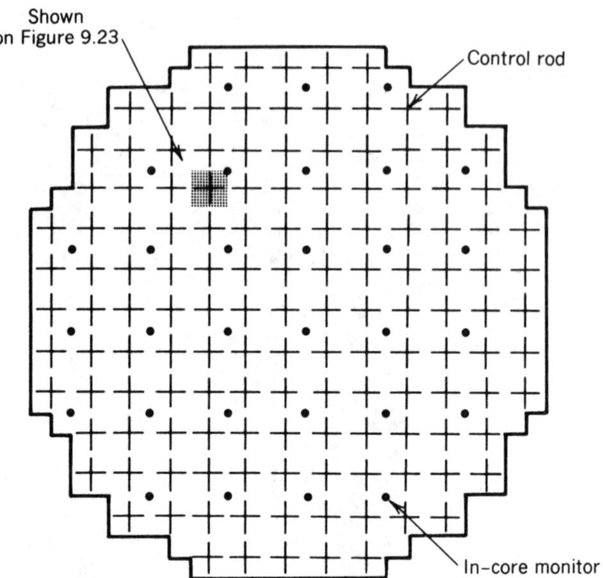

Figure 9.25. Typical core arrangement for a large BWR. Such a core contains 748 fuel assemblies, 177 control rods in the core measuring 4.9 m (16 ft) in diameter, and 4.3 m (14 ft) in height. Total number of fuel rods is 46,376 and the fuel weighs about 155 t (347,000 lb).

about 4.9 m (16 ft) in diameter and 4.3 m (14 ft) high. A schematic cross section of the core is shown in Figure 9.25. Such a large core weighing more than 200 t may contain over 750 assemblies containing 40,000 to 50,000 individual rods. The uranium oxide necessary to fuel the core could be more than 150 t (330,000 lb). More technical data, descriptive of a large BWR core of 1220-MWe size, are given in Table 9.2.

BWR Control Blades and Drives

Cruciform control blades are inserted through the bottom of the reactor vessel to provide both reactivity control and power shaping. Boron carbide (B_4C, a neutron absorber), in powder form is compacted into stainless steel tubes (72 tubes in the current design, 4.8 mm or $\frac{3}{16}$ in. in diameter), which are then arranged in a stainless steel sheath as shown in Figure 9.26. The individual stainless steel tubes retain the helium gas released by the neutron bombardment of boron. The top casting and handle provide structural rigidity at the top of the control blade. A bottom casting also provides rigidity; it contains positioning rollers and a shaped cup to limit the blade's velocity in the case of a rod drop accident.† A BWR has one control blade for every four fuel assemblies. Figure 9.27 shows newly assembled blades being inspected and readied for shipment to the plant site. The blades have an active length of 3.7 m (144 in.) of absorber material, a span of 0.25 m (9.75 in.), and an overall length of 4.4 m (about 174 in.).

Cooling of the blades is necessary to remove gamma-ray heating energy and nuclear energy from the boron-10 reaction. This is provided by a slow flow of coolant between the channel walls and the control blades, called bypass flow, which results from recirculation flow through a number of leakage paths. Holes provided in the blades facilitate the flow of coolant and heat removal from the blades.

As mentioned above, control rods in BWRs are used for power shaping (in addition to overall reactivity control). This is particularly important in BWRs because of the process of boiling inside the core. As bubbles form toward the upper part of the core, the amount of moderating material (water) there is reduced and power density tends to fall. Selected patterns of rods are inserted from the bottom to counterbalance (even out) the effect of bubbles forming at the top. These groups of control rods are more often used and, therefore, experience a higher exposure to neutron bombardment than the rest of the rods. For longer term reactivity control, the burnable poison gadolinium mixed with fuel is used as mentioned in the previous section. This poison is burned gradually to

†See Chapter 18.

Table 9.2. Typical Characteristics of Current BWR Designs

Plant	
Core thermal power	3579 MWt
Electric output (gross/net)	1269/1233 MWe
Plant efficiency	33.5%
Core	
Active core height	3.76 m (148 in.)
Core diameter	4.65 m (183 in.)
Fuel inventory	138-t UO_2
Number of fuel assemblies	748
Assembly pitch	15.2 cm (6 in.)
Rod pitch	1.63 cm (0.64 in.)
Average power density	56 kW/liter
Fuel	
Fuel material	UO_2
Enrichment	Average 2.8 ^{235}U (initial core 1.77–2.1%)
Pellet dimensions (diameter × height)	1.06 × 1.0 cm (0.416 × 0.420 in.)
Assembly array	8 × 8 with fuel channel around fuel rods
Total number of fuel rods	46,376
Cladding material	Zircaloy-2
Cladding outer diameter	1.25 cm (0.493 in.)
Cladding thickness	0.86 mm (0.034 in.)
Control	
Number of control rods	177
Material	Boron carbide (B_4C)
Control rod type	"Cruciform" blades inserted hydraulically from below between sets of four assemblies
Other control systems	Use of burnable poison
Vessel	
Material	SA533 (or 533B) manganese molybdenum nickel steel with a inner layer of cladding $\frac{1}{8}$ in. of austenitic stainless steel
Wall thickness	16.4 cm (6.45 in.)
Vessel height	21.6 m (70.75 ft)
Vessel inner diameter	6 m (19.7 ft)
Vessel weight (including head)	885 t (1,950,000 lb) approximately
Coolant	
Material	Ordinary water (H_2O)–two phase
Pressure	7 MPa (1040 psi)
Number of recirculation loops	2
Core coolant flow	13.2 Mg/hr (105 × 10^6 lb/hr)
Core coolant outlet temperature	288°C (550°F)
Core coolant inlet temperature	277°C (532°F)
Feedwater flow rate	1.94 Mg/sec (15.358 × 10^6 lb/hr)
Feedwater temperature	216°C (420°F)
Average coolant exit quality	14.7% steam by weight
Fueling	
Type	off-load, radial shuffling
Refueling sequence	$\frac{1}{3}$ of core every 18 months or $\frac{1}{4}$ of core every 12 months
Shutdown for refueling	60 days
Annual spent fuel discharge	32 t/yr
Design fuel burnup	28,400 MWd/t at equilibrium

Source: General Electric Co. See also *Nuclear Engineering International,* August Supplement, 1983.

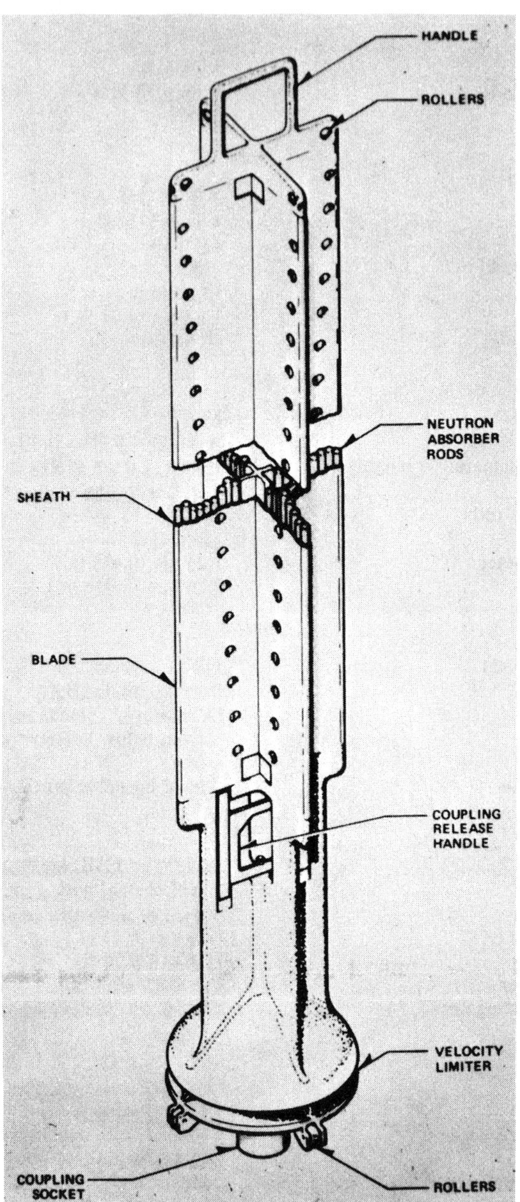

Figure 9.26. A BWR control rod is a cruciform blade. It contains a number of absorber rods made of compacted boron carbide in stainless steel tubes. The tubes are arranged in a stainless steel sheath. (Courtesy General Electric Co.)

Figure 9.27. BWR control blades being inspected and readied for shipment. (Courtesy General Electric Co.)

match the burning of fuel in the core and is almost completely depleted by the end of the fuel cycle. A third method of reactivity control is provided by varying the amount of recirculating water as explained in Chapters 8 and 12. This gives a BWR an ability to change power level without the need for changing control rod positions.

Drive mechanisms are used through coupling sockets to move the control blades. A detailed description of this system was given in Section 8.3, subsection "Control Rod Drive System."

9.4. PRIMARY COOLANT PUMPS

In a PWR these components circulate water through the primary coolant system in order to transport energy from the core to the steam generator. They develop the necessary pressure head to overcome the friction losses that the fluid suffers in flowing through the core, plena, piping, and steam generator tubes. Since the coolant temperature increase in the reactor core is only a modest 28–33°C (50–60°F), a large volume of water must be circulated to remove the heat generated in the core. Indeed, in a 1200-MWe plant the enormous amount of about 17.5 m^3 of coolant per second (corresponding to 140 million lb of water per hour) must be handled by the pumps.

Each of the primary pumps in a PWR is about 10 m (30 ft) high, requires an electric motor of 10,000 horsepower, and has a rated pumping capacity of almost 96,000 gal/min (6 m^3/sec). A cutaway view of a primary coolant pump is shown in Figure 9.28 and a list of characteristic data is given in Table 9.3. The inlet is from the bottom and discharge is on the side. In order to extend the flow of coolant through the core, in the event of a station blackout, a flywheel is provided on the shaft above the motor. The stored energy in the flywheel extends the period of coastdown.

As components of the primary system operating under high temperature and pressure and having the all-important function to provide circulating water to cool the core, primary pumps must be designed and manufactured under the stringent criteria that apply to all primary system components. They are classified Safety Class 1 and the provisions of Section III of the ASME code apply. Since the water circulated by the pumps is somewhat radioactive, their shaft must be equipped with properly designed seals to prevent the leakage of this radioactive coolant. To accomplish this, water from a separate, clean source is injected into the seal at a pressure somewhat higher than the primary pressure. The injected water leaks partly inward into the primary system and partly outward. This small outward leakage is easily collected and handled by the plant's intermediate cooling system described in Section 8.2, subsection "The Intermediate Cooling System." All plants use more than one primary loop and pump. Thus the number of pumps is redundant although not in capacity.† Each of the pumps, however, has more than enough capacity to provide adequate cooling of the core after reactor shutdown. An air-cooled, three-phase ac induction motor is mounted vertically on top of the pump as shown in Figure 9.28.

BWRs also use large pumps, external to the reactor vessel,‡ in their two recirculation loops. They are of the vertical, centrifugal type and are made of stainless steel. Multiple mechanical seals provide a pressure barrier to prevent leakage. In addition, a throttle bushing, located in the pump casing, would limit the leakage if all the seals on the shaft failed. As are PWR pumps, these pumps and their seals are cooled by cooling water from a closed circuit. A high-temperature signal in the pump cavity or cooling water alerts the operator in the control room for appropriate action.

A vertical, water-cooled, totally enclosed electric motor is used to drive each recirculation pump. This component is a three-phase, squirrel-cage induction-type motor designed to operate at constant speed from the auxiliary power system.

9.5. PRESSURIZER

The pressurizer is a large, vertical, cylindrical vessel, connected at its bottom to one of the hot legs of the primary coolant loop. There is only one pressurizer in each PWR plant regardless of the number of loops as was shown in Chapter 8, Figures 8.3 and 8.4. One pressurizer design is shown in Figure 9.29. A slightly different design is shown in Figure 9.30. The pressurizer is made of carbon or low-alloy steel shell, clad internally with a layer of stainless steel. The thickness of the steel ranges between 6 and 7 in. Other parameters are shown in Table 9.4. Section III of the ASME code applies to the design and manufacture of pressurizers.

A pressurizer is nominally filled to half its height with coolant; steam fills the other half. A spray nozzle is provided at the top and electric heater bundles are installed at the bottom of the vessel. Additional nozzles are also provided for connections to multiple relief and safety valves and to level indicators.

The purpose of the pressurizer is (a) to maintain primary systems pressure within prescribed bounds during normal operation; (b) to accommodate changes in the coolant volume due to thermal

†Rated pump capacity is usually about 30% more than full power operating requirements.
‡Except in some of the ASEA-ATOM designs.

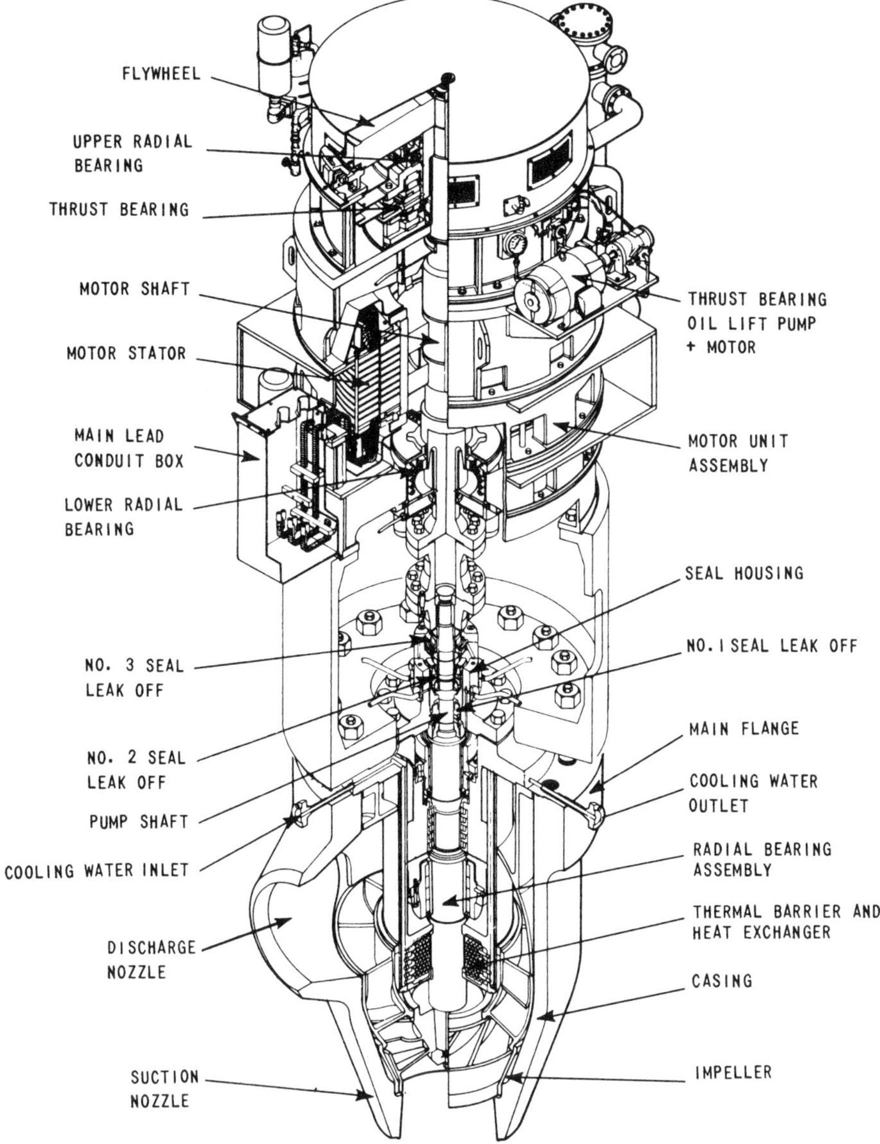

Figure 9.28. Primary system coolant pump. (Courtesy Westinghouse Electric Corp.)

Table 9.3. Characteristics of Primary Coolant Pumps for a 1200-MW Plant

Number of pumps	4	
Type	Vertical, single-stage	
Design pressure	2500 psi	(17 MPa)
Design temperature	670°F	(355°C)
Operating pressure (nominal)	2235 psi	(15.2 MPa)
Suction temperature	572°F	(300°C)
Design capacity	95,650 gal/min	(6 m^3/sec)
Total developed head	304 ft	(92.7 m)
Hydrostatic test pressure (cold)	3340 psi	(22.7 MPa)
Motor type (single-speed)	Squirrel-cage induction	
Motor rating (nameplate)	10,000 horsepower	

Source: Babcock & Wilcox, *Steam, Its Generation and Use,* 1978.

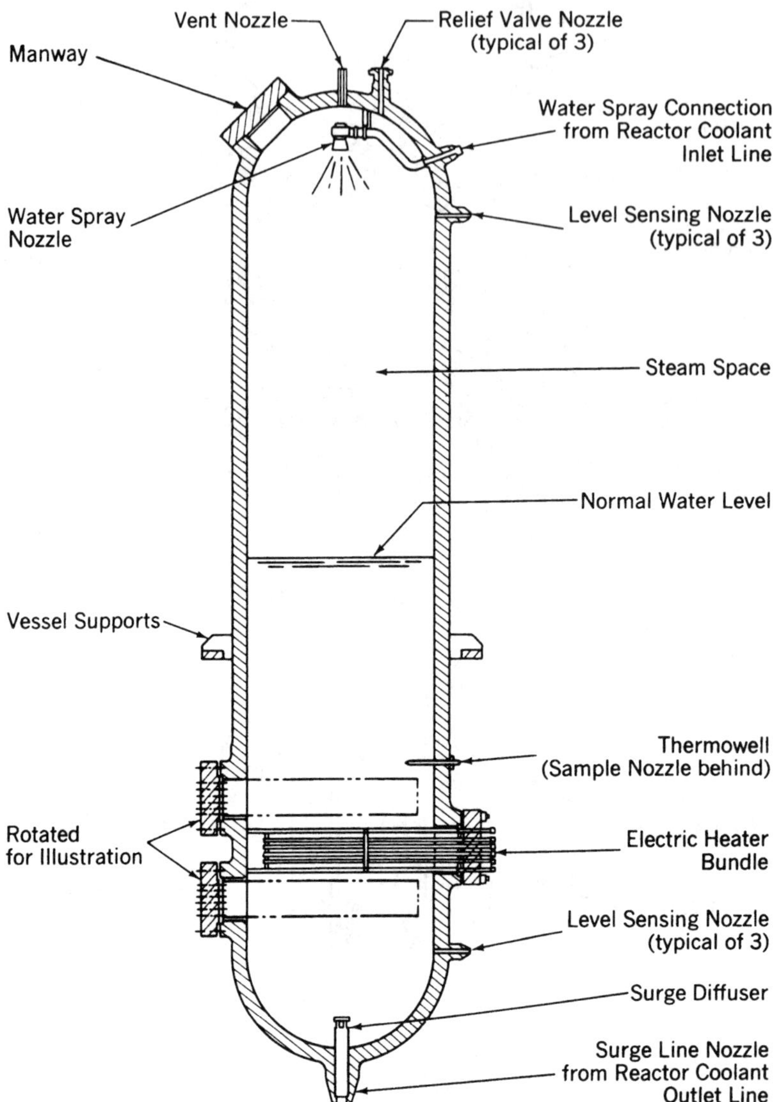

Figure 9.29. Schematic of a PWR pressurizer. The component is normally half-filled with water; the other half is occupied by steam. Spray nozzles at the top condense some of the steam and bring the pressure down when it happens to go on an upswing. Electric heaters at the bottom generate more steam if the pressure tends to go down. Thus a fairly constant pressure is maintained. Safety and relief valves are also mounted at the top of the pressurizer. (Courtesy Westinghouse Electric Corp.)

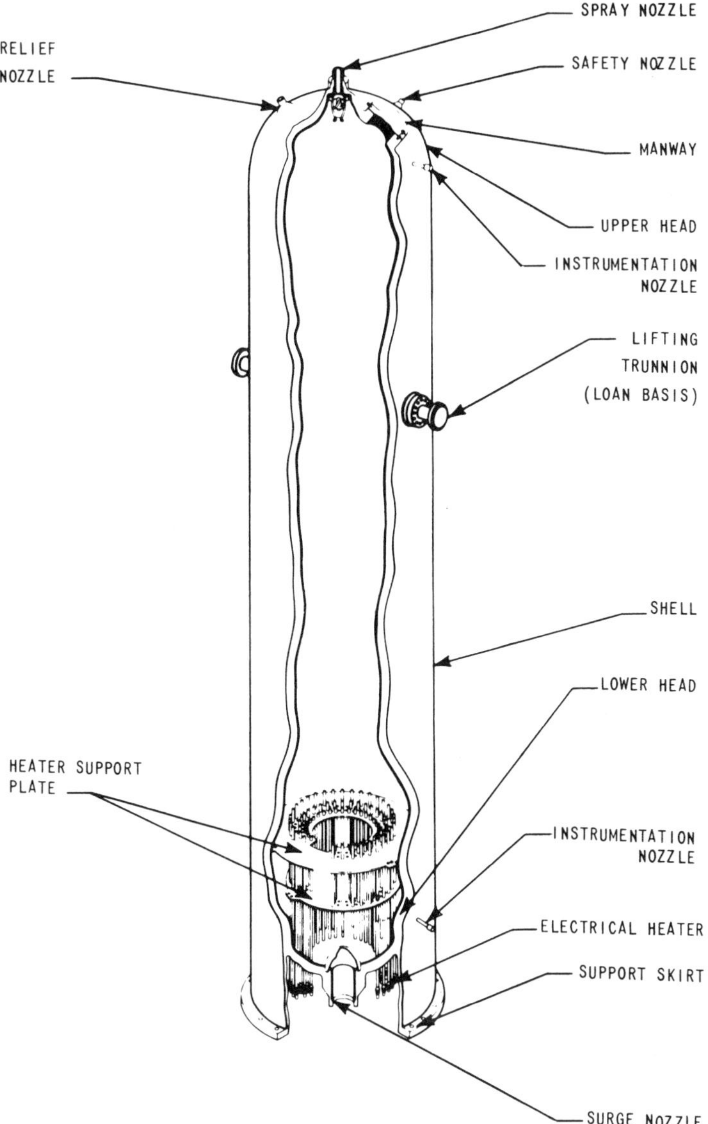

Figure 9.30. Cutaway view of pressurizer used on Westinghouse plants. In this design, the heater bundle consists of vertical rather than horizontal heating elements. (Courtesy Westinghouse Electric Corp.)

Table 9.4. Characteristic Features of Pressurizers

	860 MWe	1200 MWe
Material, shell and heads	Carbon steel Stainless steel cladding	Low-alloy steel Stainless steel cladding
Design pressure	2500 psi (17 MPa)	2500 psi (17 MPa)
Design temperature	670°F (354°C)	670°F (354°C)
Steam volume	800 ft^3 (22.6 m^3)	1200 ft^3 (34 m^3)
Electric heater capacity	1638 kW	1745 kW
Shell minimum thickness	$8\frac{3}{16}$ in. (28.0 cm)	$5\frac{15}{16}$ in. (15.1 cm)
Shell outside diameter	$96\frac{3}{8}$ in. (2.45 m)	$119\frac{7}{8}$ in. (3.04 m)
Overall height	45 ft (13.7 m)	$41\frac{1}{2}$ ft (12.65 m)

expansion during start-up, shutdown, and power level changes; and (c) to prevent the pressure of the primary coolant from exceeding prespecified limits of safety by means of the safety/relief valves. This is how the pressurizer works. When there is a decrease in the load, the temperature and pressure in the primary system move upward. An electric signal turns on the spray system at the top of the pressurizer, introducing cooler water into the vessel. This condenses some of the steam in the upper part of the vessel and keeps the pressure from rising further, without operating the pressure relief valves. Conversely, when a drop in pressure occurs, as for example, from an increase in steam flow in the turbine, the electric heaters immersed in water (ranging in capacity up to 1000-kWe) are turned on and additional steam is generated, which keeps the pressure from falling below the minimum allowable limit. The liquid level indicator is an important instrument that is meant to assist the plant operator in appropriate action. Pressurizer level figured prominently in the sequence of events at the TMI accident in March of 1979.†

9.6. SAFETY AND RELIEF VALVES—PIPING

Valves are, in general, mechanical devices that control the flow of fluid. They can be entirely passive devices; opening when pressure builds up to a point when the force of a spring is overcome, and closing when pressure drops to a lower pressure. Or they can be remotely operated, that is, the operator or process control system can send a command signal which opens or closes the valve. The same signal (usually electric) could be sent automatically when a certain set point is reached. The movement of a valve is provided either by an electric motor or by a piping system with hydraulic pressure.

Safety and Relief Valves (S/RV) are two of the more important valves in a LWR. In a PWR multiple S/RVs (number and type varying) are connected at the top of the pressurizer. Relief valves, of which there exist several designs, are also called Power Operated Relief Valves (PORVs). Figure 9.31 shows the assembly of a PORV. It consists of the main valve at the bottom of the figure and a pilot valve mounted on top of it. The main ports of a valve are its body, the disc, nozzle seat, and spring as shown.

For the case where the relief valves fail to keep the pressure from going up, safety valves are provided. The relief valves are operated much more frequently than safety valves. In fact, relief

†Some time after the accident and after the injection of safety water had been initiated, a rising water level in the pressurizer was observed. This led the operator to believe that there was excess water in the system, and he felt safe in turning off the high-pressure safety injection. Unfortunately, because of a U-shaped bend in the pipe connecting the pressurizer to the hot leg, water was trapped in the pressurizer and its level was no longer indicative of the water level in the core. Thus the gradual uncovering of the core was not detected in time to prevent the damaging of the fuel. This occurrence led to a number of revisions and modifications in nuclear plants of the TMI-type but also to a different extent to other types of plants. First, the operating procedures and instructions to the operator changed to save him from being misled by the pressurizer level indicators. Second, instrumentation is being installed to show the operator that the coolant in the primary loop is well subcooled, that is, away from the point of beginning to boil (while the limited amount of water in the pressurizer itself is at the saturation point, since it is in contact with steam). Third, efforts were intensified to provide means or to use more efficiently existing means for a water level indicator inside the PWR vessel in the event that steam is formed at the top of the vessel. These and other modifications in hardware, operating procedures, personnel training, management and so on, were put in place to ensure that a repetition of such an occurrence will be extremely unlikely.

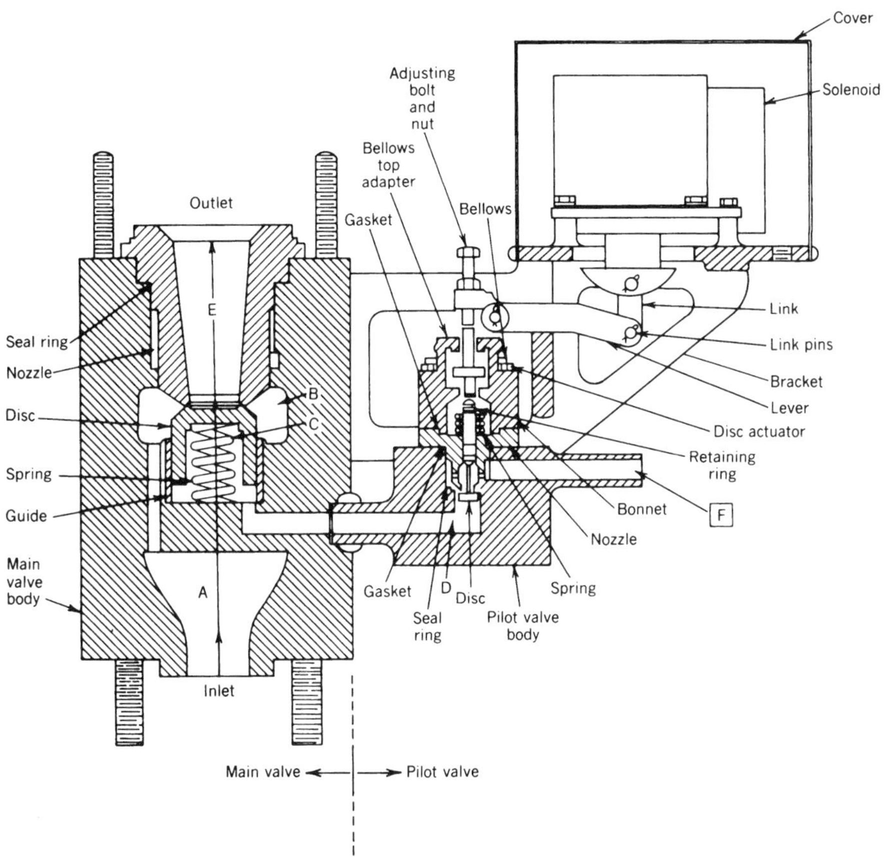

Figure 9.31. One of the relief valve designs used in PWRs (Pressurmatic Valve, Style HPV-SN). It consists of a pilot valve and a main valve. Under normal conditions, the discs of both the main and pilot valves are seated against their nozzles. When the solenoid is energized by an electric signal, the solenoid plunger hits the end of the disc actuator and breaks the tight connection of disc and seat in the pilot valve. Steam then flows from space D to the discharge space F. This causes the pressure in spaces D and C to drop and the higher pressure in cavity B pushes the disc of the main valve downward and steam flows to the discharge space E. When the solenoid is deenergized, the plunger returns to its original position, the pilot valve closes, and pressure builds up again in cavities D and C, which closes the main valve.

valves can be viewed as protective devices designed to prevent too many mechanical challenges of the safety valves. Safety valves are purely passive devices, that is, they operate without the intervention of human action or of external signals other than the pressure applied on them. A typical design, shown in Figure 9.32, exhibits the main features of a safety valve, namely the nozzle and the disc (which together form or open the pressure boundary), the valve base or body, the spindle, spring, and bonnet, and other parts. Since the effluent from these valves is radioactive, the valves discharge into a quench or relief tank filled with water and containing cooling water coils for condensing the discharge. Most of the components of safety and relief valves (those in contact with primary fluid) are made of stainless steel or Inconel. The spring is made of tungsten, whereas Stellite is often used as seating material. Valves are built to criteria of Class 1, according to the ASME code, Section III. Characteristic features of valves are inlet nozzle diameter (typically 6 or 8 in.), design pressure (2500 psig or 17 MPa), and design temperature (700°F or 370°C).

The valve capacity is the amount of steam the valve is capable of discharging. It can be calculated by the following formula (ASME code, Section III):

$$W = 51.5A\,(1.03P + 14.7)(0.975)(0.9)$$

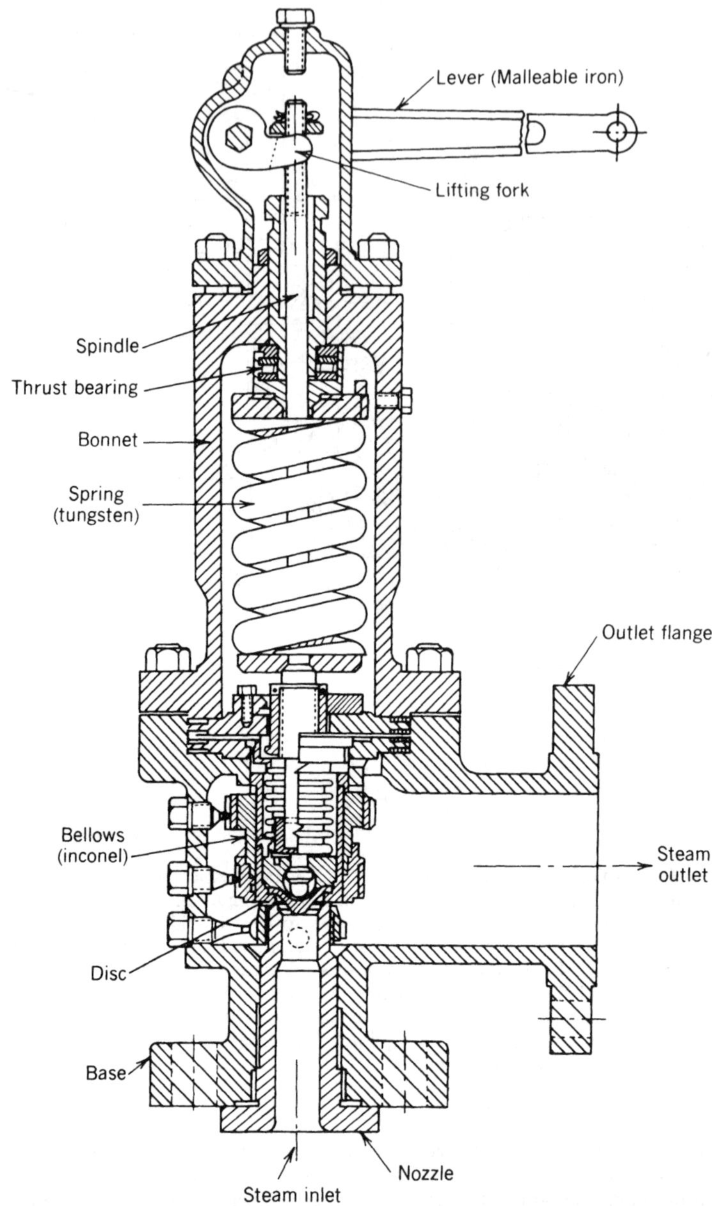

Figure 9.32. A typical spring-loaded PWR safety valve. Under normal conditions, the loaded spring holds the disc tightly against the nozzle. When an overpressure transient occurs, sufficient force develops against the disc to overcome the force of the spring and the valve lifts. With additional force developed from the flowing steam, the valve pops open to full lift. When overpressure is relieved, the force against the disc is reduced and the spring force reseats the disc against the nozzle. Closing pressure is different than opening pressure, usually by some tens of psi. Additional devices allow adjustment of opening and closing pressure and lift. (Courtesy Dresser Industries.)

where W = flow rate of saturated steam, lb/hr
A = orifice area, in.^{2}
P = set pressure, psig

This capacity corresponds to 3% overpressure, rated lift, and steady-state conditions.

Normally safety and relief valves are designed and tested to discharge saturated steam. However, because of the possibility of a pressurizer "going solid" (becoming full of water to the top) and following the events at TMI-2, interest was heightened in the behavior of the multitude of valves used in LWRs under conditions other than saturated steam. A dedicated program was mounted in the United States and abroad on the part of the utilities and vendors to test full-scale valves representative of actual installation under steam, water, and water/steam mixtures, and a variety of upstream and downstream conditions. This extensive testing investigated such behavioral patterns like valve chattering (repeated and rapid opening and closing of the valve), reseating, sticking, and dependencies on pressure, temperature, and length of pipe upstream and downstream. The conclusions were that, although anomalies were observed under certain conditions, the aggregate of the valves tested behaved as expected and their reliability should not be suspect.

Pressure and relief valves are also used in BWR plants but the pressures under which they operate and the set points are different. The BWR valves are connected to the main steam line at the steam outlet from the reactor vessel; they discharge into the pressure suppression pool.

Some of safety/relief valves in a BWR are part of the Automatic Depressurization System (ADS) of the primary system. In case of a loss-of-coolant accident and failure of the high-pressure safety injection system, the ADS reduces the system pressure, thus allowing the low-pressure safety injection systems to operate. These valves operate either automatically or manually at any pressure by operator action. The details of how these valves operate in conjunction with other safety systems are treated in Chapter 18.

Isolation Valves

Of special importance are safety valves used in BWRs to isolate the primary system within the containment from the turbine. They are called Main Steam Isolation Valves (MSIV). Their main function is to rapidly isolate the containment building in the event of an accident, such as a rupture in the primary system. In PWRs, valves are used to isolate the main steam line and/or the feedwater system in the secondary circuit. Isolation valves can close in 3–5 sec under emergency conditions.

These components must interrupt the flow of a very large amount of energy in a very short time and are therefore subject to high dynamic forces. They are massive components made of high-strength stainless steel, manufactured to exacting standards and tested under normal and accident conditions. A schematic diagram of a steam isolation valve is shown in Figure 9.33. The actual assembly of the component is shown in Figure 9.34.

In the case of full-load rejection, in order to avoid turbine overspeed, the steam flow is diverted through the bypass line into the condenser. This operation is accomplished through quick action of the turbine bypass valves. One design is shown in Figure 9.35. As the main steam line control valves close, the turbine bypass valves open to dump the steam into the condenser. These valves must help lower the temperature and pressure of large amounts of steam and therefore must withstand heavy static loads on their parts. Severe cyclic stresses occur due to rapid changes in temperature and pressure. Both the shape and the materials of the valve body must be well designed. The valve shown in Figure 9.35 is forged and has a thin wall shape that minimizes peak stresses.†

Piping

The primary loop components are connected together through pipes of various sizes. Since large amounts of water must be circulated through each loop, the pipes have diameters up to several feet. For example, the hot leg pipes (of which there are two in the two-loop 1200-MWe plant of Tables 9.3 and 9.4) have an inside diameter of almost 1 m (38 in.), whereas the cold leg pipes (of which there are four in the same plant) have a diameter of 0.71 m (28 in.). The pipe material is carbon steel, with a clad inside surface of stainless steel to minimize corrosion. The pipes of the primary loop have, in addition to the pressurizer surge line connection, several other welded connections for pressure and temperature instruments, vents, drains, and other systems, such as emergency safety coolant injection and decay heat removal.

†Thicker wall designs often have high stress due to differential thermal expansion.

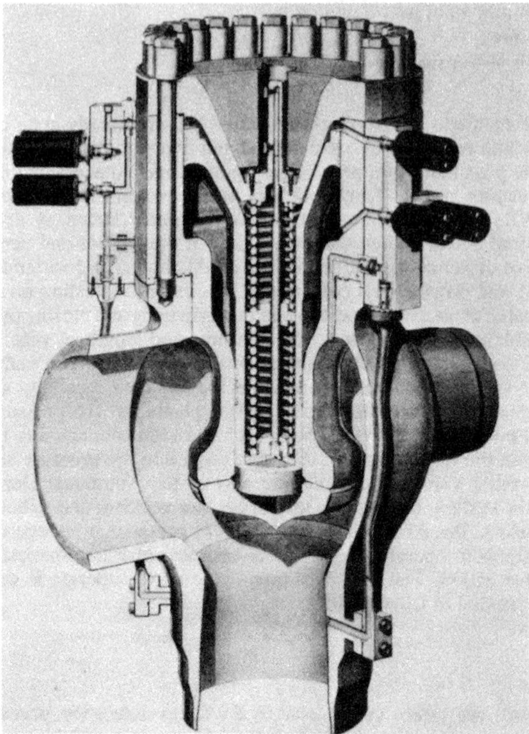

Figure 9.33. Section through a quick-closing steam isolation valve, shown in the open position. The valve is called system-medium operated because steam pressure is used to provide the closing force required. The component is also used as a relief valve. (Courtesy Sulzer Co.)

9.7. STEAM GENERATORS

The steam generators are large PWR components in which heat from the primary circuit is transferred to the secondary with the production of steam. There are two basic steam generator designs: the U-tube and the once-through steam generator. The operation of the U-tube steam generator is illustrated in Figure 9.36. This design is by far the most widely used (all but one PWR manufacturer use it). In it the hot water coming from the reactor enters at the bottom, fills the one-half space of the lower chamber, passes upward through thousands of U-shaped tubes (made of Inconel), returns to the other half of the bottom chamber, and returns to the reactor. The secondary-loop water enters through feedwater inlet into an annular space between the shell and cylindrical skirt inside the steam generator, moving first downward in the annulus and then upward in the space of the tube bundle. Because of the lower pressure (about 1100 psi) of the secondary loop, water boils to create steam, which moves upward. The upper part of the steam generator, called the upper shell, is of a larger diameter than the lower shell, and contains equipment to remove droplets of moisture from the steam and to provide drier steam at the outlet, which is located at the top of the vessel. A large fraction of water which does not vaporize moves back down through the annular space and repeats the process. Thus, a large amount of water recirculates in the steam generator (a phenomenon analogous to the recirculation of water in the BWR). Because of their respective function, the lower portion of the steam generator is called the evaporator section and the upper portion is called the steam drum. The U-tubes are inserted in a thick plate (called the tube sheet) at the bottom of the component and are held apart and stiffened along their height, by several thinner circular plates.† Additional metallic holders are used to provide rigidity to the tube bundle and to minimize vibrations induced by the flow of water. In more recent steam generator designs such as the one shown in Figure 9.37, feedwater enters at the lower part of the component. These steam generators include a preheater section on the shell side of the feedwater inlet.

†Sometimes a steel latticework called an "eggcrate" is used.

Figure 9.34. Assembly of a system-medium-operated, quick-closing steam isolation valve. Three such valves were provided for a 920-MWe PWR plant in Switzerland. (Courtesy Sulzer Co.)

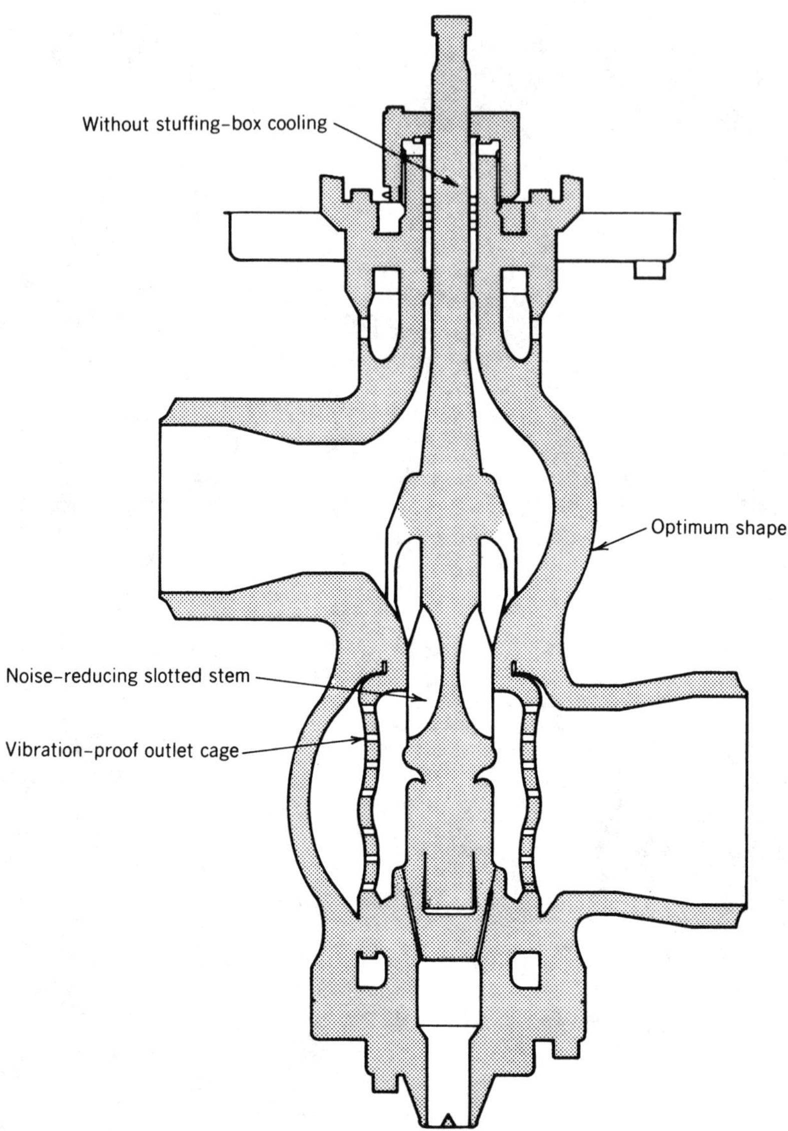

Figure 9.35. On full-load rejection of turbine plant, the safety bypass valves have to cope with all the energy delivered to the turbine. It is vital that the valves open quickly and dependably. Usually the same valve has to lower the pressure and temperature of large amounts of steam. Dissipating so much energy imposes heavy static loads on the valve parts and severe cyclic stresses due to rapid changes in pressure and temperature. This is why emphasis is placed on the choice of materials and the optimum valve body shape. Sulzer bypass valves are of forged fabricated design. The spherical form allows thin walls. Smooth shape and the absence of metal concentrations keep peak stresses low. Spray water injected into the highly turbulent zone downstream of the valve seat ensures thorough mixing of water and steam. (Courtesy Sulzer Co.)

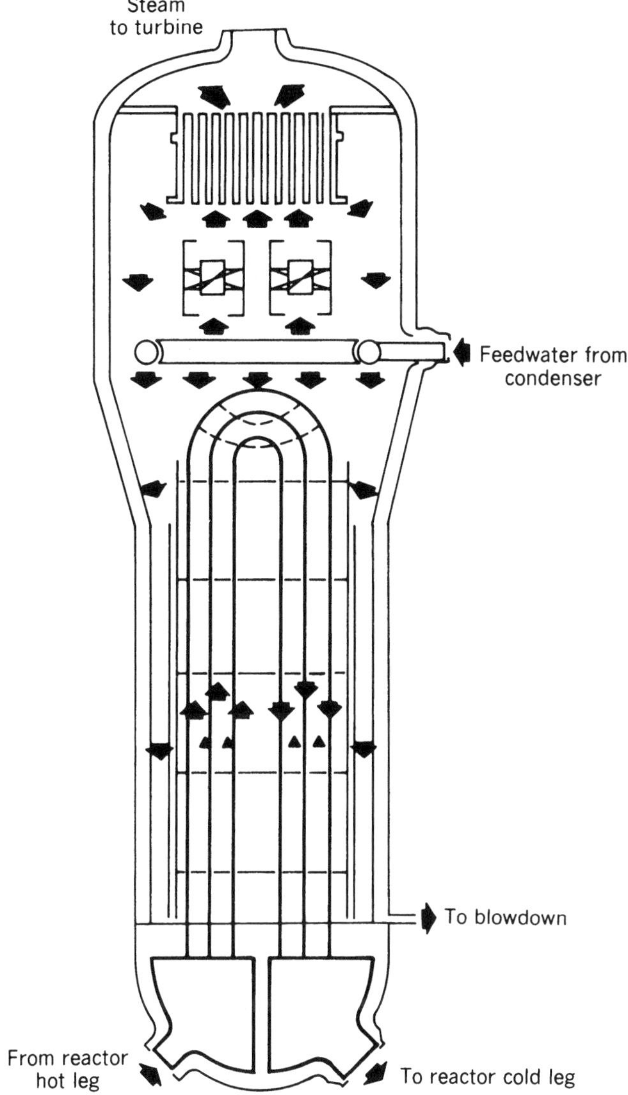

Figure 9.36. Schematic diagram showing the operation of a U-tube steam generator. Hot water enters from lower left nozzle, moves upward through the riser section of the U-tubes and returns through the downcomer section to the right-hand half of the lower plenum to return to the reactor. Feedwater moves downward through the annular space around the bundle, moves upward through the bundle section, and boils into steam. Moisture is removed from the steam through the devices at the top section of the steam generator and saturated steam of high quality exits from the top of the vessel. Water droplets fall back and move downward through the periphery to repeat the cycle.

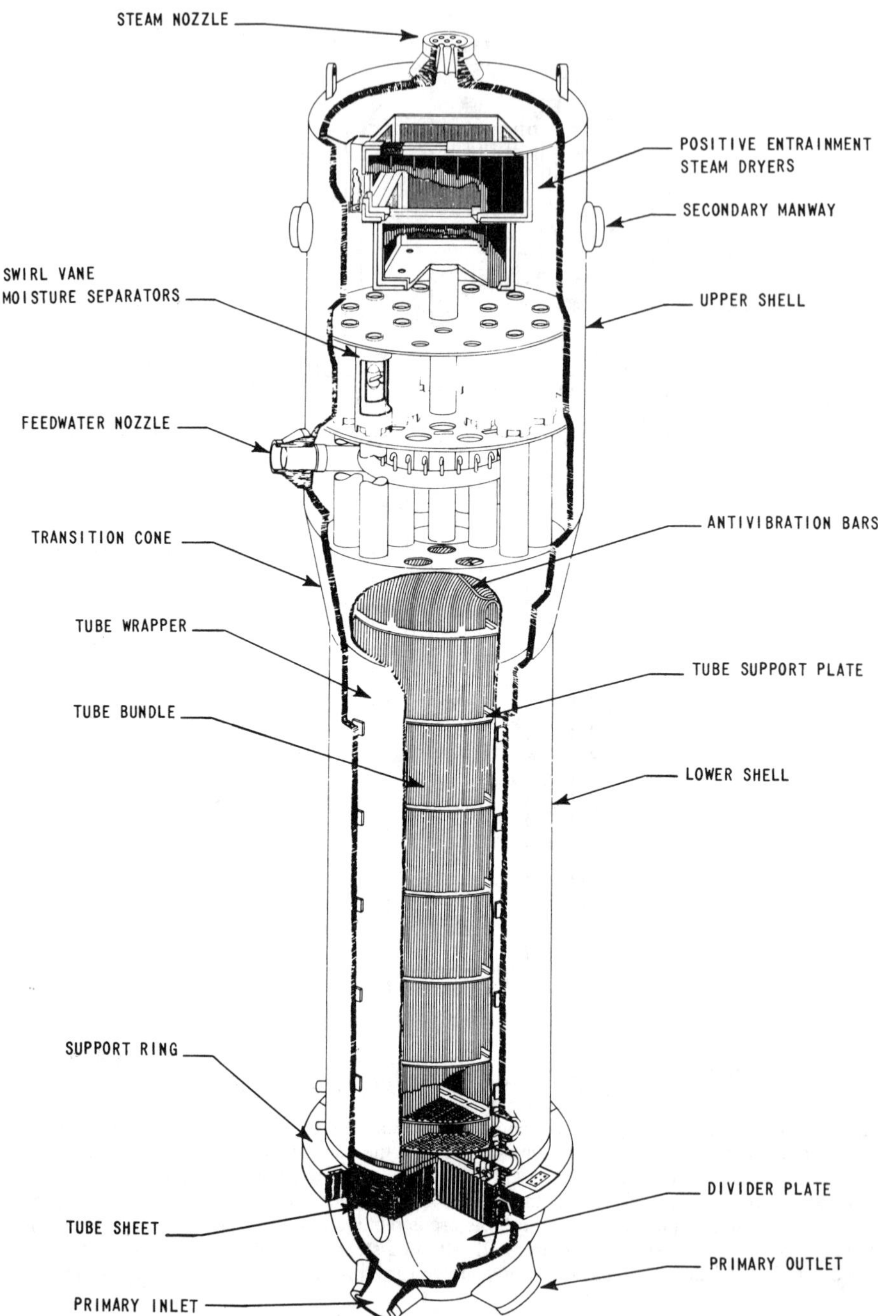

Figure 9.37. Cutout view of a steam generator using U-tubes. The lower shell is occupied by the tube bundle supported by the tube plate and held together by tube supports. The upper shell is occupied by moisture separators. In this model, feedwater is introduced at the lower part of the lower shell rather than through a circular sparger as shown in Figure 9.33. (Courtesy Westinghouse Electric Corp.)

Each loop in a PWR has a steam generator. Each steam generator is a large vessel up to 20 m (63 ft) in height with an upper shell diameter of 4.42 m ($14\frac{1}{2}$ ft) and a lower shell diameter of 3.43 m ($11\frac{1}{4}$ ft). The tube bundle incorporates 3260 individual U-tubes, of Inconel-600.

A different steam generator design is shown in Figure 9.38. It is only manufactured by Babcock & Wilcox, a U.S. PWR vendor. Made of straight tubes connected to a thick upper and lower tubesheet, it is contained in a shell, about 20.74 m (68 ft) high, with a diameter of 4 m (13 ft). The primary coolant enters at the top, flows down through the tubes (numbering upward of 15,000), and exits at the bottom. The high-pressure boundary is formed by the upper and lower hemispherical shells, the upper and lower tubesheets, and the straight tubes. The secondary water, at a pressure about one-half that of the primary side, is introduced at about the middle of the vessel from a circular manifold. The feedwater flows downward through the annular space inside the shell, enters the tube section at the bottom, and proceeds upward. Water boils and steam is produced. Toward the upper part of the heating surface, the steam becomes superheated. The boundary of the secondary side is formed by the shell, the outside surface of the tubes, and the tubesheets. The tube bundle is contained by a cylindrical shroud or baffle in two separate segments, as shown in Figure 9.38. The upper baffle together with the shell form an annulus through which the superheated steam flows from the top of the bundle downward toward the steam outlet just above the feedwater inlet. The lower baffle with the shell form the annulus through which the feedwater flows downward toward the entrance of the bundle. The shell carries additional parts corresponding to vents, drains, instrumentation, and inspection openings. Both heads have large manways to allow the entrance of personnel for inspection and maintenance. Design data for once-through steam generators are given in Table 9.5. The material used in the construction of the unit is austenitic steel but the parts coming in contact with primary coolant are covered with a layer of stainless steel. Tubes are made of a nickel–iron–chromium alloy, called Inconel-600, have an outside diameter of 15.9 mm (0.625 in.) and a thickness of 0.86 mm (0.034 in).

One important feature of the once-through steam generator is the production of superheated rather than saturated steam. This is advantageous for the turbine, yielding a somewhat higher thermal efficiency. Figure 9.39 shows the reactor coolant temperature, tube wall temperature, and steam temperature as a function of distance from the bottom. Reactor coolant temperature drops almost linearly as the fluid moves downward. In the secondary side, at about 80% of tube height, the saturated steam begins to superheat and the temperature rises sharply by about 20°C (35°F). The tube wall temperature also rises sharply at this point, approaching the temperature of the primary water, because the heat transfer coefficient on the steam side of the tube is much lower than on the water side.

At lower loads, the temperatures change as shown in Figure 9.39 to accommodate the load change with essentially constant flow through the core. The amount of heat removed is then proportional to the temperature difference across the core. The steam temperature also changes with load as shown in the figure. The amount of superheat increases somewhat as load decreases. For loads below 15% the steam temperature decreases and reaches the saturation point at a pressure of 925 psia and zero load.

Problems of Steam Generators

As experience with nuclear plants accumulated, it was found that steam generators were susceptible to a number of potentially serious problems, namely: radioactive contamination, vibration, fretting, water hammer, stress corrosion cracking, wastage (or thinning), pitting, denting, and high cycle fatigue. These problems made it doubtful that, without remedial action, the existing steam generators could complete their originally expected lifetime of 40 years. No manufacturer is immune to steam generator problems, although the kind and severity of problems may vary.

A crack through the wall of a steam generator tube opens a leakage path from the primary to the secondary system, with the potential of contaminating the secondary side and increasing exposure in areas like the turbine, which are normally free of radioactivity. A break of one or more tubes provides an opening for the loss of coolant from the primary loop which may have safety implications. Because of these concerns, steam generator tubes are inspected periodically by NonDestructive Examination (NDE) methods. Workers enter the plena through the manholes, insert specially designed probes (based, for example, on the induction of eddy currents in the wall of the tube), and look for damaged tubes. They then proceed to plug the damaged tubes, sealing off the leakage path into the secondary circuit. Many plants operate with a good number of their steam generator tubes plugged. When the plugged tubes exceed a certain fraction (about 15%), the plant's electric output must be reduced (derated) with a resultant negative impact on the plant's productivity.

An attendant problem is the radioactivity of the steam generator, exposing personnel doing maintenance work to radiation. To keep the exposure of each worker below allowable levels (no more than 3 rems of radiation may be received by any worker in any three-month period), a large number of workers often have to be hired, replacing each other inside the component at carefully monitored time intervals, in order to accomplish the job.

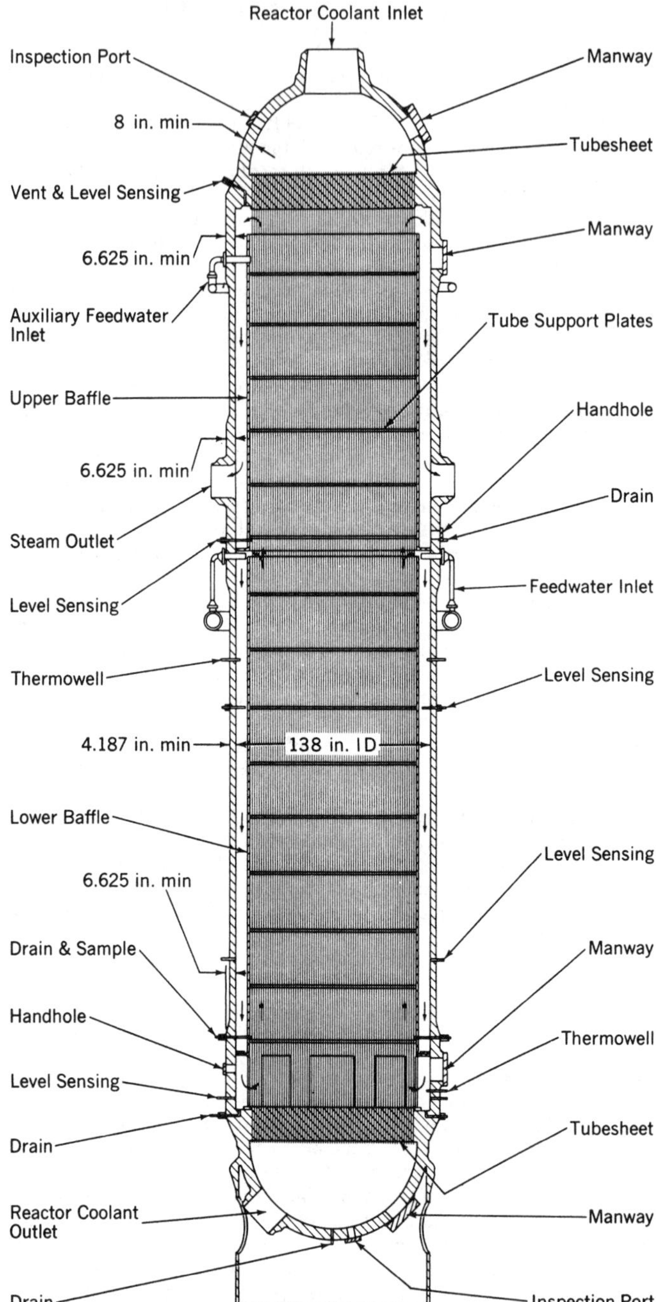

Figure 9.38. A once-through nuclear steam generator used by one of the vendors in the United States (Babcock & Wilcox). Arrows inside the unit indicate flow paths of water and steam in the secondary side. The primary water flows from top to bottom in one pass through the device. (Courtesy Babcock & Wilcox.)

Table 9.5. Nuclear Steam Generator Design Data

	Oconee Unit 1	1200-Mw Unit
Design pressure, reactor coolant, psi	2,500	2,500
Design pressure, steam, psi	1,050	1,235
Hydrotest pressure (tube side–cold), reactor coolant, psi	3,125	3,125
Design temperature, reactor coolant, °F	650	670
Design temperature, steam, °F	600	630
Reactor coolant flow, million lb/hr	65.66	69.5
Heat transferred, million Btu/hr	4,410	5,847
Steam conditions at full load, outlet nozzles		
Steam flow, million lb/hr	5.6	7.43
Steam temperature, °F	570	603
Degrees of superheat, °F	35	50
Steam pressure, psi	910	1,075
Feedwater temperature, °F	455	473
Inside diameter of pressure shell, ft-in.	11-6	11-8
Inside height of pressure shell, ft-in.	66-0	65-7
Reactor coolant water volume, ft^3	2,030	2,025
Tubes		
Approximate number	15,530	16,000
Outside diameter, in.	0.625	0.625
Minimum thickness, in.	0.034	0.034

Source: Babcock & Wilcox Co., *Steam, Its Generation and Use,* 1978.

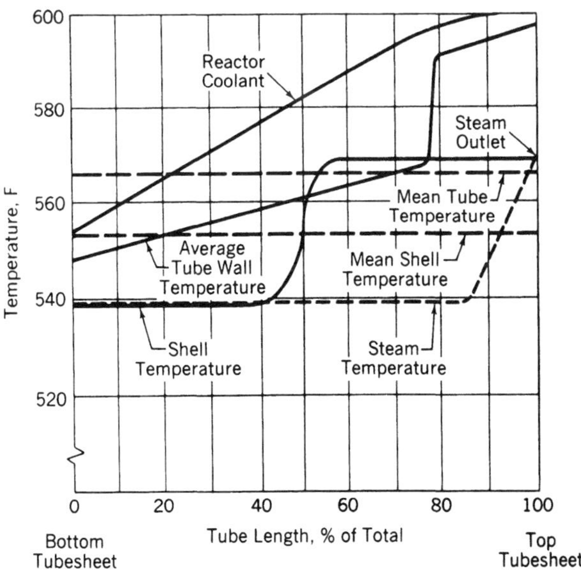

Figure 9.39. Nuclear steam generator temperatures. (From Babcock & Wilcox, *Steam, Its Generation and Use,* 1978.)

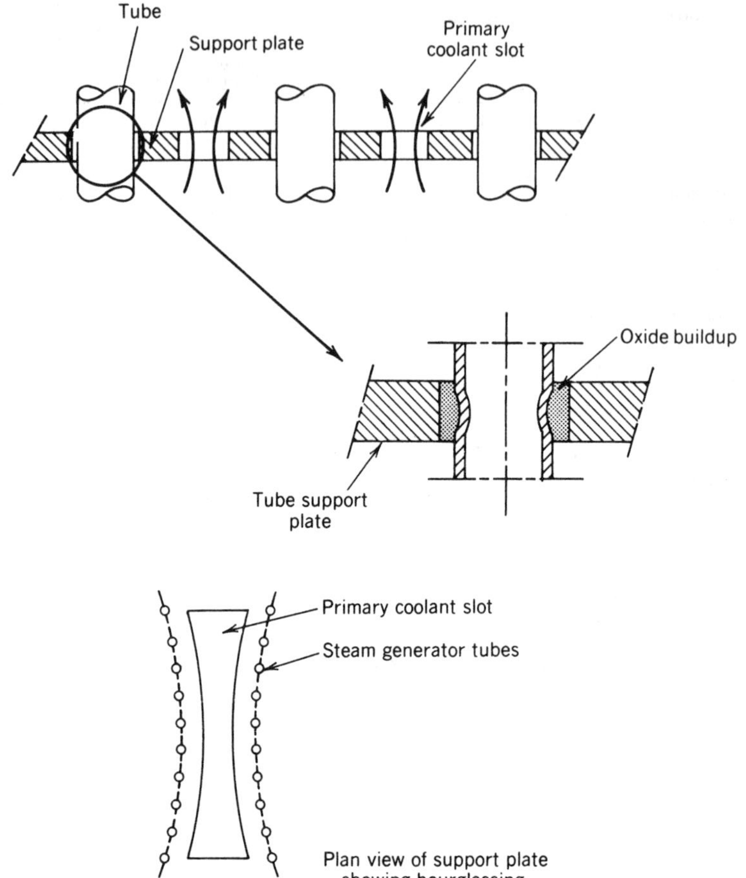

Figure 9.40. Schematic diagram showing the steam generator tube denting process. The denting occurs at the point where the tube passes through one of the several tube support plates. Corrosion products accumulate in the narrow crevice between tube and support plate and squeeze the tube by several mils. Tube may crack, creating a leakage path from the primary to the secondary side.

A particularly troublesome problem, affecting many of the units then in service, surfaced around 1975: denting of steam generator tubes at their interface with tube support plates. The problem is illustrated in Figure 9.40. Because of high temperatures at the narrow crevice between tube and tube support plate, concentration of certain undesirable ions (like clorine) occurred. The impurities entered from the secondary side through leaks in the condenser. When a low value of pH existed (meaning an acid environment), the corrosion at the crevice accelerated. Carbon steel, the material of the tube support plate, was then attacked in a "run-away" reaction to produce a hard oxide, called magnetite:

$$3Fe + 4H_2O \rightarrow Fe_3O_4 + 4H_2$$

The magnetite had approximately twice the volume of the original metal from which it was formed. As the crevice closed, the magnetite layer put tremendous stress on the tube and the support plate. In fact, rectangular slots cut out in the thick support plates for the flow of secondary water were found distorted, a phenomenon which was called hour-glassing. Some tubes were found to have minor denting (about 0.005 in. or less), but several had denting up to 0.015 in. In at least two plants† the damage was so extensive that the unprecedented decision was made to remove the damaged steam generator tube bundles and to replace them with new assemblies, a monumental task requir-

†Surry and Turkey Point.

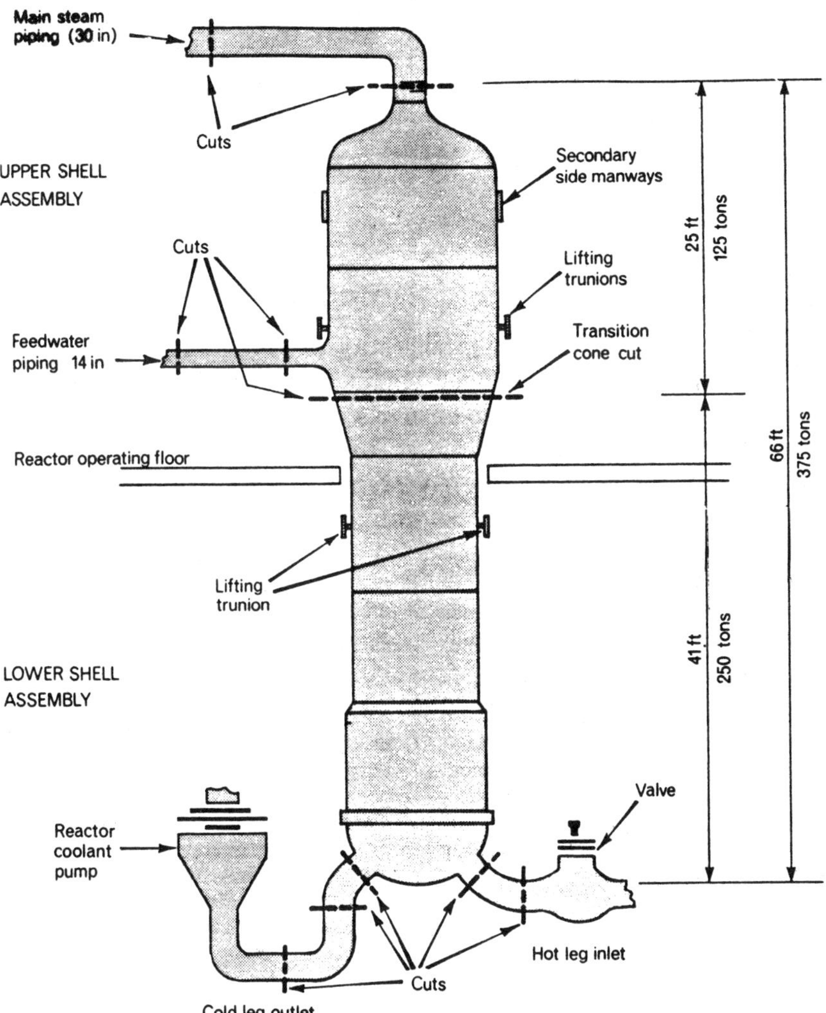

Figure 9.41. Shown in this figure is a steam generator and its connections to the primary and secondary systems in one of the plants where replacement was performed. Several cuts were made to allow removal of the upper shell assembly which stayed in containment and of the lower shell assembly which was shipped from the plant for complete replacement. [From *Nuclear Engineering International,* **25,** 21 May (1980).]

ing years and a high cost (about $100 million per plant) to accomplish. Some of the details of this large and unprecedented operation are shown in Figures 9.41 and 9.42.† The affected vendors have now developed advanced procedures to retube steam generators in place.

It appears that the denting problem results from a synergism of several adverse conditions. First, the secondary water chemistry played an important role in promoting corrosion because of unexpected chemical effects of additives‡ or because of impurities entering through leaking condenser tubes. The latter was a particular problem in plants using sea or brackish water as coolant. Blowdown was not found effective in removing the solids from steam generators: 80–90% of solids

†It is interesting to note that one of the removed steam generators from unit 2 of the Surry PWR plant has been taken to a newly built Steam Generator Examination Facility at the Hanford reservation of the U.S. Department of Energy, to be subjected to a thorough, if belated, investigation of the causes of steam generator problems as well as of the proposed remedies.

‡Corrosion inhibiting agents, such as sodium phosphate or hydrazine.

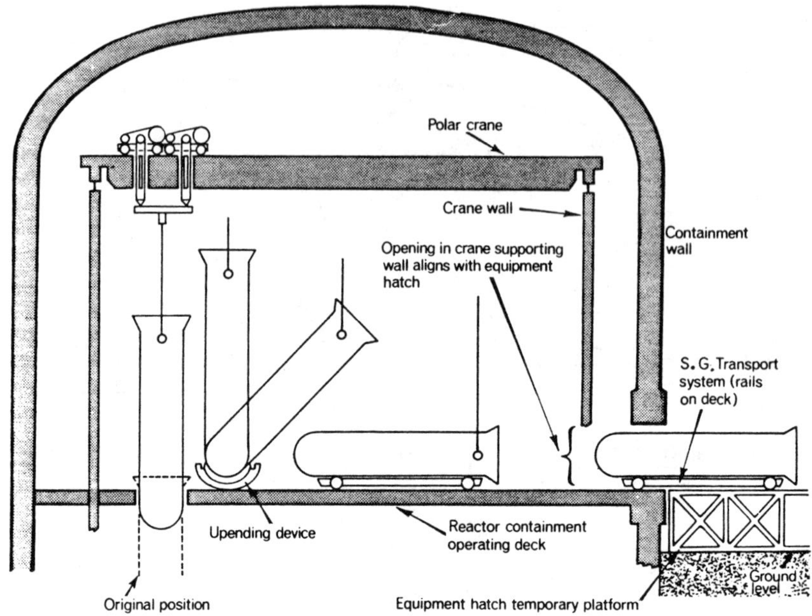

Figure 9.42. The diagram shows how the lower shell of the steam generator with its dented tubes was lifted by the polar crane out of its original position, was passed through a hole in the crane wall especially opened for this operation, and out the equipment hatch for shipment to the manufacturer's shop. The reverse procedure was followed for the installation of the new S.G. lower shell. The old upper shell was reused. [From *Nuclear Engineering International,* **25,** 21 May (1980).]

remain inside and less than 5% of copper† was removed. Second, the flow patterns and temperature distribution around the crevice created conditions favorable to the buildup of magnetite in the crevice; and third, the carbon steel used for the support plates was susceptible to the type of chemical reaction leading to an expanding hard oxide layer. Accordingly, the remedies proposed fall in three categories: (a) a more effective and stringent control of water chemistry; (b) elimination of condenser leaks and copper-bearing alloys in the feedwater lines; and (c) a change in flow patterns around the tube to alleviate the high-temperature regions in the crevice. As a result of the third item, new designs of tube support plates were implemented like the one shown in Figure 9.43. The new designs utilize broaches instead of circular holes, allowing the flow of secondary water around the tube and minimizing the hot spots at the interfaces. The use of alternate materials (e.g., ferritic type-400 stainless steel) in new units could help eliminate the problem.

In existing units that are not so severely damaged as to require replacement, it is important to arrest or retard the process of denting. Chemical cleaning to remove the layer of magnetite deposited could be used if no further thinning of the tubes would occur and the gap created from the removal of the oxide could not cause excessive fretting and eventual damage to the tubes.

Another problem, not as severe as the denting problem, arose more recently in certain designs of steam generators in which the incoming flow of feedwater hits the tube bundles with sufficient velocity to cause tube wearing or thinning. When the problem was detected, the flow velocity of the feedwater was reduced to minimize the effect but this caused a certain amount of derating (reduction of output) of the plant. The long-term solution is, however, to modify the internal structure of the steam generator, by replacing the now used impingement plate with a new manifold, flow splitter, and flow limiter that dissipates the kinetic energy of the incoming feedwater, and reduces its velocity before it reaches the tube bundle.

9.8. FEEDWATER HEATERS

Most large thermal plants have a number (up to seven or eight) of feedwater heaters. Their principle of operation stems from thermodynamic theory whereby a process of heat transfer is most efficient

†Copper is a catalyzing agent that comes from the corrosion of the feedwater lines in plants using copper alloys in this system.

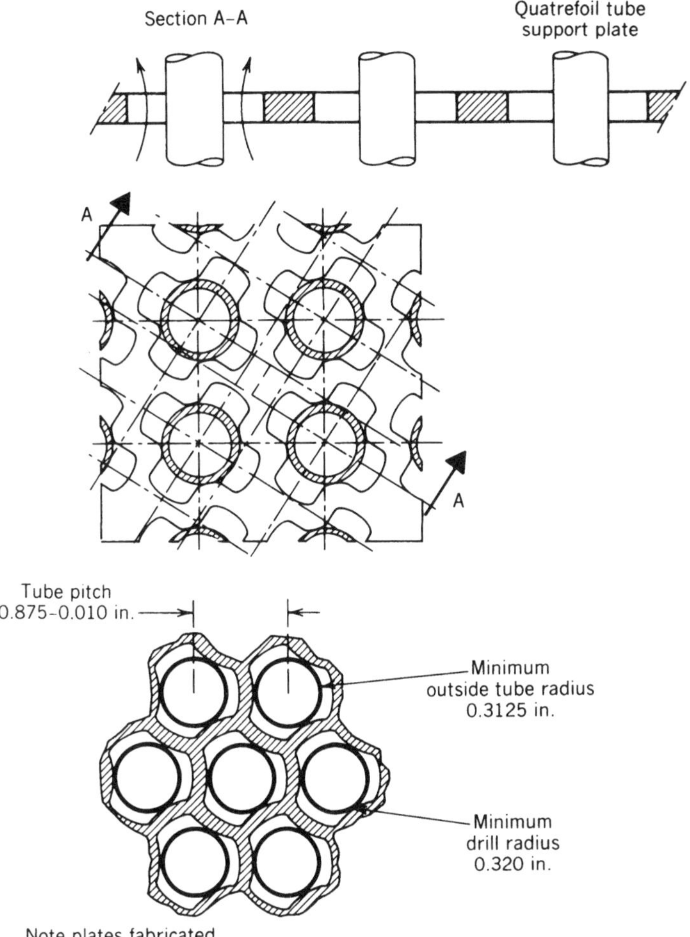

Figure 9.43. Part of the solution to the denting problem was the redesign of the support plate to the quatrefoil shape shown. The broached plates improve the circulation of secondary water through the plates and minimize the accumulation of corrosion products and high-termperature fields. The other parts of the solution were careful specifications of secondary water chemistry and the use of stainless steel in the support plates.

when the temperature difference between the heat source and the heated medium is minimum, ideally equal to zero. If this theoretical ideal could be achieved, the cycle would be fully reversible and the maximum thermal efficiency (also called Carnot efficiency) could be obtained. Even though this ideal condition cannot be achieved, approximations that yield improvements in thermal efficiency can be used (refer to Figure 8.12).

Instead of introducing the cold condensate directly into the reactor (or the steam generator) for heat-up, a series of intermediate heating steps are introduced. Small amounts of steam are extracted from several points of the turbines and introduced in a series of heat exchanges to raise the temperature of the condensate. The lowest temperature steam is used to heat the coldest water (coming from the condenser), whereas the highest temperature steam (extracted from the high-pressure turbine) is used to heat the warmest water immediately before its entrance in the reactor. Thus, the temperature difference, ΔT, across these heat exchanges is reduced.

A typical horizontal feedwater heater is shown in Figure 9.44. It is essentially not much different than the steam generator. Feedwater enters through an inlet on the hemispherical head, circulates through a bundle of tubes, and exits through the feedwater outlet.

Steam enters from above, comes in contact with the tubes by circulating through a series of

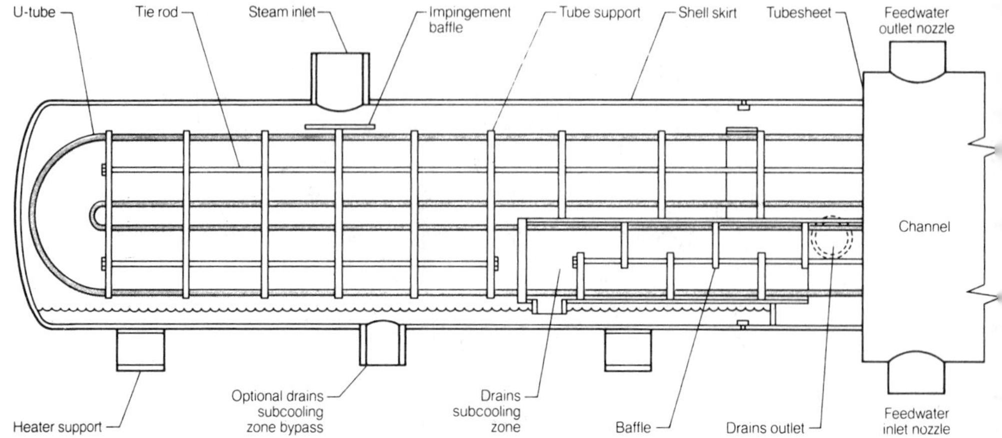

Figure 9.44. Schematic of a typical two-zone feedwater heater. The first zone condenses the steam and the second subcools the condensate. The main problem encountered in feedwater heaters is erosion of the U-tubes near the water inlet. The effect of water inlet velocity and turbulence for various geometric configurations is under study to minimize the erosion.

baffles, designed to maximize circulation and contact, is condensed, and goes into the next cooler feedwater heater unit until it reaches the condenser where it is mixed with the main feedwater flow. In many instances, a pump is used to introduce the condensed steam into the feedwater stream. The shell side pressure of the feedwater heater varies, according to the point of extraction between vacuum and 1200 psig, while the feedwater side operates under either the intermediate low pressure of the condensate booster pumps or the full pressure of the feedwater pumps. The temperature range is approximately between 38 and 260°C (100 and 500°F). The material used in nuclear system feedwater heaters is usually stainless steel-304, selected because of its excellent resistance to corrosion, its compatibility with other ferrous and nonferrous materials, and its good strength under the required pressures and temperatures. The major problem encountered in these components is the erosion of tubes due to the impingement of steam. Although a stainless-steel impingement plate is provided to dissipate the high velocity of the entering steam (Figure 9.44), tube erosion affects to some extent the stainless steel tubes in the superheater zone. The process is very sensitive to the velocity of steam, changing approximately as its fifth power.

9.9. STEAM TURBINES–GENERATORS AND ACCESSORIES

A steam turbine is a device in which the energy stored in steam in the form of high temperature and pressure is converted into an impulse on the moving blades of the rotor and hence into rotating energy of the shaft. The methods of operation can be divided into two categories: (1) impulse and (2) reaction. The basic flow patterns are shown in Figure 9.45. Some turbines use both methods for their operation. In an impulse turbine steam is expanded in stationary turbine nozzles, generating its energy in high-steam velocity. The steam jet flows over moving blades without further expansion and imparts its kinetic energy onto the blades by impact. The blades or buckets are fastened to the rims of rotating discs mounted on the turbine shaft. In the reaction turbine steam expands in both fixed blades and moving buckets. The stationary nozzles or buckets are attached to the turbine casing, whereas the moving blades are mounted onto discs which are shrunk onto the turbine shaft, as shown in the low-pressure rotor shown in Figure 9.46.

In order to increase the efficiency of the energy conversion, turbines have been designed for higher and higher temperatures and pressures, up to levels where the materials reach their performance limitations. Thus pressures up to 34 MPa (5000 psig) and temperatures up to 650°C (1200°F) were reached. However, in the light-water reactor applications the turbine operating conditions are determined by the available steam with a pressure ranging from 2.8 to 7.4 MPa (410 to 1075 psi) and a temperature ranging from 280° to 310°C (535 to 590°F).

Steam in most LWR designs is saturated, whereas in fossil fuel plants it is superheated. (One PWR vendor provides a small amount of superheat.) The turbine systems for LWRs are designed to fit these conditions. Similarly, the rotating speed of the units has to be selected with due regard to the strength of materials. Because the turbine is usually directly coupled to the generator which produces 60-Hz in the United States (50 Hz in most of the rest of the world), the rotating speed of turbines is either 3600 or 1800 rpm (3000 or 1500 rpm outside the United States). A high speed

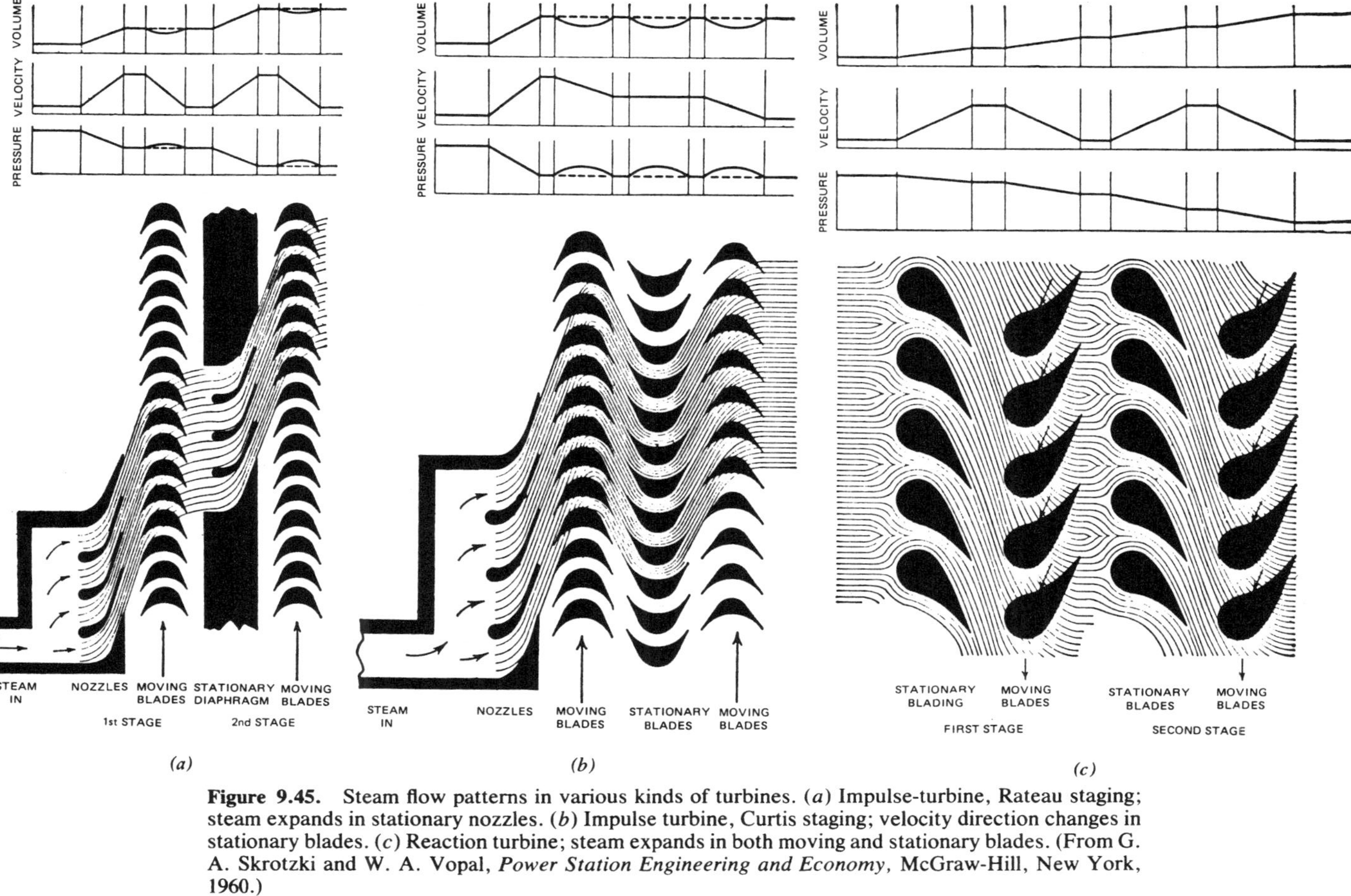

Figure 9.45. Steam flow patterns in various kinds of turbines. (*a*) Impulse-turbine, Rateau staging; steam expands in stationary nozzles. (*b*) Impulse turbine, Curtis staging; velocity direction changes in stationary blades. (*c*) Reaction turbine; steam expands in both moving and stationary blades. (From G. A. Skrotzki and W. A. Vopal, *Power Station Engineering and Economy*, McGraw-Hill, New York, 1960.)

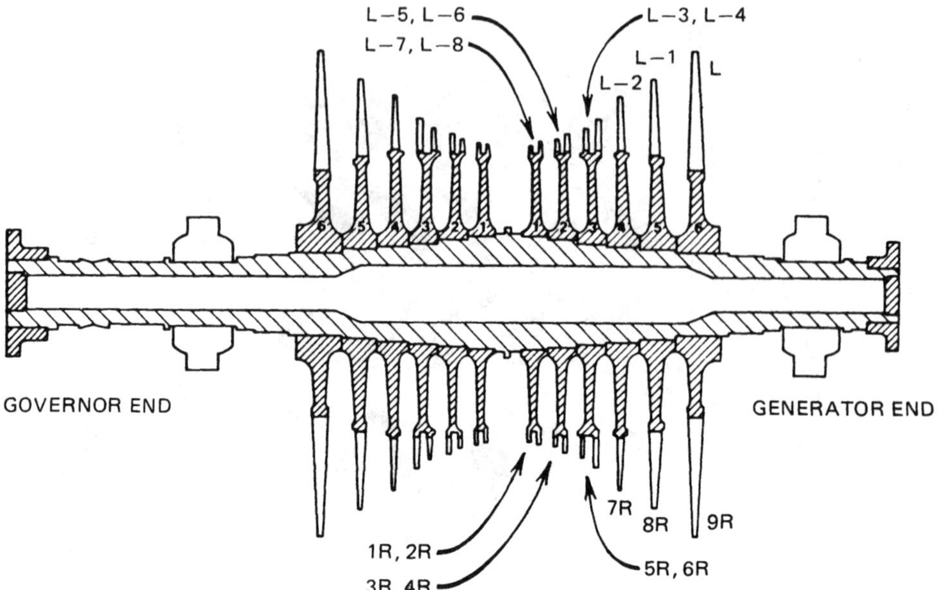

Figure 9.46. Typical configuration of a low-pressure turbine rotor. The blade-carrying discs are mounted onto the hollow turbine shaft by thermal shrinking. The inner, shorter blades are cast with the disc in one piece whereas the outer, longer blades are cast separately and then mounted onto the disc. The figure also shows the sources of potential failures, which can be anticipated and prevented by proper monitoring. (Courtesy EPRI.)

creates high centrifugal forces at the tip of the longest blade. In order to stay well within safe limits of material strength, the 3600-rpm units may have only 26-in. last-stage blades, whereas 1800-rpm units may go up to blades 48 in. in length. The large nuclear plants use predominantly the 1800-rpm turbine–generator units.

In order to generate the power produced by modern nuclear power plants, a combination of turbines must be used. A typical arrangement is shown in Figure 9.47. Three cylinders are shown, one High Pressure (HP) and two Low Pressure (LP) cylinders. The arrangement is called tandem compound because steam flows in series from the HP cylinder to the LP cylinders mounted on a single shaft and moving a single generator, an arrangement preferred in nuclear plants over the use of two shafts and two generators. Turbine rotors and discs are usually fabricated from Ni–Cr–Mo–V low-alloy steel, while 12% Cr (ANSI-403) or 17-4 PH (ANSI-630) stainless steel is used for blades.

High-pressure steam enters the central part of the HP cylinder and flows in opposite directions. As the steam expands it occupies a larger volume; hence the disc diameter and the blade sizes grow bigger. The arrangement of flow in opposite direction minimizes the axial forces on the shaft and on the axial bearings. Steam exiting from the HP cylinder is quite wet (since it was saturated at the inlet). In PWRs part or all of the steam flow exiting the HP stage goes through a Moisture Separator and Reheater (MS/R) which removes moisture and raises the temperature (and also the enthalpy) of the steam (see Figure 9.48). Reheating is accomplished by using some of the high-pressure steam extracted directly from the steam generator. The steam from the MS/R is divided into two parallel streams feeding at the center of the two low-pressure cylinders. At full load, the steam entering the LP cylinders from the reheater is about 260°C (500°F) and 1.4 MPa (200 psig). Because the steam in the low-pressure turbine may become excessively wet (see Mollier diagram of Figure 9.48) and because water droplets can damage the turbine blades, most units have special drainage devices to remove moisture between turbine stages, shown in the diagram as small upward jumps in the expansion path; in some units the entire flow of steam passes through a moisture separator before continuing. Some plants do not use reheat but moisture separation is always present. A discussion of the materials used in turbines, and problems leading to turbine failure are given in Chapter 10.

A three-cylinder nuclear turbine–generator unit can produce up to about 900 MW with 40-in. last-row blades, and up to 1000 MW with somewhat larger blades (up to 44 in.). For higher capacities, up to 1500 MW, a four-cylinder, tandem compound, six-flow nuclear turbine must be used. Such an arrangement, including the HP cylinder, three LP cylinders, the MS/Rs, electric

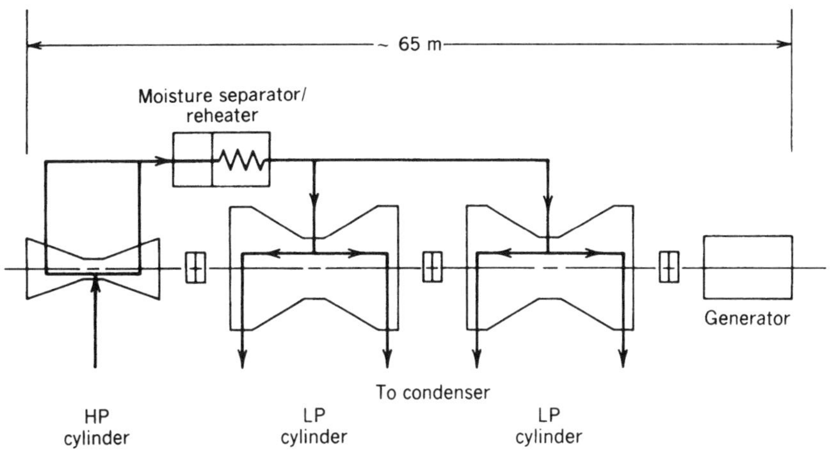

Figure 9.47. Steam flow diagram in a typical nuclear plant. Normally, one HP cylinder and two or three LP cylinders are used. In PWRs, wet steam exiting from the HP cylinder passes through a moisture separator/reheater before entering the LP cylinders. BWPs do not use a reheater. Individual loop designs vary from plant to plant. Total length, including the electric generator could be 65 m (213 ft).

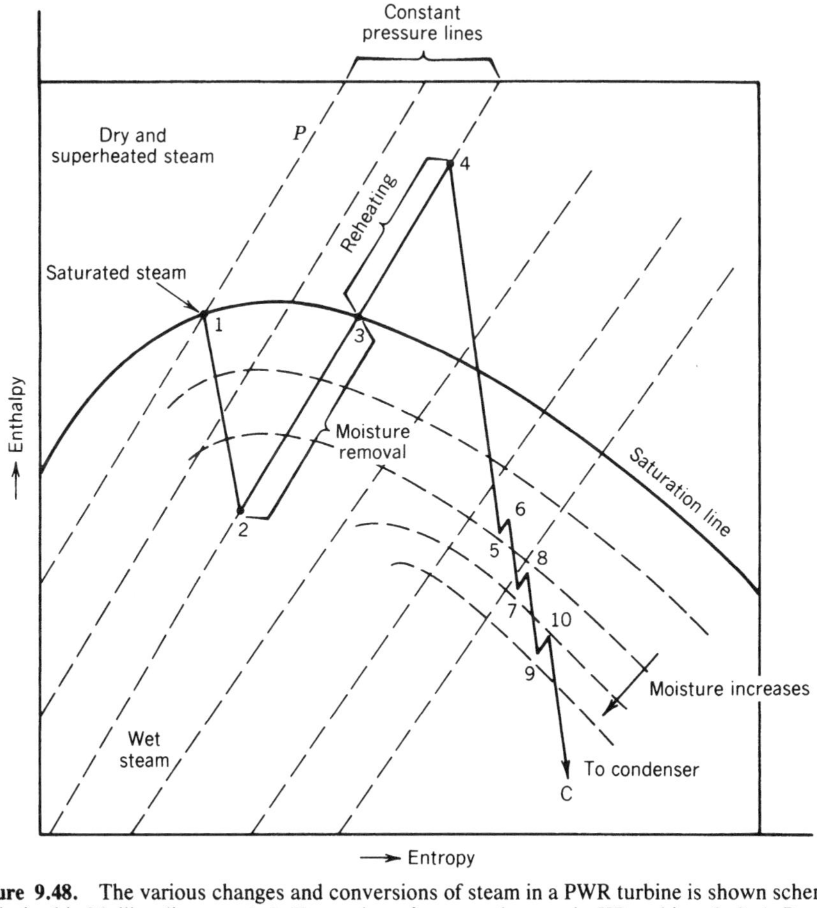

Figure 9.48. The various changes and conversions of steam in a PWR turbine is shown schematically in this Mollier diagram. 1–2: Expansion of saturated steam in HP turbine. 2–3–4: Passage through the MS/R where temperature and enthalpy are raised at constant pressure. 4–5–C: Expansion through the LP turbine with intermediate moisture removal.

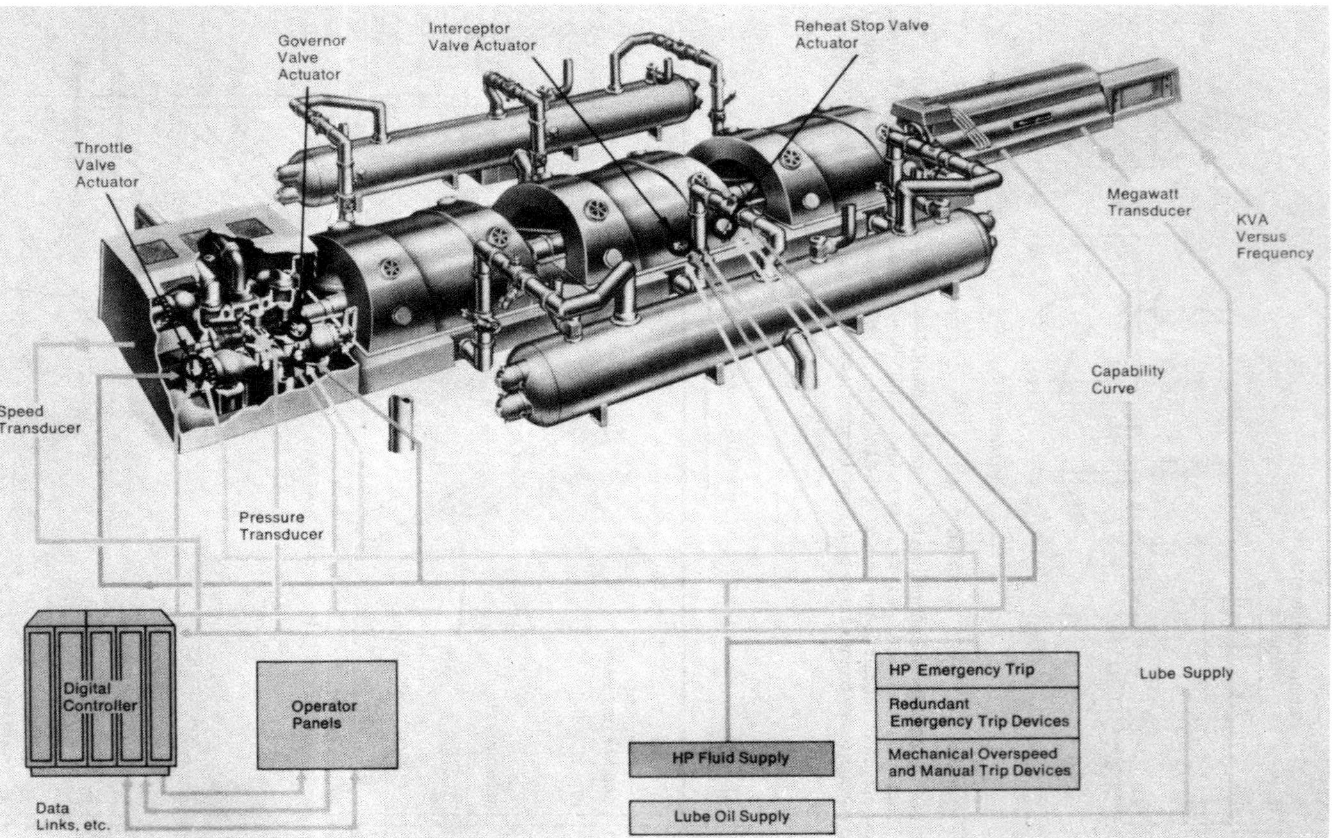

Figure 9.49. Turbine generator assembly with control systems. (Courtesy Westinghouse Electric Corp.)

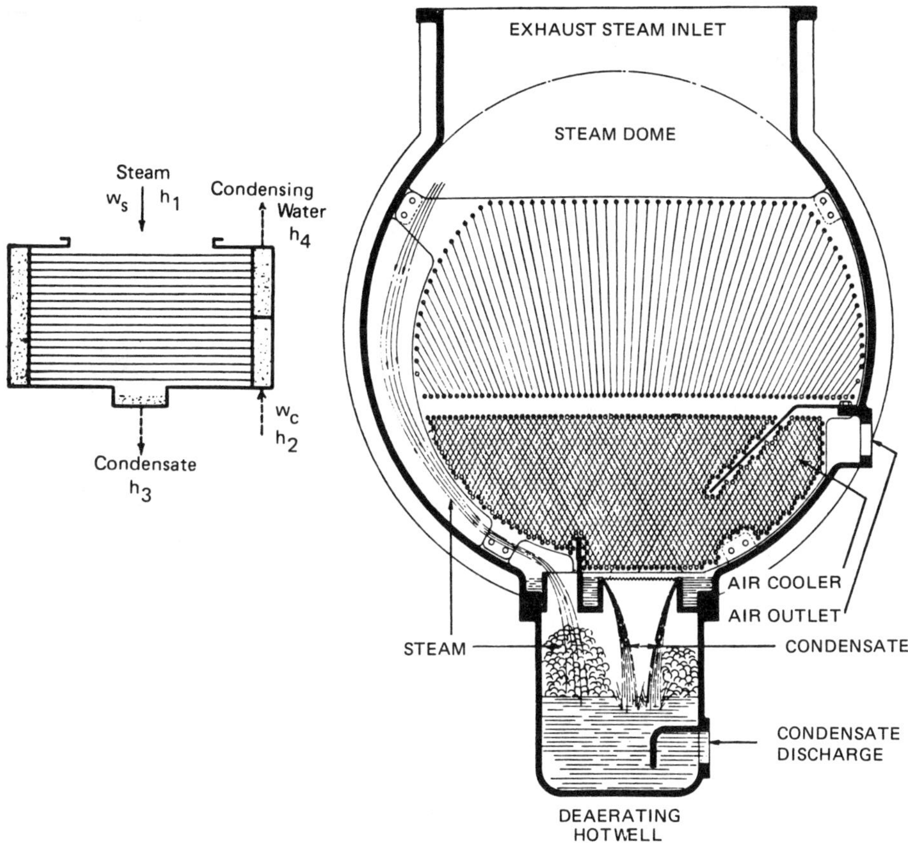

Figure 9.50. (*a*) Schematic diagram showing the principle of operation of a steam condenser. This type is called surface condenser because steam comes in contact with the surface of the tubes which contain cooling water. (*b*) Condenser cross section. Steam enters from the top coming from the turbine exhaust, comes in contact with a large number of tubes (up to 10,000 shown vertical to the cross-section plane), and condenses. Condensate is gathered in the hotwell from which it is pumped into the condensate system and back to the heat source (reactor core). A vacuum is maintained in the condenser in order to maximize the enthalpy drop which is converted into mechanical energy. Air and other gases are continuously removed to keep the pressure in the condenser low. (Courtesy Elliot Co.)

generator, and exciter is shown in Figure 9.49. The assembly can exceed 65 m (213 ft). A turbine–generator assembly requires a large number of devices and systems for the control of the energy flow, according to demand and to operator commands.

The governor is a device that controls the speed of the turbine shaft. Turbine speed directly affects the frequency of the ac generator output and must be kept within certain units for satisfactory operation. To accomplish this, the governor regulates the opening of the inlet and bypass valves according to the electrical load. In large units, the primary signal is directed to a servormotor which in turn controls the steam control valves. A number of other control and regulating systems are also shown in Figure 9.49.

9.10. CONDENSERS

The condenser is another massive component in any thermal plant. It is a heat exchanger consisting of a large metal shell, located directly under the turbine, which contains a large number of tubes connected on tube plates to the water boxes at the two ends of the shell as shown in Figure 9.50*a*. Cooling water from the sea, a river, lake, or closed-circuit cooling tower flows through the tubes. Steam enters the condenser shell from the turbine exhaust and condenses. The condensate is collected at the bottom of the condenser in the hotwell (see Figure 9.50*b*). Up to 10,000 tubes may

Figure 9.51. Steam condensers for power plants comprise an array of some 50,000 tubes fitted at either end with tubesheets. The tubes are conduits for water to pass through and cool the steam. Leaks at the tube-to-tubesheet joints can allow contaminants to enter and corrosion to occur throughout the entire plant.

Table 9.6. Typical Chemical Analysis of River Water

pH	6.9 to 8.2	NO_3^- (ppm)	32.7
Ca^{2+} (ppm)	51	SO_4^{-2} (ppm)	72
Mg^{2+} (ppm)	34	Cl^- (ppm)	24
Fe (ppm)	3.7	S_iO_2 (ppm)	8.9
Na^+ (ppm)	9.0	Dissolved solids (ppm) 384	
O_2 (ppm)	11.6	Suspended solids (ppm) 78	

be contained in a nuclear plant's steam condenser (Figure 9.51). In nuclear plants roughly two-thirds of the total enthalpy contained in the high-pressure steam ends up as waste heat in the condenser, one-third having been converted into useful energy in the turbine–generator. Large quantities of steam and of cooling water are handled by the condenser. A simple calculation of the heat balance in a surface condenser is given in Section 8.2, subsection "Ultimate Heat Sink."

The main problem encountered in condensers is the failure of the condenser tubes. This allows impure cooling water to enter the condensate system. A typical analysis of river water is given in Table 9.6. As was seen in Section 9.7, the ingress of chlorine ions from brackish or seawater into the condensate system of PWRs aggravates the corrosion processes in steam generators.

The condenser pipes in nuclear plants are presently made either of austenitic (type-316) stainless steel or newer materials.† Earlier plants made wide use of copper-based alloys for tubing but their use has been phased out because it was found that the presence of copper ions and copper oxides was accelerating corrosion and denting in steam generator tubing. Because of the persistent problems encountered in condensers, many designers have adopted titanium tubing for their ad-

†AL6X (50% Fe, 24% Ni, 20% Cr, 6% Mo) or IN-838 (16% Ni, 0.5% Cr, 0.8% Fe, 0.5% Mn) have had good results.

vanced condenser designs (the French nuclear plants make exclusive use of titanium tubing). Titanium is an expensive material and causes considerable increase in the capital cost of the component. However, the overall economics of titanium tubes is considered favorable because of sharply higher reliability of operation. Tubing must be either welded or explosively bonded into the tube sheet for best results; rolling techniques have proved unsatisfactory.

9.11. SECONDARY WATER CHEMISTRY

General

As discussed in the steam generator section of this chapter, chemistry of the secondary loop water makes a big difference in the performance of these components. The other component that is also drastically affected is the steam turbine, particularly the discs and blades of the low-pressure cylinders (a discussion of turbine failures is given in Chapter 10).

All PWR plants utilize chemical treatment of the secondary side water to control the pH, which is a measure of the acidity or alkalinity of a solution. A value of 7 represents a neutral solution.† When pH drops below 7, the solution is acidic (meaning a concentration of hydrogen ions, H^+, in excess of OH^- ions), whereas with pH higher than 7 the solution becomes alkaline (meaning an excess concentration of hydroxide ions, OH^-). BWR plants do not use chemical additives in the fluid but depend instead on full-flow demineralizers to keep the water free of impurities (see also Section 8.3, subsection "Reactor Water Cleanup System").

The chemical treatment of secondary water stems from the observation that an acidic environment tends to promote many forms of corrosion including a phenomenon called stress corrosion cracking (see Chapter 10). Under the combined effects of stresses and a corrosive environment (created by an acidic solution), metals tend to exhibit cracks, which when propagated can lead to failure. Therefore, the plant operator must keep the chemistry of the secondary water in the alkaline region, which is equivalent to saying that the pH value must be well above 7, preferably higher than 9. At this pH range most of the materials used in LWRs become passivated by a tightly adhering oxide layer on their surface which greatly reduces corrosion. Vendors provide more or less detailed specification of both water and steam chemistry to protect the components (primarily steam generator and turbines) from failures.

Early fossil plants added sodium hydroxide (NaOH) to maintain water alkalinity. This practice has been almost completely abandoned, because of the tendency of the hydroxide to come out of solution in the form of solid, when steam pressure dropped in the turbine, causing damage to the blades. The majority of nuclear power plants in the United States control the pH of the water either by addition of phosphates or by addition of volatile chemicals. Most nuclear plants with recirculating (or U-tube) steam generators initially used phosphate addition. This practice was later changed to the use of All-Volatile Treatment (AVT) in all but a couple of plants. All PWR plants with once-through steam generators employ AVT.

Phosphate Control

In this method the water alkalinity is adjusted by the addition of phosphates, that is, either disodium phosphate or a mixture of trisodium phosphate and disodium phosphate. The phosphates can release sodium hydroxide through the reaction

$$Na_3PO_4 + H_2O \rightleftharpoons Na_2HPO_4 + NaOH$$

In the conventional method (called coordinated phosphate treatment), the formation of free sodium hydroxide is avoided by maintaining a balance of the phosphate to sodium (3:1). Thus the sodium hydroxide formed is "buffered" by the phosphate, precluding free caustic and stress corrosion cracking. The reaction goes both ways: excess hydroxide in the solution drives the reaction to the left, while excess acidity neutralizes the hydroxide and drives the reaction to the right.

The main advantage of phosphate treatment is its ability to buffer, that is, to protect, against both acidic and basic imbalances and to maintain a pH value between 9 and 11. However, the phosphate treatment has the disadvantage that the salts added to the secondary water can accumulate and concentrate. Moreover, the Na/PO_4 ratio is hard to maintain when this occurs. Phosphates may also cause "wastage" of tubes when they concentrate in the heated crevices in the steam generator, producing an acidic solution, which in turn leads to tube thinning.

Because corrosion problems continued due to the presence of caustic (NaOH), particularly in

†This is only true at 25°C. Neutral pH occurs when the concentration of H^+ and OH^- are equal; the dissociation of water into H^+ and OH^- is temperature dependent. At 200°C, neutral pH is around 6.3 or $10^{-6.3}$ ions of each H^+ and OH^- per mole of water.

high-temperature and high-pressure boilers, the so-called "congruent" treatment† was introduced specifying that the sodium-to-phosphate ratio be maintained less than 2.65 below which free hydroxide cannot form. In short, in order to successfully control pH level without creating free caustic, two parameters must be kept within specified limits: the phosphate concentration (typically the specs for blowdown water were 10–80 ppm phosphate for plants with freshwater condenser coolants) and the Na-to-PO_4 ratio (typically between 2.0 and 2.6).

All-Volatile Treatment (AVT)

Newer plants adopted and older plants substituted AVT for secondary water. In this method, the introduction of solids into the system is avoided by using volatile alkaline chemicals to control the value of pH. The method is, therefore, particularly suitable for once-through steam generator plants. The main disadvantage of AVT compared to phosphate treatment is that the volatile chemicals do not buffer the solution and the protection offered against alkaline or acidic upsets is not as strong as with phosphates.

To perform AVT treatment any one of the following amines is used: ammonia (NH_3), morpholine (C_4H_9NO), and cyclohexylamine ($C_6H_{11}NH_2$). The most widely used chemical is ammonia. Since these substances are volatile, they are carried with the steam and are contained in the condensate. How effective each amine is in controlling the pH of the condensate depends on the following three factors: (1) concentration of the amine leaving the steam generator; (2) its partitioning (or distribution) between liquid and gaseous phase as steam undergoes temperature and pressure changes in the turbine and the condenser; and (3) their relative basicity, that is, how strong a base each of them is and how its strength changes with temperature. The properties of the three chemicals are different. For example, as temperature drops the ammonia partitioning in the gaseous phase (relative to the liquid phase) increases, whereas that of the other two decreases. The basicity of all three chemicals increases with decreasing temperature, that is, they become stronger bases. For the temperature ranges encountered in a power plant and for equivalent concentrations, the strongest base is cyclohexylamine, and morpholine the weakest.

The concentration of the amine used is based on the observation that corrosion of iron or steel stops when pH is in the range of 9.0 to 9.2. To calculate the necessary concentration of each amine in the condensate one assumes that the steam entering the turbine will produce water with a pH equal to 9.0 if çondensed and cooled to 25°C (77°F). Given these assumptions and the physical and chemical properties of the amines the following can be derived.

Ammonia must have a steam concentration of 0.27 ppm and the pH at the LP outlet is 1.2 pH units above neutral (which is about 6.3 at 200°C). Even though the volatility of ammonia increases at lower temperature, it becomes a stronger base. For morpholine, 3.8 ppm is required at the turbine inlet to produce a pH of 9 in condensed steam. The outlet from the LP cyclinder has a pH of about 2.2 above neutral. Finally, cyclohexylamine has effects similar to those of morpholine. It is seen that for equivalent inlet conditions, both morpholine and cyclohexylamine provide a higher value of pH in the condensate at the exit of the LP cylinders. Hence, these two compounds provide greater protection against corrosion throughout the turbine system than ammonia.‡ However, they cost more due to the higher concentrations required; it is perhaps mainly for this reason that most plants utilize ammonia for pH control.

Another chemical used with AVT in secondary water is hydrazine. It acts to remove oxygen, which is generally a deleterious element, in the same way it acts in the primary system (Section 8.2, subsection "The Chemistry and Volume Control System"). Hydrazine solution, a clear, waterlike liquid, removes oxygen through the reaction

$$N_2H_2 + O_2 \rightarrow N_2 + 2H_2O$$

Any excess hydrazine not used to capture oxygen adds alkalinity to the solution since, at the temperature prevailing in the steam generator, it decomposes as follows:

$$3N_2H_4 \rightarrow 4NH_3 + N_2$$

or

$$2N_2H_4 \rightarrow 2NH_3 + N_2 + H_2$$

†The name "congruent" came from the fact that the value of 2.65 for Na/PO_4 ratio corresponds to the temperature and pressure conditions at which the composition of liquid and solid trisodium phosphate are identical, or congruent.

‡Another amine, quinuclidine, currently under investigation, shows promise for use in nuclear systems.

Table 9.7. Feedwater Specifications for PWR Plants[a] (All Volatile Treatment)

Parameter	Westinghouse Recirculating Steam Generators	Combustion Engineering Recirculating Steam Generators	Babcock & Wilcox Once-Through Steam Generators
pH at 25°C (77°F):			
Cu alloys in system	8.8–9.2	8.8–9.2	8.5–9.3
Cu alloys not in system	Up to 9.6	9.2–9.5	9.3–9.5
Oxygen (ppb):			
Normal	<5	<10	7 max.
Abnormal	—	>10(4 hrs)[b]	—
Start-up	—	—	100 max.
Shutdown	—	100	—
Cation conductivity (μmhos/cm) at 25°C (77°F):			
Normal	4 max.[c]	<0.5	0.5 max.
Abnormal	—	>1.5(4 hrs)[b]	—
Start-up	—	—	1.0 max.
Hydrazine (ppb)	$[O_2]$ + 5	10–50	20–100
Iron (ppb):			
Normal	<10	<10	10 max.
Start-up	—	—	100 max.
Copper (ppb)	<5	<10	2 max.
Silica (ppb)	—	<10	20 max.
Ammonia (ppm)	<0.5	<1	—
Sodium (ppb)	—	<10	—
Lead (ppb)	—	—	1 max.
Total solids (ppb)	—	—	50 max.

Source: EPRI Report CS-1969.

[a]Tabulated values are for normal operation unless otherwise noted.
[b]Corrective action or shutdown recommended within time indicated.
[c]Specific conductivity.

Ammonia (NH_3) dissolved in water adds alkalinity because

$$NH_3 + H_2O \rightarrow NH_4(OH)$$

and NH_4OH produces hydroxide ions (OH^-) which make the solution alkaline. Hydrazine can be used for both oxygen and pH control, but in the United States use of hydrazine alone for pH control is not widespread.

Feedwater specifications for PWRs are shown in Table 9.7. With the systematic study of plant performance in recent years, it became apparent that maintenance of strict control over the chemistry of the water was a paramount factor in minimizing corrosion effects. Particularly important is the maintenance of low levels of chloride and sodium ions, which become a serious threat to plants using seawater as coolant. The key to maintaining very low concentrations of these harmful ions is a leak-proof condenser. To maintain leak-tight condensers, some utilities perform inspection of part or all of the condenser tubes at every outage using the eddy-current technique to spot weak or faulted tubes. Tubes whose walls are found weak (for example, with 50% loss of wall thickness) are then plugged to prevent coolant water circulation through them. During plant operation, the conductivity of the coolant is monitored. High readings are indicative of impurity in-leakage. If the levels are high enough, the plant may have to be shut down to correct whatever fault is causing the chemical imbalance.

9.12. CONTAINMENT OR REACTOR BUILDING

General

The term "containment" refers to the technical means provided to contain radioactivity, primarily fission products, and prevent its escape to the environment. In a LWR there are four successive barriers to such escape: the first barrier is provided by the fuel matrix, the second barrier is the fuel cladding, and the third barrier consists of the primary system (pressure vessel, pumps, steam

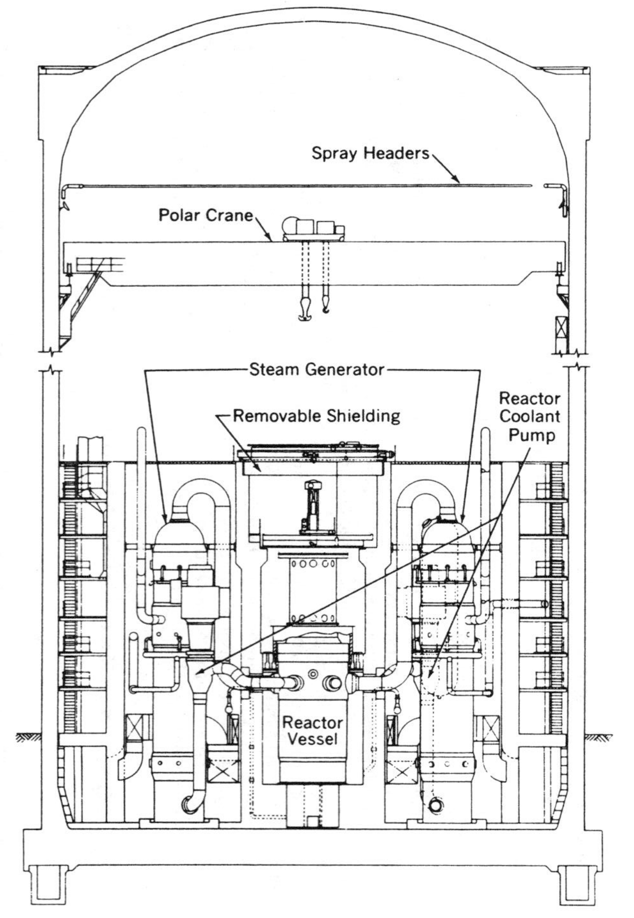
Spray Headers
Polar Crane
Steam Generator
Removable Shielding
Reactor Coolant Pump
Reactor Vessel

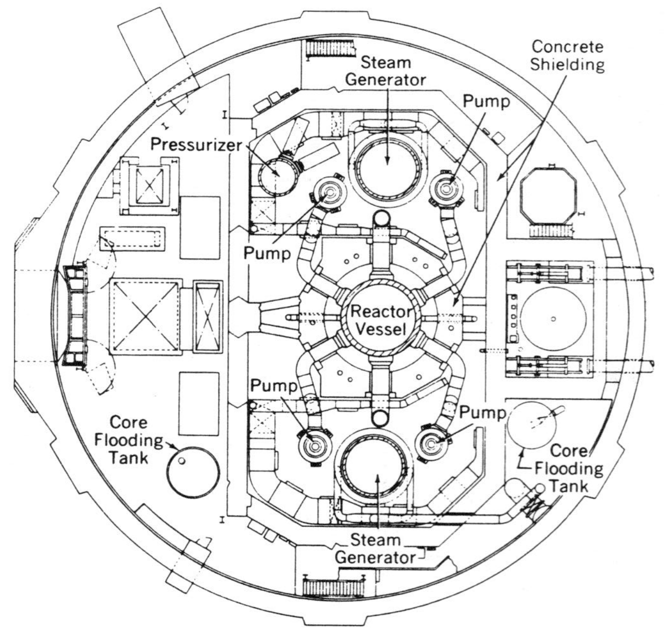
Steam Generator
Concrete Shielding
Pump
Pressurizer
Pump
Reactor Vessel
Pump
Pump
Core Flooding Tank
Core Flooding Tank
Steam Generator

generator primary side, pressurizer, etc.). A fourth barrier is provided by the reactor containment proper (some of the early, smaller plants built in the Soviet Union had no containment as such, but used a large building to contain radioactivity). It consists of a large building, usually about 42 m (140 ft) in diameter (but occasionally up to 64 m or 210 ft) and about 60 m (197 ft) in height built as a pressure vessel and capable of withstanding an internal pressure as high as 65 psig (0.44 MPa). The pressure at which failure would occur is, however, quite higher. There are two basic reasons for the use of a containment building. Under normal operating conditions, the primary water contains some radioactivity through activation (corrosion products or nitrogen-16 produced from oxygen in water) and from any leaky fuel. If a leak developed in the primary system (e.g., through a faulty pump seal) radioactivity would be released. The second reason is to guard against the likelihood of an accident such as a major break in a primary loop pipe which could lead to a Loss Of Coolant Accident (LOCA). The possible scenarios for such accidents vary widely, ranging from relatively mild to very serious. The most serious could be a core meltdown in which fission products contained in the fuel could escape the primary system. A detailed discussion of accident scenarios and their mitigation is given in Chapter 17. The containment structures with their associated systems are designed to withstand a set of postulated internal and external loads and to effectively contain radioactivity that may be released from the primary system. They also provide a shielding function, namely protection of personnel from exposure to radioactivity contained inside containment.

PWR Containment Design

Containment buildings vary considerably in design. Many are vertical cylindrical structures covered with a hemispherical or a shallow domed roof and with a flat foundation slab as in the typical arrangement shown in Figure 9.52. (A cylindrical wall has roughly double the strength of a flat wall of equivalent thickness. Also, a cylindrical building provides a smaller target for missiles for the same volume, similarly, for spheres.) One of the main factors influencing containment design is economic: since the containment is a major cost item the plant designer tries to minimize its size (within the constraints of safety and maintainability) to save money.

A brief review of the historical development of containment structures provides interesting insight. The early reactor facilities were experimental, low-power reactors installed in water pools. The large amounts of water present were considered adequate to absorb the energy generated in any power excursion and relatively small amounts of steam were expected. Accordingly, reactor buildings were made of reinforced concrete (concrete with a network of criss-crossed steel bars imbedded in them) and designed for an inside pressure of 5 to 8 psig (pounds per square inch gauge, i.e., above atmospheric pressure). A elastomer coating of the inner walls was enough to provide an impermeable membrane. With the construction of the first commercial PWR plant at Shippingport, Pennsylvania in 1957, the total energy stored in the primary coolant jumped by orders of magnitude, giving rise to much higher pressures and temperatures that needed containment. Plain reinforced concrete was no longer adequate to fulfill containment requirements economically and designers turned toward steel. A thick steel shell was used to provide the necessary strength and a layer of concrete was used to provide shielding. Later, as plant size grew to 1000 MWe, the design shifted again, as designers turned to prestressed reinforced concrete for structural strength using the steel liner primarily as an impermeable membrane.

Figure 9.52 shows such a reinforced concrete containment with such a steel liner. The approximately 1-m (3.25-ft) thick wall is made of reinforced concrete to provide mechanical strength. The ¼-in. (6.4-mm) liner provides primarily a membrane for leak-tightness against escape of gases. In the design shown in the figure prestressing was provided by a network of reinforcement steel bars placed in the concrete and tensioned after the concrete was poured and set. For this reason, it is called a "prestressed, post-tensioned" building. The main advantage of a prestressed, post-tensioned building is an efficient use of concrete, and therefore a leaner and cheaper construction. There are, however, some additional important advantages. Since a large number of tendons are used, the failure of one or two tendons would not be as serious as the failure of a steel shell structure. The tendons provide redundancy of design, an important feature of all safety systems.

Figure 9.52. Sectional and plan views of a containment building (Oconee Nuclear Station 900 MWe). The containment is a post-tensioned reinforced concrete cylinder with a shallow domed roof and a flat foundation slab. Horizontal and vertical tendons (rebar) provide the post-tensioning system while a three-way post-tensioning system is used in the dome. The foundation slab is also reinforced conventionally with high-strength reinforcing steel. The structure is lined with a 6.4-mm (¼-in.) welded steel plate to provide vapor tightness. Approximate dimensions are: inside diameter 116 ft (35m); inside height 208 ft (63.4 m); vertical wall thickness 3¾ ft (1.14 m); dome thickness 3¼ ft (1 m); foundation slab 8½ ft (2.60 m). (From Babcock & Wilcox, *Steam, Its Generation and Use*, 1978.)

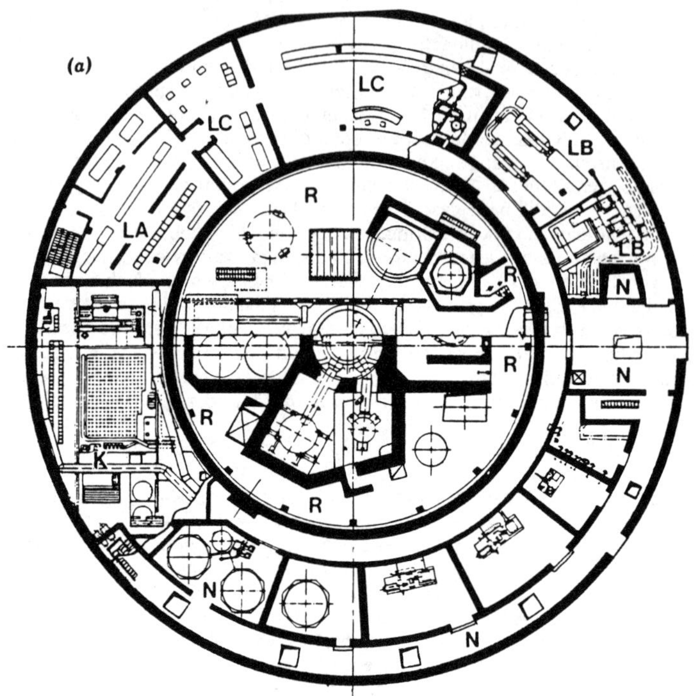
(a)
LC
LC
LB
LB
LA
R
R
R
R
R
N
N
N
N
K
Reactor building
and
ring building

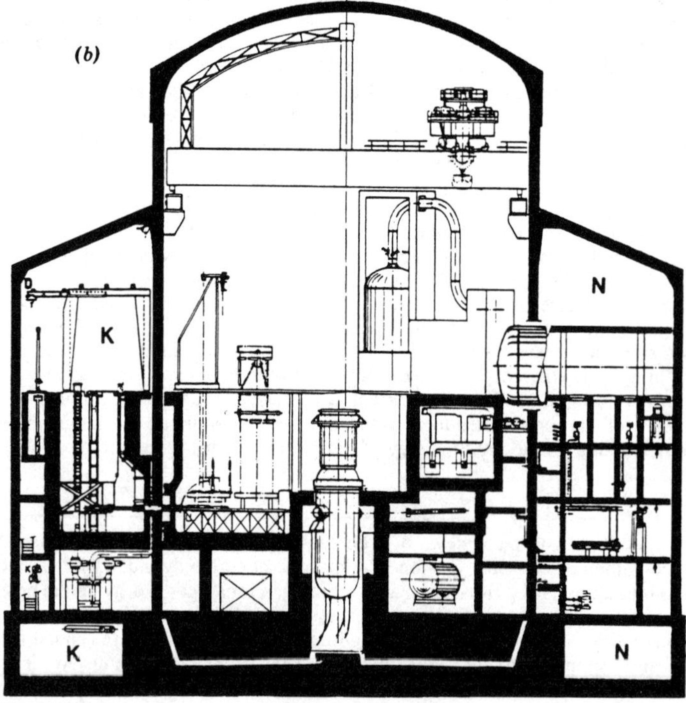
(b)
N
K
K
N
Ring building
Fuel building
Reactor building
Ring building

The individual tendons, each installed in a separate conduit, can be regularly and efficiently inspected to detect incipient failure, and to initiate timely repair.

A variation of the reinforced concrete containment with a steel liner is the design shown in Figure 9.53. This two-loop PWR design offered by French designers is a 600-MWe plant intended for export markets in developing countries where smaller plants are needed for integration in their smaller electrical grids. The annular or ring building, containing safety systems, fuel handling, control room, and so on, completely surrounds the cylindrical reactor building on a common mat and provides compactness and, it is hoped, economy of construction.

A different design of PWR containment called the ice-condenser type whose function will be discussed later is shown in Figure 9.54. It consists of a free-standing inner steel shell, about 45 mm ($1\frac{3}{4}$ in.) thick around which an outer containment of reinforced concrete is built, with an air space between the two.

There are also spherical shell designs like the one shown in Figure 9.55 with the sphere eccentrically placed within the concrete building by a German designer (KWU) of nuclear plants. A similar spherical shell design, but with a concentric arrangement of inner shell and outer concrete building, has been adopted for the latest design of one of the U.S. vendors (Systems 80 by Combustion Engineering).

The containment buildings enclose the entire primary system and have a number of compartments for the housing of auxiliary equipment, safety systems (of which there must be two redundant and physically separate trains), accumulators, electrical equipment, and ventilation equipment, as well as facilities for the handling of spent and fresh fuel. In the design of Figure 9.54 the fuel-handling and storage system is entirely enclosed in the outer containment and in the design of Figure 9.52 even the control room is housed in the annular building which is part of the compact containment building providing extra protection from external threats.

Containment Internal Loads (PWR)

The containment building is designed to contain the energy and materials released in a complete, double-ended break of the largest pipe of the reactor coolant system and to withstand the impact of internally generated missiles. A simplistic calculation will reveal the magnitude of these internal static loads.

A typical large PWR plant operates at about 2200 psia and between 550° and 590°F with a total primary water inventory of between 311 and 368 m^3 (11,000 and 13,000 ft^3), equivalent to 300,000–355,000 kg (660,000–780,000 lb). The enthalpy of the subcooled water at these conditions can be found from steam and water tables to be 580 Btu/lb. In the case that the primary boundary is breached and the system is completely depressurized, the coolant will flash to steam. Assuming that the final pressure of steam and air in the containment will be equal to atmospheric (in reality it will be several atmospheres higher but the value is not yet known), the enthalpy of saturated water at that pressure will be 180 Btu/lb. Therefore, the total amount of heat available for vaporization (assuming an inventory of 12,000 ft^3 or 720,000 lb) will be $580 - 180$ Btu/lb $\times$ 720,000 lb = 288×10^6 Btu. The heat necessary to produce 1 lb of saturated steam from 1 lb of saturated liquid (called latent heat of vaporization) is about 970 Btu/lb. Consequently, the total amount of steam produced will be $288 \times 10^6/970 = 300{,}000$ lb of steam. At atmospheric pressure this steam would occupy a volume of 300,000 lb $\times$ 26.8 ft^3/lb = 8.0×10^6 ft^3.

This volume is much larger than what is available; the containment structures in current larger power plants have a free volume varying from 1.5 to 2 million ft^3. In order to fit 300,000 lb of steam into, say, 1.5×10^6 ft^3, the volume per unit mass (called specific volume of steam) could be 1.5×10^6 ft^3/300,000 lb = 5 ft^3/lb. This volume corresponds (from steam tables) to a pressure of about 90 psia (and a temperature of 320°F). The gauge pressure will be lower, namely $90 - 14.7 = 75$ psig. The assumption of final pressure being equal to atmospheric was, therefore, wrong and one must repeat the calculation with the newly calculated pressure. By an iterative process one arrives at the final pressure at which the steam and containment air will come to an equilibrium in the free volume available in the containment. It must also be taken into account that the total pressure is made of the partial pressure of air and steam. The calculation presented above is simplistic because a number of other effects were neglected. The energy stored in the fuel and other structures of the

Figure 9.53. Containment building for the two-loop, 600-MW PWR standard design by the French vendor Framatome. Compactness of design and economy is achieved by carefully arranging safety functions, control room, and so on in an auxiliary building completely surrounding the containment. The main part of the containment, enclosing the nuclear island, has been reduced to an internal diameter of 33 m (108 ft) and is of reinforced, prestressed concrete. The auxiliary building is reinforced concrete and houses the emergency core cooling system with control and power equipment (L), safety-related auxiliary systems (N), and the fuel building (K). The auxiliary (ring) building has a diameter of 62 m (203 ft).

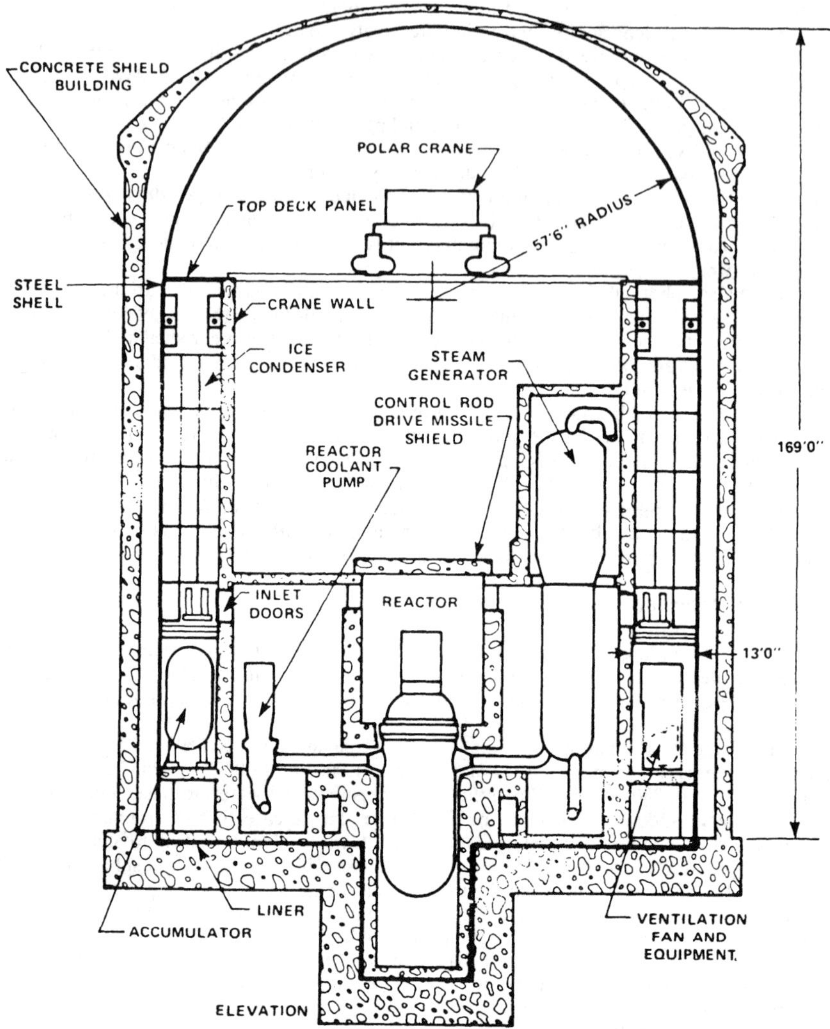

Figure 9.54. PWR containment building of the ice-condenser type. This design incorporates an inner steel shell, and an outer concrete containment with an air space between them. The steel shell encloses the primary system and safety-related and ventillation systems. Stored in an annular space around the inner shell wall are packs of ice. They are provided to condense steam if it is released in great amounts from the primary system.

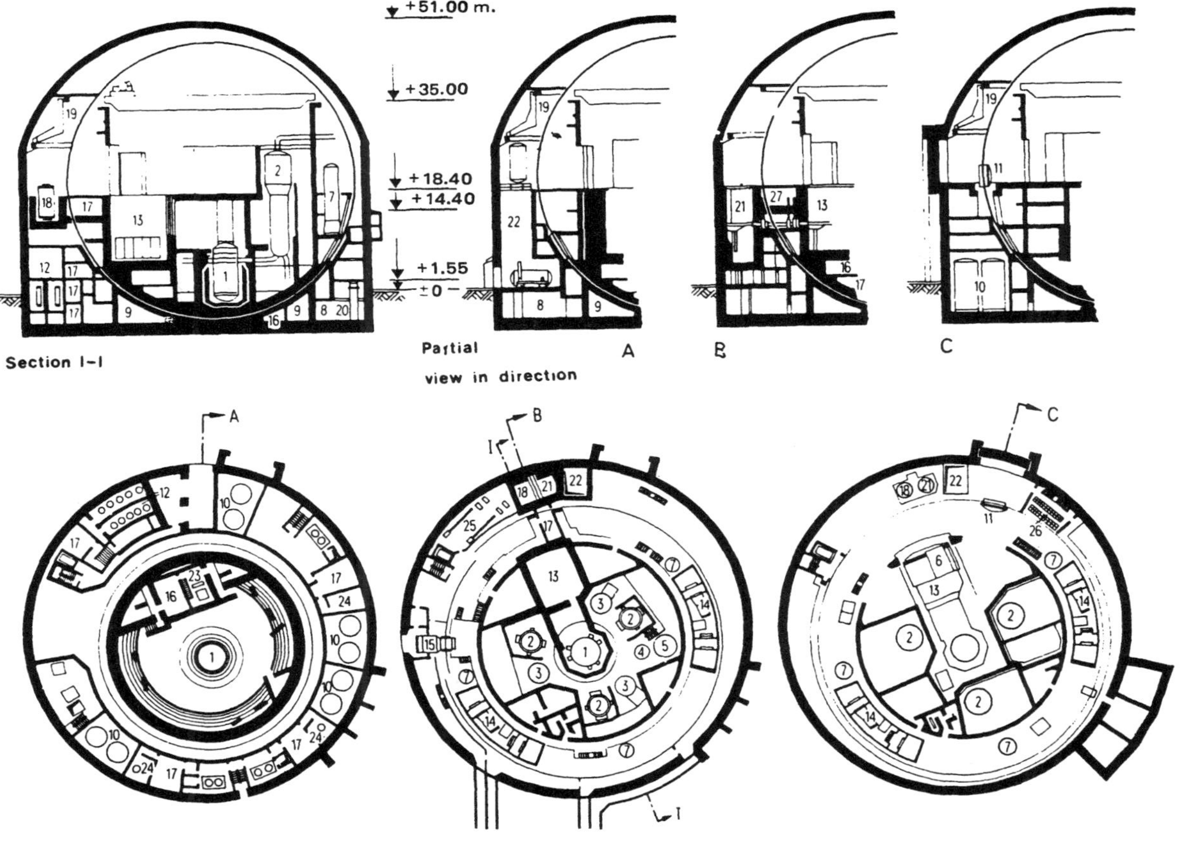

Figure 9.55. Sections of the containment used at the first standard, three-loop, PWR built in Gösgen, Switzerland by Kraftwerk Union (KWU), the West German supplier. It utilizes a spherical shell, 32 mm thick eccentrically placed in a larger reactor building. The latter was made of reinforced concrete, with a thickness of 1.6 m (5.25 ft) in the cylindrical part (reduced to 1.2 m in the dome) and was designed to withstand the full impact of a Boeing 707 type commercial airplane crashing at a speed of 370 km/hr (224 mph). *Key:* 1—reactor; 2—steam generator; 3—coolant pumps; 4—pressurizer; 5—pressurizer relief tank; 6—refueling machine; 7—accumulator; 8—high-pressure safety pump; 9—service cooling water pump; 10—borated water storage tank; 11—construction opening; 12—delay bed; 13—fuel storage pool; 14—ventilation system; 15—personnel lock; 16—transducer room; 17—valve room; 18—tank storage place; 19—loading crane; 20—component cooling heat exchanger; 21—refueling pool; 22—lifting shaft; 23—oil supply main coolant pipe; 24—residual heat exchanger; 25—cooler refueling pool/lock; 26—storage of new fuel elements; 27—fuel element transfer equipment. (Courtesy KWU.)

primary system was not accounted for. Neither did we account for any additional heat produced in the core by fission products (we assume that the fission energy was stopped by a reactor shutdown). On the other hand, we neglected the absorption of thermal energy by the large number of components in the containment, by air, the containment walls, and by extra cooling water (or ice) provided for this purpose. When these effects are taken into account a much more accurate figure of pressure and temperature can be obtained.

When the correct pressure is calculated, say, 50 psig, a 15% margin of safety is allowed and the building is then designed to withstand a pressure of 58 psig. Actual failure will occur at two to three times this pressure, that is, not below 140 psig. The designer has, of course, the option of choosing a larger building which will result in lower pressure, versus a smaller volume which must be designed to a higher pressure. An optimum solution can be found through detailed analysis if the various cost elements are known. The design pressure for current PWR containments is in the range of 40 to 70 psig and the temperatures are those corresponding to saturated steam at these pressures (approximately 300°F).

The design must also take into account impacts from missiles that might be generated inside containment. In the case of pipe guillotine rupture, the reaction forces from the high-speed stream of water and steam discharged from the break could hurl the loose pipes against the containment wall in a phenomenon called pipe whip. Whip restraints attaching long stretches of pipe to a firm support (floor, wall) are used to guard against this risk. Another possibility is the failure of a mechanism that holds the control rods down. Internal devices are provided inside containment to protect against these missiles.

PWR Containment Function

In some PWR plants, the pressure inside containment is kept below atmospheric so that any leakage (through penetrations) would be inward. Other plants use double barriers to prevent any release of radioactive material to the environment.

In case of an accident that causes the pressure inside containment to rise above a certain level, a command will be given to isolate the containment by closing all valves on lines that lead to the outside world. At the same time the blowers will be started to collect leakage from the reactor building, pass it through filters and absorption beds to remove radioactive materials, and discharge it through the station stack. The suction for the blowers is located at the penetration room located outside the reactor building, where leakage is most likely to occur. For this reason, penetrations are grouped together and penetration rooms are constructed around them.

In order to mitigate the effects of large releases of steam (and potentially of radioactivity) in the containment two full capacity independent safety systems are provided: the reactor building spray system and the reactor building emergency coolers. The systems are designed to provide cool water to condense discharge steam and to prevent containment pressure from reaching its design limit. Individual systems differ considerably but a typical system may be described as follows: The initial capacity of the systems in removing heat from the containment atmosphere is typically 253 GJ/hr (240×10^6 Btu/hr).

When a containment pressure of 4 psig is reached, the emergency coolers of the reactor building are actuated. In their postaccident mode, the system consists of three units each with a fan and an emergency cooler. As the reactor building air is circulated across a tubular heat exchanger, a portion of steam is condensed. These coolers alone would be capable of returning the containment pressure to near atmospheric within 24 hr after an accident. When the pressure reaches a level of 10 psig, the second safety system, the reactor building spray system, is automatically actuated. It consists of a pump, piping, headers, and spray nozzles arranged uniformly under the containment dome. It can spray borated water into the reactor building at a rate of 11.35 m^3/min (3000 gal/min). A sodium hydroxide (or thiosulfate) additive is also provided in the spray water to increase the retention of iodine, and, hence, to reduce its concentration in the containment atmosphere in the event of a sizable breach of fuel cladding.

The containment spray and cooling system is part of the safety provisions described in more detail in Chapter 18. For each such safety system two independent, redundant systems are provided to ensure reliability of safety function.

An alternative method for condensing steam is provided by the ice-condenser design introduced by Westinghouse in 1967 (Figure 9.54). The containment space is divided into two compartments by concrete walls and partitions. The two spaces communicate through a vertical, annular space in which a number of ice packs are stored, at about 10°C (18°F) below freezing. Since all heat sources are located in the lower compartment, any produced steam would flow through the annular space coming in contact with the ice packs. The large sensible and latent heat of ice is used in this design to condense the steam (144 Btu are needed to melt 1 lb of ice). The design requires a refrigeration system and an antifreeze (ethyleneglycol) circulation system to cool the ice machine and maintain low temperatures in the cold storage compartment. With the high heat capacity of the stored ice a considerably lower design pressure results. Thus, containment buildings of this design are smaller

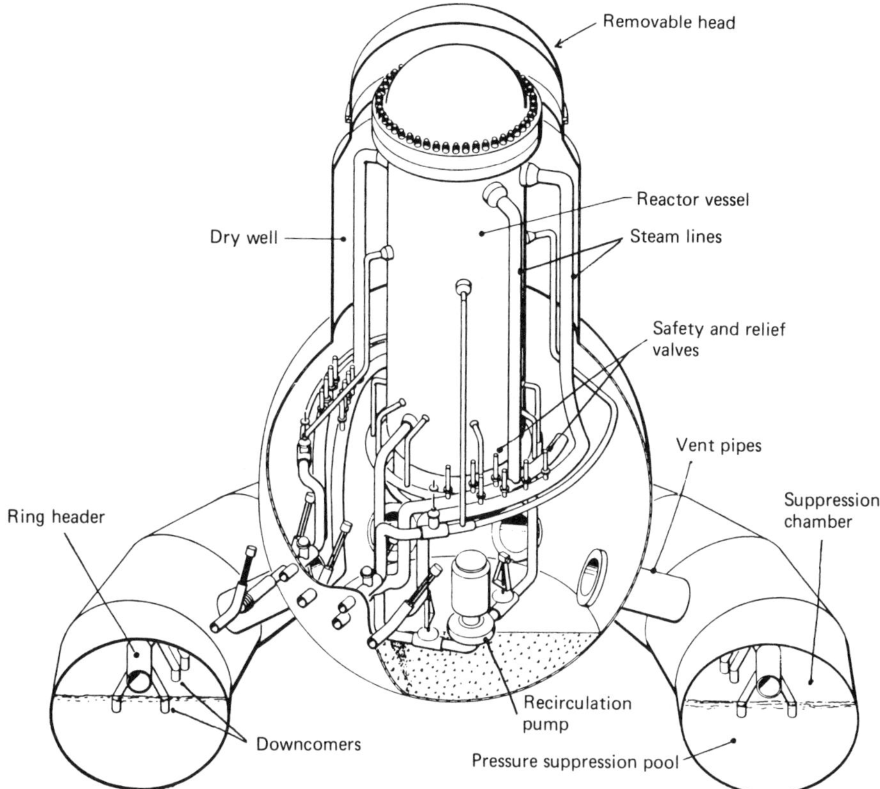

Figure 9.56. BWR primary containment system; Mark I type. This type of containment was installed in older versions of the BWR design. It is also known as the inverted light bulb. The vessel is enclosed inside a drywell which communicates with a large body of water contained in a large torus beneath the light bulb. The torus is called the pressure suppression pool. The entire structure is enclosed in the reactor building. (From WASH-1250.)

and lighter, with a design pressure of 10–15 psig. The ice contains boron poison (needed to ensure a subcritical core when the water is used for core cooling) and caustic (sodium hydroxide) for the same reasons as in the containment spray designs.

BWR Containment

The development of the BWR containment followed a somewhat different path. The first BWR plants used a steel containment in the shape of an inverted lightbulb, completely surrounding the reactor vessel pressure relief valves on the main steam lines and the recirculation system, as shown in Figure 9.56. The light bulb shell, called the drywell, is connected through a number of radially extending vent pipes to a large torus (called the wetwell), somewhat less than half filled with water. This large quantity of water is used as a heat sink to condense steam that might escape from the primary system through the opening of the relief or safety valves, or from a break in the piping. The drywell is actually connected to a ring header which runs at the center of the torus and which is provided with a large number of downcomer open-ended tubes. Should steam be released in the drywell, the pressure there would rise and the steam/air mixture would be forced through the vent pipes to the ring header and downward into the pool of water where it would mix and be condensed. The top of the light bulb forms a head which is removable during refueling. The steel light bulb is surrounded by concrete, which provides a radiation shield. The drywell and wetwell along with many other compartments are part of the reactor building as shown in Figure 9.57. The outer concrete wall of the rectangular structure provides a secondary containment. It is designed to have low leakage, and is provided with sealed joints and double door entries. The BWR containment is provided with a normal and a standby ventilation system. Under accident conditions, the normal system would be shut down and the two parallel standby systems would take over to maintain a

Figure 9.57. BWR secondary containment building showing the primary Mark I containment system enclosed. (Courtesy General Electric Co.)

negative gauge pressure inside containment. The discharged air is forced through banks of filters, including High-Efficiency Particulate Air (HEPA) filters and solid absorbents which would retain any radioactivity contained in the flow, particularly iodine.

A typical, inverted light bulb containment has a neck diameter of 8.9 m (35 ft) with a sphere diameter of 19.8 m (65 ft). These dimensions result in a free volume of about 7400 m^3 (260,000 ft^3) which is quite smaller than PWR containment volumes (typically 1.5 to 2 million ft^3). What enables a BWR to accommodate an equivalent energy release in a much smaller volume is the pressure suppression pool with its large inventory of water.

The containment described above was labeled by its designer (General Electric Co.) as Mark I. In 1969 a modified design, the Mark II, was offered. Shown in Figure 9.58, it consists of a frustum of a cone sitting on top of a cylinder. The reactor vessel is located inside the cone near the top with its head parting line at the same level with that of the drywell head. A floor separates the top conical section (drywell) from the bottom cylindrical section (wetwell) with vertical pipes connecting the two. The design is also known as the over- and under-design.

A further modification of the BWR containment resulted in an even more advanced version, the Mark III, which is currently offered by the U.S. manufacturer of BWRs. It is shown in Figure 9.59. It features a cylindrical drywell made of concrete, a free-standing steel shell providing secondary containment and an outer concrete building providing radiation shielding. The pressure suppression pool is an annular space around the drywell formed by the floor of the containment, the containment liner, and the drywell wall. Drywell and suppression pool communicate through horizontal vents in the drywell wall. A weir wall keeps the water from covering the floor of the drywell. An additional pool of water is formed above the drywell as shown. The steel containment encloses all the equipment of the reactor building; it is designed to withstand the temperature and pressure that could be produced in a large loss-of-coolant accident, and to contain any radioactivity

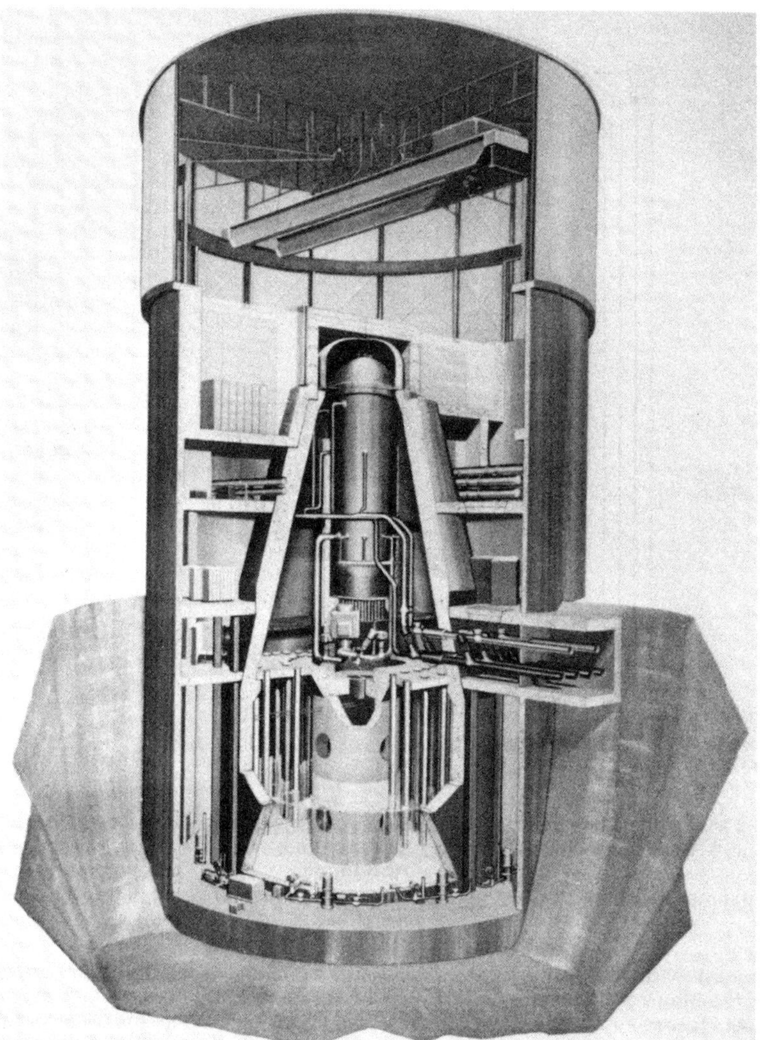

Figure 9.58. BWR containment, Mark II type. The inverted light bulb was replaced by a frustum on top of a cylinder. Vertical pipes connect the upper compartment (drywell) to the lower compartment (suppression pool). Steam and feedwater lines leave the cylindrical secondary containment through the concrete tunnel to the right. At the bottom level, just outside the pressure suppression pool are the pumps and pipes of the residual heat removal system. (Courtesy General Electric Co.)

released. The exterior concrete building provides further isolation from the environment and additional protection against external missiles. A variation of BWR containment, but with the same basic principles and features as already discussed, is shown in Figure 9.60. It is used by the Swedish manufacturer ASEA-Atom.

The large amount of water in the suppression pool is also used as a source of water for a variety of safety functions. One of these functions will be mentioned here since it is equivalent with similar systems in PWRs: a spray system with nozzles along a ring header inside the secondary containment is provided as shown in Figure 9.61. The purpose of this system is, as with PWRs, to condense any steam that escapes from the drywell and to prevent overpressure in the secondary containment. It can also trap radioactivity by solution or entrainment and minimize the potential of their release into the environment. The residual heat removal system is used for this function in its containment spray mode. Water from the suppression pool is pumped through either or both of the two identical but completely independent loops. Initiation and termination of containment spray is

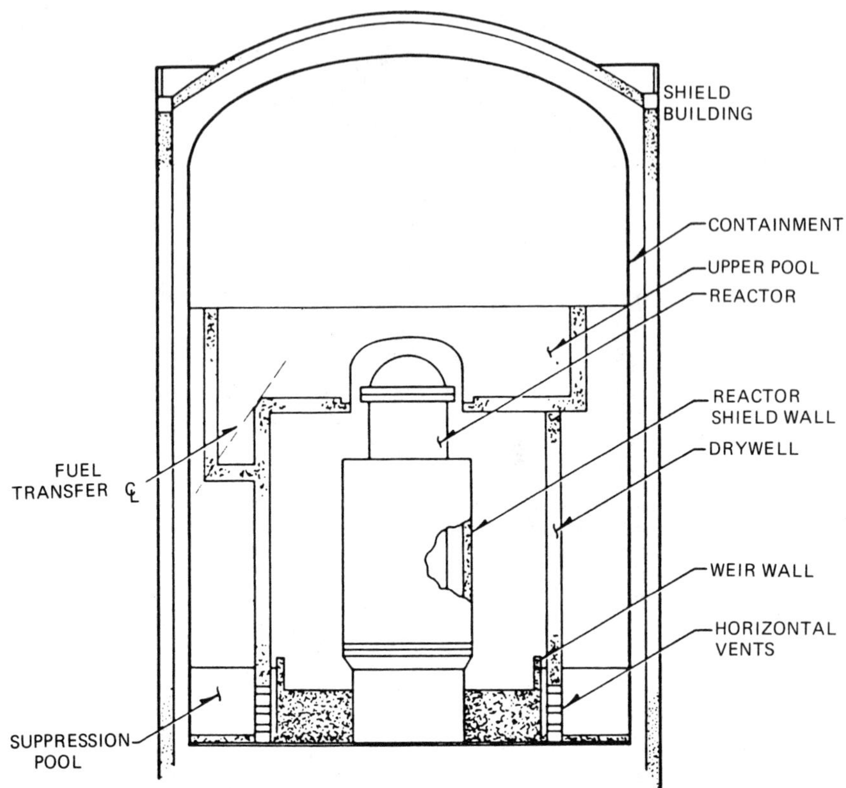

Figure 9.59. BWR multiple containment system and shield building; Mark III type. In this design, the drywell is made of concrete, inside a containment structure made of steel. The large pressure suppression pool is an annular channel between drywell and containment. Communication is effected through horizontal vents. A pool of water is also provided above the reactor.

done manually, with full flow achieved within about 3 min of initiation. The heat exchangers are provided to ensure that the temperature in the pool immediately after blowdown does not exceed a preset limit (generally 77°C or 170°F). The suppression pool water is the supply source for other safety functions, such as safety injection. It is the ultimate return of any lost coolant, thus closing the loop. Thus the suppression pool water serves two functions: to condense the steam from the reactor loop and to provide a large reservoir of water for emergency functions.

Penetrations, Air Locks, Leakage, Testing

Although containment structures must be as integral as possible, a number of penetrations are unavoidable. Penetrations are required for electric wire, pipes, air locks, and equipment hatches. Leaks frequently occur around penetrations. Therefore, they are grouped together and rooms are built around them to better detect and control leakage.

Penetrations are complex devices that must be properly designed and installed to avoid leakage. They must accept any loads applied to them. Welds used in installing penetrations must be individually testable for leaks. This means that a specially designed pressure-tight channel must be provided to allow testing of the weld at any time. Figure 9.62 shows a cross section of a typical electrical penetration. Many electrical leads are usually grouped together in one penetration. Pipe penetration comes in two categories: cold penetration and hot penetration (Figure 9.63).

Another type of opening in the containment structure is provided for personnel entrances. Since they must be available for use at any time, an air-lock construction is employed. It consists of a chamber with two doors; one toward the containment space and the other toward the exterior. An interlocking mechanism allows only one door to be open at any time. The doors are power operated with manual operation possible in case of a power failure. An assembled personnel air lock is shown in Figure 9.64.

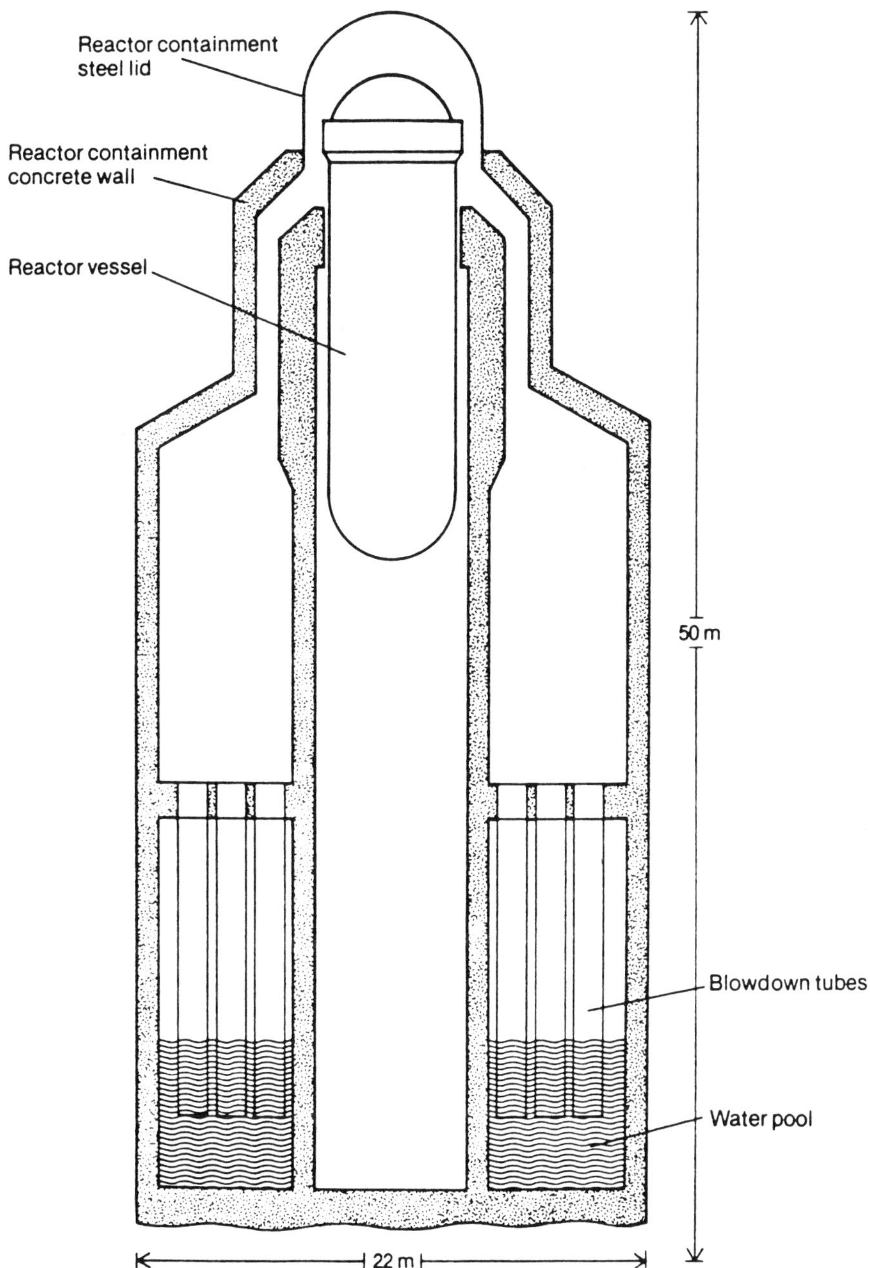

Figure 9.60. BWR inner containment design used at the Forsmark station in Sweden (by the Swedish manufacturer ASEA-Atom).

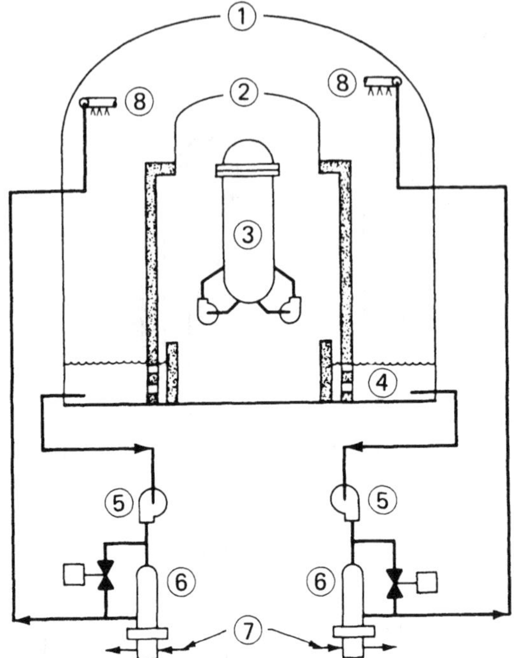

Figure 9.61. A spray system is provided inside the secondary BWR containment. It is designed to condense any steam that might escape from the drywell and to trap radioactivity. The residual heat removal system is used for this purpose and water is derived from the pressure suppression pool. 1—containment; 2—drywell; 3—reactor pressure vessel; 4—suppression pool; 5—system pump; 6—heat exchanger; 7—service water; 8—containment spray.

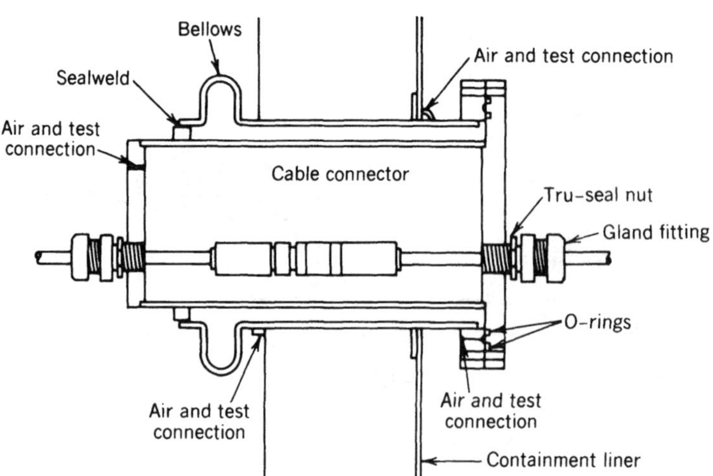

Figure 9.62. Cross section of a typical electrical penetration. Usually many electric leads are grouped in one penetration. Each penetration can be individually pressurized to test its leak tightness. (Courtesy Westinghouse Electric Corp.)

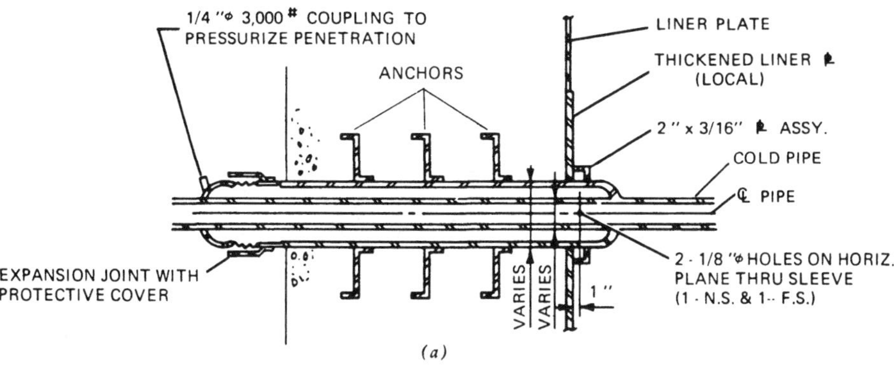

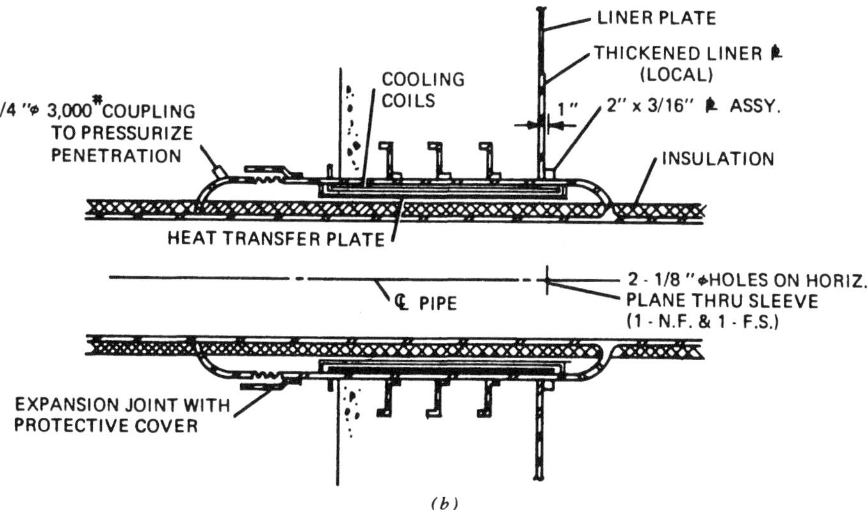

Figure 9.63. (*a*) Typical cold pipe penetration through containment wall. (*b*) Hot pipe penetration with insulation and cooling coils to prevent concrete temperature from rising too high. Expansion joints, anchors, locally thickened liners, and pressure testing openings are features of both penetration categories.

Equipment hatches are openings in the containment wall for the movement of equipment in and out of the reactor building. Their size is dictated by the size of the largest equipment to be moved through them. For PWRs this is usually a reactor vessel O-ring. It will be recalled (Section 9.7) that the existing equipment hatch in the PWR in which steam generator replacement was decided, allowed the removal from reactor of the lower shell but not of the upper shell. Normally, steam generators and reactor vessels are installed before the reactor building is closed, and removal during the plant lifetime was not anticipated. Equipment hatches are usually not of the air-lock type for reasons of economy. They can be used only when the plant is shut down.

Leakage from reactor buildings must be kept to a minimum. Door-type openings can be made leak-tight through various designs, the most reliable of which has double, inflatable pneumatic seals. Air locks are built to strict requirements of leak-tightness specified in Section III of the ASME code. Materials used in the seals are elastomers, usually neoprene, although other substances (like ethylenepropylene terpolymers) are being introduced.

The reactor building is tested initially and then periodically for leak tightness. Hatch seals, air-lock doors, and penetrations are individually tested and an overall building leak-rate test is performed. The leakage allowed depends on plant location. Values of leakage range between 0.1 and 2% per day of the net volume.

Figure 9.64. Inflatable seal personnel air lock. Rating 103 kPa (15psi). (Courtesy W.J. Wooley Co.)

Hydrogen Control

Hydrogen production in LWRs is possible during accidents due to (a) the radiolytic decomposition of water, and (b) the zirconium-water reaction. The latter is the dominant potential contributor. At temperatures above 870°C (1600°F) zirconium reacts with metal according to the reaction

$$Zr + H_2O \rightarrow ZrO_2 + 2H_2$$

The reaction rate increases with temperature and becomes very rapid above 1500°C (2700°F).

If this hydrogen is released to the containment, through either a pipe break or through relief and safety valve action, flammable mixtures of hydrogen and oxygen could be formed in containment. There are a number of limits of hydrogen flammability: an air mixture with low moisture (1 ppm to 10%) at room temperature has a lower limit of upward flammability of 4% hydrogen. The lower limit for downward flame propagation is 8% and the lower limit at which a detonation might occur is 19%. The burning of hydrogen would also produce a rise in temperature. In fact, records from the TMI-2 accident indicate that on March 28, 1979, there was a hydrogen burn in the reactor containment about 10 hr after the turbine had tripped with a pressure spike reaching 28 psig (Figure 9.65) and a temperature rise of about 40°F. The dynamics of hydrogen behavior in the environment of a postaccident containment are quite complex. They depend not only on hydrogen concentration but on direction and turbulence of flow, moisture content, size of water droplets, and so on. An extensive program of research in hydrogen generation, behavior, and management was launched following the TMI-2 accident, and many interesting results are beginning to emerge. The presence of turbulence generally tends to lower flammability limits, whereas the presence of moisture (particularly in the 15–30% range) tends to increase them.

Both PWRs and BWRs must have provisions to ensure that flammable concentrations of hydrogen are not reached in the containment. Particular concern was raised for the integrity of small containments, such as Mark I and Mark II containments of BWR. A release of hydrogen from metal/water reactions tends to give a higher relative percentage of hydrogen content in a small free volume than in a larger one, as shown in the diagram of Figure 9.66.

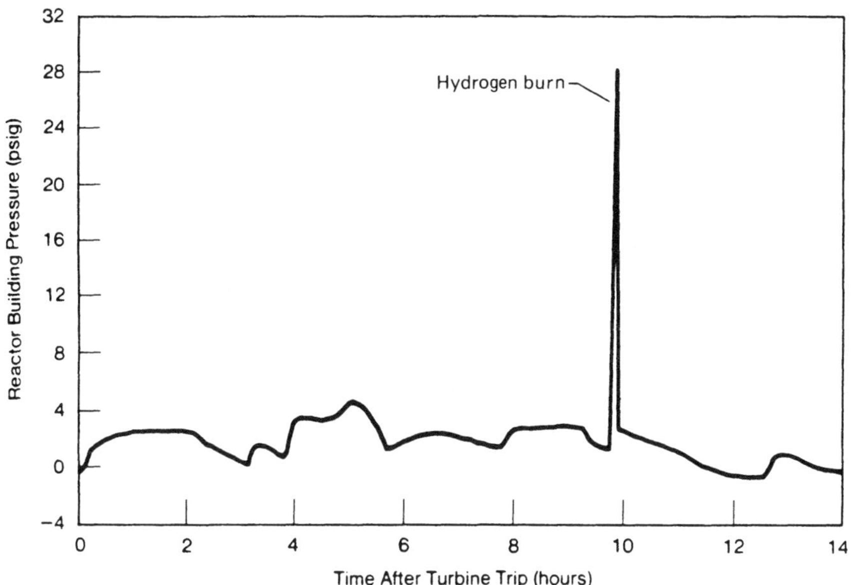

Figure 9.65. A pressure spike from a hydrogen burn of about 28 psig occurred at the TMI-2 reactor about 10 hr after reactor trip. The accident produced hydrogen through chemical reaction of zirconium and steam at elevated temperatures when the core was uncovered.

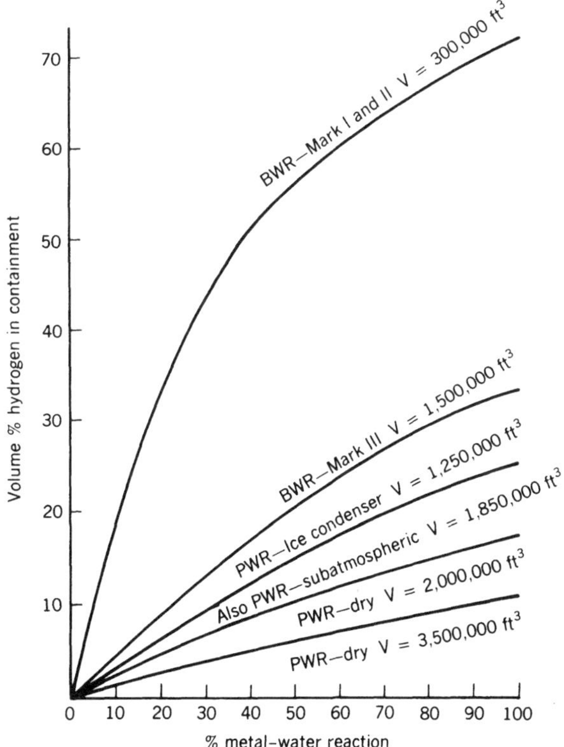

Figure 9.66. Hydrogen concentration in containment as a function of metal–water reaction. The various curves correspond to different types of containment. Those with a smaller free volume have a higher hydrogen concentration for the same amount of metal–water reaction. Mark I and II containment cause a greater concern than the others in this respect. An inert containment atmosphere could be used to eliminate the problem.

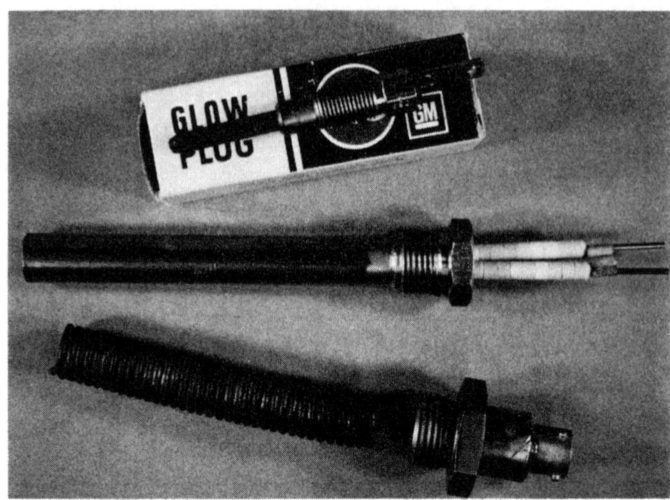

Figure 9.67. Various types of igniters for hydrogen control in containment buildings. (From EPRI.)

One of the ways to accomplish hydrogen control is the installation of igniters at selected locations in the containment to cause a gradual burn of hydrogen gas as soon as it is formed and to prevent concentrations from approaching dangerous levels at which an explosion might be possible. Figure 9.67 shows three such igniters. The first is a common glow plug which uses low voltage (hence, it needs a transformer) to heat a filament to red-hot temperatures. A second type of igniter uses a heater coil to create high temperature and can be fed directly from a 120-V line, thus eliminating the need (and cost) of a transformer. Both these kinds have been installed in nuclear plants in an arrangement shown in Figure 9.68.

Another method of coping with the hydrogen hazard is to fill the containment with inert gas (usually nitrogen); in the absence of oxygen, hydrogen cannot burn. Boiling water reactors with Mark I containment have operated successfully with inert containments. However, the maintenance of equipment and operational flexibility are hampered considerably because the inert atmosphere limits access of personnel to equipment inside containment. For this reason, inerting is not a very popular method with plant operators. Nevertheless, the inerting of all reactors with small containments (particularly Mark I and II) has been proposed as a licensing requirement to allay the concerns of containment failure from a hydrogen burn.

Among PWRs, the type of containment most vulnerable to the hydrogen threat is the ice-condenser type because of its relatively smaller volume (see Figure 9.66) and of its relatively lower design pressure (12 psig). At least a 25% metal/water reaction could be tolerated by the ice-condenser containment without inerting. This latter measure, if taken, would eliminate the problem, but its adoption would impose restrictions on the access to important components for maintenance.

Other means of reducing the hydrogen problem are use of halon suppressants,† filtered-vented systems, use of chemical catalysts, and gas turbines.‡

External Threats—Missile Protection

The containment is also subject to a spectrum of threats from the external world. Natural phenomena, such as earthquakes, tornadoes, floods and hurricanes, and tsunamis, as well as external manmade events such as nearby explosions and aircraft crashes, and possibly acts of sabotage, are taken into account in the designs of the containment. The specific design depends on the plant site and the probability and magnitude of such external threats. For example, plants built in areas plagued by tornadoes or hurricanes are designed to withstand the direct impact of various objects lifted up by the strong winds and accelerated to postulated speeds.

U.S. Regulatory documents have divided the country in three regions of varying tornado

†Chemical compounds with a halogen substituting for hydrogen in a hydrocarbon molecule, for example, $CBrF_3$ or $CBrClF_2$.

‡Gas turbines would consume the oxygen in containment before it could react with H_2.

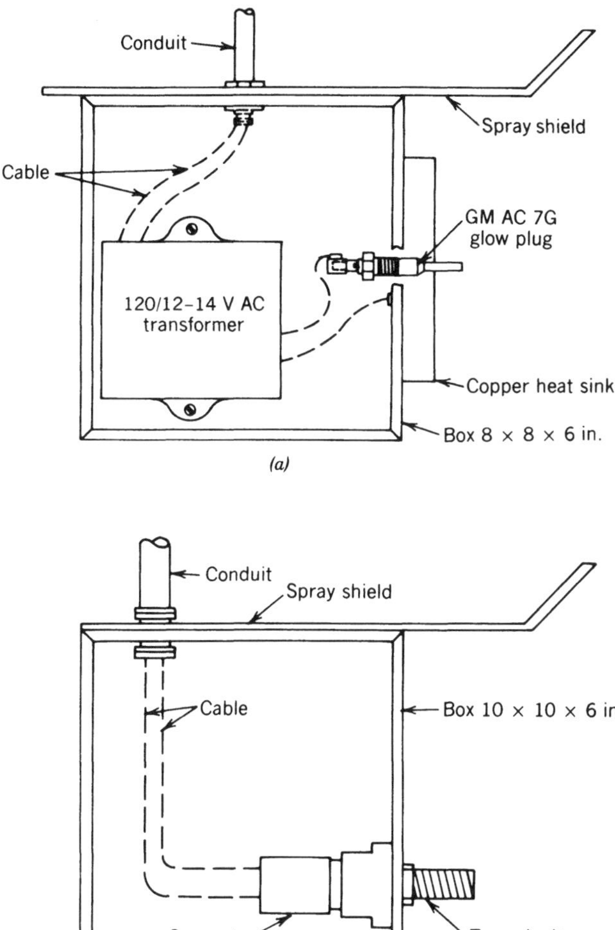

Figure 9.68. (*a*) Installation of a glow plug (type GM AC 7G) for hydrogen control in LWR containment. A transformer is needed with this design to provide 14-V ac from the electric supply line. A box and shield are used to protect the assembly from containment sprays. (*b*) This simplified design uses a heater coil with power directly derived from the line. The weight and cost of the transformer is eliminated. (From EPRI.)

intensity. In region I, the maximum speed of a tornado is taken to be 360 mph (528 ft/sec or 161 m/sec). In such a location the design must include an impact of a 1500–lb, 35-ft wooden utility pole at a speed of 150 mph, a 12-in. diameter by 15-ft long steel pipe at the same speed, an 8-lb, 1 in. × 3 ft long rebar flying at a speed of 26 mph, and a 4000-lb automobile flying at a speed of 72 mph. A full list is given in Table 9.8.

These postulated conditions, along with the conservative guidelines used in the design of containment buildings, are one of the reasons of increasing costs in the construction of plants. Recent experiments with full-sized missiles in wind tunnels and with full-sized mockups of the containment walls demonstrated that: (1) the postulated missile speeds were aerodynamically impossible to achieve even under a strong tornado (Table 9.9 shows significant reductions in missile speeds when realistic assumptions and models are used); and (2) missiles moving at the high speeds postulated failed to damage the reinforced concrete to the extent predicted by conservative formulas. The empirical relationships for the calculation of necessary thickness and reinforcement incorporate a high degree of conservatism. A test program with full-scale missiles demonstrated the margins of conservatism in reactor building standards. Figure 9.69 shows a wooden utility pole

Table 9.8. Spectrum of External Missiles[a]

	Fraction of Total Tornado Velocity
A. Wood plank, 4 in. × 12 in. × 12 ft, weight 200 lb	0.8
B. Steel pipe, 3-in. diameter, schedule 40, 10 ft long, weight 78 lb	0.4
C. Steel rod, 1 in. diameter × 3 ft long, weight 8 lb	0.6
D. Steel pipe, 6 in. diameter, schedule 40, 15 ft long, weight 285 lb	0.4
E. Steel pipe, 12 in. diameter, schedule 40, 15 ft long, weight 743 lb	0.4
F. Utility pole, 13 in. diameter, 35 ft long, weight 1490 lb	0.4
G. Automobile, frontal area 20 ft^2, weight 4000 lb	0.2

Source: USNRC Standard Review Plan, NUREG-0800, July 1981.

[a]These must be considered in the design of a reactor building. The fraction given must be multiplied by the maximum tornado velocity postulated in each of the three regions of the country. In the highest tornado activity region, called Region I, the design basis tornado maximum speed is taken to be 528 ft/sec (360 mph).

impacting a full-scale mockup of a reactor building wall at a speed of about 150 m/sec (490 ft/sec). The pole totally disintegrated with no damage to the wall. Similar experiments were performed with steel pipes and with fragments of failed turbines, accelerated to velocities representing turbine overspeed. Figure 9.70 shows a turbine disc fragment penetrating a mockup of a turbine casing at 120% turbine overspeed. Between 60 and 100% of the fragment energy was absorbed by the casing, thus greatly reducing the threat to the containment wall.

9.13. SEISMIC DESIGN

Seismic Design Principles

The design of nuclear plants must take into account the possibility of seismic disturbances. If a large earthquake occurs, the reactor must be shut down safely and all vital safety functions must be maintained. The first requirement implies the integrity of the pressure boundaries and barriers to radioactivity; the second one implies that critical systems such as control rods, valves, heat exchangers, pumps, and emergency power must remain operational to provide their necessary function.

Two magnitudes of earthquakes are used as design bases: the Operating-Base Earthquake (OBE) and the Safe Shutdown Earthquake (SSE), also called the Design Basis Earthquake (DBE). The first has a reasonable probability of occurring based on the seismic records of the region in which the plant is located. The loads caused by the OBE, combined with any additional loads from internal pressure and thermal expansion, must be within normal design stresses. The plant is expected to function without interruption. The second kind, the DBE, is a more severe condition. The reactor must be guaranteed a safe and orderly shutdown and must be kept in a safe condition afterward. The reactor coolant pressure boundary must maintain its integrity and core cooling must be reliably provided.

The most characteristic parameter for the dynamic loading of components and systems is the ground acceleration at zero level, which is transmitted to the structure from the surrounding soil (acceleration times the mass of a component gives the force applied). Other parameters are also specified such as the frequency spectra of the ground motion, and damping factor. The basic figure, however, is the so-called Zero-Period Ground Acceleration (ZPGA), which is usually given as a fraction of the acceleration of gravity, g. This figure varies, depending on location. In the U.S. values of $0.1g$ for the OBE and a value of $0.2g$ for the SSE have been frequently used. In Japan, the range of values considered is from 0.1 to $0.3g$. Using the ground acceleration, the designer develops a set of loadings for the different elevations of a structure (for example, the containment) using amplification and damping factors. If, for example, the ZPGA was taken to be $0.1g$, he may find that at an elevation of 40 m (120 ft) in the building, the horizontal loading is $0.3g$. In addition to horizontal loads there are also vertical loads, usually taken to be about 75% of the horizontal. Each piece of the structure and equipment must then be subjected to seismic analysis for the appropriate combination and intensity of loads. After an SSE has been decided upon, the designer must convince the regulators, through calculations validated with scale tests, that a number of vital components and systems will perform necessary functions: the control rod drives and backup shutdown system remain operational, and control rod channels maintain necessary clearances to prevent control rod sticking; fuel rods and assemblies maintain sufficient distances to allow adequate core cooling; primary or recirculation pumps do not lock, and the primary pressure boundary

Table 9.9. A Comparison of Maximum Horizontal Velocities for the Tornado Missiles Postulated for the Design of Nuclear Plant Containment[a]

Missile	Mass, kg	Dimensions, m	Maximum Horizontal Velocity, m/sec Region I S&C	Region I JPL	Region II S&C	Region II JPL	Region III S&C	Region III JPL	JPL Tornado S&C	JPL Tornado JPL
A. Wood plank	52	JPL: 0.102 × 0.305 × 3.66 S&C: 0.092 × 0.289 × 3.66	83	63	70	58	58	51	70	55
B. 6-in. schedule 40 Pipe	130	0.168D × 4.57	52	24	42	15	10	5	35	17
C. 1-in. steel rod		0.0254D × 0.914	51	51	40	40	38	6	33	18
D. Utility pole	510	0.343D × 10.62	55	53	48	44	26	14	39	21
E. 12-in. schedule 40 pipe	340	0.324D × 4.57	47	25	28	15	7	4	29	13
F. Automobile[a]	1810	JPL: 5.15 × 1.77 × 1.37 S&C: 5.00 × 2.01 × 1.31	59	32	42	20	41	7	46	23

Source: EPRI Report NP-748, May 1978.

[a]S&C stands for work performed by Simin and Cordes, used as guideline by regulators; JPL stands for work performed by the Jet Propulsion Laboratory performed under the auspices of the Electric Power Research Institute. The assumption was made that the missiles were located at an initial height of 40 m (131 ft) and had a zero initial velocity. The long axis of the missile was perpendicular to the direction of the storm.

(a)

(b)

(c)

Figure 9.70. Fragments of a failed turbine disc were accelerated by a rocket sled to velocities of 150 m/sec (490 ft/sec) representing a 120% turbine overspeed. It was demonstrated that as the missile hits the surrounding turbine casing, about 60% of its energy was dissipated, thus greatly reducing the threat from a subsequent impact on the containment wall. Impact with the rounded side of the fragment led to 100% energy absorption. (From EPRI.)

Figure 9.69. Frames from high-speed film showing impact of utility pole on mockup of containment wall. The 1500-lb pole impacted the 18-in thick wall at a speed of about 140 mph (200 ft/sec.). Similar tests were performed with 3-in. pipes and 1-in. rebar. The general conclusion was that the missiles did not produce scabbing in the thinnest panel tested even at impact velocities greater than those currently required for design. (From EPRI Report NP-440, July 1977.)

maintains its integrity; emergency core cooling systems can start if called upon; nonessential portions of safety systems can isolate from essential portions; if systems nonessential to safe shutdown fail, the radioactivity releases are kept within acceptable limits.

Codes and regulations specify the various kinds of loads to be analyzed (dead, live, and seismic loads) and exactly how they must be combined to calculate stresses. The codes prescribe the levels of stress that are permissible in a safe shutdown earthquake. For example, stresses may exceed the yield point (see Chapter 10) and deformation may occur, something not permitted under normal circumstances. Earthquakes as initiating events of accidents are discussed in Chapter 18.

Seismic Design Classes

For design purposes, all structures and components in a nuclear reactor plant fall under three seismic categories.

Seismic Class I. Comprises all structures, systems, components, and instruments that might cause, if failed, a loss-of-coolant accident of increasing severity; could result in an uncontrolled release of excessive radioactivity; are essential for the safe shutdown of the reactor.

Seismic Class II. Comprises those structures, systems, components, and instruments that are important to reactor operation but not essential to safe shutdown and reactor isolation. If failed, they could not result in the uncontrolled release of substantial amounts of radioactivity.

Seismic Class III. Comprises all other structures and components whose failure could result in some interruption of station operation but are not directly important to reactor operation.

Aseismic Designs

The philosophy prevailing in the United States regarding aseismic designs is to render the structure and its components as rigid as required to prevent excessive motion which could cause damage. Various kinds of rigid or elastic supports are provided such as metal struts, springs, anchors, and so on, each designed to carry the calculated loads. A special need arises with respect to pipes which must expand and contract from temperature changes (often as high as 540°C), but must be rigidly held against the wall, floor, or other fixed point in the case of a seismic event. Snubbers are used for this purpose. Since PWR primary system pipes are short, snubber application is mainly in the secondary loop. A hydraulic snubber or shock arrester is a double-acting hydraulic cylinder with two chambers connected through a restriction orifice. They act much like the air dampers used to keep the doors from slamming shut. As the pipe tends to move slowly due to thermal expansion or contraction, the piston follows as liquid moves slowly through the orifice, offering little resistance. In an earthquake, when the pipe tends to move violently, the orifice resists sudden changes and the cylinder acts as a rigid member, transferring the load from the pipe directly to the structure.

Hydraulic snubbers have a number of problems: the use of fluid requires seals which may wear out; periodic inspections are needed to inspect fluid level; radiation may degrade the fluid and hence the snubber's operation. To avoid these problems, mechanical shock arresters† were introduced, one of which is shown in Figure 9.71. Several designs exist, but they all rely on mechanical devices with no liquid for their operation. The internal structure of one design and its principle of operation is shown in Figure 9.72. These devices use the principle of mechanical inertia similar to the one used in automobile safety belts. Slow motion is allowed, but abrupt, violent motion is resisted. When abnormal, rapidly induced loads or motion occurs, the snubber becomes rigid and prevents the overstressing of the component. A typical snubber limits the acceleration to a maximum of $0.02g$. Mechanical snubbers are finding increasing application in nuclear plants, because they eliminate the shortcomings of the hydraulic snubbers. Figure 9.73 shows two common installations of shock arrestors on power plant pipes. Snubbers are characterized by their load-carrying ability, typically from hundreds to a few hundred thousand pounds and by limit to acceleration. Snubber placement incorporates a considerable factor of safety.‡

Another philosophy in tackling seismic events is the isolation of the entire plant from the surrounding soil. By placing the entire power plant with its foundation on a large number of layered

†First used in the aviation industry.

‡For example, during tests conducted in 1981 and 1982 with segments of full-size pipes supported and restrained by snubbers, the following results were obtained: a large snubber (PSA-1) designed to carry a maximum load of 2100 lb was dynamically loaded to 6900 lb with no sign of failure; a smaller snubber (PSA-1/4) with a maximum design load of 500 lb failed at a peak load of 1900 lb. These results imply that even when the wrong size snubber has been installed, or when the calculated loads are in error, failure will probably not occur under earthquake conditions because of the large safety factor.

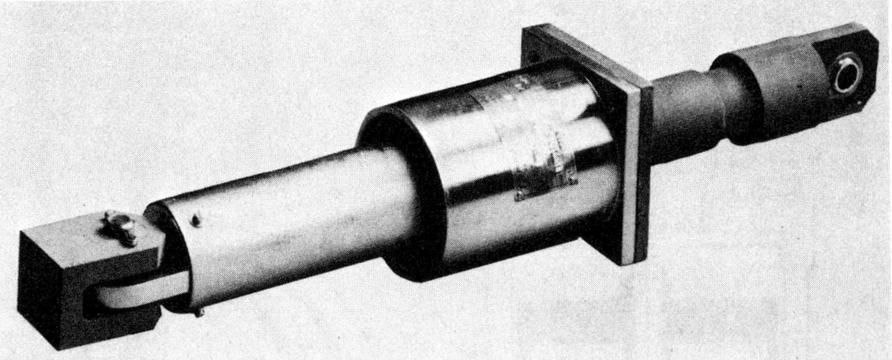

Figure 9.71. Mechanical shock arrester (snubber) used to attach pipes or components to rigid structures. They prevent shock forces, like those caused by an earthquake, from causing damaging motions to the piping or components, by becoming semirigid, load carrying members. The snubbers, however, allow slow motions such as those created by thermal expansion and contraction. (Courtesy Pacific Scientific Co.)

columns of energy-absorbing material (for example, layers of steel and neoprene), coupling of the soil to the structure is loosened and the acceleration transmitted is reduced by a large factor. Another possibility for decoupling is the digging of a deep trench around the plant backfilling the trench with soft soils or sand. This has not been widely adopted in the United States but is finding increasing favor elsewhere. The first nuclear plants in South Africa are using isolation. The French have applied it successfully to their breeder plants (the seismic design of the French Phénix breeder reactor† is based on isolation and on free dampened and energy-absorbing movement of piping).

Large-Scale Seismic Tests

To properly design components and systems to withstand seismic events, a number of assumptions must be made: earthquake magnitude, which defines peak ground acceleration; frequency content; soil-to-structure interaction; damping factors; and response of the component to a given excitation. Many of these assumptions must be made from often scant data and small-scale experimental studies, which are not always easy to extrapolate to the full-size components. The result is a tendency to be overconservative and, at the same time and despite the conservatism, to doubt the seismic robustness of the plants.

With the attention given to the response of nuclear plants to seismic events, particularly in seismogenic areas like California and Japan, data from large-scale experiments become essential. Several examples show the present emphasis and future trends. These are:

1. The earthquake simulation tests performed in a deserted area of New Mexico using underground explosives to test scale models of containment buildings.
2. The vibration tests of the actual piping at Indian Point I, a plant which has ceased operation.
3. The world's largest shake table newly completed at the Nuclear Power Engineering Center in the town of Tadotsu on Shikoku Island, Japan.

The Japanese shake table, which began testing in 1983, has the capacity to simulate the most severe earthquake and can carry a component weighting up to 1000 t; this allows the testing of full-sized reactor components or scale models of the entire plant. Reactor core internals could be tested there to full scale, whereas pressure vessels and primary loops will be tested in a one-half scale and reactor containment in a one-third scale.

All these large-scale experiments are intended to demonstrate experimentally that the safety and reliability of components and systems are assured under conditions of a design earthquake. The margin of safety that exists according to calculations has not been actually demonstrated, although in Japan, nuclear plants have performed well during the large earthquake experienced there in 1980. The large seismic demonstration will fill this need.

†The seismic design of piping used in breeder reactors is complicated by the high temperatures (i.e., the piping is less rigid and more plastic) and by the thinner wall piping used.

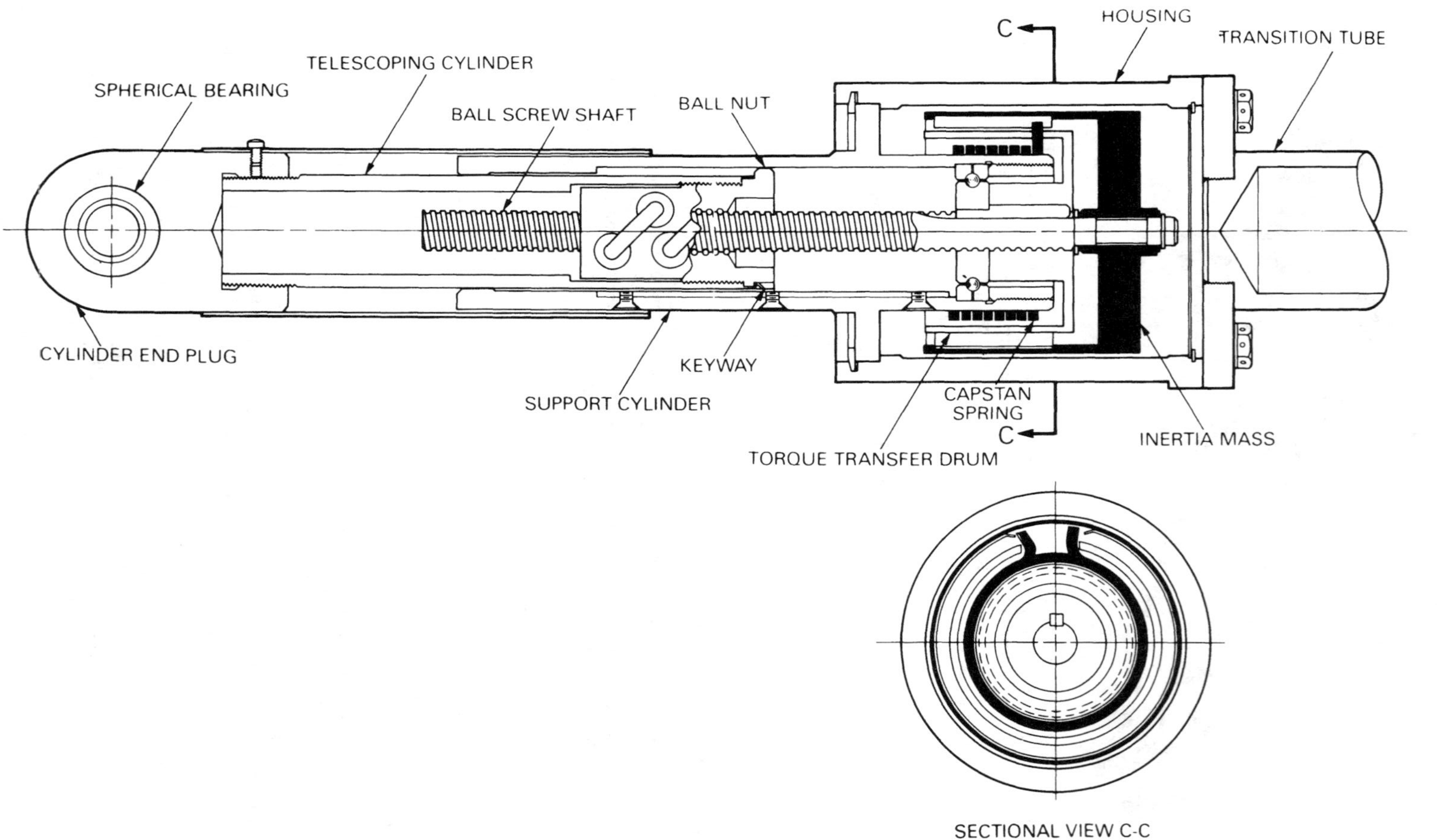
HOUSING
TRANSITION TUBE
TELESCOPING CYLINDER
SPHERICAL BEARING
BALL SCREW SHAFT
BALL NUT
C
CYLINDER END PLUG
KEYWAY
SUPPORT CYLINDER
CAPSTAN SPRING
C
INERTIA MASS
TORQUE TRANSFER DRUM
SECTIONAL VIEW C-C

Figure 9.73. Mechanical shock arrester shown installed in power plants. Their application in nuclear power stations is mostly to the secondary loop and associated components. Their operation should be guaranteed in any orientation. (From EPRI.)

Figure 9.72. A cutaway view of a typical Pacific Scientific arrester. Any movement of the pipe to which the snubber is connected causes a compressive or tension load in the left end of the unit. This force converts any change in length to rotary motion through a ball screw. The screw is keyed to a torque-transfer drum, which encompasses a capstan spring and causes it to rotate also. The two ends of the capstan spring protrude through a slot in the torque-transfer drum and contact shoulders located on the inside of the inertia mass. When the torque-transfer drum turns, the capstan spring is carried with it by bearing against one end of the capstan spring. The opposite end of the capstan spring, in turn, bears against the inertia mass, which is also free to turn, on a bearing located on the extreme end of the ball-screw shaft. Whenever normal thermal motion is involved, the motion is gentle and the entire mechanism will turn. If the force is in the opposite direction, the torque-transfer drum picks up the opposite end of the capstan spring and the inertia mass is driven by the other end. If, however, the pipe attempts to accelerate beyond a predetermined threshold, it will cause the torque carrier to attempt to accelerate angularly also. The inertia mass resists acceleration, which, in turn, causes a relative angular displacement between the torque carrier and the inertia mass lagging behind. In so doing, the capstan spring will be tightened around the mandrel that is integral with the main housing. This boa-constrictor-like action provides a braking force to the angular rotation.

9.14. INSTRUMENTATION

Neutron Sources

Neutron sources are placed in the reactor core to help control the fission reaction during reactor start-up. As the fuel is loaded in the core, the total amount of fissile material exceeds the critical mass necessary for a chain reaction but the control rods and other parasitic absorbers in the core (coolant, structural material, etc.) keep the reactor subcritical. When the reactor is to begin producing energy criticality is achieved (multiplication factor $k = 1$) by slowly withdrawing control rods. However, in the absence of an initial measurable neutron flux, the chain reaction could be started by a stray neutron and could build up to a higher power level very quickly before the control rods could be moved in to control power output.

By placing a neutron source in the core, a neutron flux measurement is available before any control rod movement. The gradual increase of this reading as control rods are withdrawn provides a safe and efficient means of bringing the reactor to criticality and to the desired power level.

Neutron sources are often in the form of metallic rods placed in a cylindrical holder and are held in place by notches in the upper and lower support plates (Figure 9.74). Two types of sources are commonly used: antimony–beryllium and polonium–beryllium. The first consists of a rod of radioactive antimony (^{124}Sb) whose gamma rays produce neutrons from beryllium-9. The source

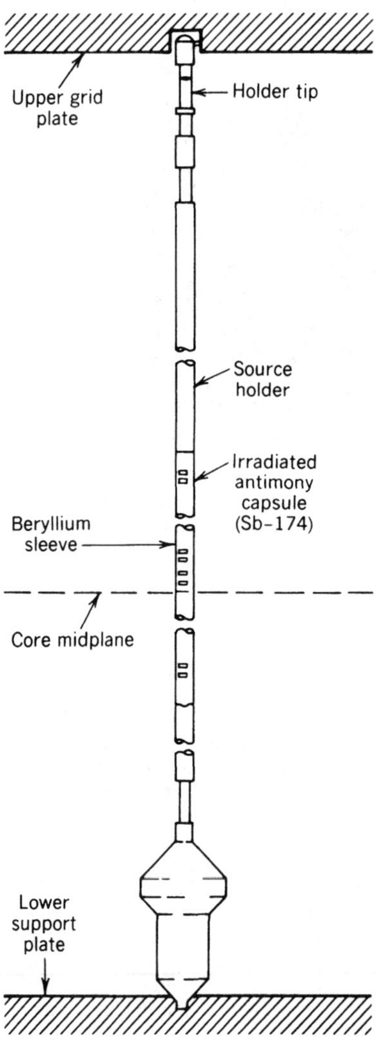

Figure 9.74. Neutron source held between the upper grid and thc lower support plate in a PWR installation. Capsule contains irradiated antimony (emitting energetic gamma rays) surrounded by a beryllium sleeve (which, under γ bombardment, emits neutrons).

produces neutrons of roughly uniform energy (0.03 MeV). The second type uses polonium-210 as a source of alpha rays which, by bombarding beryllium-9, produce neutrons, through an (α, n) reaction,†

$$^{9}Be + \alpha \rightarrow {}^{12}C + n$$

Redundant neutron sources are always placed in the core. A vendor may provide primary and secondary neutron sources. The polonium–beryllium source is preferred as a primary source, because it has a half-life of 138 days, compared to a half-life of 60 days for the antimony–beryllium source. A primary source of Po—Be gives the operator twice as many days to load the reactor. "Live" neutron sources (sometimes ^{252}Cf is used during the first cycle) having a high neutron emission strength are brought to a new installation from other reactors. "Dead" sources, which have lost their strength through decay, are also stored at the reactor and can be reactivated for use at the next start-up operation. When the reactor is shut down, all neutron sources installed in it contribute to the shutdown neutron population of the reactor.

Nuclear Instrumentation

A great variety of measuring instruments and sensors is installed in nuclear plants. They are nuclear instruments for the measurement of different types of radiation (primarily neutrons and gammas), as well as non-nuclear instrumentation for the measurement of process parameters such as temperature, pressure, flow, acidity (pH), humidity, and so on. Each instrumentation channel comprises the sensor, a signal transmission line, amplifier, or other electronics, and meters, indicators, or recorders at the other end. The measured parameters can be channeled, according to type and importance, in different ways: they are fed to instruments in the control room to inform the operator of the status of the plant; they can trigger optical or audio enunciators when certain limits are exceeded; they can be fed to the reactor protection system which automatically shuts the reactor down above certain limits, or combination of limits are crossed; they can be used in the process control system which automatically adjusts the state of the plant (by moving, for example, the position of a valve or of a control rod); they can cause other automatic or manual action for radiation protection purposes.

Most nuclear radiation detectors operate on the following basic principle: when a particle of radiation (α, β, or γ) passes through a gas, it kicks off electrons from the atoms, creating ion pairs in the detector volume. By applying voltage across the two electrodes of the detectors, these ions (negative electrons and positively or negatively charged atoms) can be collected, creating a current in the circuit (Figure 9.75*a*). The size of this current gives a measure of the extent of ionization, and hence of the intensity of radiation going through it. The characteristics of the various types of radiation detectors are illustrated in Figure 9.75*b*. The amount of charge collected depends on two parameters: the amount of ionization produced in the chamber and the voltage applied across the electrodes. The basic radiation detectors, ion chambers, proportional counters, and Geiger–Müller tubes, operate in regions II, III, and V, respectively.

Ionization chambers operate at an applied voltage of 100–200V so as to collect all ionization charges produced in the sensitive volume of the detector. The charge collected is proportional to the energy deposited in the gas by the impinging particle, but not sensitive to the applied voltage. When the number of particles passing through the detector is high, a continuous current is produced rather than individual pulses. The flowing current or the voltage across a resistance in the external circuit is a measure of the intensity of radiation surrounding the chamber. The usual shape of ionization chambers used in reactors is cylindrical with a wire running along its axis serving as the anode. Depending on the details of design and on the fill gas used ionization chambers can be used as pulse counters or current devices.

Two kinds of radiation are of special interest in reactors, neutrons and gammas (alphas and betas have a very short range and do not travel far). Ionization chambers are widely used for gamma detection. They are made with metal walls for strength, which also release electrons that enhance the ionization produced. In order to be insensitive to neutrons, these gamma detectors use materials having a low cross section for neutron interactions.

There are two approaches to detecting neutrons. One can use in the ionization chamber a substance that interacts with neutrons and releases, in turn, ionizing radiation. Boron is one such substance, producing alpha particles through a neutron–alpha reaction. Detectors filled with boron–trifluoride gas (called BF_3 counters) find wide use in neutron detection. It is also possible to coat the electrodes with boron.

The second kind of ionization chamber for neutron detection is the "fission chamber." A

†This beryllium reaction has historic significance since it was through it that the neutron was first identified.

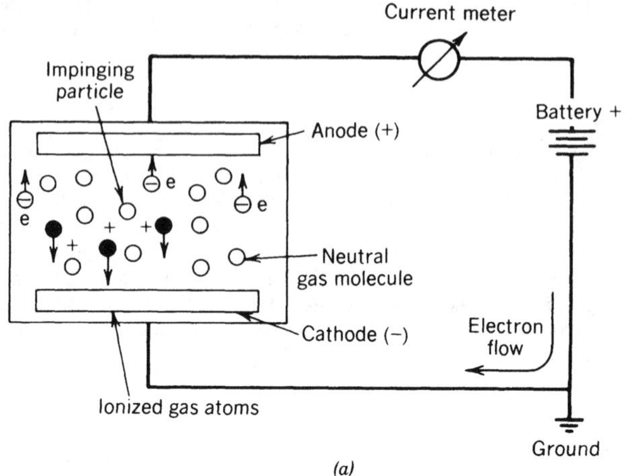

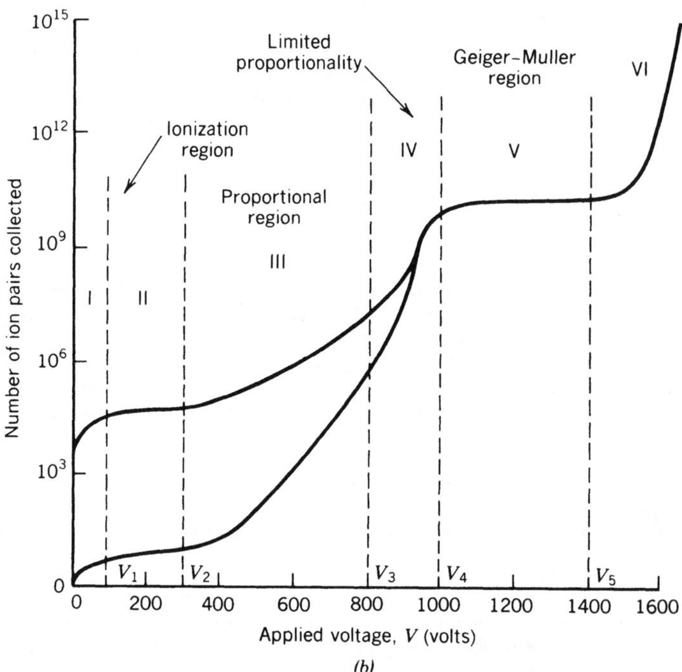

Figure 9.75. (*a*) Radiation and neutron detectors are based on the ionization of gas atoms or molecules. A voltage is applied across two electrodes so that ions formed in the space between them by impinging particles are attracted to electrodes of opposite polarity, thus creating a current in the circuit. (*b*) The curve shows how the charge collected (i.e., current) varies with applied voltage. The graph shows also the regions in which the various types of detectors operate. Upper curve in regions I, II, and III is caused by a more energetic particle than lower curve.

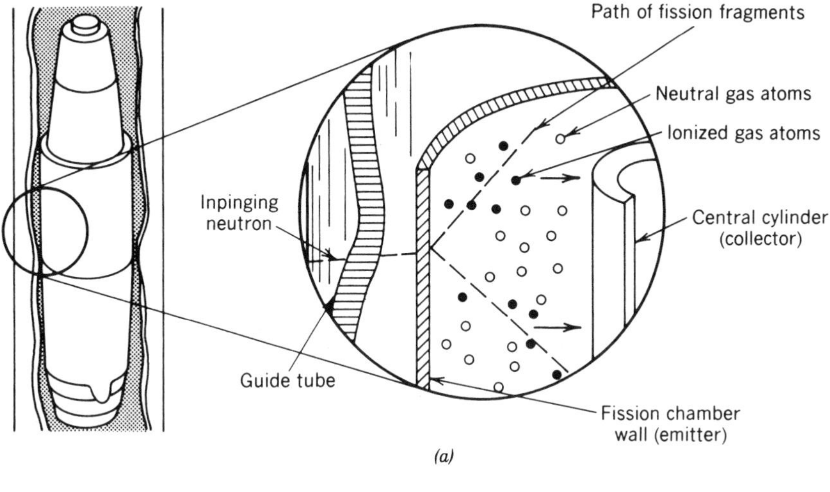

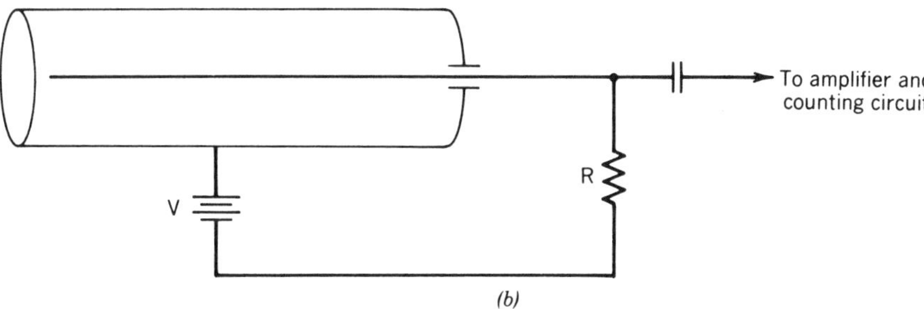

Figure 9.76. Neutron detectors are ion chambers with neutron-sensitive material. When ^{235}U is used as lining, fission fragments produce strong ionization pulse. Device is a fission chamber, shown in in-core guide tube (*a*) and in pulse-counting circuit (*b*).

coating of fissile ^{235}U is applied to the electrodes (Figure 9.76). Neutrons impinging on the ^{235}U layer cause fissions, which in turn produce two heavy charged fission fragments that travel through the chamber fill gas, causing ionization. By making the fission chamber small, the pulse created by one fission is much larger than those created by other particles (betas or gammas). The system can be easily designed to discriminate against the small pulses and the detector measures neutron flux only. A third method is to include a hydrogen-rich material in the chamber and count the protons caused by neutron collisions. In some instances, the mixing of strong gamma fields with a neutron flux can lead to inaccuracies in the measurement of power level. To correct the error, the "compensated ion chamber" was introduced. By an ingenious combination of two subchambers and properly designed circuitry, the gamma contribution is subtracted from the total signal so that the resulting net current is due only to neutrons. Figure 9.77 shows a cutaway view and the circuitry of a compensated ion chamber.

A variation of the ionization chamber is the "proportional counter." It operates at a higher voltage (region III in Figure 9.75*b*) and provides not only collection of all primary ions but also amplifies them several orders of magnitude through secondary ion collisions and enhanced ionization. The amplification makes detection of weaker signals easier and provides for discrimination of a higher signal against a weaker one. For this reason, proportional counters find wide use in the operation of source-range channels during reactor start-up (see discussion below). Proportional counters resemble ion chambers in mechanical design and could be used either with BF_3 or with ^{235}U coatings for neutron detection (Figure 9.78).

The "self-powered detector" is based on an entirely different principle: an energetic particle (photon or neutron) striking an electrode causes the ejection of an electron (beta particle), leaving the surface positively charged. This is a solid-state detector having no fill gas, and is made of two electrodes separated by a solid insulator needing no power source (Figure 9.79). Electric charges

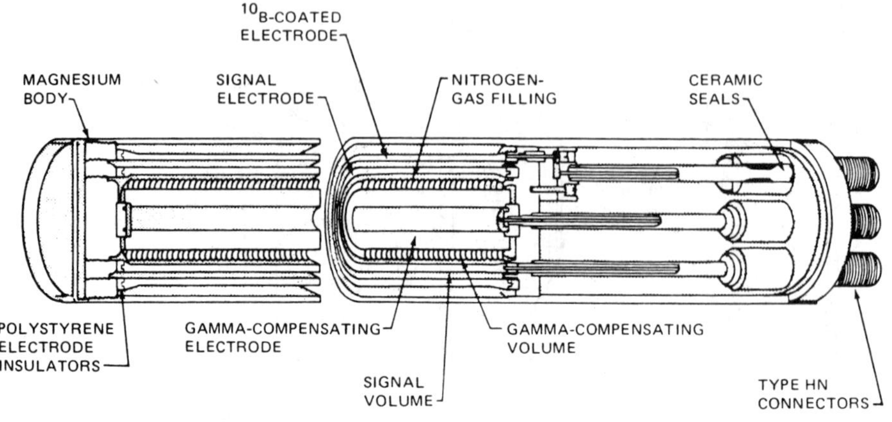

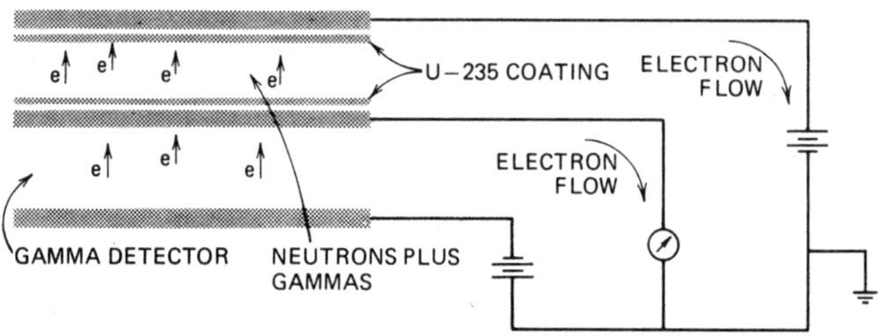

Figure 9.77. The compensated ion chamber solves the problem of detector sensitivity to both neutrons and gammas. In order to measure power levels one needs to count neutrons only; the gamma counts introduce errors. The compensated detector is made of two chambers as shown schematically in the bottom part of the figure. One chamber (boron-lined) counts both neutrons and gammas, whereas the other only gammas. With a properly designed circuit the effect of the gammas on the reading is canceled (to within 2–3%).

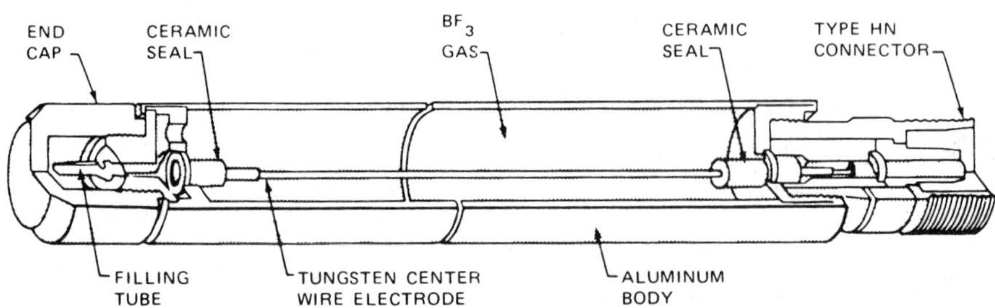

Figure 9.78. A proportional counter operates in region III of the ionization curve shown in Figure 9.75*b*. The larger voltage prevailing there causes an amplification of the ionization pulse, which allows discrimination between forms of radiation. Boron gas fill or boron coating adds capability for neutron detection.

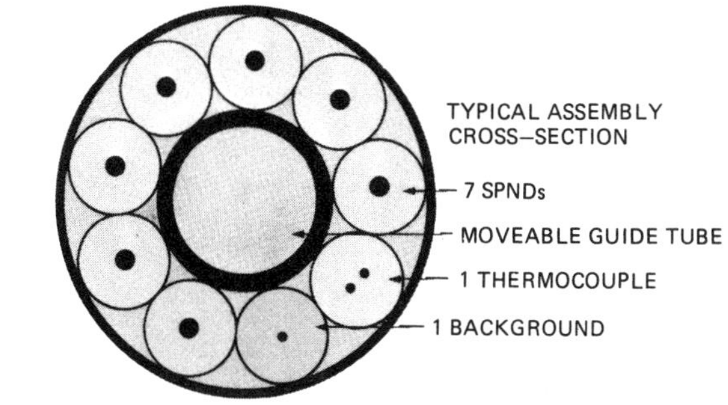

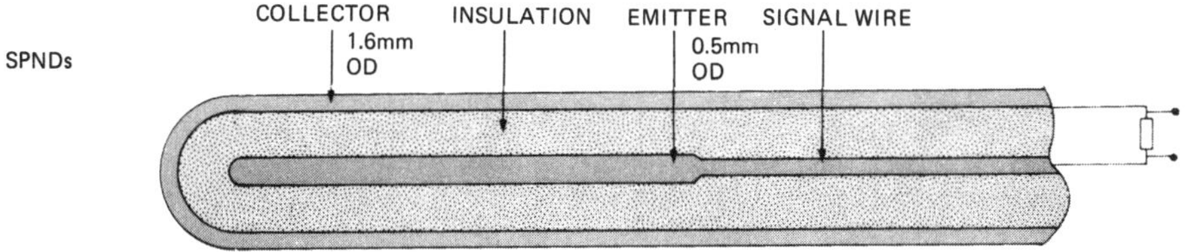

Figure 9.79. Self-Powered Neutron Detectors (SPND), shown at bottom, can be made very thin and require no source of power for operation. When a neutron or gamma ray impinges on the central emitter, a beta particle (electron) is emitted. As charges penetrate the solid insulator and reach the collector, a current is produced in the external circuit. A commercial unit (top) may have seven SPNDs, one thermocouple, and one background detector placed around a central guide tube.

that penetrate the insulator and are collected on the outside electrode cause an electric current to flow in the external circuitry. The signal can be measured as current or voltage and is a measure of neutron (or gamma) flux. For neutron detection, rhodium or vanadium are used as neutron absorbers, which then become beta emitters; cobalt and platinum also absorb neutrons but emit a gamma ray which in turn ejects electrons from the emitter surface. Self-powered detectors can be made as small as 1–3 mm in outer diameter and are particularly suited for use inside the reactor core. They have some disadvantages, particularly a slow response time (rhodium and vanadium) or low detection sensitivity (cobalt and platinum), which makes them unsuitable for reactor control. They are, however, quite useful for neutron flux mapping, fuel management, and verification of physics calculations. Finally, the self-powered detectors have to be periodically recalibrated to account for the gradual depletion of the emitter material. The change is small, amounting to a few percent each year of operation.

Power Monitoring in PWRs

The power production level in a PWR is monitored through two instrumentation systems: the ex-core and the in-core instruments. The ex-core instruments measure gross neutron flux and hence total power level, whereas the in-core instruments measure local power levels.

The ex-core instrumentation must cover a very wide range from full power (or more) to very low levels, about 10 orders of magnitude lower than full power. The latter corresponds to start-up conditions when a good fraction of all neutrons come from the neutron sources. Because it is practically impossible for one instrument to cover the entire range, three groups of instruments cover parts of the range as shown on the left of Figure 9.80. The range overlaps considerably so that the total spans almost 13 decades. All ex-core neutron detectors are located outside the reactor vessel, in the inner side of the shielding wall as shown in Figure 9.81*a*. On plan view, the ex-core channels are located around the core as shown in Figure 9.81*b*. Each group of neutron detectors incorporates more than one unit to provide redundancy as mandated by regulatory requirements. Figure 9.80 shows a total of eight channels of instrumentation feeding into electronic equipment and from these into the control and protection system of the reactor. There are two source-range, two intermediate-range, and four power-range detectors. Two identical source-range detectors are placed on opposite sides of the vessel and at about the midplane of the core. Since they cover a weak signal region (low count rate), they are proportional counters in lead-shielded thimbles to keep out the gamma rays. They cover 6–7 decades from below the neutron source range to a 2-

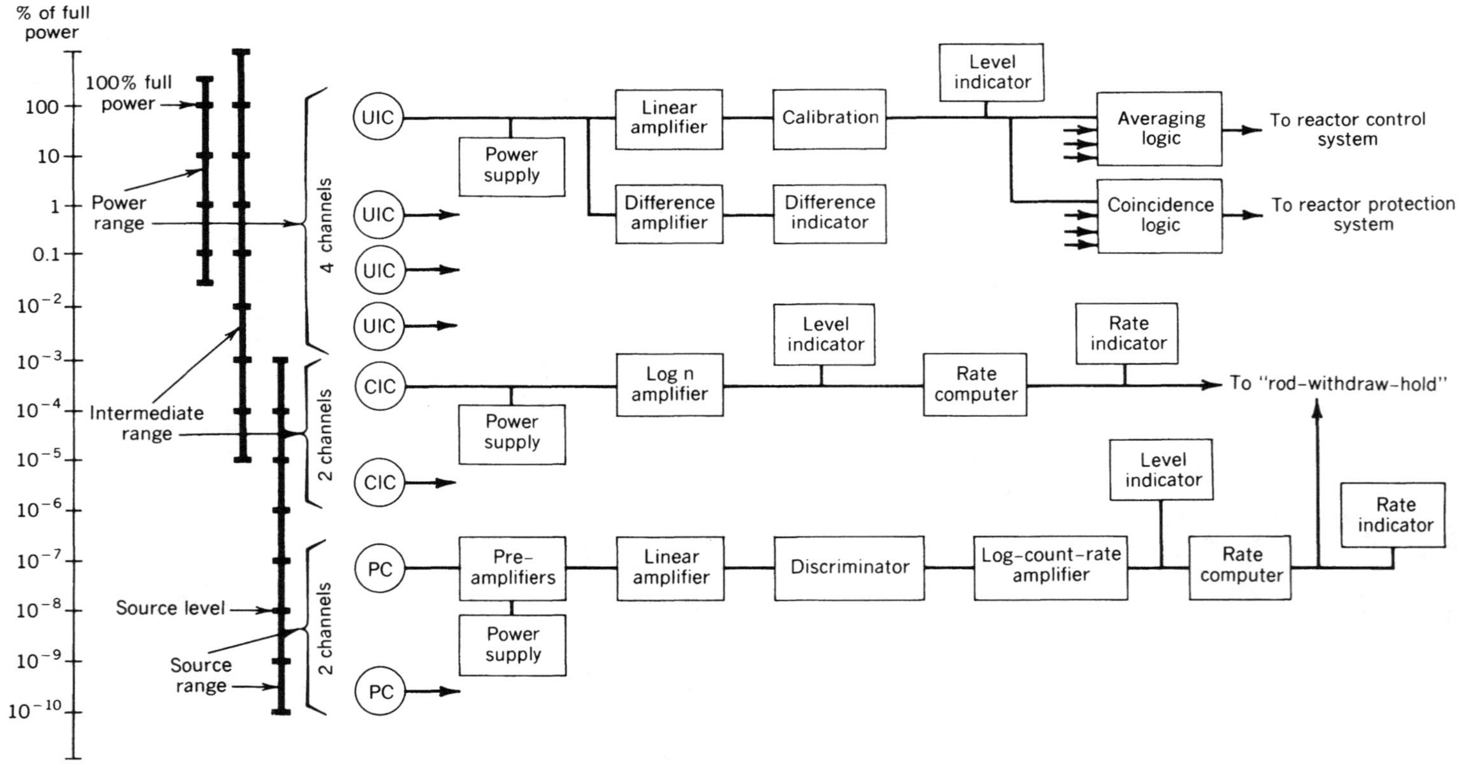

Figure 9.80. Three sets of detectors, each set with redundant channels, are used in nuclear plants to cover the full power range, with at least two decades of overlap. They cover a total of 10 decades (a range of 10^{10}) with additional margins on both ends. The figure also shows how the signals are fed into the control system of a PWR. (From Babcock & Wilcox, *Steam, Its Generation and Use*, 1978.) CIC—Compensated Ion Chamber counters; PC—Proportional Counters; UIC—Uncompensated Ion Chamber counters.

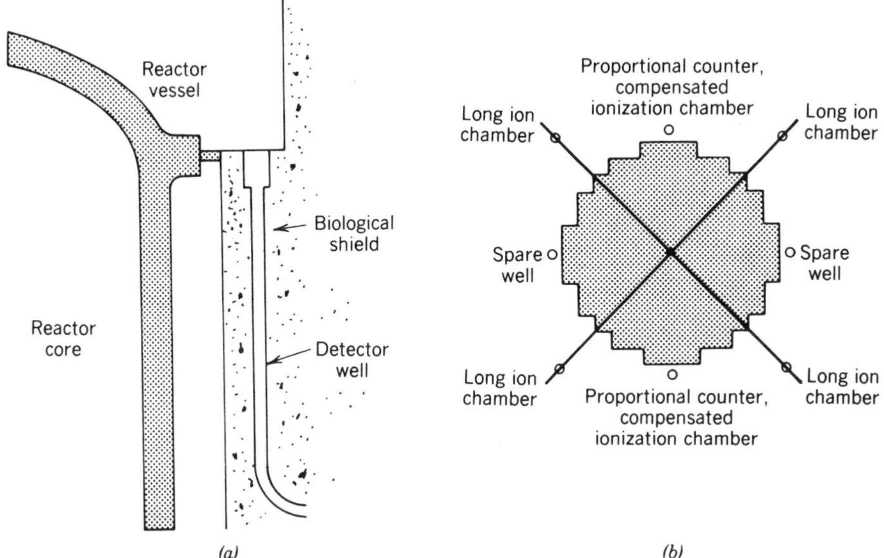

Figure 9.81. Excore power monitors in a PWR are located in wells provided in the biological concrete shield just outside the reactor vessel. Two proportional counters serve as source-range detectors and two compensated ionization chambers as intermediate-range detectors. They are placed on opposite sides of the core and sit at about the core midplane. Four long ion chambers outside the four quadrants of the core serve as power-range detectors.

decade overlap with the intermediate range detector, and give readings in counts per second (from 1 cps at the lower end to more than 1 million cps at the high end of the scale). The readout of the count rate is given in a logarithmic scale using appropriate electronic circuitry. Such a counter is called a "log *n*" meter. If it covers 6 decades, say from 1 to 10^6, the six equal subdivisions on its scale will read 10^0, 10^1, 10^2, . . . , 10^6. Naturally, the accuracy of the reading is not very high over the major portion of the range covered. These detectors are used at reactor start-up as control rods are slowly withdrawn from the core and the count rate increases. Besides providing a neutron flux level indication, the signal is also fed to an electronic differentiating circuit that calculates the "rate of change" of neutron flux. This quantity is displayed on the "period meter" or "rate meter." If the rate of increase is too fast (say more than a decade per minute), a signal is generated that stops the further withdrawal of the control rods.

Two identical intermediate-range channels are located on opposite sides of the core and at the core midplane, usually in the same lead-shielded thimble with the source-range detectors. They are turned on well before the source-range meters reach their upper limit. They cover a range of about 8 decades, from about 7 decades below full power to several times more than full power. As seen in Figure 9.80 each channel provides an indication on a "log *n*" meter, a rate meter, and rate information for the control rod withdrawal if rise to power is too fast. Compensated ion chambers are used in these meters to subtract the contribution of gamma rays, thus providing an accurate measurement of neutron flux alone. In this range the pulses occur too close to each other to be resolved and the output is a constant current with some random fluctuations.

Finally, four power-range channels are provided, located outside four quadrants of the core as shown in Figure 9.81*b*. They cover the range from about 1 to 125% of full power. Uncompensated ion chambers in unshielded thimbles are used, since gamma rays are no problem here compared to the large neutron flux. Each detector is about 12 ft long and covers the full length of core, thus "seeing" an integrated picture of the core power. However, each is divided into two half-length sections and thus can provide two measurements reflecting power in the upper and lower half of the core. From the two measurements in each channel both a sum and a difference is produced. The sum of the power signals is then calibrated by comparison with power calculated in the plant computer from other reactor process quantities, such as flow rates, and temperature rise. The difference gives the operator an idea of unevenness in power generation in the top and bottom half of the core and helps him to correct it.

The signals from the four power-range channels are further combined in the "averaging logic" which feeds the reactor control system (which moves the control rods in order to maintain the

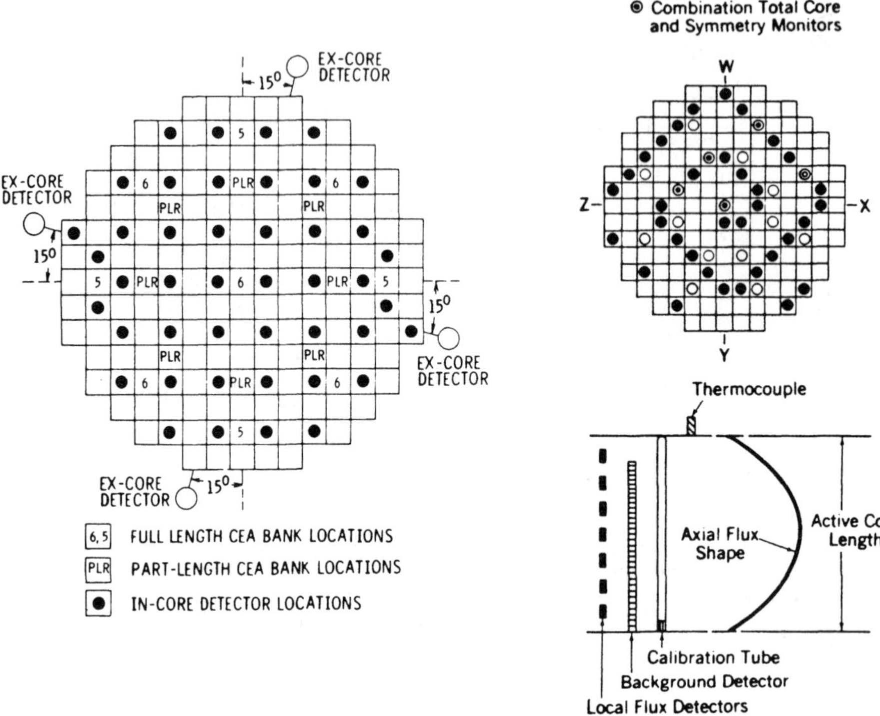

Figure 9.82. Two alternative ways of positioning in-core neutron flux detectors. Along each thimble there are seven self-powered detectors. (From Combustion Engineering, Inc. and Babcock & Wilcox Co.)

desired power level); the "coincidence logic" on the other hand compares the four signals and, if two of them are found to be outside of prescribed safety limits, produces a signal for the reactor protection system, which causes a quick shutdown (this is called a two-out-of-four logic).

In-core instrumentation is used in PWRs to provide a more detailed picture of power levels inside the core. In order to avoid disturbing the core excessively, small channels and detectors must be used, a requirement that brought about the wide use of self-powered, very thin detectors described above. Because of the slow response of these detectors, their output cannot be used either for control or for reactor protection functions. There are various means of distributing the detectors in the core; Figure 9.82 shows two of the alternative ways used by different designers. About 30% of the assemblies in the core incorporate instrument channels in which the instrument is inserted. Penetration for lead wire connections are located at the bottom of the reactor vessel (Figure 9.83). Each channel contains up to seven local neutron-flux detectors spaced evenly along the length of the core, one background detector, and one thermocouple above the upper core plate to measure the coolant temperature at the core outlet. The neutron flux and temperature signals from these in-core detectors (which could total 400) are fed to the reactor computer which combines them and synthesizes power distribution and core performance parameters for the benefit of the plant operator.

Power Monitoring in BWRs

In BWRs all power monitoring is performed from inside the reactor core. Since a BWR reactor vessel is bigger and the spacing between core elements a little wider than in a PWR, space is not as critical. More importantly, locating detectors for control and reactor protection functions inside the core provides maximum sensitivity to control rod movement during the start-up period and optimum monitoring in the intermediate and power ranges. Detector channels are located in the channel between four assemblies and are distributed in the core in a pattern shown in Figure 9.84. Some monitors are stationary and some are movable.

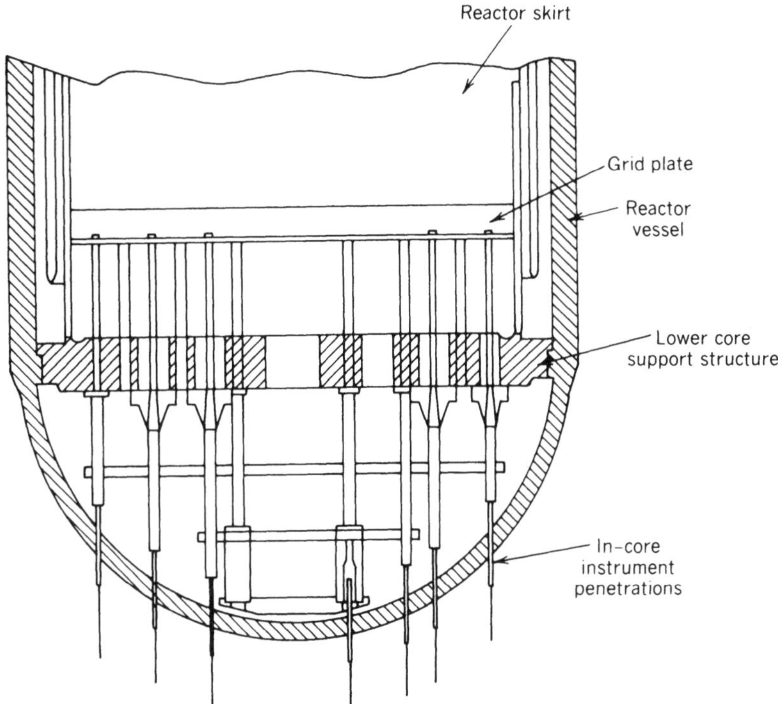

Figure 9.83. The lower reactor vessel structure of a PWR. Penetrations for electric connection to the in-core neutron detectors are provided at the bottom of the vessel. The in-core detectors are thin self-powered neutron detectors inserted in instrument tubes of selected fuel assemblies.

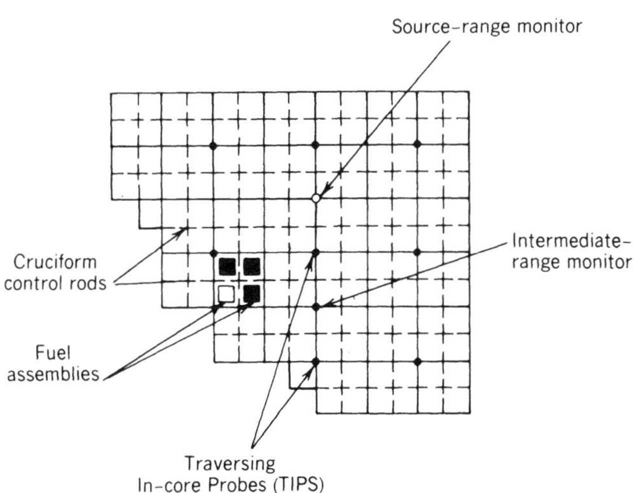

Figure 9.84. BWR core quadrant showing the location of in-core neutron monitors.

The full range of power is covered by three groups of detectors: source range, intermediate range, and local power range, as shown in the diagram of Figure 9.85. A movable probe, capable of traversing any chosen instrument channel through a mechanical system, performs a continuous neutron flux measurement and allows the operator to periodically calibrate the stationary detectors. The *source-range monitors* are fission counters, inserted to about the core midplane by a drive mechanism shown in Figure 9.86. Instrument thimbles attached to the bottom of the pressure vessel and extending upward into the core are used to insert the monitors through vertical, controlled motion of a metallic rod. These detectors cover a range from source level of 0.001 of full power but they can then be partially withdrawn to a lower neutron flux area, giving an apparent drop in count rate. This extends their range of usefulness and provides overlapping with the intermediate range monitors. As reactor power increases toward full power, the source-range monitors are withdrawn to approximately 0.61 m (2 ft) below the core to minimize their activation and the depletion of fissionable material that would result, unnecessarily, from intense neutron bombardment.

The intermediate-range counters used in BWR are fission chambers based on the voltage variance method. The method utilizes the variable component of the voltage which is due to the random collisions of neutron in the detector chamber. The measurement is not affected by direct current components that may be due to leakage or gamma radiation and is thus suitable for measuring lower neutron fluxes.

Local Power-Range Monitors (LPRMs) are power-range monitors in fixed locations inside the core and cover the range from 1 to 125% of rated power on a linear scale (a linear scale gives a much higher accuracy throughout the range, as opposed to the logarithmic scale). These detectors are ion chambers (based on fission of ^{235}U) arranged in a uniform pattern throughout the core as shown by the black circles in Figure 9.84. Each detector assembly contains four fission chambers and a guide tube for a Traversing In-core Probe (TIP) based also on the ion chamber principle, and used to calibrate the fixed monitors. The fixed detectors thus provide power measurements for four different axial levels inside the core. The useful life of each of these detectors is about 1×10^{22} *nvt*.† The detectors can be removed and replaced through the thimble openings at the bottom reactor head.

The TIP is a feature of BWRs. An ion chamber can be inserted in the calibration guide tube provided in each instrument assembly and moved continuously along its length, allowing a continuous profile of the axial power shape. An example of such a profile, shown in Figure 9.87, exhibits a local perturbation of neutron flux and a rather large imbalance between the top and bottom of the core. The calibration tubes connect to nozzles at the bottom of the reactor vessel and connect to an indexing mechanism located inside containment, which allows the operator to direct the TIP to any of a number of detector assemblies. There are several individual traversing probes. One TIP and its associated drive mechanism is used for a group of fixed instrument assemblies (seven to nine in each group, depending on reactor size). To obtain a flux profile, a TIP is first inserted to the top of the calibration guide tube and then gradually withdrawn as measurements are taken. The data from the TIP are fed directly to the process computer.

There are also in a BWR four Average Power-Range Monitors (APRM). Each of these monitors averages signals from as many as 24 individual in-core detectors to measure the total power produced in the core. The signals from the average power monitors provide input to the reactor protection system. When the total power level, the average from all APRMs, becomes too high for the coolant system to handle, a signal is generated that causes reactor shutdown. The APRM output is also displayed in the control room.

Non-nuclear Instrumentation

It was already mentioned that the in-core instrument channels in PWRs contain, in addition to neutron flux monitor, thermocouples for the measurement of coolant temperature. A large variety of instruments is used in nuclear plants to measure process variables such as pressure temperature, flow, water level, and so on. Both the primary and secondary side of a PWR and the single thermal circuit of a BWR are continuously monitored. Signals from these instruments are fed to the control room panel, and to the plant process computer. They provide input signals to the reactor protection system for quick shutdown, if certain limits are exceeded; to the reactor control system to maintain power level; and to the systems that control primary coolant and feedwater.

The center processing this large amount of information generated at over 2000 points in the plant is the plant computer. It collects, stores, and manipulates signals from all instruments and provides the operator with valuable assistance in the safe and efficient operation of the plant. Both primary parameters directly from the detectors and calculated figures can be provided upon request. Significant advances in the use of modern computers, both for safety and optimized productivity purposes, have been made in recent years. They are discussed more fully in Chapter 12.

†The integrated flux or fluence, the product of the neutron flux at the location (neutrons/cm^2/sec) times the duration of exposure (in seconds).

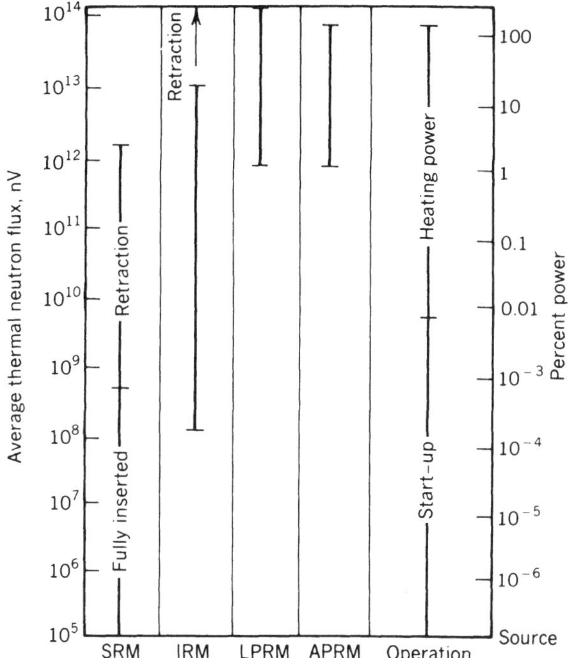

Figure 9.85. A BWR has three groups of monitors covering about 10 decades of power range. The source range monitor covers normally from 10^{-7} to 10^{-3} of full power, but when pulled out of the core, it extends to 1% of power. Similarly, the other detectors cover a range of power indicated by the vertical bar. (Courtesy General Electric Co.)

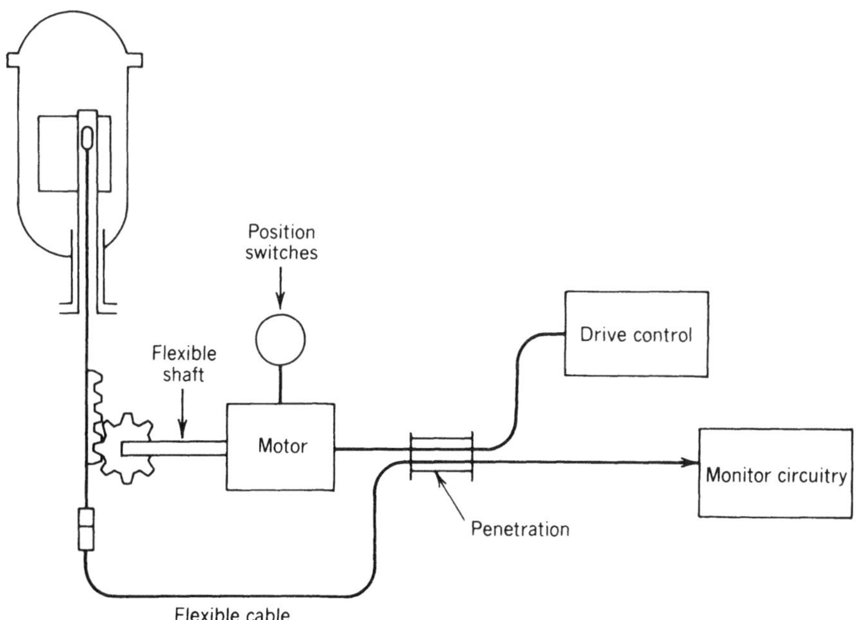

Figure 9.86. Shown in the figure is the system used in BWR to drive power monitors in the core. In addition to fixed neutron flux detectors distributed uniformly throughout the core (at four different planes), there are Traveling In-core Probes (TIPs) which can be inserted in any desired channel through the drive system to give a continuous profile of power along that channel.

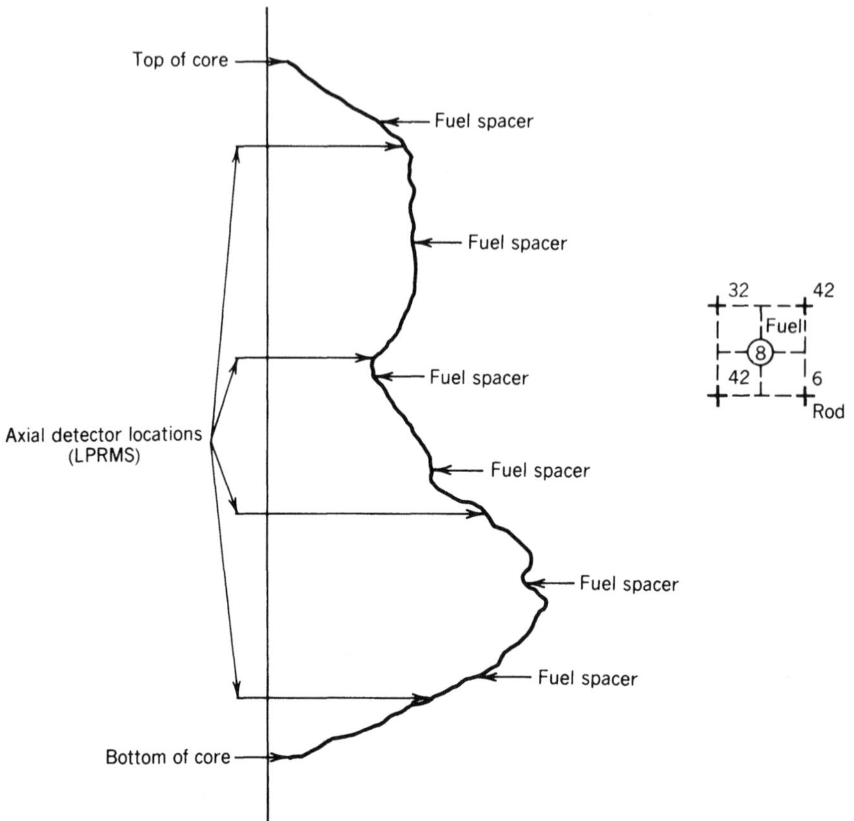

Figure 9.87. Vertical flux profile is mapped out by the movable probe and system depicted in Figure 9.86. Inset shows positions of control rods adjacent to channel (0, fully inserted; 42, withdrawn). Sharp dips indicate presence of fixed in-core detectors and spacers.

BIBLIOGRAPHY

Babcock & Wilcox Co., *Steam, the Generation and Use,* 1978.

Combustion Engineering, *System 80, C-E Standard Safety Analysis Report,* Vols. 1–9, 1983.

de Tonnac, A., "A Framatome 600 MWe Nuclear Island for Export Markets," *Nuclear Engineering International* **26,** 33 (1981).

Framatome, "Standard 3-Loop Plant, Nuclear Island," M30, 21.VI, June 1981.

General Electric Co., *BWR/6, General Description of a Boiling Water Reactor,* September 1980.

Helander, L. I. "The ASEA-ATOM BWR," *Nuclear Europe* (1982).

Lish, U. C., *Nuclear Power Plant Systems and Equipment,* Industrial Press, New York, 1972.

Nuclear Safety Analysis Center, "Workshop on Hydrogen Burning and Containment Building Integrity," NSAC-32, July 1981.

Tsoulfanidis, N., *Measurement and Detection of Radiation,* McGraw-Hill, New York, 1983.

Straus, S. D., "Nuclear Instrumentation," *Power Magazine* **119,** 35 (1975).

U.S. Atomic Energy Commission, "The Safety of Nuclear Power Reactors and Related Facilities," WASH-1250, July 1973.

Vogt et al., H. W., "Gösgen: The First Standard PWR for Switzerland," *Nuclear Engineering International* **25,** 37 (1980).

———. "First Soviet 1000 MWe PWR Reaches Design Capacity," *Nuclear Engineering International* **26,** 26 (1981).

Westinghouse Electric Corporation, *Reference Safety Analysis Report,* RSAR-3. Westinghouse Nuclear Energy Systems, 1973.

CHAPTER 10
MATERIALS

10.1. INTRODUCTION

General Remarks

As the number of reactors increased rapidly in the 1960s and 1970s with larger and more complex units coming on line, it became apparent that a number of technical problems were surfacing to plague the industry. The protagonist of these problems was deterioration of materials in service under the combined effects of a corrosive environment, high stresses, and neutron irradiation. The advent of these problems should not have been unexpected since experience with many other technologies that preceded nuclear had shown that it is only through experience that problems are discovered and appropriate measures are put in place to correct them; a painstaking process of trial and error. The accumulation of over 2000 reactor-years of operation worldwide (counting only civilian reactors) has focused attention on the importance of the many aspects related to materials in nuclear plants. These include: selection of the appropriate material and of design parameters such as temperature and pressure, the careful control of the chemical environment in which they operate, control of manufacturing processes such as welding and annealing, inspection and detection of cracks or other flaws before installation, and in-service monitoring of the operation for the detection of abnormal conditions, and remedial techniques. Furthermore, damage to materials from the intense radiation originating in the reactor core is a consideration unique to nuclear service and deserving of special attention.

This chapter presents a description of the major categories of materials used in nuclear reactors. The principal modes of failure and the methods to mitigate or to eliminate them will also be reviewed. The subject is very extensive both in breadth and depth and could not be exhaustively covered. The most important material categories are discussed. Materials used in LWRs are given extensive discussion, whereas those for other types of reactors are only mentioned in passing. It must be expected that the challenge to materials posed by advanced nuclear technologies will be tougher and a continuing and more demanding effort will be needed to meet the future material requirements. Liquid Metal Fast Breeder Reactors (LMFBRs), for example, operate at much higher temperatures and fusion reactions impose a much higher bombardment by high-energy neutrons on structural materials. This implies that, apart from physical feasibility, a great number of engineering problems must be solved to ensure economic operation of a developing technology.

In addition to the applications of the various materials, and the most important generic problems, inspection and detection methods, and remedies will also be discussed.

Some Definitions in Strength of Materials

Two basic concepts in the study of material behavior are stress and strain. When an external force is applied to a solid body, the atoms will be slightly displaced and internal forces will develop to counter the external force. "Stress" is, therefore, the internally distributed forces that tend to resist deformation. "Stress" is force per unit area as the area becomes very small. For example, a cylindrical rod with a cross section A which is tensioned (or compressed) by a force F is subject to an average stress equal to F/A (tensile if extended and compressive if compressed). However, the stress may not be even across the cross section in which case one must consider local rather than average stress.† "Strain" is the relative change in dimension that a solid undergoes under a given stress; it is dimensionless and often given in percent. If a compressive force is applied in one direction, the distance between atoms will be decreased in that direction and increased in directions perpendicular to it. The ratio between the strains in the two directions is called Poisson's ratio.

†The unit of stress in the modified metric system (Système International) is the pascal (Pa) equal to 1 N/m^2. In the British system, it is the pound per square inch or psi.

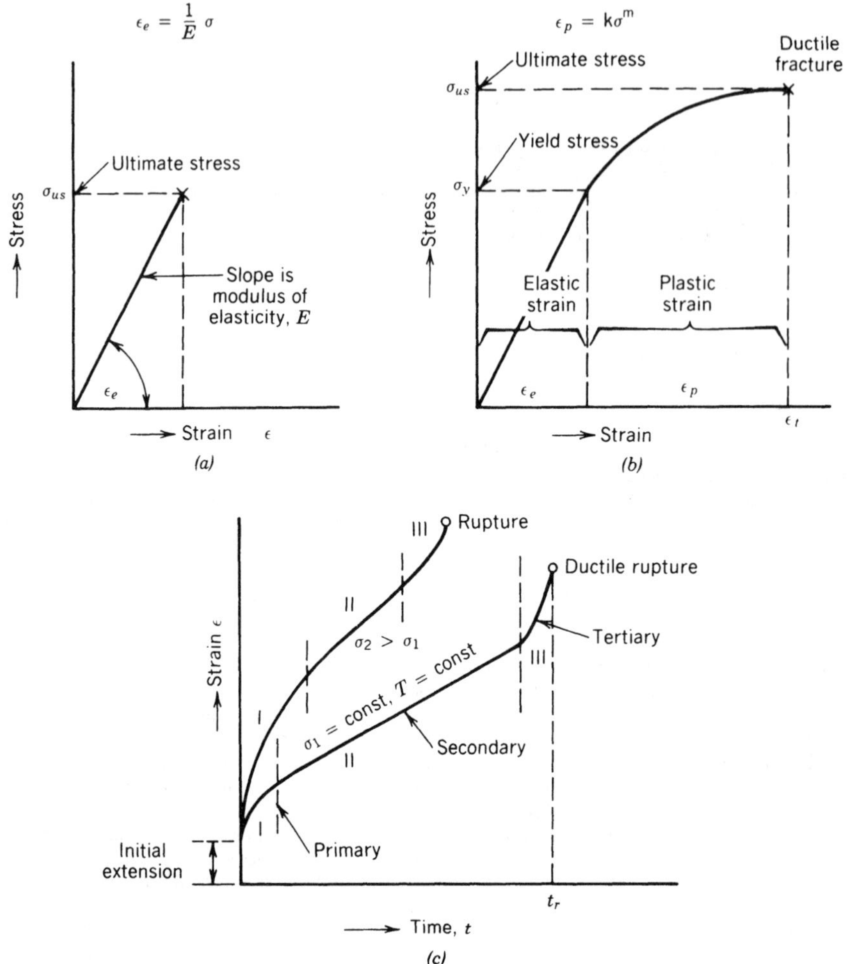

Figure 10.1. The mechanical behavior of materials is described by their stress/strain diagrams. Elastic behavior (*a*) is characterized by a linear relation between stress and strain. Beyond the elastic limit a material may exhibit plastic behavior (*b*) where strain increases faster than stress. Finally, creep behavior (*c*) is evident at high temperatures. The material flows under constant stress. Upper curve is for higher stress.

There are three basic ways to describe the behavior of materials under stress: linear behavior, plastic behavior, and creep. Figure 10.1 illustrates in graphic form these three behaviors. In the first, the stress and strain maintain a linear (elastic) relationship. If the applied force is removed, the material recovers its previous shape, and the strain disappears. Some materials fracture as the applied force is increased at a point on the elastic region; this is called brittle fracture. The slope of the line, measured as a ratio of σ/ϵ is the modulus of elasticity and is expressed in the same units as stress, since strain has no dimensions.

Ductile materials go into a different regime of behavior when stressed beyond the elastic limit. They undergo plastic deformation, which means that a certain amount of deformation will remain even when the applied force is removed. The relationship between plastic deformation and stress is not linear; it is expressed by a relationship of the form

$$\epsilon_p = k\sigma^m$$

As the applied force is increased, there will come a point where the material will fail, by ductile fracture. In both cases, the stress at the point of rupture is called "ultimate strength." The point at

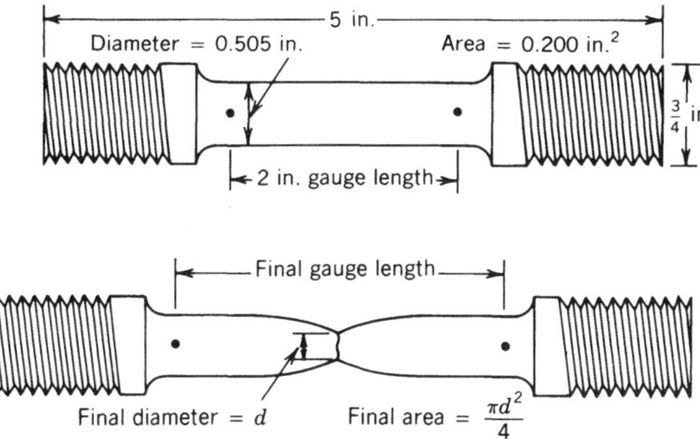

Figure 10.2. Schematic showing a metal specimen before and after a tensile test (ASTM standard). The elongation of the specimen after fracture and the cross-sectional reduction at the neck give a measure of the ductility of the material.

which the material departs from the elastic behavior is called "yield point" and the corresponding stress is "yield strength." Total strain in the elastic–plastic case is made up of two components, elastic and plastic strain.

In the third case, we observe the phenomenon of creep (Figure 10.1*c*). Under a constant but relatively high temperature and while keeping the stress constant, the material continues to deform, until it reaches a certain point of ductile rupture. Three consecutive regions can be discerned in a creep experiment: the primary, with relatively faster strain rate; the secondary, with a constant strain rate; and a tertiary, with an accelerated strain rate until failure. For a higher stress, a creep curve higher than the first will be shown. The relationships between stress and strain (cases *a* and *b* of Figure 10.1) and between strain rate, stress, strain, and temperature for case *c*, are called the constitutive relations of the given material.

"Fatigue" in materials is a phenomenon resulting from repeated cycles of stressing. A turbine shaft, for example, which carries the weight of the turbine discs and blades as well as its own, is subject to alternating states of tension and compression as it turns. Its strength to this kind of dynamic loading is much lower than its strength to the same magnitude of stationary load. The behavior of materials subject to repeated cycles of loading must be known in order to design components to resist failure from "fatigue."

Testing of materials takes place under controlled conditions in order to determine its strength characteristics. The characteristics of the curves shown in Figures 10.1*a* and 10.1*b* are determined through a tensile test with a specimen like the one shown in Figure 10.2, specified as a standard size specimen by the American Society of Mechanical Engineers (ASME). Total tensile force and elongation are accurately measured in steps of increasing force. After the elastic region is exceeded, the specimen deforms plastically and a neck begins to form, with a reduced cross section where rupture ultimately occurs. In addition to Young's modulus of elasticity, yield strength, ultimate strength, and Poisson's ratio, the test also provides a measure of the material's ductility. This quantity is defined as the total specimen elongation at rupture over the initial length as a percent. Alternately, it can be defined as the percent reduction of the cross-sectional area at the neck at rupture over the initial area. Ductile materials have a relatively high permanent elongation (or neck formation) at rupture. Brittle materials fail without much deformation.

Another test measures the ability of a specimen to withstand concentrated stresses. This property of the material is called "fracture toughness." The test is performed with a small material specimen in which a notch has been deliberately created as shown in Figure 10.3. Two types, Charpy and Izod specimens, are struck by a swinging pendulum and the energy absorbed by the specimen for fracture is measured. An application of the Charpy fracture toughness is discussed in Section 10.9, subsection "Changes in Physical Properties."

In addition to stresses from external loads, such as weight and pressure, materials are also subject to internal stresses. Such stresses may arise from uneven temperature across the material. Take, as an example, a steel pipe which contains high-temperature fluid. The innermost layer of the pipe will be at a temperature very close to that of the hot fluid, say, about 288°C (550°F) in a nuclear power plant. The outer layer, even with the thermal insulation around it, will be at a somewhat lower temperature. The thermal expansion of the inner layer will tend to be larger than that of the outer layer, which creates internal stresses known as "thermal stresses." They can be calculated if

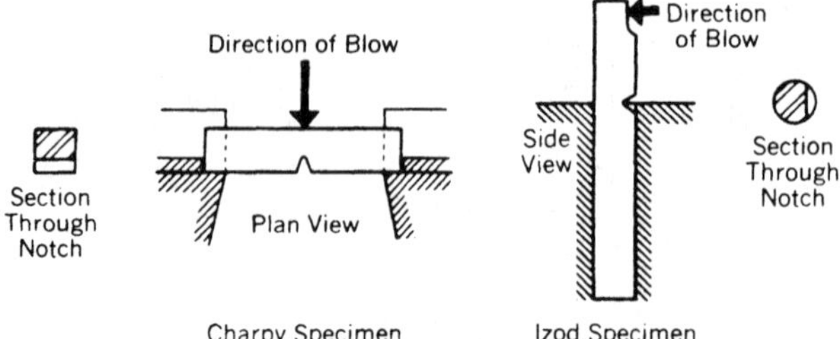

Figure 10.3. Two methods of measuring the fracture toughness of a steel. A notched specimen bar is either supported by both ends (Charpy specimen) or is cantilevered (Izod specimen). They are then struck by a swinging pendulum and fractured in a single blow. The energy absorbed by the specimen is measured by the height of the pendulum's rebound and can be read directly in kg-m (or ft-lb or J) on a calibrated dial or scale. This energy is a measure of the material's "toughness," that is, its ability to withstand concentrated stresses (in other words, its ability to withstand rupture once a flaw or crack exists in its body).

the temperature gradient across the material is known and they must be added, in the calculation, to the externally generated stresses to ascertain that the allowable limits are not exceeded. Repeated heating and cooling of a component, such as those occurring in plant shutdown and restart, subject the materials to "thermal cycling," an undesirable condition for the strength of the material. Another cause of internal stresses is the welding of metal pieces together. The local heating and the freezing wedge of welding material between the solid metal pieces cause stresses in the weld and its surrounding area.

"Annealing" is often applied to such welds to relieve the internal stresses. Annealing is the process of gradual heating of the material to a specified uniform temperature and the maintenance of this temperature for a specified length of time after which a gradual cooling takes place. Annealing allows rearrangements in the microstructure of the metal, whereby crystal dislocations are repaired and the stresses they cause are greatly reduced.

Choice of Materials

In choosing the material for a certain application, the designer must take several factors into consideration. Strength of the material under a set of given conditions such as external and internal loads, temperature, and chemical environment is a major factor. The materials must be capable of withstanding the imposed loads for their entire lifetime without serious deterioration of performance and with considerable margins of safety. Materials intended for use inside the nuclear core must also have appropriate neutronic characteristics. This means, in general, a low neutron absorption cross section, to avoid the impairment of the neutron economy. In the case of control rods, the opposite is desired; materials with a high neutron cross section are used there. Table 10.1 gives the

Table 10.1. Capture Cross Sections of Structural Metals for Thermal Neutrons at Energy Level 0.025 eV

Group A, <0.5 barn		Group B, 0.5–5 barns		Group C, >5 barns	
		Mo	2.4		
C	0.0045	Fe	2.5	Ti	5.8
Be	0.009	Cr	2.9	Mn	12.6
Mg	0.059	18–8 stainless	2.9	W	19.2
Si	0.13	Cu	3.6	Ta	21.3
Pb	0.17	Inconel X	4.1	Co	34.8
Zr	0.18	Monel	4.2	B	750
Al[a]	0.22	Ni	4.5	Cd	2400
		V	4.8		

Source: C. Bonilla, *Nuclear Engineering*, McGraw-Hill (1957).

[a] Structural aluminum alloys contain small percentages of Mn, by which their cross section is almost doubled.

neutron capture cross section for several elements used in reactors. For structural components other than control rods, a low-absorption cross section is desirable. A third, but very important consideration, is the cost of acquisition. Other material characteristics also enter into the picture. Availability, the machinability or ease of manufacture, the toxicity or health impact, the potential for activation under neutron bombardment, and susceptibility to chemical attack and corrosion, are taken into account in the selection of materials. Table 10.2 lists some of the important physical properties of reactor materials. Often there are no clear choices of materials possessing all the desirable features and judicious compromises must be made for an acceptable combination of features. In several cases, different manufacturers of nuclear plants have made different choices to meet the same overall objective.

10.2. STRUCTURAL STEELS

Iron, alloyed with varying quantities of carbon and other metals such as chromium, manganese, and nickel, forms a large array of structural materials used in industrial applications. The properties of these materials vary; the selection is made according to the requirements of each application. To understand the behavior of the various steels, an introduction to the physical metallurgy of iron and its alloys is necessary.

Physical Metallurgy Considerations

Iron in solid state has crystalline structure; its atoms are arranged in a regular pattern in space to form a crystalline lattice. The study of the iron structure, performed through X-ray diffraction, has revealed that its crystal has a cubic space lattice. Figure 10.4 shows the two variations of the cubic lattice in which iron may exist: the Body Centered Cube (BCC) and the Face Centered Cube (FCC). At room temperature, the crystal takes the form of a BCC, which is called the "alpha phase." Iron in the "alpha ferrite" phase is a soft, ductile, and magnetic material. If the crystal is heated, first it loses its magnetism (at a temperature of 708°C), and then is transformed to a face centered cube at a temperature of 910°C (1670°F). In this phase, it exists as "gamma iron." With further heating to 1410°C (2570°F), the crystal reverts back to a BCC and is now called "delta iron"; it remains stable until the melting point is reached, 1535°C (2795°F). If molten iron is gradually cooled, the solidified crystal will go through the transformations in reverse. Because of these changes in crystalline structure with heating or cooling, iron is said to be an "allotropic" material; it undergoes allotropic changes, among the various possible allotropic phases.

Pure iron rarely exists. It would be expensive to obtain and would not have characteristics that are desirable in its various applications. The element commonly formed in combination with iron is carbon. Similar transformations in crystalline structure exist in the iron–carbon system, but they now include carbon itself and chemical combinations of carbon and iron, the iron carbides. These are shown in the diagram of Figure 10.5 for any carbon content in the range 0–5% in carbon. Combinations with a carbon content higher than 2% correspond to the cast irons. Combinations with less than 2% carbon are called steels. Figure 10.4 is an equilibrium diagram. It implies that at any point the phases are at equilibrium among themselves, which in turn means that the temperature changes are performed slowly and all the necessary time to complete the transformation is available. The addition of carbon alters the properties of the mixture. For example, the melting point is lowered with increasing carbon up to a minimum of about 1125°C (2057°F), which is called a eutectic. At a content of 0.1% carbon, delta iron as a single phase is eliminated (point H). In the area confined by the line $NJESG$, gamma iron contains a substantial amount of carbon in the form of solid solution; in this form, it is called austenite or austenitic steel. Corresponding to 0.8% carbon, point S, is called a eutectoid because it looks like the eutectic and represents the minimum temperature at which austenite may exist in single phase. Contrasted to the austenite which can dissolve considerable amounts of carbon is the alpha ferrite, which can only contain very small amounts of carbon in solution (corresponding to the line QP). Steels with very low amounts of carbon are, therefore, called ferritic steels. If a steel with a 0.5% carbon content is cooled from a temperature of, for example, 1600°F, it first crosses the line GS at which point two phases will begin to form: ferrite with very low carbon (less than 0.05%) and austenite, with a higher carbon content (a little higher than 0.5%). With further cooling, the material will cross the PS line at 1333°F below which a mixture of ferrite and pearlite will exist. The two points at which the transformations are initiated (crossing the GS line and then the 1333°F line) are called the critical points of steel. The difference in solubility of carbon in the two iron phases (alpha and gamma) is the crux of all heat treatment of steel.

The transformations shown in the phase diagram of Figure 10.5 assume an infinite time. In practice, however, processes may take from a few seconds (as in the case of spot welding) to several days (as in the case of heat treatment of large vessels). The effect of time is shown in time diagrams like the one shown in Figure 10.6. The diagram, which corresponds to a certain steel of less than 0.8% carbon, shows that when austenite is cooled rapidly from a high temperature (about

Table 10.2. Principal Physical Properties of Several Reactor Materials[a]

		Fuels			Structural Materials					
Property	Temper-ature	Ura-nium	Thorium	Graphite	Alumi-num	Beryl-lium	Magne-sium[b]	Zir-conium	Molyb-denum	Stainless 18–8
Density ρ (g/cm^3)	Room	19.1	11.7	2.2	2.7	1.85	1.74[b]	6.5	10.2	7.9
Melting point (°C)	—	1133	1690	3700	660	1350	650	1850	2620	1420
Coefficient of linear expansion α ($\times 10^6$/°C)	Room	22	11.2	2–3[c]	23.9	12.4	26	4–10[c]	5.5	16.7
Thermal conductivity k (cal/cm-sec-°C)	Room	0.06	0.09	0.3	0.53	0.38	0.35	0.05	0.53	0.04
Elastic modulus E ($\times 10^{-6}$ psi)	Room	30	10	1.0	10	42	6.5	12	45	30
Poisson ratio ν	Room	0.23	0.26	0.20–0.33	0.3	0.03	0.35	0.33	0.31	0.38
Yield stress σ_0 ($\times 10^{-3}$ psi)	Room	25	27	—	15–21	33	15–33	18	57–85[d]	45[d]
	600°F	18	12	—	1.5	15	5	10	—	30[d]
Tensile strength σ_t ($\times 10^{-3}$ psi)	Room	90	38	—	16–24[d]	45–80[d]	25–45[d]	35–85[d]	100–250[d]	90[d]
	600°F	32	22	—	2.5	40	8	16–45[d]	60–80	65[d]
Elongation at fracture in 2 in. (%)	Room	14	40	—	35	2	5–15[d]	16–31[d]	5–20[d]	55[d]
	600°F	43	38	—	90	17	23	60	—	40[d]
Thermal-neutron capture cross section σ_a (barns/atom)	Room	—	—	0.005	0.215	0.009	0.059	0.18	2.4	2.9

Source: C. Bonilla, *Nuclear Engineering*, McGraw-Hill (1957).

[a]See also NUREG/CR-0497.

[b]Characteristic alloy.

[c]Depending on orientation.

[d]Depending on heat treatment and cold working.

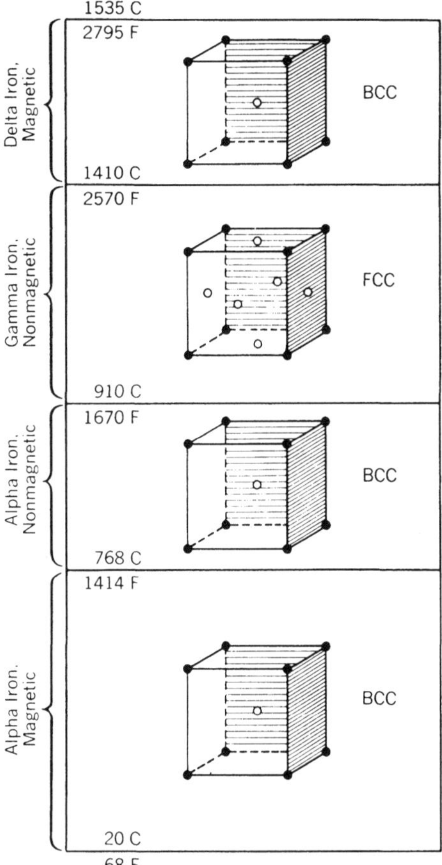

Figure 10.4. Allotropic transformations in pure iron.

1600°F) to a temperature of 900°F and is kept there, the transformation (called isothermal, since it takes place at constant temperature) proceeds along a horizontal line from pure austenite to a mixture of austenite, ferrite, and carbides and, finally, to an agglomeration of ferrite and fine carbides. The total time required is about 700 sec.

The metallurgist distinguishes the different kinds of steels (resulting from various carbon or other element additions and heat treatments) through microscopic examination of suitably prepared (ground, polished, and etched) metal surfaces (Figure 10.7). The main phases of mixtures of iron and steel, corresponding also to the areas of the phase diagram (Figure 10.5), can be summarized as follows.

Austenite is a solid solution of carbon in gamma iron. It may contain a maximum of 2% carbon (at 2090°F) and about 0.80% carbon at the critical temperature of 1333°F. It can exist in ordinary steels only at elevated temperatures (above critical) but can also be found at lower temperatures in certain alloys (the 18 chromium–8 nickel type). Austenite is characterized by high-impact strength and high ductility.

Ferrite is alpha iron containing in solution a small amount of carbon (0.04–0.05%). It is a soft, ductile material with low strength which is dramatically reduced below 40°F. Its tensile strength is about 274 MPa (40,000 psi), elongation about 40%, and hardness 90–95 Brinell.†

Pearlite is a mixture of ferrite and iron carbide (cementite). The carbide separates out in lamellar form as austenite is slowly cooled below the critical temperature of 1333°F. The process,

†Hardness measures the resistance to penetration. One of the most commonly used scales is the Brinell scale. Values range from about 40 (very soft) to 700 (very hard). Cutlery knives have a Brinell hardness of about 500.

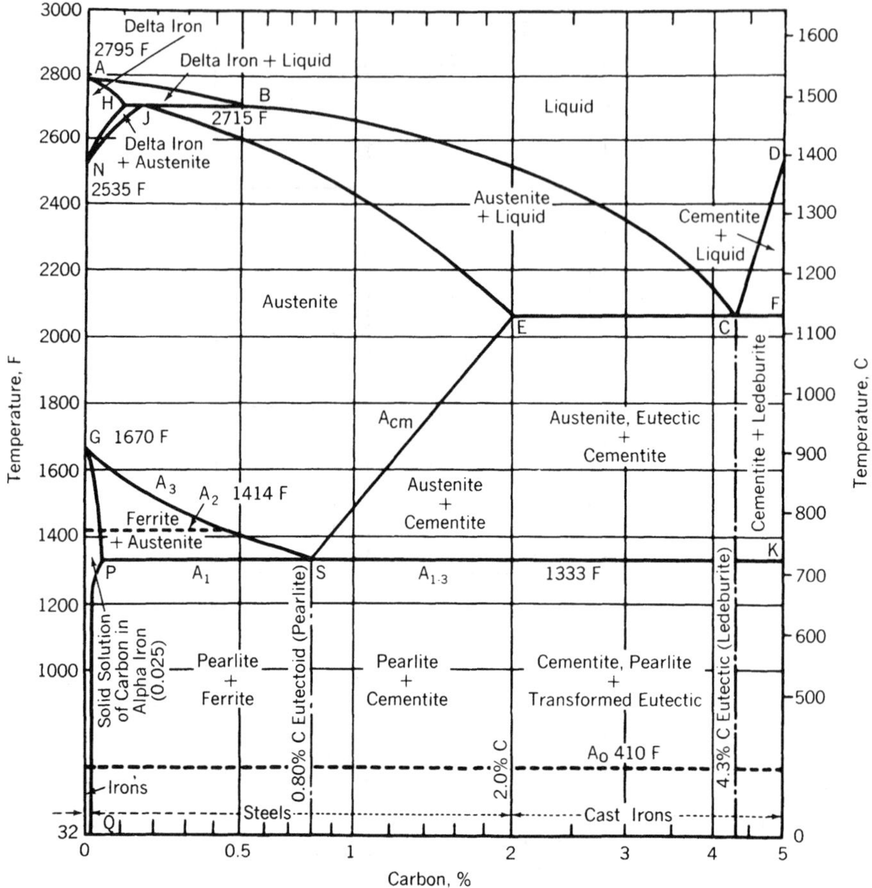

Figure 10.5. Equilibrium diagram showing phase solubility limits, carbon in iron.

called annealing or normalizing, produces metal with high strength and adequate ductility and machinability.

Cementite is iron carbide (Fe_3C) containing 6.67 wt% carbon. It is a very hard material (650 Brinell) and extremely brittle. As shown in the Fe—C phase diagram, it appears in steels with higher than 0.80% carbon as they are slowly cooled. It is also a constituent of pearlite in lamellar form as shown in Figure 10.7*b*. The form in which cementite precipitates out of solution depends on the kind of heat treatment.

Bainite is also a mixture of ferrite and cementite but is formed from austenite just above the M_s temperature in many steels with small components of other metals (low-alloy steels). Its strength is higher than that of either ferrite or pearlite, but its hardness is lower than that of martensite. It is becoming increasingly important in nuclear applications where other steels developed stress-corrosion cracking problems.

Martensite is a very hard constituent formed below the M_s temperature (see Figure 10.6) which varies with steel composition.

Classification of Steels

The steels used in industrial applications can be classified in a variety of ways according to kind (method of production), class (form and use), grade (composition), and quality (control exercised in manufacturing, heat treating, etc.). A few useful definitions pertaining to the composition or grade of steel will be given here.

"Plain carbon steel" is steel whose properties derive primarily from carbon. Small quantities of other elements, such as manganese, silicon, phosphorus, and sulfur may be present but their presence is more or less accidental and not intended to modify the properties of steel. The carbon content of carbon steel may range from very low to 1.7%, usually not more than 1.3%. One may

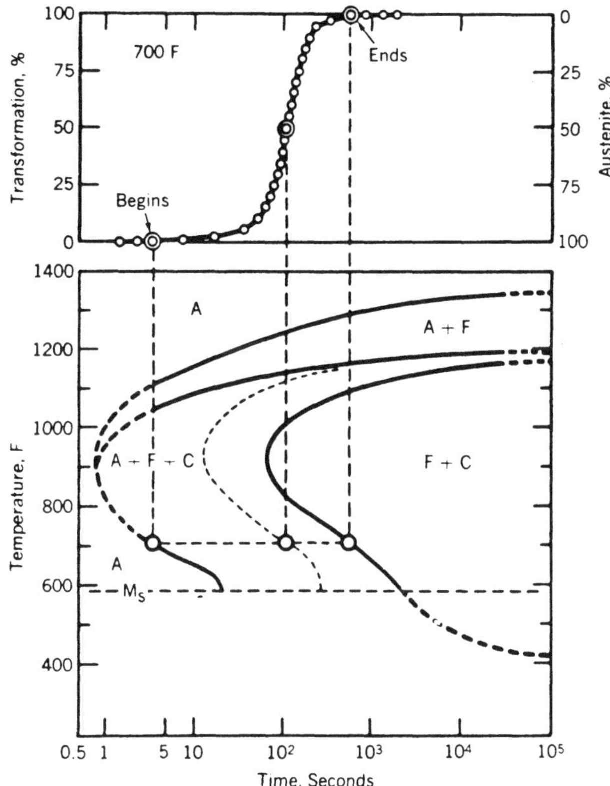

Figure 10.6. The time diagram for phase transformation in a certain composition steel (below 0.8% carbon) shows the gradual changes taking place along the horizontal line corresponding to a temperature of 900°F. A denotes austenite, F ferrite, and C carbide. When an austenitic steel is quickly cooled from 1600°F in a furnace or bath at 700°F, nothing happens for the first 3 sec. Then a gradual transformation occurs: austenite is converted to ferrite with the formation of a third phase, carbides. After 700 sec, the transformation to a mixture of ferrite and carbides is complete. The top diagram shows the time evolution of this transformation. Notice the logarithmic scale of time. It takes about 100 sec for 50% of the transformation to occur and another 600 sec for the other 50%. At temperatures below 600°F (the M_s line) austenite transforms to martensite, a very hard and brittle constituent of heat-treated steels.

distinguish further: low-carbon steel (with 0.10–0.30% carbon); medium-carbon steel (with 0.30–0.85% carbon); and high-carbon steel (with 0.85–1.3% carbon).

When other elements are added to modify the physical and chemical properties of steel, "alloy steel" is produced. Specifications for the different carbon and alloy steel grades have been prepared by various organizations, including the Society of Automotive Engineers (SAE), the American Iron and Steel Institute (AISI), the American Society for the Testing of Materials (ASTM), and others. Each steel is designated by a sequence of four to five characters which codify class and grade. The AISI designation, for example, utilizes four characters XYZZ. The first designates class, the second, modification of class, and the last two, carbon content in points, where each point is 0.01%. The four-number group is prefixed with a letter from A to E which designates the melting practice used in manufacturing. A steel AISI C1020 is one produced in a basic open hearth (letter C), is a true plain carbon steel (digits 10), and has a carbon content between 0.18 and 0.23% (digits 20).

Plain carbon steel can be successfully used where the requirements for strength and corrosion resistance are modest. Because its strength is decreased considerably at high temperatures and because of other shortcomings, the range of usefulness of carbon steels is limited in nuclear applications.

Alloy steels contain amounts of alloying elements (other than carbon) to modify their properties. They are classified as low-alloy (with less than 10% total alloy content) and high-alloy (more than 10% total alloy) steels.

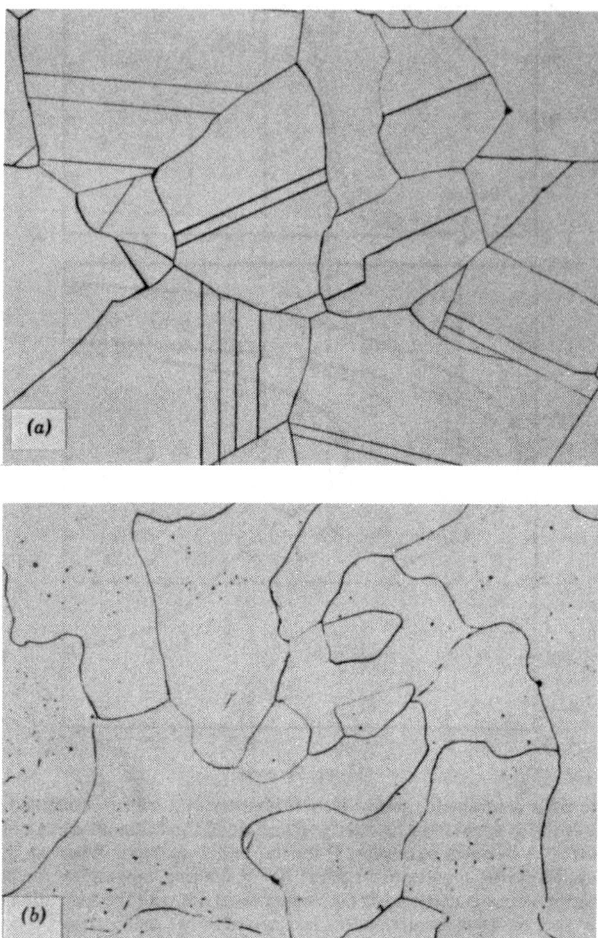

Figure 10.7. Microscopic photographs of surfaces of typical steels. A variety of methods is now available for the study of microstructures of metals and other materials. The surface is ground and highly polished to reflect back incident light and etched in acid. Dark lines, spots, and areas represent discontinuities, that is, grain boundaries, inclusions, and so on. The appearance of these samples gives clues as to the composition of the material, its fabrication, and prior heat treatment. (*a*) Austenite, typical microstructure (500×) reduced about two-thirds. (*b*) Ferrite, typical microstructure (1000×) reduced about two-thirds. (*c*) Lamellar pearlite in 0.8% carbon steel (500×). (*d*) Martensite, typical microstructure in quenched steel (500×) reduced about two-thirds.

Alloy Steels

To overcome the deficiencies of plain carbon steel, alloying elements are added to steel. They modify the properties of steel and render it more capable to respond to applied challenges. The effect of alloying elements in steel is (depending on element and content) to increase the following properties:

1. Hardenability.
2. Resistance to softening on tempering.
3. Resistance to corrosion and oxidation.
4. Strength at high temperatures.
5. Resistance to abrasion.
6. Strength of steels that cannot be quenched.

(c)

(d)

Figure 10.7. (*Continued*)

An example of the change in steel properties by the addition of alloying elements is shown in Figure 10.8, which pertains to alloys of pure iron with various metals. In practice, all alloys contain carbon in addition to iron and the alloying metal, which makes a three-component system. The addition of an element leads to modified phase diagrams, of the kind shown in Figure 10.5, sometimes involving additional phases. For example, the addition of chromium shrinks the area corresponding to austenite (*GSEJN* in Figure 10.5). Above 13% of chromium, austenite does not exist at all. At a content of about 45% chromium and below 1500°F, a pure, nonmagnetic compound is formed, called the "sigma phase," which produces a brittle alloy. Small quantities of sigma phase may exist in the ferrite of alloys with a chromium content as low as 15%.

The effect of nickel addition on the phase diagram is opposite that of chromium. It widens the region of austenite; at a nickel content of 24% the alloy is practically austenitic at all temperatures. The effect of all other alloy elements can be characterized as akin to chromium (ferrite formers);

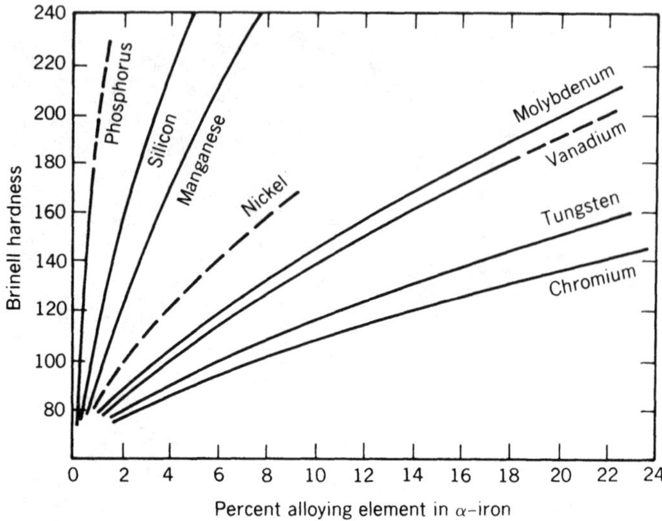

Figure 10.8. Probable hardening effects of various elements as dissolved in pure iron (From E. Bain, *Alloying Elements in Steel,* American Society for Metals, Metals Park, Ohio, 1939.)

akin to nickel (austenite formers); or those forming compounds. The effects of alloying elements on the properties of steel are summarized below.

Carbon, which is not generally considered an alloying element, since it is always a component in steel, has dramatic effects on the properties of the material. As shown in Figure 10.9, tensile strength, yield strength, and hardness all increase with increasing carbon content. On the other hand, ductility (measured by elongation and reduction of area) and toughness (measured by the Charpy impact strength) decrease. In low-alloy steel for high-temperature application, the carbon content does not exceed 0.15% in order to provide adequate ductility for welding, expanding, and bending operations. Stainless steel has an upper limit of 0.08% for carbon. It is designed to minimize the intergranular corrosion which is the result of chemical attack at the grain boundaries where carbide precipitates. In certain kinds of stainless steel, the carbon content is further limited to 0.03% for maximum corrosion resistance.

Phosphorus has the ability to increase the strength and hardness of steels (see Figure 10.8).

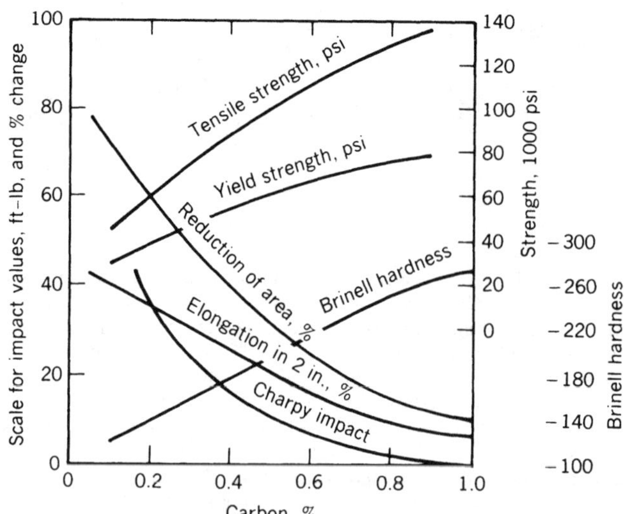

Figure 10.9. General effect of carbon on the mechanical properties of hot-rolled carbon steel.

However, it is considered highly undesirable because of its harmful effect on ductility, resistance to shock, and weldability. Phosphorus enhances the embrittlement of carbon steel mainly by enlarging grain size and by causing segregation. The harmful effect is enhanced as the carbon content increases. *Sulfur* is also an undesirable element in steel. Pressure vessels for reactor applications must have very low levels of phosphorus and sulfur content to limit the embrittlement and susceptibility to thermal shock as the neutron irradiation of the vessel increases with time.

Silicon in small quantities (up to 1%) is beneficial to many properties of steel because of its deoxidizing and degasifying action. Ultimate strength is increased without loss of ductility; above 2.5% silicon causes brittleness of the material and above 5% loss of malleability.

Manganese additions act as deoxidizer and neutralizer of sulfur. Manganese improves the mechanical properties of steel (ratio of yield to tensile strength), prevents brittleness, and improves hardenability and wear resistance. Manganese has a beneficial effect on resistance to creep (flow at elevated temperatures) but no influence on corrosion or oxidation resistance.

Chromium is the element known to improve the resistance to corrosion; hence, it is an indispensable constituent of stainless steel. In addition, chromium raises yield strength, ultimate strength, hardness, and toughness of steel at room temperature, but not so markedly at higher temperatures. Other notable properties are improvement of resistance to wear or abrasion. The resistance of chromium steel to corrosion in the atmosphere and many reagents is steadily increased when chromium content exceeds 12%, although the chemical properties of the alloy depend also on the carbon content. For maximum corrosion resistance, chromium must be maximized and carbon minimized to the extent possible. At higher temperature operation over long periods of time, chromium, in sufficient content, prevents the graphitization of steel and makes it resistant to high-temperature oxidation. Chromium is, therefore, an essential ingredient of steels intended for high-temperature service.

Nickel dissolves in iron at all proportions. It increases its ultimate strength without impairing its ductility. The principal effect of nickel addition is an increase of toughness, a measure of the resistance of an existing crack to extend under stress, an important property of structural steels. The effect is more pronounced at nickel contents above 1%. At contents above 5%, nickel also improves resistance to corrosion. The most common use of nickel is in combination with chromium, to produce alloys called 18–8 type (18% chromium and 8% nickel) with much improved properties which cannot be produced by equivalent amounts of either element alone. These alloys are known for their high resistance to corrosion, and oxidation at high temperatures and greatly enhanced creep strength. Nickel (up to 4%) is also used in low-alloy ferritic (or bainitic) steels with a modest beneficial effect on their creep properties.

Molybdenum is used in small amounts (up to 2%) in all steels. In combination with other alloying metals (mainly nickel and chromium), it serves to enhance their effect on the mechanical properties of steel. Molybdenum addition to steel improves its strength, elastic limit, resistance to wear, impact qualities, and hardenability. The beneficial effect of modybdenum is most evident at elevated temperatures: (a) the "red-hardness" of steel is greatly improved (i.e., steel can be heated to a red-hot temperature without losing its hardness); (b) chromium steel is made less susceptible to temper embrittlement; and (c) the high-temperature creep strength of steel is markedly improved. *Tungsten,* a refractory metal, has effects similar to those of molybdenum. *Vanadium* is used as an alloying element in small contents (0.30% or less) to increase strength, toughness, and hardness. It forms carbide compounds and tends to stabilize the crystal structure, especially at elevated temperatures. It inhibits grain growth and, therefore, allows heat treatment at higher temperatures without loss of strength. It also enhances the properties of other steel ingredients. For example, the addition of 0.1–0.5% vanadium to 0.5–1.0% molybdenum steels can produce a remarkable improvement of creep behavior at high temperatures.

Titanium and *niobium* are used in small quantities in combination with other elements. Because of their greater affinity to carbon than chromium, they are used in chromium–nickel austenitic alloys (18–8 type) to react with carbon and to allow chromium to remain in solution. Thus, the corrosion resistance of the alloy is maintained. These elements have been used in the development of the "super alloys" known for their superior stability at elevated temperatures. *Copper* is an ingredient which, in contents of up to 1%, improves yield strength and resistance to atmospheric corrosion. However, copper, as is the case with sulfur and phosphorus, has a detrimental effect on radiation embrittlement and its presence in reactor pressure vessels must be minimized.

Mechanical Working of Steel

To produce a component, metals must be shaped either by casting in a mold or by mechanical working. This latter also imparts to the metal certain desirable properties. There are two methods of working metals: cold and hot.

Hot working takes place at a temperature above the recrystallization temperature and the simultaneous annealing that occurs prevents stress and work hardening. Hot work is usually performed above the transformation temperature (1333°F in Figure 10.5 but variable for other alloy steels) at which the material has satisfactory plasticity. Hot working is normally involved in forging, pressing, rolling, and piercing.

Cold working is a process taking place below the recrystallization temperature of the material and usually takes place after the initial hot working. Cold working includes drawing, forming, and stamping.

The temperature at which steel is worked has a marked effect on its properties. Hot work improves the quality of steel by closing voids in the ingot; this produces a more homogeneous and sound material. The crystals of the material are reduced in size, which improves its ductility and toughness. Hardness is not increased by hot working. Hot working is an effective, and comparatively inexpensive method (mainly because of the relatively lower energy required) of shaping metals with adequate dimensional accuracy and surface quality.

Cold work, on the other hand, increases the hardness, tensile strength, and yield point of the metal but reduces its ductility. In this process, grains are elongated in the direction of working, the exact amount depending on the amount of cold work and on the material. If cold working produces excessive hardening of the material, it may fracture upon further working. In such cases, it may be necessary to give the material some heat treatment to restore its ductility.

Forging is often the first step of hot working to bring a piece of metal to a desirable shape. A forging hammer works the metal piece by the application of intermittent blows whereas a forging press applies a continuous force as it kneads the steel in every direction. Suitably shaped dies are used with hydraulic or steam-hydraulic presses to form nozzles, vessel heads, and other parts. Hot working by forging presses is also used to produce the round metal pieces for the manufacture of seamless tubes.

Rolling is the most common method for reducing steel to shape. The cast of the forged piece of metal (in the form of ingot, slab, bar, or billet) is first heated throughout its mass to an appropriate temperature and then passed through rolls rotating in opposite directions. As the metal passes through the rolls, its thickness is reduced, its internal structure is refined by a reduction in grain size, and the metal is shaped to the desired form. Figure 10.10 shows the production of a course segment for a pressure vessel for a nuclear application.

Heat Treatment

Heat treatment is a means of modifying the properties of steel by altering its microstructure. Various heat treatments are used to produce different effects such as hardness, ductility, improved machinability, relieving of internal stresses, higher strength, or impact resistance.

Annealing is applied in two variations: full anneal and process anneal. In full anneal, the metal is heated, at a specified heating rate, to a temperature about 55°C (100°F) higher than the upper limit of the critical range. It is held there for an appropriate time and then is subject to a controlled cooling in a furnace. The full annealing of a hypoeutectoid steel (less than 0.8% carbon) results in a mixture of ferrite and perlite with a fine grain structure. The metal thus produced is relatively soft, ductile, and free of internal stresses. Process anneal is carried out at temperatures below the critical range (usually between 950 and 1300°F) and its main purpose is to reduce residual stresses in work-hardened steel and to improve ductility.

Normalizing is a special form of annealing: steel is heated above the critical temperature range and then is allowed to cool in air. Normalizing relieves internal stresses caused by previous working and increases softness and ductility; yet it leaves steel with a higher tensile strength and hardness than full annealing.

Spheroidizing is another type of annealing steel with the purpose of increasing its softness and machinability. It consists of heating the material to just below its critical temperature followed by very slow cooling. The process causes the agglomeration of iron carbide (Fe_3C) in a globular or spheroidal form from which the name of the process is derived. The treatment is usually applied to steels with a higher carbon content (more than 0.45%) and hypereutectoid steels. The product has properties similar to those of coarser pearlite.

Quenching consists of very rapid cooling of steels (usually of higher carbon content), heated to temperatures where austenite is formed. The rapid cooling to below 204°C (400°F) leads to the formation of a very hard and brittle material, martensite. Its microstructure is shown in Figure 10.7*d*. Details of properties and behavior will depend on carbon content and on the type and amounts of alloying elements in the steel. Martensite is the hardest form of heat-treated steels. It has a high strength and resistance to abrasion but a poor resistance to impact and is almost impossible to machine.

Tempering is a secondary treatment intended to reduce the brittle characteristics of some steels which have been subjected to normalizing or quenching. Heating to a specified temperature, below the critical range, followed by a controlled cooling allows certain transformations to occur in hardened steel. Some of the hardness is lost in tempering, but its toughness is increased and stresses created by quenching are relieved. The effect of tempering is larger the higher the tempering temperature.

Figure 10.10. Production of a steel course for a reactor pressure vessel by rolling.

Steels Commonly Used in Nuclear Plants

A variety of steels is used in the components of a nuclear plant. A list of the most common materials by U.S. and overseas manufacturers is given in Table 10.3 which gives the content of each material in carbon and other alloying elements. Carbon steels have a carbon content of 0.10–0.30%. They are widely used as base metal for pressure vessels for both PWRs and BWRs as well as for other large pressure vessels such as pressurizers. Typical materials are A508/Class 2† forgings and A533/Grade B Class 1 plate. The first is a manganese–molybdenum steel modified with small amounts of nickel and chromium‡; the second has a similar composition but much reduced chromium. Both materials are first heated to a temperature of 870–900°C (1600–1650°F) where austenite is formed, quenched, and finally tempered to about 650–675°C (1200–1250°F), for a

†These designations are according to the American Society for Testing and Materials (ASTM).
‡Gases (H_2 and N_2), sulfur, and phosphorous are maintained as low as possible in A508 steels.

Table 10.3. Nominal Compositions of Alloys Used (or Candidates for Use) in Nuclear Components (Steels)

	Composition, wt%									
AISI Type	Fe	Cr	Ni	Mn	Mo	Si	V	C	S	Other Constituents
Carbon (ferritic) steels										
A501	Balance	4–6	—	1.0	0.40–0.65	1.0	—	0.10	0.030	0.40 (P)
A508/2	Balance	0.35	0.7	0.7	0.6	—	0.05	0.27	—	
A508/3	Balance	—	0.6	1.3	0.52	—	0.05	0.20	—	
A508/4	Balance	1.7	3.3	—	0.5	—	0.03	0.23	—	
A508/5	Balance	1.7	3.3	—	0.5	—	0.1	0.23	—	
A533	Balance	—	—	1.15–1.50	0.45–0.60	0.15–0.30	0.05	0.25	—	
Low-alloy (bainitic) steels										
1Cr–1Mo–0.25V	96.07	1.0	—	0.85	1.25	0.25	0.25	0.33	—	
2¼Cr–1Mo (Grade 22)	95.7	2.42	—	0.49	0.98	0.28	—	0.026	0.009	0.012 (P) and 0.05 (Cu) Nb in stabilized version
Ni–Cr–MoV (A469 Class 8)	Balance	1.25–2.00	3.25–4.00	0.60	0.30–0.60	0.15–0.30	0.05–0.15	0.28	0.018	0.015 (P)
Ni–Cr–MoV (A470 Class 8)	Balance	0.90–1.50	0.75	1.00	1.00–1.50	0.15–0.35	0.20–0.30	0.25–0.35	0.018	0.015 (P)
Ni–Cr–MoV (A471 Class 8)	Balance	0.75–2.00	2.00–4.00	0.70	0.20–0.70	0.15–0.35	0.05	0.28	0.015	0.015 (P)

Ferritic (martensitic) stainless steels										
403 (S40300)	Balance	11.5–13.0	—	—	1.0	0.5	—	0.15	0.030	0.040 (P)
410 (S41000)	Balance	11.5–13.5	—	—	1.0	1.0	—	0.15	0.030	0.040 (P)
Sandvik, Sweden (HT-9)	Balance	11.5	0.05	1.0	0.55	0.4	0.3	0.20	—	0.5 (W)
(HT-7)	Balance	9	—	1.0	0.45	0.65	—	0.1	—	
French (R8)	Balance	9.5	—	2.0	1.0	0.3	0.35	0.10		0.5 (Nb)
French (EM-12)	Balance	9.0	—	2.0	1.0	0.75	0.3	0.15	—	0.5 (Nb)
Combustion engineering developmental alloy (U.S.)	Balance	9	—	1.0	?	?	1.0?	0.01	—	1.0? (Nb)
Japanese (HCM9M)	Balance	8/10.0	—	1.8/2.2	0.3/0.7	≤0.5	—	≤0.06	≤0.03	
Austenitic stainless steels										
304 (S30400)	Balance	18–20	8–10.5	—	2.0	1.0	—	0.08	0.030	0.045 (P)
304L (S30403)	Balance	18–20	8–12	—	2.0	1.0	—	0.03	0.030	0.045 (P)
316 (S31600)	Balance	16–18	10–14	2.0–3.0	2.0	1.0	—	0.080	0.030	0.045 (P)
316L (S31603)	Balance	16–18	10–14	2.0–3.0	2.0	1.0	—	0.030	0.030	0.045 (P)
321 (S32100)	Balance	17–19	9–12	—	2.0	1.0	—	0.08	0.030	0.045 (P) Ti = 5 × C min.
347 (S34700)	Balance	17–19	9–13	—	2.0	1.0	—	0.08	0.030	0.045 (P)

Source: J. T. A. Roberts, *Structural Materials in Nuclear Power Systems*, Plenum, New York, 1981.

Table 10.4. Mechanical Properties of Selected Austenitic Stainless Steels at Room Temperature

	304	304L	316	316L	347
Tensile strength (psi, min.)	80,000	70,000	75,000	70,000	80,000
Yield strength (0.2% offset) (psi, min.)	30,000	25,000	30,000	30,000	30,000
Elongation in 2 in. (%, min.)	50.0	40.0	40.0	40.0	40.0
Reduction in area (%, min.)	60.0	60.0	50.0	60.0	50.0
Young's modulus (10^6 psi)	29.0	29.0	29.0	29.0	29.0
Brinell hardness (max.)	180	180	200	180	200
Rockwell hardness (max.)	B90	B90	B95	B90	B95
Izod impact, (ft-lb, min.)	85	80	70	80	80
Creep strength (psi at 1000°F)					
1% flow in 10,000 hr	19,000	19,000	24,000	24,000	32,000
1% flow in 100,000 hr	13,000	13,000	15,000	15,000	27,000

Source: ASTM.

minimum of 1 hr/25 mm (1 in.) of thickness. These materials are optimized for high strength and toughness and to ensure weldability. Carbon steels lose strength rapidly with increasing temperature and are not particularly resistant to corrosion. For this latter reason, the inside surface of all primary system components must be covered with a stainless steel cladding.† The stainless steels most common in reactor system applications are the 300 series of the American Iron and Steel Institute (AISI), listed in Table 10.3. Their overall characteristics are similar; some of them are listed in Table 10.4. Austenitic stainless steels combine good strength, ductility, and resistance to corrosion at high temperatures; they resist corrosion by many agents under oxidizing conditions. The main types of stainless steel are 304, 316, 347, 304L, and 316L. The L following the number indicates a steel with low carbon content, typically 0.03% compared to 0.08% of normal stainless steel. When corrosion resistant cladding is required, 308 stainless steel weld overlay, normally about 5 mm (0.20 in.) thick, is used. After the welding of the pieces and of the overlaying of stainless steel, the entire vessel is given a heat treatment for 1 hr/25 mm (1 in.) of thickness at a temperature of 595–620°C (1100–1150°F). The total postweld heat treatment of a vessel may last 40 hr.

The dominant material in primary coolant piping of operating BWR plants is 304 stainless steel; types 304L, 316, and 347 stainless steels are also used in smaller quantities, as is Inconel 600. The low-carbon stainless steel has an enhanced resistance to corrosion. For this reason, types 304L, 316L, and 347 are introduced increasingly in applications, particularly where the 304 stainless steel has shown susceptibility to stress corrosion cracking. These steels have shown superior resistance (over a factor of 20 compared to 304 stainless steel) to integranular stress corrosion cracking. Ferritic steels are commonly used in steam lines, feedwater lines, and so on, in forms including seamless, welded, and small amounts of cast pipe. The use of carbon steel piping and components has increased significantly in the evolution of BWR designs because of problems exhibited by the austenitic steels. The current BWR/6 standard design uses carbon steel in almost all primary pressure boundary piping. PWR piping materials are mostly 304 and 316 stainless steels. In many cases, ferritic steels clad with 308L austenitic stainless weld overlay are used.

Low-alloy steels find a major application in the construction of turbine rotors and discs (see also Chapter 9). The rotor and the discs are made of low-alloy bainitic steels (alloying elements are Ni, Cr, Mo, V); the turbine blades are typically made of 12% chromium martensitic stainless steel (AISI Type 403) which combines creep strength along with oxidation and corrosion resistance. Large turbine rotors (also called spindles) are machined from forged ingots and can weigh 200 to 400 tons. The production of high-quality, homogeneous, defect-free ingots for this application is of great importance to the reliability of turbine operation. The technique used presently is vacuum-arc casting technology, a combination of melting in an electric furnace and degassing under vacuum. The ingot is given a long thermal soak to minimize the chemical segregation of nonmetallic inclusions upon solidification of the melt. The ingot is then forged, in order to bring it to the desired shape and size and to work it mechanically. This latter breaks up the microstructure of the cast and imparts a normal ingot porosity. The material is subjected to double normalizing and temper treatment in order to refine the microstructure. A further heat treatment gives the ingot the desired mechanical properties.

Almost all large-turbine rotors and disc forgings in the United States come under three ASTM

†A few exceptions exist. The head of a BWR vessel which is in contact with steam rather than water does not have to be clad with stainless steel.

Table 10.5. Mechanical Properties of Rotor Steels

Property	A469 (1971) Class 8	A470 (1974) Class 8	A471 (1970) Class 8
Tensile strength, min. (MPa)	829	725–860	1105
Yield strength, min. (MPa)	691	585	1000
Elongation in 50 mm. min. (%)	16	14–17	13
Reduction of area, min. (%)	45	38–43	37
Ductile–brittle transition temperature, max. (K)	277	394	283
Room temperature impact energy, min. (J)	55	8.2	41

Source: EPRI Report NP-1023, March 1979.

specifications, A469, A470, and A471. Some of their mechanical characteristics are given in Table 10.5.

High-Temperature Behavior of Steels

High operating temperatures pose exceptional challenges to structural steels. Their yield strength and ultimate strength decrease with increasing temperature. Figure 10.11 shows the decline in tensile strength with temperature for several classes of steels. The drop in strength is remarkable above about 480°C (900°F). Although LWRs do not operate at such high temperatures, breeder reactors and High-Temperature Gas-cooled Reactors (HTGRs) do. The selection of materials for these latter applications is far more exacting than in LWRs.

The phenomenon leading to degraded performance of materials at elevated temperatures is "creep," described in Section 10.1, subsection "Some Definitions in Strength of Materials." At ordinary temperatures, most metals and alloys exhibit hardening and strengthening as a result of plastic deformation. Above a certain temperature, plastic deformation of the materials does not

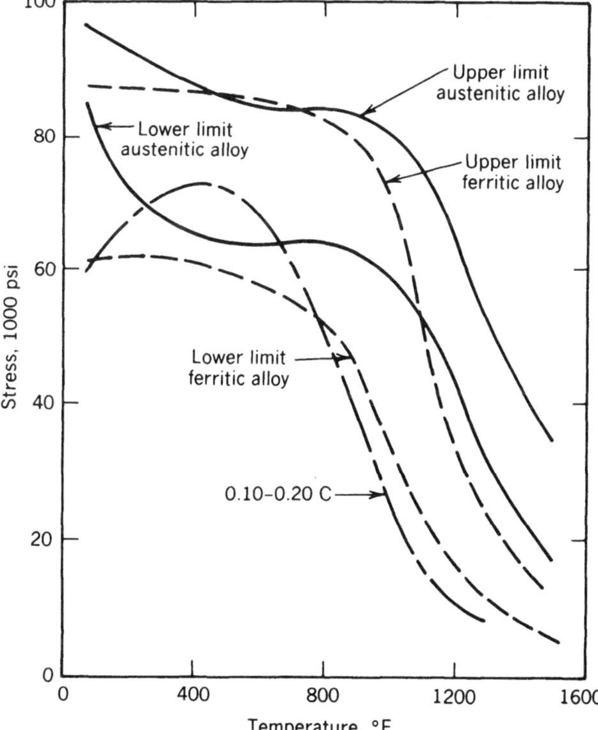

Figure 10.11. Tensile strength of various steels at temperatures to 1500°F.

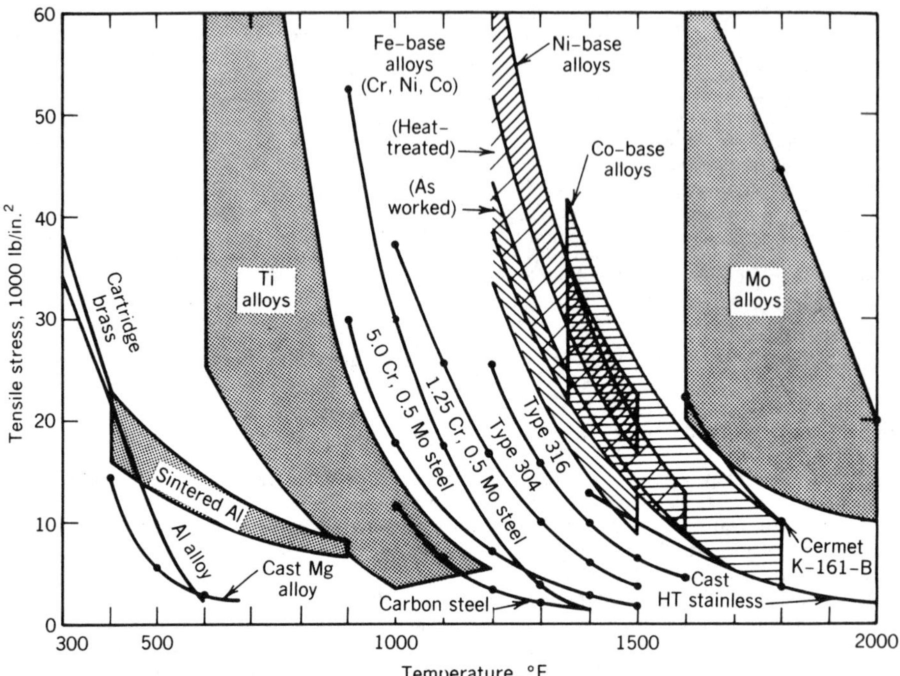

Figure 10.12. Stress–temperature curves for various alloys (rupture in 1000 hr). (From *Metals Handbook,* American Society for Metals, Metals Park, Ohio, 1954 Supplement.)

produce hardening; the metal continues to deform under constant load until fracture occurs. The fracture type depends on temperature and the rate of strain, that is, the slope of the curve shown in Figure 10.1*c*.

Data from extensive creep tests are collected to aid in the design of components expected to operate at high temperatures. Creep data are obtained by subjecting specimens to a constant load at a given temperature and by observing the change in length as a function of time. Several curves of the type shown in Figure 10.1*c* are obtained, each for a given temperature. Higher stress and higher temperature will increase the minimum creep rate during the secondary creep period and will shorten the time to rupture. Because full creep tests are expensive in time and money, they are seldom carried out to rupture. They are extended only so far as to allow a determination of the most important feature of the creep curve, that is, the slope of the secondary creep segment. This requires a minimum of 1000 hr of testing, depending on material, stress, and temperature. The results of the creep tests can be used in several ways: the most common usage is to quote the stress that will produce a 1% elongation in 10,000 or 100,000 hr at a given temperature.

Carbon steel has poor creep resistance above about 315°C (600°F) because it is subject to tempering (i.e., softening). Alloying elements improve the creep behavior of steels. Low-alloy steels containing molybdenum, vanadium, chromium, and tungsten, strong carbide-forming elements, have satisfactory creep resistance up to 425°C (800°F). Molybdenum is the single most important element in improving high-temperature creep of steels. A comprehensive comparison of various alloys in terms of their high-temperature tensile strength is shown in Figure 10.12.

The ASME code requires high-temperature design for temperatures above 427°C (800°F) with austenitic steels. The design of LMFBR components which operate in a range of 480–570°C (900°–1050°F)† must take into account the effect of temperature on the selection of materials. As seen in Figure 10.12, a difference of 28°C (50°F) could make a substantial difference in the tensile stress of the material.

The LMFBR vessel of the Clinch River Breeder Reactor (CRBR) has a diameter about 6 m and a relatively thin wall (~75 mm) since the internal pressure is quite low (about 1 MPa or 145 psi). It is constructed entirely of stainless steel (SS) types 304 and 316. Type 304 SS is selected for piping in

†The Fast Flux Test Facility at Hanford has a maximum sodium outlet temperature of 566°C (1050°F), while the Prototype Fast Reactor (PFR of the U.K.) and Phénix (France) a slightly lower sodium outlet temperature of 560°C (1040°F).

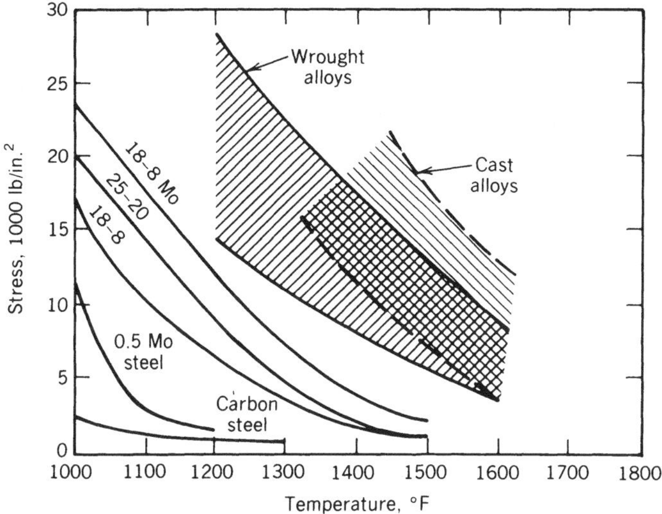

Figure 10.13. Creep strength of superalloys versus steel (creep rate of 0.0001%/hr). (By permission from *Properties of Metals at Elevated Temperatures*, by G. V. Smith, copyright © 1950, McGraw-Hill, New York.)

LMFBRs, although, in some designs, type 316 SS is selected for the hot leg regions where the higher temperatures exist. The 316 stainless steel is more expensive than 304 SS but has superior strength properties as shown in Figure 10.11. Welds or fills are made with type 308, 316, or 16–8–2 (i.e., 16% Cr, 8% Ni, and 2% Mo) materials.

The HTGR, in its several design variations, operates at an even higher temperature. The helium exiting from the core has a temperature in the range of 680°C (1260°F) and a pressure of about 7.25 MPa (1050 psi). Stainless steel used in cladding materials and other core internals must have good strength characteristics at these elevated operating temperatures. High-alloy austenitic steels of the type 18–8 are required for satisfactory strength up to about 705°C (1300°F). A number of "superalloys" has been developed for high-temperature service. Such are the N-155 (Multimet), S-90, Refractory 26, and Refractory 80; they contain almost equivalent amounts of chromium, nickel, cobalt, and iron. The superior creep behavior of superalloys versus steel in the temperature range up to 870°C (1600°F) is shown in Figure 10.13. Creep strength of a wrought superalloy could be double that of a 18–8 type steel at 650°C (1200°F) and the advantage is larger at higher temperatures. Nickel-base and cobalt-base alloys have excellent high-temperature strength characteristics and corrosion resistance. They include the nickel–chromium series known as Inconel alloys (to be further discussed in the next section); the nickel–chromium–molybdenum alloys like the "Hastelloys," Cosmoloy F, GMR-235, Inconel 713C, and so on; the nickel–chromium–cobalt alloys (Nimonic 90 and K-42-B); and the nickel–chromium–cobalt–molybdenum series (Inco 700, M-252, René 41, Udimet 500, Waspaloy, etc.). The cobalt-base alloys include the original alloy of this group known as Stellite or HS-21, a cobalt–chromium–nickel–tungsten type (HS-31), and alloy HS-25 suitable for applications up to 1095°C (2000°F). Stellite is used in nuclear reactors as a hard facing material on valves and control rod drive mechanisms. It has excellent wear resistance and corrosion properties. Its principal components are 27Cr–3Ni–64Co. The cobalt, however, can cause activation problems in the primary coolant system (see Chapter 12).

Most of these alloys find application in the manufacture of gas turbine blades, electric heating elements, combustion liners, jet engines, and other high-temperature service. For temperatures above 870°C (1600°F), one must look to the use of refractory metals and their alloys. Because of cost and availability considerations, attention has been focused on the nonprecious refractory metals chromium, molybdenum, and tungsten with melting points of 1888°C (3430°F), 2727°C (4760°F), and 3410°C (6170°F), respectively. The upper limit of application for these alloys is about 1093°C (2000°F).

Sensitization of Stainless Steel

Sensitization of 18–8 type stainless steels can result in the localized depletion of chromium with the loss of its anticorrosion properties. Cracks in the steel can then occur, especially under stress in high oxygen environments. The sensitization of steel permits corrosive attack to start at the grain boundary where there is a chromium deficiency. Corrosion follows the grain boundary, which is typical of intergranular corrosion. Sensitization can occur during welding when chromium carbide precipitates in the grain boundaries (Figure 10.9). This precipitation happens not in the weld itself, but in the Heat-Affected Zone (HAZ) immediately adjacent to the weld. During welding, the HAZ is heated to the temperature range 800–1600°F (425–870°C) necessary for carbide precipitation. The weld area itself is heated to much higher temperature, but rapidly cools through the precipitation range, retaining the austenite structure.

10.3. MATERIALS FOR HEAT EXCHANGERS

Steam Generator Tubing

As described in Chapter 9, PWRs utilize large steam generators to transfer heat from the primary to the secondary side. This heat transfer occurs across the walls of thousands of tubes in either of the two types of steam generators (U-tube or once through). It is very important and desirable to minimize corrosion on the secondary side of the steam generator. Although a stainless steel of the 18–8 type could be well suited to the coolant environment on both sides, it is still subject to some corrosion on the steam side. The search for a more corrosion-resistant material led to the selection of nickel-base alloys (alloys whose largest constituent is nickel). The composition of the various nickel-base alloys is shown in Table 10.6. Almost all steam generators use cold-drawn tubes made of commercial Inconel 600. It contains 60.5% nickel, 23% chromium, 14.1% iron with small amounts of other elements. An exception is tubing made in West Germany where Alloy 800H (which is an iron- rather than nickel-base alloy) is used for its superior high-temperature properties. For the same reason, in steam generators designed for the High-Temperature Gas Reactors (HTGRs) a combination of Alloy 800H and $2\frac{1}{4}$ chromium–1 molybdenum is used.

In LMFBR heat exchangers, the dominant material in use is $2\frac{1}{4}$ Cr–1 Mo steel (SA336), known as Croloy. The steam generator shell and support plate as well as the tubing is made of this material, although tubing can also be made of 9 Cr–1 Mo steel (SA213) and Incoloy 800. For the intermediate heat exchangers materials used are 304 and 316 stainless steel and $2\frac{1}{4}$ Cr–1 Mo steel.

The French Phénix breeder reactor, now in operation for many years, utilizes the $2\frac{1}{4}$ Cr–1 Mo steel and a niobium-stabilized version of this alloy in the evaporator section of the steam generator and type 321 stainless steel in the superheater section. The larger Super-Phénix design, presently under construction, has changed to type 316L stainless steel for the shell and internal structures and Alloy 800 for the tube bundle. The reason offered for the switch is the higher resistance of Alloy 800 to stress corrosion cracking on the water side and lower susceptibility than that of austenitic or ferritic steels to wastage from the sodium/water reaction. This latter could be caused by small leaks in the sodium-to-water barrier. Other materials for LMFBR steam generator tubing include the ferritic 9 Cr–1 Mo used in the United Kingdom's Commercial Demonstration Fast Reactor (CDFR) and a niobium-stabilized version of Croloy ($2\frac{1}{4}$ Cr–1 Mo) in the West German SNR-300 reactor.

Incoloy 600 is the predominant material used in LWRs. It has good strength and creep properties up to about 627°C (800°F), but beyond this temperature its creep behavior is degraded rapidly. Tables 10.7 and 10.8 give these properties as a function of temperature. An important advantage of this material is a low coefficient of thermal expansion. This causes a smaller differential expansion between tubes and the low-alloy shell of the steam generator as compared to 18–8 stainless steel.

The various problems encountered in steam generators were discussed in Chapter 9, particularly the tube denting problem. Here we discuss additional aspects of steam generators caused by a phenomenon called Stress Corrosion Cracking (SCC). Through a combination of stress and a corrosive chemical environment the material develops a crack which may progress with time, leading ultimately to tube failure. If the chemical attack is limited to the regions between the grains of the material, the process is an Inter-Granular Stress Corrosion Cracking (IGSCC); if it proceeds through the grain itself it is called Trans-Granular Stress Corrosion Cracking (TGSCC). Tubes develop susceptibility to SCC primarily on the secondary side where the chemical conditions are less likely to be ideal. The cause of most failures is attributed to caustic stress corrosion.

Caustic environments are believed to exist in areas of poor secondary side circulation and are mainly due to impurity ingress. The susceptibility to IGSCC in high-temperature caustic solutions increases near the active–passive transition region.†

Copper oxide added to caustic (NaOH) increases the susceptibility of steam generators to SCC while mixtures with silica appear to decrease the crack depth. For this reason, the use of copper alloys in the secondary side must be avoided. Temperature appears to be an important parameter

†The passive region corresponds to lower temperatures where a protective oxide film is formed which inhibits further corrosion. As the temperature increases the reaction rate is accelerated to a point where active oxidation occurs.

Table 10.6. Composition of Various Types of Inconels (Nickel-Base Alloys)

Type	Composition, wt%									
	Ni	Cr	Fe	C	Mn	Si	Ti	Mo	S	Others
Inconel 600	60.5	23.0	14.1	0.08	0.5	0.2	1.4	—	—	
Inconel 690	60.0	30.0	9.5	0.03	—	—	—	—	—	
Inconel (Alloy) 800H	32.5	21.0	46.0	0.05	0.8	0.5	0.4	—	—	0.4 Cu
Inconel (Alloy) 800	34.0	21.0	43.0	0.02	0.64	0.3	—	—	—	—
PE 16	42.3 max.	16.6	34.1	0.06	0.12	0.24	1.31	3.63	0.004	0.99 Al 0.003 P

Source: J. T. A. Roberts, *Structural Materials in Nuclear Power Systems*, Plenum, New York, 1981.

Table 10.7. Tensile Properties of Cold-Drawn, As-Drawn Inconel Alloy 600 Bar

Temperature, °F	Tensile Strength, psi	Yield Strength 0.2% Offset, psi	Elongation, %
85	128,500	120,500	14.5
200	124,500	118,000	13.0
400	120,500	—	—
500	119,500	113,000	12.5
600	118,000	113,000	13.0
700	118,000	111,000	14.0
800	117,500	109,500	14.0
900	113,500	103,000	17.0
1,000	110,500	100,000	14.0
1,100	105,000	93,500	13.0
1,200	92,500	81,500	20.0
1,300	68,500	61,000	43.0

Source: Babcock & Wilcox Co., *Steam, Its Generation and Use,* 1978.

[a]Strain rate 0.005 in./in. to yield strength, then 0.05 in./in.

for crack initiation and propagation in deaerated high-temperature water. The kinds of impurity present in the water play an important role. Some impurities (like lead), change the corrosion process from integranular to transgranular. Dissolved gases (e.g., hydrogen, oxygen, or ammonia) can affect the electrochemical potential of the metal and can, therefore, have an important effect on SCC. The behavior of three tubing materials in terms of susceptibility to SCC as a function of caustic is shown in Figure 10.14. Alloy 800 has the highest resistance to cracking of the three materials compared. Indeed, there have been no reports of tube cracking in steam generators designed by the German manufacturer KWU, which uses Alloy 800 as tube material.

Steam Condensers

As described in Chapter 9, the condenser is a large heat exchanger in which steam enthalpy not converted to mechanical energy is rejected to the environment. This rejected energy could be up to

Table 10.8. Creep Properties of Cold-Drawn, Annealed[a] Inconel Alloy 600

Temperature, °F	Stress, psi for a Secondary Creep Rate of: 1%/10,000 hr	1%/100,000 hr
800	40,000	30,000
900	28,000	18,000
1,000	12,500	6,100
1,100	6,800	3.400
1,200	—	2,200
1,300	—	1,400
1,400	—	970
1,500	—	660
1,600	880	450
1,700	—	—
1,800	560	340
1,900	—	—
2,000	270	160
2,100	170	100

Source: Babcock & Wilcox Co., *Steam, Its Generation and Use,* 1978.

[a]3 hr at 1750°F—air cooled.

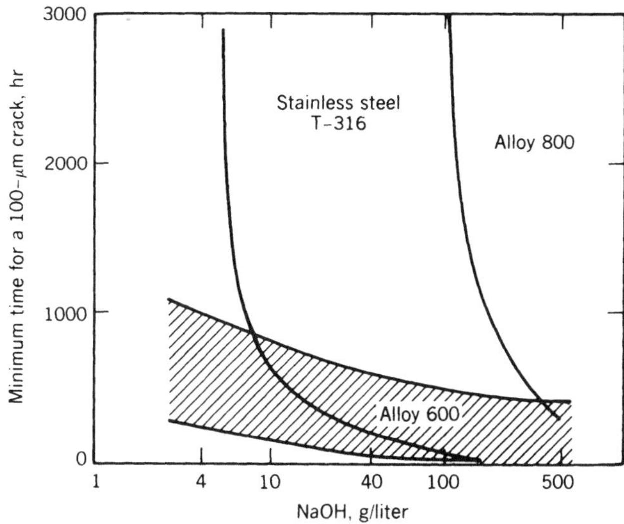

Figure 10.14. Influence of the NaOH concentration at 350°C on the minimum time to induce a 100-μm crack in C-ring specimens. Comparison of the SCC resistance of Inconel 600, Inconel 800, and type 315 stainless steel.

twice the amount converted to useful energy. The condensers used in nuclear applications have a configuration similar to those used in fossil fuel plants. The materials used for condenser tubing are aluminum–bronze, aluminum–brass (SB 261), cupronickel (SB 111, 251), titanium, and type 304 stainless steel (SA 249). A list of copper-base alloys used in condensers is shown in Table 10.9. Historically, admiralty brass has been used for condensers with freshwater service, while the copper–nickel, aluminum brass, and aluminum bronze have been used predominantly in plants with seawater-cooled condensers. The reason is that the latter exhibit a somewhat higher resistance to corrosion by seawater. All of the copper alloys are highly susceptible to erosion-corrosion. This phenomenon is mainly caused by air release and by the flow of turbulent, high-velocity water. The performance of admiralty brass, used primarily in freshwater service, has been excellent. The 90–10 copper–nickel alloys, especially with seawater service, have shown a relatively poor performance with problems arising from erosion–corrosion and localized (pitting) corrosion on the waterside. A primary weakness of these alloys (and most other copper alloys) is their weak resistance to waters containing sulfides, compounds that result from the decomposition of organic matter.

Because of the adverse effects of the presence of copper in the secondary side of steam generators and of the importance of having a leak-tight condenser in nuclear plants, the trend has been to replace the copper base alloys with stainless steel or titanium. Since the early 1960s, a good fraction of the tubes were made of either type 304 or type 316 stainless steel, the dominant type being 304 SS. These materials have a greater resistance to erosion–corrosion than copper-base alloys. Because of its erosion resistance, stainless steel tubing has been particularly used in the areas of steam impingement. Because of its resistance to ammonia attack and ammonia-induced SCC, stainless steel has also been applied to areas with high ammonia concentration. Although chloride ions increase the susceptibility of stainless steel to pitting and crevice corrosion, this has not been observed in condensers because they operate at temperatures below the critical temperature for SCC, 47°–57°C (116–135°F). Titanium as tubing material has been relatively limited, but operating experience has been very good. Titanium presents the unique feature that it is the only condenser material used in an unalloyed form. Its application has been mostly as retubing of existing condensers and has taken place mostly overseas, notably in Japan, France, and the United Kingdom. Experience, so far, has shown that titanium tubing has a high degree of reliability, with a high probability of operating for 40 yr with no more than 1% plugged tubes.† Clearly, titanium offers a significant advantage over conventional condenser tube materials, especially in the presence of very aggressive environments (such as seawater). Its high cost, however, inhibits its wide use and has to be weighted with its relative advantage in each situation.

†Tubes in condensers and steam generators which leak are plugged at each end to maintain system integrity.

Table 10.9. Copper-Base Alloys Used in Condenser Tubing

	Composition, wt%											
Type	Cu	Sn	Al	Ni	Pb	Fe	Zn	Mn	As	Sb	P	Cr
Admiralty brass (443)	70–73	0.9–1.2	—	—	0.07	0.6 max.	R[a]	—	0.02–0.10	—	—	—
Admiralty brass (444)	70–73	0.9–1.2	—	—	0.07	0.6 max.	R[a]	—	—	0.02–0.10	—	—
Admiralty brass (445)	70–73	0.9–1.2	—	—	0.07	0.6 max.	R[a]	—	—	—	0.02–0.10	—
90–10 copper–nickel (706)	86.5 min.	—	—	9.0–11.0	0.05	1.0–1.8	1.0 max.	1.0 max.	—	—	—	—
70–30 copper–nickel (715)	65.0 min.	—	—	29.0–33.0	0.05	0.40–0.70	1.0 max.	1.0 max.	—	—	—	—
Aluminum brass (687)	76.0–79.0	—	1.8–2.5	—	0.07	0.06 max.	—	—	0.02–0.10	—	—	—
Aluminum bronze (608)	93.0 min.	—	5.0–6.5	—	0.10	0.10 max.	—	—	0.02–0.35	—	—	—
IN-838	82.3	—	—	16.0	—	0.8	—	0.5	—	—	—	0.4
IN-848	68.6	—	—	30.0	—	0.3	—	0.7	—	—	—	0.4

Source: J. T. A. Roberts, *Structural Materials in Nuclear Power Systems*, Plenum, New York, 1981.

[a]R = remainder.

10.4. FUEL STRUCTURAL MATERIALS

General

In both LWR and current LMFBR designs, the fuel, in the form of oxide pellets (uranium or mixed uranium/plutonium oxide) is placed in long tubes to form fuel rods. The fuel designs used in PWR and BWR plants were discussed in Chapter 9. The tube containing the fuel is called cladding and forms the barrier containing radioactive fission products released in the fuel pellets during irradiation.

Fuel design seeks to achieve an economical fuel cycle, while providing the necessary fuel characteristics for a safe plant operation. The first requirement implies the selection of structural materials with low neutron cross section and low cost, while the second requirement implies materials with adequate mechanical corrosion resistance characteristics. Proper design of fuel assemblies allows the operation of the reactor at the design power and for the highest possible burnup without breaching the cladding and releasing radioactive products to the primary coolant. However, in addition to operation under normal conditions, nuclear regulatory procedures have increasingly required that the fuel be designed to respond to a set of postulated transients and accidents. As a result of these requirements, the trend in fuel design has been toward more conservative designs. The materials used for fuel cladding and other fuel assembly structural materials are stainless steels and zirconium-base alloys.

Stainless Steel as Cladding

Stainless steel, particularly type 304, was used as cladding in a few, early LWRs, because of its good mechanical and corrosion resistant characteristics. However, since the early 1960s, the designers quickly moved to the use of zirconium primarily on account of its low neutron absorption cross section (an improvement of a factor of 15 as shown in Table 10.2). Another reason was a rash of fuel failures in BWRs using stainless steel cladding (e.g., Dresden 1, Humboldt Bay, Big Rock Point). Today only one small BWR (LaCrosse) and several PWRs (Connecticut Yankee, San Onofre 1) still use stainless steel cladding. The experience with this cladding in PWRs has been flawless until some failures were reported at Connecticut Yankee.

In LMFBR applications, type 304 stainless steel was first considered as a candidate, based on existing thermal reactor experience. Eventually, however, type 316 stainless steel or a variation called D-9 has been adopted for both cladding and fuel subassembly ducts because of its superior mechanical properties and resistance to swelling at the elevated temperatures of LMFBRs. Swelling of stainless steel (and of other materials) at elevated temperatures is caused by neutron irradiation. This dimensional instability must be taken into account in the design of the core by allowing the components subject to swelling (cladding and ducts) to expand axially.

Zircaloy Cladding

Zirconium alloys have been introduced in fuel design because they combine desirable nuclear, physical, and mechanical properties. Because nuclear-grade zirconium is expensive, its alloys are used only where its neutron economy advantage is mostly felt: in the active zone of the nuclear core. Two slightly different alloys were developed, Zircaloy-2 and Zircaloy-4; their composition is shown in Table 10.10. Zircaloy-2 has a small content of nickel while in Zircaloy-4 the nickel content is replaced by iron. This small change in composition reduces the hydrogen absorption rate during service in high-temperature water. The physical and mechanical properties of the two alloys are nearly identical.

PWR fuel is made with Zircaloy-4 clading, while BWR fuel utilizes Zircaloy-2. However, the channel containing a BWR fuel assembly is made of Zircaloy-4. Lower and upper tie plates are

Table 10.10. Zirconium-Base Alloys

	Composition, wt%				
Type	Zr	Sn	Fe	Cr	Ni
Zircaloy 2[a]	Balance	1.5	0.12	0.1	0.05
Zircaloy 4[b]	Balance	1.5	0.2	0.1	—

Source: J. T. A. Roberts, *Structural Materials in Nuclear Power Systems*, Plenum, New York, 1981.

[a]Zircaloy-2 is also called Zirconium 20.

[b]Zircaloy-4 is also called Zirconium 40.

Table 10.11. Some Physical Properties of Zircaloy-4

Temperature, °F	Density, lb/ft^3	Thermal Conductivity, Btu/ft^3, hr,°F/in.	Coefficient of Linear Expansion[a] (in./in.-°F) 10^6	Specific Heat	Modulus of Elasticity in Tension (Static Value), psi/10^6
70	412	98		0.070	14
200		101	3.24	0.073	13
400		107	3.33	0.077	12
600		113	3.43	0.081	11
800		120	3.53	0.085	9
1000		131	3.62	0.086	7
1200		142	3.72	0.086	6

Source: Babcock & Wilcox Co., *Steam, Its Generation and Use,* 1978.
[a]Between 70°F and temperature shown.

fabricated from type 304 stainless steel. The spacer grids, which keep proper distance between rods along the length of the fuel assembly, are usually made of Zircaloy-4. The end grids, however, are made of Inconel-718, chosen for its high corrosion resistance and high strength. Guide thimbles, for the insertion of control rods, are also made of Zircaloy-4.

Some variations in fuel design exist among the fuel vendors. For example, Exxon-Nuclear (not a nuclear reactor vendor), which supplies some reload fuel batches, makes BWR fuel with a thicker cladding than that supplied by General Electric and uses cold-worked and stress-relieved rather than fully annealed Zircaloy-2 tubing.

Some of the important physical properties of Zircaloy-4 are shown in Table 10.11. The combination of a low thermal expansion coefficient and a low modulus of elasticity† leads to lower thermal stresses compared to other structural materials, at a given temperature gradient. Other important properties are its melting point of 1845°C (3353°F) and a phase transition which it undergoes in the temperature range of 782–954°C (1440–1750°F).

An undesirable property, from a safety point of view, is the exothermic chemical reaction of zirconium with water at temperatures beginning at about 760°C (1400°F) and accelerating rapidly with increasing temperature. If the temperature were to increase to such high levels during an accident, two adverse effects would result: first, the production of hydrogen and second, the production of additional heat from the exothermic chemical reaction. These phenomena complicate the analysis of accidents in which elevated temperatures may occur (see also Chapter 7).

Mechanical properties of Zircaloy are generally satisfactory as long as the operating temperatures remain below the temperature range of 370–425°C (700–800°F). The strength of the material depends on a number of factors, often acting in a synergistic manner. The amount of cold work and the kind of heat treatment strongly influence strength characteristics. Figure 10.15 shows the gradual decline of strength properties of Zircaloy-4 as temperature increases. Heat treatment cannot be used to strengthen Zircaloy but cold work can.

An important feature of zirconium is its anisotropic structure and behavior. This means that because of the internal crystalline structure of the material, it exhibits different properties in different directions. For example, the yield strength along one axis of a specimen may be much larger than that obtained by stressing the specimen in a direction perpendicular to the first. The fabrication method strongly determines the texture or the orientation of the crystal structure and hence, the anisotropic behavior of the finished product. Creep characteristics of Zircaloy are satisfactory and do not limit the designer, primarily because the approximately three years of in-reactor operation is relatively short compared to that required for significant creep to occur under normal conditions of temperature and pressure.

Ductility is, generally, a desirable property for reactor materials, allowing the material to gradually deform under stress before rupture. Ductility and strength generally change in opposite directions. Mechanical work and heat treatment are used to obtain an optimum combination of the two material properties for the intended application. Zircaloy ductility is typically between 10 and 30%, depending on degree of cold work received. The design of fuel rods for normal steady-state operations must allow no more than 1% permanent strain. The ductility is influenced not only by temperature, cold work, fabrication method, and anisotropy, but also by chemical characteristics such as hydriding. This latter results from a chemical reaction between zirconium and hydrogen that renders the material more brittle.

†The inverse of the modulus of elasticity, that is, stiffness, is important in the fuel's seismic design.

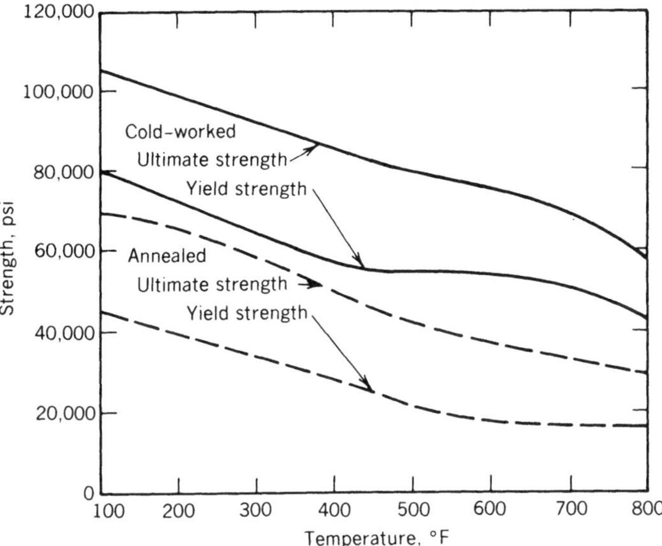

Figure 10.15. Mechanical strength of Zircaloy-4 in the cold-worked and annealed conditions.

An important consideration in the performance of cladding is the degree of embrittlement suffered through neutron irradiation. As explained in a later section, the fast neutron flux to which the material is exposed over a long period of time alters its mechanical properties. The general effect of neutron bombardment is an increase of ultimate strength with a simultaneous loss of ductility; the material becomes embrittled. However, the temperature at which the material operates must also be taken into account. At temperatures above 343°C (650°F), both the strengthening effect of neutron bombardment and the strengthening from the original cold work are being reduced through annealing. As a result, the overall strength of the material is reduced and ductility is partially restored. Creep behavior is similarly dependent on the interacting effects of neutron flux, neutron fluence (time-integrated neutron flux), stress, and the degree of cold work.

Corrosion of Zircaloy can occur either at the water side or at the fuel side. On the water side, Zircaloy tends to form a very thin oxide layer which protects the metal from further corrosion without significantly reducing tube thickness. The initial formation of a protective oxide film, which adheres tightly to the outer tube surface may, with continued irradiation, be followed by an additional oxide formation which may not be protective and which may flake off to expose fresh metal area to further oxidation. This may cause problems, leading, in extreme situations, to the failure through the wall. The first kind of limited corrosion that leads to the formation of a thin, uniform, adherent layer, 1–10 μm thick is actually benign and leads to the so-called "passivation" of the metal. This layer may remain stable even after 10 yr of exposure. In some cases, localized nodular attack occurs, leading to the buildup of up to 200 μm of oxide. A third kind is accelerated uniform corrosion that begins to spall at thicknesses above 70 μm. Water-side corrosion has not limited the life of fuel rods so far. However, some BWR channels have exhibited spalling of oxide layer and had to be replaced prematurely. An attendant problem of the waterside oxidation is that the hydrogen released in the oxidation process can be absorbed by the base zirconium metal. The formation of hydrides and their precipitation along grain boundaries in the form of platelets can cause a reduction in the ductility of the metal.

The other form of Zircalogy corrosion occurs at the inner surface of the tubing. Not only is the temperature there higher, but a hostile chemical environment exists from the presence of fission products, the most harmful of which is iodine. The phenomena involved in the cladding cracking and failure from the inside of the rod are quite complex. They involve the presence of the fuel pellet which, through expansion and relocation, may come in contact with the cladding and apply localized high stresses and strains. This phenomenon is known as Pellet-Clad Interaction (PCI). On the other hand, the presence of chemically aggressive species among the fission products promotes corrosion at points of high stress; this is stress corrosion cracking. Many combinations of adverse conditions may exist in the PCI–SCC process of Zircaloy. Figure 10.16 illustrates the process of crack initiation and propagation inside the cladding. Current data support the concept of a threshold stress. A sustained critical tensile stress in combination with a sustained environment of aggressive fission products will lead to crack propagation and failure. The threshold stress is

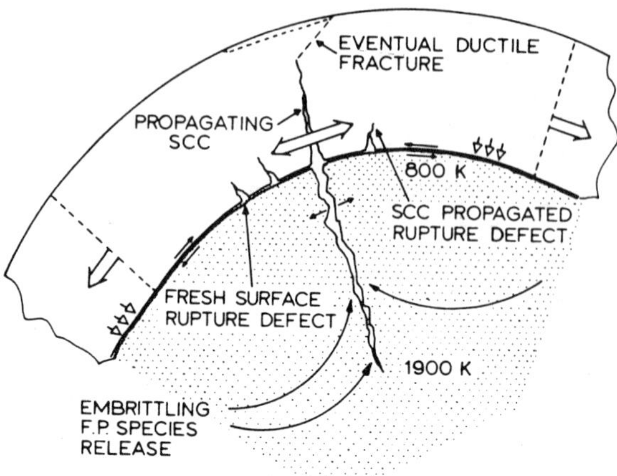

Figure 10.16. Schematic of PCI Zircaloy-fuel rod failure mechanism.

associated with the formation of a crack at inhomogeneities in the Zircaloy surface. Data have shown that there exists a threshold of iodine concentration, about $1–3 \times 10^{-2}$ g I_2/m^2 below which no cracking was observed, as illustrated in Figure 10.17. Other variables such as temperature and irradiation time play an important role. For example, neutron irradiation results in a reduction of the threshold stress for failure.

To combat the SCC occurring inside cladding tubes, various schemes have been suggested, mostly relying on a thin barrier between pellet and cladding to protect the cladding from fission product attack. These designs are called barrier fuels. The Canadians have developed a graphite coating for their CANDU fuel, called CANDLUB, and are investigating a new siloxane coating. For LWR application, two materials have been under investigation: copper (plated as a 5–10 μm layer on the inner tube surface) and pure zirconium coextruded with the Zircaloy tubing. Initial tests, with these fuel types, have shown a higher resistance to SCC. The barrier fuel cladding is available commercially.

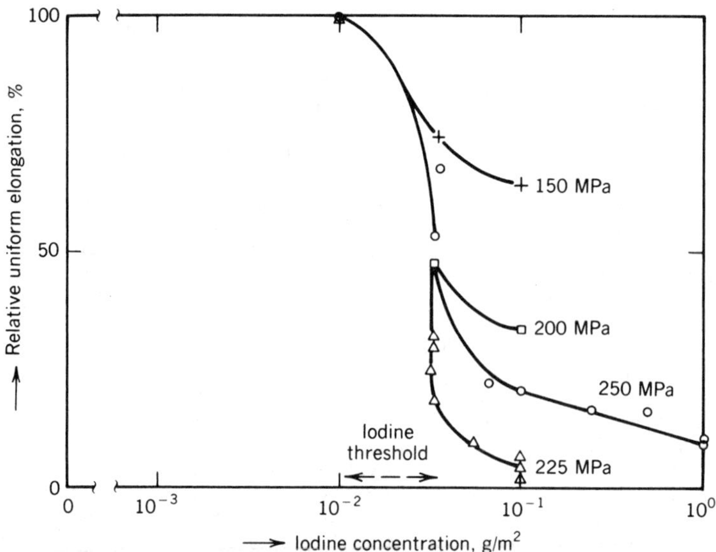

Figure 10.17. Iodine concentration threshold for SCC of stress-relieved Zircaloy at 673 K. (Courtesy M. Peehs, H. Stehle, and E. Steinburg.)

Table 10.12. Neutron Absorption Properties of Some Strong Absorbers

Element	Thermal Neutron Cross Section, in barns or 10^{-24} cm^2
Cadmium	2,400
Boron	750
Iridium	440
Mercury	380
Hafnium	115
Rare-earth metals:	
Gadolinium	44,000
Samarium	6,500
Europium	4,500
Dysprosium	1,100
Erbium	166
Lutecium	108

10.5. CONTROL MATERIALS

General

Continuous operation of a reactor requires that the core be critical. However, to compensate for the gradual depletion of fissile material with time, as burnup accumulates, and to compensate for other phenomena such as the buildup of fission products, an excess of reactivity must be built into the nuclear core. This excess reactivity must be compensated as needed at any given time to keep the reactor critical for steady-state operation. This task is accomplished by the use of materials that are strong neutron absorbers. The control system and its operation were described in Chapter 8 and the components used in commercial reactors were described in Chapter 9. Control elements in various forms perform the following tasks: regulate power generation according to demand; provide quick shutdown and account for short-term and long-term reactivity changes that result from temperature changes, fission product accumulation, and fissile material depletion.

The foremost characteristic of a control material is its neutron absorption properties. These vary with the energy of the impinging neutrons but one can lump together the detailed absorption features into a "thermal absorption cross section," which is of interest in thermal reactors (LWRs and HTGRs) and into a fast "absorption cross section," which is of interest for fast reactors where the neutron energy spectrum is relatively high. A list of elements with high thermal absorption cross section is given in Table 10.12. The most commonly used elements are boron, cadmium, gadolinium, and hafnium.

It must also be noted that a very high cross section, such as that of gadolinium, will lead to a quick depletion of the material through conversion to another nuclide which is not neutron absorbing. Therefore, control elements made of very strong neutron absorbers would lose their effectiveness toward the end of the fuel cycle. For this reason the class of strong neutron absorbers (rare earths) are mostly used as burnable poison, that is, as poison intended to gradually deplete and thus to match the depleting inventory of fissile material in the core.

In addition to neutron absorption, other properties are of importance in the reactor environment and the form of control material must provide them. These properties include:

1. Adequate mechanical strength.
2. Corrosion resistance.
3. Chemical and dimensional stability under the prevailing conditions of temperature and irradiation.
4. Relatively low mass to allow rapid movement.
5. Availability and reasonable cost.
6. Fabricability.

Control Rod Materials

The dominant materials used in control rods in LWRs are boron carbide (B_4C) and an alloy containing 80% silver–15% indium and 5% cadmium. BWRs use a boron carbide powder (or boron carbide pellets) compacted into tubes of austenitic stainless steel type 304 (Section 9.3, subsection

"BWR Control Blades and Drives"). In PWRs the dominant material is the silver–indium–cadmium alloy, clad in cold-worked 304 stainless steel or Inconel 627 tubes (Section 9.3, subsection "PWR Control Rods and Drives"). Some PWRs (those made by Combustion Engineering) use boron carbide but the other vendors are also moving toward use of this material for economic reasons. Fast reactors use boron carbide in their control rods.

The AgInCd alloy was originally developed on neutronic considerations and as a less expensive substitute to hafnium but has now greatly surpassed it in cost. The alloy has a reactivity worth lower than that of boron carbide (by ~15%) and poor corrosion resistance in high-temperature oxygenated water. Consequently, if the cladding develops a leak, corrosion would be a problem. Its melting point is about 800°C (1472°F)† compared to a LWR operating temperature of about 400°C (752°F). Its dimensional stability is quite adequate‡ and performance has complied to design goals for over 10 yr of operation. Space is provided inside the cladding to allow for volume increase. Another problem with AgInCd alloy rods is the production of long-lived activation products that emit gamma rays. This complicates the disposal of control rod assemblies at the end of their useful life. The main disadvantage of the AgInCd alloy is, however, high cost (totaling up to $2 million for a full PWR core), primarily from the high cost of silver and indium.

Boron carbide (B_4C) is the predominant control material for BWRs and LMFBRs. Natural boron is made of two isotopes (19% boron-10 and 81% boron-11) one of which (boron-10) has a very large thermal neutron cross section (3838 barns). Natural boron has a smaller absorption ability because of the dilution of boron-10 with boron-11. Boron is seldom used in pure form. Powder metallurgy is the preferred mode of fabrication of boron carbide which is the commonly used form of the element. Boron carbide is a refractory material with a melting point of between 2340 and 2480°C (4244 and 4496°F). Vibratory compacting (vipac) is used to fill stainless steel rods with boron carbide; pellets made by hot pressing in graphite molds at 2200°C (~4000°F) can also be used. Another form in which boron is used is in combination with a metal binder such as aluminum, copper, or iron. Mixtures of aluminum with 35–50% boron are known as "boral." This material, sandwiched between aluminum sheets, has been used principally for shielding but can also be used for control. The main problems with boron carbide are swelling and the production of helium gas from neutron reactions as follows:

$$^{10}B + n \rightarrow {}^{3}H + 2[{}^{4}He]$$

and

$$^{10}B + n \rightarrow {}^{7}Li + {}^{4}He$$

The released helium gas and the swelling can stress the stainless steel tube and lead to failure. If this happens, the boron can be subjected to leachout by the coolant water, which accelerates boron depletion.

The decision of control blades for BWRs was made on the basis of 7–10 yr lifetime after which replacement must take place. Some BWR control blades have operated successfully for longer times, but the current trend is to plan for replacement at intervals of 4–7 yr. The prevalent explanation for failures of the type 304 stainless steel tubes in several BWRs is as follows: boron carbide sinters under irradiation and temperature conditions in the reactor; it then swells, and applies stress on the containing tube which leads to conditions conducive to stress-corrosion cracking from the outside surface. The process is akin to the SCC observed in BWR fuel rods clad in stainless steel, and is related to the amounts of impurities (particularly phosphorus and sulfur) contained in the steel. It must be noted that control rod tubes made by European manufacturers who use steels of higher purity are not prone to SCC and no such failures have been reported to this time. An alternate design of control rod provides horizontal holes drilled into the body of the stainless steel blades where boron carbide powder is packed. The design is presently being tested in commercial reactors.

Alternate Control Materials

Because of the high cost of AgInCd and the technical performance problems of B_4C, designers have been looking for alternate materials for reactor control. A number of them and their properties are listed in Table 10.13.

Hafnium is a control material attracting increasing attention as offering an alternative solution to the expensive AgInCd alloy and to the gas-producing boron carbide. Hafnium is an element similar to zirconium and titanium. It is associated with zirconium in all its minerals, and is normally

†Compare the pure metal melting points: indium 156°C; silver 960°C; cadium 321°C.

‡Volume expansions of only 2% have been reported at fluences of 4×10^{24} n/m^2 at neutron energies above 1 MeV and at temperatures of 317°C (600°F).

Table 10.13. Materials Characteristics of Alternate Control Rod Materials Compared to B_4C and AgInCd

Material[a]	Number Atoms per Boron	Density $cm^3 \times 10^{22}$ Metal	Density g/cm^3	Worth Relative to B_4C	Swelling upon Irradiation	Fabricability	Commercial[b] Availability	Cost Relative to B_4C	Corrosion Resistance in Water at 315°C	Comments
B_4C–73% dense	8.0		1.78	1	High	Good	Good	1		Reference material
AgInCd	—	—	10.2	0.85	Low	Good	Good	10 to 15 times more	Moder.	Reference material
Ag		4.8								
In		0.059								
Cd		0.023								
Hafnium	—	4.4	13.1	0.85	Low	Good	Good	4 to 8 times more	Good	Best overall alternate material
Boron	13.0			1.1	High	Poor	Poor	3 to 5 times more	Poor	Performance poor
Europium	—	1.9	4.8	~0.9	Not known		Poor	30 times more	Poor	No technical advantages high cost
Eu_2O_3	—	2.3	6.7	~0.95	High	Moderate	Poor	20 to 25 times	Not	No technical advantages high cost
EuB_6	7.4	1.2	4.5	~1.1[c]	High	Poor	Poor	20 to 30 times more	Not known	High worth, but high cost
Eu_2O_3–70 vol% B_4C	6.9	0.7	3.6	>1[c]	Not known	Poor	Poor	Unknown > 10	Poor	High worth, no existing technology
GdB_6	7.6	1.5	4.7	>1[c]	Not known	Poor	Poor	Unknown > 5	Poor	High worth, no existing technology
Pyrohafnates	—	*e*	8.3	0.93	Not known	Moderate	Poor	Unknown > 2	Good	High worth substitute
W–70 vol% B_4C	6.9	1.7	6.8	~1[c]	Not known	Moderate	Poor	Unknown > 2	Poor	High worth substitute

Source: EPRI NP-1974.

[a]All materials listed except europium metal have melting points greater than 2000°C.
All materials listed are expected to be compatible with iron- and nickel-base cladding alloys.

[b]In pellet or rod form in production quantities.

[c]No quantitative data on worth in LWR neutron spectrum available. Values given are estimates.

[d]All densities except for wrought metals and B_4C pellets given as 90% of theoretical value.

[e]Mixture of hafnium and rare-earth metal oxides, typical composition Dy Sm Hf_2O_7.

Table 10.14. Physical and Mechanical Properties of Unirradiated Hafnium

Physical Properties	
Density (g/cm^3)	13.64 ~13.0 (Commercial nuclear grade with 4.5 wt% Zr)
Crystal structure Alpha phase to 1760°C	HCP
Beta phase 1760–2230°C	BCC
Transformation temperature—alpha to beta	1760°C (3200°F)
Melting point	2230°C (4046°F)
Boiling point	3100°C (5612°F)
Coefficient of linear thermal expansion (per °C)	
0–1000°C	5.9×10^{-6}
Thermal conductivity (W/cm-°C)	
At 50°C	0.223
300°C	0.210
400°C	0.207
500°C	0.205
Specific heat [cal/(g-atom) (K)]	
At 298.15 K	6.15
1300 K	7.98

Source: EPRI NP-1974.

obtained by separating it from zirconium. Natural hafnium is a mixture of six isotopes, two of which (^{174}Hf and ^{177}Hf) have a fairly high thermal neutron absorption cross section. What makes hafnium particularly effective is its large epithermal resonance capture cross section. Other properties of hafnium are given in Table 10.14. Some of the principal advantages of hafnium are: a resistance to corrosion higher than that of Zircaloy, a fact that allows its use without cladding; adequate mechanical strength; good stability and retention of mechanical properties under irradiation; good fabricability using normal metal-working techniques; a cost lower than that of the AgInCd alloy but higher than that of boron carbide. The reactivity worth of a hafnium rod at the beginning of life would be equal to that of the AgInCd alloy but lower than that of boron carbide. However, its design life could be longer than control rods of either material. Hafnium has been used extensively in many U.S. naval nuclear reactors and in the Shippingport PWR; its performance there has been good. Published in-reactor performance data are, however, lacking. A testing program to qualify hafnium for BWR control rod application has been established in anticipation of commercial introduction. The control rods projected for BWR application are unclad solid hafnium rods alloyed with a small amount of zirconium. Combinations of control materials have also been considered. Pyrohafnates, one of the alternate materials included in Table 10.13, are mixtures of one or more rare earths with hafnium.

Burnable Poisons

In addition to the movable control rods used in all LWRs and to the soluble poison used in PWRs, present LWR designs utilize "burnable" poisons. These are solid poisons placed in selected rods in the reactor. As they are subject to neutron irradiation, the absorber material is gradually depleted, thus matching, roughly, the depletion of fissile material. Burnable poisons are used to counterbalance excess reactivity at the beginning of the fuel cycle and to provide a means for power shaping and optimum core burnup. In PWRs boron-base materials are used in the form of either aluminum oxide–boron carbide (Al_2O_3—B_4C) pellets or borosilicate glass. They are placed, in varying numbers, in thimble locations (otherwise reserved for control rods) of specified assemblies, or in fuel rod locations. In BWRs, pellets of a homogeneous mixture of uranium oxide and gadolinia (UO_2—Gd_2O_3) are used to entirely fill selected rods in each fuel assembly. The concentration of gadolinia ranges from 1 to 5%.

Homogeneous dispersions of uranium oxide and gadolinia have been used in BWRs for some time, because BWRs did not use soluble poison to control reactivity over the life of the fuel cycle. Experience with this ceramic material has been generally satisfactory. The use of burnable poisons in PWRs was introduced primarily to avoid the need for a high boron concentration at the beginning of life, which could cause a safety concern for the following reasons: with a sudden increase in power, and consequently in temperature, the water expansion causes the loss of some boron poison from the core; the negative moderator temperature coefficient is thus not as negative as it would be

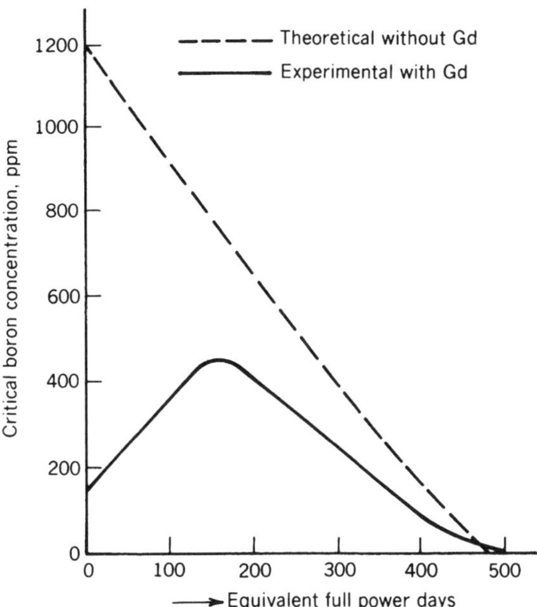

Figure 10.18. Critical boron concentration versus core lifetime. Without burnable poison the critical concentration peaks to a high value at beginning of life. With gadolinium it is greatly reduced (by a factor of more than 6) at the BOL. It peaks at a later time due to the buildup of plutonium but the value at peak is much lower.

if the water were free of boron. This concern is particularly acute at the beginning of life when boron concentration is highest to compensate for the high fuel reactivity. The addition of burnable poison reduces the fuel reactivity at the beginning of life and hence, the needed boron concentration is lower. PWRs have used two materials as burnable poisons. Aluminum oxide–boron carbide pellets, with a boron carbide content of 3.5 to 6.9% in volume are produced by hot pressing or cold pressing and sintering powders. With a density lower than 90% of theoretical, these pellets are clad in Zircaloy tubes and placed in selected assemblies. They occupy either thimbles reserved for control rods or certain fuel rod locations. The main potential problem is the hydriding of the Zircaloy cladding from hydrogenous contaminants trapped in the porous bodies of the poison pellets. Manufacturing procedures must be, therefore, carefully monitored as they are in the manufacture of uranium oxide fuel rods to minimize the potential for hydriding. The use of borosilicate glass as burnable poison (about 12.5 wt% in B_2O_3) minimizes any possibility for leaching but all of the helium gas is released and an adequate free volume must be available inside the stainless steel cladding to avoid excessive stresses. Operating experience has been satisfactory.

Considerable interest exists for increasing the use of gadolinium as burnable poison in PWRs. There are several reasons for this trend. First, gadolinium provides a good reactivity holddown at the beginning of life, as shown in Figure 10.18. The boron concentration at BOL can be held down to low levels.

Second, gadolinia, unlike boron compounds, can be readily mixed with uranium oxide and does not have to be lumped in separate rods. Its high thermal cross section (due mostly to its odd-A isotopes ^{155}Gd and ^{157}Gd) results in a more complete burnout toward the end of cycle, which yields better neutron economy and hence a higher fuel utilization. With proper design and location of the poisoned rods, flatter power distributions and low neutron leakage can be achieved. Additional advantages of increased usage of gadolinium (in mixtures with uranium oxide) in PWRs are: no displacement of water, and very little displacement of fuel; an easier lattice optimization and the elimination of the problems of handling and disposal of the extra burnable poison rods at the end of cycle. Potential disadvantages of gadolinium are: a degraded thermal conductivity and lower melting point of the Gd_2O_3—UO_2 mixture which leads to a lower power generation; a more complex configuration which is harder to analyze; and an increased cost of fuel assembly fabrication. It appears, however, that the plus points outweigh the minuses and vendors are moving in this direction. Several design configurations have been examined as shown in Figure 10.19. The duplex

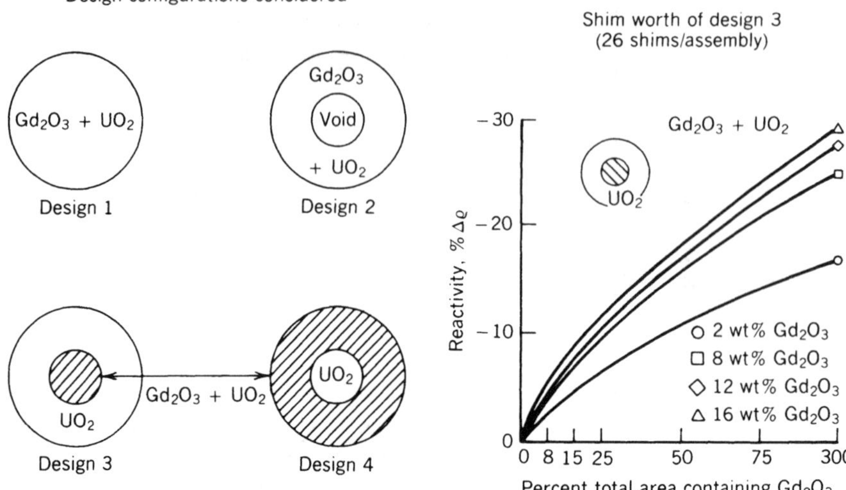

Figure 10.19. Alternate pellet designs for mixtures of gadolinia and uranium oxide. Design 1 is the simplest to manufacture. The graph at right shows the reactivity worth of the shim rods of design 3 for different gadolinia contents.

pellet design may offer certain physics advantages but is more complicated and more expensive to make. The homogeneous pellet offers simplicity and adequate reactivity control; it may be the obvious choice for the first applications of gadolinium-loaded fuel in PWRs. The effect of homogeneous pellets on the total fuel reactivity as a function of burnup is shown in Fig. 10.20. The graph shows that with solid pellets containing a homogeneous mixture, the reactivity worth of the fuel can be made quite flat over the core lifetime. The peak in boron concentration is eliminated, which eliminates certain safety-related concerns.

10.6. MODERATOR AND REFLECTOR MATERIALS

Introduction

Thermal reactors operate with low or thermal energy neutrons (about 0.025 eV in energy) to take advantage of the fact that such slow neutrons are absorbed more readily by ^{235}U nuclei. This leads to a higher number of absorptions and fissions than at higher energies. However, neutrons produced from fissions have a high energy, on the average between 1 and 2 MeV. Moderators are used in thermal reactors to slow down and moderate fast neutrons from fission. The process can be visualized as analogous to billiard balls colliding with other balls. In a collision with a ball of the same mass, a moving billiard ball can loose a large amount of its energy, even all of it, if the collision is head-on and there is no spin. If a billiard ball collides with a much heavier ball, say a bowling ball, very little energy will be transferred to the latter and the billiard ball will simply bounce in a different direction. This shows that materials with light nuclei are more effective as neutron moderators. A hydrogen nucleus with a mass almost identical to that of a neutron would be the best moderator from this point of view. Water, which contains a high amount of hydrogen, would be a good moderator. Calculations show that, on the average, it takes 19.6 collisions in water for a neutron to slow down from an energy of 2 MeV to an energy of 0.025 eV. Another requirement of a good moderator is a high scattering cross section, which implies many collisions per unit time, and therefore, a better chance that the neutron will be slowed down before it is captured or lost through leakage. The product of average number of collisions to thermalize (represented by the Greek letter ξ) times the macroscopic scattering cross section (Σ_s) gives the slowing down power of a material.

Another requirement of a good moderator is a low neutron absorption cross section, to ensure that the neutron economy will not suffer too much through unproductive absorptions in the moderator mass. A figure of merit can be constructed by taking the ratio $\xi\Sigma_s/\Sigma_a$, which is called moderating ratio. Table 10.15 lists the most widely used moderators and some of their important characteristics.

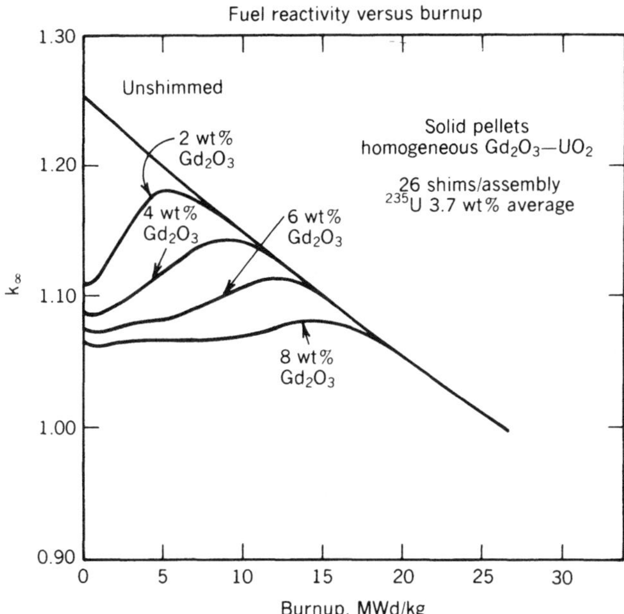

Figure 10.20. The total fuel reactivity of a core with gadolinium shims is shown as a function of burnup. The higher the gadolinium content, the flatter the reactivity curve is over the core lifetime.

Table 10.15. Characteristics of Selected Moderators

	Light Water	Heavy Water	Metallic Beryllium	Beryllium Oxide	Graphite
	H_2O	D_2O	Be	BeO	C
Atomic weight	18.0	20.0	9	25.0	12.0
Density (kg/m^3)	1000	1100	1840	2860	1570
Macroscopic scattering cross section (epithermal) Σ_s (cm^{-1})	1.64	0.35	0.74	0.66	0.39
Macroscopic absorption cross section (thermal) Σ_a (cm^{-1})	22×10^{-3}	85×10^{-6}	1.1×10^{-3}	0.62×10^{-3}	0.37×10^{-3}
Average number of collisions to thermalize, ξ (2 MeV to 0.025 eV)	19.6	35.7	88.4	107	115
Slowing down power $\xi\Sigma_s$ (cm^{-1})	1.5	0.18	0.16	0.11	0.063
Moderating ratio $\xi\Sigma_s/\Sigma_a$	70	2100[a]	150	180	170

[a]Pure heavy water has a moderating ratio of 12,000. The figure of 2100 corresponds to 99.8 at% heavy water (0.2% is light water).

Ordinary Water

Water has the highest slowing down power but it also has the highest absorption cross section (due to a microscopic hydrogen absorption cross section of about 0.33 barn). This sometimes rules out the use of ordinary water as a moderator. For example, a nuclear pile using natural uranium cannot be made critical if it is moderated by ordinary water. It can be used successfully as a moderator if the fuel is slightly enriched. The low cost of water, its excellent slowing down power, and its capability as a coolant led to the development of the most widely used commercial nuclear reactor, the LWR, which uses fuel enriched to 2–4%. Water used in nuclear reactors must be free of impurities in order to minimize corrosion and scale formation as well as the formation of radioactive activation products. Water is subject to radiolytic decomposition, which produces gaseous hydrogen and oxygen. The process must be controlled with appropriate means as was described in Chapter 8. Another related potential problem with water is its chemical reaction with zirconium at elevated temperatures with the production of zirconium oxide and hydrogen. A major drawback of water is its low boiling point. This on one hand limits the highest steam temperatures that can be achieved (and, hence, limits the plant thermal efficiency) and on the other requires a high pressure in the primary system which poses a challenge to structural materials.

Heavy Water

A heavy-water molecule contains deuterium atoms instead of hydrogen atoms. Its slowing down power is not as high as that of water but its absorption cross section is far lower; its moderating ratio is the highest among all moderators. A heterogeneous reactor with natural uranium can be made critical if heavy water is used as moderator. This route was followed by the Canadians who have successfully developed and operated several units of this kind. In one reactor, heavy water is used as moderator and light water as coolant but the norm is to use heavy water for both purposes.

The main disadvantage of heavy water is its cost. One out of 6666 molecules of water is heavy water and industrial processes have been established to perform the separation. Its physical properties are close to those of ordinary water. It freezes at 3.82°C (38.87°F) and boils at 101.42°C (214.56°F). Its density is 1100 kg/m^3 at room temperature. Heavy-water reactors require high operating pressures, just as LWRs do.

Other Hydrogenous Moderators

Hydrogen as a moderator has also been used in the form of organic hydrocarbons and metallic hydrides. A reactor concept utilizing organic polyphenyls (waxlike materials) has been studied for several years but did not progress beyond the experimental stage. The moderators investigated were different mixtures of isomeric polyphenyls with moderating characteristics not much different than those of water. The materials were found, however, to be subject to degradation due to the combined effect of radiation and temperature.

Another form of hydrogenous moderator is zirconium hydride (ZrH_2), produced by heating zirconium metal in hydrogen gas at about 350°C (660°F). The material has good moderating properties and has been used in a few experimental reactors. Notable among them are the TRIGA (Training, Research, Isotope, General Atomics) reactors now in operation in many laboratories in the United States and abroad. In the TRIGA design, the zirconium hydride moderator is incorporated with the uranium in the fuel elements, forming a homogeneous mixture. Thus the moderator temperature follows closely and promptly the fuel temperature. This provides a prompt negative temperature coefficient of reactivity, giving the TRIGA reactor built-in safety and stability.

Graphite

The use of graphite as moderator in power reactors has been extensive. The dominant type of reactor deployed in the United Kingdom is the gas-cooled, graphite–moderated type. Several reactors of similar type were installed in France until that country decided to adopt the LWR. In the USSR, a few reactors with graphite moderator and light-water coolant are in operation and in the United States one operating plant (at Fort St. Vrain) is a helium-cooled graphite-moderated reactor, while the first such commercial plant, the small Peach Bottom-1 reactor, has been decommissioned.

Graphite of high purity has good moderating characteristics, and satisfactory mechanical properties; is a good conductor of heat; and can be obtained at reasonable cost. Reactor-grade graphite is made artificially (since the naturally occurring graphite is relatively impure) by graphitization of petroleum coke.

Graphite is an allotropic form of carbon, representing the stable phase at all temperatures barring the extreme. It does not melt by heating at atmospheric pressure but is converted directly to the gaseous phase (a process called sublimation) at 3650°C (6600°F). Its crystalline form is hexa-

Table 10.16. Properties of Reactor-Grade Graphite

Property	Longitudinal	Transverse
Thermal expansion coefficient (per °C)	1.4×10^{-6}	2.7×10^{-6}
Thermal conductivity [cal/sec-cm^2 (°C/cm)]	0.41	0.31
Tensile strength (psi)	2000	700
Flexural strength (psi)	2100	2100
Compressive strength (psi)	6000	6000
Modulus of elasticity (psi)	1.5×10^6	1.1×10^6

Source: A. M. Freudenthal, Thermal Stress Analysis and Mechanical Design, in *Nuclear Engineering,* C. F. Bonilla, Ed., McGraw-Hill, New York, 1957.

gonal and consists of layers of carbon atoms on top of each other. Because the distance between layers is relatively large, the material presents little resistance against slippage of the parallel layers.† The crystalline form of graphite makes it a highly anisotropic material. Its electrical, thermal, and mechanical properties vary depending on orientation. Graphite properties vary widely among different products. The actual density of reactor-grade graphite ranges between 1600 and 1700 kg/m^3. This figure is much lower than its theoretical density of 2260 kg/m^3, due to the porosity of the manufactured product. Table 10.16 gives some important characteristics of reactor-grade graphite in two directions: one along the axis of extrusion and one perpendicular to it. Tensile strength is sharply different in the two directions. Its value increases with temperature, reaching a maximum at about 2500°C (4530°F) at which temperature its strength is almost double that at ordinary temperatures. Above this temperature, the value declines rapidly. Resistance to creep is high at temperatures below 1500°C (2730°F) but deteriorates at higher temperatures. The resistance of graphite to thermal shock and to thermal stresses is good. These properties make the material particularly suitable for high-temperature applications such as the environment of an HTGR.

The main problems with graphite stem from its chemical affinity with oxygen, water vapor, carbon dioxide, and metals. The use of the chemically inert helium gas as coolant and the strict control of water vapor in the primary systems are among the measures to minimize these problems.

Particular attention has been given to the behavior of graphite under irradiation. Neutron bombardment can produce dimensional instability although at higher temperatures this effect is less pronounced because of the annealing of the effects on the crystalline structure.

A well-known effect of graphite irradiation is the stored energy and its consequences, also known as the Wigner effect. Below a certain temperature of about 350°C (662°F), at which annealing of defects cannot take place, radiation damage increases with time, causing the accumulation of stored energy in the crystal lattice. If the metastable material (loaded with stored energy) is suddenly transformed to the stable form, the excess stored energy can be released at once, causing a large increase in temperature. An integrated flux of 10^{19} nvt at ordinary temperature can store up to 400 cal/g of graphite which, upon release, can cause the temperature to rise to 1000°C (1800°F).‡ Graphite-moderated reactors operating at fairly low temperatures follow procedures to allow the controlled and gradual heating of the material so that annealing of radiation damage can take place and a catastrophic temperature rise can be prevented. At high temperatures, this problem does not exist since the annealing and heat release proceed continuously.

Reflectors

Neutrons found near the surface of a nuclear core tend to escape and be lost for the purpose of furthering the chain reaction. This leakage of neutrons outside the assembly impairs the neutron economy, and must be minimized. To cut down on leakage losses, a reflector material is used, surrounding the reactive region. Its purpose is to scatter back escaping neutrons into the core, without absorbing them. The ratio of neutrons scattered back from the surface of the reflector to the amount reaching the surface is called the "albedo."§

The requirements for a good reflector are the same as for moderators. Therefore, the same materials, water, heavy water, beryllium, and graphite, are used as thermal reflectors. Their albedo ranges from 0.82 (H_2O) to 0.97 (D_2O). In fast reactors slowing down of neutrons is not desirable and

†This property makes graphite powder a good lubricant.

‡Large-scale overheating occurred in a British plutonium producing reactor at Windscale in 1957. The accident happened during a normal periodic stored energy release and seriously damaged the reactor, causing a large release of radioactivity to the environment.

§A similar concept is used to describe the reflectivity of various objects to different kinds of radiation. The albedo of the earth to solar radiation is about 0.34.

many materials that scatter neutrons strongly can be used as reflectors. Fast reactor reflectors are high-density, heavy elements with a high-scattering cross section for fast neutrons such as iron, bismuth, and lead. Fertile materials such as ^{232}Th and ^{238}U are also used.

10.7. SHIELDING MATERIALS

Shielding materials are used in nuclear installations to protect personnel and equipment from the damaging effects of radiation. This is accomplished by surrounding the radiation source with the shield or by building protective walls that absorb a large part of the emitted radiation to a harmless level. There are three basic kinds of radiation: heavy ionized particles, including alphas, protons, fission fragments, and so on; beta particles, that is, positively or negatively charged electrons; and gamma rays and neutrons. The heavy ions and betas do not travel far from where they are produced and shielding against them is no problem. Gammas and neutrons must be carefully attenuated to protect personnel. It must also be noted that beta rays do produce secondary radiation in the process of being decelerated and absorbed in matter: this secondary radiation consists of a continuous X-ray spectrum (called "bremsstrahlung," meaning "braking radiation") and production of two gamma rays, each with an energy of 0.51 MeV whenever a positron (e^+) and an electron (e^-) meet to annihilate each other.

To shield against neutrons, the material must have good moderating capability (which implies light elements) and a reasonable absorption cross section. To shield against gamma rays, a material with good gamma-ray scattering and absorption properties is required.† Water is a common shielding material because of its good properties and low cost. It provides excellent neutron moderation, good neutron absorption, and, in sufficient quantities, adequate gamma shielding. A number of experimental reactors operate with a reactor core immersed in a deep pool of water which provides cooling, moderation, reflector, and shielding, all in one, while allowing visual inspection of the core. Spent fuel discharged from LWRs is stored in a water pool (see Chapter 8) with enough water over the fuel (about 4 m of depth) to provide adequate shielding. Other hydrogenous materials used as reflectors are paraffin and polyethylene.

To attenuate gamma rays, heavy elements in various forms (sheets, bricks, etc.) are used, such as lead, iron or tungsten. Boral, a metallic matrix of boron carbide in aluminum, clad in aluminum sheets has been used extensively as a combination neutron/gamma shield (see also Section 10.5, subsection "Control Rod Materials"). It is seen that both light and heavy elements are useful to shield against reactor radiation. However, one need not choose the most effective material, since any kind of matter will interact with radiation and, in sufficient quantity, stop it. The optimum choice must take into account cost and space availability. In a commercial power reactor where space is no problem and cost must be minimized, abundant and cheap materials are used, such as water and concrete. This latter material is an inexpensive and effective shielding material, also used for structural elements. It is discussed in detail in the following section.

10.8. CONCRETE

Concrete, in several varieties, finds extensive use in nuclear power installations. It serves two basic purposes: as structural element; and as shielding against ionizing radiation. It could also serve, with or without special design, the safety function of containing the molten aggregate material resulting from the unlikely event of a core melt which melts its way through the bottom of the reactor vessel. Concrete is relatively inexpensive to build, effective for strength and radiation shielding, easy to form into any desired shape, and quite stable against radiation damage and other environmental factors. These aspects will be discussed in the following paragraphs.

Portland Cement: Composition and Properties

Normal concrete (portland cement concrete) is made of a mixture of small and large aggregates (sand and gravel), portland cement binder, and water, in appropriate proportions. When the mixture solidifies, the inert materials (mostly silica, SO_2) are bound together by the continuous matrix of the hydrated portland cement. In large castings, large solid pieces could be added as aggregate such as stone, crushed rock, or manufactured products. To give desired properties to concrete, special ground minerals or manufactured materials may be added. For example, mineral barytes (mostly barium sulfate), limonite, or even iron punchings can be added to concrete to enhance its shielding ability. Small quantities of admixtures are sometimes added either to change the behavior of the fresh mix (retard or accelerate its setting) or to improve the durability of the hardened

†Gamma rays are attenuated by interaction with the electrons and electric-magnetic field surrounding a nucleus. Therefore, heavy materials (e.g., lead) with more electrons make better shielding material on a per unit volume basis, although all materials have more or less the same gamma-ray shielding ability on a per unit mass basis.

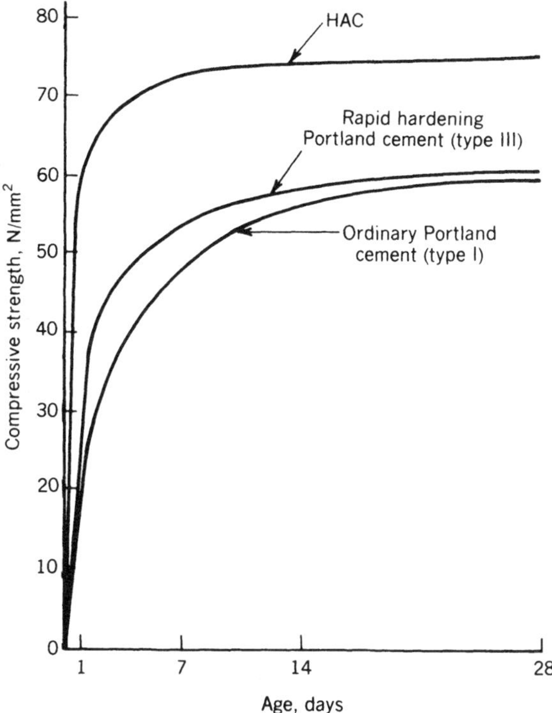

Figure 10.21. Comparison of strength development of High Alumina Cement (HAC) and Portland cement concretes. (Courtesy A. M. Neville.)

concrete. Water is contained in concrete in three basic forms: as a chemical ingredient bound to the compounds formed during setting; as moisture absorbed onto internal surfaces of the cement paste; and as free moisture in the voids contained within the concrete.

Because water is used in making concrete from portland cement, it is called a "hydraulic cement." The process of the chemical reaction of the cement ingredients with water is called hydration. As time passes, concrete becomes gradually harder and stronger, in a process that takes many days to complete as shown in Figure 10.21. Depending on the relative quantities of its chemical constituents, concrete is classified into five types (I to V). The major constituents of portland cement are: tricalcium silicate, dicalcium silicate, tricalcium aluminate, calcium alumino-ferrite, and gypsum. Although most of the cement ingredients interact with water, concrete strength is mostly attributable to the hydration of the calcium silicates, which form calcium silicate hydrate sometimes called cement or tobermorite "gel" and calcium hydroxide.

Many factors contribute to the buildup of strength in the concrete: the proportions in the mix, relative humidity during curing, and temperature. Limiting the amount of water used in the mix to the bare minimum for the chemical reactions is very crucial for ultimate strength. However, in practice, larger amounts of water are used to make the fresh mix softer and easier to manipulate. This excess water increases the porosity and permeability of the hardened concrete and decreases its strength. Various methods are used in the preparation of the mix (e.g., mechanical vibrators) to limit the water added and to reduce voids. A proportion of 36–42% water of the cement weight is needed for complete hydration but in practice, the hardened cement will contain typically a few weight percent of unbounded water.

The density of normal concrete is about 2450 kg/m^3 (150 lb/ft^3) and contains up to about 10 wt% water. When water-reducing techniques (or admixtures) are used to limit water-to-cement ratio to below 0.4, concrete can be built to a compressive strength of about 82 MPa (12000 psi), measured after 28 days of curing. Conditions in actual locations, however, produce concrete with a strength typically in the range of 17–55 MPa (2000–8000 psi). Tensile strength in concrete is relatively low, amounting to between 10 and 20% of its compressive strength. For this reason, in cases where concrete is expected to sustain tension or bending, steel bars are used for reinforcement (rebar). Other important characteristics of concrete are its modulus of elasticity, which varies from 14 to 48 GPa (2 to 7 million psi) and its Poisson ratio, which ranges from 0.15 to 0.25.

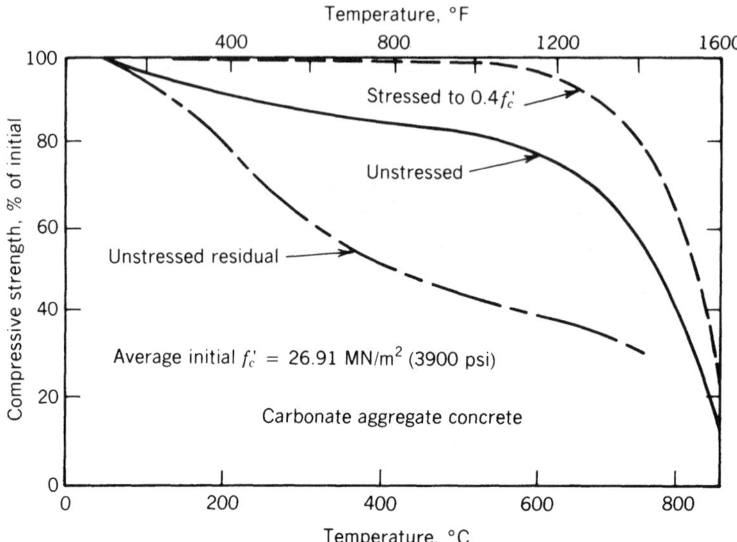

Figure 10.22. Compressive strength of carbonate aggregate concrete as a function of temperature. (Courtesy of M. S. Abrams.)

Nuclear reactors must be designed and built under a set of hypothetical accident scenarios which may expose components to extreme ranges of pressure and temperature. Because of these requirements it is useful to discuss briefly some additional features of concrete and how they change at higher temperatures.

At room temperature, saturated structural concrete contains between 2 and 10% (by volume) of evaporable water. As temperature rises above 100°C, the loss of this water proceeds rapidly. At temperatures above 105°C, the water that is strongly absorbed or chemically bound is gradually lost from the hydrates in the cement paste. (For example, calcium hydroxide decomposes into lime and water: $Ca(OH)_2 \rightarrow CaO + H_2O$.) Dehydration proceeds and becomes complete at 850°C. Heating breaks the bonds of the chemical compounds in concrete and as a result its strength decreases with increasing temperature. Further weakening is due to differences in the thermal expansions of the aggregates and cement paste. Also, the increasing porosity, due to the evaporation of unbounded water, contributes to the loss of strength, which becomes significant above about 450°C (842°F). Figure 10.22 shows the decline of compressive strength as temperature rises. Similarly, the modulus of elasticity decreases almost linearly with increasing temperature and could be almost 50% lower at 400°C compared to its value at room temperature.

Heat capacity of normal concretes is of the order of 0.2 cal/g-°C (or Btu/lb-°F) and rises slowly with temperature. Because of the large masses of concrete in a nuclear plant, this quantity is important in calculating the amount of heat absorbed by the concrete as its temperature rises, and, hence, in calculating the course of an accident (for example, pressure buildup inside containment). Similarly, thermal conductivity is a quantity of interest since it is needed to calculate the amount of heat transmitted through a reactor building. The value of thermal conductivity varies widely (sometimes by an order of magnitude), depending on the constituents in the concrete, including the pores. A typical value is 0.003 cal/cm-sec-°C (0.75 Btu/hr-ft-°F) remaining fairly constant with rising temperature. Thermal diffusivity of concrete can be calculated by dividing thermal conductivity per unit density by the heat capacity ($d = k/c\rho$). Typical values are 0.5 to 1.5 mm^2/sec at room temperature. The above considerations are particularly important for concretes that are exposed to high-temperature fields and steep temperature gradients. Such a case is the prestressed concrete reactor vessel used in the HTGR, a design used presently at the Fort St. Vrain nuclear plant and in gas reactors abroad, notably gas-cooled reactors in the United Kingdom. Provisions are made in these reactors to minimize the exposure of concrete to temperature by providing radiation shields, thermal insulation, and cooling coils.

Concrete as Radiation Shield

Concrete is considered a good shielding material because of its water content, its low cost, and the ease to shape as necessary. In order to shield against neutrons, light materials are used. Fast neutrons colliding with a light nucleus (the lightest of which is hydrogen, about equal in mass with the neutron) lose their energy quickly by transferring their energy to the target nucleus (the collison of a moving billiard ball with a stationary one is a good analogy). Water, since it contains hydrogen, is an excellent medium for slowing down neutrons, which can then be easily absorbed by surrounding matter. Concrete is a good material for slowing down of neutrons because of its high content of hydrogen atoms. Even when the evaporable water is lost due to heating, there remains an adequate amount of chemically bonded hydrogen in the concrete for shielding purposes.

In order to enhance the shielding capacity of concrete, substances can be added that are strong absorbers of neutrons. Boron is such a strong neutron absorber. Therefore, boron-loaded concretes have been made with a number of additives including boron carbide (B_4C), colemanite ($2CaO \cdot 3B_2O_3 \cdot H_2O$), and boron frit. Admixtures can be added to increase the hydrogen content of concrete. Serpentine and bauxite will retain their chemically bound water even above 100°C but will lose all water when heated to 1000°C.

To improve concrete's gamma shielding properties, heavy metals (as high-density aggregates) can be used in concretes. Magnetite, hematite, barite, or even steel punchings have been used, but only in special applications because of constructability and QA problems associated with such dense materials. Limonite ($2Fe_2O_3 \cdot 3H_2O$) adds both to the neutron and gamma shielding capability of concrete. It is possible to add aggregate that combines high-density and refractory properties that are needed in special applications concrete. These include: zirconia, chrome ore, corundum, tabular alumina, magnesia, and silicon carbide. Concrete incorporating heavy aggregates is called "high-density concrete," with a density of about 6000 kg/m^3.

Concrete for Special Applications

The portland cement concrete described is quite adequate for applications where temperature is not expected to rise above 400°C. To account for accident scenarios involving a core melt in a LWR or in a core disruptive accident in a LMFBR where a mixture of core materials and sodium may come in contact with concrete, special concretes must be considered. Such concretes may include refractory aggregates mixed with portland cement, aluminous cement, and those using nonhydraulic binders, also called anhydrous cements (waterglass and others). These latter are considered because they contain no water to interact with sodium or corium† for the production of hydrogen.

The potential exposure to liquid sodium suggests the use of concretes that do not contain large amount of silica such as high-alumina cement. For enhanced resistance to high temperature, dense refractory brick linings could be used since they have proven successful in industrial application and tests with molten sodium. For best performance, refractory aggregates must be chosen such as tabular alumina, corundum, zirconia, silicon carbide, and magnesia.

For the biological shielding in LMFBRs such as around the reactor cover, the concrete must be capable of withstanding sustained high temperatures (100–300°C) and possible transients up to 840°C under upset conditions. It is desirable that they do not release any water when heated and they do not react exothermically with sodium. Dense refractory bricks made from tabular alumina, zirconia, or other similar aggregates would provide an adequate anhydrous shielding in LMFBRs. Other possibilities include concrete made with waterglass or phosphate binders with dense refractory aggregates.

If the ability to contain a core melt must be provided, this can only be met by the use of dense refractory brick linings and nonhydraulic concretes, such as the phosphate or magnesia concretes. These materials have been successfully tested to prove their ability to greatly slow down the attack of molten metals.

The choice of materials and designs must take into account not only the material properties but also the degree of damage incurred as the hypothetical accident proceeds. Given a certain concrete thickness in the wall or floor, a certain degree of damage, perhaps several feet of thickness could be allowed as the molten material interacts with the concrete. The molten core, however, cools down and the process of interaction would be stopped before the molten mass goes through the entire thickness. In this case, a safe containment of the accident would have been achieved. For such a performance, the use of common portland cement concrete seems to be quite adequate.

10.9. RADIATION DAMAGE

General Principles

What distinguishes the environment of a nuclear reactor from other industrial applications is the presence of intense radiation. The effects of radiation (primarily gamma rays and neutrons) on materials must, therefore, be considered to ascertain adequate performances throughout plant

†"Corium" is a term used to describe a mixture of core materials, mainly fuel, and steel.

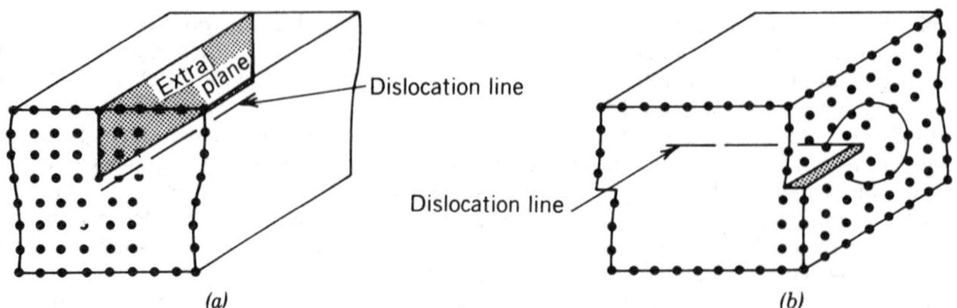

Figure 10.23. Schematic representation of dislocations. (*a*) Edge dislocation. (*b*) Screw dislocation.

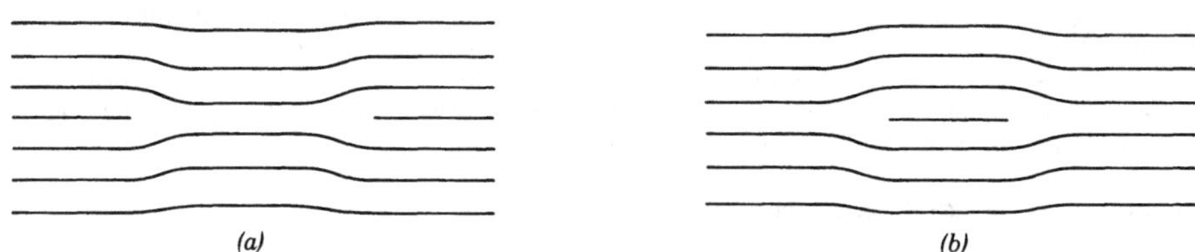

Figure 10.24. Formation of dislocation loops by aggregation of vacancies or interstitials into platelets.

lifetime. The principles of radiation effects on materials, mainly those encountered in power reactors, will be reviewed first.

The type and extent of the effect depend on both the structure of the material and the type and energy of the incident radiation. Beta particles and gamma rays produce mainly electronic excitation or ionization, that is, they perturb only the atomic electrons of the material. This causes very little permanent damage in metals since the displaced electrons quickly lose their energy which is dissipated as heat.† This is not the case with heavy particles such as protons, neutrons, alphas, and so on. As these particles enter the material, they collide with whole atoms in the crystalline structure, transfer a considerable amount of energy to them, and may displace them from their original position. This introduces defects in the solid which, in sufficient quantity, cause permanent changes in the properties of the material. These changes are generally undesirable and the effect is often called radiation damage.

To cause the displacement of an atom in a solid crystal, a minimum amount of energy must be transferred to it from the bombarding particle. This amount varies somewhat but is of the order of 25 eV for metals. If the struck atom has sufficient energy, it will knock other atoms as it moves through the mass of material and a whole concatenation of such knock-on events will occur. Some of the displaced atoms may find vacant positions in the lattice to occupy. Others will become lodged at irregular (nonequilibrium) locations in the crystal lattice and will become "interstitials." For each interstitial there is a vacant place somewhere in the lattice. It is these interstitials and vacancies that constitute defects in the crystal and cause a change in its physical properties. These radiation-induced interstitials are in addition to existing defects in the crystal structure which are always present from the manufacturing process and working of the material. Figure 10.23 shows two kinds of common dislocations. These dislocations become natural sites where the interstitials tend to congregate. Figure 10.24 shows the formation of additional dislocation loops from the aggregation of interstitials or vacancies.

In a reactor core, fission neutrons are generated at energies averaging between 1 and 2 MeV.‡ Each of these energetic neutrons can cause a large number of dislocations in solid materials found in the reactor core. In thermal reactors, neutrons are eventually slowed down to low energies at which they lose their ability to cause dislocations. Hence, the main concern in radiation damage is caused by fast neutrons. Enough fast neutrons exist even at the reactor pressure vessel, originating

†Organic materials, such as oil, rubber, or plastic, become extremely brittle, however, when the radiation dose exceeds 10^6 R.
‡A 1-MeV neutron can dislocate an average of about 400 atoms in iron, 440 in beryllium, and 900 in graphite.

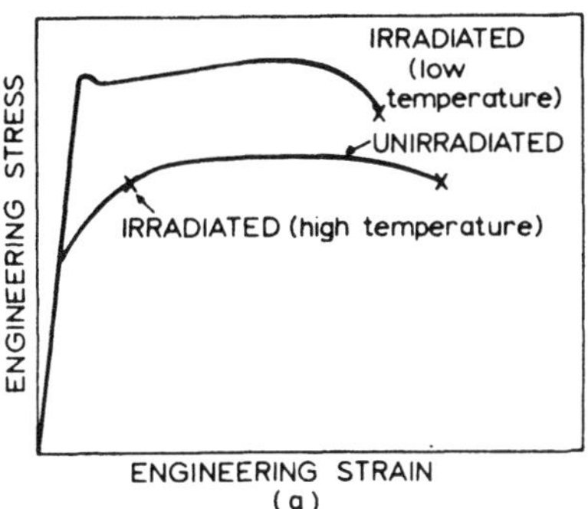

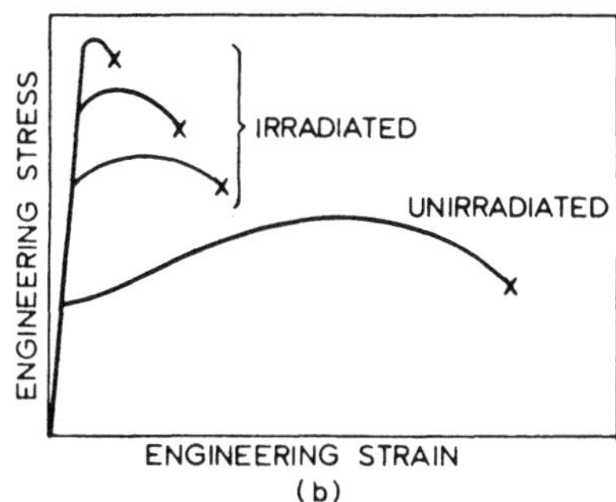

Figure 10.25. Effect of fast neutron irradiation on the tensile properties of steels. (*a*) Face centered cubic structure. (*b*) Body centered cubic structure. Irradiation increases yield strength, that is, extends upward the steep linear portion of the curve. At the same time, it reduces strain at rupture, which means it reduces the material's ductility. The upper figure shows the effect of temperature. Irradiation at low temperature (upper curve) shows the expected increase of yield strength and decrease of ductility. Irradiation at high temperature, where annealing occurs, shows no increase in yield strength but loss of ductility.

mainly from the outer zone assemblies to warrant consideration of the irradiation effects on the properties of the material.

Changes in Physical Properties

The defects introduced in the crystal structure increase the resistance of the material to distort under applied forces since additional obstacles are presented to the slippage of one crystalline plane against another. Generally, therefore, the effects of neutron irradiation are an increase in yield stress, the "hardening effect" of radiation, accompanied by loss of ductility. These effects are shown in Figure 10.25. An important effect of neutron irradiation on certain materials such as low-carbon structural steels used in reactor pressure vessels is a shift in the transition temperature at which the material goes from ductile to brittle, and a reduction in the upper-shelf energy, as shown in Figure 10.26. The shift of both these quantities means an embrittlement effect of neutron

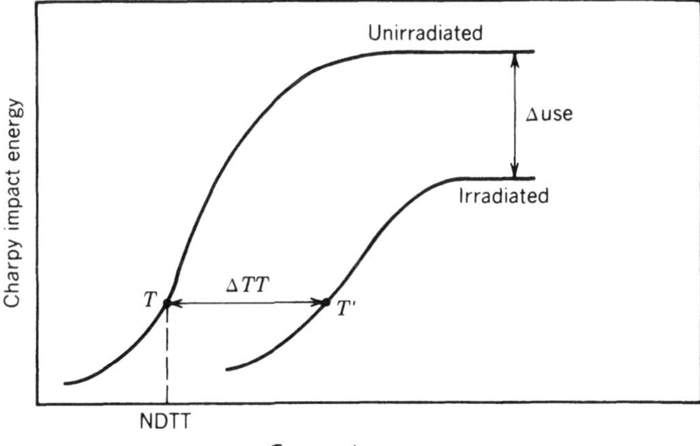

Figure 10.26. Schematic showing two important changes caused by neutron irradiation of steels. The curves for unirradiated and irradiated steels were derived from Charpy impact tests (see Section 10.1) as a function of temperature. Two effects are evident. The energy required to break a Charpy specimen is reduced (the energy corresponding to flat portion of the curves is called "upper shelf" energy). The temperature at which the material undergoes a transition from ductile to brittle (point *T*) is increased. (This temperature is called "Nil Ductility Transition Temperature," NDTT, or "Reference Temperature for Nil Ductility Transition," RT_{NDT}.)

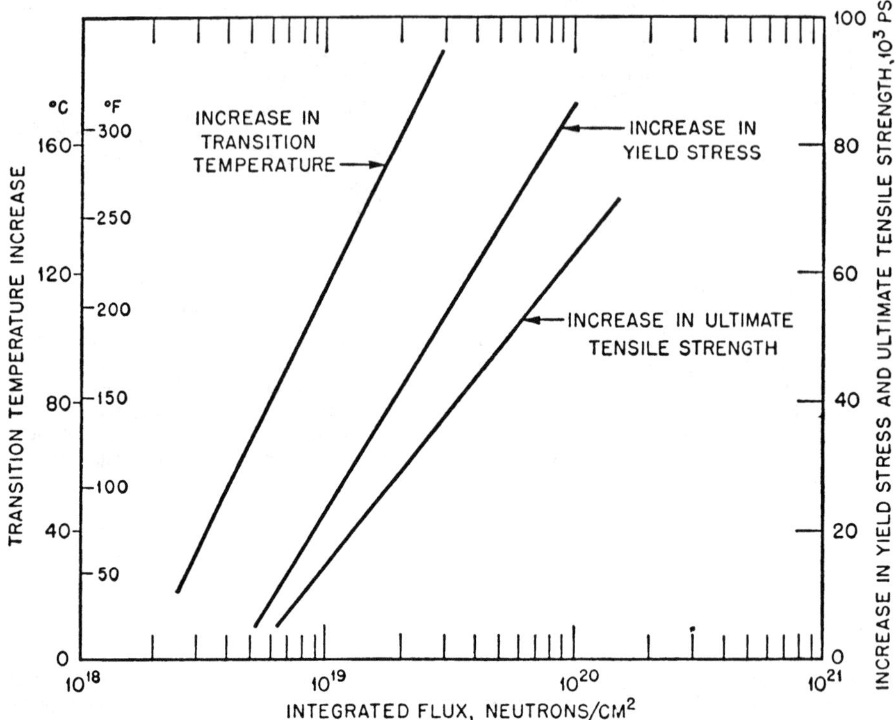

Figure 10.27. Changes in properties of low-carbon steel. [Data from L. F. Porter, ASTM-STP-276, p. 161, 1959 and W. S. Pellini, et al., "Radiation Damage in Solids," *IAEA* **II,** 138 (1962).]

irradiation on reactor pressure vessels. Although temperature has no effect on the production process of defects in the material, it does affect the rearrangement of the damaged zone. At elevated temperatures, atoms can diffuse more easily from one point to another in a crystal lattice. Interstitials can move faster into existing vacancies, thus removing some of the irradiation-caused defects. This constitutes an annealing of defects and reduces the hardening and embrittlement process. Stress and other variables also affect the rearrangement of the damaged zone. The changes of some of the important mechanical characteristics of low-carbon steel are shown in Figure 10.27. These measurements were made at a temperature below 232°C (450°F). The increase would not be as marked if the irradiation exposure were done at higher temperatures, because of the annealing effect.

Radiation effects in LMFBRs are far more severe than in LWRs. A much larger amount of power is produced per unit of core volume in a LMFBR and the neutron flux is higher by about a factor of 100 than in an LWR. Temperatures are higher and the fuel burnup is almost three times as high as in LWRs. Under these severe conditions additional damaging processes occur. Helium production becomes significant from (n, α) reactions, particularly in the stainless steel cladding, creating voids and leading to material embrittlement. Other effects are "swelling," an increase in volume, and "growth," an anisotropic change of shape. Swelling is the result of trapping of interstitials by dislocations. When the material is stressed (as in the case of cladding due to external or internal pressure) dimensional change is greatly accelerated through a phenomenon called "irradiation creep." Because of these effects, the lifetimes of LMFBR fuel assemblies are limited by radiation damage, specifically, by distortions caused by irradiation creep and swelling.

BIBLIOGRAPHY

Babcock & Wilcox Co., *Steam, Its Generation and Use,* 1972, Chapters 28–30.

Clark, D. S., and W. R. Varney, *Physical Metallurgy for Engineers,* Van Nostrand, New York, 1962.

Freudenthal, A. M., "Thermal Stress Analysis and Mechanical Design," in *Nuclear Engineering,* C. F. Bonilla, Ed., McGraw-Hill, New York, 1957.

Glasstone, S., and A. Sesonske, *Nuclear Reactor Engineering,* Van Nostrand Reinhold, New York, 1967.

Hagrman, D. L., and G. A. Reyman, Eds., *MATPRO-Version 11, Revision 2, A Handbook of Materials Properties for Use in the Analysis of Light Water Reactor Fuel Rod Behavior,* NUREG/CR-0497, TREE-1280, Rev. 2, EG&G Idaho, Inc., Idaho Falls, Idaho, August 1981.

Hanford Engineering Development Laboratory (HEDL), *Nuclear Systems Materials Handbook,* Vols. 1 and 2, TID-2666.

Roberts, J. T. A., *Structural Materials in Nuclear Power Systems,* Plenum, New York, 1981.

Shrager, A. M., *Elementary Metallurgy and Metallography,* Dover, New York, 1969.

Smith, C. O., *Nuclear Reactor Materials,* Addison-Wesley, Reading, Massachusetts, 1967.

S. M. Stoller Corp., "Control Rod Materials and Burnable Poisons," EPRI NP-1974, July 1980; also Combustion Engineering Report CEND-391.

CHAPTER 11
FUEL UTILIZATION

11.1. INTRODUCTION AND OVERVIEW

Fuel utilization is the degree to which one is capable of deriving energy inherent in the unit mass of fuel. In the case of fission reactors, this is expressed as energy that can be obtained through fissioning of fissile nuclei. The importance of higher fuel utilization relates to resource management (less fuel will need to be purchased), environmental considerations (less mining of uranium will be necessary), future strategies (depending on projected depletion of reserves), and economies of fuel cycle in general.

The most important factor in achieving good fuel utilization is appropriate design and operation of the plant for the best neutron economy possible. Neutronic calculations for various configurations and at various time points in the fuel cycle are performed to determine the best design and the optimum fuel management scheme. If neutron absorptions in moderator, poisons, control elements, and structural materials are minimized, more neutrons will be available for energy-producing processes. Hence, fuel utilization will improve. Another effort in fuel management is to achieve a power distribution in the reactor core as flat as possible. If power distribution is very uneven in a fuel bundle (large peaking factors), the fuel will have to be discharged when the most exposed† part has reached its limits, while the rest of the bundle has yet to deliver its maximum potential.

One factor that limits fuel utilization is the necessity that a certain amount of fissile material must always be present in the core to make it critical. In many types of reactors where refueling is accomplished in batches (for example, once a year), a certain excess reactivity must be built into the core at the beginning of life to last until the next refueling. This ties up extra fuel in the core, causing many neutrons to be wasted, since absorbers must also be added to equalize this initial excess of reactivity. The process limits fuel utilization. Minimizing excess reactivity and poisons in the reactor core yields higher fuel utilization.

Another factor related to fuel utilization is the process of enrichment and the parameter called "tails assay" (see also Chapter 6). When natural uranium is enriched for use in light-water reactors (LWRs), two streams result: the product stream yielding an enrichment of 2–4% (higher enrichments for other applications) and a waste or tails stream, usually set at 0.2–0.3%, down from the natural uranium content of uranium-235 which is 0.71%. The value picked for the tails assay affects the amount of feed (uranium hexafluoride), and hence the amount of uranium oxide (U_3O_8) needed to produce a given amount of product. It will also affect the amount of separative work needed for the same amount of product.‡ For comparison of fuel utilization among various reactor options, one must always normalize to the same tails assay.

Although fuel utilization affects fuel cycle economics, it should not be considered alone in a very complex picture in which many other factors play an important, and sometimes overriding role. Such aspects are the costs of yellowcake and enrichment (as hinted above), transportation costs, the availability and cost of spent fuel storage, and above all, the cost of plant downtime which depends on frequency and duration of reactor shutdowns and the cost of replacement power. As we shall see later in this chapter, it may be preferable to lengthen the fuel cycle (longer times between refueling shutdowns) even if it means a degradation in fuel utilization.

Several other considerations may interact with and impact fuel management and utilization. Regulatory concerns regarding radiation embrittlement of pressure vessels over their 30- or 40-yr lifetime (see Section 10.9) may require a low-leakage fuel management scheme to minimize fast neutron bombardment of pressure vessel welds even though this may affect power output. Another

†The burnup of fuel is referred to as "exposure"; its units are MWd/t.
‡As a rule of thumb, a decrease of tails assay of 0.1% (e.g., from 0.3 to 0.2%) will decrease the feed and will increase the amount of SWUs on the order of 20%.

aspect is the politics of recycle. Although reprocessing of spent fuel and recycle of its uranium and plutonium content lead to considerably higher fuel utilization, this option may not become practically available for a variety of regulatory, political, international, and economic reasons.

In the following sections, the various aspects of fuel utilization will be discussed in more detail.

11.2. NUCLEAR FUELS

Nuclear fuels are materials capable of releasing energy through nuclear reactions. Even though this definition would include fusion reactions and fuels (such as deuterium and tritium), we shall limit the discussion to nuclear fuels that release energy through fission. We distinguish nuclear fuels into "fissile" and "fertile" materials.

A "fissile" material is one whose nucleus will fission when bombarded with a slow-moving or "thermal" neutron. The only "fissile" material found in nature is the isotope of uranium ^{235}U. This isotope constitutes only 0.711 wt% of natural uranium; the balance is made of the more abundant isotope ^{238}U (99.283 wt%) and traces of ^{234}U. ^{238}U is not fissile, a property related to its even number of nucleons. However, it is "fissionable" since it can be split when bombarded with fast neutrons, that is, with neutrons of sufficiently high energy, for example, with 1–2 MeV neutrons like those produced in fission.† ^{238}U and ^{232}Th (also found in nature) have another interesting property. Upon absorption of one neutron and after a series of radioactive decays, they give birth, respectively, to two artificial fissile isotopes, ^{239}Pu and ^{233}U. These artificial isotopes can also be regarded as nuclear fuels. The nuclear transformations are described by the following equations:

$$^{238}U + n \rightarrow [^{239}U]^* \rightarrow \beta^- + {}^{239}Np \rightarrow \beta^- + {}^{239}Pu \text{ (fissile)} \tag{11.1}$$

$$^{232}Th + n \rightarrow [^{233}Th]^* \rightarrow \beta^- + {}^{233}Pa \rightarrow \beta^- + {}^{233}U \text{ (fissile)} \tag{11.2}$$

Because of their ability to absorb thermal neutrons and to produce new fissile materials, ^{238}U and ^{232}Th are called "fertile" materials. This important property is utilized in the converter and breeder reactors discussed below. Thus there are three main fissile isotopes of interest in the nuclear industry: one found in nature, ^{235}U, and two artificial, ^{239}Pu and ^{233}U, which are produced from the fertile isotopes ^{238}U and ^{232}Th.

11.3. BASIC NOTIONS IN CORE PHYSICS

Neutronic Characteristics of Fuels

The principal neutronic characteristics of these isotopes (or nuclides) are shown in Table 11.1. The absorption cross section, σ_a, is given for thermal neutrons having a representative speed of 2200 m/sec. It is measured in barns (10^{-24} cm^2) and gives a measure of the probability of a nucleus absorbing a thermal neutron. Multiplied by the number density of a nuclide (number of atoms/cm^3) it yields the macroscopic cross section $\Sigma_a = N \cdot \sigma_a$ (in units of cm^{-1}). The macroscopic cross section multiplied in turn by the thermal flux yields the absorption rate

$$F_a = \Sigma_a \cdot \phi_{th} \qquad \text{(absorptions/cm}^3\text{-sec)}$$

The microscopic fission cross section, σ_f, is smaller than the absorption cross section. The balance makes the radiative capture cross section σ_c, which represents the probability that a neutron absorbed by a fissile nucleus will not lead to a fission but to the emission of a gamma ray,‡ an unproductive process (except in the case of fertile materials). The fission cross section plus the radiative capture cross section make up the total absorption cross section,§ that is

$$\sigma_a = \sigma_f + \sigma_c$$

The ratio of capture-to-fission sections, σ_c/σ_f, is denoted by the letter α and is an important parameter in neutron physics.

Neutrons per fission, ν, is a quantity averaged over a large number of fissions, since in each fission an integer number of neutrons are emitted, usually 2 or 3, but, occasionally, even more. The parameter η denotes the number of neutrons emitted per absorption (as opposed to ν which is per

†In fact, many nuclei in the periodic table of the elements could fission when bombarded with very energetic neutrons but the required energies are well above those encountered in nuclear reactors.

‡This is sometimes referred to as radiative capture.

§Other reactions are possible but are usually unimportant in reactor physics.

Table 11.1. Some Important Properties of Fissile Nuclides

Property	^{233}U	^{235}U	^{239}Pu
Thermal cross section			
(at 2200 m/sec, in barns)			
Fission, σ_f	528.7	583.9	741.7
Radioactive capture, σ_c	45.8	98.4	270.2
Total absorption, σ_a	574.5	682.3	1011.9
Neutrons produced			
Average number per fission, $\bar{\nu}$	2.495	2.437	2.891
Average number per absorption,[a] η	2.291	2.078	2.079

Source: ENDF/B-V, BNL-NCS-17541, July 1979. Also EPRI, NP-2510, July 1982.

[a]The values of η were obtained from $\bar{\nu}$ by multiplying by the ratio $\bar{\sigma}_f/\bar{\sigma}_a$, where average cross sections over a Maxwellian spectrum were used.

fission) in order to take into account the unproductive captures. It is easy to show the relationship

$$\eta = \frac{\nu}{1 + \alpha}$$

Let us now review the process occurring in a reactor fueled with a mixture of ^{235}U (enriched to 2–5%) and ^{238}U. Out of 100 thermal neutrons absorbed in ^{235}U, about 85 of them will lead to fissions, and the remaining 15 will cause radiative capture and will lead to the production of ^{236}U. This isotope is merely a poison. It can absorb a neutron to produce the short-lived ^{237}U, which decays to nonfissile ^{237}Np.

Neutrons produced in fission of ^{235}U are also absorbed by ^{238}U and the chain shown in Eq. (11.1) will result. Since ^{239}Np decays quickly, it is usually assumed that neutron absorptions in ^{238}U lead to ^{239}Pu nuclei whose gradual production adds fuel and reactivity to the reactor core. As this artificial fissile element builds up in the fuel, a good proportion of total fissions (up to 40%), and hence of total energy produced, comes from plutonium fissions. A portion of absorptions in ^{239}Pu will produce ^{240}Pu which, with an additional neutron absorption, produces ^{241}Pu, a fissile material with favorable neutronic characteristics. When a neutron is absorbed by ^{241}Pu, either fission or radiative capture occurs; the latter produces ^{242}Pu. This element is neither fissile nor fertile but simply a poison, like ^{236}U. ^{241}Pu can also decay, with a half-life of 13.2 yr, to ^{241}Am. Further neutron absorptions in ^{242}Pu produce ^{243} Pu, which decays to the nonfissile isotope ^{243}Am. These nuclear transformations of ^{235}U and ^{238}U are shown in Figure 11.1.

Certain types of reactors were designed to take advantage of the fissile isotope ^{233}U produced from fertile ^{232}Th. Such reactors must start with an existing fuel, namely, fissile uranium, mixed with the fertile thorium. The nuclear reactions occurring in the thorium chain are shown in Figure 11.2, the main portion of which consists of the abbreviated chain shown in Eq. (11.2).

Critical Mass and Reactivity

Even though an average of 2.4 neutrons are released per fission, the continuation of the chain reaction can only be guaranteed by careful consideration of the total neutron economy. Neutrons can be "lost" by nonfission reactions in the fuel (radiative captures), by absorption in nonfuel materials in the core (called "parasitic" absorptions), or by leakage of neutrons through the surface of the core to the surrounding space. The fraction of neutrons leaking out can be reduced by increasing the size of the core (the volume is increased faster than the surface area) or the concentration of the fissile material. The minimum amount of fissile material needed to sustain the chain reaction is called "critical mass." At a given concentration, one can calculate the "critical size." The critical mass can be as little as 10 kg (in an assembly of highly enriched, almost pure ^{235}U) to more than 200 kg (in a natural uranium-graphite reactor).† Natural uranium alone (i.e., without a moderator) can never reach critical size, because of the relatively high number of neutron reactions that do not lead to fission.

Criticality is measured by the multiplication factor, k. It is the ratio of neutrons born in one generation to the neutrons born in the previous generation. The reactor is critical when $k = 1$; the fission chain can be maintained indefinitely at a constant pace. When k is larger than 1, the reactor

†Modern power reactors have 100 t of uranium in their cores.

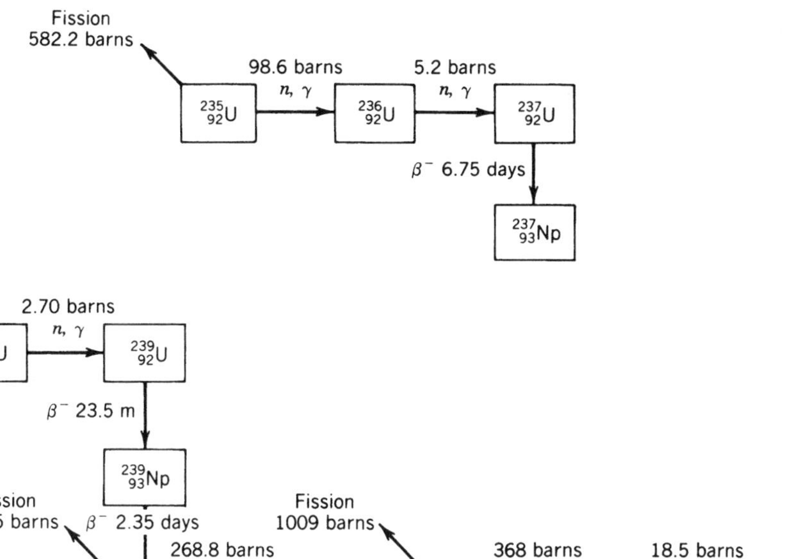

Figure 11.1. Principal nuclear reactions in uranium-fueled reactors.

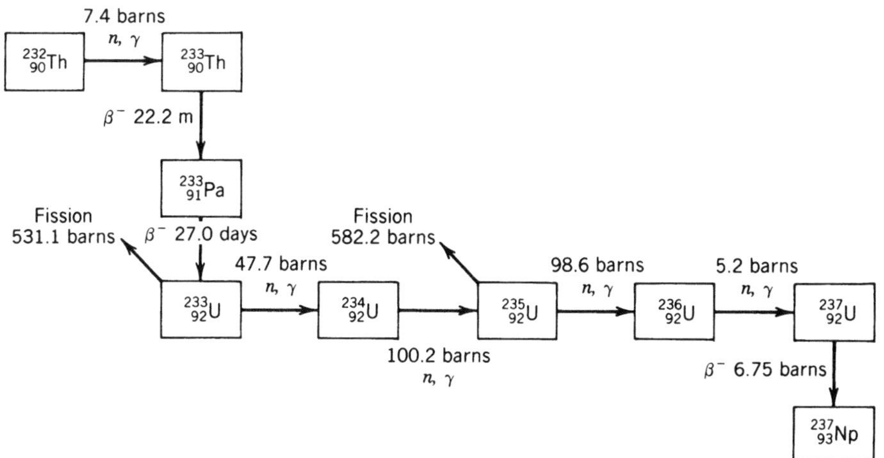

Figure 11.2. Principal nuclear reactions in thorium-fueled reactors.

is "supercritical"; the neutron population and power level rise until k is brought back to a value of 1 either through external control or through inherent mechanisms (e.g., rise in temperature or increase of steam bubbles). If k is smaller than 1, the reactor is said to be "subcritical"; any fission chain that may start will eventually die. The only way to maintain a chain reaction when $k < 1$ is by insertion of an independent neutron source. The ratio $(k - 1)/k$ is called the reactivity, ρ, and it ranges from 0 to 0.25† in standard power reactors.

The above discussion leads directly to the following two conclusions. First, it is essential to maintain an adequate inventory of fissile material in the reactor core to achieve criticality throughout core life. Hence, whenever the fissile fuel is depleted below a certain level, at least part of the core must be replaced. This refueling operation, according to present practice in the LWR industry today, is done once a year although longer fuel cycles (18 months) are also being used, as we shall see later in this chapter. At each refueling outage, lasting normally 4–8 weeks, one-fourth (boiling water reactors, BWRs) or one-third (pressurized water reactors, PWRs) of the core is replaced with fresh fuel, thus adding the necessary reactivity to the core, while the removed fuel is placed in the spent fuel pool for cooling. Other operations of repair and maintenance are scheduled concurrently with the refueling to minimize the duration of plant downtime, and hence the economic loss. In the CANDU reactor, refueling is performed on-line, and shutdown is not required for this operation. The second consideration is the absolute necessity to maintain control over the fission chain reaction at all times and to allow the reactor to become only slightly supercritical whenever there is a need to increase power level. An elaborate and redundant control system is, therefore, incorporated in all nuclear reactors for the purposes of controlling power level and shutting down the reactor in normal and emergency situations.

Fission Product Poisoning

Each fission results in the production of two large fission fragments which deposit all their energy very close (a few micrometers) to the site of fission (see also Chapter 2). Some of these fission products or their radioactive products, notably xenon-135 and samarium-149, are strong thermal neutron absorbers and therefore poison the core. The chain that produces ^{135}Xe is shown below:

$$
\begin{array}{ccccccccc}
^{135}\mathrm{Te} & \xrightarrow[29\ \mathrm{sec}]{\beta^-} & ^{135}\mathrm{I} & \xrightarrow[6.7\ \mathrm{hr}]{\beta^-} & ^{135}\mathrm{Xe} & \xrightarrow[9.2\ \mathrm{hr}]{\beta^-} & ^{135}\mathrm{Cs} & \xrightarrow[3\times 10^6 yr]{\beta^-} & ^{135}\mathrm{Ba}\ \text{(stable)} \\
\uparrow & & \uparrow & & \uparrow & & & & \\
\text{Fission} & & \text{Fission} & & \text{Fission} & & & &
\end{array}
$$

^{135}Xe has a very large absorption cross section, 2.65×10^6 barns for thermal neutrons. It is produced both directly from fission and from decay of two other fission products, tellurium-135 and iodine-135. Since ^{135}Te decays so rapidly to ^{135}I it is possible to combine the yields per fission in ^{235}U of these two nuclides into one value, 0.061. The yield of ^{135}Xe is 0.003 (values of yields differ for fission in ^{233}U and ^{239}Pu). Xenon is destroyed by two processes: decay into cesium-135 and neutron absorption which is proportional to flux. The rate of accumulation of ^{135}Xe depends on all these processes and their time constants, and can be readily calculated. For a given flux, xenon begins to build up after reactor start-up and reaches equilibrium (a flat constant level) after about 20 hr for neutron fluxes normally encountered in reactors. The level of equilibrium depends on flux and is higher, the higher the flux. Figure 11.3 shows the xenon buildup after start-up for various flux levels. It also shows the so-called xenon transient which occurs after reactor shutdown. Since the main cause of xenon destruction, namely neutron flux, disappears, xenon production from the decay of ^{135}I overwhelms the process until the production rate of xenon equals and then trails its destruction rate from xenon decay into ^{135}Cs. The result is a large peak (depending on previous neutron flux), which constitutes one of the main reactivity components that the control system must be able to override at the operator's command.

The second most important fission product poison is ^{149}Sm. With a thermal neutron cross section of 40,800 barns, this isotope is much less of a poison in reactor core but its effect must, nevertheless, be taken into account. Its simplified chain of production is

$$
\begin{array}{ccccc}
^{149}\mathrm{Nd} & \xrightarrow[2.0\ \mathrm{hr}]{\beta^-} & ^{149}\mathrm{Pm} & \xrightarrow[54\ \mathrm{hr}]{\beta^-} & ^{149}\mathrm{Sm}\ \text{(stable)} \\
\uparrow & & & & \\
\text{Fission} & & & &
\end{array}
$$

†This is the maximum value a core would have without the addition of various control materials and poisons. At any point in time, the reactivity of the core is always in the range 0.0–0.0064, the prompt critical value (see Chapter 2).

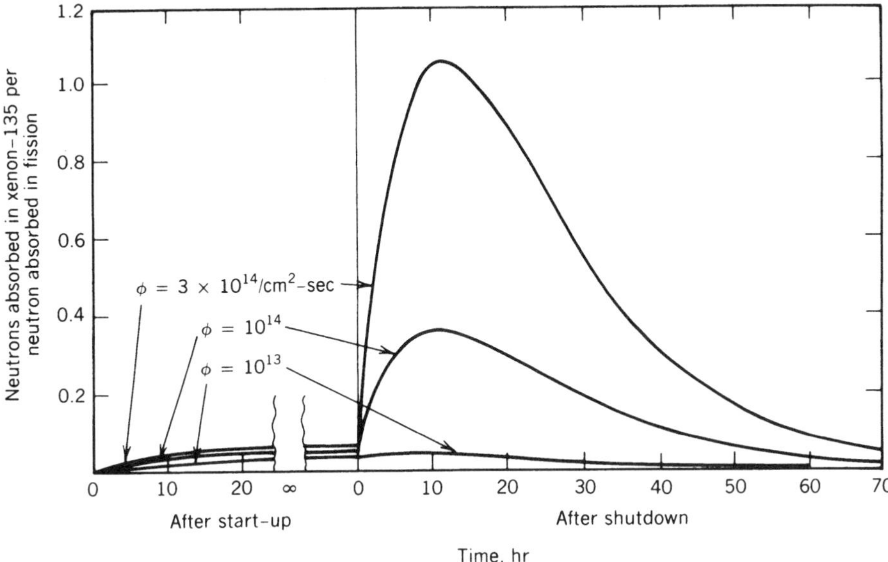

Figure 11.3. The xenon poison ratio is defined as the fraction of neutrons absorbed in xenon-135 relative to the number of neutrons absorbed in fission-producing reactions. It is proportional to the concentration of xenon nuclei in the fuel. The buildup of xenon after reactor start-up, shown for three flux levels, reaches a flat level after a few tens of hours. After reactor shutdown, the xenon undergoes a transient which adds negative reactivity for a few tens of hours. The control system must have enough worth to over-ride this poison effect if reactor start-up is needed during the period of 40–50 hr following shutdown.

Since ^{149}Nd decays rapidly into ^{149}Pm, one can assume that the latter is produced directly in fission of ^{235}U with a yield of 0.0113. Because of the different characteristics of this chain, samarium builds up to an equilibrium which is independent of flux and equivalent to a value of reactivity $\rho = -0.463\%$. Following reactor shut-down, samarium builds up as the accumulated promethium-149 decays. However, unlike ^{135}Xe, which decays by beta decay, ^{149}Sm is stable and remains in the fuel until the reactor is started up again, whereupon it drops back to its operation level, as shown in Figure 11.4.

Total Reactivity Requirements

The changes in reactivity can be distinguished as long term and short term. Long-term reactivity changes are caused by the slow burning (depletion) of the fissile material, adjusted by the buildup of new fissile material produced by neutron captures in fertile material. They can also be caused by similar depletion of burnable poisons (see Section 10.5) through neutron irradiation. Short-term reactivity changes are those caused by xenon and samarium buildup and by the changes in reactor temperatures as the reactor is brought up to power from shutdown (Chapter 12). Because the so-called "temperature coefficient of reactivity," composed of moderator and fuel coefficients, is negative in LWRs, heating up the reactor from room temperature to an operating temperature of 300°C (570°F) means a net loss of reactivity. The reactor control system must be capable of compensating for these reactivity losses in order to keep the reactor critical at all times during its core lifetime. The total control system of a PWR has a capability of about 25%.† About 10% is dedicated to fuel burnup, permanent poisons, and fissile isotope buildup; 3% for temperature compensation; 3% for equilibrium xenon; 3% for xenon transient override; and 1% for equilibrium samarium. This leaves a margin of 5% to ensure that the core is well subcritical with the entire control system effective. In fast reactors, reactivity worths are generally smaller because of the lower absorption properties of materials in a fast neuron spectrum.

†This means that it can keep under control a core with a maximum $k = 1/(1 - \rho) = 1/(1 - 0.25) = 1.33$. This was derived from the definition of reactivity $\rho = (k - 1)/k$.

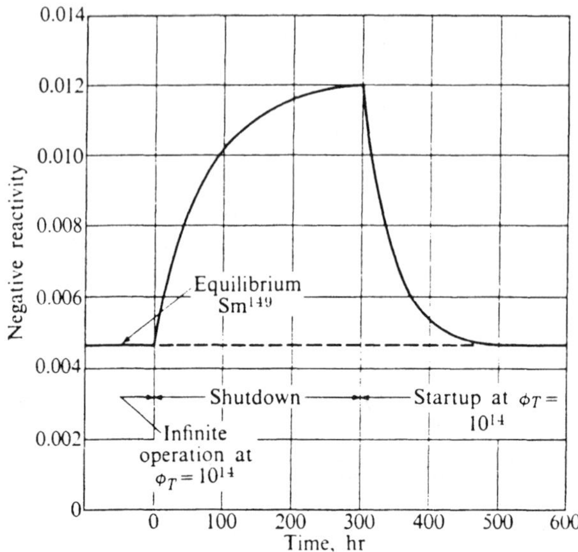

Figure 11.4. Samarium-149 buildup after shutdown of a reactor operating at a flux of 10^{14} neutrons/cm^2-sec and the subsequent burnout of the samarium after start-up.

Fission Energy, Burnup, and Fuel Consumption

When a thermal neutron is absorbed by a fissile nucleus, the internal balance of the forces inside the nucleus is perturbed. The excited nucleus then may split into two lighter nuclei, much like a water droplet that has become too large splits into two smaller droplets. Beta and gamma rays, neutrons, two fission fragments, and energy are the products of fission.† The energy released is equivalent to the mass lost in the process, since the total sum of the products weighs slightly less than the mass of the original nucleus plus the absorbed neutron.

The mass deficit in the fission reaction emerges in the form of energy, according to Einstein's formula of mass-energy equivalence, $E = mc^2$. The energy released is mostly in the form of kinetic energy carried by the moving fission fragments. These fragments, however, are quickly slowed by collisions with other nuclei; thus the kinetic energy is converted to heat, in the vicinity of the fission event (within a few micrometers). About 20% of the total energy released is carried away by the beta and gamma rays, as well as by the fission neutrons. This energy is also eventually converted into heat, although this conversion takes place farther away from the fission event.

The amount of energy released in fission is on the order of 200 MeV, or 3.2×10^{-11} J as shown in Table 11.2. Although small in absolute terms, this amount of energy is extremely large in relation to the amount of mass involved in the fission process.

Let us now consider a reactor operating at a power level of P megawatts thermal.‡ Using a figure of 200 MeV of energy per fission we can obtain the fission rate by using the appropriate conversion factors:

$$R_f = P\,(\text{MW}) \times \frac{10^6\ \text{J}}{\text{MWsec}} \times \frac{1\ \text{fission}}{200\ \text{MeV}} \times \frac{\text{MeV}}{1.60 \times 10^{-13}\ \text{J}} \times \frac{86{,}400\ \text{sec}}{\text{day}}$$

$$= 2.70 \times 10^{21} \times P\,(\text{MW}) \text{ in } \left(\frac{\text{fissions}}{\text{d}}\right)$$

This figure can be converted into grams of fissile material burned by dividing it by Avogadro's number and multiplying by 235 (since we are considering fission in ^{235}U).

†Other particles, such as neutrinos, are also produced and carry with them a certain small fraction of energy. Because of near zero cross section and zero charge, these particles are nearly impossible to capture or detect.

‡To obtain the electric output one must multiply P by the plant's thermal efficiency, typically 0.33 for LWRs.

Table 11.2. Emitted and Recoverable Energies for Fission of ^{235}U

Form	Emitted Energy, MeV	Recoverable Energy, MeV
Fission fragments	168	168
Fission product decay		
β-rays	8	8
γ-rays	7	7
neutrinos	12	—
Prompt γ-rays	7	7
Fission neutrons		
(kinetic energy)	5	5
Capture γ-rays	—	3–12
Total	207	198–207

We thus obtain a burnup rate

$$\text{burnup rate} = R_b = 1.05\ P\ (\text{MW})\ \text{in g/d}$$

This means that a reactor operating at a thermal power output of 1 MW requires the fissioning of about 1 g of ^{235}U. Stated differently, 1 MWd of energy is equivalent to the energy content of 1 g of ^{235}U. This figure must be adjusted to account for the nonfission absorptions in ^{235}U. This is done by multiplying the burnup rate by the absorption to fission ratio $\bar{\sigma}_a/\bar{\sigma}_f = 1 + \alpha$, which now yields the uranium consumption rate (or specific consumption).

$$\text{consumption rate} = C = R_b(1 + \alpha) = 1.05(1 + \alpha)P\ (\text{g/day})$$

By using a value of $\alpha = 0.169$ for ^{235}U, we obtain a consumption rate of about 1.24 g/day per megawatt of power, assuming primarily thermal fission.†

Expressed in another way, the inverse of C gives the amount of energy released per unit mass, or burnup:

$$B = \frac{1}{C} = \frac{1}{1.24}\frac{\text{MWd}}{\text{g}} = \frac{10^6}{1.24}\frac{\text{g}}{\text{ton}}\frac{\text{MWd}}{\text{g}} = 800{,}000\frac{\text{MWd}}{\text{t}}$$

This figure is expressed per ton (metric) of ^{235}U and is to be compared with 0.35 MWd/t of coal. This very large amount of energy can be released only if every nucleus of ^{235}U in fuel of pure ^{235}U is consumed. In practice, however, the fuel is a mixture of fissile and fertile isotopes, and this must be periodically replaced. Thus the actual burnup achieved in LWR fuel is from 25,000 to 35,000 MWd/t‡ of fuel. In breeder reactors, the burnup can be increased to 100,000 to 150,000 mWd/t, which implies a higher utilization of the energy inherent in the fuel. Burnup is calculated on the basis of the total mass of uranium in the fuel or total mass of heavy metal to include any initial or subsequently produced plutonium. Since different fuel bundles and different parts of the fuel within the same bundle are exposed to different fluxes, one has local burnup, bundle average, core average, and batch average burnup.

Yet another definition of burnup is the number of fissile nuclei that fissioned, over the total number of fissile and fertile nuclei originally present in the fuel. In LWRs, with 2–4% enrichment, the fuel is designed to sustain a few percent fission. One percent fission corresponds to about 10,000 MWd/t of burnup.

Burners, Converters, and Breeders

It was seen earlier in Section 11.3 that the number of neutrons released in fission (η) is larger than two. Besides one neutron, which is necessary to perpetuate the fission reaction, and the fractions

†This quantity is usually called "specific consumption" in other fuel applications. Compare C = 1.24 g/MWd for ^{235}U to the equivalent amount of coal. Using a heating value, HV = 30,230 kJ/kg, or 13,000 Btu/lb, we obtain 2860 kg/MWd or a ratio to uranium of 2,300,000 : 1.

‡We use consistently the notation MWd/t to denote megawatt-days per metric ton of uranium or heavy metal (which includes all isotopes of uranium and plutonium). We will use "st" to denote short ton equal to 2000 lb = 0.9072 t. Alternate ways of expressing burnup units in literature are: MWD/TeU, MWD/MTM, GWd/tU, MWD/THM, and so on.

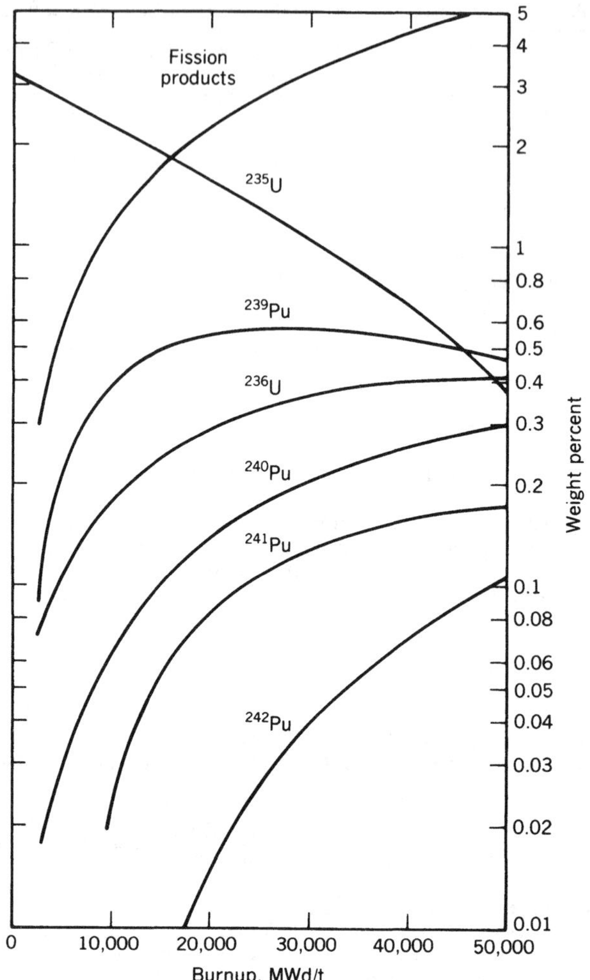

Figure 11.5. The concentration of various nuclides changes with time (or burnup). Fissile ^{235}U starts at about 3.2% and decreases exponentially with burnup while the plutonium isotopes build up quite rapidly at first and much slower afterward. Fuel discharged from the reactor at an average burnup of 35,000 MWd/t will have about 0.85% ^{235}U, 0.55% fissile ^{239}Pu, and 0.15% fissile ^{241}Pu. ^{236}U and ^{242}Pu are poisons while ^{240}Pu is fertile, leading to ^{241}Pu. The concentration of fission products (some of which are strong poisons) will be about 3.8%.

going into radiative captures, parasitic absorptions, and leakage, some neutrons are left for absorption in fertile material to produce new fissile material. This process is known as "conversion." The conversion ratio, CR, is the number of new fissile material produced per unit of fissile material destroyed. It turns out that LWRs have a conversion ratio of about 0.6. There is some build up of new fissile nuclei from fertile material in the core, but the dominant process is the burning of existing fissile nuclei, hence these reactors are also called "burners." The changes in composition that occur in a PWR during irradiation are shown in Figure 11.5, made by the computer code CELL, as a function of burnup. The concentration of ^{235}U decreases almost exponentially over burnup while ^{239}Pu builds up rapidly at first and then levels off at a value of about 0.6%. An additional fissile material, ^{241}Pu, builds up, through absorptions in ^{240}Pu, giving a fissile advantage. The concentration of ^{240}Pu, however, is quite low.

Reactors designed to achieve a higher conversion ratio, between 0.7 and 1.0, are called "converters." As the conversion ratio approaches unity, almost one new fissile nucleus is produced for every nucleus destroyed, and the reactor can, in principle, run indefinitely. The high-temperature gas-cooled reactor (HTGR) can be designed to have a CR of about 0.75 and it is a converter reactor.

Obviously, with higher conversion ratios, the fuel utilization is improved and there are several ideas and methods to improve the conversion factor of LWRs as we shall see later.

The most interesting case arises when the conversion factor becomes larger than unity. Now more fissile material is produced than burned and it is possible, in due time, to accumulate enough additional fissile material to fuel another reactor. Hence, these are called "breeder reactors." The ability of a reactor to breed is measured by the "breeding gain," G, which is the number of fissile nuclei "gained" in the system per fissile nucleus consumed. It is clear that the gain is the excess of the conversion ratio, above unity.

$$G = \mathrm{CR} - 1$$

For breeding it is imperative that the value of η be greater than 2: one neutron to continue the fission reaction, one to produce a new fissile nucleus (by absorption in a fertile nucleus), and a little extra for various losses. As can be seen in Table 11.1 in the thermal energy region, only ^{233}U has an η of 2.3 substantially larger than 2.0. For this reason, the thermal breeders considered so far have been designs using ^{233}U as fuel and ^{232}Th as fertile isotope. But since ^{233}U does not exist in nature one must start any such reactor with an initial loading of ^{235}U and later utilize ^{233}U when it becomes available in sufficient amounts.

It is possible to design and build breeder reactors by using a fast neutron spectrum where the neutronic characteristics of ^{239}Pu are most favorable. The η value for this isotope rises markedly above the value of 2 at energies above 10 keV and reaches almost 3 at an energy of 1 MeV.

Fast reactors do not contain any moderator materials to slow neutrons down, and the bulk of fissions occur at energies of the order of 100 keV. The most developed type of breeder reactor is the liquid-metal fast breeder reactor (LMFBR) of which several prototypes have been built in several countries (see also Chapter 13). It utilizes liquid sodium metal as coolant. Its core consists of fuel enriched to a high degree in fissile material (more than 25%) and of a blanket of fertile material where the new fissile material is generated. The first core of breeder reactors has been, so far, made of highly enriched ^{235}U, because ^{239}Pu was not available.† Breeder reactors can, of course, start and then continue operations entirely on plutonium fuel. The fertile material comes primarily from large stockpiles of depleted uranium (below 0.35% ^{235}U content). These are produced from the "tailings" of the gaseous diffusion plants in several countries. In the United States alone, 200,000 tons of depleted uranium, stored in steel drums at enrichment plants, represent a very large potential energy resource were they to be converted into fissile material in breeder reactors. Their use would also delete the need for large amounts of additional mining of uranium ore.

Because of the low absorption and fission cross sections at fast neutron energies, fast breeders require a larger mass of fissile material to become critical. For a given amount of power the fissile inventory in the core of a fast breeder reactor is about twice that required in an equivalent LWR core. This additional front-end cost may impact negatively the breeder even though the fuel utilization is, in the long run, far superior. A summary of conversion ratios and fuel utilization figures corresponding to current LWRs, advanced converter designs, and fast breeders is given in Figure 11.6.

Measures of Fuel Utilization

We have already discussed fuel burnup and percent fissions as measures of fuel utilization. The latter is the measure used in Figure 11.6. It shows that the parameter ranges from a few percent in current LWRs to a maximum of 60% in fast breeders. Percent fissions is a more direct and more readily usable measure than burnup to obtain the degree to which the energy inherent in uranium (including both fissile and fertile) is utilized in a specific reactor.

Another commonly used measure is the amount of yellowcake (or uranium oxide, U_3O_8) needed to produce a certain amount of energy, for example, 1 MW-yr. Another, similar measure is the total amount of uranium oxide needed per reactor lifetime. This widely used measure is useful for the calculation of total commitment and total resource production needed as a function of time. Care must be exercised when comparisons are made on the basis of reactor lifetime uranium requirements. One must specify power output, plant lifetime, plant capacity factor, tails assay, fuel management scheme, and even plant thermal efficiency for the comparison to be meaningful. The comparisons that will be presented in the rest of this chapter should be viewed in this light. Changes in the projections made with regard to these parameters‡ could cause large differences in the results.

†The reasons of this unavailability were that national production programs reserved plutonium for military uses and fuel reprocessing which could produce plutonium from civilian spent fuel was not taking place.

‡The manipulation of capacity factor has been notorious in its usage by opposing sides of nuclear power issues to show results favorable to their respective viewpoints.

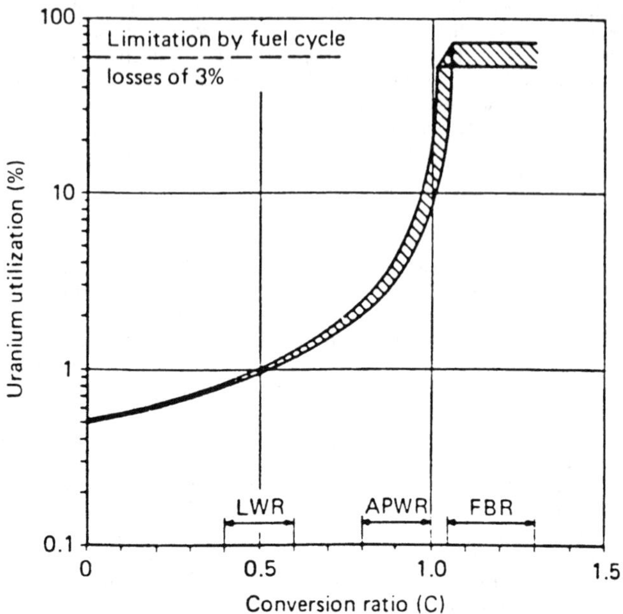

Figure 11.6. Utilization of natural uranium in closed fuel-reprocessing cycles as a function of conversion ratio. Current designs can utilize about 1% of total uranium (including fissile and fertile isotopes). Advanced converters can approach utilization of 10% while fast breeders can go up to 60%. [From W. Oldekop et al., *Nuclear Technology* **59** (1982).]

11.4. FUEL CYCLE MANAGEMENT IN THERMAL REACTORS

As the fuel is burned to produce energy, there comes a time (sooner or later, depending on reactor type) when the reactor can no longer be critical, even when all control rods and soluble poison are removed from the core. The operator must then decide on a course of action to restore reactivity in order to operate the reactor. The options available to him form a fairly large number of possible combinations and include: removal of old fuel and replacement with fresh at preselected time intervals; movement of fuel from one region of core to the other (shuffling); composition of new fuel in terms of both fuel enrichment and, possibly, burnable poisons and composition of soluble poison. The set of procedures regarding the above parameters constitute the "fuel and poison management" of the reactor.

The main purpose of fuel management is to replenish the reactivity of the core and enable it to operate at the maximum possible power output level. There are, however, a number of subsidiary, but important objectives aimed at optimizing the overall productivity of the plant. These goals, already alluded to in the introduction to this chapter, are the following:

Power shape should be as flat as possible. With a flat power distribution, every part of the core operates at its maximum allowed conditions, and therefore, the maximum total power output can be obtained from a given amount of fuel. A uniformly fueled reactor, with a uniformly distributed poison is far from this condition. Power is highest at the center of the core and falls off to near zero levels at its edge, so that the average power level is about a third of the maximum value. Therefore, in commercial reactors the fuel composition and poison distribution in the core is not uniform, in order to achieve a more even power distribution.

Maximum burnup of the fuel implies the largest economic advantage from a given investment, although other factors enter in the economic equations such as fuel enrichment. In general, the operator tries to operate the fuel close to its thermal limits† and for the maximum length of time possible without incurring an inordinate amount of fuel failures which might eventually impact the economics of the plant. It is also important to achieve as uniform a burnup as possible for the discharged fuel.

Neutron economy affects indirectly the economic performance of the plant, since neutrons absorbed in poisons are forever lost for any productive purpose. Neutrons saved could be absorbed

†These are specified in the operating license of a plant.

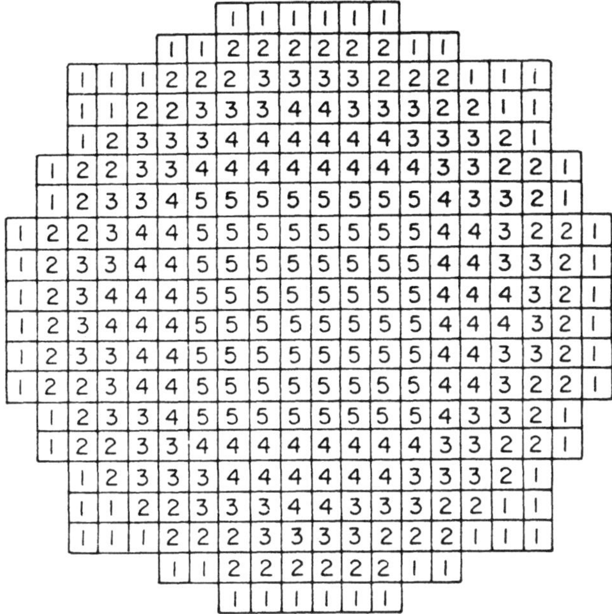

Figure 11.7. Fuel zones for partial batch replacement or out–in fueling.

in fertile materials (such as ^{238}U which is abundant in reactors with slightly enriched fuel) to produce fissile fuel and enhance the production of energy.

Fuel Management Schemes in LWRs

There are various strategies for fuel management in LWRs. The simplest method would be the use of uniform fuel and its complete replacement with fresh fuel when reactivity can no longer be maintained. This method, called "batch irradiation," is not used because of its serious drawbacks. The power density in the core is uneven with a peak-to-average power ratio higher than 3; the depletion of fissile material, which is proportional to neutron flux, is much higher in the center than at the periphery, resulting in very uneven burnup. At core discharge, when the central portion of the core has reached its maximum allowable burnup, large portions of the fuel have yet to deliver their full energy potential. In addition, a large excess reactivity must be built into the core which leads to the need for a control system with large reactivity worth with all the attendant problems, and to a waste of neutrons. All these factors have a negative impact on the economics of the fuel cycle and on the cost of a kilowatt-hour.

To flatten power distribution, one can use a "zoned loading" of the reactor. In this scheme, the central flat power region is loaded with fuel of lower enrichment, while the outer regions, called the buckled zones because of a more rapid fall-off of flux and power in them, are loaded with fuel of higher enrichment. One can also use a heavier poison loading (using burnable poison rods) in the inner regions than in the outer buckled regions. Although the inner zone has a flatter power distribution and uniform burnup, in the buckled zones these quantities are, by necessity, very uneven.

Refueling operations, in current LWRs, take place annually, when the reactor is shut down for 4 to 6 weeks. Only partial fuel replacement takes place, typically one-third or one-fourth of the core. A number of different methods are available.

In "partial batch replacement," the portion of the core that has sustained the highest exposure or burnup is removed and replaced by fresh fuel, while the rest of the fuel remains in place. In the next refueling, again the fuel with the highest burnup will be replaced, and so on. Figure 11.7 shows a reactor core divided in five concentric zones, with equal numbers of assemblies. Each zone, starting with the innermost and proceeding outward, is replaced with fresh fuel in successive refuelings. The main advantage of the scheme is that each zone has a fairly uniform burnup at discharge. However, the method leads to large peaking factors as when fresh fuel is placed at the center of the core, and it requires more frequent refueling than in batch irradiation. "Scatter refueling" is a variation of the partial batch refueling and is intended to solve the peaking factor

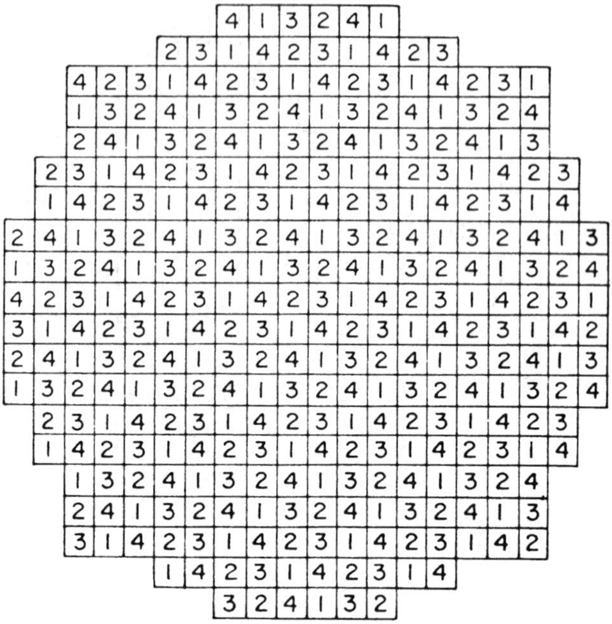

4 1 3 2 4 1

2 3 1 4 2 3 1 4 2 3

4 2 3 1 4 2 3 1 4 2 3 1 4 2 3 1

1 3 2 4 1 3 2 4 1 3 2 4 1 3 2 4

2 4 1 3 2 4 1 3 2 4 1 3 2 4 1 3

2 3 1 4 2 3 1 4 2 3 1 4 2 3 1 4 2 3

1 4 2 3 1 4 2 3 1 4 2 3 1 4 2 3 1 4

2 4 1 3 2 4 1 3 2 4 1 3 2 4 1 3 2 4 1 3

1 3 2 4 1 3 2 4 1 3 2 4 1 3 2 4 1 3 2 4

4 2 3 1 4 2 3 1 4 2 3 1 4 2 3 1 4 2 3 1

3 1 4 2 3 1 4 2 3 1 4 2 3 1 4 2 3 1 4 2

2 4 1 3 2 4 1 3 2 4 1 3 2 4 1 3 2 4 1 3

1 3 2 4 1 3 2 4 1 3 2 4 1 3 2 4 1 3 2 4

2 3 1 4 2 3 1 4 2 3 1 4 2 3 1 4 2 3

1 4 2 3 1 4 2 3 1 4 2 3 1 4 2 3 1 4

1 3 2 4 1 3 2 4 1 3 2 4 1 3 2 4

2 4 1 3 2 4 1 3 2 4 1 3 2 4 1 3

3 1 4 2 3 1 4 2 3 1 4 2 3 1 4 2

1 4 2 3 1 4 2 3 1 4

3 2 4 1 3 2

Figure 11.8. Fuel pattern in scatter refueling.

problem. The core is divided in small local groups with an equal number of assemblies. Figure 11.8 shows the plan view of a core subdivided into four-assembly groups. Each group contains fuel labeled 1, 2, 3, and 4. At the first refueling, all assemblies labeled 1 will be replaced with fresh fuel, at the second refueling assemblies labeled 2 will be removed and replaced with new fuel, and so on. The sequence is repeated and each assembly is irradiated for four cycles. Thus the fresh fuel is no longer concentrated in one region but is scattered throughout the core. The method drastically reduces the peaking factor although some peaking still occurs in the fresh, most reactive assemblies. A scatter refueling scheme with four zones allows a burnup about 60% higher than that achievable in simple batch irradiation, and the poison needed for reactivity control is 40% lower. However, the time between refuelings is also 40% shorter in four-zone scatter refueling than in batch refueling.

Out–in Refueling

To alleviate the problem of power peaking in the central region of the core, which is present with the previous schemes, an alternative method can be employed. The core is again divided into concentric zones with equal number of fuel assemblies, as shown in Figure 11.7. At the end of the first cycle, the fuel of the central zone (zone 5) with the highest burnup is removed. But instead of replacing it with fresh fuel, the bundles from the next outer zone (zone 4) is moved to the center; fuel from zone 3 is moved in zone 4, and so on. Fresh fuel is then placed in the outermost zone 1. Thus the least reactive fuel is placed in the region that normally tends to have the highest flux, while the most reactive fuel is placed in the region where flux drops off. At the next refueling, the same operation of central zone removal, inward movement of zones, and fresh fuel placement at the periphery is repeated. The name "out–in" for this scheme derives from this fuel movement from outer to inner zones. The scheme tends to depress power density in the center of the reactor. Figure 11.9*a* shows how the shape of power distribution in a three-zone core (a 260-MWe PWR) with a relatively small radius (1.25 m) is flattened at the beginning of the fuel cycle with a peaking factor of 1.3. Figure 11.9*b* shows the power distribution in a large core (1000-MWe PWR). In a large core, the inner and outer regions are loosely coupled and the more reactive outer zone does not react strongly with the inner zone, which is less reactive. The flux depression at the center is now quite large and the peaking factor about 2.0, a rather unfavorable condition. To obtain satisfactory results in large reactor cores, a combination of "out–in" and "scatter" refueling is used. The method, called modified scatter refueling, is illustrated in Figure 11.10. The reactor core is divided

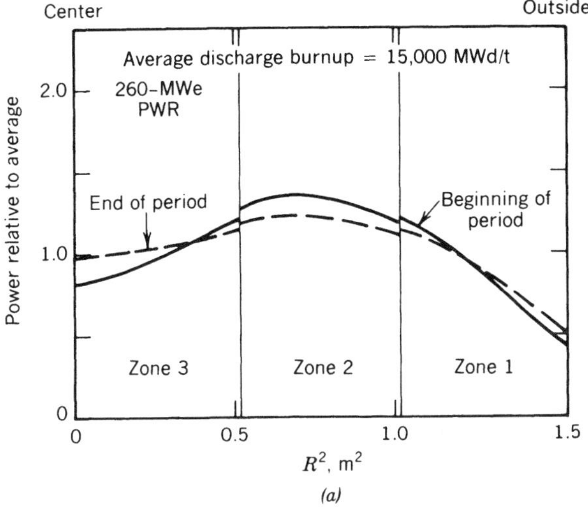

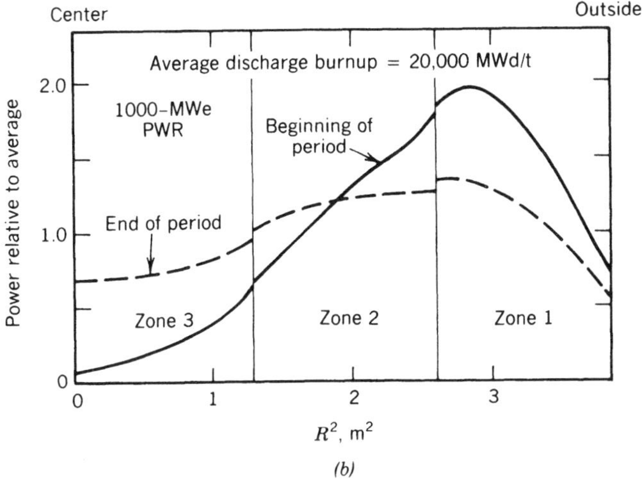

Figure 11.9. Radial power distribution with three-zone out–in fueling.

into an outer zone (labeled 1) containing one-fifth of the total assemblies and an inner zone containing the remaining four-fifths.

The inner zone is further subdivided in groups of four assemblies in the manner used in scatter refueling. At refueling time, the most burned assembly in each four-assembly group is removed and replaced by one assembly from the outer zone. Thus the entire outer zone is emptied and replaced with fresh fuel. This scheme leads to a fairly flat power distribution in the central core region, avoiding both the central power peaking of scatter refueling and the central power depression of the out–in scheme.

Optimization of Fuel Cycle Cost

The ultimate objective of the plant designer and operator is to minimize the cost of power production (see Chapter 19). Assuming that plant construction cost can be separated, the cost of the fuel cycle must be minimized. To illustrate the degrees of freedom that the designer has in the selection of parameters, we refer to Figure 11.11. The figure gives unit fuel cycle cost for a steady-state operation, as a function of enrichment. The curves were drawn for a varying availability-based

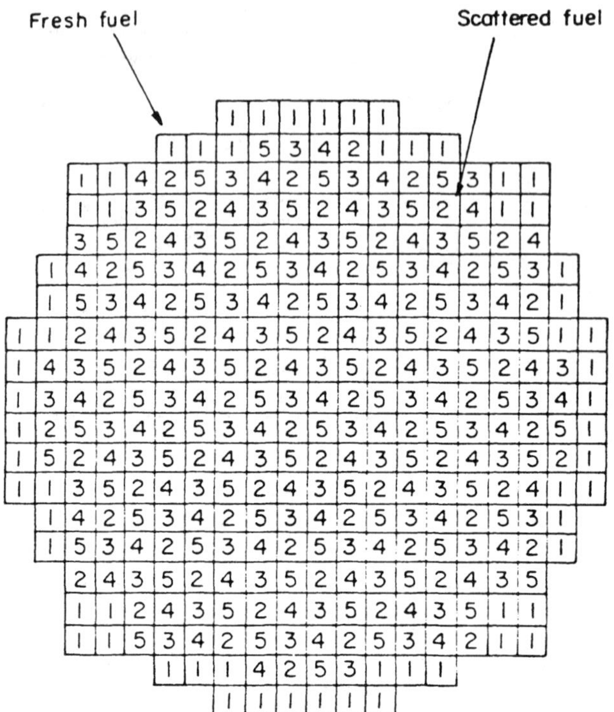

Figure 11.10. Modified scatter refueling.

capacity factor† L', ranging from 0.5 to 1.0. The plant's capacity factor and the burnup at discharge play an important role in determining fuel cycle cost. The usual choice for current LWRs is to have one-third or one-fourth of the core replaced at annual intervals with a burnup ranging from 30,000 to 40,000 MWd/t, and enrichment between 3 and 4%. In BWRs, the design burnup is somewhat lower (27,500 MWd/t). Since the power density in the core is much lower than in PWRs, fuel residence in the core may be longer, particularly if burnups comparable to those in PWRs are to be achieved. One possible scheme suggested by General Electric Company is replacement of one-third of the core every 18 months. The subject of extended fuel cycles will be discussed in more detail later.

Succession of Fuel Cycles in a Large PWR

When a new reactor is first fueled, all fuel is unirradiated as it begins its operation in cycle 1. A typical initial loading of a PWR is shown in Figure 11.12. It represents a three-region or three-lot core (meaning three different enrichments) with burnable poisons distributed so as to flatten the power distribution to the extent possible. During normal power operation, the movable control rods are fully withdrawn. Burnable poisons, in combination with the adjustable soluble boron composition in the reactor coolant, are used to account for long-term reactivity changes. The condition of the core at the beginning and end of cycle 1 is given in Figure 11.13, which represents one quadrant of the core. Rotational symmetry is assumed for the other three quadrants. Each square represents one assembly described by three lines of symbols, giving lot number and bundle location (first line), final burnup (second line), and peaking factor (third line) which must be kept below safe limits (a value of 1.58 is maximum). These figures are average for the assembly; they

†Availability-based capacity factor is defined as the ratio of electric energy generated during a period of time when the power plant was not shut down for refueling, to the amount of electric energy that would be generated at full capacity:

$$L' = \frac{\text{energy generated}}{(\text{full capacity}) \times (\text{time between refueling})}$$

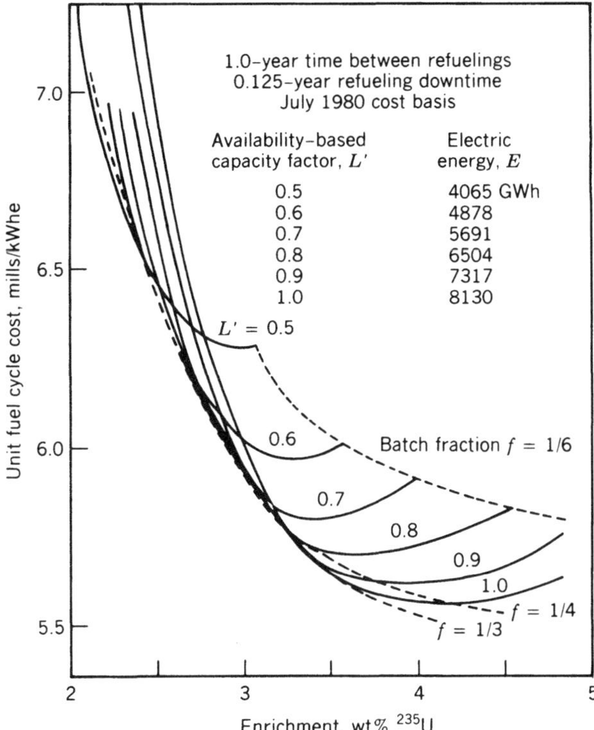

Figure 11.11. Fuel cycle cost in mills/kWh as a function of fuel enrichment at steady-state conditions. The effects of availability-based capacity factor and batch fraction are shown. The values were obtained by dividing total fuel cycle cost by the amount of electric power produced per cycle. The beneficial effect of increasing plant factor on unit energy cost is evident.

vary from the bottom to the top of the assembly, roughly symmetrically about the core midplane. The total amount of energy obtained from each assembly and from the core in the first cycle can be calculated by integrating the burnup figures over the entire core. In the specific example, a total energy of 1341.1 GWd or 32,188 × 10^6 kWh were produced in the first cycle of operation.

At the end of cycle 1, 64 of the 65 assemblies of lot 1 are removed; assemblies (almost all) from the periphery, belonging to lot 3 (Figure 11.12), are moved in positions of the inner zone and 64 fresh fuel assemblies with a 3.2% enrichment and no burnable poison are placed in the outer zone (and a very few in the inner zone) to begin cycle 2. All subsequent cycles are the same fixed enrichment, in this case 3.2%. The refueling pattern is similar to modified scatter refueling. Results of cycle 2 are somewhat different than those in cycle 1; total thermal energy is 835.2 GWd, much lower than in cycle 1. The third cycle will also differ from the second but the differences gradually diminish and the cycle eventually reaches equilibrium. These cycles are reached after seven or eight annual refuelings and are also called steady-state cycles with an average burnup slightly higher than 10,000 MWd/t. Fuel that has remained in the reactor for three cycles will have received a burnup of somewhat higher than 30,000 MWd/t. The evolution of fuel cycle parameters and their approach to equilibrium values is given in Table 11.3.

Lifetime uranium requirements of LWRs are relatively high because only a small percentage of total metal uranium is utilized for energy production. Assuming a 40-yr life, a realistic average capacity factor of 57%,† a tails assay of 0.2%, and the availability of plutonium recycle, a 1000-MWe LWR has a life-long uranium requirement of between 4000 and 4100 st of yellowcake (U_3O_8). If no reprocessing of spent fuel takes place (as is the case at this writing) and no plutonium is available for recycling, the requirements increase by about 23% to a range of 4900 and 5050 st of yellowcake (see also Table 11.4).

†This calculation assumes CF = 40% in the first year, 65% in the next 2 yr, and 75% in the following 12 yr. After the fifteenth year, it falls by 2% each year until it reaches 25% in the last (fortieth) year.

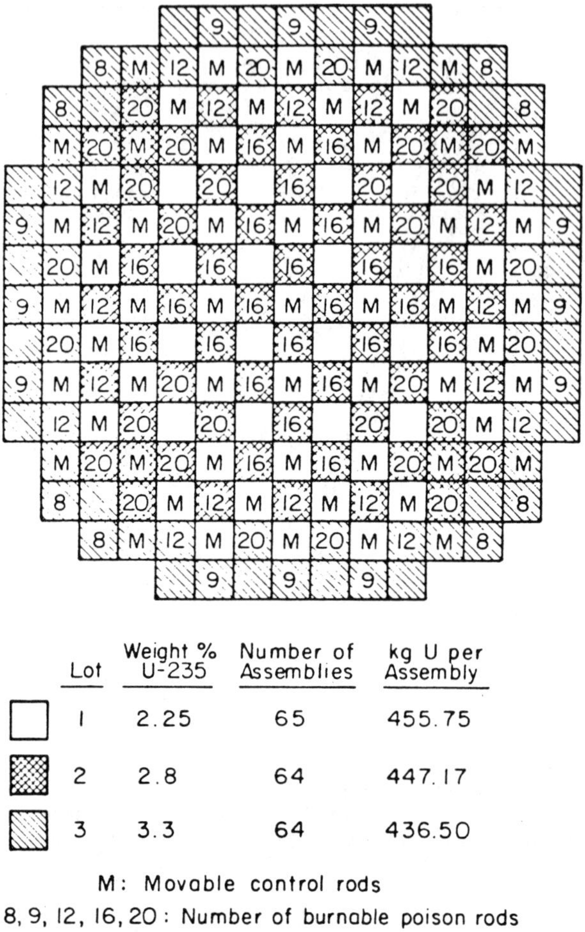

	Lot	Weight % U-235	Number of Assemblies	kg U per Assembly
(blank)	1	2.25	65	455.75
(dotted)	2	2.8	64	447.17
(hatched)	3	3.3	64	436.50

M: Movable control rods

8, 9, 12, 16, 20 : Number of burnable poison rods

Figure 11.12. Initial fuel loading of a large PWR, of 1060-MWe capacity. It is called a three-region core because it contains three distinct kinds of assemblies representing different fuel enrichment and burnable poison loading. Each region has the same number of assemblies (region 1 has one extra assembly) and is designed for a modified scatter refueling scheme. The enrichment and burnable poison distributions are designed to create a flat power distribution in a large portion of the core. (Courtesy Westinghouse Electrical Co.)

Fuel-Management in CANDU Reactors

The CANDU reactor system, described in more detail in Chapter 13, has a distinct advantage, in terms of fuel utilization, over equivalent LWR. This is mainly due to its on-line, continuous refueling. To maintain criticality, the CANDU reactor does not need a large excess amount of reactivity to be "locked up" in the core for a year or more, as in the LWR. The designers of the CANDU have opted for a different approach. Natural uranium is used as fuel, thus eliminating the need and cost for enrichment. This in turn excludes the use of water as moderator and coolant (because of its relatively high absorption cross section); heavy water is used instead (99.7% pure). About 1 t of heavy water is needed per megawatt of electric output with 2–3% annual losses from leakage. The additional cost of heavy water tends to counterbalance the savings from the elimination of enrichment services.

Fuel consists of 0.5-m-long fuel bundles inserted in horizontal pressure tubes that run axially through a thin walled tank, the calandria, which contains the heavy-water moderator. Twelve bundles are needed to fill each fuel channel. The core is always maintained with a reactivity level of slightly in excess of unity. As soon as power cannot be maintained, refueling is necessary to add reactivity to the core. This is done by on-line refueling that proceeds on a daily basis. Two refueling

Centerline	A	B	C	D	E	F	G	H
A	1AA 17302 1.04	2AB 16578 0.88	1AC 17063 1.04	2AD 16666 0.94	1AE 17442 1.19	2AF 17184 1.12	1AG 16220 1.16	3AH 12775 0.88
B	2BA 16578 0.88	1BB 17049 1.02	2BC 15844 0.82	1BD 17210 1.10	2BE 16716 0.99	1BF 17296 1.23	3BG 16041 1.00	3BH 13596 0.99
C	1CA 17063 1.04	2CB 15844 0.82	1CC 17050 1.05	2CD 16600 0.94	1CE 17260 1.16	2CF 16951 1.09	1CG 15950 1.15	3CH 11985 0.82
D	2DA 16666 0.94	1DB 17210 1.10	2DC 16600 0.94	1DD 17099 1.10	2DE 15981 0.90	1DF 16698 1.16	3DG 15945 1.06	3DH 10194 0.72
E	1EA 17442 1.19	2EB 16716 0.99	1EC 17260 1.16	2ED 15981 0.90	2EE 18303 1.24*	2EF 14934 0.87	3EG 14014 0.99	
F	2FA 17184 1.12	1FB 17296 1.23	2FC 16951 1.09	1FD 16698 1.16	2FE 14934 0.87	3FF 16484 1.16	3FG 9449 0.62	
G	1GA 16220 1.16	3GB 16041 1.00	1GC 15950 1.15	3GD 15945 1.06	3GE 14014 0.99	3GF 9449 0.62		
H	3HA 12775 0.88	3HB 13596 0.99	3HC 11985 0.82	3HD 10194 0.72				

* = Maximum relative power

Fuel lot 1 2.25 wt% ^{235}U
Fuel lot 2 2.80 wt% ^{235}U
Fuel lot 3 3.30 wt% ^{235}U

Cycle average burnup = 15,535 MWd/t
Cycle thermal energy = 1341.1 GWd

Key

1AA	Assembly number
17302	EOC burnup, MWd/t
1.04	BOC relative power (Assembly/average)

Figure 11.13. Quarter-core representation of PWR at the end of cycle 1. The three fuel lots are indicated by the first figure in the first line in each assembly. Fuel bundle location, burnup at end of cycle, and relative power are also shown as explained in the key to the figure. (From M. Benedict, T. H. Pigford, and H. W. Levi, *Nuclear Chemical Engineering*, 2nd ed., McGraw-Hill, New York, 1981.)

Table 11.3. Fuel-Cycle Performance of PWR in Successive Cycles

Cycle Number	Fuel Lot Number: Charged	Fuel Lot Number: Discharged	wt% ^{235}U Charged	Burnup, MWd/t: Cycle Average	Burnup, MWd/t: Fuel Discharged	Peak Radial Power Ratio: Max Value	Peak Radial Power Ratio: Position
1	1	1	2.25	15,535	16,943	1.24	EE
	2[a]		2.8				
	3[a]		3.3				
2	4	2[b]	3.2	9,652	25,115	1.34	DG
3	5	3[b]	3.2	9,894	32,076	1.36	DG
4	6	4[b]	3.2	10,284	30,306	1.34	DG
5	7	5[b]	3.2	10,038	30,401	1.38	DG
6	8	6[b]	3.2	10,084	30,419	1.37	DG
7	9	7[b]	3.2	10,081	30,399	1.37	DG
8	10	8[b]	3.2	10,081	30,400	1.37	DG

[a]Contains burnable poison.
[b]Sixty-three assemblies from this lot and one from previous lot.

Table 11.4. Thermal Reactor Fuel Characteristics

Characteristics[a]	BWR	PWR	Std HTGR	High-Gain HTGR	CANDU (Thor)	CANDU	ATR
Thermal efficiency (%)	34	33	39	39	30	30	31
Specific power (MWth/t)	28	38	82	69	25.6	22	13
Initial core (and blanket)[b] average							
Irradiation level (MWd/t)	17,000	22,600	54,500	33,500	18,500	6,900	13,700
Fresh fuel assay (wt% ^{235}U)	2.03	2.26	93.15	93.15	93.15	0.711	1.2
Spent fuel assay (wt% ^{235}U)	0.86	0.74	~60	~60	~60	0.31	0.33
Fissile Pu recovered (kg/t)[c]	4.8	5.8	—	—	—	1.7	4.3
Feed required (st U_3O_8/MWe)[d]							
at 0.2% tails	0.494	0.422	0.367	0.388	0.520	0.199	0.516
at 0.3% tails	0.581	0.498	0.456	0.419	0.646	0.199	0.577
Feed required (st ThO_2)[b,d]	—	—	42.5	52.8	160	—	—
Separative work required (SWU/MWe)[d]							
at 0.2% tails	239	222	366	336	519	—	—
at 0.3% tails	185	174	311	286	441	—	—
Replacement loadings (annual rate at steady state; 75% capacity factor)							
Irradiation level (MWdth/t)	27,500	32,600	95,000	48,800	27,000	9.600	20,000
Fresh fuel assay (wt% ^{235}U)	2.73	3.21	93.15	93.15	93.15	0.711	0.711
Spent fuel assay (wt% ^{235}U)	0.84	0.90	30	30	—	0.15	0.2
Fissile Pu recovered (kg/t)[c]	5.9	7.0	—	—	—	2.3	—
Feed required (st U_3O_8/MWe)[d]							
at 0.2% tails	0.144	0.154	0.85	0.045	0.20	0.125	—
at 0.3% tails	0.179	0.191	0.106	0.055	0.24	0.125	
Feed required (st ThO_2/MWe)[b,d]	—	—	8.7	19.7	41.5	—	—
Separative work required (SWU/MWe)							
at 0.2% tails	105	117	85	45	19	—	—
at 0.3% tails	84	94	73	38	16	—	—
Replacement loadings (annual rate with Pu recycle[e], 75% capacity factor)							
Fissile Pu recycled (kg/MWe)	0.163	0.167	—	—	—	—	0.3
Fissile Pu recovered (kg/t)[c,f]	8.1	9.5	—	—	—	—	5.5

Fissile ^{233}U recovered (kg/MtTh)[b]	—	—	—	—	—	—	—
Feed required (st U_3O_8/MWe)[d,g]							
at 0.2% tails	0.121	0.129	—	—	—	—	—
at 0.3% tails	0.148	0.158	—	—	—	—	—
Separative work required (SWU/MWe)[d]							
at 0.2% tails	82	93	—	—	—	—	—
at 0.3% tails	66	75	—	—	—	—	—
Lifetime[h] commitment required, 40-yr life, st U_3O_8/MWe[b] 40 (replacement requirements) + initial core and blanket							
Without Pu recycle							
at 0.2% tails	5,130	5,330	—	—	—	4,160[i]	—
at 0.3% tails	6,340	6,550	—	—	—	4,160[i]	—
With Pu recycle							
at 0.2% tails	4,020	4,100	—	—	—	—	2,600
at 0.3% tails	4,900	5,050	—	—	—	—	2,660
With thorium and ^{233}U recycle							
at 0.2% tails	—	—	2,980	1,920	1,440	—	—
at 0.3% tails	—	—	3,700	2,400	1,780	—	—

Source: Adapted from *Report of the Liquid Metal Fast Breeder Reactor Program Review Group*, U.S. ERDA report, ERDA-1 (January 1975).

[a]MWth is thermal megawatts; MWe is net electrical megawatts; MWdth is thermal megawatt days; t is metric tonnes (thousand of kilograms) of uranium; and st U_3O_8 is short tons of U_3O_8 yellowcake from an ore processing mill. One SWU is equivalent to one kg of separative work.

[b]Information requested not previously in Table 12, WASH 1139(74), page 24.

[c]After losses.

[d]For replacement loadings, the required feed and separative work are net, in that they allow for the use of uranium recovered from spent fuel. Allowance is made for fabrication and reprocessing losses.

[e]Plutonium available for recycle ratchets up each pass because not all the plutonium charged is burned. Therefore, more plutonium is recovered from mixed oxide fuel than from standard uranium fuel, and this increment increases with each cycle (5–6 yr per cycle) requiring several passes to reach steady state. The data shown represent conditions for the 1980s when most reactors will be discharging fuel which has only seen one recycle pass.

[f]Average fuel discharged with full recycle of self-generated plutonium. For mixed oxide fuel (natural U spiked with self-generated plutonium) the spent fuel from BWRs contains 15.1 kg Pu/t and from PWRs, 18.7.

[g]Includes natural uranium to be spiked with plutonium; 0.0087 st U_3O_8/MWe for BWR and 0.0067 for PWR.

[h]Lifetime commitments assume operation at 40% capacity factor (CF) for the first year, 65% CF for the next two years, followed by 12 yr at 75% CF. Therefore, CF drops two points per year, reaching 25% in the last (40th) year.

[i]A burnup of 9600 MWd/t has not yet been achieved, so that the current generation of CANDUs requires about 15% more uranium feed than indicated in this table.

Figure 11.14. A typical fueling machine used for on-line fueling of CANDU reactors. Two such machines are used on each side of the reactor core, attaching simultaneously to one channel. As the spent bundles are removed by one machine, new bundles are inserted in the channel by the other.

machines are provided, one on each side of the horizontally placed cylindrical reactor (Figure 11.14). The fuel machines look and function as revolving pistols. Each machine is equipped with a barrel that attaches onto the fuel channel, unlocks the end plug, removes it, and replaces it at the end of a fueling. Each of the six storage chambers of the barrel can store two fuel bundles; therefore, up to 12 fuel bundles can be inserted (or removed) in each visit to the reactor face. Both refueling machines must be attached to the same channel during the refueling of this channel. One machine inserts fresh fuel bundles while the other, at the opposite end, is ready to receive the spent fuel bundles as they are ejected into its barrel. The motion takes place in the direction of coolant flow which alternates between adjacent fuel channels.

As in the LWR's successive cycles, an equilibrium in the condition of the core takes some time to develop in the CANDU but the time scale is much shorter. After initial criticality with all fresh fuel in the core, and for a period of 100 to 150 full-power days, no refueling is necessary. A transition period of 300 to 350 full-power days follows with some periodic refueling, as the core approaches equilibrium. The final period at equilibrium covers about 95% at the reactor's lifetime and is characterized by continuous on-line refueling. Even though optimium performance is achieved with regular replacement of spent fuel, the reactor can be operated, if desired, for many weeks without refueling.

Although it is possible to perform refueling of a CANDU by replacing one or two bundles at a time, the method proved impractical, especially in large systems. It was found that 4- or 8-bundle refueling is much more efficient without causing a large penalty in fuel utilization. These schemes are illustrated in Figure 11.15. In implementing a fuel management scheme, the behavior of fuel that is moved from a lower to a higher power level and the probability for failure must be considered. Fuel defects have a negative impact on fuel economics. For example, the economics associated with the 8-, 10-, and 12-bundle shifting, with due consideration to fuel failure, led to the conclusion that for the Pickering station, a 10-bundle shift was the most favorable for all but the outer two rings of fuel channels. In the larger Bruce A reactors, however, the fueling scheme consists of a 4-bundle shift in the central core zone and an 8-bundle shift in the periphery.

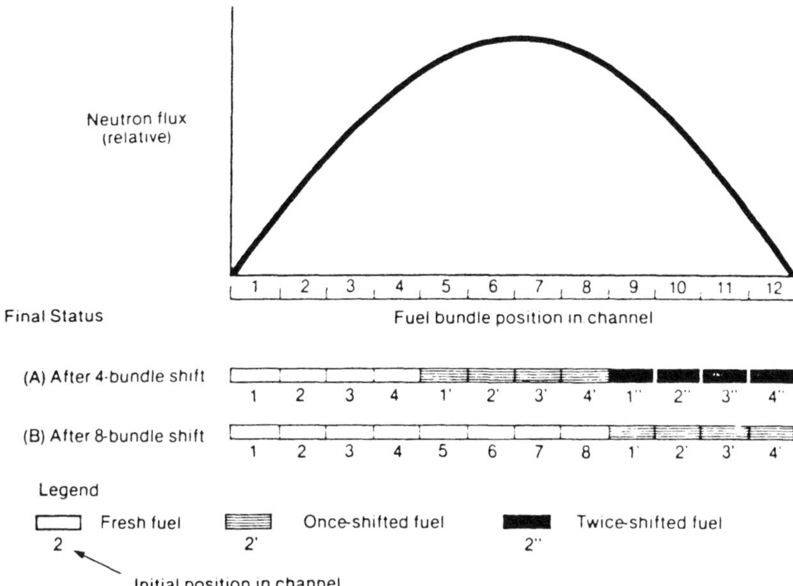

Figure 11.15. Four-bundle and eight-bundle shifts in an unflattened CANDU core.

The continuous refueling of the CANDU reactors leads to a number of important advantages. Since there is no need for large excess reactivity, the waste of neutrons in the core is minimized. Absorptions of excess neutrons in the fertile ^{238}U lead to the production of fissile ^{239}Pu. This leads to a conversion factor of about 0.75 (compared to 0.6 for LWRs). It must be noted, however, that this advantage is fully realized if spent fuel is preprocessed to recover its fissile content. In a once-through strategy (no reprocessing and recycle), the lifetime uranium requirements of the CANDU are about 4160 st, comparable to that of a LWR with recycle (see Table 11.4 for comparison), but still about 20 to 25% lower than that of LWRs on a once-through basis. The second important advantage of the CANDU is that refueling does not require reactor shutdown; this increases the productivity of the plant. In rough numbers, the plant factors for CANDUs have been historically about 20% higher than LWRs (about 80% compared to 60%). Although the various shutdowns have a multitude of causes, it is estimated that at least half of this differential advantage, namely about 10%, is due to the continuous refueling of the CANDU.

Since the fissile content of the CANDU fuel is only 0.7%, the amount of energy that can be drawn from a given amount of uranium is low. The burnup of the fuel at discharge is about 7500 MWd/t, as compared with a design burnup of 9500 MWd/t. The burnup of discharged fuel and average burnup in the core is shown in Figure 11.16. Discharged fuel contains about 0.5% fissile isotopes, of which slightly more than half is plutonium. The recycle of fuel in CANDU reactors would significantly decrease the lifetime uranium requirements. However, the economics of reprocessing and recycle for CANDUs is questionable. The large amounts of fuel that would have to be reprocessed and fabricated (because of the much lower concentration of fissile elements) represent a cost component that reduces the incentive for plutonium recycle in CANDUs compared to the case for recycle in LWRs. Even though reprocessing and recycle is kept open as an option, it has not yet been practiced commercially. The present policy of once-through fuel cycle is likely to continue as long as uranium remains plentiful and relatively inexpensive.

Additional features of CANDUs will be discussed elsewhere: its good potential for utilizing thorium, by converting it into ^{233}U, will be discussed later in this chapter. The proliferation perspective of the features of the CANDU fuel cycle and particularly of on-line refueling will be discussed in Chapter 20; economics will be examined in Chapter 19.

Fuel Management in HTGRs

The HTGR has not found extensive commercial application, the only operating plant in the United States being the Fort St. Vrain reactor. However, this type of reactor has continued to attract attention as a good future option because of the following features: thermal efficiency (about 0.39 versus 0.33 for LWRs); a large thermal inertia, and hence, an intrinsic safety advantage; a potential

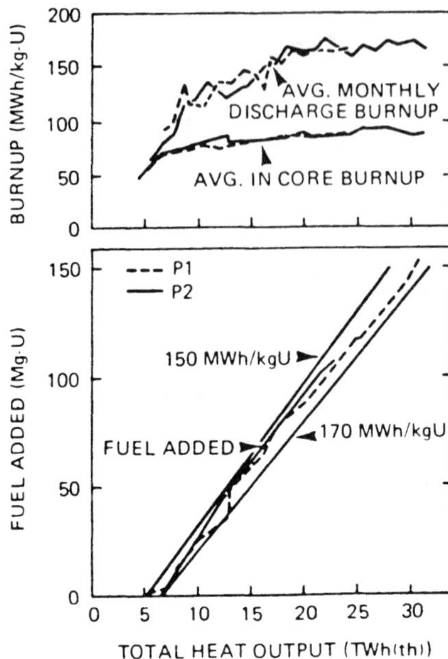

Figure 11.16. Fuel consumption and burnup for Pickering units 1 and 2. (From J. A. L. Robertson, *Science* **199,** 10 February, 1978.)

for using the thorium resources by conversion into fissile ^{233}U; its potential as a source of process heat; the possibility of using a direct thermal cycle in a gas turbine.

The fuel designs of the HTGR (see Chapter 7) use hexagonal graphite blocks containing fuel rods made of a graphite matrix incorporating two kinds of spherical particles. The TRISO particle contains highly enriched uranium (93.5 wt% ^{235}U) in the form of uranium carbide (UC_2) and the BISO particle contains thorium oxide (ThO_2). During irradiation, about three-fourths of the ^{235}U (TRISO spheres) is replaced by ^{233}U, some of which undergoes fission. The fuel cycle scheme envisions replacement of a quarter of the core annually. To realize the potential of the HTGR, the removed fuel must be reprocessed to recover leftover uranium as well as the newly generated fissile ^{233}U. This operation requires a whole series of chemical processes for separation of various streams of materials and the fabrication of new fuel. The HTGR cycle has not been "closed" and its closure is not a near-term possibility, given the minimal levels of presently installed capacity. In view of the experience in the LWR fuel cycle, current design concepts envision a once-through cycle with no need for reprocessing and recycling.

Assuming that reprocessing and recycling is available, lifetime requirements of the HTGR are on the order of 3000 st of yellowcake, compared to over 4000 st for the LWR with recycle. Conversion ratio of a typical design is of the order of 0.7 but it can be made higher with appropriate changes. By increasing the amount of fertile material in the core (^{232}Th) and by reducing the burnup level, the conversion factor could be substantially increased and the lifetime requirement further decreased to about 2000 st (Table 11.4). The fuel is designed for a burnup of about 96,000 MWd/t, a figure three times that in LWRs. It is not a surprising figure since the fuel is highly enriched ^{235}U.

Following the proliferation concerns and the search for alternate designs in the late 1970s, the HTGR was redesigned to operate with fuel enriched to only 20% in ^{235}U, since this figure seemed to be accepted as a threshold in terms of proliferation potential. This conceptual design, however, loses much of the high conversion advantage of the HTGR.

11.5. FUEL MANAGEMENT IN BREEDERS

The breeder has a breeding ratio substantially higher than 1; it produces more fuel than it consumes. A typical breeder core contains three different regions: core, axial blanket, and radial blanket. The core region is made of either 20% enriched uranium oxide or a mixture of about 20% PuO_2 and 80% UO_2 made of depleted uranium (about 0.3 wt% ^{235}U). The axial blankets, contained in the same rods with the fuel but placed below and above it, are made of depleted uranium, as are the radial blanket rods.† The core and axial blankets remain in the reactor for about 2 yr (at 80%

†In some newer core designs, blanket assemblies are placed in the core region to improve the reactor's response to loss of sodium coolant (see Chapter 13).

capacity factor), whereas the radial blankets remain in the reactor for up to 6 yr to accumulate sufficient amounts of fissile ^{239}Pu. Radial blanket material is mixed with axial blanket and core material for reprocessing. This produces a dilution of the highly exposed fuel in fuel with lower exposure. LMFBR design burnup is high, on the order of 70,000 MWd/t although even higher burnups have been successfully reached. The high exposure makes discharged fuel highly radioactive. A short turnaround time is proposed for fuel recycling. This means a short time (about 60 days) between discharge and reprocessing and refabrication of fresh fuel in order to minimize the amount of plutonium inventory outside the reactor. Economic and nonproliferation advantages result from such a scheme.

An 1000-MWe LMFBR produces a net gain of plutonium on the order of 250 kg/yr. After steady-state cycle operation has been achieved, an LMFBR does not need any fissile material input external to its own production cycle. Furthermore, it produces enough extra plutonium to fuel, in due time, an additional reactor. The parameter used in this context is the system's "doubling time." It is defined as the time required for extra material (in addition to the reactor's own needs) to be accumulated to form the core fissile inventory for a new reactor. A 1000-MWe LMFBR would require a fissile inventory of 2000- to 3000-kg fissile material. Using an inventory of 3000 kg and a fissile annual gain of 250 kg, the doubling time would be 3000/250 = 12 yr.

This simplistic calculation should be corrected for two reasons. First, it is not necessary to wait for 12 yr for adequate fissile material build up if several breeder reactors are available and contributions from them are added. In this way, a new reactor inventory can be quickly accumulated and extra plutonium can start producing its own gain. As with money in the bank, bred plutonium must be compounded with the actual compounding period, which could be only a few months, to yield the real doubling time.

The second correction pertains to the amount of plutonium residing in the fuel cycle, that is, in storage, reprocessing, fabrication, and so on.

Therefore, a more realistic definition of doubling time is the time it takes the LMFBR and its support facilities to produce enough extra fissile material to supply an additional reactor *and its* fuel cycle facilities. The fissile material residing in the fuel cycle is comparable, although normally smaller, than the core inventory of 2000–3000 kg, so that the total fissile material committed to a plant is on the order of 4000 kg. If the inventory of a given system is made smaller, the doubling time is made shorter.

The significance of the doubling time, and hence, of the conversion ratio, is high in a scenario of fast capacity growth where resource could be a limiting factor. If plutonium from LWR spent fuel were to be used to start up a LMFBR, and given that about 300-kg plutonium can be produced from the annual LWR spent fuel discharge (i.e., per 1000 MW × 1 yr × 0.80 = 800 MWy of energy), of which about 200 kg is fissile, it would take approximately 20 reactor-years of LWR operation to start up one LMFBR. Today, however, more than 10,000 tons of LWR spent fuel have been discharged in the United States alone and more than 1500 tons are discharged annually. This represents an already existing inventory of more than 60,000 kg and an additional annual production of 9000 kg of fissile plutonium compared with the 4000 kg needed per 1000-MWe LMFBR system. Given that breeder development is not proceeding vigorously at this time, fissile resources are not a constraint and consequently the importance of high gain has been downplayed. The optimization of LMFBR system is now focused on other parameters of importance such as safety features, high reliability and maintainability, and capital cost. The only external input to a breeder is depleted uranium (about 1500-kg U annually under equilibrium conditions) or ^{232}Th. The annual consumption of natural uranium in a breeder is much lower than that in burner and converter reactors. Stated in different terms and referring to Figure 11.6, breeders are able to utilize up to 60% of the energy inherent in uranium resources (counting both fissile and fertile isotopes), as compared to only a few percent that the other types of reactors use. If one takes into account that a stockpile of over 200,000 t of depleted uranium already exists at the U.S. enrichment plants, a large number of breeders can be supplied for a long time with no need for additional mining. It is from this point of view of virtual independence from natural energy resources, that the development of the breeder is so important.

11.6. FUEL UTILIZATION COMPARISONS

A summary of fuel cycle characteristics of the current thermal reactors (LWR, CANDU, and HTGR) is shown in Table 11.4 and Figure 11.17. On a strict basis of resource conservation, the CANDU reactor and the HTGR are preferable to the LWR with no recycle. However, with a reprocessing strategy, allowing the recycling of fissile uranium alone as was originally envisioned, annual feed requirements of the LWR are about the same as those of the CANDU without recycle.

This occurs for the following reasons: (a) The CANDU discharged fuel contains about 0.2% ^{235}U which is about the same as the tails in the enrichment process. The wastage of natural fissile material per unit of mined ore is the same in both systems. (b) Although the CANDU has a higher conversion rate, this is offset by a lower thermal efficiency. (c) The discharge rate of fissile

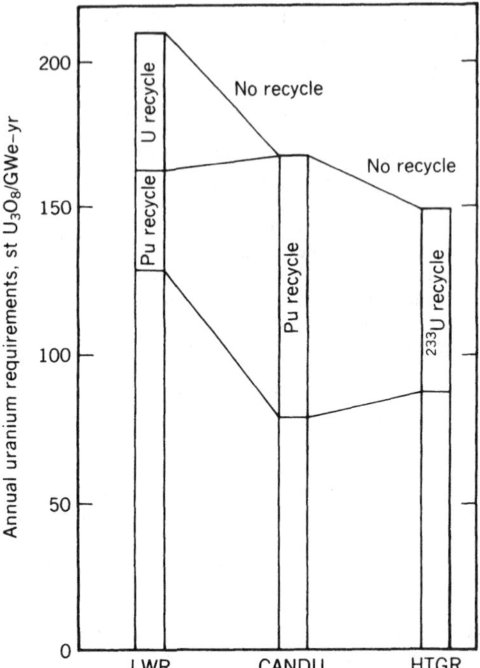

Figure 11.17. Comparison of annual uranium requirements (capacity factor = 80%, tails assay = 0.2%). (ANL neg. no. 116-77-55.)

plutonium from a CANDU reactor is higher (340 kg/GWe-yr) than that from a LWR (200 kg/GWe-yr).

With recycle of both uranium and plutonium, the LWR requirements become more favorable than the CANDU's for which little economic incentive exists for reprocessing as mentioned earlier, because of the dilute fuel and the large amounts of material involved. If, however, self-generated plutonium recycle is assumed for both systems, the annual requirements of the LWR are further reduced by 20%, whereas those of the CANDU are reduced by 50%. The high conversion ratio of the CANDU, and the resulting high plutonium content of spent fuel accounts for this large decrease. The uranium savings accruing from recycling of CANDU spent fuel are, however, offset by the high cost of reprocessing. This fact renders fuel reprocessing and recycle in CANDUs much less attractive, and hence less probable than in LWRs.

The annual requirements of the HTGR, with no recycle, are lower than both LWR and CANDU. If a thorium/uranium-233 cycle is commercially available, the annual feed requirements of the HTGR are slightly higher than the CANDU and much lower than the LWR.

It must be emphasized that annual uranium requirements should not be considered in isolation. The total energy production costs include several other factors such as capital costs of construction, the price of uranium and enrichment services, plant availability and productivity, the availability and cost of the fuel cycle, and so on. For example, consider the two main components of fuel: cost of yellowcake and cost of enrichment services. The quantities of yellowcake and separative work needed depend on the volume of tails assay. If the prices are fixed, an optimum tails assay can be calculated which minimizes total fuel cost. If the tails assay of 0.2%, used in Figure 11.18, were changed to 0.3%, the annual uranium requirements for both LWR and HTGR would be increased by 20–25% while the separative work units would be decreased by a similar amount, while CANDU requirements would remain the same. Whether the rise of tails assay is favorable or not cannot be judged only by the fact that the uranium requirements are increased, but by the total effect on cost, given the current prices of uranium and the separative work unit.

11.7. ADVANCED REACTOR DESIGNS

With the objective of improving fuel utilization, several designs have been proposed, ranging from relatively simple to substantial modifications to existing systems to entirely novel concepts. Their main impetus came from a search for schemes that would utilize natural resources more efficiently

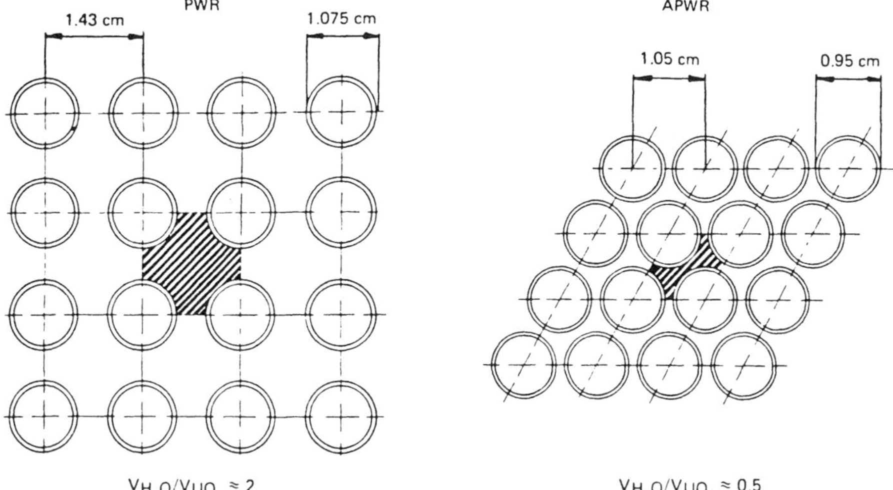

Figure 11.18. Fuel lattices of a standard PWR and an Advanced PWR (APWR). Comparing the unit cells of the two lattices, one finds a much reduced amount of water in the advanced design. The volumetric ratio of moderator to fuel, which is about 2 in PWRs, could go as low as 0.5 in APWRs. [From W. Oldekop et al., *Nuclear Technology* **59**, 212 (1982).]

and would cut down uranium demand and hence price increases. The atmosphere for this search was greatly enhanced by the following: first, dramatic price hikes of uranium yellowcake from levels of $7/lb to $40/lb in the seventies; second, drastic modification of the early projections of steep increases in nuclear capacity; third, doubts regarding the early deployment of breeder reactors; and fourth, proliferation concerns that pressed for nuclear power alternatives with high fuel utilization. (The validity of this latter attitude will be further discussed in Chapter 20.) In the 1980s, however, the picture has changed considerably with respect to uranium prices, nuclear capacity projections, and relative proliferation concerns. As a result, the advanced concept designs for high fuel utilization have lost some of their appeal. Although they do not represent designs with foreseeable prospects of implementation, they will be briefly reviewed here. The concepts that were specifically intended for thorium utilization will be examined in the next section.

The "spectral shift reactor" concept is based on the existing PWR technology. It replaces common water with heavy water as moderator. The effects are twofold: the parasitic absorption of neutrons in the coolant/moderator is drastically reduced and the neutron economy improves; also, more subtly, because heavy water is a less effective moderator than water, the neutron spectrum is shifted (hence the name "spectral shift") toward higher energies. Under certain conditions the conversion ratio increases with an epithermal neutron spectrum; more fissile isotopes are produced from fertile material. The fuel cycle scheme of this concept actually requires that the moderator be a gradually changing mixture of light and heavy water. At beginning of life, the moderator is almost entirely heavy water. As burnup proceeds, light water is added, which shifts the spectrum toward lower energies where absorption and fission cross sections are higher. This spectral shift increases the reactivity of the core and compensates for reactivity loss through burnup.

A variation of the above concept is the "heavy-water breeder reactor." With a redesigned fuel lattice and with heavy water as coolant moderator, the reactor can surpass the conversion ratio of 1 and breed excess material, which can then be used to start a new reactor. However, it was found that the moderator temperature coefficient of reactivity is positive, a condition that might give problems in licensing the concept in the United States. (It must be noted that the CANDU has a positive moderator temperature coefficient and is, nevertheless, licensed in Canada and other countries.) To make this coefficient negative, the designers settled on a mixture of 80% heavy water to 20% light water with severe penalty to the breeding gain. The heavy water adaptations of LWRs have the disadvantage of introducing a serious new cost component and an additional system of handling heavy water, particularly in the spectral shift scheme.

The benefit of an epithermal spectrum has been investigated also in a series of studies based on a "tight lattice" and use of a light-water moderator. The concept is also called a "low-moderator volume fraction" or "dry lattice" reactor because more fuel is packed within a given area as shown in Figure 11.18, which compares the unit cells of a standard PWR to those of an advanced PWR (APWR). The core was designed to fit in existing PWR vessels without major modifications. To

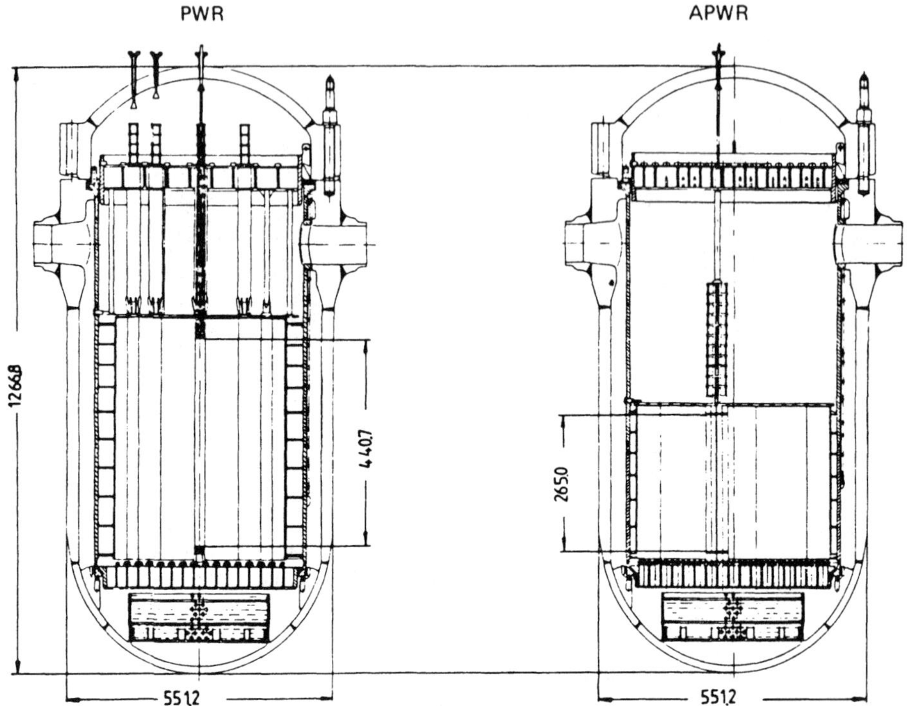

Figure 11.19. An advanced PWR core can fit in the same PWR vessel, as shown, without major modifications. Because hydraulic friction in the tight lattice is higher and power density is greater, a shorter core must be used in the APWR. [From W. Oldekop et al., *Nuclear Technology* **59,** 212 (1982).]

compensate for the higher friction loss in the tight core, and since a much higher power density can be achieved, a shorter core and a slightly lower flow rate are used, as shown in the schematic of Figure 11.19. Calculations have shown that a conversion ratio of 0.9 or more can be achieved at a final fuel burnup of about 45,000 MWd/t and a reload fuel with 7.5% fissile plutonium. Other tight lattice designs use a higher moderator-to-fuel ratio of about 1.0 and still maintain a high conversion ratio with appropriate fuel design. To maintain reactivity with increasing burnup, this concept utilizes mechanical means for spectrum shift. By withdrawing Zircaloy filled rods from the core the moderator-to-fuel ratio is increased, neutrons are moderated to lower energies, and reactivity increases (in a manner analogous to the heavy-water spectral shift reactor). Tight lattice reactors could reduce uranium requirements by as much as 25%.

In new designs, great attention to thermal performance and safety parameters must be given. Calculations on the APWR (not yet substantiated in experimental test facilities) show that the moderator temperature coefficient and the void coefficient are negative, critical heat flux margin is adequate, and accident conditions can be accommodated. If, however, the moderator-to-fuel ratio seems too low, a higher ratio can be adopted with resultant loss in the conversion ratio, as shown in Figure 11.20.

A High-Gain Light-Water Breeder Reactor (HGLWBR) has been recently proposed as a concept amenable to retrofitting in existing PWRs with only minor modifications. The concept, still in its preliminary conceptual design states, utilizes the seed and blanket design pioneered in the Shippingport LWBR. But whereas the latter is based on the thorium cycle, and has a breeding ratio close to 1, the light-water plutonium breeder is based on the uranium/plutonium cycle with a very substantial breeding gain. This concept takes advantage of the following properties:

1. The use of geometry control, of which satisfactory experience exists in the Shippingport LWBR. The core is controlled by varying the flow of neutrons from the seed to the blanket regions. This is accomplished by a suitably zoned moving seed and stationary blanket. The loss of neutrons to parasitic absorbers, as occurs in conventional methods of control, is avoided.
2. The tight lattice spacing, the feasibility of which was also demonstrated in the LWBR. In lattices containing ^{238}U fertile material, the tight spacing results in a very large fast fission factor.
3. The use of a novel fuel management system which results in a high buildup of ^{241}Pu. In the

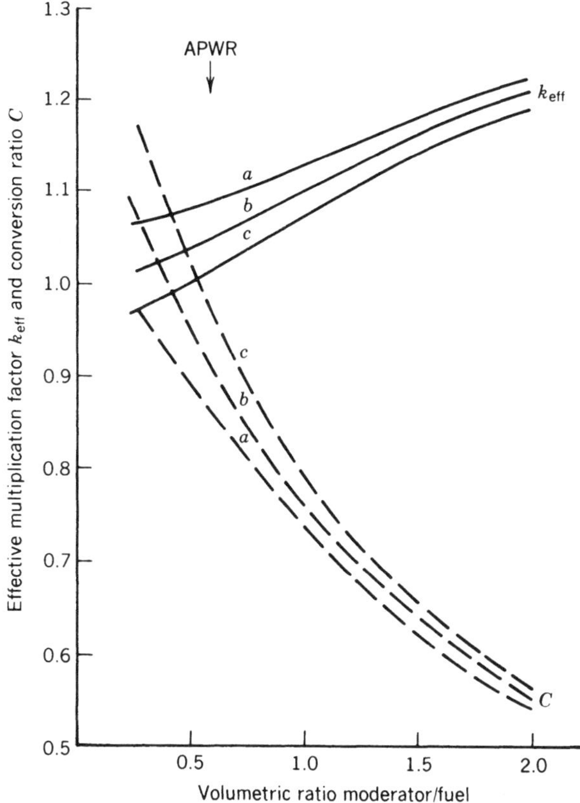

Figure 11.20. Variation of the effective multiplication factor k_{eff}, and of conversion ratio, C, with moderator-to-fuel volume ratio. At a V_M/V_F of 0.5 conversion ratios of more than 0.9 can be achieved. If V_M/V_F must be increased to 0.75 for thermal hydraulics reasons, the conversion ratio drops to 0.85 (for 7.5% fissile plutonium). Notice that reactivity and conversion ratio move in opposite directions. a = 8.5% fissile plutonium, b = 7.5% fissile plutonium, c = 6.5% fissile plutonium.

largely epithermal spectrum, ^{241}Pu has a very high value of η, rising as high as 2.8 at some energy points. An external input of fissile plutonium, discharged from LWRs, is necessary for start-up and in prebreeding stages. Preliminary calculations indicate the potential of a breeding gain of more than 0.35 under equilibrium conditions.

In the area of BWRs, an improved fuel design called "SVEA" was introduced by ASEA-Atom, the Swedish BWR vendor. Its main objectives were to flatten the power shape and improve neutron economy. These objectives were accomplished by the placement of a cruciform channel of Zircaloy filled with water inside each fuel bundle, as shown in Figure 11.21. The extra amount of nonboiling water in the assembly interior balances the peaking effect of the water in the interassembly spaces (reserved for insertion of the cruciform control blades). With a flatter power distribution across the assembly, a more uniform burnup is possible and hence there is a higher average burnup per assembly at discharge.

There are added advantages to the concept: the Zircaloy cross provides extra mechanical rigidity to the channel walls and minimizes creep deformation. In fact, the walls can be made thinner than in the standard designs so that the total amount of zirconium in a fuel bundle is reduced, even with the additional zirconium of the internal cross. Thus, the neutron economy is further improved. The improved neutron economy enables the designer to use a lower average fuel enrichment and reduce the number of different rod types from five to two or three (five types of rods, each with a different enrichment are used in a standard BWR to reduce power peaking). Part of the neutron economy advantage is used to lower average enrichment and part is used to increase average fuel assembly burnup by 12 to 14%.

A reduction in fuel cost of about 10% is claimed, which is on the same order as the total fuel

Figure 11.21. The "SVEA" concept is a new BWR fuel assembly design introduced by ASEA-Atom, the Swedish BWR vendor. Its main feature is an additional cross of Zircaloy internal to and running the length of the assembly, filled with water. The design lowers power peaks, improves neutron economy, and allows an increase of average assembly burnup.

manufacturing cost. The internal nonheated wall also improves heat transfer in the case of loss-of-coolant accidents. The concept can be used as replacement fuel in the ASEA-Atom reactor and with slight modifications in any other BWR core.

11.8. THORIUM UTILIZATION

Thorium is of interest for nuclear power because of its ability to capture a thermal neutron and to produce a new fissile isotope, ^{233}U, as discussed in Section 11.2. Since thorium is about four times as abundant as uranium in nature, it represents an additional and substantial energy resource. Normally the schemes assume that spent fuel will be reprocessed to recover fissile ^{233}U, but in some concepts the fissile ^{233}U is burned in place, without reprocessing and refabrication. Since no ^{233}U exists in nature, the cycle must be started with existing fissile materials, that is, ^{235}U or ^{239}Pu. If enough ^{233}U is accumulated, a system based on thorium alone and its derivative ^{233}U could be sustained for a very long time. In the transition period, however, the cycle would have to start with fissile plutonium or uranium which would be progressively decreased if a certain amount of self-generated ^{233}U were recycled. Eventually, all reactors would be fueled with ^{233}U and a portion of enriched uranium if the conversion ratio were less than 1. Thus the need for uranium would taper off.

The thorium/uranium cycle differs from the uranium/plutonium cycle in several ways. An important difference is that the neutronics for thorium/^{233}U are favorable at thermal neutron energies, whereas plutonium exhibits better neutronic properties at high neutron energies. Hence, thermal reactors are best suited as either converters or breeders for the thorium/^{233}U cycle while fast reactors are more favorable for the uranium/plutonium system.

Reactors that have been designed or that could accommodate a thorium cycle include the following systems in either standard or modified form: CANDU, HTGR, LWR, LWBR, Molten Salt Breeder Reactor (MSBR), and LMFBR. Development of the MSBR (a thermal breeder) has been discontinued. Almost all schemes designed to utilize thorium depend on the availability of a complete thorium fuel cycle, which allows the reprocessing of the extraction and refabrication of ^{233}U. Thorium and ^{233}U-bearing fuels are characterized by a hard 2.6-MeV gamma ray originating in the element thallium-208, produced by radioactive decay of ^{232}U, which in turn is produced from ^{233}U through an $(n, 2n)$ reaction. The hard gamma makes it necessary to handle all operations in the cycle remotely from a control room protected with shielding, a fact that adds complication and cost to the thorium cycle, relative to the uranium/plutonium cycle.

Neutronic Features of the Thorium/^{233}U Cycle

The fertile ^{232}Th has a higher thermal neutron absorption cross section than ^{238}U (7.4 versus 2.7 barns). Assuming equal concentration and neutron flux, a higher conversion to fissile material takes place in ^{232}Th, although it also means that more fissile material must be loaded in the core to compensate for the higher absorption in the fertile material. As we shall see later, this feature requires the use of high (or medium) enrichment fuel. The second important feature of the thorium/^{233}U system is a high thermal value of η. Its value of 2.2 is higher than that of both ^{235}U ($\eta = 2.0$) and ^{239}Pu ($\eta = 1.9$) and gives a substantial margin above the value of 2 which is the minimum necessary for breeding. In a thermal reactor fueled with ^{235}U and fertile thorium, the destruction of fissile nuclei gives birth to new fissile material which is neutronically superior to that it replaces. In the uranium/plutonium system, the produced nucleus (^{239}Pu) has worse thermal neutronic characteristics than the destroyed nucleus (^{235}U). A reactor that combines fissile ^{233}U and fertile ^{232}Th can be designed and built with a conversion ratio close to 1, which makes the system self-sufficient.

Thorium in CANDUs

The heavy-water moderated CANDU with its favorable neutron economy offers a high degree of flexibility in the design of a fuel cycle operating on thorium/^{233}U. To begin the cycle, either highly enriched uranium or plutonium would have to be used as fissile material along with fertile thorium. In the first case, the cost of enrichment services (and, possibly, the difficulty of procuring them from the few countries that provide them) must be considered. In the second, and more likely case, spent fuel would have to be reprocessed to produce enough plutonium to start the thorium CANDU. With appropriate fissile concentration, a conversion rate close to 1 can be achieved, to make the reactor self-sustained. The range of possible designs and their implications in terms of burnup, conversion ratio, uranium requirements, and so on are shown in Table 11.5. The optimum choice of lattice pitch and burnup level is determined by a number of parameters such as prices of uranium yellowcake, price per SWU or reprocessing, cost of fabrication, and price of heavy water.

The lifetime uranium requirement for a CANDU reactor operating on a highly enriched thorium cycle is about 1100 st of yellowcake. In fact, since its conversion factor is almost 1, the reactor's fissile inventory would be sufficient to start a second reactor after the decommissioning of the first, and so on indefinitely. If plutonium recycled from existing natural uranium CANDUs is used as feed, the lifetime requirements are twice as high, that is, about 2200 st since about 0.5 atom of plutonium is produced per atom of ^{235}U consumed.

The low figure of lifetime uranium requirements is, of course, desirable, but it must be examined against a very high front-end uranium yellowcake (and, possibly, enrichment) requirement. The introduction of thorium systems eases the long-term resource requirement but strains the short-term ability of the supply system. Furthermore, the discounting of future advantages relative to present values further erodes the long-term cumulative savings of the thorium system. This is true of all thorium utilization schemes.

Thorium in HTGRs

Among the reactor types that reached commercial operation, the HTGR is the only one specifically designed to operate with thorium as fertile material. The standard design starts with a core loaded with highly enriched ^{235}U until such time when enough ^{233}U becomes available for the fueling of a new core. An entirely new fuel cycle capable of handling and reprocessing discharged fuel and

Table 11.5. CANDU-PHW Th Cycle Characteristics

	Fixed Lattice Pitch and Specific Power							Fixed Burnup				
Lattice pitch (cm)				28.6				28.6	28.6	28.6	22.9	22.9
Specific power (kWth/kgHM)				29				22	29	38	29	38
Burnup (MWd/kgHM)	10	20	25	33	40	44	47			30		
Conversion ratio	1.0	0.96	0.93	0.90	0.87	0.85	0.84					
Reactor ratio, Th/NU[a]	—	5.79	4.21	2.73	2.14	1.80	1.66	4.78	3.01	2.14	1.38	1.13
Th-fuel residence time (yr)	1.2	2.4	3.0	3.9	4.7	5.2	5.6	4.7	3.5	2.7	3.5	2.7
Pu makeup (gm/kgHM[b])	0	1	2	4	6	8	9.3	2.0	3.4	4.9	7.6	9.3
Equilibrium loading[c] (MTHM/GWe-hr)												
Natural uranium	0	18.8	24.5	34.2	40.7	45.6	48.0	22.1	31.8	40.7	53.6	59.9
Th + ^{233}U	95.7	40.8	30.9	21.2	16.3	14.0	12.7	26.4	24.0	21.8	18.5	16.9
U_3O_8 requirements[c] (st/GWe-yr)	0	24.7	32.2	44.9	53.4	59.9	63.0	29.0	41.8	53.4	70.4	78.7

Source: C. Till et al. ANL, RSS-TM-1, 1977.

[a]Ratio of CANDU reactors operating on the Th-U cycle to CANDU reactors operating uranium cycle.
[b]Pu makeup is supplied by natural fueled CANDU reactors.
[c]At 80% capacity factor.

refabricating new fuel rods and assemblies is needed. Under the assumption of a commercially available fuel cycle, uranium lifetime requirements are less than 3000 st of yellowcake, substantially below current LWR requirements. Several variations of the standard HTGR have been studied. One of them is a variation seeking to achieve a higher fuel utilization by halving the burnup of the standard HTGR and by using shorter refueling intervals. It is called the high-conversion HTGR. It has a conversion ratio of more than 0.8 and a lifetime uranium requirement of about 2000 st of yellowcake, a 33% improvement over the standard HTGR (see also Table 11.4).

As mentioned earlier, in spite of the several attractive features of the HTGR system, it has not become a commercial option at the time of this writing. Interest, however, persists in the United States and several foreign countries, notably the Federal Republic of Germany and Japan.

Thorium in LWRs

Thorium can also be used in LWRs using the current core configuration with beneficial results on lifetime uranium requirements. The obvious incentive is to use fuel more efficiently in the large number of existing LWRs. The initial fuel must be highly enriched uranium (as in the case of the CANDU or the HTGR) with ^{232}Th as fertile material. Again reprocessing of spent fuel would be necessary to recover and recycle the produced ^{233}U. The use of light water as moderator and of the standard fuel design (as opposed to the optimized LWBR core design to be discussed later) imposes a penalty on the neutron economy and limits the conversion ratio to a value of 0.75, still much higher than that in standard LWRs. In a state of equilibrium, fresh fuel would contain enriched uranium and recycled ^{233}U from the reactor's own cycle. A 1000-MWe plant would require about 90 st of uranium yellowcake per year (at a 75% capacity factor). A fairly large commitment of about 800 st of yellowcake is required for reactor start-up. When this is added to the refueling requirements (90 st $\times$ 30 yr $=$ 2700 st) a total of 3500 st per lifetime is obtained. This figure is lower than the 4000 st requirement for a standard PWR with plutonium recycle. Fuel burnup and fuel cycle are assumed the same as in a standard LWR.

The advantage of this option is the possibility of retrofit in existing LWRs with practically no alterations other than a change in fuel composition. Moderate design changes, such as reducing the water fraction by tightening the lattice, could further improve neutron economy and hence conversion ratio. Such a change would decrease the annual and lifetime uranium requirement. However, the need for highly enriched uranium in the initial loadings imposes a significant penalty, a recurring theme in the effort for improving fuel utilization. Figure 11.22 shows the front-end penalty versus the long-term savings of the thorium cycle compared with the standard LWR cycle.

A more drastic redesign of the reactor core would lead to a break-even reactor, one which, in equilibrium, is self-sustained and even repays the initial fissile inventory from converted fuel. This is the case of the light-water breeder reactor to be discussed next.

Thorium in LWBRs

The LWBR has been developed by the Department of Energy under the sponsorship of Admiral M. Rickover, Director of the U.S. Naval Reactor Program. It has been implemented as a replacement core in the Shippingport PWR. The 72-MWe reactor went critical in 1977, following two PWR cores that produced heat in the reactor since 1957, its first year of operation.

The reactor core is made of several hexagonal modules of the seed and blanket type. It is based on the thorium cycle and will, eventually, use ^{233}U. However, the start-up material is enriched uranium (medium enrichment in the seed and low enrichment in the blanket regions). The use of medium rather than high enrichment is made possible by good neutron economy which is achieved by using movable seed to control reactivity. Thus soluble poison, normally used in PWRs, with all its problems, is avoided (although it is still available as an emergency shutdown system). The LWBR core was designed to fit in existing PWR pressure vessels (as in the case of other, advanced designs discussed earlier) in order to take advantage of the large investment already made by utility companies in LWR plants. Certain modifications are still necessary, for example, to the vessel head, control system, and, of course, to the core and vessel internals.

The design of the LWBR claims that conversion ratio is actually larger than 1 by a few percent. Given the unavoidable material losses in the cycle, it is questionable that this reactor actually "breeds." Detailed isotopic measurements will clarify this point. The reactor was scheduled for decommissioning at the end of 1983 to be followed by an array of measurements and end-of-life testing to substantiate the concept and reactor performance. Since the plant must be started with externally supplied ^{235}U, a lifetime commitment of about 2000 st of uranium yellowcake (for 1000 MWe) is needed. If it is started with fissile plutonium, the figure is doubled. A comparison of fuel requirements of the thorium reactors discussed above is shown in Table 11.6. The CANDU operating on highly enriched uranium has the lowest lifetime requirements, except for the MSBR (whose development was discontinued).

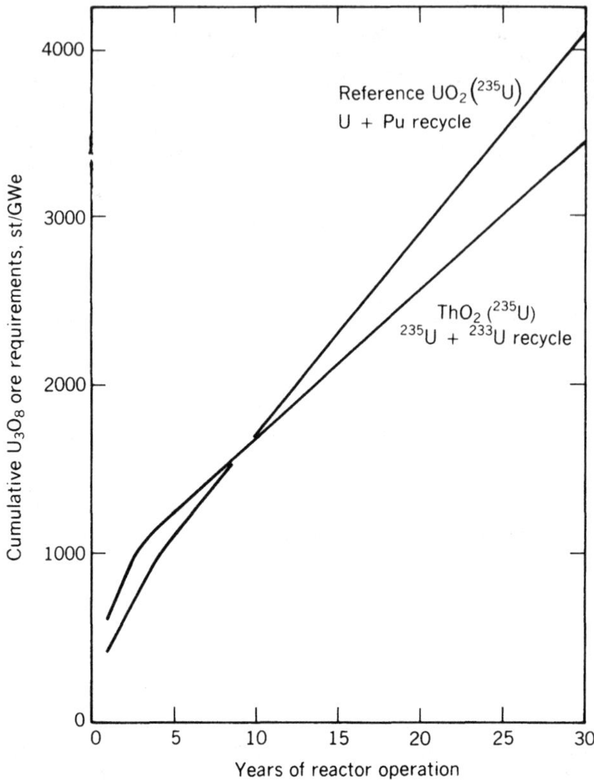

Figure 11.22. Cumulative U_3O_8 ore requirements versus reactor lifetime. (From EPRI Report NP-359.)

11.9. ONCE-THROUGH FUEL CYCLE IMPROVEMENTS

All commercial reactor types were originally developed with reprocessing and recycling in mind. Reprocessing of spent fuel allows the recovery of unburned original fissile material and newly produced fissile material produced through neutron captures in fertile materials. During the first decades of nuclear power development, reprocessing was very limited since there were not enough quantities of spent fuel to make the large-scale reprocessing and recycle worthwhile. Later on, when the quantities accumulated in the United States warranted the commercial processing and

Table 11.6. Fuel Utilization Characteristics of Thermal Converters and Near-Breeders (1000 MWe) on the Thorium Cycle

	CANDU	LWBR	HTGR	MSBR
CR or BR	1.0	1.0	0.9	1.07
Initial core fissile Inventory (kg)[a]	2000	2000–4000	4800	1500
Annual uranium requirement (st U_3O_8/yr)	0	0	35	0
Lifetime uranium requirement[b] (st U_3O_8)	1100	1800–4000	2300	~0[c]

[a]Indicated data are estimated based on fissile Pu for CANDU, ^{235}U, or fissile Pu for LWBR, ^{235}U for HTGR, and ^{233}U for MSBR.
[b]U_3O_8 required to achieve equilibrium cycle plus annual feed (if required) for 30 yr.
[c]Excess fissile production of 50 kg/yr is assumed to compensate the initial core inventory.

Table 11.7. Reduction in U_3O_8 Requirement for Various Potentially Retrofit Improvement Options in PWRs

Improvement Type	Reduction in 30-yr U_3O_8 Requirement (%)[a]
Increased burnup	
50 MWd/kg, annual refueling	11
50 MWd/kg, 18-month refueling	5
Lattice changes	
Annular pellets; reduced fuel-rod diameter	2–3
Variable-lattice fuel assembly design	1–4
Improved fuel management and control design	
Low-leakage fuel management	2–3.5
Other	1
Enrichment zoning/fertile blankets	
Pinwise enrichment zoning within assembly	0.1
Axial blanket	2–4
Radial blanket	*b*
End-of-cycle coastdown	3
Full use of batches in start-up core	0.5

Source: DOE/NE-0001/9, Vol. 9, 1980.

[a]Relative to 30 MWd/kg, annual refueling.

[b]No feasible retrofit scheme has been identified.

recycle, this route was stopped, partly because of technical problems encountered in the building of reprocessing plants, but mainly because of concerns about the proliferation of weapons-grade materials from a large-scale plutonium economy. In April 1977, reprocessing and recycle was officially banned by presidential decision. The ban was lifted by the Reagan administration in 1981 but reprocessing and recycle has yet to become available or to show promise in the foreseeable future in the United States. France, however, has proceeded vigorously in this area and provides reprocessing and refabrication services to its customers and Japan is proceeding along similar lines.

The result of these developments is that a "once-through" (or in somewhat less elegant terms, a "throw-away") cycle has become a real, perhaps inevitable, mode of operation.

If fuel cannot be reprocessed and recovered fissile material reused, spent fuel must be called "waste" (an inaccurate characterization given the amount of usable energy and usable elements inherent in it). The sudden increase in temporary and permanent storage requirements (either on-site or away from reactor) imposed new conditions on reactor operators and changed the parameters for fuel cycle optimization.

The once-through strategy leads to a desire to extract as much energy from a given amount of fuel as long as it stays in the reactor. With this perspective, a search was launched to find ways to improve fuel utilization in current LWR designs. A list of such modifications, along with a range of corresponding fuel savings, is shown in Table 11.7. The list was compiled during the Nonproliferation Alternative Systems Assessment Program (NASAP) in the late 1970s and was made with inputs from many government and industry participants.

The first method, increased burnup, will be discussed separately in the next section. The addition of *radial* or *axial blankets* decreases the leakage of neutrons outside the core. In one concept, used by Babcock & Wilcox and already being demonstrated at the Rancho Seco Plant, the axial blanket consists of 15-cm (6-in.) segments of natural uranium pellets at the top and bottom of the fuel column, replacing the slightly enriched uranium of the standard design. The reduced neutron leakage is estimated to yield a reduction of initial fissile inventory, and an overall savings of 3% in uranium and 2.8% in separative work. A full core of such radial blanket assemblies is expected by the mid-1980s.

Another method for achieving fuel economy is to use *structural materials with a lower neutron absorption*. For example, the periphery of the core could be modified by changing the steel shroud with one made of Zircaloy which has a lower neutron absorption. Similarly, Zircaloy-4 has been used to replace Inconel in intermediate spacer grids in more recent fuel designs, a modification estimated to yield a uranium and separative work savings of about 2%.

Cycle stretchout consists of extending the time between refuelings by a few days to weeks.† It could be accomplished by lowering the average core moderator temperature to below the nominal design value, thus adding positive reactivity to the core via moderator feedback. During a first

†It is already routinely used to adjust cycle length and time of refueling.

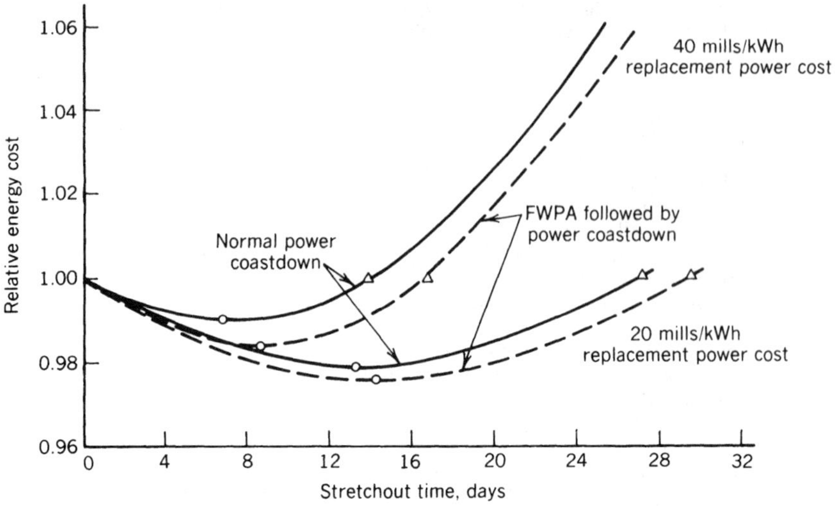

Figure 11.23. Equilibrium cycle stretchout: relative energy cost versus stretchout time. Cycle stretchout may be accomplished by several different methods. The most common method, power coastdown, is accomplished by reducing reactor power and secondary pressure so that the lower fuel and moderator temperatures and lower xenon poisoning provide excess reactivity, thereby permitting additional burnup to be accumulated. An effective (from the standpoint of both economics and fuel resource conservation) method of cycle stretchout, called FeedWater Pressure Augmentation (FWPA), is included. In this operational mode, the extraction flow to the feedwater heaters is sequentially decreased, and the turbine throttle valve is maintained in the fully open position. The decrease in extraction steam flow for the feedwater heaters permits lower pressure operation before the volumetric flow limit on the turbine admission valve is reached. This method permits extended operation at full core thermal power by reducing core average moderator temperature but at a lower thermal efficiency. Once full thermal power can no longer be transferred to the turbine, power coastdown can be employed to achieve further cycle extension. FWPA is always followed by power coastdown to achieve the maximum cycle stretchout. *Economic Assumptions*: uranium ore, \$40/lb U_3O_8; separative work, \$100/kg SWU: conversion, \$4/kg U; fabrication, \$140/kg U; spent fuel disposal, \$135/kg U; tails assay, 0.20 wt%. *Key:* ○, economic optimum; △, breakeven stretchout time.

phase, full thermal power can be maintained, but some replacement electric power is needed because of a decrease in thermal efficiency. The extent to which average temperature can be lowered is limited by the plant trip set points and by limits on the amount of moisture at turbine inlet. A typical value of temperature drop is 11°C (20°F). Further stretchout can be accomplished by gradually reducing power (power coastdown), while maintaining criticality via power feedback. In this method, the moderator temperature is changed to a lower level through the maintenance of a lower power level, which adds reactivity to the core. A similar method can be used in BWRs. By the use of feedwater temperature reduction, the favorable energy impact of cycle stretchout is limited by the cost of replacement power. The total impact on the cost of energy production is shown in Figure 11.23 where the dependence on cost of replacement power is evident.

Lattices Changes

While in a recycle scenario tight lattices are favorable because they increase the conversion ratio, in a once-through strategy the opposite is true. A higher moderator-to-fuel ratio (or a wetter lattice) softens the neutron spectrum toward energies where cross sections are higher and the fuel more reactive. Thus a lower fissile inventory is necessary to maintain a certain power level. A "wet lattice" can be achieved by a couple of means: reducing fuel rod diameter increases the water fraction; using an annular instead of a solid pellet decreases the amount of fuel in the same lattice (in addition to providing better fuel performance). Manufacturers of reactor cores are actively considering these modifications. Fuel utilization improvements of 1–4% for the first method and 2–3% for the second method are expected.

Fuel Cycle and Poison Management

An improved fuel and poison management also holds considerable promise for better fuel utilization. The first steps were taken quite a few years ago when burnable poisons were introduced in PWRs to partially replace soluble poison whose uniform distribution in the core is far from optimum. (In addition, soluble poison has safety and corrosion drawbacks.) By placing lumped burnable poison in selected positions in the core, better control of power shape and higher fuel cycle flexibility is achieved. The improved, low-leakage fuel cycle specifies the placement of once burned fuel in the core periphery in a scheme called in–out–in (fuel goes first in the inner zone, then in the outer zone and then back to the inner zone). The reduced neutron leakage in the lumped burnable poison scheme more than compensates for the loss of reactivity in the residual burnable poison. Savings of ~4% in uranium yellowcake have been measured. A low-leakage scheme is adopted in the extended fuel cycles/high-burnup strategies, described in the next section.

The future trend in poison management is to adopt increased use of gadolinia as burnable poison, in a homogeneous mixture with fuel. The method has a potential of further improving power distribution in the core, and hence of further improving fuel utilization. Programs to demonstrate the feasibility of the concept and to gain experience with the performance of gadolinia/uranium oxide rods are under way.

The methods proposed for improved fuel utilization in once-through LWR fuel cycles can be placed in three categories. The first category consists of the concepts that can be readily retrofitted in the existing plants. They include mostly fuel design and management improvements. They are estimated to yield a total uranium savings of ~15%. The second category includes modifications which require considerable capital investment and time for demonstration and implementation, since their economic and technical feasibility must be assessed. When the composite savings from this category is added to those of the first, a total of about 25% savings could be realized (21% for PWRs and 28% for BWRs). A third category could be conceived of even longer term modifications which cannot be retrofitted in current LWR designs.

It must also be noted that the individual savings from various concepts are not always additive. If both retrofittable and nonretrofittable options are combined a total of 30% in uranium savings may be achievable, although the practicality and net economic benefit of many of these options have yet to be assessed. A goal of 15% of overall savings might be a reasonable figure for the near term (the next decade or so).

11.10. EXTENDED CYCLES/HIGH BURNUP FUEL

One of the more attractive avenues toward improved fuel utilization and economics, in the context of indefinite deferral of reprocessing and recycle, is a combination of two actions: an extended fuel cycle associated with high burnup fuel. The two factors work at odds with each other but in combination produce a favorable result.

With the refueling interval as a variable, and from a point of view of strict fuel utilization, the operator would have an incentive to go to a shorter fuel cycle, say, 6 months instead of 1 year. The reason for this advantage is that with more frequent refueling less excess reactivity, and hence, less fissile inventory need to be locked up in the core. This leads to less absorptions in control poisons and produces a better neutron economy. The ideal case is that of the CANDU where refueling is done on a daily basis. This strategy, however, is not favored by the utilities. The more frequent shutdown would impact economics adversely and would increase personnel exposure. The trend is, therefore, toward extended cycles, typically 18 months long.† Assuming that burnup remains about the same, the fuel utilization would deteriorate as shown in Figure 11.24.

If, on the other hand, one keeps the same fuel cycle length but increases burnup, fuel utilization increases as shown in the same figure. Higher burnup is achieved by increasing the number of batches from three to four or five (i.e., the core fraction removed in each refueling becomes one-quarter or one-fifth), which allows the fuel to stay longer in the reactor. Naturally, for longer cycles a higher enrichment would be required to maintain reactivity during a longer period. The savings to be derived from progressively higher burnups are shown in Figure 11.25. Each cycle individually enjoys a modest saving with increasing burnup. The preliminary analysis on which Figure 11.4 is based shows that on a 12-month cycle and a 5-yr residence time (leading to burnups of 50,000 MWd/t) savings for a PWR would be 14–18% for uranium, 2–4% for enrichment, and 40% for storage and transportation. The total savings for a 1000-MWe plant could be as high as \$3–5 million/yr, which translates into 0.5–0.8 mill/kWh. Similarly, significant savings could be obtained in BWRs even though burnups may be limited to lower values.

†U.S. utilities usually have high electricity demands in the summer and winter, lower demands in spring and fall. Therefore, to schedule refueling outages in low-demand periods, 6-, 12-, 18-, or 24-month cycles are required.

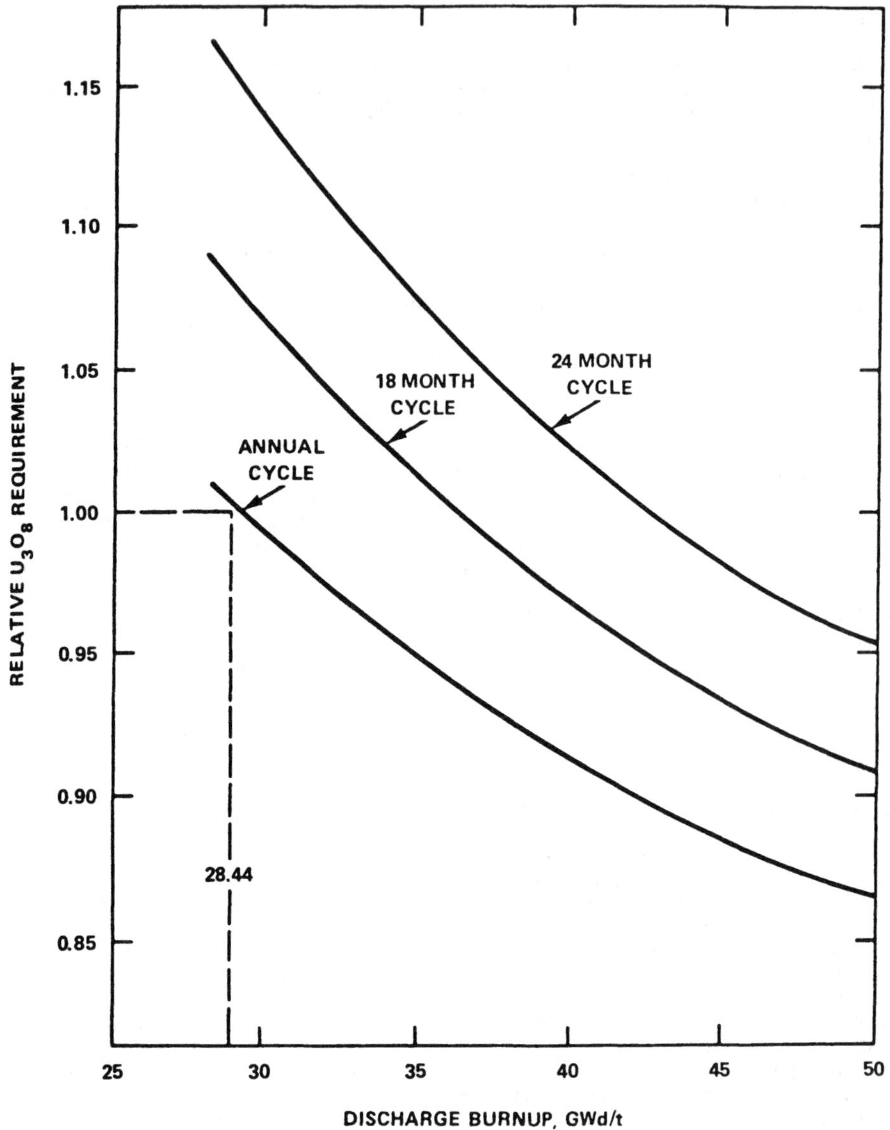

Figure 11.24. Relative U_3O_8 requirement versus burnup for various cycle lengths in BWRs. (From DOE/NE-0001/9.)

When one compares the two cycles (18- and 12-month), significant disadvantages are experienced in both uranium and enrichment services by going to the longer cycle. However, the storage and transportation savings from the 18-month cycle dominate the economic picture and explain the utility operator's preference for it. To express it in different terms, the penalty in uranium and enrichment costs caused by a longer cycle is, to a great extent, compensated by exposing the fuel to higher burnups, while other fuel savings (storage and transportation) increase dramatically. These differences are reflected on the cost of the kilowatt-hour. The unit energy cost drops off with increasing burnup and is also dependent on refueling time because of the cost of replacement power. The dependence is shown in Figure 11.26. One extra week of refueling time could make a difference of more than 1 mill/kWh in fuel cycle cost.

Because of the attractive characteristics of the longer cycles in conjunction with high burnup fuel, several utilities are actively studying its introduction to their system. The combined effect is

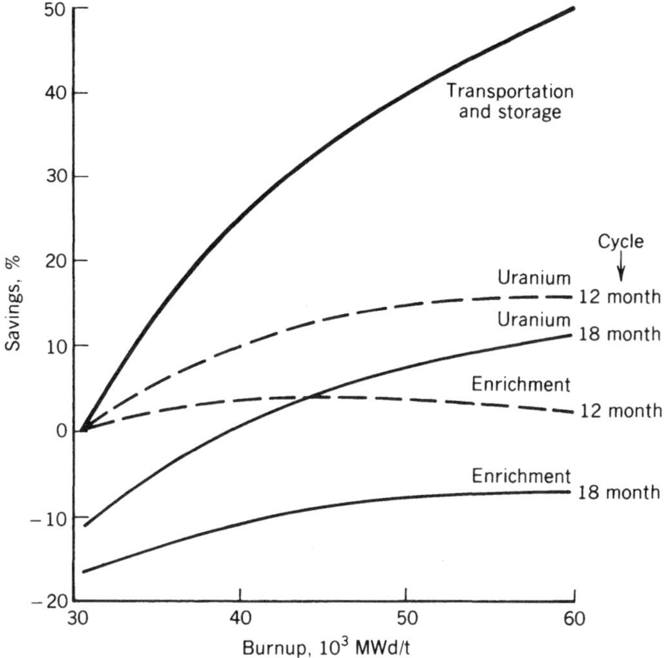

Figure 11.25. Percentage savings predicted for the three major components of the fuel cycle (uranium, enrichment, and transportation and storage) for 12- and 18-month irradiation cycles. Savings in uranium and enrichment level off above 50,000 MWd/t burnup and are higher for a 12-month cycle. Savings in transportation and storage become appreciable as burnup is extended. Other factors such as replacement power costs during refueling are also important. [From *EPRI Journal* (December 1978).]

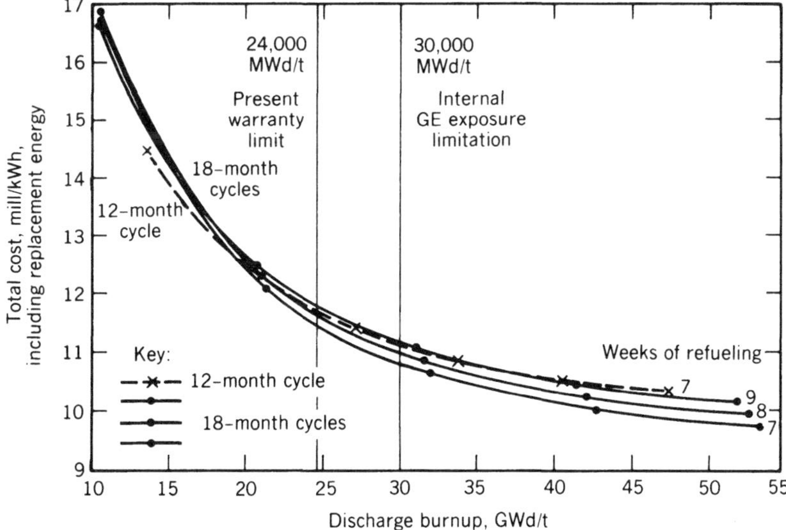

Figure 11.26. 12- and 18-month equilibrium cycles—base case. Total cost (mills/kWh) versus discharge burnup.

It takes enrichments of 3.0 wt% to make the cost of the 18-month cycle comparable to the 12-month cycle. The fuel costs (including replacement energy costs) were plotted against discharge burnup. For discharge burnups on the order of 30,000 MWd/t U, the 18-month cycle looks better than the 12-month cycle provided the reload downtime is comparable to the 12-month cycle (7 to 8 weeks).

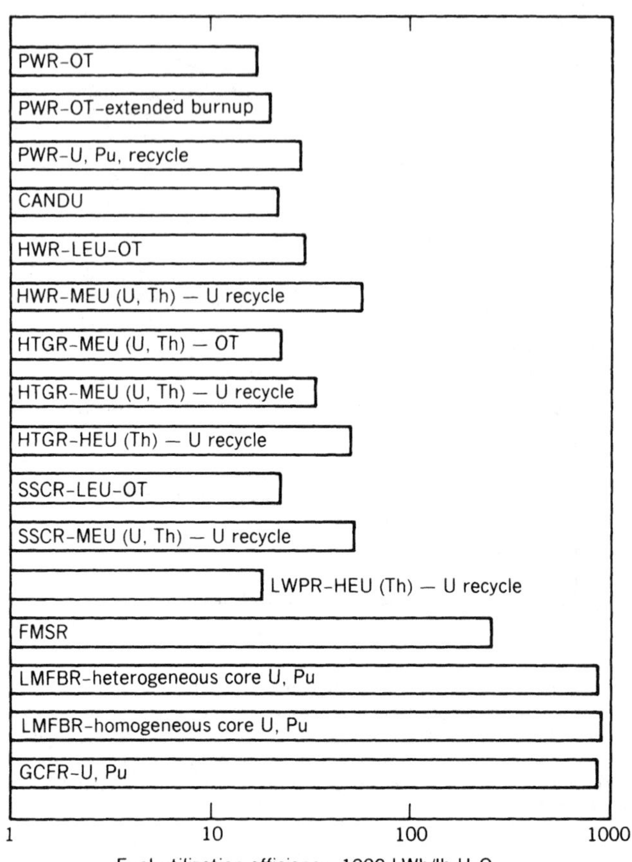

Figure 11.27. Fuel utilization efficiency for LWRs, ACRs, and FBRs. (From B. R. Sehgal, C. Braun, and A. G. Adamantiades, *Proceedings, ASME Winter Annual Meeting*, November 1980.)

expected to be a 5–8% savings in uranium and 6–8% penalty in enrichment. The overriding consideration, however, is that the replacement of three annual refuelings by two, 18-month refuelings holds the possibility of reducing total outage time to afford greater flexibility to utilities operating more than one nuclear plant. The estimated overall annual savings to a two-unit PWR plant site, from a switch to a 18-month fuel cycle, could be as high as $6 million.

The strategy depends heavily on the ability of fuel to perform well under high burnup conditions. An average burnup of 40,000–50,000 MWd/t implies peak burnup in excess of 60,000 MWd/t (compared to a current value of 40,000 MWd/t). Since few statistics exist at these high burnup levels, vigorous programs by government and industry agencies are under way to study behavior of Zircaloy-clad fuel rods under these conditions. Effects, such as dimensional stability, pellet-clad interaction, pressure buildup from fission gas release, and water-side corrosion must be studied to ascertain adequate fuel reliability. These studies include tests of rods with higher enrichment and burnable poison loadings, fuel management schemes, and annular pellets.

11.11. WILL THERE BE ENOUGH FUEL?

The topic of fuel utilization is only important to the extent that it impacts fuel resources and cost of energy. Much of the impetus of the activity in the late 1970s was provided by the abrupt policy change of the Carter administration in April 1977 regarding reprocessing and recycle, and by the subsequent efforts of the Nonproliferation Alternative Systems Assessment (NASAP), which produced the nine-volume DOE/NE-0001/9 and the International Nuclear Fuel Cycle Evaluation (INFCE) program. A plethora of paper studies was produced on the subject by national laboratories, universities, government contractors, and by government agencies themselves (Department of

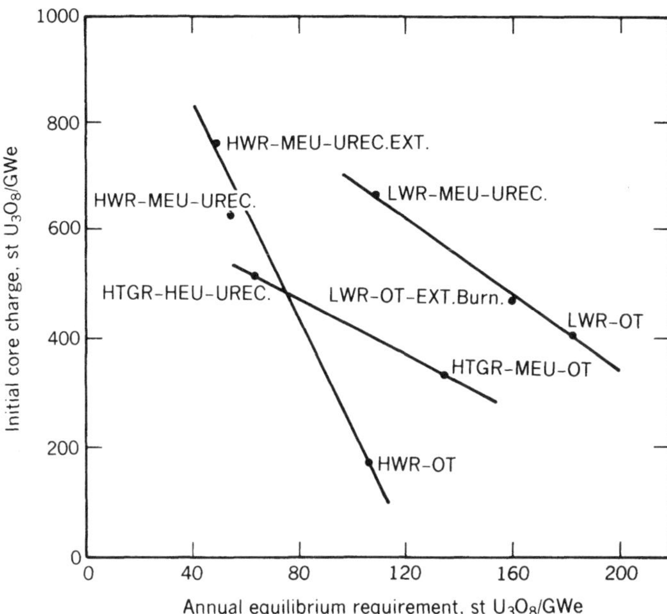

Figure 11.28. Comparison of uranium requirements of advanced converter reactors and standard designs operating on a once-through cycle. Initial core requirements are invariably much higher for the ACR due to the high or medium enriched uranium needed to realize the higher conversion efficiency of these concepts versus standard designs. The ACR annual and lifetime requirement is lower than those of standard designs. The choice depends not only on relative price of uranium and enrichment services but also on discount rate, and economic and regulatory disincentives for the commercialization of novel designs. (From B. R. Sehgal, C. Braun, and A. G. Adamantiades, *Proceedings, ASME Winter Annual Meeting*, November 1980.)

Energy, State Department, Nuclear Regulatory Commission, and the Arms Control and Disarmament Agency). Fifty some countries participated and contributed to INFCE studies. Most of these studies focused on a large number of "Advanced Converter Reactors" (ACRs) to forestall the need for the development of the breeder, which was considered prone to proliferation (more on that subject in Chapter 20). The large number of concepts examined and their estimated potential for fuel utilization in terms of kilowatt-hour of energy produced per pound of uranium yellowcake are shown in Figure 11.27.

There are two major problems with the development of ACRs. The first is that ACRs have front-end requirements which are higher than standard LWRs. The relationship of ACR to standard design in terms of requirements is shown in Figure 11.28. There is a trade-off to be made between high front-end requirements and longer term savings from the lower annual loading needs. It would take several years before the two systems break even as was shown in Figure 11.22. This would produce higher pressure on the supply of uraniun (and on price) in the near term. The second problem is that the ACR's higher utilization of uranium stems from the use of bred fissile material after reprocessing and fabrication into fresh fuel for the next fuel loading. Therefore, the closure of the fuel cycle is of paramount importance for the ACRs. Without it the benefit to fuel utilization simply evaporates. The ACR on a thorium cycle suffers from the same limitation. The benefit to uranium utilization is not felt until enough ^{233}U is produced and recycled into the reactor. For the first 10 yr of operation, total uranium requirements for most ACRs will be less than for LWRs. However, enrichment requirements of ACRs are similar or higher than LWR needs. The relative advantage is, of course, dependent on prices for these two items. At the time of this writing, prices for uranium at $20/lb fell substantially compared to the prices prevalent in the late 1970s (spot prices were about $40/lb). In a softening uranium market, due to revisions of nuclear power growth and to numerous cancellations, interest in the development of new ACR designs has faded. As far as long-term overall uranium savings are concerned, those are diminished to relatively small present worths by discounting.

Additional impediments to the development and introduction of the ACRs are the development and market introduction cost and uncertainties regarding licensing. This leaves two realistic alternatives for fuel utilization improvements: relatively near-term changes that do not require large investments and those that can be easily installed in existing LWRs. Many of these modifications are actually pursued with an expected gain in uranium utilization of 15% in the short run and perhaps up to 30% in the longer term. The second option is, of course, the breeder reactor, specifically the LMFBR with its potential of completely flattening the uranium feed cumulative demand. In some countries, notably France, Japan, and the USSR, the option is a likely commercial reality and is actively pursued. In other countries, notably the United States, the Federal Republic of Germany, and the United Kingdom, high estimated construction costs and a moderated capacity growth projection makes its deployment problematic.

BIBLIOGRAPHY

Nuclear Fuels, Core Physics, Fuel Cycles, General Issues

Benedict, M., T. H. Pigford, and H. W. Levi, *Nuclear Chemical Engineering,* 2nd ed., McGraw-Hill, New York, 1981, Chapter 3.

Ford Foundation, *A Time to Choose; America's Energy Future, Report of the Energy Policy Project,* Ballinger, Cambridge, Massachusetts, 1974.

Ford Foundation/MITRE Corp., *Nuclear Power: Issues and Choices, Report of the Nuclear Energy Policy Study Group,* Ballinger, Cambridge, Massachusetts, 1977.

Pigford, T. H., et al., *Comprehensive Standards: The Power Generation Case,* U.S. EPA Report PB-259-876, March 1975.

Pigford, T. H., and K. P. Ang, "The Plutonium Fuel Cycles," *Health Physics* **29,** 451 (1975).

Turner, S., H. J. Elgin, and R. P. Hancock, *Historical Survey of Nuclear Fuel Utilization in U.S. LWR Power Plants,* Southern Science Applications Inc., Report SSA-122, DOE/ER/10020-T1, Dunedin, Florida, August 1979.

U.S. Department of Energy, *Nuclear Proliferation and Civilian Nuclear Power,* Vols. 1–9, DOE/NE-0001/9, June 1980.

U.S. Nuclear Regulatory Commission, *GESMO: Final Generic Environmental Statement on the Use of Recycle Plutonium in Mixed Oxide Fuel in Light-Water Cooled Reactors: Health, Safety and Environment,* 5 Vols., NUREG-0002, August 1976.

von Hippel, F., and R. H. Williams, "Energy Waste and Nuclear Power Growth," *Bulletin of the Atomic Scientist* **32** (December 1976).

Alternate Reactor Systems

Bertin, L., "Management Practices Complement CANDU's On-Load Fuelling" *Nuclear Engineering International* (November 1981).

Dahlberg, R. C., et al., *NTGR Fuel and Fuel Cycle Summary Description,* General Atomic Co., GA-A12801, Rev. January, 1974.

Foster, J. S., and E. Critoph, "The Status of the Canadian Nuclear Power Program and Possible Future Strategies," *Annals of Nuclear Energy* **2** (1975). *Study of the Developmental Status and Operational Features of Heavy Water Reactors,* EPRI Report NP-365, February 1977.

Merril, M. H. *Use of the Low Enriched Uranium Cycle in the HTGR,* General Atomic Co., Report GA-A-14340, March 1977.

Robertson, J. A. L., "The CANDU Reactor System: An Appropriate Technology," *Science,* Vol. **199,** 10 (February 1978).

Till, C. E., et al., *A Survey of Considerations Involved in Introducing CANDU Reactors into the U.S.,* Argonne National Laboratory, RSS-TM-1, February 1977.

U.S. ERDA, *Advanced Nuclear Reactors,* ERDA-76-107, May 1976.

U.S. ERDA, *Final Environment Statement, Light-Water Breeder Program; Commercial Application of LWBR Technology,* 5 Vols., ERDA-1541, June 1976.

U.S. ERDA, *Report of the Liquid Metal Fast Breeder Reactor Program Review Group,* ERDA-1, January 1975.

Advanced Concepts

Edlund, M. C., "Physics of the Uranium Plutonium Fuel Cycle in Pressurized Water Reactors," *Trans. Am. Nucl. Soc.* **24,** 508 (1976).

Matzie, R. A., and F. M. Sider, *Evaluation of Spectral Shift Control Reactors Operating on the Uranium Fuel Cycle,* EPRI Report, NP-1156, August 1979.

Oldekop, W., et al., "General Features of Advanced Pressurized Water Reactors with Improved Fuel Utilization," *Nuclear Technology* **59,** 212 (1982).

Perry, A. M., and A. M. Weinberg, "Thermal Breeder Reactors," *Annual Review of Nuclear Science* **22** (1972).

Radkowsky, A., et al., *A Heavy Water Breeder Conceptual Core Design,* EPRI Report, NP-2176, December 1981.

Radkowsky, A., et al., *Feasibility Study for a High Gain Light Water Breeder Reactor (HGLWBR),* EPRI Report in preparation.

Uotinen, V., and M. C. Edlund, *Technical Feasibility of a PWR Design with a Low Water Volume Fraction Lattice,* EPRI Report NP-1833, May 1981.

Thorium Utilization

Banerjee, S. E. Critoph, and R. G. Hart, "Thorium as a Nuclear Fuel for CANDU Reactors," *Canadian Journal of Chemical Engineers* **23,** 291 (1975).

Kasten, P. R., et al., *Assessment of the Thorium Fuel Cycle in Power Reactors,* ORNL-TM-5565, Oak Ridge National Laboratory, January 1977.

Sehgal, B. R., C. L. Lin, and J. Naser, "Performance of Various Thorium Fuel Cycles in LMFBRs," *EPRI Journal* **2,** 40 (1977).

Shapiro, N. L., J. R. Rec, and R. A. Matzie, *Assessment of Thorium Fuel Cycles in Pressurized Water Reactors,* EPRI Report, NP-359, February 1977.

U.S. Atomic Energy Commission, *The Use of Thorium in Nuclear Power Reactors,* WASH-1097, June 1969.

Higher Fuel Utilization in Once-Through Cycles

Coleman, T. A., et al., "Improved Uranium Utilization in Pressurized Water Reactors," *Trans. Am. Nuclear Soc.* **39,** 133 (1981).

Hoshino, T., "Optimum Fuel Loading and Coastdown Operation for LWR Power Stations," *Trans. Am. Nuclear Soc.,* **27,** 466 (1977).

Jamal, M., and R. D. Williams, "Feasibility of GE BWR Cycle Extension via Feedwater Temperature Reduction," *Trans. Am. Nuclear Soc.* **33,** 182 (1981).

Kusner, D. E., M. A. Mann, and P. J. Turinsky, "Planned Cycle Stretchout in PWRs," *Trans. Am. Nuclear Soc.* **27,** 467 (1977).

Matzie, R. A., et al., *Uranium Resource Utilization Improvements in Once-Through PWR Fuel Cycle,* CEND-380/000-2426-199, Combustion Engineering Co., 1980.

Shapiro, N. L., and Y. Liu, "Improvement of Fuel Utilization for Once-Through PWR Cycles," *Trans. Am. Nuclear Soc.* **30,** 147 (1978).

High Burnup Fuel/Extended Cycles

Anderson, C. K., and M. C. Andrews, "Higher Burnups Being Achieved with New Management Programs," *Nuclear Engineering International* (November 1981).

Antonopoulos, P., and R. A. Woehlke, "Vermont Yankee 18- and 12-Month Cycle Economics," *Trans. Am. Nuclear Soc.* **32,** 408 (1979).

"LWR Extended Burnup-Fuel Performance and Utilization," Vols. 1 and 2, Am. Nuclear Soc. Topical Meeting, Williamsburg, Virginia, April 1982.

Roberts, J. T. A., R. Williams, and E. Zebroski, "Incentives for Extending Fuel Burnup," *EPRI Journal* (December 1978).

U.S. Department of Energy, *Nuclear Proliferation and Civilian Nuclear Power,* Vols. VIII and IX, Report DOE/NE-0001/2, U.S. Government Printing Office, Washington, D.C., June 1980.

CHAPTER 12

OPERATION OF A NUCLEAR POWER PLANT

12.1. INTRODUCTION

The usual measure of nuclear power's operational efficiency is the total amount of electricity produced and the cost of producing that electricity. A small number of plants may have somewhat different criteria; for example, some reactors are designed to produce both process heat for industrial companies and electricity for the utility grid.† In any case, because the capital cost associated with a nuclear power plant far exceeds its operating costs and because its power is often the least expensive on the electric power grid, utilities try to run their nuclear units as close to 100% power level as long as possible. This is called base load operation. When a nuclear plant is out of service, replacement power from a fossil fuel plant will often have an incremental cost in excess of $750,000 per day for a 1000-MWe plant. With such a large cost penalty, even the start-up rate of a nuclear unit can have significant financial impact. Therefore, an attempt is usually made to come to full power (from 0 to 100% power) as fast as possible without compromising the safe and efficient operation of the unit.

Plant Performance

Load and operation factors (also called availability factor or service factor) are regarded as the overall performance parameters of power plants. Since these factors vary considerably from plant to plant and from year to year because of refueling outages and maintenance requirements, it is not valid to predict future operational performance for a single plant. Load and operations factors for the principal reactor types are given in Figures 12.1 and 12.2.

On a worldwide basis, load factors averaged 59% for 1983, a decrease of 1% over 1981. The highest load factors in 1983 (79%) were recorded in Canada, in part, because the CANDU reactors can be fueled while in operation. Other countries had lower results: Sweden (60%), Germany (64%), France (62%), Japan (70%), and the United States (54%). Light-water reactors (LWRs) are the primary reactor type in these countries. In general, the older plants, which tend to be smaller, have better load factors than the larger plants, which have less operational experience. This is seen in Figure 12.3. It is normal for all power plants, both nuclear and fossil units, to improve their availability during the first two years of operation.

Plant Safety

Safety requirements that restrict the operations of a nuclear plant necessarily are a judgment between the benefits and potential hazards of nuclear power. At one end, the safest nuclear power plant would not be allowed even to approach criticality; of course, no public benefit would be derived from the plant. At the other end, a nuclear plant allowed to operate without operable safety systems would be an undue risk to the public. The question of benefit versus acceptable risk is examined in detail in Chapter 17. Examples of unacceptable reactor operations are given in Table 12.1. Unacceptable operations are ones that threaten the safety of the public or might lead to plant damage. In the United States, criteria protecting the former are contained in 10CFR Parts 20, 50,

†Experience in the large-scale use of nuclear energy for industrial heat applications in the United States is currently quite limited. Consumers Power Company's Midland Nuclear Cogenerating Plant, which is designed to provide approximately 2×10^6 kg/hr (4×10^6 lb/hr) of saturated steam to the adjacent Dow Chemical Company complex, is the sole large-scale example. Other countries, such as Canada, Russia, Sweden, Switzerland and W. Germany, have used nuclear power to produce steam for process heat and district heating.

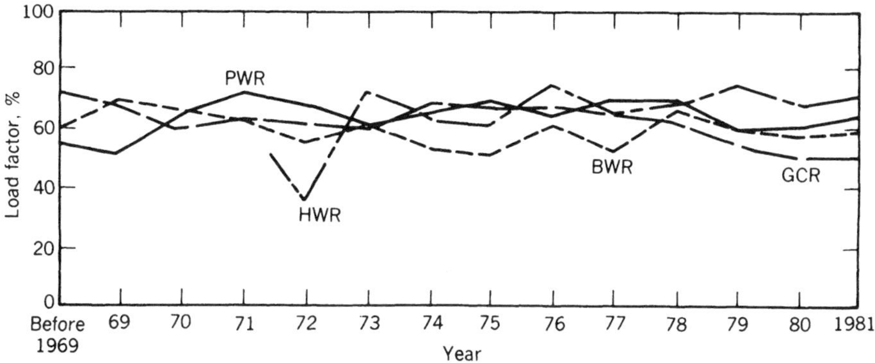

Figure 12.1. Average load factors for world reactor units, shown by year for the principal types. COMECON nations are excluded for lack of data.

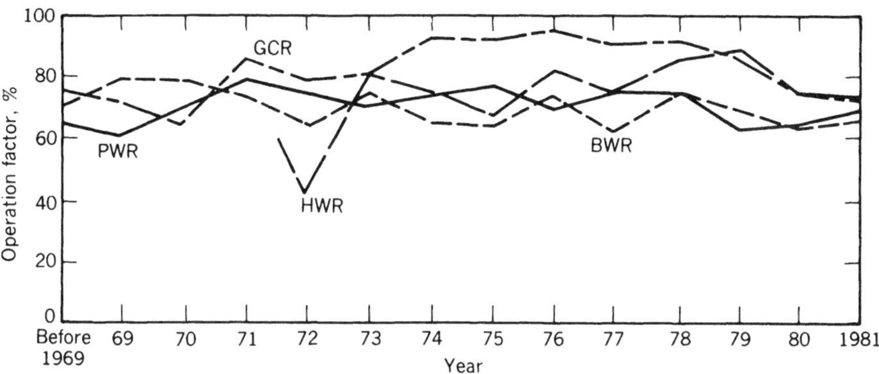

Figure 12.2. Average operation factors for world reactor units, shown by year for the principal types. COMECON nations are excluded.

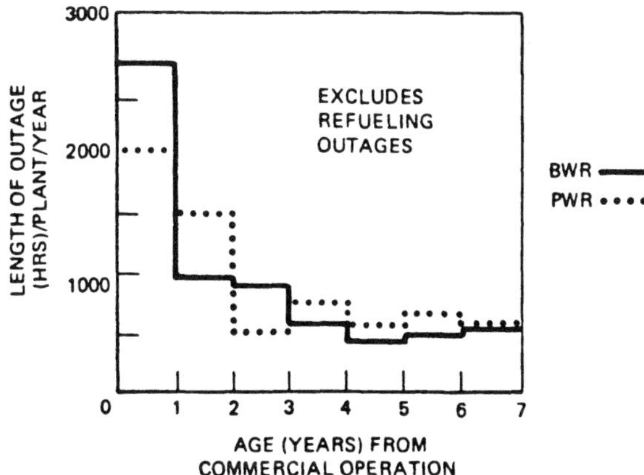

Figure 12.3. Outages per plant year. (From EPRI Report NP-755.)

Table 12.1. Results Inconsistent with the Safe Operation of a Reactor

Plant Event Category	Unacceptable Result
1. Planned operation	1-1. Release of radioactive material to the environs that exceeds the limits of either 10CFR20 or 10CFR50.[a]
	1-2. Fuel failure such that radioactivity released via the normal discharge paths would exceed the limits of 10CFR20.
	1-3. Nuclear systems stress exceeding that allowed by industry codes.
	1-4. A plant condition not considered by plant safety analyses.
2. Abnormal operational transients	2-1. Release of radioactive material to the environs that exceeds the limits of 10CFR20.[a]
	2-2. Any fuel failure directly resulting from the transient.
	2-3. Nuclear system stress exceeding that allowed by industry codes.
3. Accidents	3-1. Radioactive material release exceeding the guideline values of 10CFR100.[a]
	3-2. Failure of the fuel barrier.[b]
	3-3. Nuclear system stresses exceeding that allowed by industry codes.
	3-4. Containment stresses exceeding that allowed by industry codes when containment is required.
	3-5. Overexposure to radiation of plant control room personnel.
4. Additional plant capability events	4-1. Inability to shut down reactor by manipulating controls and equipment outside the control room.
A. Shutdown from outside control room	4-2. Inability to bring the reactor to the cold shutdown condition from outside the control room.
B. Shutdown without control rods	4-3. Inability to shut down the reactor independent of control rods.

Source: BWR/6 Generic Safety Report.
[a]Unacceptable results more important.
[b]Failure of the fuel barrier includes fuel cladding fragmentation (loss-of-coolant accident) and excessive fuel enthalpy (control rod drop accident).

and 100, while the latter is the subject of engineering codes. This chapter examines how safe operation is achieved, how a plant is operated, and what is necessary for high reliability.

12.2. PLANT OPERATIONS

Normal plant operation refers to planned maneuvers needed to run a plant without significant incidents. Operations during an incident are not considered normal until the plant returns to preincident status. A plant operates according to prescribed guidelines called procedures. There are many volumes of these procedures in a plant's control room. They specify the steps required to go from one operating state to another and the plant's operating limits.

Only two operating states are desired for a nuclear plant: refueling outage and full power operation. The former should be as short as possible. As more nuclear units are built a third operation, load following, may become important in some sections of the United States.† Occasionally, plants must shut down because of equipment failure, or for safety inspections mandated by the NRC. Many planned maintenance operations and periodic safety inspections required by the NRC take place during a refueling outage.

In the United States, NRC licensing procedures overlay a degree of formality on all nuclear plant operations. Operational requirements restrict both the plant's condition and the range of

†Because electricity from a nuclear plant usually has the lowest incremental cost of production, full power (i.e., baseload) operations are the norm. If the nuclear capacity in a given system exceeds the baseload demand, however, nuclear plants would also supply some of the variable load (i.e., load follow).

Table 12.2. Nuclear Safety Operational Criteria

Applicability	Criteria
Planned operation, normal operational transients, and accidents.	The plant shall be operated in a safe manner at all times.
Abnormal operational transients and accidents.	The plant shall be operated so that no single active component failure can prevent vital safety actions. However, this requirement is not applicable during system repair if the availability of the safety action is maintained.

operability of plant systems. Such requirements must be observed during all modes of plant operation (not just while the plant is at power) to assure safe operation. Two kinds of requirements are placed on plant equipment:

1. Performance criteria while the reactor is operating.
2. Surveillance requirements to assure that the system is capable of performing its essential functions.

Table 12.2 shows the nuclear safety criteria used to set operational requirements. These criteria reflect the NRC approach to protecting the public health and safety by assuring a nuclear plant operates only in a safe way. These criteria are reinforced by technical operating specifications and limits that are a part of the licence for every nuclear power plant.

Operational requirements are systematically selected to assure the existence of a failure proof way of controlling the reactor should a transient or accident occur. Particularly important in Table 12.2 is the criterion that no single component failure prevents vital safety actions. This is known as the "single failure" criterion. It is central to the NRC safety philosophy, and determines the design of many systems.

The emphasis on safety has resulted in all operations being conducted according to written procedures. Modern instrumentation, by reducing the complexity of monitoring and controlling the plant, has greatly simplified these procedures. The procedures are intended to keep the plant running evenly and to allow smooth transitions between operating states.

Steady-state operation implies that the plant is not undergoing any change; we are also concerned with plants undergoing changes of state (i.e., from one power level to another), referred to as transients. Both steady-state and transient conditions are classified according to mode: normal, abnormal, and off-normal. The following three sections describe these basic modes of plant operations.

Normal Modes

Those operations that are routinely performed in producing the electric power, including starting up and shutting down the plant, are considered normal. Also included is dealing with random changes in output which are not planned for but which happen frequently enough that handling them is a routine matter. An example of the latter is a sudden change in demand for power caused by transmission lines downed in a storm.

The five following transients are considered normal conditions:

1. *Heat-up and Cooldown.* Heat-up and cooldown are limited by plant-operating specifications to a rate of 55°C/hr. In actual practice, the rate of 55°C/hr will not be usually attained because of:

(a) Criteria for preventing brittle failure of components in the primary coolant system, which establish lower permissible temperature rates.
(b) Slower initial rates achieved when energy from the coolant pumps is only used to heat the system.
(c) Interruptions in the heat-up and cooldown cycles. These interruptions might be due to various operating procedures such as drawing a pressurizer steam bubble,† control rod withdrawal, or coolant sampling.

†To control the thermal hydraulic behavior of a PWR, a steam bubble is created in the pressurizer. This facilitates changes in power level of the reactor.

Ideally, heat-up and cooldown would occur only before and after refueling. In practice, additional unscheduled plant cooldowns may be necessary for plant maintenance.

2. *Unit Loading and Unloading.* The loading and unloading of a unit's electrical generator on the utility's grid causes power changes. A load swing of 5%/min is the maximum that the automatic reactor control system for most reactors can handle. The reactor coolant temperature will vary with the load during such a transient.

3. *Step Increase and Decrease of 10%.* A ±10% change in load demand is a transient which occasionally occurs. If a turbine control valve were to open, such a transient would be possible. It might also be caused by disturbances in the electrical network into which the plant output is tied. Nuclear plants have reactor control systems that restore plant equilibrium without a reactor trip.† In effect, during load change conditions, the reactor control system attempts to match turbine and reactor outputs in such a manner that peak reactor coolant temperature is minimized and gradually restored to its desired value. For example, following a decrease in turbine load, the steam pressure and temperature in the primary system increase since the nuclear power does not decrease as fast as the turbine load. In a PWR, this power mismatch between the turbine and reactor causes the control system to insert the control rods partially to reduce core power. In a BWR, the expanding steam fraction inside the core automatically reduces the power. Following a load increase in turbine load, the reverse situation occurs.

4. *Large Decrease in Load.* This transient is caused by a major decrease in turbine load from full power. The resultant rapid increase in reactor coolant temperature initiates the steam dump system. This prevents a reactor shutdown or lifting of the coolant system safety valves. For example, in a 95% load decrease from full power to 5% power, the steam dump system‡ accepts 85% of the turbine load. The remaining 10% of the total change is handled by the rod control system (pressurized water reactor, PWR) or void expansion (boiling water reactor, BWR). If the steam dump system could not cope with the transient, the reactor would trip and the safety valves would lift.

5. *Steady-State Fluctuations.* According to commonly used operating specifications, the reactor coolant temperature may not increase or decrease more than 3°C in 1 min. These temperature changes are assumed to fluctuate around the average temperature value ($T_{avg} \pm 1\frac{1}{2}$°C). Temperature changes lead to pressure changes according to the equation of state for the coolant. The reactor coolant pressure, therefore, fluctuates up and down proportionally to the system's (absolute) temperature.

Abnormal Mode

Abnormal operation can result from unplanned transients. Such transients are more severe than those encountered in the previous section. There are eight conditions that are considered potentially serious.

1. Nuclear system pressure increase.
2. Moderator temperature decrease.
3. Positive reactivity insertion.
4. Coolant inventory decrease.
5. Coolant flow decrease in the core.
6. Coolant flow increase in the core.
7. Coolant temperature increase.
8. Excess coolant.

These variations, if uncontrolled, could result in damage to the reactor or the fuel, or both. A pressure increase threatens the reactor piping and will cause the safety/relief valves to open. In a BWR, a pressure increase also collapses voids in the moderator, causing an insertion of positive reactivity§ which threatens fuel damage as a result of overheating. On the other hand, a temperature decrease of reactor vessel water (i.e., the moderator) in either BWRs or PWRs also results in an insertion of reactivity as density increases, again leading to fuel overheating. A coolant temperature increase also threatens the integrity of the fuel; such a variation could be the result of a heat exchanger or steam generator malfunction during operation. Moreover, reactivity insertions are possible from causes other than moderator temperature or pressure changes. Such reactivity insertions are obviously undesirable.

†An automatic shutdown of the reactor core by means of control rod insertion (sometimes called a scram).

‡Steam can be made to bypass the turbine, "dumping" directly into the condenser.

§More (or denser) moderator in the core leads to more power being produced.

Both a coolant inventory decrease and a reduction in coolant flow through the core are more serious in a BWR than in a PWR since they both reduce the void content of the moderator, resulting in an increased power. Another serious condition, an excess of coolant inventory, could be the result of malfunctioning water level control equipment; this can result in a turbine trip, which causes an increase in nuclear system pressure and an increased power level.

The above abnormal conditions could result from either equipment failure or an operator mistake. Examples of the latter are opening the wrong valve or withdrawing the control rods in the wrong sequence. To prevent damage to the plant, detailed procedures are available to the operators to handle such abnormal system states.

Off-Normal (Upset) Mode

The following transients are considered upset conditions:

1. *Loss of Load Without Immediate Turbine or Reactor Trip.* This transient is caused by a rapid decrease in turbine load from full power. It represents the most severe transient on the reactor coolant system. The reactor and turbine will eventually trip; however, before any serious damage to the system occurs in a PWR, the trip would be caused by a high pressurizer level.

In a BWR, the situation is more serious, since the reactor would continue to operate, although at much lower power (~20%). The safety/relief valves would open, but the steam continuing to be generated would eventually lead to a core meltdown due to depletion of the cooling water if not terminated. This scenario is referred to as an ATWS (Anticipated Transient Without Scram) in safety analysis reports. Since redundant means of tripping all reactors are provided as a part of the reactor protection system, transients of this nature are very rare.

2. *Loss of Power.* This transient might result because of an area-wide electrical blackout around the plant resulting in the loss of outside electrical power. Under these circumstances, the reactor coolant pumps are without power and will "coast down." Following the coastdown of the coolant pumps, natural circulation will permit removal of core residual heat (i.e., through the steam generators in a PWR). Diesel generators are also available to provide emergency power to the plant.

3. *Loss of Flow.* This type of transient could be caused by a reactor coolant pump inadvertantly shutting down, for instance, due to a faulty signal, resulting in partial loss of coolant flow. The reactor and turbine will trip because of low reactor coolant flow, terminating the transient. The steam dump system will subsequently open, helping to control pressure in the system. Flow reversal of the coolant may occur, however, in the effected loop.

4. *Reactor Trip from Full Power.* A reactor trip from full power may occur for a variety of reasons, such as a problem on the electrical grid. A plant trip results in temperature and pressure transients in the reactor coolant system. The transients continue until the reactor coolant and the heat sink temperatures are in equilibrium. A continued supply of feedwater to the core will remove any residual heat in the system and prevent the safety valves from lifting.

5. *Inadvertent Auxiliary Spray (PWR).* In a PWR, a transient will occur if the pressurizer auxiliary spray valve is opened inadvertently. This will introduce cold water into the pressurizer; a very sharp pressure decrease will result. The reactor trip that would occur would only accelerate the pressure decrease. The pressure is finally stabilized at the hot leg saturation pressure.† This transient is more severe on a two-loop PWR plant than on a three- or four-loop plant.

6. *Earthquakes.* Mechanical stresses on the plant and equipment can occur from the deflections caused by earthquakes. The plant components, especially those that perform safety functions, are engineered to handle such stress. Their design incorporates margins according to the seismic conditions where the plant is located (see Chapter 18).

12.3. PLANT START-UP

A nuclear plant may be started up from one of two conditions: cold or hot standby. A "cold condition" refers to the plant temperature when the plant is started up for the first time, or after an extended outage, as for refueling. When the plant has been shut down for only a few hours, however, and the coolant systems are still near operating temperature and pressure, the term "hot standby" is used. This often is the case after a minor outage such as turbine trip, small plant transient, or a false instrument reading that causes a quick shutdown of reactor power, known as a scram. The difference between these two initial conditions is given in Table 12.3. Typical times needed to achieve full power are given in Table 12.4.

If a plant has never been operated before, a series of tests are performed during the final stages of construction before the unit is licensed by the Nuclear Regulatory Commission. The main

†That is, flashing of coolant to steam in the pressure vessel exit piping prevents the pressure from dropping below the steam saturation pressure.

Table 12.3. Initial System Start-up Conditions for a PWR Reactor

	Cold Condition	Hot Standby
Reactor coolant temperature	Below 60°C	290°C
Reactor coolant pressure	28 bars	150 bars
Pressurizer temperature	Below 60°C	340°C
Pressurizer level	100%	25%

objective of these tests, which are outlined in Table 12.5, is to assure that the plant will operate as designed and in a safe manner. The testing period also allows a certain amount of training for the staff prior to the plant's entering commercial operation. In addition, this phase is necessary prior to its final acceptance by the owner utility to demonstrate that the plant meets the performance warranted by the manufacturer.

Start-up of a PWR

A PWR at ambient conditions (i.e., a cold plant) is started up by using the heat generated by the reactor coolant pumps. To run these pumps requires about 5% of the normal electrical output of a plant. While the reactor is shut down, this energy comes from an outside source. The pumps heat the system to a hot condition within 6 hr by friction energy dissipated in the coolant. Prior to this heat-up phase, however, precriticality checks of electrical power and system configurations are performed to assure that the plant is ready to function.

The primary coolant system is then charged with borated water. The boron is in the form of boric acid (H_3BO_3) dissolved in the water. Figure 12.4 shows the chemical structure of boric acid and comments on how it is introduced into the coolant. Its concentration is carefully monitored at all times. The boric acid controls the neutron reactivity in the core prior to start-up, and allows the reactor to operate with the control rods almost fully withdrawn.

There are four ways to control the reactivity in a PWR: (1) control rods; (2) boron addition to the coolant; (3) burnable poisons (e.g., gadolinia) added to the fuel (see Chapter 7); and (4) changing the coolant (i.e., moderator) temperature. Each of these methods is used. The choice of technique is governed by how much of a power change (i.e., change in reactivity) is needed and how quickly. These methods are summarized in Table 12.6. [A BWR does not use boron in the coolant system. More reliance is placed on burnable poison placed in the fuel. Since a BWR normally operates with

Table 12.4. Typical Start-up Times to Achieve Full Power for a PWR

	Time, hr	
Operation	Cold Start-up[f]	Hot Standby[f]
Raise coolant systems to hot condition[a]	6	—
Drain pressurizer from solid condition[b] to operating level	2	—
Withdraw control rods from core[c] and achieve minimal power	$\frac{1}{2}$	$\frac{1}{2}$
Raise coolant system temperature[d] and pressure to no-load levels	4	—
Ascend to full power[e]	$\frac{1}{2}$	$\frac{1}{2}$
Total	13	1

[a]Primary coolant temperature and pressure of 205°C and 27 bars.
[b]"Solid" refers to a pressurizer completely full of liquid coolant. During normal operation a gas vapor bubble is allowed to form in the top of the pressurizer. System pressure is controlled by varying the size of the bubble.
[c]Control rods are nearly completely withdrawn from a PWR. Criticality is controlled by the amount of boron in the reactor coolant. For BWR, boron is not used in the coolant; the control blades are only part-way removed in this case.
[d]Same as hot standby conditions, 290°C and 150 bars. Preparation of the secondary system must be complete by this stage. This preparation includes establishing a vacuum in the condenser and starting the turbine generator in motion.
[e]Power increase may be up to 5%/min.
[f]See Table 12.3 for definition.

Table 12.5. Precritical Tests Performed Before a Nuclear Plant Is Licensed to Operate

1. Inspection—Examine equipment for proper installation, review the quality control and documentation, "walk-through" all the systems.
2. Electrical testing—Check for proper connection of all electrical equipment, complete testing equipment under "no-load" conditions.
3. Instrumentation—Calibrate all instrumentation and control systems to assure they operate within prescribed ranges.
4. Hydro-testing[a]—Test all liquid and gas systems to hydrostatic loads according to code (ASTM, ASME, etc.) specifications for which they were designed. These conditions are in considerable excess of normal operating conditions.
5. Functional tests—Demonstrate by operation that all components will perform the operations for which they were designed.
6. Hot-ops[a]—Hot operational testing of all equipment under conditions to be encountered in service.
7. Zero-power test—After initial fuel loading, a usually prolonged period of physics testing of the reactor core to measure certain parameters necessary for operation and to assure the safety of the system.
8. Power testing—The plant is tested at various power levels, with steam dumped to the condenser through the turbine bypass system. The objective is to verify the steady state and transient control of the plant. In the final phase of this period, the plant is run for several days at 100% power for final acceptance testing and warantee performance evaluation.

[a]Industry jargon.

coolant voids (steam) in the core, it has still another mechanism for reactivity control, namely system pressure which controls the amount of moderator in the core by collapsing or expanding the void region.]

When all safety systems, including the Emergency Core Cooling System (ECCS), are operational, the pressurizer heaters can be turned on to form a steam bubble in the pressurizer. The bubble greatly increases the pressure stability of the primary coolant system and allows the pressure to be regulated. During the start-up, the pressure of the primary coolant system must remain below certain specified values for any given temperature. This is to protect critical components, particularly the pressure vessel, from operating at high pressure in a temperature range where low ductility of the steel might cause a problem. This temperature/pressure restriction is shown in Figure 12.5. The pressure eventually reaches about 27 bars, and is maintained until the pressurizer water level reaches the no-load set point (25%).

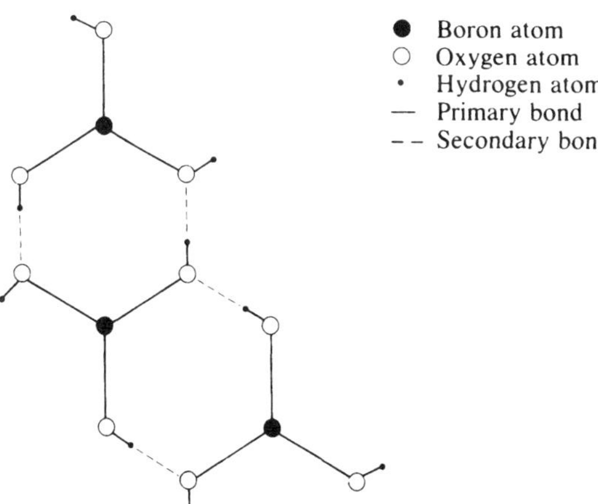

Figure 12.4. Boric acid structure showing molecular bonding. The boric acid used in PWRs for power control purposes is a hydrated form of boric oxide $B_2O_3 \cdot 3H_2O$ [but is perhaps best thought of as $B(OH)_3$]. Hydrogen saturated water containing 4–12% boric acid is fed to the primary coolant system from the volume control tank under gas pressure by a positive displacement pump. For a typical Zircaloy clad fuel assembly, a boron concentration of 100 ppm in the coolant will result in a 1% change in reactivity.

Table 12.6. Methods for Changing Reactivity and Power Levels in LWRs

Technique	Reactor Type	Purpose
1. Control rods	BWR, PWR	Quickly raise or lower power level Important safety feature when a reactor transient occurs and the plant must be scramed Fast acting but perturb power shape
2. Boron in primary coolant system	PWR	Used as a chemical "shim" so that control rods can be nearly fully withdrawn Allows more uniform power distribution across the core Relatively slow acting 1% change in reactivity requires about 100 ppm in a Zircaloy clad fuel matrix, about 70 ppm when stainless steel is used
3. Burnable poison in fuel	BWR, (PWR)	Allows axial power shaping at beginning of fuel life Particularly useful in BWRs where power is perturbed by partially inserted control rods and void formation in the core
4. Changing coolant temperature	PWR, (BWR)	Fast acting means of changing power when small changes are required Does not perturb power shape Minimizes boron duty Provides fast return to power
5. Changing coolant pressure	BWR	Will expand or reduce voids in the core decreasing or increasing the rate of nuclear reactions Important safety feature; if power were to quickly increase the void formation would self-limit power Negative feedback mechanism

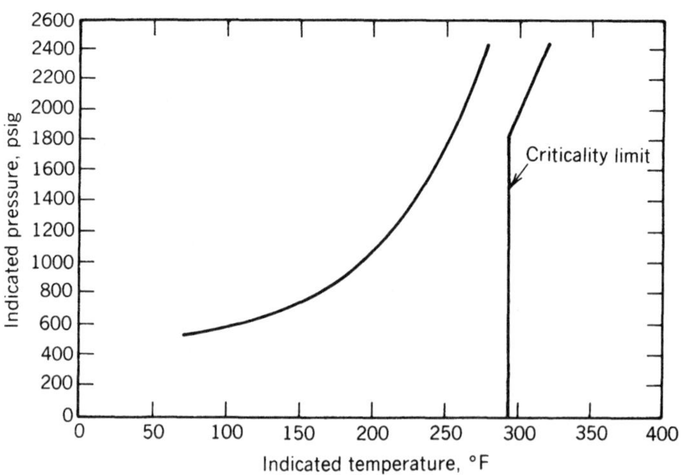

Figure 12.5. Reactor coolant system heatup curve. Limitations on pressurization of the primary coolant system are determined by the ductility of the material used in the pressure vessel. The maximum pressure at any temperature is based on stress limits for brittle fracture. Since neutron radiation can adversely affect the temperature at which degraded ductility occurs, the maximum pressure is set conservatively to allow for accumulated radiation effects throughout the life of the plant. (Courtesy Westinghouse Electric Corp.)

Table 12.7. Control Rod Groupings and Functions[a]

Type of Control Rod	Typical Number	Function
Shim or control (full length)	61, ganged together in groups of 4, 8, or more	Be available for emergency shutdown of the core (scram) Control the power level
Axial shaping (part length)	8, not always ganged	Control xenon oscillations Improve axial power pattern

[a]The control rod assemblies (typically 69 in number in a PWR) are symmetrically placed throughout the core. When they are operated, they are ganged together in various control rod banks. In that manner they can be symmetrically withdrawn from the core without causing power imbalance in various parts of the core. Of the 69 assemblies, 61 may be shim rods and have both a safety and power control function. The other 8, called axial power shaping rods, are part-length rods. They are moved in and out of the core to improve the axial power distribution. The (accidental) removal of a single control rod, or even a ganged set of control rods, is not enough to allow the core to go critical.

Up to this point, the reactor core is still shut down, with the control rods fully inserted. After the preheating of the system using the main coolant pumps is complete, the reactor core is made critical. The system is brought up to low power as follows:

1. The shutdown group of control rods is withdrawn slowly in a prescribed sequence. Table 12.7 gives the function of the various types of control rods available to change the reactivity of the core. The neutron rate is monitored and the reactor period (inversely proportional to power-doubling time) observed. A start-up rate of about ½ decade/min† is established.
2. As criticality is approached, the count rate of the neutron monitors no longer reaches equilibrium between control rod withdrawals. The reactor coolant temperature increases, while the pressurizer spray maintains the system pressure required by the temperature/pressure curves already given in Figure 12.5.
3. The reactor power is then increased by further withdrawals of the control rods from the initial critical position. The control rod groups still remaining in the core are used for power-range control. They are usually operated manually‡ at low power, but are put on automatic control above 15 or 25% power.

As the reactor is brought to power and the system temperature reaches 205°C, steam is drawn from the steam generators. This steam is used to heat up the secondary systems, to establish a vacuum in the condenser, and to start the turbine moving. The latter is not connected to the electrical grid at this point, and will not be until the plant start-up is completed and it is rotating at synchronous speed with the main grid.

The heat-up and pressurization of the primary system continues until zero load conditions are established (290°C, 150 bars). The plant is now in a hot condition. This is the same point the plant would be at if it were recovering from a brief outage and was in a "hot standby" condition. The turbine can then be synchronized to the grid, and pressurizer spray and heaters are put on automatic mode. The feedwater and temperature controls remain on manual control. If the entire system is correctly functioning at this point, the plant goes on automatic control. The power can then be increased to full power, but at a rate of increase that does not exceed 5%/min. Full power is reached in about 13 hr during a normal start-up.

Plant Start-up Operations (BWR)

Much of the description in the previous section also pertains to a BWR. The major exception is the actual sequence of operations needed to bring the plant on-line. This is because of the differences in system design between a PWR and BWR. A BWR is a direct cycle plant and boiling occurs directly in the core. This leads to a greater stability for BWRs and considerably different transient response.

†This refers to the time it takes for the neutrons in the core to increase by a factor of 10 (decade). Various neutron monitors exist in and around the reactor core. These are called the source-range, intermediate-range, and power-range monitors. Normally, control rods are withdrawn a little bit, and the neutron level in the core stabilizes before the rods are withdrawn further.

‡That is, by the operator controlling switches in the control room.

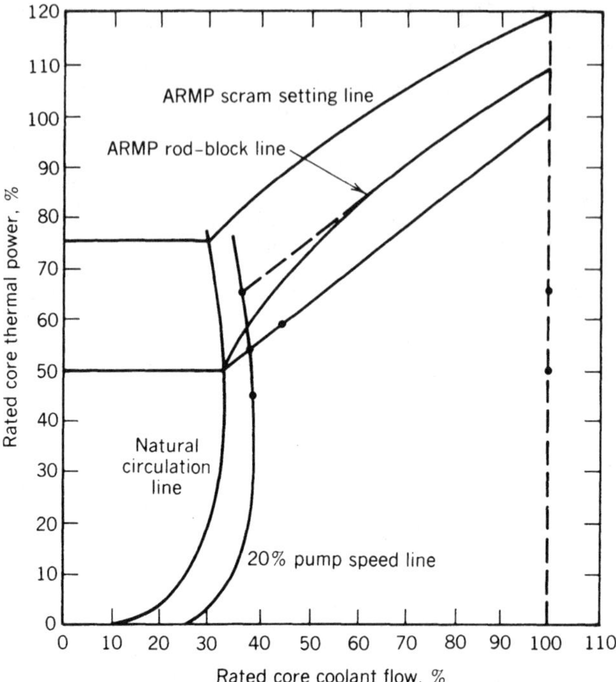

Figure 12.6. The power map (i.e., the chart of core thermal power versus core coolant flow) for Peach Bottom-2. The rod-block power–flow line represents the points for any combination of coolant flow and core power at which any further withdrawal of control rods (to increase power) is automatically blocked. The 20% pump speed line shows power flow conditions when the recirculation pumps are running at 20% of rated speed. [From *EPRI Journal* (August 1977).]

The initial approach to criticality entails the usual preoperational system status checking. As with a PWR, if the system is on hot standby conditions, the start-up period is considerably shortened. Once the system's status is verified, the coolant system is readied by placing the main coolant pumps and the feedwater pumps in gear, followed by starting up the condensate and condensate feedwater systems. The condenser vacuum† is next established. At this point, the reactor is ready to begin control rod withdrawals. The control rods are removed sequentially in groups (sometimes called banks).

Unlike the PWR, a BWR is heated up and pressurized by nuclear heat via rod withdrawal from the core. The heat-up rate is usually 25–50°C/hr. All control rods in a BWR are hydraulically actuated. They are gradually removed from the core several notches‡ at a time. If the plant is on hot standby, the start-up begins at this point. As the plant reaches key pressure levels, various additional checks are made and various systems brought on-line. When the plant reaches its operational set point, the turbine/generator is started up, synchronized with the grid, and loaded. The plant is now producing net power.

Going from zero power to full load conditions is determined by the plant's natural circulation capability and the speed of the main coolant pumps. An example is given in Figure 12.6. Generally, a BWR cannot be operated on natural circulation much above 25% of rated power. Moreover, power increases above this point must proceed more slowly to avoid potential damage to the reactor fuel including pellet clad interaction (see Chapter 7 and Figure 12.7) and the onset of transition to film boiling in the core, shown in Figure 12.8.

†In order to operate efficiently, all steam plants establish a vacuum in the condenser to "pull" the steam through the turbine. The vacuum is created by a pump, such as the steam jet air ejector. This vacuum also helps remove oxygen from the system which can cause corrosion and other problems.
‡In a BWR there are 48 latch positions for a control rod. These are referred to as notches.

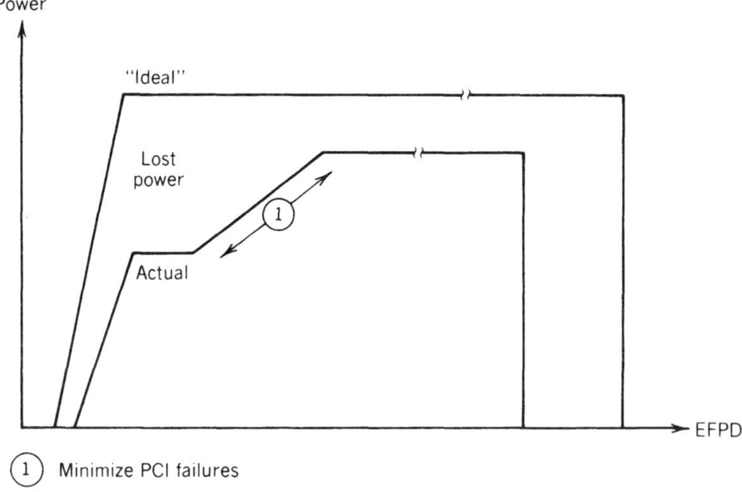

Figure 12.7. EFPD = Effective Full Power Days. Concerns about a too rapid increase in the temperature of the fuel require a BWR to reduce the rate at which approach to full power is made. This is indicated by ① in the figure. The mechanism to be avoided is Pellet-Clad Interaction (PCI). This could cause small perforations in the clad material and limit the life of the fuel.

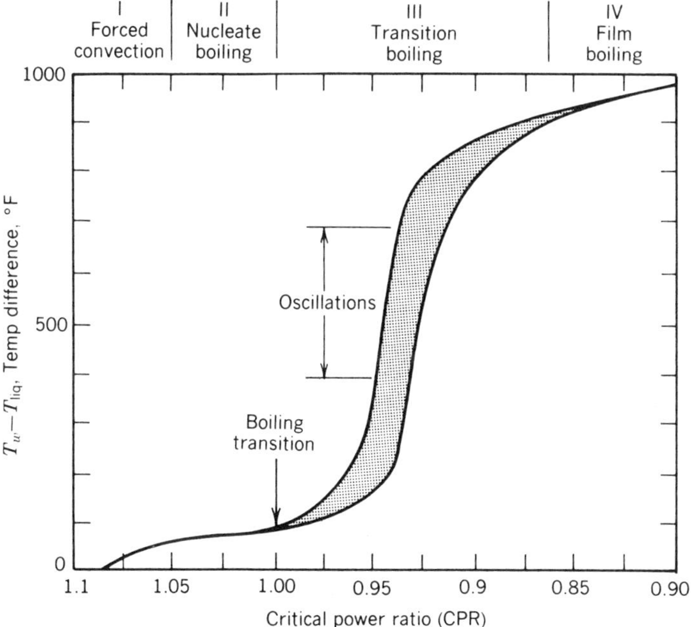

Figure 12.8. Variation of heat flux with surface-liquid temperature difference in boiling system. There are three different types of boiling heat transfer to water in forced convection systems: nucleate boiling, transition boiling, and film boiling. Nucleate boiling, at low heat transfer rates, is an extremely efficient mode of heat transfer. As heat transfer is increased, the boiling heat transfer surface alternates between film and nucleate boiling, leading to fluctuations in heat wall temperatures. The point of departure from the nucleate boiling region into the transition boiling region is called the boiling transition. Transition boiling begins at the critical power and is characterized by fluctuations in cladding surface temperature. Film boiling occurs at the highest heat transfer rates; it begins as transition boiling comes to an end. The boiling transition does not necessarily correspond to the fuel damage threshold, especially in the high steam-quality range. Boiling transition is identified as the heat transfer rate below which clad overheating does occur. Damage would not actually occur until well into the film boiling regime.

BWR Operating Limits

For purposes of maintaining adequate thermal margin during normal operation, the Minimum Critical Power Ratio (MCPR)† must be below the operating limit and the maximum Linear Heat Generation Rate (LHGR)‡ must be above the design rate for the plant. The MCPR operating limit specifies that no more than 0.1% of the fuel rods in the core undergo boiling transition during the most severe abnormal operational transient. Thus, no fuel damage would be expected even if a few fuel rods actually experience a boiling transition.

The steady-state operating limit for MCPR is 1.24 and the peak LHGR heat generation rate is 13.4 kW/ft for a current generation BWR. These transient thermal limits are established to prevent fuel cladding failure, even during severe transients. Mechanisms that can cause fuel damage are:

1. Severe overheating of fuel cladding.
2. Fracture of the fuel cladding caused by expansion of the uranium dioxide pellet (PCI).

The linear heat generation rate required to cause unacceptable cladding strain is approximately 25 kW/ft in new fuel, but decreases with burnup to approximately 20.5 kW/ft toward the end of fuel life (40,000 MWd/t).

The MCPR and peak LHGR limits are sufficiently general so that no other limits need to be stated. For example, cladding surface temperatures will always be maintained within 6°C of the coolant temperature as long as the boiling transition is not reached and the boiling process stays in the nucleate regime. Fuel integrity is, therefore, assured as long as MCPR and LHGR limits are met. Thus, no additional design criteria are required on coolant void fraction, coolant velocities, or flow distribution.

For BWRs, which use control rods for reactivity control, however, additional operating procedures are usually followed to further minimize PCI failures. A strategy of "preconditioning" fuel has been devised. This calls for operating the fuel at high power (over 13 kW/ft) for a while to allow some minor deformation of cladding. Once accomplished, subsequent high-power operation will not excessively stress the fuel cladding (see Chapter 7). In summary then, the steady-state operating limits assure that the plant will perform satisfactorily.

12.4. COOLDOWN OPERATIONS

Plant Cooldown (PWR)

Plant cooldown operations bring the reactor system from no-load operating status to cold shutdown. During a plant cooldown, the boron in the reactor coolant is increased to the concentration required for cold shutdown by adding boric acid to the reactor coolant system (RCS) from the boron recovery system. If refueling is planned, the reactor coolant is degassed during cooldown to reduce the volume of hydrogen and fission gas.

Plant cooldown is a two-phase operation. First, heat is removed by the steam generators, then the decay heat removal system is used. When the cooldown starts, fission product decay is still generating significant heat in the reactor core. Thus, the steam generators are used to remove the decay heat, plus the heat from the reactor coolant pumps, and the sensible heat from the system components. One reactor coolant pump per loop provides forced circulation of the coolant. If the reactor coolant pumps are not available, the RCS can remove the decay heat by natural circulation of the coolant.

The second phase of cooldown begins about 6 hr after shutdown when the temperature reaches approximately 150°C. The reactor coolant pumps are stopped and the decay heat system is actuated, cooling the pressurizer with spray flow. This phase continues for about 18 hr. When the pressurizer has been sufficiently cooled, the spray is stopped. The RCS can then be depressurized by venting the pressurizer.

Plant Cooldown (BWR)

A BWR is cooled down by the residual heat removal system directly. This normally takes 15–20 hr. During the initial phase, most of the heat can be removed by dumping steam directly to the condenser, bypassing the turbine. The residual heat removal system completes the cooldown.

†MCPR is the ratio of the power at which non-nucleate boiling occurs to the power being produced (see Figure 12.8). It varies from location to location in the core.

‡LHGR is power produced in a given length of a fuel rod. It is usually measured in kW/ft. It varies from location to location in the core.

12.5. NORMAL PLANT OPERATING PARAMETERS

Control Rooms and Instrumentation

The actual operation of a nuclear plant is usually no more difficult than operating a modern fossil fuel power station. In some sense it may be easier, since the operational strategy calls for constant full power operation, if possible. As a result, very little load following (power maneuvering to keep up with daily fluctuations in the demand for power) occurs. Also, much of the actual control of the plant is automatic. Consequently, a few trained people could actually run a nuclear plant, aided, of course, by the automatic instrumentation and process computers.

Reliance on plant process computers has grown with the demands for improved availability, efficiency, and safety. In the early plants, process computers were frequently designed as elements peripheral to plant operation, and as a result, performance suffered. The newer plants use techniques that improve plant operations.

A typical control room for a nuclear plant is illustrated and described in Figure 12.9, while Figure 12.10 shows an advanced control room currently available for order in new plants. Also shown in these figures are a series of modern operational aids designed to help the reactor operators. Some of these aids were developed as a result of the accident at Three Mile Island in 1979, which revealed shortcomings in the control rooms of nuclear units.

Advanced control rooms and instrumentation in nuclear plants are currently being used to assist operators with the analysis and integration of plant status information. These new designs incorporate the concept of functional modularity at the hardware level. This simplifies validation and modification, thereby minimizing obsolescence. Such systems help overcome the increasing complexity of plant control required to maximize availability and still meet stringent safety and environmental requirements. Almost all reactor control rooms now have a "safety panel" to inform the operator of the status of the plant during an accident. The panel groups together all relevant information, presenting it more clearly. It helps find the cause of the accident,† and determines the action needed. The safety panel emphasizes the validation of system parameters. Thus, values recorded by the sensor are compared, to assure the information is consistent. The safety panel computer functionally integrates the information, verifies it, and interprets it. As an example, coolant level, density, temperature, and pressure information are processed to yield the coolant inventory, void fraction, and subcooling (see Figure 12.11).

During the last decade, there has been a dramatic escalation in costs of plant construction, operation, and fuel, as well as a growing public concern about conservation. As a result, utilities are committed to the improvement of plant performance. This commitment, the increasing size and complexity of power plants, the greater stringency of regulatory requirements, and the rapid advances in the electronics industry are all contributing to the introduction of new instrumentation and control technology.

Consequently, in a power-generating facility there are thousands of monitoring and control points that must be individually hardwired between the field and the control building. Hardwiring requires that hundreds of miles of cable be strung, costing millions of dollars in materials and labor. Cable separation and fire protection requirements compound the complexity of plant wiring.

Recent advances in electronics make it possible to reduce instrumentation and control wiring through the use of remote multiplexing.‡ Remote Multiplexing Systems (RMSs) are able to transmit many signals on a small number of wires. The individual field sensors and actuators are wired to remote terminals that are strategically distributed throughout the plant and sequentially sampled for transmission by the remote multiplexers. Figure 12.12 shows how such a system might work. In the control building, the signals are separated and distributed on short cables to their final destinations.

System Parameters

During normal operation of a nuclear reactor, the temperature and pressure of the coolant are carefully controlled. In a PWR, the operating pressure is maintained by the pressurizer as is the coolant volume. The latter is adjusted by a water level control system. The water level is designed to change with the operating conditions of the reactor. In contrast, a BWR maintains coolant inventory by changing the rate at which the feedwater pumps operate.

System temperature is controlled by the nuclear heat produced in the core, that is, by the regulation of the core reactivity by the reactor control system. At low power levels, the control

†The first sign of an accident a plant operator receives is usually the emergency reactor shutdown (scram) or the start of the Emergency Core Cooling System (ECCS).

‡Multiplexing (or time division) means sending different signals over the same wire using different frequencies, much as the telephone system operates.

(a)

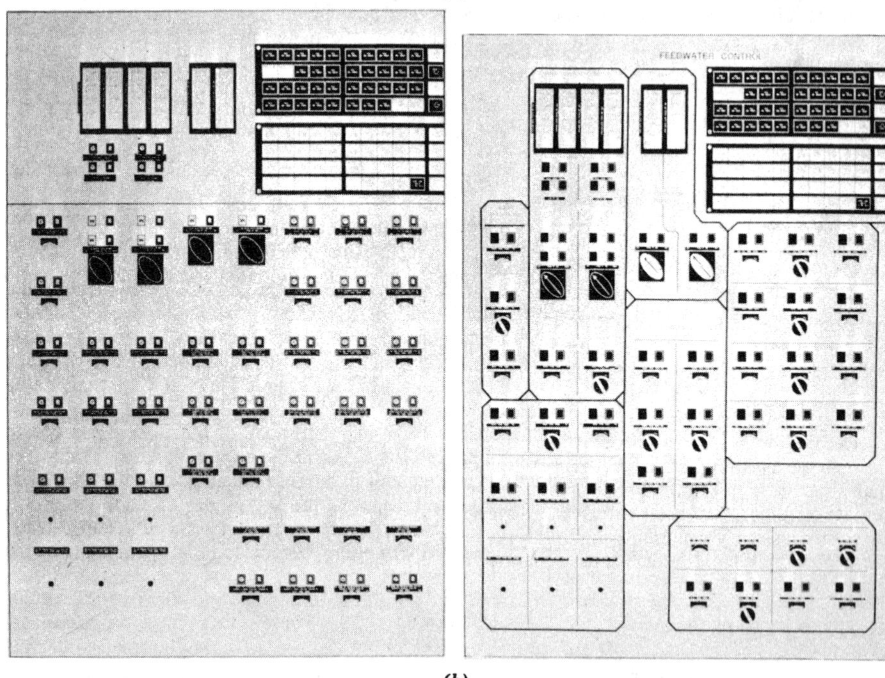

(b)

Figure 12.9. (*a*) A typical reactor control room is exemplified in the Ginna Nuclear Station control room. Shown are the various dials, meters, and controls needed to operate the plant. It is not uncommon, if the plant has two nuclear reactor units, that both control panels are located in the same room. When this is done, it is important for human factors purposes that the control panels be identical. It is particularly poor design to have "mirror-image" panels. This can lead to confusion in times of stress. (Courtesy Rochester Gas and Electric.) (*b*) Many nuclear control rooms are being upgraded to include operator decision support aids. One simple aid is the use of taped lines to group indicators so that relationships are apparent to operators. Prior to the accident at TMI, some control room designs clustered elements, but used no markings. (Courtesy EPRI.) Left: a representative control panel. Right: Human factors enhancement of panel. Note no switches or indicators have been moved.

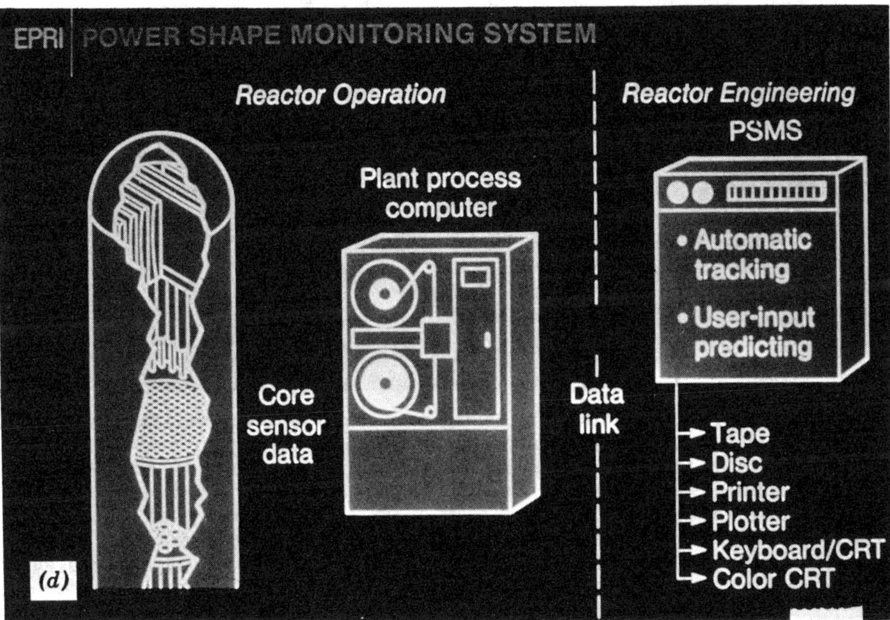

Figure 12.9. (*c*) Another operator aid is a Disturbance Analysis and Surveillance System (DASS) which gives an operator a real-time analysis of system transients. The DASS will diagnose the cause of the transient and display for the operator suggested strategies to allow system recovery. (Courtesy EPRI.) (*d*) Still another operator aid is a Power Shape Monitoring System (PSMS). This is particularly useful in a BWR. It provides a greatly enhanced capability to monitor operating limits in the core. The user-interactive system automatically tracks the state of the core with calculations for power, exposure, and fuel reliability. It can also be used in a predictive mode to predict the effects of anticipated operational strategies. (Courtesy EPRI.)

Figure 12.10. Advanced control rooms. During severe transients, operators in the past had problems finding and analyzing critical information about reactors. To improve this situation, the newest control rooms have more diagnostic aids, CRT displays, and computer controls. Part (*a*), showing an advanced Westinghouse control room, is one such concept. The extensive use of CRT displays allows an operator to receive all necessary information on the system and to execute system commands from a single location. (Courtesy Westinghouse Electric Corp.) Part (*b*) shows a new type of display, called a Safety Panel Display System (SPDS). Its function is to monitor all the parameters that are the operational safety indicators for the system: reactivity, coolant, inventory, heat removal, and containment integrity. These indicators are displayed in real time. (Courtesy EPRI.) Part (*c*) shows one of the parameters, reactivity, that could be instantaneously displayed by the SPDS. Other parameters that are available include temperatures, pressures, flows, coolant levels, etc. (Courtesy EPRI.)

SECONDARY HEAT REMOVAL A
PRIMARY COOLANT INVENTORY A
CONRAC
(b)

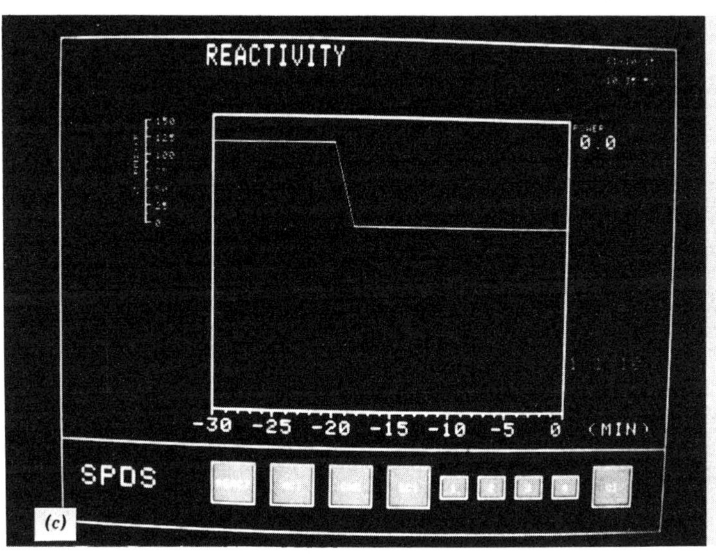
REACTIVITY
0.0
-30 -25 -20 -15 -10 -5 0 (MIN)
SPDS
(c)

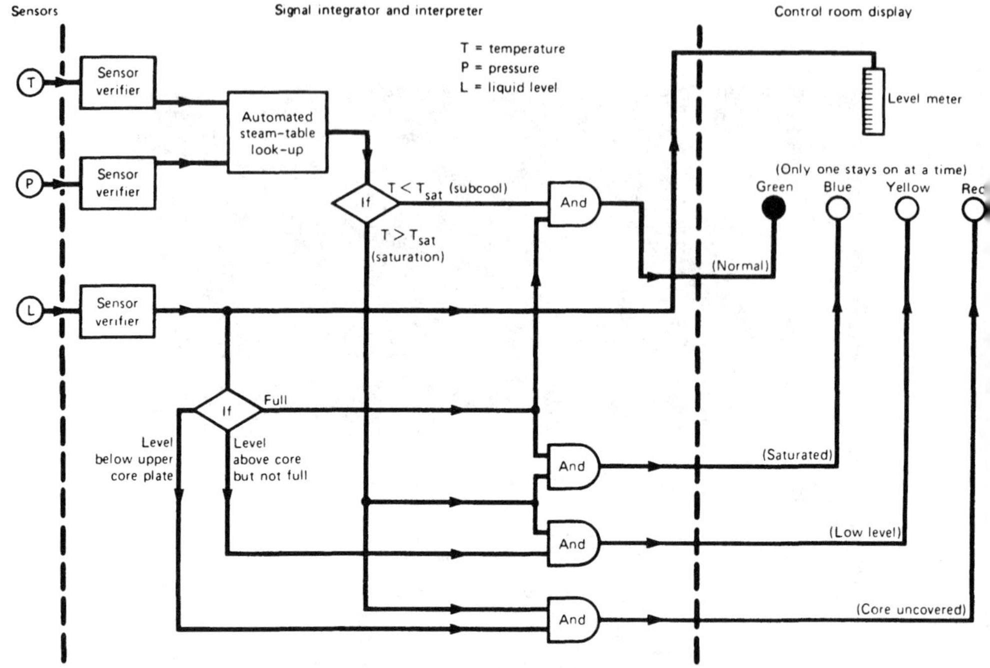

Figure 12.11. Example of a "smart" coolant monitor. [From Y. Y. Hsu and A. Hon, *Nuclear Safety* **22,** 149 (1981).]

system is operated manually. Above a pedetermined percentage of full power, the reactor control system operates automatically, thereby regulating the system temperature. The details of a typical reactor protection system are given in Figure 12.13.

The actual power in the reactor is monitored by neutron level detectors which are sensitive to the wide range (10 decades) of power levels that the reactor might produce (Figure 12.14). To cover so wide a range of power, three sets of neutron detectors are used: source range, intermediate range, and power range. Any change in core reactivity can be inferred by the rate of change of the neutron flux seen by these monitors, while the core power level is proportional to their signal.

The long-term control of core reactivity is usually accomplished by means of chemical "shims." This means use of boric acid in the coolant for PWRs and burnable poisons (usually gadolinia, although europia and hafnium are sometimes considered) in the fuel for BWRs. In the case of a boron shim technique, the concentration of the boric acid must be adjusted downward as the nuclear fuel builds up fission products throughout core lifetime. This is referred to as boron "letdown." As seen in Figure 12.15, the boron concentration is usually dropped quite rapidly during the first 200 MWd/t of fuel burnup after refueling due to the effects of the new fuel elements. Thereafter, the boron concentration is more slowly adjusted downward until the next loading of new fuel. The burnable poisons are routinely used in BWRs to control excess reactivity, especially in the first fuel cycle. How this might work is illustrated in Figure 12.16, which shows how various amounts of gadolinia level the reactivity of a BWR fuel assembly throughout its fuel cycle. This reduces power peaking in the core and leads to better fuel utilization. However, more recently, the use of such materials in PWRs is being contemplated. Table 12.8 summarizes the effects of burnable poison used in PWRs. The main disadvantage of burnable poisons seems to be the more difficult design and manufacture of the fuel assemblies. Their considerable effect on the boron letdown curve is shown in Figure 12.17.

System Chemistry

In all LWRs, the coolant chemistry, in both primary and secondary systems, must be closely controlled for good plant operations. The coolant system water chemistry must be selected to minimize corrosion, and its composition must be periodically analyzed to verify that the reactor coolant quality meets the specifications. Otherwise, costly equipment failures with long plant

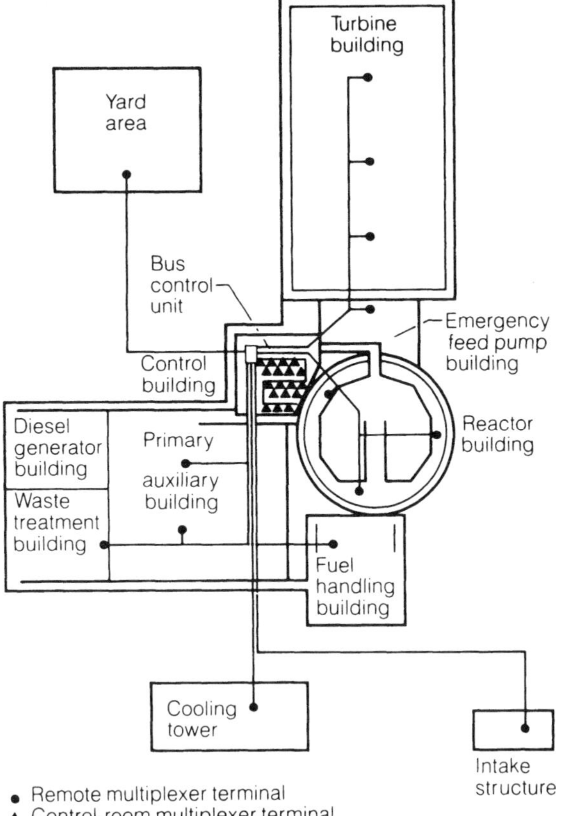

Figure 12.12. Typical multiplexing system installation, showing distribution of remote terminals through the plant. The typical RMS (Remove Multiplexing System) has approximately 20 field terminals, 20 control building terminals, and a pair of redundant control units. The communication highway also contains redundancy and supports transmission rates close to one million bits of information per second. There is a growing interest in using fiber optics as the transmission medium because of advantages in noise immunity and isolation. [From *EPRI Journal* (May 1978).]

outages may result. One notable example is the corrosion problem in the steam generators of some PWRs.

In PWRs, chemicals are added to the reactor coolant system to control the coolant pH during initial start-up and subsequent operation, to scavenge coolant oxygen during start-up, and to control the oxygen level due to radiolysis during power operation. Dissolved oxygen markedly increases the corrosion potential of steels. Figure 12.18 demonstrates the necessity for oxygen control showing that even in highly pure water type 304 stainless steel corrodes rapidly when the oxygen levels exceed 100 ppb. Typical oxygen content and pH limits for operations are shown in Table 12.9 for PWRs.

The pH control chemical employed in PWRs is lithium hydroxide. This chemical is chosen for its compatibility with the materials and water chemistry of borated water/stainless steel/zirconium/Inconel systems. The lithium hydroxide is introduced into the reactor coolant system via the charging flow. The lithium hydroxide concentration is maintained in the range specified for pH control.

During reactor start-up from the cold condition, hydrazine is employed as an oxygen scavenging agent. The hydrazine is introduced into the reactor coolant system the same way as the pH control agent.

Dissolved hydrogen is employed to control and scavenge oxygen produced by water radiolysis in the core region. Sufficient partial pressure of hydrogen is maintained in the volume control tank to attain the specified equilibrium concentration of hydrogen in the reactor coolant. A pressure

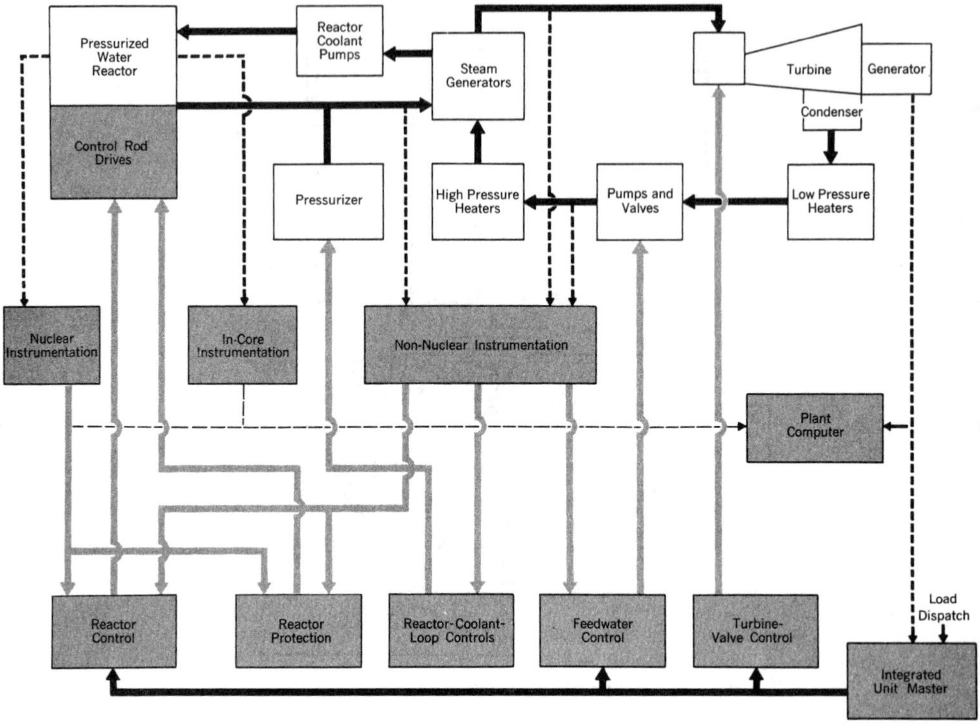

Figure 12.13. Instrumentation, control, and protection functions for a PWR. The broken lines represent the instrumentation inputs from the plant, including reactor measurements by the nuclear and in-core instrumentation, and reactor coolant loop, steam, feedwater, turbine, and generator measurements by the non-nuclear instrumentation. The thin dashed lines represent inputs to the information and computing system, which acquires and processes data from all the instrumentation systems. (From *Steam, Its Generation and Use*, 39th ed., Babcock & Wilcox Co., 1978.)

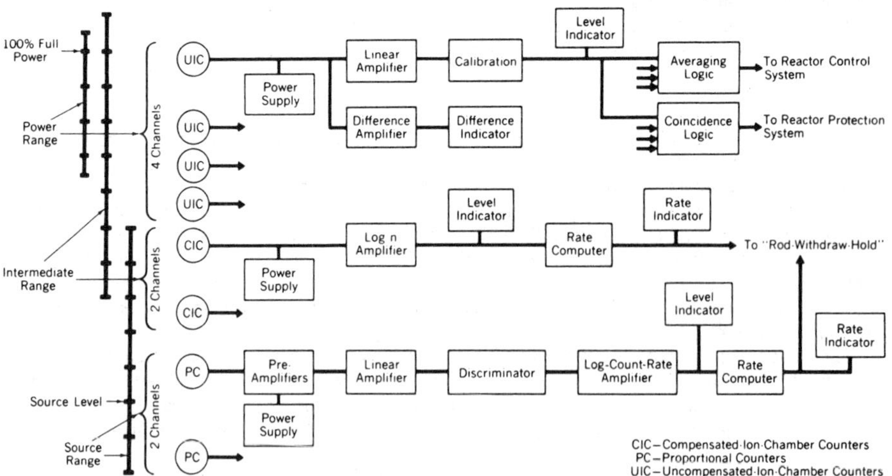

Figure 12.14. Nuclear instrumentation system. The nuclear instrumentation system monitors the reactor neutron power from below source level when the reactor is shut down to over 125% of full power. The instrumentation provides 13 decades of neutron flux information to include margins at both ends of the operating scale and allow for variations in source strength and leakage flux at full power. (From *Steam, Its Generation and Use*, 39th ed., Babcock & Wilcox Co., 1978.)

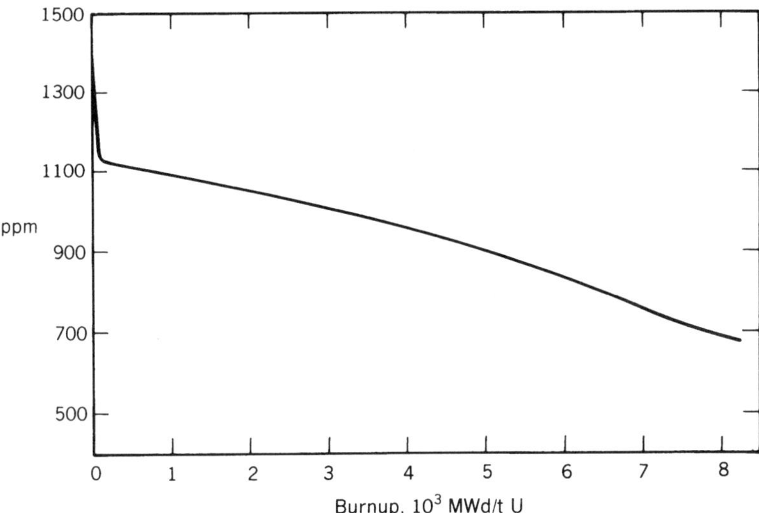

Figure 12.15. Boron letdown curve. Chemical shim control of reactivity in PWRs is provided by the addition of boric acid to the coolant. This allows the reactor to be controlled with the control rods nearly removed from the core, resulting in a more uniform power distribution. As the fuel builds up fission products during operation, less boron is required in the coolant. This is referred to as boron "let-down." A typical PWR fuel assembly is discharged at 33,000 MWd/t, but there are only 11,000 MWd/t exposure between refueling outages.

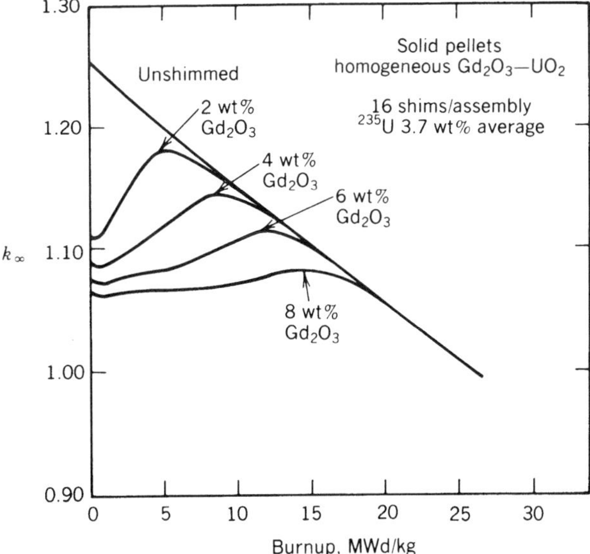

Figure 12.16. Fuel reactivity versus burnup for various concentrations of Gd_2O_3. (From CEND-391.)

Table 12.8. Summary on the Effects of Gadolinium Insertion in PWRs

	Items	Advantage	Disadvantage
1.	Design of the gadolinium distribution	Four more parameters for flux shaping and reactivity control (enrichment, number, distribution), better control of transient cycle	Complicated design, more experience required
2.	Control of the reactivity investment	Boric acid reduction and concentration, more constant or longer cycle length	
3.	Boric acid reduction and concentration kept more constant: effect on core behavior	Larger reactivity worth of boron, temperature coefficient more negative, less dilution operation	
3a.	Increase of reactivity worth of boric acid	SIBA system more effective	
3b.	Temperature coefficient more negative	LOCA, LOF, transient overpower	Steam line break, increase of load
3c.	Increase of reactivity worth of safety rods	Better control, advantageous for plutonium recycle	Rod ejection, more effective
4.	Environmental impact (population and workers' doses)	Less production of *T*, less liquid waste, less boron poison waste, improvements in storage and handling.	

Source: C. Vandenberg et al., *Nuclear Technology* **46,** 500 (1979).

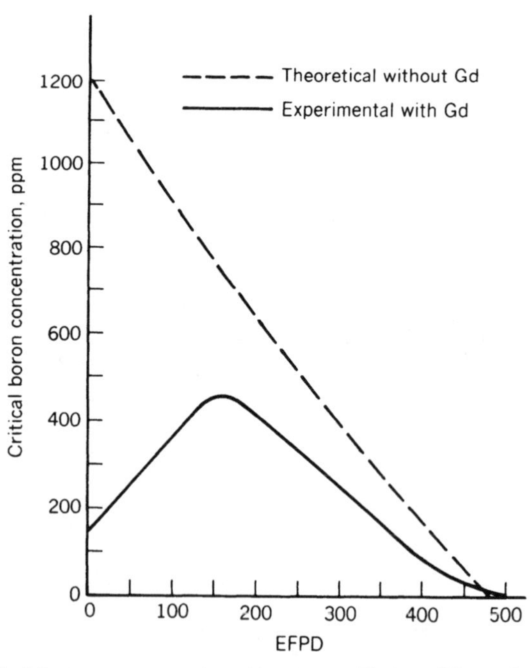

Figure 12.17. Critical boron concentration versus core lifetime. [From C. Vandenberg et al., *Nuclear Technology* **46,** 500 (1979).]

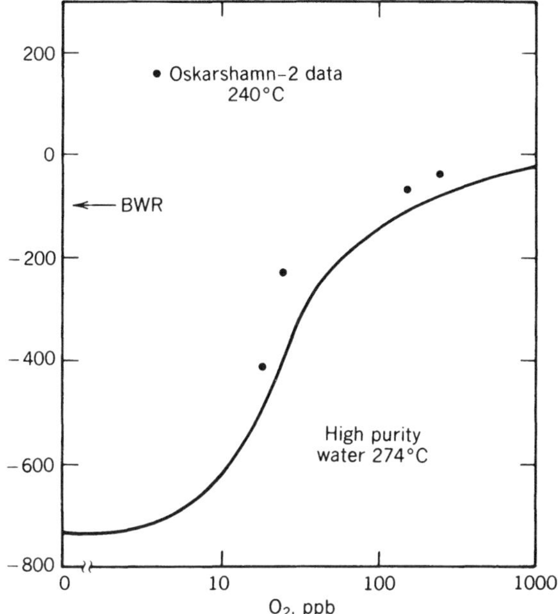

Figure 12.18. The effect of dissolved O_2 on the corrosion potential of type 304 stainless steel. [From B. Gordon and M. Indig, *Trans. Am. Nuclear Soc.* **35,** 491 (1980).]

control valve in the vapor space of the volume control tank can be adjusted to provide the correct hydrogen concentration needed.

In BWRs it is more difficult to control coolant chemistry using volatile chemicals such as hydrazine and hydrogen because, unlike PWRs, the system is not closed. The chemicals can leak out through the turbine glands and condenser seals. This is one of the primary reasons why BWRs operate close to neutral pH. However, new techniques have been recently developed in Sweden to use hydrogen to reduce the corrosion potential of BWRs.

Another new possibility is being developed to control corrosion. Technetium (^{99}Tc), a fission product available from spent fuel, has the potential to reduce corrosion in primary and secondary cooling loops in power reactors. It works as a corrosion inhibitor. About 5 ppm of ^{99}Tc in the coolant water is sufficient to coat any steel surface in contact with the water. Technetium, still being researched, is not yet available for reactor use.

Steam and Water Purity in Secondary Systems (PWRs)

The combination of oxygen and dissolved salts from impurities in the steam or water of reactor secondary systems invariably leads to corrosion. This corrosion can be accelerated in components under mechanical stress, severely impacting their reliability and economic performance. The turbine and steam generators are particularly affected. The secondary loop of a PWR cycles steam through the high-pressure and low-pressure turbines. The steam then turns to liquid in the condenser and returns to the steam generator to be revaporized. Figure 12.19 shows how fine tuning the water chemistry can help reduce corrosion in the secondary system.

Table 12.9. Reactor Coolant Water Chemistry in a PWR

pH	Between 4.2 (high boric acid concentration) and 10.5 (low boric acid concentration)
Dissolved oxygen	0.1 ppm (max)
Chloride	0.15 ppm (max)
pH control agent (LiOH)	0.2–2.2 ppm Li
Boric acid	Variable from 0 to 4000 ppm boron

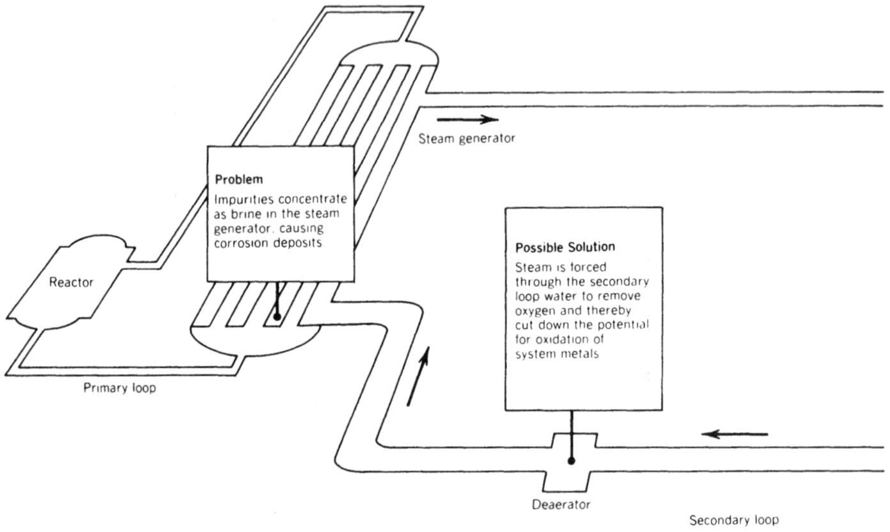

Figure 12.19. Fine-tuning the chemistry of water and steam as a way of avoiding corrosion

The most common source of impurities is the condenser, where water and air can leak from the thousands of cooling-water tubes into the secondary loop, a problem exacerbated by the vacuum conditions in the steam cycle that tend to draw fluid through leaks. Other sources of impurities are boiler feedwater from inside the loop, which can carry oxide deposits from corrosion in the condenser and feedwater heater chain, and makeup water from outside the loop, which can contain particles (clay, sand, or silt) and dissolved organic substances from river or lake water.

As we have seen in the last section, primary-loop water, because it surrounds the uranium fuel rods, is controlled after demineralization to maintain conditions that preclude corrosion of the fuel rod cladding. Secondary-loop water, however, has only recently been acknowledged as a generic troublemaker that warrants comprehensive monitoring and analysis. Relatively few PWRs as yet control secondary water to a similar degree. Several plants have effectively reduced impurities, and therefore corrosion, by installing a demineralizer for the makeup water, a resin-bed system to clean condensed steam from the condenser, and a deaerator to remove oxygen from the water and so lower the risk of system metal oxidation.

In PWRs, 90% of all cracks in turbine discs have occurred at the dry-to-wet transition zone, dubbed the Wilson line. At full operating load, steam enters a PWR low-pressure turbine at about 500°F (260°C) and 200 psi (1380 kPa). As the steam rushes through the turbine, its pressure and temperature drop. At some point, which differs with different turbine load conditions, the steam begins to condense, some of it contacting the turbine surfaces, where salts accumulate. This dew point area receives the brunt of concentrated acid or caustic impurities. The concentration phenomenon at the Wilson line occurs in both evaporation and condensation. To illustrate, the evaporation of a dilute hydrochloric acid solution results in an increased concentration of acid in the liquid phase because the steam removes more water than acid. Correspondingly, at the initial stages of condensation, all the steam has not yet condensed to completely dilute the solution to its original low concentration in the steam.

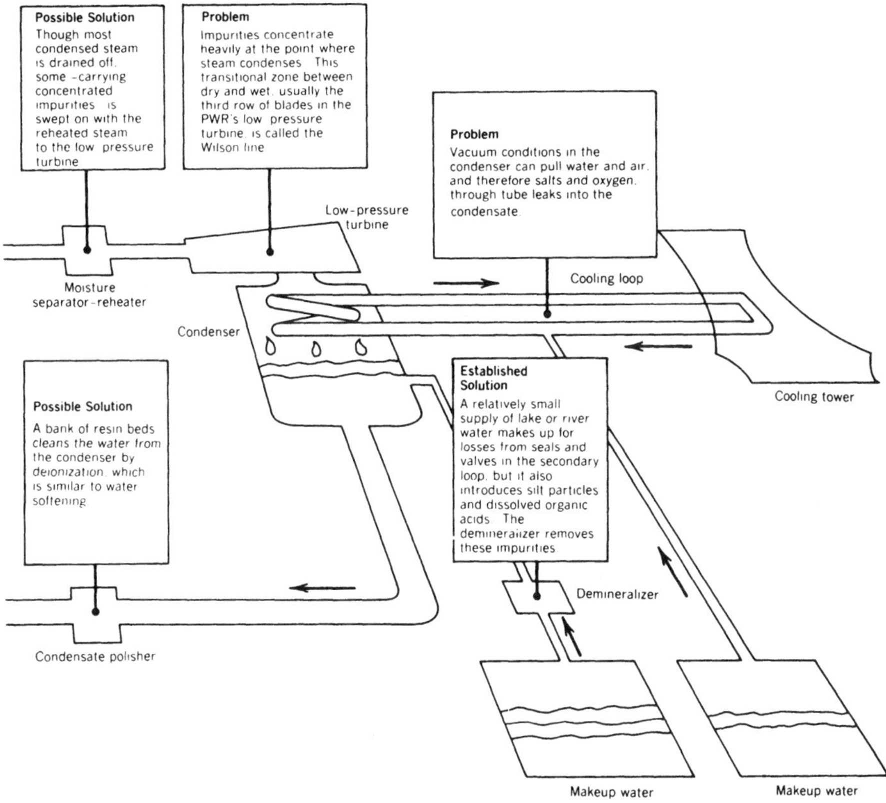

damage in the secondary loop of pressurized water reactors. [From *EPRI Journal* (October 1982).]

Most of the iron oxide tends to remain in the steam generator. Of the 10 million lb (4.5×10^6 kg) of feedwater that pass through the secondary circuit each hour, 1–10 ppb (by weight) is iron oxide. That proportion is common for a fairly clean system; in a more heavily contaminated system, the proportion could reach 10–20 ppb, translating to about 1 ton/yr of iron oxide that travels with the feedwater and deposits in the steam generator. Corrosion products from various sources not only initiate cracking but also can inhibit heat transfer in heat exchangers, cause blocking and denting of tubes, and occlude flow regions because of their porosity.

The degradation of steam generator tubes is of concern because they are part of the reactor coolant pressure boundary. In addition to this safety concern, the excessive maintenance and repair requirements caused by steam generator tube corrosion have resulted in high occupational radiation exposures. To properly monitor the state of the steam generators, In-Service Inspections (ISI) are made. The ISI requirements provide for periodic inspections of steam generators to demonstrate pressure boundary integrity. Tubes that are degraded to the extent that their integrity cannot be assured before the next inspection are removed from service. This is usually done by plugging any damaged tubes.

Turbines are also periodically inspected. The concern is that corrosion of the turbine components may lead to their disintegration under high mechanical stress or transient loads. Several catastrophic failures of turbines have occurred at fossil fuel plants (Table 12.10). Chunks of metal in excess of 2000 kg have been thrown out of the turbine building on occasion. Although such failures have not occurred at nuclear plants,† continual inspection is carried out to detect incipient failures early.

†Yankee Rowe recently failed the L-1 disc of its turbine. The debris was retained in the turbine casing.

Table 12.10. Known Turbine Generator Failures at Operating Speed in Fossil Fuel Power Plants

Manufacturer/Station	Size, MWe	Year of Failure	Type of Failure	Cause of Failure	External Missiles
1. General Electric (Tanners Creek 1)	100	1953	First-stage disc brake	High-temperature rupture	No
2. G.E.C. Turbine Generators, Ltd. (Hinkley Point A-5)	87	1969	Disc failure	Brittle fracture	Yes
3. G.E.C. Turbine Generators, Ltd. (Hinkley Point A-4)	87	1969	Disc failure	Brittle fracture	Yes
4. G.E.C. Turbine Generators, Ltd. (Hinkley Point A-6)	87	1970	Disc failure	Brittle fracture	Yes
5. Mitsubishi (ENESA)	330	1970	Rotor failure	Flawed	Yes
6. Westinghouse (Gallatin 1—TVA)		1974	Rotor failure	Fatigue	Yes
7. Westinghouse (Shippingport—Duquesne)	150	1974	Disc failure	Brittle failure stress corrosion	No
8. Allis-Chalmers (Oak Creek Power Co. 3—Wisconsin Electric)	130	1977	Last stage disc—low-pressure turbine	Probably brittle fracture	Yes

Source: R. H. Broadhurst et al., *Trans. Am. Nuclear Soc.* **35**, 391 (1980).

Water Quality in BWRs

BWRs use high-purity water without additives. Impurity levels in the coolant are controlled by the reactor water cleanup system and by using high-quality feedwater. To reduce impurities, several procedures are used, including oxygen control, full-flow condensate demineralization, and shutting down reactor operations when the level is too high. Component materials are also very important. For instance, stainless steel is used for feedwater heater tubes. Condenser designs must prevent in-leakage; superior performance is being obtained with titanium alloys for condenser tubing.

BWR primary coolant contains 0.2–0.4 ppm oxygen during normal operation. These levels are inherent in the operating characteristics of a BWR: the oxygen content is the direct result of radiolysis. Radiolysis cannot be controlled in the core, but is minimized to prevent accelerated corrosion of the system. Since the BWR is an open system, hydrogen cannot be easily introduced into the system to scavenge oxygen. The pH of the coolant water in a BWR is close to neutral (between 6 and 8 at 25°C). Unlike a PWR, boron and lithium are not added to the coolant.

Chemistry Control and Radiation Exposure

Good chemistry control is important for keeping radiation levels around a nuclear plant to a minimum, and reducing occupational exposure. Corrosion-product contaminants within the nuclear cycle are the primary source of radioactivity associated with out-of-core surfaces. As the metals of the system corrode, impurities are released to the process stream and can deposit on fuel surfaces. While residing in the core, these impurities can be activated to radioactive isotopes. If this material becomes resuspended in the primary coolant, it can deposit on out-of-core plant surfaces. Such deposits are the primary source of plant radiation fields.

Most of the corrosion products present in the water of power plant systems have magnetic susceptibility and exist as particulates. In PWRs the principal primary-system contaminant is the strongly magnetic nickel ferrite. The iron oxides magnetite (strongly magnetic) and hematite (weakly magnetic) are the dominant corrosion products in BWRs. One device for reducing fission product transport by electromagnetic filtering is shown in Figure 12.20.

Good chemistry (especially in the feedwater) is also important for reducing corrosion in key components to prevent extensive plant outages for repair. A good example is the accelerated corrosion in many PWR steam generators. Close attention to coolant chemistry has led to greatly reduced corrosion rates in many instances. Chemical feed equipment, shown in Figure 12.21, is provided to ensure proper chemistry control of the steam system during all modes of operation. This not only helps minimize corrosion of the steam generators but also reduces turbine deposits due to carry-over from the steam generators and free caustic formation.

When nuclear units were changed from phosphate-based water treatment to all-volatile treatment to avoid wastage corrosion (see Chapter 9), a different form of corrosion resulted. This attack, called denting, occurs when magnetite (Fe_3O_4) forms in steam generator crevices. Research showed that chloride, copper, and oxygen were the principal chemical aggravators of denting. Various chemical procedures, such as treatment with $Ca(OH)_2$ and boric acid as shown in Figure 12.22, can control denting.

The corrosion products formed in the reactor primary system can become radioactive due to neutron activation in the core. They are referred to as activated corrosion products, although the term "crud" is often used. The rate at which radioactivity can build up is given in Figure 12.23. Cobalt is the most serious corrosion product. When activated, it forms ^{60}Co, an isotope with a 5.3-yr half-life and high-energy, very penetrating gamma rays. A large fraction of the radiation doses around primary systems comes from ^{60}Co. In addition to first entering the coolant as a corrosion product,† cobalt can enter the system by erosion of hard-faced surfaces. Many valve seats and control rod drive mechanisms use cobalt alloys‡ for hard-facing, that is, to protect bearing and wear surfaces (Tables 12.11a and 12.11b). Minute quantities of the cobalt can erode or be worn away from these surfaces and be activated. This process is illustrated in Figure 12.24. Reactor manufacturers are attempting to reduce the use of cobalt to eliminate this problem.

Design Changes

Corrosion problems have led to many design changes. One example is the redesign of PWR U-tube steam generator support plates to reduce denting. Quatre-foil broached supports and egg-crate designs help minimize the corrosion buildup which otherwise leads to failure. Recent research work has developed chemical systems capable of cleaning tube-to-tubesheet and support plate crevices that further help the situation.

†Cobalt is present in trace amounts in steel and Inconel materials.
‡Principally stellite.

Figure 12.20. High-temperature filter for reduction of primary system radioactivity. (Courtesy EPRI.)

Other design changes that reduce corrosion, however, can have an impact on plant performance. An example of this is the routing of moisture separator drains in once-through steam generators. Two possibilities exist: route them to the high-pressure feedwater heaters or to the condenser hotwell. The former is more thermally efficient, while the latter greatly reduces corrosive impurities because the flow passes through the condensate demineralizers. As in this example, the choice often is not clear cut, and the various economic factors must be closely evaluated.

12.6. CONTROLLING SYSTEM TRANSIENTS

Nuclear reactors are designed for stable, steady-state operation. To achieve this, the key system parameters must be carefully controlled. There exist complex relationships between the neutronic behavior of the core, temperature and pressure of coolant, system flow rates, control rods and poisons, just to name a few. Any of these parameters can be used to change the power level of the core. An inadvertent change in any of these parameters, however, can cause a system transient which must be controlled for safe and economic operation of the plant.

The power level of the reactor is governed by a complex set of differential equations:

$$\frac{dP}{dt} = \frac{\rho - \bar{\beta}}{\Lambda} P + \Sigma\lambda_i C_i \tag{12.1}$$

$$\frac{dC_i}{dt} = \frac{\beta_i}{\Lambda} P - \lambda_i C_i \tag{12.2}$$

C_i = precursor concentration
P = power

Figure 12.21. Chemical feed equipment in a PWR. (Courtesy ENEL.)

β_i = delayed neutron fraction
$\bar{\beta}$ = average delayed neutron fraction
Λ = prompt neutron generation time
λ_i = parameter related to delayed neutron half-life

These are referred to as the Inhour equations because they determine the period (i.e., the time rate of change) of the reactor core, usually calculated in units of *in*verse *hours*. This formulation treats the core as if it were a point, although more complicated formulations treat its three-dimensional spatial aspects. The importance of delayed neutrons in controlling a reactor was already covered in Chapter 2.

The key parameter in these equations for our present discussion is the reactivity, ρ. Its size at each instant determines the system behavior. The net reactivity is calculated from the control rod positions, thermal hydraulic feedback, and all the other power feedback mechanisms of the system. It is the perturbations of these reactivity mechanisms that give rise to transients, which go by such names as (control) rod withdrawal accident, loss-of-flow condition, turbine trip, cold water injection accident, and so on. As an example, Figure 12.25 shows a system response to an uncontrolled rod withdrawal.

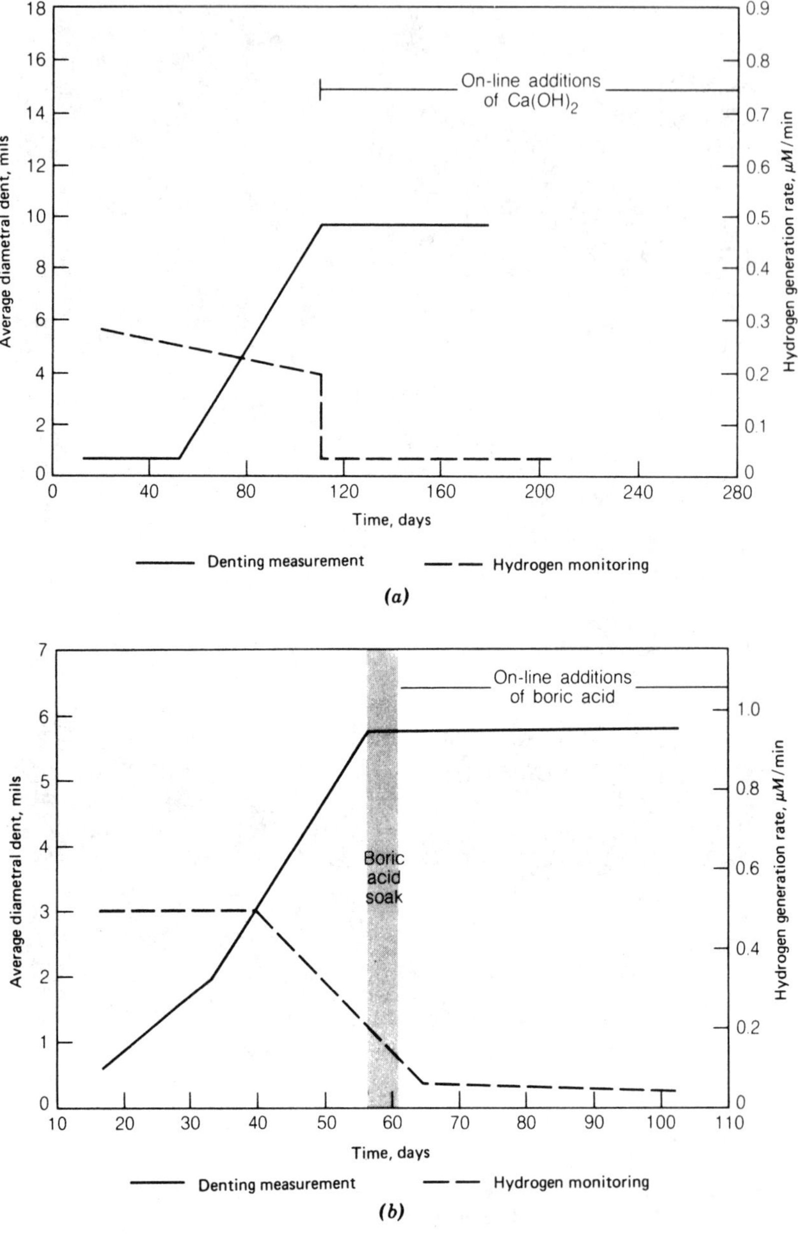

Figure 12.22. (*a*) On-line treatment with $Ca(OH)_2$. This process is effective in arresting denting. [From *EPRI Journal* (October 1981).] (*b*) Soak followed by on-line treatment with boric acid is also effective in arresting denting. [From *EPRI Journal* (October 1981).]

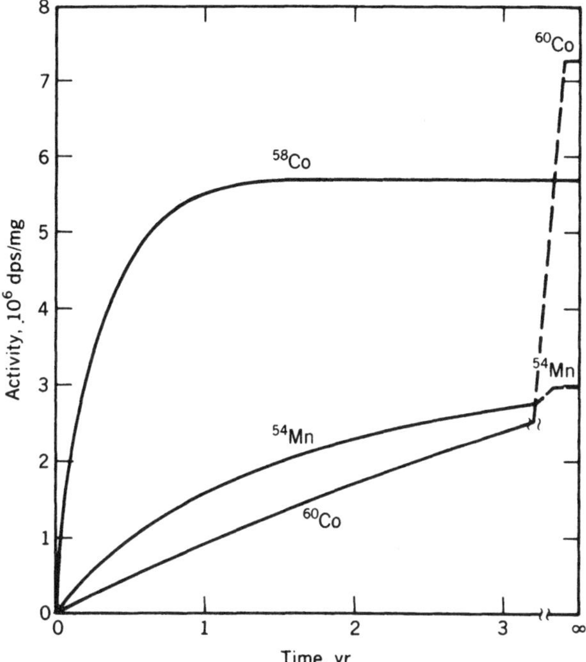

Figure 12.23. Core induced activity 304 SS. (From P. Cohen, *Water Coolant Technology of Power Reactors*, American Nuclear Society, 1969.)

During the first minute of the transient, the power and moderator temperature in the core slowly increase, until the reactor scrams, then both fall rapidly to low values. The response to transients varies considerably between reactor types, as does the reactivity in the core between hot and cold conditions, and so on. The gross reactivity parameters for various reactors are given in Table 12.12. For LWRs, the shutdown margin is 1% assuming the most effective control rod is stuck. This margin is sufficient to rapidly reduce a reactor's power, as was evident in this example.

When a transient occurs, the reactor control system automatically tries to counteract the transient and to restore the system to its original operating state. In mathematical terms, this requires the reactivity change be brought back to zero. This can be accomplished by either reversing the initiator of the transient (for example, restoring feedwater flow in a loss-of-feedwater transient), or by modifying some of the other system parameters (e.g., partly inserting control rods to accommodate a step decrease in turbine load). If the transient is severe enough, the system scrams and steam is dumped directly into the condenser, bypassing the turbine. Such a situation is illustrated in Figure 12.26. In less than a minute, the system had scramed and stabilized, while the power was reduced to its decay heat level.

For extremely severe transients, for example, a coolant pipe break, the plant goes into a mode of operation designed to mitigate the consequence of such accidents. At this point, maintaining the various safety functions of the plant becomes of primary importance. As shown in Figure 12.27, auxiliary services, containment integrity, and radiation control are vital. The decisions of the operator now become critical. His mission is to get the plant in a safe shutdown condition, and maintain vital safety functions. He can rely on the operating procedures, process computers, and safety panel to help him. He follows the strict logic sequence shown in Figure 12.28. In emergency situations, the operator is also helped by the design of the plant, particularly by the multiple ways that can be used to accomplish safety functions. Figure 12.29 illustrates this point. Figure 12.29*a* is the method preferred to control the primary and secondary coolant pressure. If the system pressure drops and off-site power is available, shown in Figure 12.29*b*, then the Safety Injection System (SIS) and Auxiliary FeedWater (AFW) system come on. If off-site power also fails, Figure 12.29*c*, the SIS and AFW still operate, but the Atmospheric Dump Valve (ADV) opens in the secondary system. On the other hand, if the system pressure is too high, as in Figure 12.29*d*, the Primary Safety Valve (PSV) and Pressure Operated Relief Valve (PORV) open in the primary while the ADV opens in the secondary coolant system. Thus all vital safety functions can be maintained

Table 12.11a. BWR Systems, Materials, and Cobalt Release Estimates

	Surface Area, dm^2				Estimated Cobalt Release, g/yr
	Carbon Steel	Stainless Steel	Ni–Cr–Fe	Cobalt-Based Alloys	
Reactor vessel and internals	5,000	983,000	28,000	285	56.4
Recirculation system	—	21,000	—	98	18.0
Control rod drives	—	101,000	38,000	103	6.0
Reheat steam system	1,618,000	148,000	—	469	141.6
Low-pressure turbine and heater drains	105,000	675,000	—	6	1.2
Main condenser	525,000	5,451,000[a]	—	—	—
Condensate system to no. 3 heater	168,000	756,000	—	42	7.2
Main steam and high-pressure heater drains	1,002,000	2,280,000	—	375	124.8
High-pressure feedwater system	74,000	780,000	—	84	15.6

Note: This analysis is based on Carolina Power & Light Co.'s Brunswick-2 reactor, a 2436-MW/(th) BWR/4.

[a]Condenser tubes 90-10 Cu–Ni.

Table 12.11b. PWR Systems, Materials, and Cobalt Release Estimates

	Inconel		Stainless Steel		Cobalt-Based Alloys		Total Estimated Cobalt Release, g/yr
	Surface Area, dm^2	Cobalt Release, g/yr	Surface Area, dm^2	Cobalt Release, g/yr	Surface Area, dm^2	Cobalt Release, g/yr	
Reactor coolant system[a]	1,520,000	32.8	179,000	3.7	684	63.9	100.4
Chemical and volume control system	—	—	21,000	0.7	41	1.7	2.4
Boric acid system	—	—	21,000	0.6	22	0.9	1.5
Shutdown cooling system	—	—	111,000	0.5	57	0.6	1.1

Source: M. Naughton, *EPRI Journal* **7**, 58 (June 1982).
Note: This analysis is based on a two-loop, 2560-MW/(th) PWR of Combustion Engineering, Inc., design.
[a]This system also contains Zircaloy (surface area 597,000 dm^2).

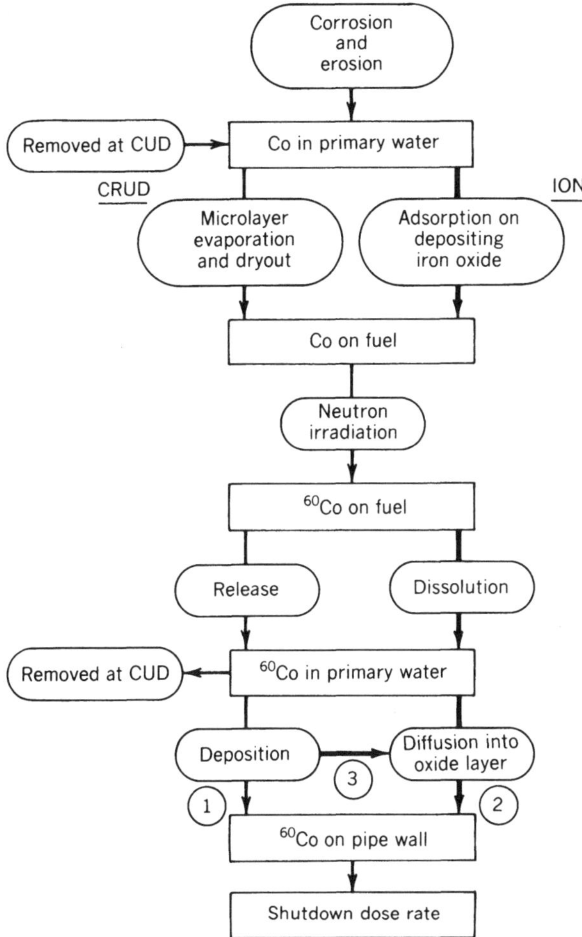

Figure 12.24. Basic processes in Co and ^{60}Co transport. (1) Insoluble cobalt is deposited directly on the fuel surface, while soluble cobalt is adsorbed on iron-oxide deposits on fuel surface. (2) ^{60}Co activated on the fuel surface is dissolved in the water as ion and some is released with iron-oxide as crud. (3) ^{60}Co in the water deposits on the pipe surface through three different processes: Process 1—Deposition of crud ^{60}Co on the surface. Process 2—Diffusion of ionic ^{60}Co into the iron-oxide layer on the surface. Process 3—Release of ^{60}Co from the crud on the surface and diffusion into the iron-oxide layer. [From Y. Matsushima et al., *Trans. Am. Nuclear Soc.* **32,** 759 (1979).]

through multiple system configurations. Of course, the effectiveness of any particular way depends on which systems are operable and the capacity of the subsystem used.

Power Distribution Transient

Reactors commonly undergo gross power transients during several normal operating procedures, such as reactor start-up, control rod adjustments, or load following. These transients are accompanied by significant changes in the core ^{135}Xe inventory, which in turn causes a reactivity transient. ^{135}Xe is a fission product which accumulates in the reactor core during operation. It has an exceptionally large neutron capture cross section of 3×10^6 barns, about 100,000 times greater than all the other long lived fission products together. A small part (about 0.2%) of ^{135}Xe comes directly from fission, but the majority comes from the radioactive decay of another fission product, tellurium:

$$^{135}\mathrm{Te} \xrightarrow{1\ \mathrm{min}} {}^{135}\mathrm{I} \xrightarrow{6.7\ \mathrm{hr}} {}^{135}\mathrm{Xe} \xrightarrow{9.2\ \mathrm{hr}} {}^{135}\mathrm{Cs} \tag{12.3}$$

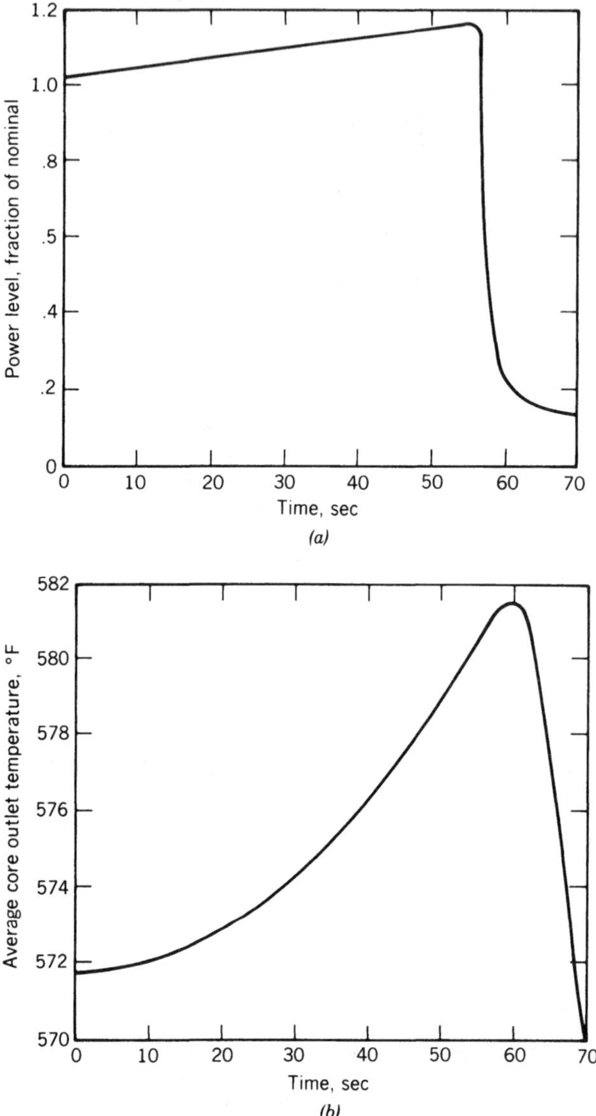

Figure 12.25. (*a*) Power response to uncontrolled rod withdrawal at full power; $\dot{\rho} = 2 \times 10^{-5}$/sec. (*b*) Temperature response to uncontrolled rod withdrawal at full power $\dot{\rho} = 2 \times 10^{-5}$/sec. (From E. E. Lewis, *Nuclear Power Reactor Safety*, Wiley-Interscience, New York, 1978.)

The buildup rate (6.7 hr) and decay rate (9.2 hr half-life) of ^{135}Xe are important in the concentration of this reactivity poison. When a reactor operates at constant power, ^{135}Xe equilibrium is reached in about one day. Because the amount of ^{135}Xe produced in a given part of the core is proportional to the local power, and delayed in time by the 6.7-hr ^{135}I decay rate (i.e., ^{135}Xe buildup rate), different parts of the core respond differently as the control rods are moved in and out at various times to adjust the power.

To maintain criticality during periods of changing xenon concentration, compensating reactivity must be added. In a PWR, the control rods are used for this purpose, while a BWR can adjust the moderator void fraction. Automatic control systems are available to execute control rod and void adjustment strategies. These systems considerably improve the operator's ability to respond to xenon transients. In a BWR, however, axial power variations are important because of the reactiv-

Table 12.12. Reactivity Values in Power Reactors

Item	Indian Point-2 (PWR)	Browns Ferry (BWR)	Fort St. Vrain (GCR)
Temperature defect ($\Delta\rho$); cold to hot zero power	0.050	0.028	0.028
Power defect ($\Delta\rho$); zero power to full power	0.020	0.040	0.037
Equilibrium xenon and samarium ($\Delta\rho$)	0.035	0.062	0.026
Fuel depletion and gross fission products ($\Delta\rho$)	0.170	0.120	0.055
Total installed reactivity ($\Delta\rho$)	0.275	0.250	0.146
Shutdown margin	1% with highest worth rod stuck	1% with the highest worth rod stuck; 4% with all rods in	0.077 Δk (80°F); all control rods inserted; 0.111 Δk (400°F), all rods in

Source: T. J. Thomson and J. G. Beckerley, *The Technology of Nuclear Reactor Safety,* MIT Press, Cambridge, 1973.

ity feedback† due to the voids in the core. Decreasing coolant flow increases the void fraction (i.e., decreases reactivity) in the upper part of the core. Increasing the flow has exactly the opposite effect. Older BWRs maintain constant coolant flow, letting the core power set the void fraction necessary for criticality.‡

Other fission products also build up in the reactor core during operation. These are "poisons" also, but they are mostly long-lived isotopes, reaching a maximum concentration just before a fuel element is discharged. These are relatively stable poisons, building up in the fuel at the rate of about 30 barns per fission. One notable exception is ^{149}Sm, which produces transients similar to ^{135}Xe, but of much smaller magnitude.

Reactor Start-up After Shutdown or Scram

Because ^{135}I has a shorter half-life than ^{135}Xe, the xenon concentration quickly increases to a peak value. This occurs because the iodine decays to xenon at a rate that is initially greater than the decay of the xenon [see Eq. (12.3)], and xenon is no longer being lost to neutron capture. The buildup reaches its peak 4–12 hr after shutdown, then slowly decays. Figure 12.30 illustrates this phenomenon. In large power reactors,§ the xenon transient following shutdown can be minimized by slowly reducing the power (coasting down) to burn out some of the xenon.

Because the xenon concentration grows after shutdown, it is often desirable to start the reactor up again as soon as possible, particularly after a rapid shutdown (scram). If this is done quickly ($\frac{1}{2}$ hr or less) then the xenon will not have yet built up to appreciable levels. Moreover, start-up after a brief shutdown is somewhat easier because the neutron level in the core is still high.¶ When the reactor is then started up, this neutron source will give an instrument response on the power monitors even before the control rods are withdrawn, and assist in rapidly coming up to full power. When a longer outage is required, the xenon concentration can be partly reduced by operating the reactor at low power levels prior to shutdown.

†The reactivity changes are such that they tend to destabilize the reactor, producing slow power oscillations. This is analogous to the ouput–feeding–input mechanisms of some electronic devices, and is referred to as feedback.

‡This "self-adjusting" ability is an important stability and control feature of BRWs.

§Xenon transients are smaller in power reactors than in research and other special reactors because the neutron flux is lower.

¶After 10-min shutdown, the neutron flux will have decayed only by a factor of 10^5 because of the presence of delayed neutrons.

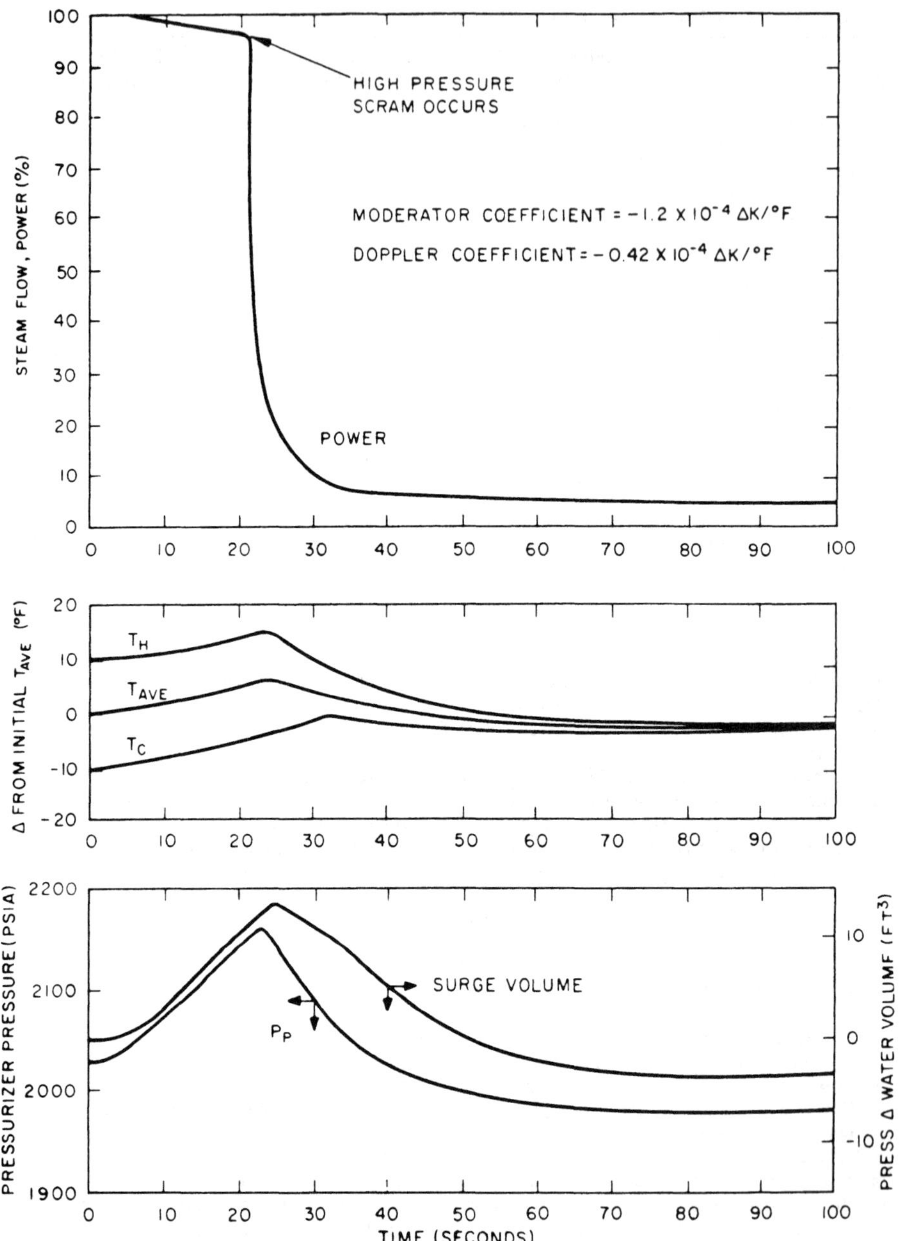

Figure 12.26. Complete loss of load with high-pressure scram at 2150 psia; four-loop PWR. (From Shippingport FSAR.)

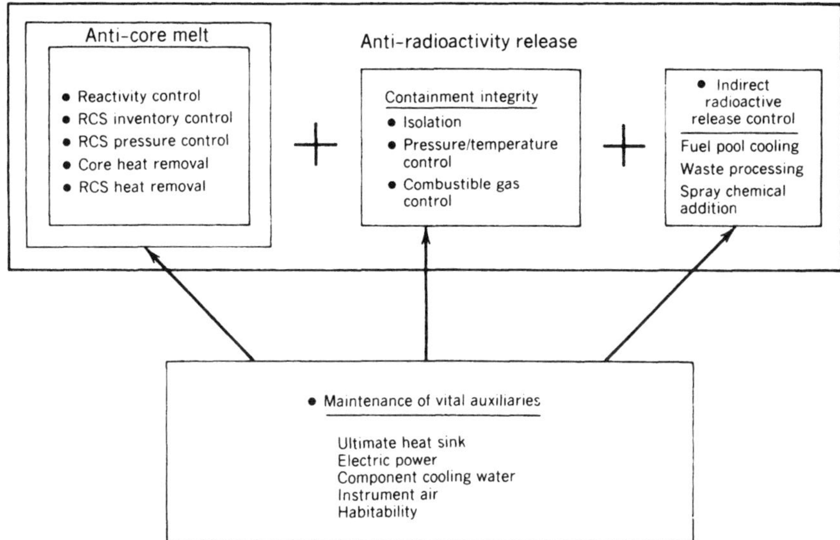

Figure 12.27. Classes of safety functions. [From W. R. Corcoran, *Nuclear Technology* **55**, 690 (1981).]

Hypothetical Severe Transients and System Behavior

Anticipated Transients Without Scram (ATWS) have been the subject of debate in the regulatory community for many years. It refers to a scenario in which an anticipated incident causes a reactor transient requiring the reactor protection system to scram the reactor, but for some reason the scram does not occur. The transient proceeds to its natural termination; potentially, the core is damaged and radiation may be released beyond the plant site, resulting in property damage and personal injuries.

An example of such a situation is the loss of feedwater flow to the steam generators of a PWR. This particular initiating event will produce a high system pressure if the reactor does not scram. The steam generator could dry out about 50 sec after the loss of main feedwater flow, resulting in the rapid increase in primary system pressure. The relief and safety valves will open at 2350 and 2500 psia, respectively, typically the setpoints for commercial plants. Because of the limited capacity of these valves, the pressure rises above 2700 psia about 50 sec later. The maximum pressure will be limited by the moderator temperature coefficient. The pressurizer will fill with coolant (i.e., go solid) and the relief and safety valves will start to discharge subcooled liquid.

Recovery from such an ATWS could still be accomplished even though the control rods cannot be inserted. The recovery procedure might start about 600 sec into the transient by manually opening the pressurizer relief valve to depressurize the primary system and injecting a highly concentrated boron solution through the high-pressure emergency core coolant system. The auxiliary feedwater system could be used to regulate the cooldown rate of the primary system. No radioactivity would be released in this ATWS scenario.†

12.7. REFUELING, MAINTENANCE, AND PLANT OUTAGES

A generating plant is designed to operate consistently at a given electric output. Obviously a plant can produce its maximum kilowatt-hours only if all essential equipment works perfectly and the power is always needed. A plant may not reach this ideal for various reasons: shutdowns (i.e., full outages) for refueling, equipment maintenance or component failure; operation at reduced power

†On February 25, 1983, the nuclear power industry's first ATWS occurred at the Salem 1 nuclear plant. The first sign of trouble was when operators received an indication that the water in one steam generator dropped to the low-low level, a condition at which automatic scram is to be triggered by reactor-trip circuit breakers. There are two such circuit breakers, but neither functioned, and the manual trip system was used to shut down the reactor. The ATWS was thusly terminated by the operator in approximately 30 sec.

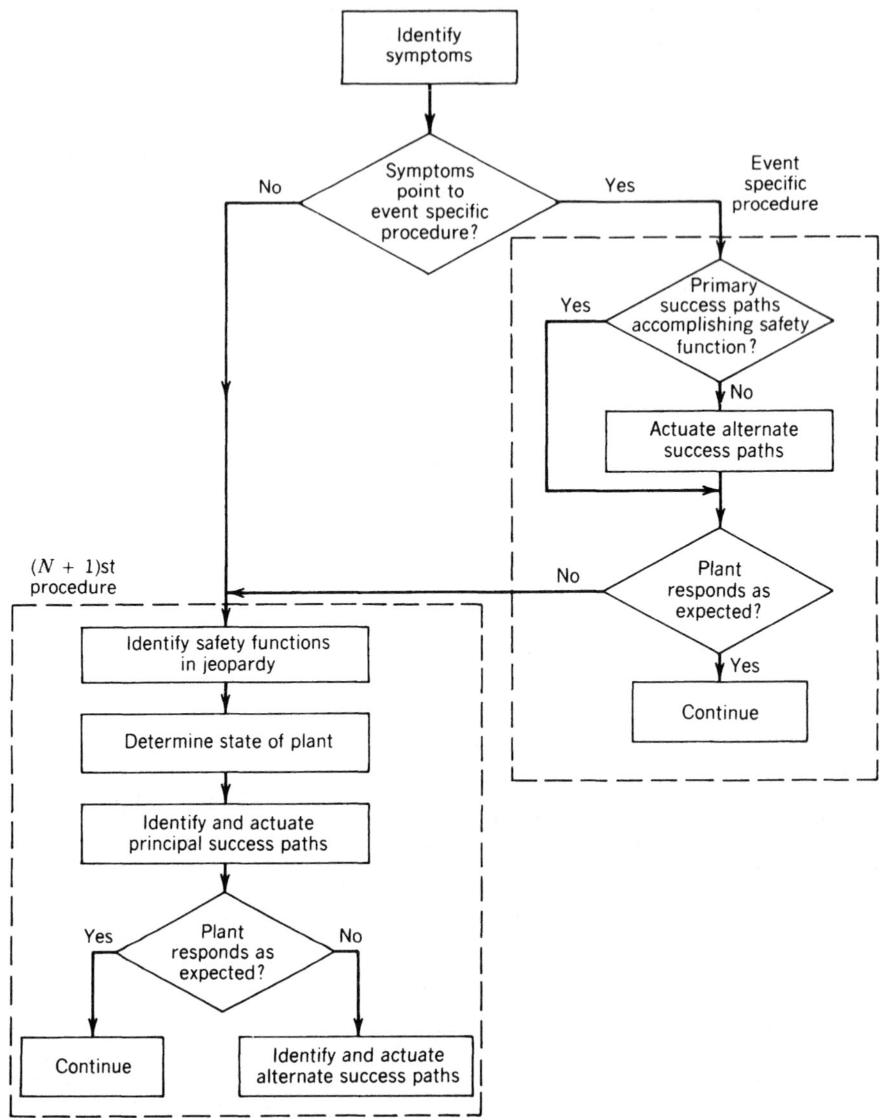

Figure 12.28. Operator action during an event. [From W. R. Corcoran, *Nuclear Technology* **55**, 690 (1981).]

(i.e., partial outages) caused by equipment problems or restrictions imposed by regulatory bodies; or lack of need for the power (load-following or economy outages). The way some of these factors might affect a plant's performance is given in Figure 12.31.

Of particular concern are nuclear plant outages which limit plant availability. These limiting factors may be due to a wide variety of causes. Some factors (such as refueling) are necessary to normal operation of a plant. Although plant availability for all nuclear plants has steadily improved over the years, utilities are always looking for further improvements.

The dominant cause of plant unavailability (other than refueling) varies with the reactor type and the manufacturer of the system. For example, with BWRs it has been due to nuclear fuel problems that lead to leaks. Table 12.13 shows that on average 749 hr/yr of full-power electrical production has been lost in BWRs for this problem alone, and that 560 hr/yr of this lost power could be possibly regained through operating improvements. When all the current fuel is replaced by advanced (8 × 8) fuel, much of this potential improvement will be achieved. Another cause of BWR unavailability is scram recovery, which can take up to 12 hr. This recovery time is being shortened by more sophisticated control rod withdrawal verification procedures. Table 12.14 gives some other systems and equipment-related activities that have been large contributors to plant downtime. For most of these limiting factors, potential improvements have been identified and are being implemented. Often a large fraction of the outage time has been for one-time modifications that are not expected to occur in future years.

The longest normal outage in LWRs is the refueling of the core with new fuel. About one-third of the fuel elements in a PWR (one-quarter in a BWR) are replaced each year. It is common to rearrange the rest of the fuel elements at this time to optimize fuel economics. Because the refueling outage takes several weeks, it is usually scheduled in the spring or fall of the year in the United States, when most utilities have low demand for power. Greater consideration is now being given to stretching the time between refueling outages to 18 months from the more common 12 months. This would improve the economics of the plant.

The annual refueling cycle common in most commercial nuclear power plants in the United States has evolved based upon the belief that refuelings can be performed in three weeks and that other plant maintenance can also be conveniently handled on the same annual basis. Refueling outages have proven to be highly complex operations requiring large efforts in planning, organization, and coordination, including supplementation of the normal contingent of plant personnel with outside contractor personnel. The refueling outage has attracted an increasing amount of diverse, nonrefueling operations. An example of this trend is shown in Figure 12.32 for one outage at the Zion reactor. Many equipment overhauls and modifications extended the outage over 60 days, much longer than normally desired. Many of the refueling operations are complex and require precise execution to minimize outage time. One such operation, shown in Figure 12.33, involves the removal of the reactor pressure vessel head.

A refueling outage may include 2000–3000 work orders, including such tasks as:

1. Tests of operating and safety-related equipment.
2. Inspections of key equipment.
3. Repairs.
4. Equipment replacement.
5. Maintenance (preventive and required).
6. Refueling operations.

Some of the major tasks are shown in Figure 12.34, which also gives the operations on the critical path to restarting the plant. To shorten the outage time, extensive planning is involved. As in any complex operation that is well run, the planning stage is essential to make on-schedule, on-budget outages possible. Equally important is the postoutage review that evaluates problems and successes of the outage and feeds the results to future planning activities. Some of the steps necessary for an efficient outage are given in Table 12.15.

Much maintenance is scheduled concurrent with the refueling outage. Of the various environmental impacts on maintenance activities, radiation and the ALARA measures required to reduce personnel exposure have the most profound effect. The need to accommodate maintenance workers who work in protective garments is a requirement sometimes overlooked in the past design of nuclear facilities. The maintenance manager is faced with restrictions in using available manpower while keeping exposure levels as low as possible and reasonably distributed among his staff. Furthermore, the productivity of maintenance personnel is reduced by many physical and administrative restrictions placed on activities at radioactive work sites. To overcome these restrictions, work is being done to develop remote viewing approaches, long handled tools, remote control mechanisms, and to apply robotic principles in future power plant design. One such advanced maintenance operation is shown in Figure 12.35.

12.8. PLANT SIMULATORS AND OPERATOR TRAINING

All plant operators are required by regulation to be specifically trained on the specific operation of the plant they will be licensed to run. A typical training schedule is shown in Figure 12.36. Much of this training is done at a power plant simulator nearly identical to the plant itself, as shown in Figure 12.37. The training requirements for license candidates and requalification training require control manipulations that cannot all be performed at the plant but require some to be performed on an applicable simulator having similar characteristics to the operator's own plant. For example, simulators with conventional control rooms are not acceptable for training of operators for plants with advanced control center designs.

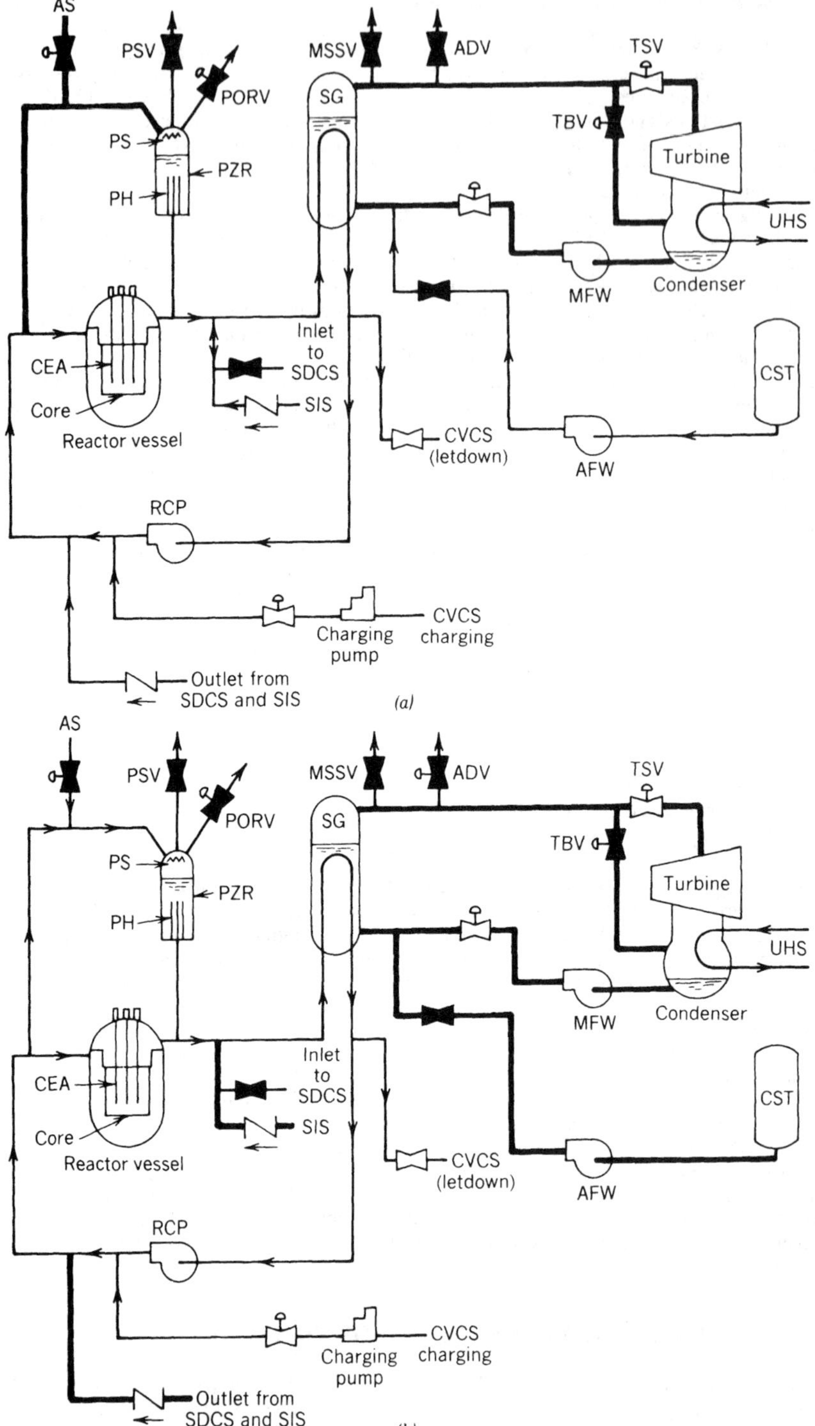

Figure 12.29. RCS pressure control. Multiple means of controlling the pressure in the reactor coolant system in a severe transient (accident) improve safety. If the preferred method (*a*) is not available, methods (*b*) (off-site power/low pressure), (*c*) (loss of ac/low pressure), and (*d*) (overpressurization) might be used. The redundant methods are necessary to assure operation of critical safety functions. AFW = auxiliary feedwater, ADV = atmospheric dump valve, AS = auxiliary spray, BRS = boron recovery system, CST = condensate storage tank, CEA = control element

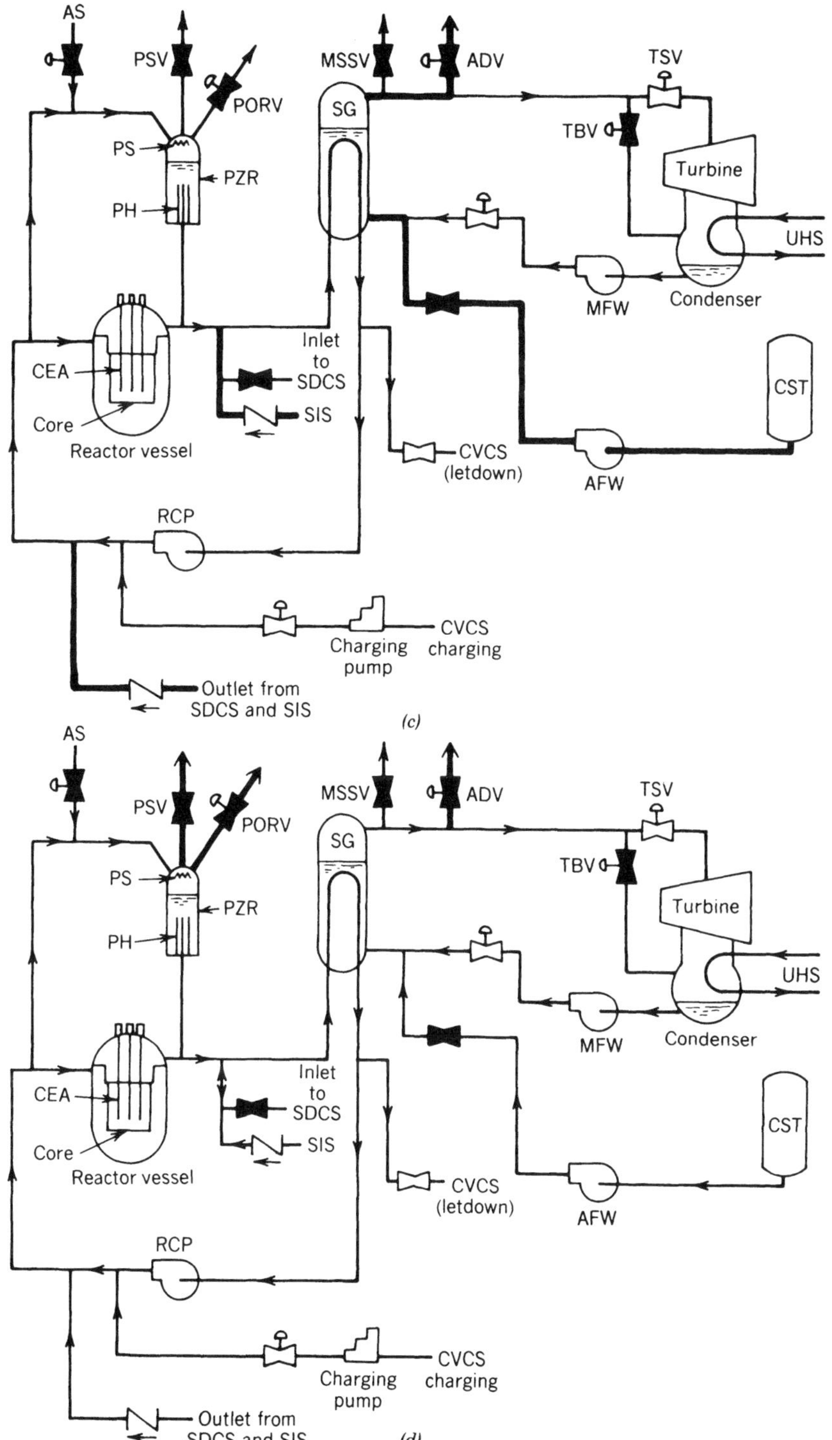

assembly, MFW = main feedwater, MSSV = main steam safety valve, PH = pressurizer heater, PORV = power operated relief valve, PS = pressurizer sprays, PSV = primary safety valve, PZR = pressurizer, RCP = reactor coolant pump, RWT = refueling water tank, SDCS = shutdown cooling system, SG = steam generator, SIS = safety injection system, SP = safeguards pumps, TBV = turbine bypass valve, TSV = turbine stop valve, UHS = ultimate heat sink, VCT = volume control tank. [From W. R. Corcoran, *Nuclear Technology* **55,** 90 (1981).]

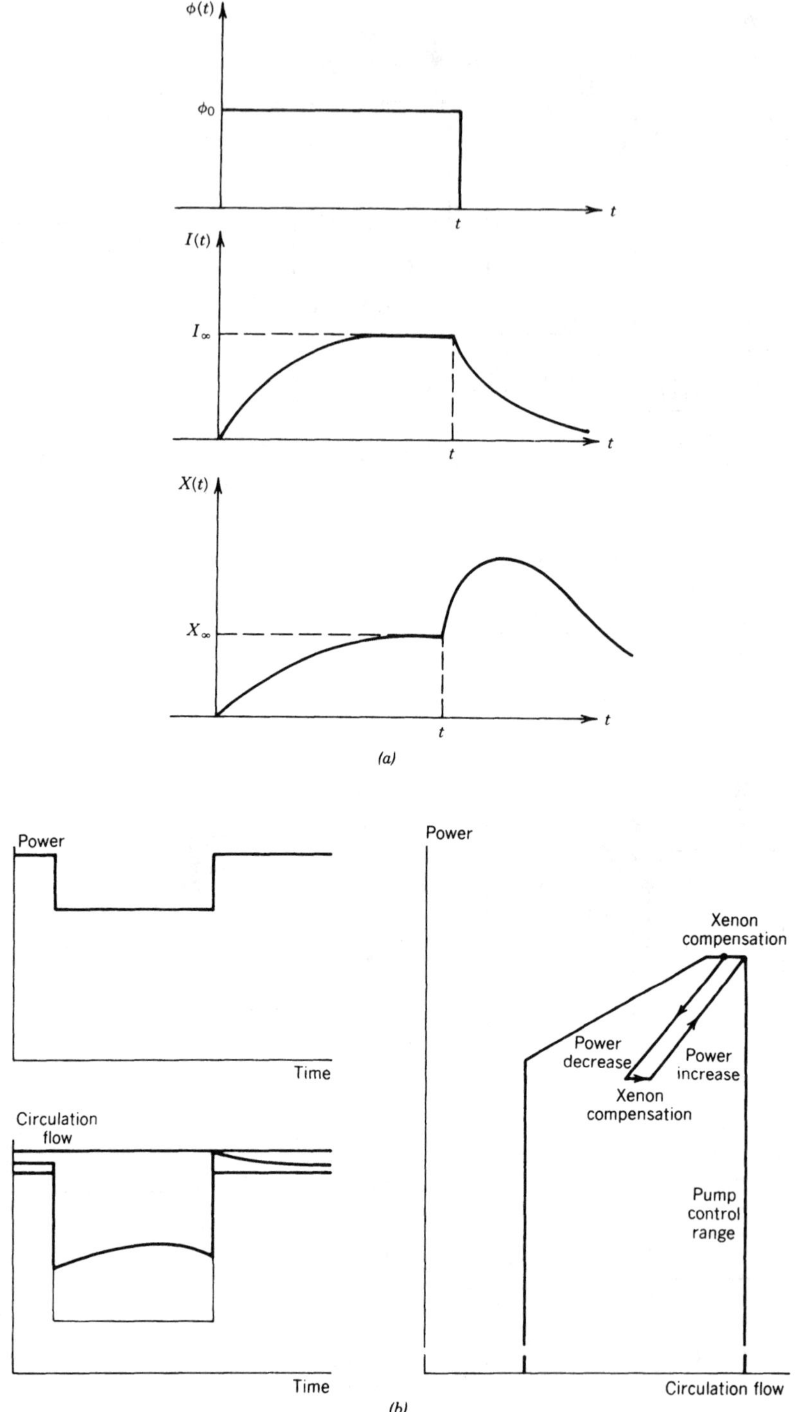

Figure 12.30. (*a*) Qualitative behavior of ^{135}I and ^{135}Xe concentrations following a start-up and then shutdown. φ, the flux as a function of time, is proportional to the reactor's power level. Both the iodine and xexon initially build up to equilibrium values I_∞ and X_∞, but at shutdown the iodine decays while thc xenon builds up to a peak 4–12 hr after the shutdown. (*b*) In a BWR, power control is carried out by varying main circulation flow with automatic compensation for xenon poisoning. Changing the flow through the core causes steam void formation which, in turn, affects the power level through reactivity feedback. (Courtesy ASEA-ATOM.)

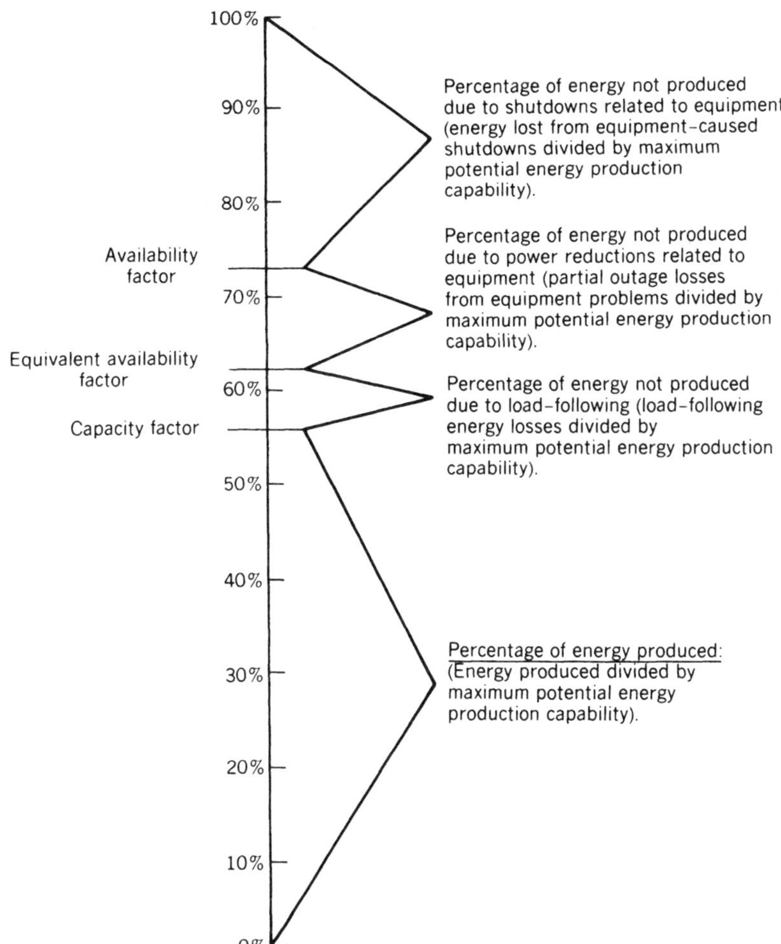

Figure 12.31. Relationships among performance indices for a typical generating facility. (EPRI Report NP-842.)

Table 12.13. BWR Unavailability Due to Fuel

Activity	Effect on Plant Production in Equivalent Full-Power Unavailability (hr/plant-yr, all plants)	Estimated Potential Improvement (hr/plant-yr, all plants)
Fuel preconditioning	350	265
End-of-cycle coastdown	96	46
End-of-cycle thermal-hydraulic restrictions	90	90
Control blade replacement	88	44
Fuel sipping	69	60
Fuel channel inspection/replacement	26	26
Rod pattern changes	26	26
High off-gas	4	3
Total	749	560

Source: EPRI Report NP-1136.

Table 12.14. The 10 Leading Causes of BWR Downtime in 1981

Activity	Effect on Plant Production in Equivalent Full-Power Unavailability	Estimated Potential Improvement
	hr/plant-yr, all plants	
Core spray piping repairs[a]	230	230
Main condenser tube plugging	122	75
Feedwater sparger inspection/ repair/replacement[a]	88	75
Recirculation pump seal re- pair/replacement	68	35
Safety/relief valve seat leaks	63	50
MSIV maintenance	60	30
Control rod driver overhaul/ maintenance	54	45
Recirculation bypass line re- moval/repair[a]	52	52
Turbine maintenance	51	0
Plugging core bypass holes[a]	48	48

Source: EPRI Report NP-1136.

[a]These activities are modifications that, once completed, are not expected to recur.

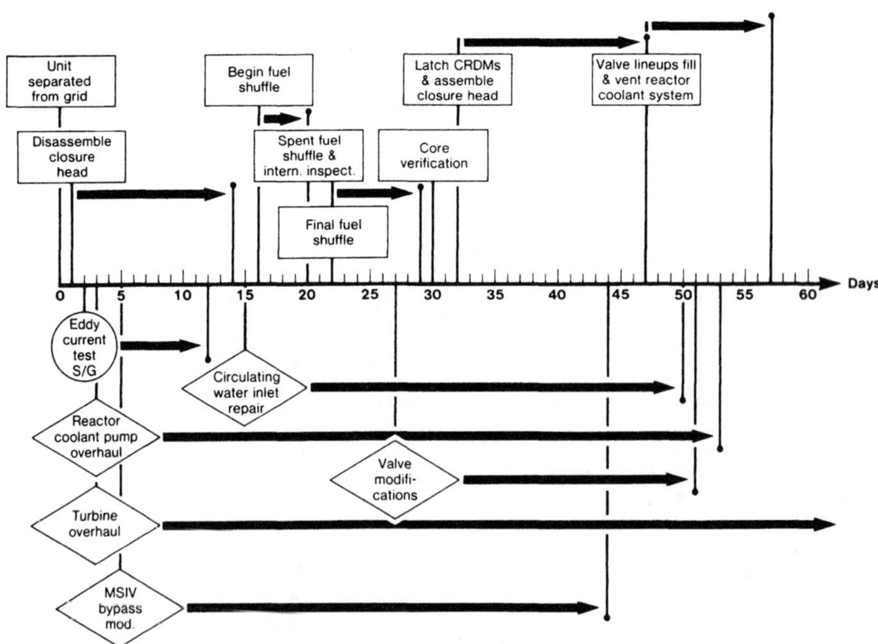

Figure 12.32. Summary of a Zion 1 refueling outage. (Courtesy EPRI.)

Figure 12.33. Installing a reactor head during a refueling outage at Omaha Public Power District's Fort Calhoun Plant. (Courtesy of Omaha Public Power District.)

Table 12.15. Nuclear Power Plant Outage Planning

1. Advance planning
   a. Establish job selection
   b. Update regulatory agency developments
   c. Evaluate past plant operating problems and success
   d. Update maintenance program
2. Outage preplanning
   a. Establish organizational responsibility for outage
   b. Prepare outage worklist 6 to 12 months in advance
   c. Prepare job scopes 6 to 9 months in advance
   d. Order long lead materials
   e. Validate plant configuration
   f. Calibrate instrumentation
   g. Train personnel
   h. Prepare testing program
   i. Prepare waste handling procedures
3. Conduct of outage
   a. Provide on-site technical support
   b. Monitor daily work progress
   c. Support operations, QA, and health physics groups
   d. Provide adequately trained manpower
   e. Provide rapid material turnaround for shortages
   f. Update cost and schedule
4. Post outage
   a. Complete evaluation and feedback of outage problems and successes to subsequent outage planning activities

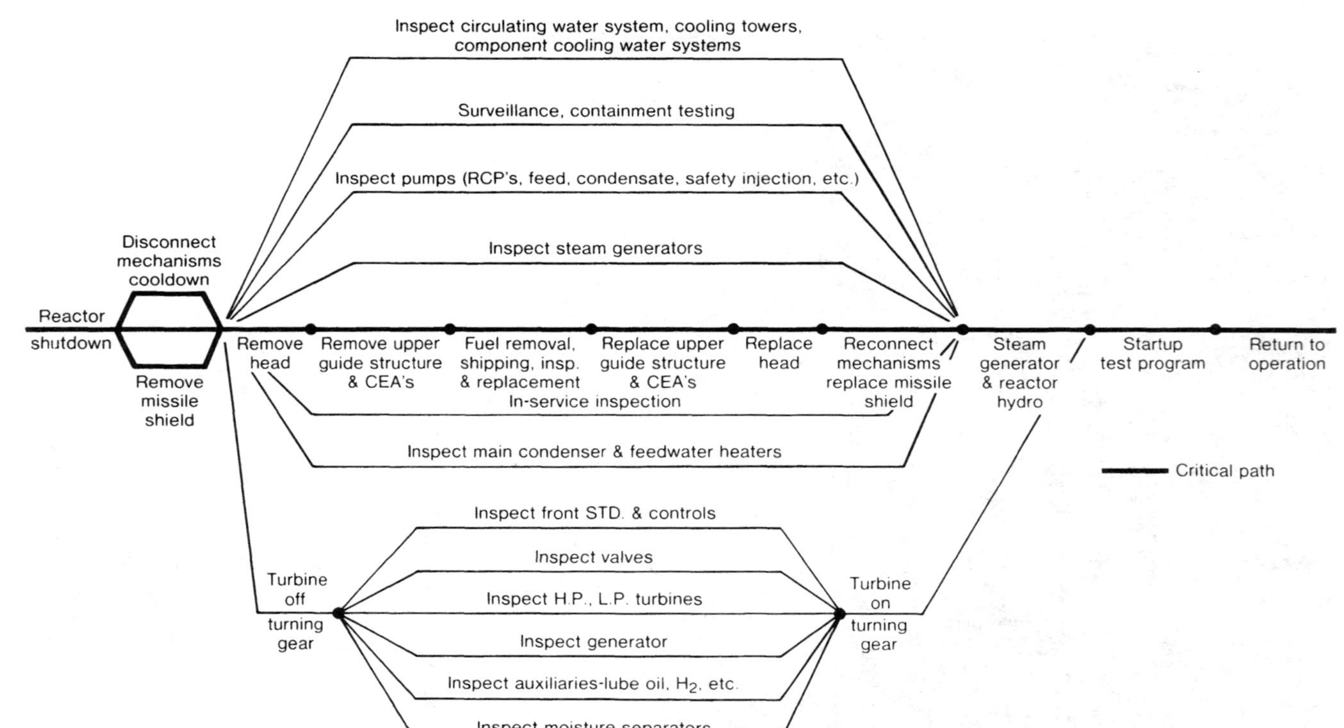

Figure 12.34. Typical nuclear unit outage schedule. (Courtesy EPRI.)

Figure 12.35. Periodic inspection and maintenance is required on all key components of nuclear plants. Shown is an operation on the control rods of a BWR. When such operations are conducted in high radiation zones, mockups are often used to familiarize personnel with the task. More and more of the maintenance in high radiation zones is being done by automatic equipment to lower occupational exposure, improve quality, and to shorten the downtime of the reactor. (Courtesy General Electric Co.)

Level	Student 1	Student 2	Student 3	Student 4
Steps	Step 1 (POTC)[a] Orientation Safety First aid Math (alg. & trig.) Physics Chemistry Nuclear seminar (10 Weeks)	Step 1 (POTC) Electrical theory AC & DC circuits Motors & generators Relay & protective ckts. Principles of solid state Electrical components Switchgear Composition I (13 Weeks)	Step 1a (POTC) Reactor theory Fuel core design (BWR & PWR) Thermal hydraulics Health physics Fuel loading and start-up Power operation & shutdown Industrial psychology (9 Weeks) Step 1b (POTC) Reactor technology (BWR or PWR) Instrumentation Systems Reactor internals Operating procedures Accident and transient analysis (7 Weeks)	(Assigned plant) Electrical training (2 Weeks) On the job training Plant familiarization (20 Weeks)
	Step 2 (POTC) Plant systems (pri. & sec.) Pumps Heat exchangers Systems designs Thermodynamics Calculus & analytic geometry Print reading Speech & communication (19 Weeks)	Step 2 (POTC) Turbines Design Operations Precautions Control Report writing (12 Weeks)	Step 2 (assigned plant) Plant systems Plant procedures Fire fighting training (20 Weeks)	
Total time per level	29 weeks	25 weeks	36 weeks	22 weeks

[a]POTC refers to the utility's off-site training center.

Figure 12.36. Training syllabus required by TVA to qualify a trainee for Assistant Unit Operator of a nuclear plant. [From I. Berman, *Power Engineering*, (January 1981)].

Figure 12.37. Operator training at a nuclear plant simulator. (Courtesy Consolidated Edison.)

An operator must demonstrate satisfactory understanding of the normal and abnormal operation of all apparatus and mechanisms and know the operating procedure in each area for which he is licensed. These demonstrations and manipulations require actual plant maneuvering unless an applicable simulator is used.

A great many changes have taken place in U.S. nuclear training since the accident in 1979 at Three Mile Island. In the area of training in particular, U.S. nuclear utilities were faced with the need to upgrade programs, staff, facilities and, most of all, to increase the attention of management toward training.

Unlike the utility industries in other countries, the U.S. nuclear utility industry includes 58 separate organizations. Each is unique and operates independently. Prior to the accident at Three Mile Island (TMI), each determined for itself, within federal regulations and a few training standards, the training that it would provide to its personnel. Training programs varied widely in quality, duration, scope and depth of content. Government regulations established only minimum training standards in a limited number of areas.

Following the accident at TMI, the industry recognized this need and took action. The utilities formed the Institute of Nuclear Power Operations (INPO) and directed it, as part of its function, to evaluate utility training and assist in making needed improvements. The U.S. NRC and the U.S. Department of Energy were directed to cooperate and assist in these industry efforts. Additionally, the NRC upgraded a number of its requirements in the areas of operator qualifications, training, and supervision. Some immediate rules, for instance, limited operator overtime, added an extra operator to each shift crew, and made licensing tests more difficult.

By contrast with 1979, today's typical nuclear plant training staff has increased from four or five to as many as 20 or 30, and many instructor training programs have been established. The typical training facility is a new building equipped with modern classrooms and equipment. A plant-specific simulator is also a part of the training facility at a typical larger utility. In fact, the use of simulators has increased dramatically. The number of simulators has tripled from 10 in 1979 to approximately 30 in 1984. Twenty more plant-specific simulators will be added in the next several years.

The emphasis on training is such that a typical nuclear plant has five shifts of workers, with one shift dedicated to training. Several utilities have implemented a six-shift program to permit more

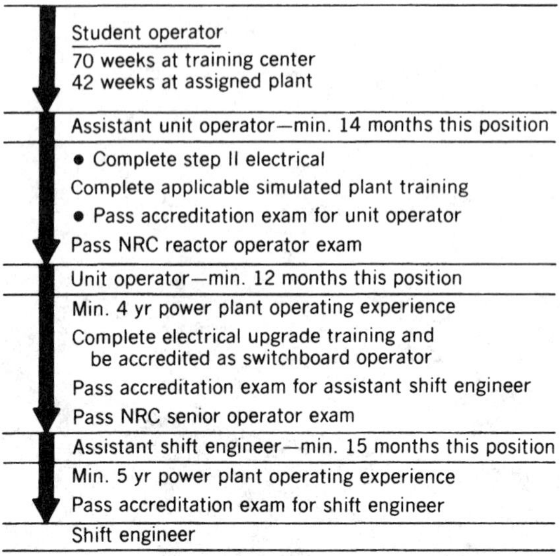

Figure 12.38. TVA nuclear operator progression leading to the position of Shift Engineer. [From I. Berman, *Power Engineering* (January 1981).]

time in training. The training for licensed operators today focuses more on job-related knowledge, and the licensing exam is also becoming more operations-oriented. Although the emphasis and priority are still on licensed operators, most nonlicensed operators and maintenance personnel now also receive formal training in the classroom, as well as on the job. Persons in these positions also must be qualified formally before being assigned job responsibilities. Supervisory personnel, too, receive training on how to carry out their duties.

Many of the reactor vendors run training schools to instruct new operators. Because of the amount of training now required, the trend has been for utilities also to run their own training centers. After the initial training of an operator, certain minimum amounts of on-the-job training and experience are required for the operator to advance. One utility's progression chart is shown in Figure 12.38. About 10 yr of training, requalification, and experience is required to become a shift engineer at a nuclear plant. The value of training is shown by improvements in plant operations as experience is gained. The improvement curve shown in Figure 12.39 is in great part due to this type of training, although increased equipment reliability is important also.

12.9. IN-SERVICE INSPECTION

In-Service Inspection (ISI) is a procedure mandated by the U.S. NRC regulations (10CFR, Section 50.55) to assure the continuing integrity of a reactor's primary system and safety-related equipment.† The guidelines for ISI are given in Section XI of the ASME Boiler and Pressure Vessel Code. In addition to the inspection of the pressure vessel and piping, the code also requires periodic testing of the plant's main pumps and valves. While some pressure vessel welds may only have to be tested every 10 yr, pumps in critical safety systems, such as the safety injection pump, must be checked for operability every 3 months. The frequency and priority for in-service inspections are determined for each component according to its safety significance. Three classes of equipment have been established by the code:

Class 1. Components containing primary coolant and components that can not be isolated from the core.

Class 2. Auxiliary systems which are not part of, but communicate with, the primary coolant pressure boundary [e.g., Residual Heat-Removal (RHR) system].

Class 3. Components which support class 2 components, but are not part of them (e.g., the water system supplying the RHR heat exchangers).

†Particular technical specifications are incorporated into the operating licence for each nuclear plant.

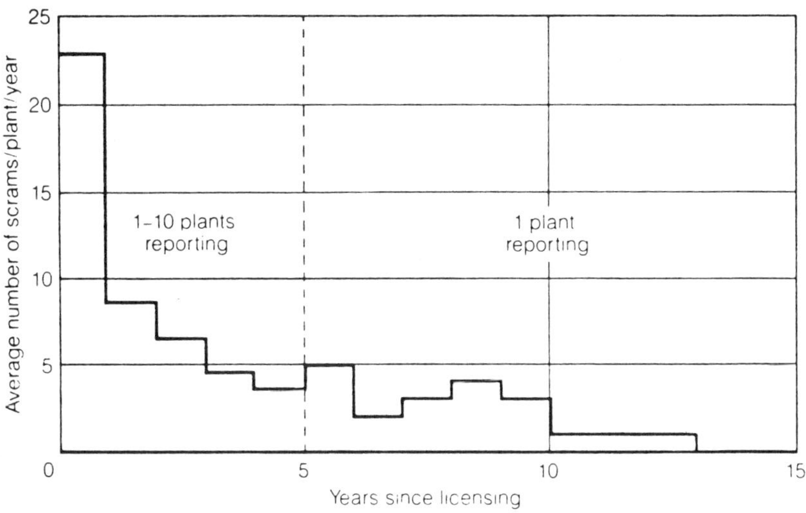

Figure 12.39. The learning curve for an average BWR shows sharp dependence on the length of time the plant has been in service; the number of scrams per year decreases with unit maturity. [From *EPRI Journal* (May 1977).]

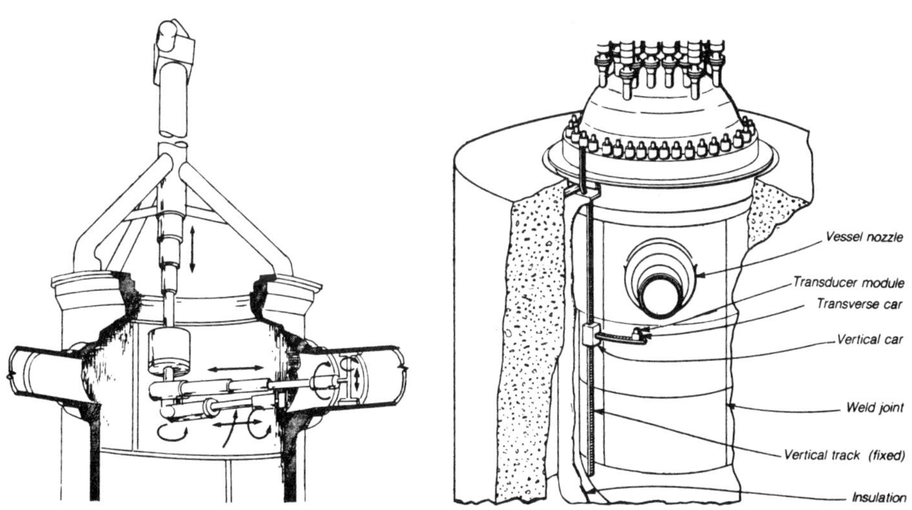

Figure 12.40. Ultrasonic techniques are used for examining all welds in the reactor pressure vessel. Primary option is whether to inspect from inner or outer surface. External inspection must be anticipated early in design stage to allow instrumentation accessibility. Inspection from inside requires removal of fuel and internals, but allows 100% access to welds. PWR vessels are inspected from within (left). The manipulating device, universally used, is mounted on vessel flange. Telescopic design and pivot joints give access to all vessel and nozzle surfaces. Ultrasonic transducers are affixed to ends of pivot arms (left). BWR-vessel welds are checked externally (right) to avoid removal of internals. Traversing tracks for transducers can be mounted on inner insulator surface and around nozzles during construction. Newer approach uses trackless vehicle with magnetic wheels. For all UT systems, transducers are driven and monitored. [From S. Strauss, *Power* (December 1982).]

Table 12.16. Forced Outage Summary for Selected Causes, All U.S. LWRs—Nuclear Part of Plant

Cause	Percent
Engineered safety features	28
Reactor coolant system	23
Instrumentation and control	14
Electric power system	8
Radioactive waste systems	6
Others	21

Source: NUREG-0483

Table 12.17. Selected NSSS System/Component Unavailability Impact

Cause	Mean Time to Failure, Months	Mean Time to Repair, Days	Cost, $/yr
Reactor coolant pump			
Impeller shaft	811	57	$0.4–1.9M
Pump seals	187	7.4	0.2–1.0
Nuclear instrumentation	9	0.6	0.2–0.6
PWR steam generator tubes	54	10	1.8–3.7
Valves			
Feedwater control valve	26	0.6	0.1–0.6
Pressurizer relief valve	125	4	0.2–0.4

Source: EPRI Report NP-2168.

Table 12.18. Summary of an Engineering Evaluation of the Benefits of Upgraded Refueling Subsystems

Subsystem	Person-hours Saved	Refueling Hours Saved	Person-Rem Exposure Saved
Improved vessel head closure system	224	32	10.6
Integrated vessel head	108	26	2.1
Improved refueling machine	476	68	5.1

Source: Courtesy of Westinghouse Electric Corp.

The ISI inspections are normally conducted during a refueling outage. If a major component such as the pressure vessel or main coolant pump is due for inspection, the refueling outage is often prolonged by several weeks. For example, a recent outage at the Salem Unit required 69 days, of which 17 days on the critical path were due to ISI. Figure 12.40 shows some of the ISI techniques currently used to inspect major components.

12.10. AVAILABILITY IMPROVEMENT PROGRAMS

All reactor vendors and the utilities that operate the plants have programs to enhance plant availability. Leading causes for plant unavailability are shown in Table 12.16, while the cost impact of some selected system/component failures is given in Table 12.17. The availability enhancement programs are designed to (1) reduce lost generation hours and the length of outages, (2) reduce maintenance costs and occupational radiation exposure, and (3) improve the safety of the plant.

The leading causes for unavailability, once identified, are systematically attacked to improve plant performance. As an example of such a program, consider a refueling operation. Primary goals might be a reduction in the amount of person-hours and a resultant decrease in radiation exposure. Of equal importance, perhaps, may be a shortening of the refueling outage. Not all refueling and maintenance outages result in the refueling being the critical path activity, but frequently the refueling manpower requirements exceed those of other operations, including turbine maintenance.

One utility wanting to improve refueling operations performed an availability study, and found that the job of opening and closing the reactor vessel head during refueling should be improved. A system was designed to automatically tension, remove, and insert the studs in the reactor vessel flange. The time and manpower savings, as well as the radiation exposure savings were significant (Table 12.18). Other causes of unavailability can be addressed in the same manner, trying to save downtime, which, as we saw in the beginning of this chapter, can exceed $750,000 per day for an average size nuclear plant.

BIBLIOGRAPHY

Berman, I., "Plant Simulators," *Power Engineering* **85,** 38 (January 1981).

Burns, E. T., *Refueling Outage Trends in LWRs,* EPRI Report, NP-842 (1978).

Corcoran, W. R., et al., "The Critical Safety Functions and Plant Operation," *Nuclear Technology* **55,** 690 (1981).

Dempsey, R. H., "Reassessment of Simulator Training Needs," *Trans. Am. Nuclear Soc.* **34,** 714 (1980).

Frederick, L. G., et al. *Limiting Factors Analysis (BWRs),* EPRI Report, NP-1136 (1979).

Hermant, C. P., "Improving (Control Room) Designs in France," *Nuclear Engineering International* **27,** 48 (November 1982).

Koppe, R. H., and E. A. J. Olson, *Nuclear and Large Fossil Unit Operating Experience,* EPRI Report NP-1191 (1979).

Lewis, E. E., *Nuclear Power Reactor Safety,* Wiley, New York, 1977.

Lombardo, T., "TMI plus 2," *IEEE Spectrum* **18,** 28 (April 1981).

Masche, G., *Systems Summary of Westinghouse Pressurized Water Reactor Nuclear Power Plant,* Westinghouse Electric Corporation, 1973.

Passel, T., "Steam Purity in PWRs," *EPRI Journal* **7,** 22 (October 1982).

Randall, J. L., "The Uncommon Sense of Outage Management," *Trans. Am. Nuclear Soc.* **39,** 680 (1981).

Seminara, et al., *Human Factors Review of Power Plant Maintainability,* EPRI Report, NP-1567 (1980).

Skarpelos, J., "Factors Influencing BWR Water Quality," *Trans. Am. Nuclear Soc.* **43,** 321 (1982).

Strauss, S., "In-Service Inspection Assures Nuclear Component Integrity," *Power* **19,** 126 (December 1982).

Szeless, A., "Performance of Nuclear Power Plants," *Power Engineering* **86,** 54 (September 1982).

Vandenberg, C., et al., "Safety Aspects of Using Gd as a Burnable Poison in BWRs," *Nuclear Technology* **46,** 500 (1979).

———, "Anticipated Transient Without Scram," *LOFT Highlights* **4** (March 1982).

———, *BWR/6 Standard Safety Analysis Report,* General Electric Company.

———, *PWR Reference Nuclear Power Plant,* Stone and Webster Engineering Company.

———, *RESAR-3, Reference Safety Analysis Report,* Westinghouse Electric Corporation, November 1973.

———, *Steam, Its Generation and Use,* Babcock & Wilcox Company, 39th ed. New York, 1978.

———, *System 80 CESSAR Final Safety Analysis Report,* Combustion Engineering Inc., 1981.

CHAPTER 13
OTHER POWER REACTOR TYPES

13.1. INTRODUCTION

It has been mentioned in Chapter 1 that there was a period, from about 1955 to 1965, when approximately a score of American industrial companies were planning to offer a power reactor product line. It was in that time that these companies were looking for the ideal reactor type, and almost every combination of feasible fuel, coolant, and moderator was suggested.

Some of these combinations have been mentioned. Many were actually built in experimental or demonstration-scale sizes in the United States. Among them were the organic moderated and cooled reactor; the sodium cooled, graphite moderated reactor; the molten salt reactor; the aqueous homogeneous reactor; and the gas-cooled reactor. A great many others were the subjects of design studies, research and development projects, or just papers presented at industry meetings.

Three reactor concepts have survived in the United States: the light-water moderated and cooled reactors, including the PWR and the BWR; the high-temperature gas-cooled reactor (HTGR); and the LMFBR or liquid-metal cooled fast breeder reactor. Another variety of fast breeder that was the subject of considerable research was the gas-cooled fast breeder reactor (GCFR). This was seen by many to hold promise because of certain inherent safety characteristics, but its development also was slowed for want of substantial funding.

Of these concepts, the first two, the LWR and the HTGR, are thermal reactors. That is, they operate using moderated neutrons slowed down to "thermal" velocities (so-called because their speed† is determined by the thermal, or kinetic, energy of the substance in which the fuel is placed, namely the moderator). The third type, the fast breeder (not, of course, so-called because it breeds rapidly), operates on fast neutrons—unmoderated neutrons that have the extremely high velocities and energies with which they are released from a fissioned nucleus. These neutrons have a low probability of fissioning ^{235}U, but they are effective in fissioning ^{239}Pu, or in causing the transmutation of ^{238}U to ^{239}Pu, as described earlier.

By a different classification, also introduced in Chapter 1, LWRs are essentially burners, or very low-efficiency converters. HTGRs are converters that can be designed to approach—but not quite reach—breeding. Breeders, as their name indicates, are designed to breed, that is to produce more fissile material than they consume. Burner, converter, and breeder reactors differ from each other in their fuel utilization, that is, the method by which they sustain fission and produce fissile isotopes. This subject is covered in Chapter 11, which also discusses conversion ratios, breeding ratios, and the other fuel cycle considerations.

Abroad, Britain and France each independently developed their own line of carbon dioxide-cooled, graphite-moderated reactors. France has abandoned them in favor of the PWR, and in late 1982, Britain was preparing to order its first PWR. Canada has developed the "CANDU" natural uranium-fueled and heavy-water moderated and cooled reactor.

In this chapter, we will discuss gas reactors, the LMFBR, and the CANDU. The safety aspects of these systems, however, are reserved for Chapter 17, and their economics for Chapter 19.

13.2. GAS REACTORS

The use of a gas for cooling a large reactor was considered seriously in the United States as far back as 1943. When the Hanford (graphite-moderated) reactors for plutonium production were first designed, helium was the preferred coolant; it was not adopted, however, largely because of the

†Thermal neutrons have mean kinetic energies of about 0.03 eV, which is the mean kinetic energy of a molecule.

difficulties anticipated in preventing leakage of the expensive helium gas from the large pressure vessels that would be necessary to contain the reactors.

Natural uranium can be used as a reactor fuel in graphite-moderated systems. However, relatively small slowing-down power of graphite leads to very large volume ratios of moderator to fuel. This leads, in turn, to low power densities and large volume cores. Significant thermal neutron capture takes place in the large mass of graphite. Therefore, if natural uranium is to be used, neutron capture must be minimized in other constituents. Thus, from a neutronic standpoint, the low atom densities of gases make them ideal coolants for graphite-moderated systems.

In the United Kingdom, the successful operation of the Windscale reactors led to the development of the dual-purpose Calder Hall and Chapel Cross stations for the production of plutonium and electrical power. These served as prototypes for a series of gas-cooled reactor power plants with an installed electrical capacity that exceeded 8500 MWe by 1983. The reactors are graphite moderated; the coolant is carbon dioxide at a pressure of 150 to 600 psi. In the first series of gas reactors developed, the fuel was natural uranium metal clad with a thin layer of Magnox. The fuel material was originally determined by the shortage of enriched uranium in the United Kingdom, but it has been retained because it proved to be economically satisfactory. Special finned designs of fuel elements of various types have been developed in order to improve heat removal. Steam temperatures were limited to about 650°F and fuel burnup was about 300 MWd/t. Eventually, 8 Magnox reactors of the Calder Hall type were operated by British Nuclear Fuels Ltd. (BNFL), 16 by the Central Electricity Generating Board (CEGB), 2 by the South of Scotland Electricity Board (SSEB), not counting the overseas units at Latina and Tokai Mura. The total net electrical output of these stations is 4420 MWe.

Due to the continuing high cost and unavailability of helium at the time, the British developed methods for using carbon dioxide at still higher temperatures and pressures. This eventually led to an Advanced Gas-cooled Reactor (AGR) design.

Another concept evolved in West Germany called a pebble-bed reactor. In the pebble-bed reactor concept, the fuel is in the form of ceramic spheres 1.5–2.5 in. in diameter. The spheres contain fissile and fertile material, for example, uranium carbide or uranium and thorium carbide particles, dispersed in graphite. A coating of impervious graphite provides resistance to the escape of fission-product gases. These fuel particles are each 0.4 mm; about 35,000 are required for each fuel sphere. The coolant is helium gas. The advantages of the pebble-bed concept arise from the use of simple fuel elements that permit easy refueling and reprocessing.

The pebble-bed design was demonstrated in the 15-MWe AVR experimental reactor, located at the Jülich Research Center, which started operating in 1967. It operated at very high temperatures, 950°C gas outlet. Contamination levels of the helium coolant circuit have been very low. A scale-up of this concept is the 300-MWe THTR, the prototype high-temperature reactor being built at Schmehausen. This reactor has suffered construction delays and funding problems but is expected to be in commercial operation by 1985. It achieved criticality in September 1983 after the loading of some 200,000 of the spherical fuel and moderator elements. The full core inventory will require 675,000 elements.

The Advanced Gas-cooled Reactor

The first phase of the United Kingdom's gas-cooled reactor program was based on metal uranium fuel, clad in Magnox (a magnesium alloy) cans, cooled by carbon dioxide, and moderated by graphite. It was always recognized that if the heat output per unit volume of the reactor core could be increased, and if this heat could be made available at higher gas temperatures, then a significant reduction in electricity costs would ensue, providing the fuel elements required in order to achieve these aims did not give rise to excessive fuel costs.† In 1965, when the Magnox program had reached its maximum development with the use of concrete pressure vessels‡ at the Wylfa power station, it was decided to start work on a new reactor system, the Advanced Gas-cooled Reactor (AGR). The AGR uses slightly enriched uranium as fuel. This has two effects. Ceramic fuels and cladding materials that can withstand higher temperatures can be used, since more thermal neutron capture can be tolerated. The slightly enriched fuel also allows the volume ratio of graphite to fuel to be reduced, leading to higher power densities and smaller core volumes.

The reactor developed for the AGR program has proved surprisingly flexible in operation, the main constraint in start-up being the steam turbine. A satisfactory load following is being achieved. However, the program suffered delays and technical problems with advanced gas-cooled reactor

†High-temperature, high-pressure CO_2 also tended to corrode the mild steel components of the Magnox reactors.

‡The prestressed concrete vessels overcome the difficulty of fabricating very large steel pressure vessels that would otherwise be needed. Graphite-moderated cores are very much larger than LWR cores.

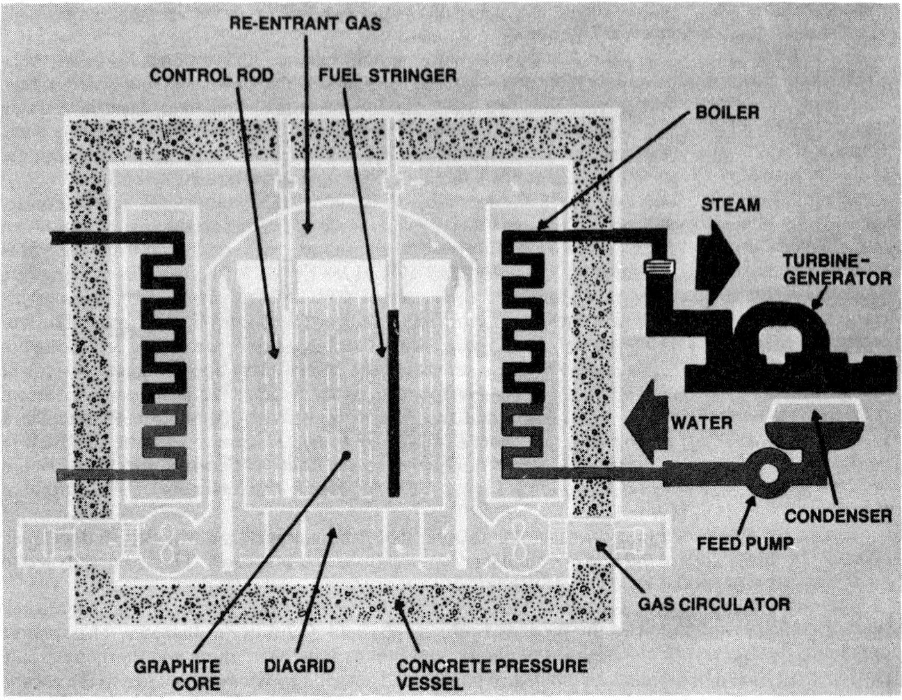

Figure 13.1. Advanced Gas-cooled Reactor system. (Courtesy CEGB.)

construction. The first of the commercial stations, one of twin 660-MWe reactors at Dungeness B, was only loaded with fuel in 1981, some 16 yr after the placing of the contract. Of four AGR stations subsequently ordered, two each at Hinkley Point B and Hunterston B, fared better and after some initial problems have been showing progressively improved operating performance over the past few years. The stations at Heysham-1 and Hartlepool—the last to be ordered in 1969 and 1970—have also suffered considerable construction delays but started producing power in 1983.

AGR Description

The reactor is fueled with uranium oxide, slightly enriched in ^{235}U, and uses carbon dioxide gas to transfer the heat from the fuel to the steam generators.

In a typical AGR system, the reactor core, steam generators, and gas circulators are housed in a single-cavity, prestressed concrete pressure vessel (see Figure 13.1). The reactor core is designed to act as a moderator and to provide individual channels for fuel stringer assemblies, control devices, and coolant flow. It is a massive 16-sided stack of graphite bricks. The bricks are interconnected with graphite keys to provide the assembly with stability and to maintain the vertical channels on their correct pitch.

The primary system for control and shutdown of the reactor comprises 89 absorber rods and drives housed in standpipes in the reactor vessel. Forty-four of these are black rods, that is, rods that absorb most thermal neutrons impinging on their surface, and seven are sensor rods, designed to detect, when raised or lowered, any gradually developing guide tube misalignment that may occur between the graphite core and the steel structures above it. The remaining 45 rods are gray (weaker neutron absorbers) regulating rods.

Slightly enriched uranium dioxide was chosen as fuel because of its anticipated higher burnup capability, and beryllium was originally chosen as cladding because of its low neutron absorption and its anticipated higher temperature of operation. However, development work showed that beryllium had a tendency to become brittle and swell due to helium generation. It also became clear that stainless steel would permit an appreciably higher clad temperature than beryllium and this, coupled with a substantial reduction in the price of ^{235}U, enabled the present concept of a stainless steel-clad, low-enriched uranium dioxide, cluster-type fuel element to emerge, in spite of the large neutron absorption cross section of stainless steel. Figure 13.2 illustrates one of the fuel elements.

The reactor is designed so that fuel may be changed when it is on- or off-load, at any pressure

Figure 13.2. A partially cutaway model of an AGR fuel element. Each element is approximately 1 m long. (Courtesy CEGB.)

from atmospheric to normal operating pressure, by a fueling machine that handles complete fuel assemblies. Routine refueling on-load has not yet been carried out. There are two reasons for this. During early reactor testing it was shown that, under certain fault conditions, it was possible for the stringer to overheat. Also, as a result of a finding in 1978 that a stringer had been damaged during loading at power, all on-load refueling operations were suspended. The reintroduction of on-load refueling is anticipated, albeit initially at low (about 50%) power levels.

Carbon dioxide coolant is used to transfer to the steam generators the heat produced by the fission of the uranium atoms in the fuel pins. The coolant composition is a compromise between the requirement to inhibit graphite corrosion and the prevention of deposition of carbon on the fuel, based upon the levels of CO, CH_4, and H_2O in the CO_2 coolant gas. The coolant gas strategy employed at Hinkley Point B is shown in Table 13.1.

The coolant is pumped through the channels of the reactor core at high pressure by gas circulators. Each reactor has eight circulators driven by induction motors. Each circulator is a totally enclosed unit located in a horizontal penetration at the bottom of the reactor pressure vessel. Cooled gas is drawn from the bottom of the steam generators by the gas circulators and is discharged into the space below the core. About half of this gas flows directly to the fuel channel inlets, while the remainder, known as the reentrant flow, passes up the annulus surrounding the core and returns downward through the core in the passages between the graphite bricks to rejoin the main coolant flow at the bottom of the fuel channels. The reentrant flow thus cools the graphite bricks, the core restraint system, and the gas baffle.

The AGR uses a prestressed concrete pressure vessel. The vessel is made gas-tight by a thin mild-steel liner which is protected from the high gas coolant temperatures by foil and blanket insulation attached to its inner surface. The liner is cooled by water pipes welded to its outer surface.

A summary of system parameters for an AGR reactor is presented in Table 13.2.

Table 13.1. Gas Coolant Composition at Hinkley Point B

Elapsed Time at Power	CO, %	H_2O, vpm	CH_4, vpm
2500–5000 hr	0.5	200–300	—
1 yr	1.0	200–300	130
After 1 full yr	1.0	300	165

Source: Adapted from R. Hall, *Nuclear Energy* **21,** 41 (1982).

Table 13.2. Full-Load Performance Parameters for a Typical AGR

Station Design	
Electrical output:	
Main plant	2 × 660 MWe gross
Station net output	1235 MWe
Thermal efficiency	40%
Heat balance:	
Heat to turbine from steam	1577 MW
Heat lost to vessel liner cooling system	8.5 MW
Heat lost to circulator cooling system	4.5 MW
Heat lost to gas treatment plant	3.0 MW
Total heat to gas	1593 MW
Power to circulators	43 MW
Heat from reactor	1550 MW
Reactor	
Reactor heat	1550 MW
Number of fuel channels per reactor	332
Number of control rods per reactor:	
Black	44
Gray	45
Bulk (average) gas temperatures:	
Channel inlet	334°C
Channel outlet	635°C
Bulk gas flows:	
Fuel channels	3910 kg/sec
Net circulator flow	4270 kg/sec
Peak channel flow	14.1 kg/sec
Peak channel temperature: channel outlet	661°C
Fuel Elements	
Material	UO_2 pellets, stainless steel clad
Type	36-pin clusters in graphite sleeve
Number of fuel elements per channel	8
Gas Circulators	
Number per reactor	8
Power consumption per reactor	43 MW
Shaft power	4.8 MW
Pressure Vessel	
Internal diameter	20.3 m
Internal height	21.9 m
Steam Generators	
Total heat transferred per reactor	1577 MW
Number of steam generators	4
Number of units per steam generator	3
Number of platens per unit	44
Feedwater temperature	156°C
Superheater: outlet steam temperature	541°C
Reheater:	
Inlet steam temperature	343°C
Outlet steam temperature	539°C
Turbine Generator	
Steam pressure	160 bars
Steam temperature	538°C

Source: *The Safety of the AGR*, CEGB (1982).

The HTGR

During the mid-1950s, Congress' Joint Committee on Atomic Energy—the "watchdog" committee on Atomic Energy Commission matters—was pushing the AEC hard to build a demonstration gas-cooled power reactor. There were those on the committee who kept one eye on Britain's successful Calder Hall gas-cooled nuclear power plant and France's equally successful (though smaller) demonstration gas-cooled power plants at Marcoule. They had misgivings that the United States might be overlooking a good bet for the "ideal" power reactor.

Meanwhile the nation's electric power companies organized to build a privately financed commercial-type gas-cooled nuclear power demonstration plant†. Fifty-one utilities banded together in a nonprofit firm, High Temperature Reactor Development Associates (HTRDA). HTRDA turned to the General Atomic Division of General Dynamics Corporation for the reactor design.

Bechtel Corporation was the engineer-constructor. The $39 million proposal provided that Bechtel would build the plant on Philadelphia Electric's system on a fixed-price, turnkey basis, provided that AEC agreed to contribute pre- and postconstruction research and development work under a contract with General Atomic.

The reactor, proposed for Peach Bottom, Pennsylvania, was to be cooled by helium gas, moderated by graphite, and fueled by uranium carbide and thorium carbide. From the start, two different fuel cores were contemplated. The first was to have metal-clad fuel elements containing homogeneous carbon compacts of 93% enriched uranium carbide together with thorium carbide, and would produce only 30 MWe from 850°F (450°C), 850 psi (57 bar) steam. Coolant helium would enter the core at 582°F (305°C) and leave at 1015°F (545°C). This core performed poorly, reaching only a fraction of its designed burnup.

By the time the second core was ready to be inserted, General Atomic expected to have ready all-ceramic fuel elements, with no metal cladding. These would be homogeneous carbon compacts containing carbides of ^{235}U and thorium nested in long impervious graphite tubes. This would permit substantially raising the temperature ceiling, while eliminating loss of neutrons to absorption in metal cladding. Thus, this second core would raise power output to 40 MWe, by raising coolant temperature to 662°F (350°C), 1382°F (750°C) outlet, and steam conditions to 1000°F (540°C), 1450 psi (99 bar). General Atomic planned to carry out R&D simultaneously on both core designs, and hoped that the second might progress fast enough that the metal-clad core might never have to be used. Gross thermal efficiency was calculated to be 37%, and fuel element lifetime 3 yr at 80% load factor.

General Atomic claimed six advantages for its new design: simplicity and compactness; use of inexpensive construction materials, thereby lowering costs, especially in larger plants; modern steam conditions and high thermodynamic efficiency; low fuel-cycle costs due to high burnup; good nuclear economy; and finally "an extraordinary degree of inherent safety." A major safety advantage claimed for the system, like other graphite-moderated gas reactors, was its ability to absorb shutdown decay heat even in case of loss of coolant. The graphite reflectors have a large heat capacity and therefore constitute a built-in heat sink to which the core could transfer heat in an emergency. Further safety was provided by the homogeneous fuel-moderator mixture which ensured a prompt-acting negative temperature coefficient. A summary of the HTGR safety features is given in Table 13.3.

The HTGR reactor concept was well received in the United States because of increased efficiency of the graphite moderator in larger core sizes, which provided potentially long fuel burnups, low fuel-cycle costs, and relative insensitivity to fuel-reprocessing charges at higher power levels.

A long row of R&D problems had to be overcome, however, before the HTGR could become a reality. These included obtaining a graphite with sufficient porosity so that fission-product gases would not build up pressures that would weaken structural integrity; learning the chemistry of uranium and thorium carbides; establishing the conversion ratio and temperature coefficient; and developing needed hardware such as helium blowers.

Peach Bottom

The problems were solved. AEC accepted the HTRDA proposal, and a construction permit was applied for in July 1960. It was issued in February 1962, and the operating license in January 1966. The Peach Bottom reactor (later called Peach Bottom 1 after Philadelphia Electric added two large BWRs at the site) first went critical on March 3, 1966; produced its first electricity on January 27, 1967; and reached full power for the first time in May 1967. After that, with allowance made for some plant modifications, it operated successfully with the exception of core performance, which was well below the goal exposure of 900 Effective Full-Power Days (EFPD). A second core was

†It was hoped that the plant would be able to operate at higher temperature, hence at higher efficiency, than the British and French models.

Table 13.3. Safety Features of HTGRs

Inherent Safety Characteristics	Design Safety Features
a. The use of large thorium loadings in the fuel elements results in negative prompt and overall temperature coefficients throughout reactor life at all temperatures of interest.	1. A core auxiliary cooling system is included to provide an independent means of cooling the reactor and primary coolant system and removing reactor afterheat. This system consists of separate and independent cooling loops, which are, in turn, completely independent of the main coolant loops.
b. The high heat capacity of the large mass of core graphite ensures that any core temperature transients resulting from reactivity insertions or interruptions in cooling will be slow and readily controllable.	2. A reserve shutdown system is provided which is independent of the normal control rod system. Neutron-absorbing material is stored in hoppers in each refueling penetration and can be released by the operator, if required, by pressurizing the hopper with gas from an external source.
c. The use of helium as coolant means that the reactivity is insensitive to changes in coolant density. Control of the reactor is inherently easier than in reactors where the coolant functions as the moderator.	3. A steam/water detection and dump system is provided to minimize the amount of water that could leak into the primary coolant as a result of a steam generator tube or subheader leak.
d. Since the entire primary coolant system is contained within the PCRV, the need for external coolant piping, which might be postulated to rupture, is eliminated. The integrity of the PCRV structure itself precludes a sudden loss of primary coolant.	

Source: J. P. Gibbons et al., *Nuclear Engineering and Design* **26,** 27 (1974).

loaded in mid-1970 and achieved its 900 EFPD design exposure. In 1971, the reactor posted 68.8% availability, below the conventional target of 80%, but respectable for a first-of-a-kind plant type. Over its entire career, the unit's nuclear steam system availability was 88%.

A schematic of the principal parts of the Peach Bottom system is given in Figure 13.3. Unique to this system are the external helium compressor and steam generator, and the steel pressure vessel. These components were to be greatly modified in future HTGRs. A summary of the plant's operating characteristics, Table 13.4, shows a core outlet temperature (728°C) and steam temperature (538°C) which are much higher than for LWRs. These are the temperatures that determine the high thermal efficiency of the plant.

In late 1973, Philadelphia Electric announced that it planned to decommission the unit when core life ran out, because it was found to be too small to be economical to continue in operation. In January 1975, the plant was shut down for the last time.

In its nine years of operation, Peach Bottom 1 generated more than 1.4 billion kilowatt hours of electricity, at an average gross plant efficiency of 37.2%.

Fort St. Vrain

At the time of its decommissioning, Peach Bottom 1 was the world's only commercial HTGR. Its European counterpart, the Dragon reactor at Winfrith, England, dumped its heat to the atmosphere. When the Peach Bottom 1 developmental plant was taken out of service, the 330-MWe Fort St. Vrain scale-up HTGR was already nearing completion for Public Service Company (PSC) of Colorado.

This unit, presently the only operating HTGR in the United States, was ordered by PSC from General Atomic in March 1965, with final contracts, to which AEC was also a party, being signed November 1, 1965.

The plant is 33 miles north of Denver near Platteville, Colorado, and the confluence of the St. Vrain Creek and the South Platte River. The plant received a construction permit in September 1968, and first went critical in 1974. After a period of "debugging," it began operation at 70% of full power in 1978. It was limited to 70% of full power by NRC until technical issues associated with core temperature fluctuations were resolved, but completed a successful full-power test run in November 1981 in which all plant systems and components performed at or near design conditions. The NRC removed the 70% limitation in 1982, and Fort St. Vrain is now running at 100% of power. Through August 1984, it had produced more than 4 billion kWh net electricity.

Fort St. Vrain has a thermal output of 842 MW (thermal) and an electrical output of 330 MWe. It

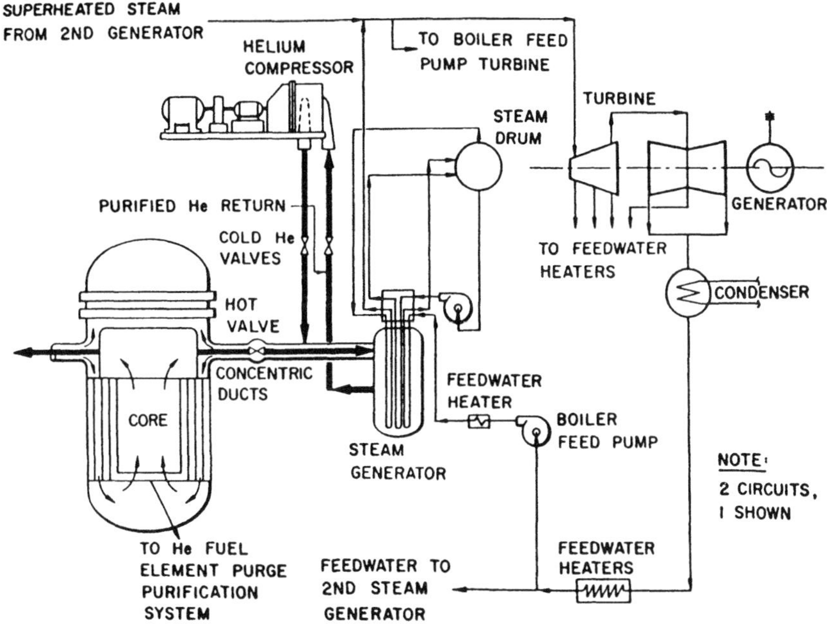

Figure 13.3. Simplified process flow diagram for the main coolant system of the Peach Bottom HTGR. (From GA-A16637.)

Table 13.4. Peach Bottom Atomic Power Station Plant Characteristics

Coolant	Helium
Pressure	2.4 MPa
Core inlet temperature	344°C
Core outlet temperature	728°C
Steam temperature	538°C
Steam pressure	10.0 MPa
Net thermal efficiency	34.6%
Reactor thermal output	115 MWth
Net electrical power	40 MWe
Pressure vessel	
Diameter	4.3 m
Height	10.8 m
Core	
Effective diameter	2800 mm
Active height	2300 mm
Fuel element diameter	89 mm
Fuel element length	3660 mm
Number of fuel elements	804
Reflector thickness	610 mm
Control rods	
Normal operating rods	36
Shutdown rods	19
Fuel life at full power	900 days

Source: GA-A16637.

produces steam at 2400 psi and 1000°F; average fuel temperature is 1830°F. Net efficiency is 39.2%, considerably higher than for LWRs.

Subsequent Developments

During the period from 1971 to 1973, U.S. utility companies placed orders with General Atomic for ten HTGRs, four 770-MWe and six 1160-MWe units. The designs were based on the Fort St. Vrain reactor except for the following: the pressure vessel was changed to improve seismic characteristics and to allow for easier replacement of equipment; much of the auxiliary equipment was modularized; and the fissile and fertile fuel was separated into two types of particles. These orders were based on the successful operation of Peach Bottom 1. Philadelphia Electric tacitly expressed its satisfaction with Peach Bottom 1 by ordering twin 1160-MWe units for a site at Fulton, Pennsylvania.

To meet the anticipated fabrication demands, General Atomic planned a fuel fabrication factory to be built at Youngsville, North Carolina, for start-up in 1978 and full operation in 1979. A construction permit application for the fuel factory was filed with AEC. Initial capacity was to be six cores a year, to be expanded to 12 in 1983, and eventually to as many as 20 a year.

At the same time, AEC included in its fiscal 1975 budget requests for funds to build two fuel demonstration projects: a $30 million reprocessing plant at the Reactor Testing Station in Idaho, and a $10 million refabrication plant in Oak Ridge capable of handling, remotely, radioactive fuel being recycled.

As events turned out, none of this came to be—except for the fuel fabrication facilities required to continue supporting Fort St. Vrain. The 1974 financial crisis in the electric utility industry resulted in the eventual cancellation, one by one, of the projects. A great many more LWRs were also canceled at that time and since, for a multiplicity of reasons: the tight financial situation of the utilities, a downturn in the historic rate of growth of power demand in the country, and the growth in the cost of projects attributable to delays caused by the length of the licensing process and intervenor actions.

Thus, except for Fort St. Vrain, the HTGR reactor type in the United States is presently dormant, although it still holds out potential advantages: higher efficiency and higher steam conditions at the turbine; the ability of using thorium as fuel by converting it to ^{233}U efficiently; and safety advantages of cooling with inert helium gas. A cooperative development effort involving the federal government, utilities, and potential supplies was launched in 1975 to keep the HTGR as a viable option.

In 1978, the utility supporters of the HTGR formed a nonprofit corporation, Gas-Cooled Reactor Associates, to develop the HTGR for production of electricity and other industrial and commercial applications. This group now acts as coordinator of the United States program.

HTGR Technology

A number of improved variations of the basic HTGR exist as designs. They are the subject of an ongoing research program supported by DOE and several private utilities in the United States. Since these improved designs have no immediate prospect of a commercial order, they are not summarized in this chapter. Rather, the Fort St. Vrain technology is described, since it serves as a basis for all the improved versions, and some of the principal offshoots are noted.

HTGR Pressure Vessel

One important way, other than size, in which Fort St. Vrain differs from Peach Bottom 1 is that it has a Prestressed Concrete Reactor Vessel (PCRV), the first reactor in the United States with this feature. Its use was first developed in England and France for their lines of carbon-dioxide cooled reactors, where they have accumulated about 35 years satisfactory operating experience. About 20 were in use in those countries and one in Germany when Fort St. Vrain was under construction. They are lined with steel to keep the coolant gas out of the porosities in the concrete, but operate at working pressures of from 200 to 700 psia, as compared with the 2200-psi pressure of the water coolant in PWRs, which is one reason they have not been adopted for water-cooled reactors. (Another reason may be the simple fact that the steel reactor pressure vessel technology was already developed by the Navy and adopted by civilian plants in the United States, at a time when there were no gas-cooled reactors being built in the United States.)

"Prestressed" means that a PCRV incorporates a large number of steel tendons within and around the concrete walls which are tensioned before the vessel is pressurized (Figure 13.4). Compressive stresses in the concrete exceed the tensile stresses generated by internal system pressure. Thus, the main mass of concrete is held in compression under all operating conditions. At operating pressure, the net stresses in the concrete are small in magnitude, and compressive in nature, to take full advantage of concrete's material properties. Therefore, PCRVs are not suscepti-

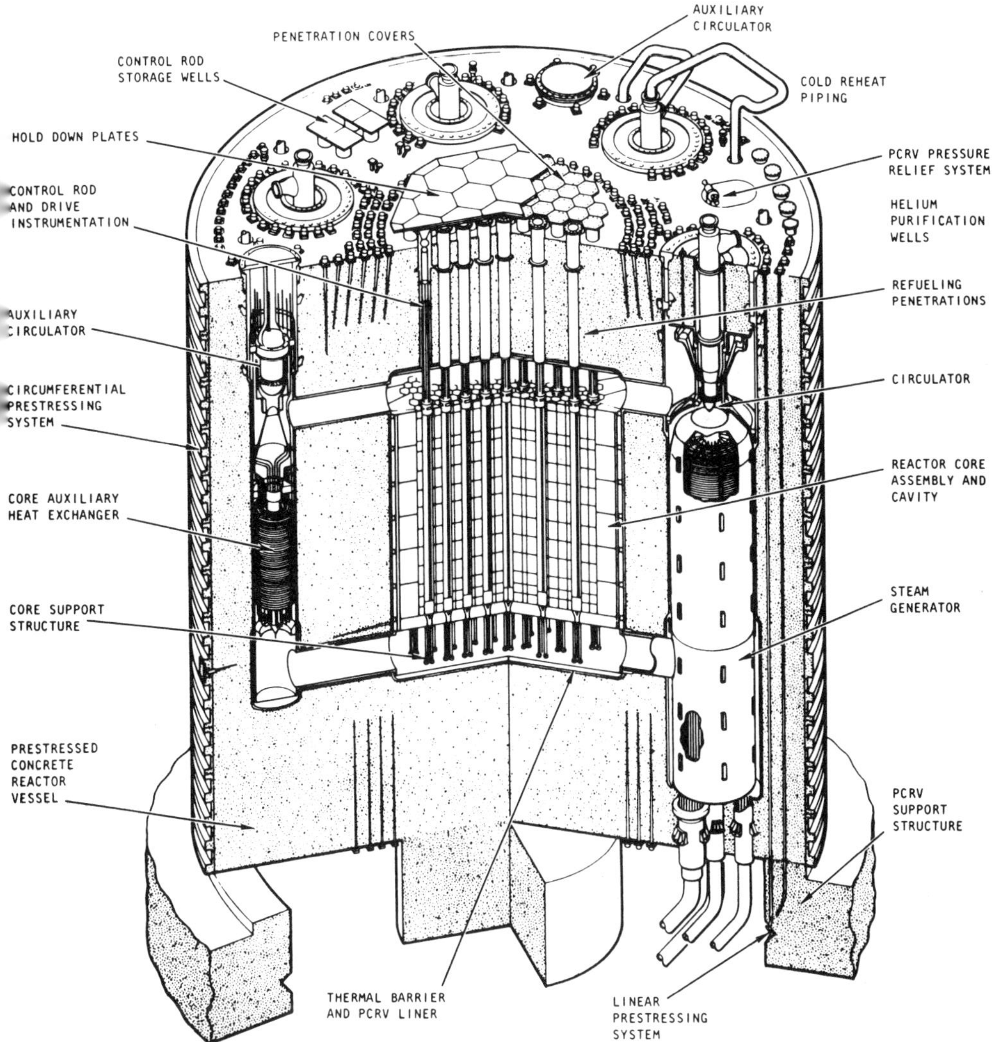

Figure 13.4. HTGR prestressed concrete reactor vessel arrangement. The primary system components are contained in a large cylinder of prestressed concrete. Penetrations exist for refueling, as well as for replacing various pieces of equipment. Several primary coolant loops, as well as secondary cooling loops, are contained in the vessel. (Courtesy General Atomic Co.)

ble to the propagation of cracking or to sudden failure, but are really self-sealing: any crack that might develop under hypothetical overpressure conditions would be closed by the prestressing system upon pressure reduction.

PCRVs have an advantage in compactness, in that they eliminate major external primary coolant piping, because the steam generators are located inside the PCRV, grouped around the core cavity. The primary helium circulators are also inside the PCRV, and in addition to housing the entire primary system, the PCRV is designed to be thick enough to provide the necessary biological shielding.

The prestressing is accomplished by linear tendons grouped in guide tubes, and anchored at one end and tensioned by jacks at the other end. Circumferential prestressing is done either by linear tendons or by wire wraps in a series of circular channels throughout the vessel's height. Preformed winding channels are built into precast, high-strength concrete elements that serve as external forms during construction. They contain all the embedded, bonded reinforcement necessary to resist local anchoring or bearing stresses that arise from the radial forces that result from circumferential wire winding. The tendons and the anchors are at or near the outer surface of the vessel

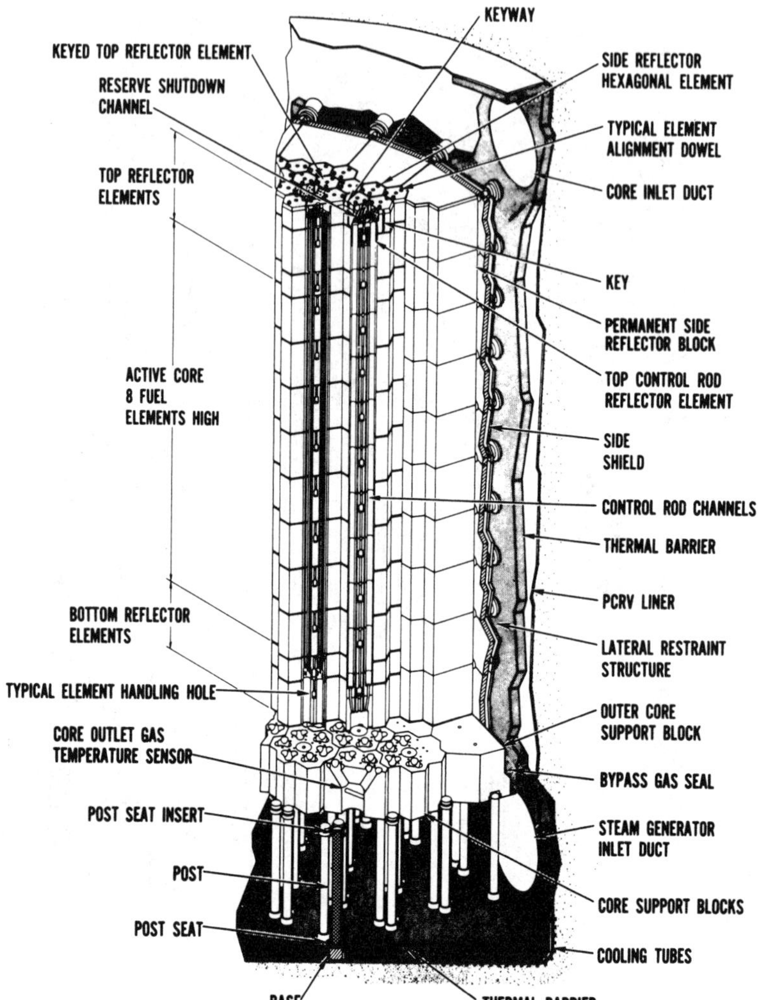

Figure 13.5. HTGR fuel element arrangement. (Courtesy General Atomic Co.)

walls, which shields them from potential irradiation damage, leaves them accessible for surveillance, and permits replacement should the need arise. Pressure loading is shared by the large number of steel tendons acting in parallel, so that failure of one tendon cannot initiate the failure of others. On the contrary, the multiplicity of independent longitudinal and circumferential tendons produces a high degree of safety redundancy.

Another feature of PCRV design is the cooling water coils welded to the exterior surfaces of the steel vessel liner before the concrete is in place. In operation these cooling coils, together with thermal insulation inside the liner, limit temperatures at the liner–concrete interface to about 150°F, which is well within the range where concrete's structural properties have been extensively investigated and are fully known.

A final advantage for the PCRV is that it is field-erected on site, thereby minimizing the problems and eliminating the cost of transportation, and simplifying the job of installing massive steel, shop-fabricated reactor vessels.

HTGR Core

The Fort St. Vrain reactor core is made up of columns of stacked hexagonal graphite blocks forming a large hexagon 19.6 ft in diameter and 15.6 ft high. Figure 13.5 illustrates the arrangement of these blocks which constitute an HTGR's fuel elements. These elements are arranged into

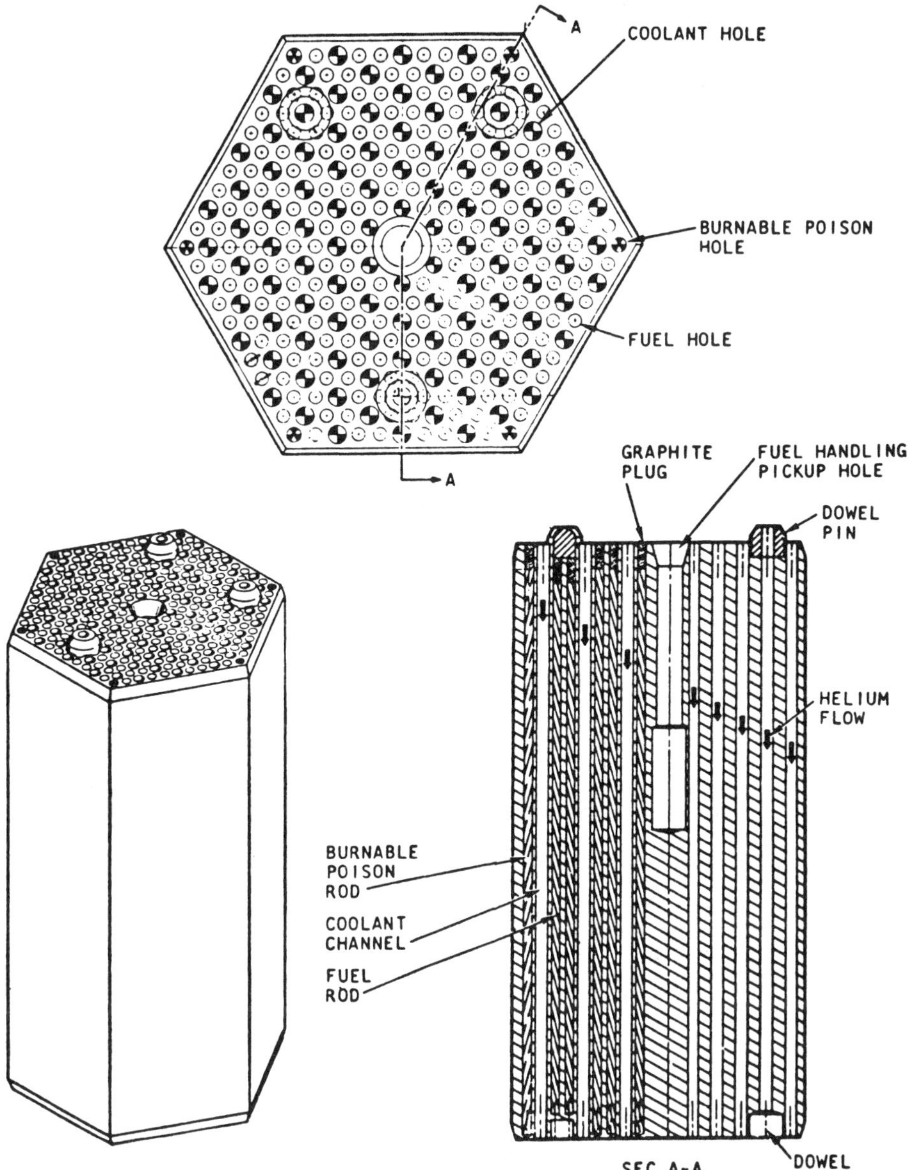

Figure 13.6. Fort St. Vrain fuel element. (Courtesy General Atomic Co.)

stacks, which themselves are arranged in groups of seven; the central stack of each group has control rod channels. The individual fuel elements are further detailed in Figure 13.6, which shows the coolant flow paths and the vertical holes drilled in them to accommodate the fuel. There are a total of 1482 fuel "compacts"—as well as 74 control rod elements driven in pairs by 37 control rod drives. A graphite reflector completely surrounds the core. The fuel compacts are graphite containing thousands of minute coated particles of uranium dicarbide and thorium dicarbide. The combination of enriched fuel and the inert helium coolant allows the use of an all ceramic core. The compacts are small sticks, 3 in. long, 0.6 in. in diameter, each containing 45,000 particles. It takes 2000 such compacts or sticks to fill the holes drilled in the hexagonal graphite moderator blocks. Thus, graphite is the moderator, the cladding, the core structure, and the reflector. Coolant gas passes downward through vertical passages in each of the fuel elements into a plenum area under the core. Thence, it passes through the core support floor into the steam generators where it gives up its heat to water and boils steam. The gas then goes to the suction side of the helium circulators, where the pressure is raised about 1 atm, and is discharged to the top of the reactor core by means of an annular space between the core barrel and the PCRV liner insulation, there to begin a new passage down through the core.

HTGR Fuel

The coated fuel particles are not just powdered dicarbides of uranium and thorium, but a painstakingly developed fuel form (Chapter 7 describes their function). These tiny microspheres are the "fuel element" of the HTGR system. There are two types, so-called "Biso" and "Triso" particles. The Biso particle has a buffer coating of low-density carbon around the kernel of uranium or thorium dicarbide, and an outer layer of high-density isotropic pyrocarbon that retains the fission products. The Triso particle has an inner buffer layer, and a layer of silicon carbide between it and the outer pyrolytic carbon layer. The principal function of the silicon coat was to provide a means of separating the two types of particles into separate streams during reprocessing after discharge from the reactor.

In Fort St. Vrain, both the uranium core particles and the thorium blanket particles are Triso coated. (It must be noted, to prevent confusion, that unlike "conventional" breeders in which the blanket of fertile material is heterogeneous and surrounds the central core of fissionable material, in the HTGR system—which is not a breeder but is called an "advance concerter" because of its high conversion ratio—fissionable particles and fertile particles are homogeneously mixed in the graphite matrix of the fuel compact.)

The initial loading for Fort St. Vrain contained 13 different compositions of rods, all having the same external dimensions and containing only two types of particles (both Triso coated)—the fuel differed in the proportion of the two types, that is, the fissionable and the fertile particles. It is in this way that neutron flux gradients were controlled and power distribution flattened to maintain the same temperature across the core. But for the larger reactors planned, the core physics was expected to become more refined, and the 13 different blends in the rods reduced to 5. It was also planned to convert Fort St. Vrain to a more advanced type of fuel.

The fuel cycle developed by General Atomic for its post-Fort St. Vrain line of 770-MWe HTGRs was to have all of the 93% enriched uranium feed or start-up fuel as uranium carbide in 500-μm-diameter Triso fissionable particles,† while the thorium would be contained, as oxide, in 800-μm-diameter Biso fertile particles. In the latter, ^{233}U would be produced, which would form the staple fissionable fuel after the initial start-up charge of ^{235}U. During the first fuel cycle, about 75% of the ^{235}U in the Triso particles is burned and about 8% of the thorium in the Biso particles is converted to ^{233}U. Fuel loadings are given in Table 13.5. This table is based on uranium enriched to 93% ^{235}U, referred to as the High Enriched Uranium (HEU) cycle. More recently, however, proliferation concerns about such highly enriched fuel material has focused concern on the Low Enriched Uranium (LEU) cycle. This, then, is currently the reference fuel cycle for post-Fort St. Vrain plants. Referred to as the LEU/Th cycle, it is based on 20% enriched uranium fissile particles,† and ThO_2 fertile particles, both of which are Triso coated. No further work on the HEU fuel cycle is being done.

If HTGRs become a successful reactor option, the actual fuel cycle will probably involve at least two and possibly three modes of operation over the lifetime of a plant:

1. Nonrecycle operation. Fuel charged to the reactor consists of enriched uranium and thorium. Spent fuel removed from the core is placed in storage awaiting reprocessing and recycle.
2. Initial recycle operation. An interim period for the early HTGRs when the stored ^{233}U is used exclusively to fuel the reactor.
3. Recycle operation. The fuel removed from the core is reprocessed and the ^{233}U is fed back into the reactor along with highly enriched ^{235}U makeup.

These three modes of operation are schematically represented in Figure 13.7. Optimum flow of fissile material in an HTGR requires a reprocessing facility, where the fissile isotopes can be separated from the waste products. The principal materials flow for a reprocessing facility which could serve 20 GWe of installed capacity is given in Figure 13.8.

†Uranium oxycarbide (UCO) may be selected as the fissile kernel material. UCO has good fission retention properties and can be formed in a gel process.

Table 13.5. HGTR Fuel Loadings

	Equilibrium Segment	
	Nonrecycle	Recycle
Metal charged (kg)		
BISO particle		
^{232}Th	8080	8080
Recycle ^{233}U	—	200
Recycle ^{235}U	—	20
Total U recycle	—	300
TRISO particle		
^{235}U	670	390
Total U	720	420
Metal discharged (kg)		
BISO particle		
^{232}Th	7470	7490
^{233}U for recycle[a]	190	200
^{235}U for recycle	10	20
Total U	240	330
TRISO particle		
^{235}U	40	30
Total U	170	100
Fissile Pu	1.0	0.6

Source: From R. C. Dahlberg, *Nuclear Engineering and Design* **26,** 47 (1974).

[a]This includes the ^{233}Pa in addition to the ^{233}U. Since the ^{233}Pa half-life is only 27.4 days, its decay to ^{233}U will be essentially complete by the time reprocessing occurs.

HTGR Control System

The reactor control system consists of two independent subsystems. One is used for normal reactor control, while the other is a reserve system designed exclusively for performing an emergency shutdown should the normal control system malfunction.

The service system has 37 control rod drives located in the penetrations through the top head of the PCRV. Each of these independent drives operates two control rods as a pair. The rods are articulated annular sections of 40% boron carbide, plus graphite, in metallic containers. They are supported from cables that are actuated by the electric drives and cable drums located in the PCRV penetrations.

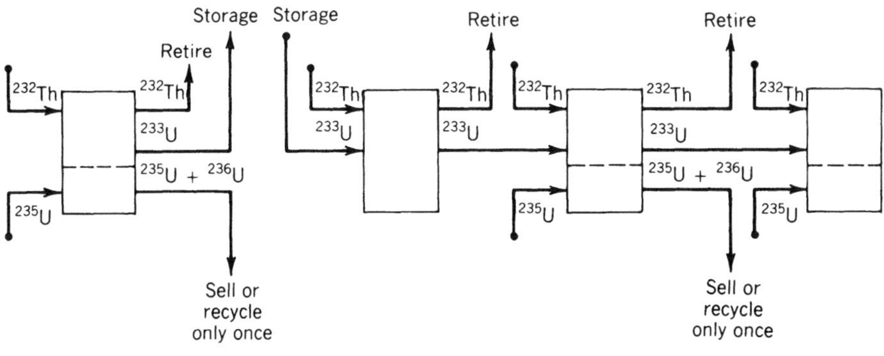

Figure 13.7. ^{235}U/Th/^{233}U fuel cycle modes. [From R. C. Dahlberg, *Nuclear Design and Engineering* **26,** 47 (1974).]

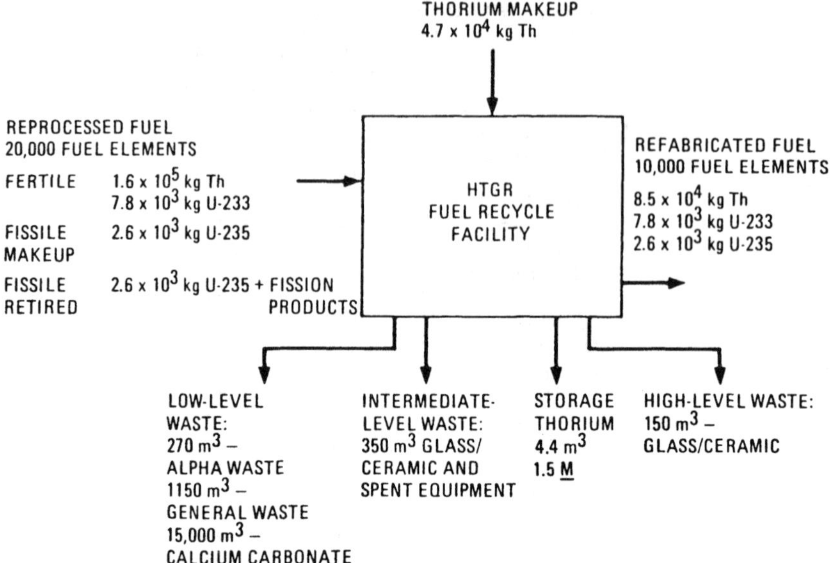

Figure 13.8. Nominal annual material flow for a central HTGR fuel recycle facility servicing 20-GWe installed capacity. (From GA-A16637.)

The reserve system consists of boron–carbide spheres that can be released by the reactor operator and fall by gravity from a reservoir in the control rod drive mechanism into the reactor core.

Steam Generator

The steam generators are of the once-through type. They take feedwater from the high-pressure feedwater heaters and produce superheated steam at 2400 psig and 1000°F at the main stop valves of the turbine–generator unit. The reheat steam circuit uses the high-pressure turbine exhaust steam to drive the helium circulator turbines, and then flows to the steam generators to produce 1000°F reheat steam. Figure 13.9 illustrates the arrangement and circulation patterns in the HTGR steam generators.

Each of the two primary coolant loops has a single steam generator consisting of six identical modules. Each module incorporates integral economizer–evaporator–superheater and reheater sections. The steam generators are designed to operate continuously at conditions from full load down to 25% or lower; steam conditions during partial load operation do not exceed the full-load values.

HTGR Power Loop

Hot helium from the reactor enters the top of the steam generator module and flows downward through reheater, superheater, and evaporator–economizer tube bundles in succession. On leaving the bottom of the evaporator–economizer tube bundle, the helium turns and flows horizontally through a plenum to the circulator inlets. Unlike the usual straight tubes or U-tubes of LWRs, the HTGR bundles are made up of helically coiled tubes. Detection and plugging of defective tubes in the reheater are accomplished by a special tube-plugging machine. In the unlikely event that removal of a module is required, it can be done.

Each of the four helium primary coolant circulators consists of a single-stage axial-flow compressor, a single-stage steam turbine main drive, and a single-stage water turbine auxiliary drive. The last is used to supply power to the circulator when the steam supply is either not available or not desirable. The helium compressors and the two drive turbines are mounted integrally on a single vertical shaft. A helium stop valve on the discharge side of each helium circulator prevents backflow through the circulator when it is not in operation. Details of the steam turbine driven

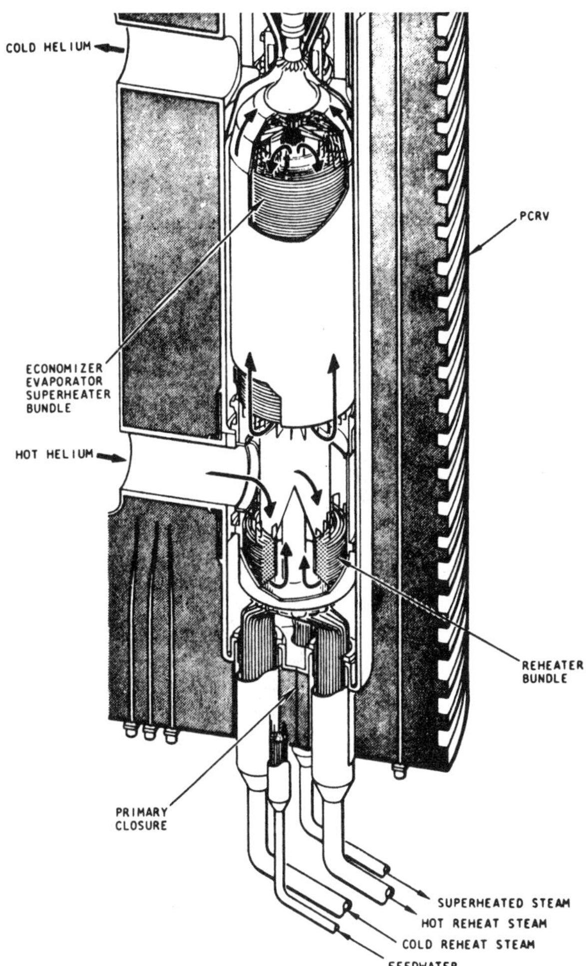

Figure 13.9. 1100-MWe HTGR steam generator. [From J. Landis, *Nuclear Design and Engineering* **26** (1974).]

circulator are shown in Figure 13.10. Fort St. Vrain will be the only HTGR with this type of drive. Subsequent plants will have electric motor driven circulators.

Refabrication of HTGR Fuel

Spent fuel reprocessing is an important part of the HTGR fuel cycle. Development work has proceeded on a small pilot plant.

General Atomic set up a radioactively cold demonstration reprocessing head-end line. This took simulated spent fuel from a reactor through crushers that reduced the graphite hex blocks unloaded from a reactor, with the fuel compacts still in them, to quarter-inch size pieces without breaking the fuel microparticles. These went into a fluid-bed combustor in which the graphite moderator and the pyrocarbon coats were burned away, leaving fertile oxide ash and silicon carbide coated fissile particles that went to a sorter for separation. Some of the more important aspects of this operation are explained in Figure 13.11.

The fertile metal oxides were leached in acid. In an operating plant, this solution would go to solvent extraction columns to separate out the new fissionable material formed in the fertile material. The other particles, containing unfissioned fissionable material, would go to a particle crusher

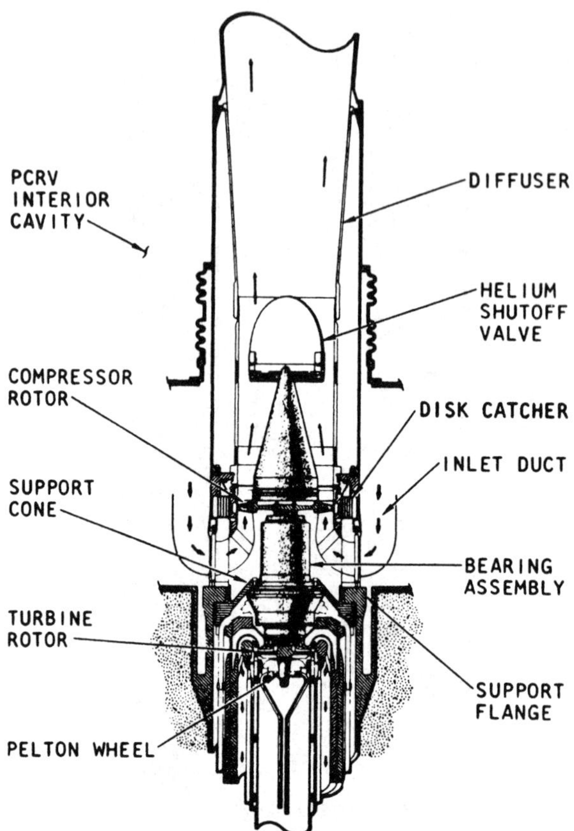

Figure 13.10. Steam turbine driven circulator for the 330-MWe HTGR. [From L. Cavallaro, *Nuclear Design and Engineering* **26** (1974).]

to break away the silicon carbide layer and expose the kernel, to begin its processing back to usable form for refabrication into new fuel. More details of this operation can be found in Chapter 7.

Future Modifications of the HTGR

The HTGR reactor developed by General Atomic Company makes use of the conventional Steam Cycle (SC) to produce power. Another variation of this design is called the Direct Cycle (DC). Instead of using hot gas to boil water to make steam which drives a turbine, hot gas is used directly to turn a gas turbine which is the power generator.

The technical developments required for gas-cooled reactors and related power plant equipment divide logically into three categories: (1) those related to the reactor and fuel, common to both HTGR-SC and HTGR-DC; (2) those related to the HTGR-SC, involving the utilization of the hot helium in the steam cycle; and (3) those related to the HTGR-DC, involving the very different closed-cycle gas turbine–compressor technology. A list of items requiring further development is given in Table 13.6.

The current utility interest in the HTGR is mainly expressed through an organization of a group of companies known as Gas-Cooled Reactor Associates (GCRA). GCRA conducts most of the forward planning for the HTGR and, in the past, stressed the HTGR-DC as the best way to utilize the high-temperature helium and make electric power. However, there is very little emphasis on the HTGR-DC at this time. All effort is being placed on commercialization of another version, the HTGR-SC/C (Steam Cycle with Cogeneration†). An HTGR is particularly well suited for the cogeneration option since it can deliver steam at high temperature and pressures.

An HTGR plant operating in a cogeneration mode has a nuclear steam supply system identical

†Steam turbine for electricity, and steam for process heat.

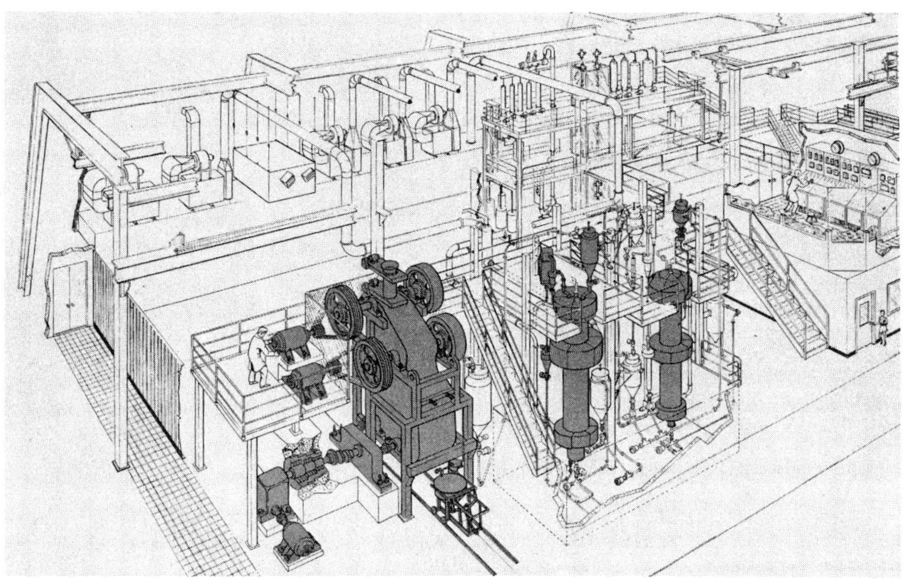

Figure 13.11. HTGR spent fuel reprocessing. The initial or head-end steps of HTGR fuel reprocessing include size reduction (crushing); burning to eliminate the graphite moderator; classification of particle types; additional crushing or grinding as required; and dissolution in nitric acid solutions (leaching). The purpose of the fluidized-bed burners is to remove the graphite moderator and the fuel coatings from the crushed fuel elements by means of combustion and to oxidize carbide-type fuel kernels in preparation for the dissolution or leaching process. (Courtesy General Atomic Co.)

Table 13.6. HTGR Improvements Under Development

1. HTGR—reactor and fuel, problems common to all applications
   (a) Continued attention must be paid to materials used and techniques employed in thermally insulating the interior of the prestressed concrete reactor vessel (PCRV) from the very hot helium gas that causes concrete deterioration. This becomes even more critical for the higher helium temperatures of the HTGR-DC. Prevention of helium leakage from the system is also important.
   (b) The increase in helium temperature at core outlet to 850°C (1562°F) for the HTGR-DC, compared to 685°C (1265°F) for the HTGR-SC, is believed to be attainable with fuel modification. The power density of the HTGR-DC core will likely be somewhat less than that of the HTGR-SC.
2. HTGR-SC—special problems of the steam cycle
   (a) The design and fabrication of the steam generators for efficient, trouble-free performance is essential since they are enclosed in the PCRV. A special requirement is the minimizing of water leaks to the helium side since, at the high graphite temperatures in the core, any water in the helium would attack the graphite.
   (b) The vertical helium circulators in the Ft. St. Vrain reactor are powered by steam turbines. Succeeding plants will utilize vertical synchronous electric motor drives controlled by variable frequency input devices.
3. HTGR-DC—special problems of the direct cycle
   (a) The salient development problem of the HTGR-DC is the closed-cycle turbine compressor at a rating of 400 MWe. While closed-cycle turbines employing helium as working fluid are by no means new, no machine in the rating range required for this application has been built.
   (b) The turbine compressor is equally important to plant efficiency as the heat exchanger, called the recuperator, which extracts the energy from the hot helium exhaust of the turbine and uses it to preheat the helium entering the reactor core. The materials, design, and producibility of this component require significant development.

Source: From R. H. Simon (GA) and R. A. Evans (HBA).

to a HTGR-SC plant. Flexibility in the process steam temperature and pressure conditions is provided by several possible turbine arrangements. Operation could, for instance, be easily shifted from the cogeneration to noncogeneration mode by adding a low-pressure condensing turbine. Such a turbine could be initially installed if the process steam load is projected to occur well after plant construction, or could be installed later if the initial steam demand falls off.

The Gas-Cooled Fast Reactor

The Gas-Cooled Fast Breeder Reactor (GCFR) is still another version of the HTGR. Their designs are quite similar; the helium-cooled technology is common to both. The similarities include the multicavity PCRV, the helically coiled steam generators, electric motor driven helium circulators, and most structural materials. The significant differences between the fast and thermal versions of the gas reactor are listed in Table 13.7. They include (1) UO_2/PuO_2 fuel pellets instead of the Biso/Triso fuel particles, (2) fuel rods with metallic cladding instead of graphite fuel blocks, (3) much higher power density, and (4) lower temperatures of the outlet gas. Since the GCFR fuel and blanket assemblies are similar to those of the LMFBR, their fuel cycle (fabrication, reprocessing, refabrication, and waste disposal) is essentially the same. Because of funding problems, however, development work on this concept was stopped in 1981.

13.3. THE LIQUID-METAL FAST BREEDER REACTOR

As mentioned in Chapter 1, the concept of the fast reactor was born even before World War II ended; and at its close in 1945, the Los Alamos Laboratory was at work on Philip Morrison's proposal for a 10-kW power reactor fueled by plutonium and operating on fast neutrons. The code designation for plutonium happened to be "49," and as Morrison's reactor was sited in a canyon at Los Alamos it acquired the nickname Clementine, after the ballad of Gold-Rush days: "in a canyon dwelt a miner, forty-niner, and his daughter Clementine."

The reactor Clementine began operating in November 1946 at a power of 10-kW thermal, later increased to 25. The fuel consisted of plutonium rods in a cylindrical cage 6 in. high, 6 in. in diameter. It was placed in the bottom of a 45-in. high steel pot in which mercury was circulated to carry away the heat. The mercury left the pot at about 175°F (80°C) and was piped to a heat exchanger where it was cooled by water. Control was accomplished by four rods, the lower half of which were of uranium and the upper half of boron. Two of the rods were for power regulation, and two for safety. When the rods were lowered, the boron replaced the uranium section of the rods, so that neutrons were absorbed by the boron to slow or halt the chain reaction. Blocks of natural uranium were placed around the core as reflectors to prevent loss of neutrons. Clementine was used principally to test the effect of fast neutrons on various materials and never produced any useful power. Clementine was permanently shut down and dismantled in 1953. (See Figure 13.12 for the chronology of U.S. LMFBR development.)

EBR-1

By 1951, however, a larger, more technically sophisticated, and power-producing fast breeder had been built. This was the Experimental Breeder Reactor (EBR, later called EBR-1 after a successor, EBR-2, had been started) run by Argonne National Laboratory at AEC's National Reactor Testing Station in the southeastern Idaho desert. EBR had a turbine generator attached that developed 200 kW of electricity. When the unit generated its first power on December 20, 1951, it became the world's first nuclear power plant to generate electricity. The power was used to run the reactor's pumps and other equipment, to light the building, and to operate tools in the machine shop. EBR-1 was also the first reactor to accomplish breeding in the sense of making a net gain of fissionable material.

EBR-1 used as fuel uranium enriched to 90% in ^{235}U. The core was described as being "about the size of a regulation football." This relatively small size compared to the core of an LWR, it may be noted, is because the use of 90% enriched fuel packs a great deal more fissionable material into a unit volume than would be possible with the 2 or 3% enriched material used in LWRs.

EBR-1 was cooled by NaK, the sodium (Na)–potassium (K) alloy that is molten at room temperatures and below.† The core was surrounded by a blanket of natural uranium. The blanket reflected some of the fast neutrons, but others were captured by ^{238}U nuclei, leading to plutonium production. The NaK coolant flowed downward from the core at a temperature of about 612°F to go to a heat exchanger where its heat was transferred to a secondary NaK circuit. This secondary loop did not require shielding as it did not pick up any radioactivity from the primary loop which,

†Actually a eutectic mixture of 76 wt% Na and 24 wt% K, having a melting point of 45°F (12.5°C). Ordinary sodium, which is solid at room temperature, melts at 208°F (98°C).

Table 13.7. Key Differences Between GCFR and HTGR

Difference	GCFR	HTGR	Reason and Effect
Fuel	UO_2/PuO_2 pellets inserted into cylindrical metal rods (cladding)	UCO and ThO_2 kernels with pyrolytic and silicon carbide coatings. The fuel particles are embedded in graphite rods, which are, in turn, placed in axial holes in graphite blocks.	Plutonium is the best fissile fuel in a fast reactor, uranium is the diluent and fertile material; ^{235}U and ^{233}U are the best fissile fuels in thermal reactors, thorium is the fertile material and transmutes to ^{233}U.
Core	Assemblies of fuel rods	Stacked graphite blocks with axial coolant holes.	Graphite is both moderator and structural material in HTGR.
Core outlet temperature, °C (°F)	520–570 (970–1060)	680–1000 (1260–1830)	HTGR has all ceramic core; GCFR has metal-clad fuel.
Core power density (MW/m^3)	120–320	6–8	No moderator in GCFR; therefore, higher pumping power required.
Core flow direction	Up	Down	Lack of significant heat capacity in GCFR core (no moderator) justifies design for higher reliability of residual heat removal (after scram), e.g., addition of natural circulation capability.

Source: From R. H. Simon (GA) and R. A. Evans (HBA).

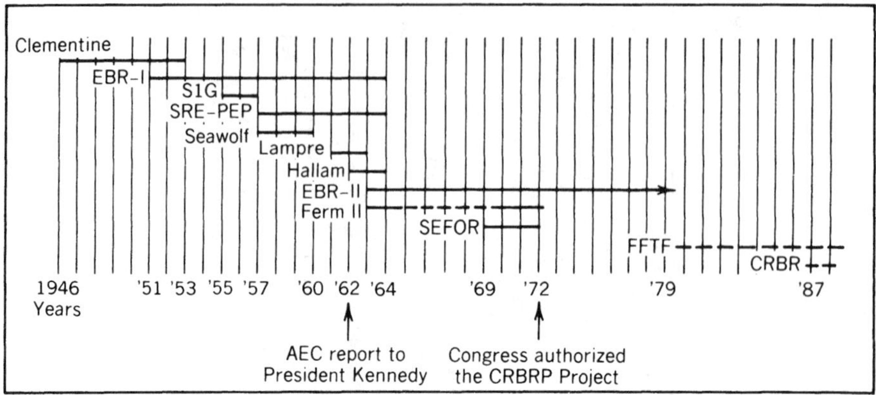

Figure 13.12. Liquid-metal cooled breeder reactor experiments in the U.S. LMFBR program, showing their operating time spans. [From *Power Engineering* (March 1979).]

like the reactor itself, of course required shielding.† The secondary NaK loop carried the heat to a second heat exchanger or boiler, which produced steam at about 550°F and 400 psi. This steam drove the turbine generator.

EBR-1 operated with four cores: Mark I, from 1951 to 1954; Mark II, from 1954 to 1955; Mark III from 1957 to 1961; and Mark IV from 1962 to 1964.

During routine operation, EBR-1 always had stable operating characteristics. The only anomalies were noted with the Mark I core during start-up at low coolant flow rates. After the Mark II core was loaded, experiments were carried out to study the reactor's stability under extreme conditions such as deliberate power oscillations and severely reduced, even zero, coolant flow. Under such conditions, the reactor developed a prompt positive temperature coefficient. (All reactors must have a negative temperature coefficient of reactivity, which means that if the temperature of the core rises, for example because of decreased coolant flow, the reactivity of the core decreases; this is a self-regulating feature that makes safe reactor control feasible.) In one of many series of reactor physics experiments for which EBR-1 was used, measurements were made of the changes in reactivity of the reactor as the fuel temperature was increased. The most difficult of these experiments involved permitting the fuel temperature to rise to 500 or 600°C. Because it was desired to obtain the temperature coefficient of the fuel only, it was necessary to shut off the flow of NaK coolant. In one such experiment, on November 29, 1955, a delay in scramming the reactor resulted in one side of the core, constituting about one-third of the fuel, melting down.

Analysis of the experimental data showed that the runaway was due to an increase in reactivity caused by thermal distortion of the core. Nevertheless, a positive aspect of the experiment was that in melting down, the core lost criticality—that is, it failed safe. Following the meltdown, an 8-month cooling period ensued before the work of removing the damaged core was started. The Mark III core, designed to minimize distortion, was installed in December 1957, and the reactor resumed operation. Reactor kinetics experiments with this core showed that it had a prompt negative temperature coefficient.

The Mark IV core was a plutonium core, consisting of 35 kg of plutonium alloyed with 1.25% by weight of aluminum, and clad in Zircaloy.

EBR-1 continued to operate successfully until it was finally shut down in 1964.

EBR-2

But before EBR-1's third core was loaded, construction had already begun in December 1957 on EBR-2. This unit, it may be recalled from Chapter 1, was one of the five reactors in AEC's 5-yr demonstration program of 1954. Unlike EBR-1's fully enriched (93%) core, EBR-2 operates on fuel enriched to 49% in ^{235}U, in the form of rods clad in stainless steel. It also has a depleted uranium blanket in which plutonium is produced. It is cooled by molten sodium at 60 psi pressure, with a reactor inlet temperature of 700°F and an outlet temperature of 886°F. Like EBR-1, it has a secondary loop of sodium that transfers the heat of the primary coolant to a second heat exchanger where superheated steam is produced at 1250 psi, 850°F. It produces 16.5-MWe net power. EBR-2

†Because irradiated sodium forms radioactive ^{24}Na, it is a potent gamma ray emitter (1.37 and 2.75 MeV) with a 15-hr half-life.

is located, like EBR-1, at the Idaho reactor test center, and its power is used there (the National Reactor Testing Station, or NRTS, is now called the Idaho National Engineering Laboratory, or INEL).

EBR-2 began power operation on August 7, 1964 and, as of the end of 1983, is still in regular operation, generating power as an experimental baseload plant. Where EBR-1 had demonstrated the *scientific* feasibility and practicality of breeding, and the use of liquid metals as reactor coolant and heat transfer fluid in a power system, EBR-2 was designed to demonstrate *technical* feasibility with emphasis on design features that could be extrapolated to large central-station application. One of its primary objectives was to extend the scientific principles demonstrated in EBR-1 to an engineering application that could provide the basis for a follow-on commercial demonstration of LMFBR power stations.

EBR-2 is a sodium-cooled fast reactor power plant. In addition to demonstrating the feasibility of the LMFBR concept for central power station application for almost two decades, EBR-2 has demonstrated considerable versatility for irradiating experimental fuel and fuel elements. Much of this work has recently been taken over by a new AEC/DOE fast reactor dedicated to research work and producing no power: the Fast Flux Test Facility (FFTF), which started up in 1980 at the Hanford Engineering Development Laboratory at Hanford, Washington, having been authorized for construction in 1966. Contrary to the major operations involved in refueling a LWR, EBR-2 can be shut down from full power, a partial refueling made, and the system restored to full power in about 24 hr.

But perhaps the most important contribution of EBR-2, one that is little known, is its demonstration that fast breeders using the ^{235}U–plutonium cycle need not be potential contributors to the problem of diversion of nuclear material. This has been done by EBR-2's use of an adjacent fuel recycling plant.

Spent fuel subassemblies from EBR-2 are moved from the reactor building into the adjacent Fuel Cycle Facility (FCF). There they are separated from the subassembly structure, the cladding is removed, and the bare fuel is chopped up. It then goes to a melt-refining furnace, where the fuel is melted down, contaminants are vaporized or removed as slag, and fresh makeup fuel is added. The process is called pyrometallurgical refining.

The next step is highly automated. The purified fuel is formed into new fuel pins by injection casting under vacuum after being melted in a graphite crucible. This operation is done in batches, with 120 pins made at one time, each in a glass mold that is broken off and discarded after the fuel has solidified. The pin castings are then sheared to length, and next cascade down through several levels of an automated inspection device that measures their length, diameter, and weight. An eddy-current tester checks the pins for flaws, porosity, cracks, and voids.

After inspection each pin is sealed in new cladding. This is a stainless steel tube with a bottom already welded in place, but open at the top. Spiral wire on the outside of each tube acts as a spacer to separate the pins when they are in the fuel assembly to create a clearance through which the sodium coolant can flow.

In the cladding step, a plug of solid sodium is first dropped into the cladding tube, the pin is inserted, resting on the sodium plug, and then the tube is heated. As the sodium melts with higher temperature, the pin drops down and forces the now-liquid sodium up the inner side of the tube, around the pin.

This pin moves along the assembly line to another station where a top plug is welded to the stainless steel tube by a remote welding machine, and the tube is leak-tested. Heat is applied to the pin and it is vibrated to eliminate any possible gas bubbles in the sodium that would prevent a perfect bond between the liquid sodium, the fuel pin, and the stainless steel cladding. The bond is then tested for integrity.

The final stage of the fabrication procedure is the arrangement of the clad, sodium-bonded fuel pins into new assemblies and final inspection. If they pass inspection, they are transferred through an air lock into the EBR-2 reactor building for reinsertion into the core of the reactor, by a remotely operated fueling machine.

Thus, it may be noted, no plutonium leaves the two interconnected buildings—the reactor building and the fuel cycle facility building next to it, both of which have walls of concrete several feet thick and neither of which can be entered because of the high level of radioactivity. While on-site reprocessing/refabrication is not necessarily required for diversion resistance of a commercial LMFBR, many of the aspects demonstrated at EBR-2, including the remote operation of the facility, are extremely important in current diversion–resistant fuel cycles (see Chapters 14 and 20).

Although EBR-2 has a core of relatively small dimensions—19.94 in. in diameter, 14.22 in. high, with a volume of 72.79 liters—nevertheless, there are 53 core subassemblies, plus 60 inner and 510 outer blanket subassemblies (in addition to the upper and lower blanket regions in the core subassemblies). The core subassemblies each contain 91 pins, and the outer blanket subassemblies 19 pins each, so that there are a total of 15,653 pins in the reactor, despite its small overall dimensions.

Over the years that EBR-2 has operated, many thousands of fuel pins have been irradiated, discharged from the reactor, disassembled, processed to separate fissionable materials from fission products (i.e., waste), and the former refabricated into new fuel and reloaded into the reactor.

Enrico Fermi Atomic Power Plant

Even before the 1954 five-reactor AEC demonstration program, including EBR-2, was announced, AEC had in June 1951 invited interested utilities, equipment manufacturers, and architect/engineering firms to set up study groups to evaluate the technical and economic feasibility of commercial atomic power generation. One of the four original such study groups consisted of Detroit Edison Company and Dow Chemical Company, who undertook to study the feasibility of commercial power-producing breeder reactors. By 1954, the Detroit Edison-Dow Chemical group had grown to 33 member companies incorporated as Atomic Power Development Associates (APDA).

In late March 1955, APDA submitted a proposal to AEC offering to build a 100-MWe fast breeder at a site near Monroe, Michigan, 33 miles south of Detroit on the shore of Lake Erie. A number of APDA companies led by Detroit Edison formed a separate syndicate, Power Reactor Development Corporation (PRDC) to own and operate the proposed plant. PRDC was to own the plant up to the turbine generator, which Detroit Edison owned, and sell steam to Edison. APDA remained as the nonprofit research and development organization and designer of the reactor.

The breeder, formally named the Enrico Fermi Atomic Power Plant, went critical for the first time on August 23, 1963, and after a long program of confirmatory low-power tests, generated its first electricity 3 yr later, on August 5, 1966.

Even before the first criticality, however, the contractor assigned to fabricate the fuel for the Fermi breeder had found it technically impossible to make as designed, and consequently, the reactor was derated from 100 MWe to 60.5 MWe. At this rating, primary coolant sodium at 80 psig pressure entered the reactor at 550°F, leaving at 800°F. The primary sodium then was pumped to an intermediate heat exchanger where it gave up its fission heat, inside the containment building, to a secondary sodium loop, which was piped out of containment to a steam generator house and into a steam generator to raise steam for the turbines. Steam conditions were 600 psi superheated steam, at 742°F. Thermal conversion efficiency was 31.3%. Control was achieved by means of 10 boron–carbide control rods.

The reactor had barely been in operation a month when, on October 5, 1966, an accident occurred. A zirconium baffleplate—ordered to be added underneath the core by the AEC regulatory staff, with the object of ensuring even flow distribution of coolant to all the core channels—began vibrating sufficiently that a small piece broke off and blocked one channel. This resulted in the partial melting of two fuel subassemblies and a protracted outage for repair.

Radiation levels during the accident were so minimal that no unusual precautions had to be taken, and dosimeter readings showed negligible venting of activity up the stack to the atmosphere.

The repairs required a little longer than 3 yr to carry out. Fermi returned to operation in 1970, but never really recovered from the setback, in that interest in the program was not restored. In 1973, the plant was shut down for good, after delivering 12 million kWh to the Detroit Edison System.

Clinch River Breeder Reactor

In 1969, Congress authorized AEC to begin a two-phase plan for a larger demonstration LMFBR plant. After a proposal by Commonwealth Edison-TVA was accepted by the government in March 1972, two nonprofit corporations were established: Project Management Corporation (PMC) and Breeder Reactor Corporation (BRC). Each of the two companies had a distinct role: BRC brought together 743 (later increased to 753) utilities throughout the United States to support the program financially; and PMC was the management arm.

The Clinch River breeder reactor was to be a 375-MWe plant. It was a joint venture of the federal government and the electric power industry.

When President Carter was elected, he opposed continuation of the project. Despite his opposition, Congress continued funding and authorization for the project throughout the Carter administration, and although no site work could begin without a construction permit, fabrication of the many components previously contracted for continued. Nevertheless, NRC environmental hearings were suspended and public hearings canceled.

In 1981, President Reagan directed federal agencies to proceed with breeder technology development, including Clinch River. In November 1982, NRC authorized site preparation activities including site clearing, excavation, and construction of temporary support and service facilities. Licensing activities were reinstituted, following the president's directive. However, in late 1983, the project failed to get congressional approval and was canceled.

U.S. Nonpower-Producing Fast Reactors

Two fast-neutron reactors have been built in the United States not to produce power or to breed, but solely for research and development purposes. Chronologically, both fall between the Enrico Fermi Fast Breeder and the Clinch River project.

Figure 13.13. FFTF, Richland, Washington. (Courtesy DOE.)

One is the Southwest Experimental Fast Oxide Reactor, more conveniently referred to by the acronym SEFOR. This unit was built in Arkansas as a joint venture of General Electric Company, U.S. utilities, the AEC, West German nuclear interests, and Euratom—the European Atomic Energy Commission. It operated from 1969 to 1972, with a thermal power of 20 MW. Its purpose was to demonstrate the inherent safety of a mixed-oxide fueled fast reactor. This inherent safety was predicted by physicists because of the negative Doppler coefficient, which was the effect verified.

The other R&D fast reactor is a test-bed for high-performance breeder fuel. This is the Fast Flux Test Facility (FFTF) at the Hanford nuclear research complex in southeastern Washington state (see Figure 13.13). Although its conceptual design was completed in 1966 and it had been scheduled to begin operation in 1973, it actually went into operation only in 1981. However, it has already been instrumental in the engineering development of large LMFBR components. It is being

Table 13.8. LMFBR Projects Throughout the World

Name	Country	Type	Power, MW(th)	Power, MWe	Initial Operation
		In Operation			
BR-10	USSR	Loop	10	—	1959
EBR-II	United States	Pool	62	16	1963
Rapsodie	France	Loop	40	—	1967
BOR-60	USSR	Loop	60	12	1969
BN-350	USSR	Loop	1000	350	1972
Phénix	France	Pool	563	250	1973
PFR	United Kingdom	Pool	600	250	1974
JOYO	Japan	Loop	75	—	1977
KNK-2	Germany	Loop	58	20	1977
FFTF	United States	Loop	400	—	1980
BN-600	USSR	Pool	1470	600	1980
		In Procurement/Construction			
SuperPhénix	France	Pool	3000	1200	1985
SNR-300	Germany	Loop	762	327	1986
MONJU	Japan	Loop	714	300	1987
CRBR	United States	Loop	975	350	Cancelled 1983
		In Planning/Design			
Super-Phénix 2 and 3	France	Pool	3750	1500	1992
BN-1600	USSR	Pool	4200	1600	1990
CDFR-1	United Kingdom	Pool	3250	1300	1992
DFBR	Japan	—	2800	1000	1993

Source: Adapted from EPRI Report NP-1972.

used to subject structural material samples as well as fuel samples to very intense, fast-neutron test irradiation. It has a thermal power of 400 MW.

Breeder Reactors in Europe and Japan

Although the United States was the first to develop a breeder, other countries have taken the lead. France, Britain, and the USSR have all proceeded with their own original plans. A listing of the worldwide LMFBR projects is given in Table 13.8, while Table 13.9 shows some key differences for the major projects now under construction.

France's 250-MWe breeder, called Phénix, Britain's 250-MWe Prototype Fast Reactor (PFR), and the Soviet Union's 350-MWe fast reactor BN-350 all went into operation about 1973–1974 (the French and Soviet units in 1973, the British in 1974). (The Russian designation "BN" stands for Bystrye Neitrony, or Fast Neutron.)

The French experience with Phénix has been outstanding, however, and that reactor has had an extremely high availability factor. Based on that experience, the French began construction in 1975 of a scaled-up, 1200-MWe version called SuperPhénix, in association with German and Italian firms. SuperPhénix is located at Creys-Malville in the Rhone Valley 50 km south of Lyon. Construction is nearing completion and the plant is scheduled to enter service in 1984. The Super-Phénix reactor is described in detail later in this chapter.

The BN-350 had some serious steam generator problems, but has been returned to service.

The Soviet Union went on to scale up BN-350 (a loop unit) with a 600-MWe pool unit, BN-600, which entered service in 1979. It is also building a still larger unit, rated at 1600 MWe, BN-1600, which is scheduled for operation starting in 1986. Reliability is a key factor in Soviet designs. For this reason, modular components, such as steam generators, are usually used. The fuel elements are designed for 10% heavy atom burnup (roughly 100,000 MWd/t), and the core height is set at 1 m. The main parameters of BN-1600 are presented in Table 13.10.

West Germany has started work on its own 300-MW prototype at Kalkar in the Ruhr region.

Table 13.9. Comparison of LMFBR Design Features

Design Feature	U.S. Clinch River	Japan Monju	France Super-Phénix	U.K. CDFR-1	West Germany SNR-300	USSR BN-600
Pool design			•	•		•
Loop design	•	•			•	
Heterogeneous core	•					
Independent, redundant, and diverse shutdown systems	•	•	•	•	•	•
Short shaft coolant pump	•					
Hot leg primary coolant pump	•				•	
Sodium-water reaction accommodation of intermediate piping	•	•	•	•	•	•
Primary and secondary system cell liners	•	•	N/A	N/A	•	N/A
Bent-tube steam generator	•			•		
Superheated steam cycle	•	•	•	•	•	•
Inconel clad upper internals	•	Not decided	N/A	N/A		N/A
Sodium-water reaction sensor at steam generator outlets	•	•	•	•	•	•

Source: Adapted from *The Energy Daily,* 12/8/1982.

Table 13.10. Main Parameters of the BN-1600 Reactor

Thermal power of reactor [MW (th)]	4,200
Sodium flow in primary loop (t/hr)	60,000
Sodium temperature in primary loop (°C)	
At core inlet	350
At core outlet	550
Sodium temperature in secondary loop (°C)	
At inlet to heat exchanger	310
At outlet from heat exchanger	505
Core parameters, mm	
Diameter	3,350
Height	1,000
Maximum neutron flux (neutrons-cm^{-2}/sec)	1×10^{16}
Maximum burnup (% heavy atoms)	10
Maximum power density (kW/L_{core})	710
Breeding ratio with plutonium in "equilibrium" state	1.4
Time between reloading, months	4–6
Steam parameters	
Pressure, kg/cm^2 (psi)	140 (1,991)
Temperature (°C)	490–500
Reactor vessel parameters	
Diameter (m)	18.3
Height (m)	18
Pressure (gauge), kg/cm^2 (psi)	0.4 (5.7)
Weight of sodium in first loop (t)	2,000
Main circulating pump in primary loop	
Flow (t/hr)	15,000
Head (m of liquid)	95
Shaft power (kW)	5,300
Number of intermediate heat exchangers	8

Source: From E. I. Inyutin and E. A. Khodarev, *Nuclear Safety* **24,** 243 (1983).

This reactor, called the SNR-300, was the first fast reactor subject to the same independent licensing procedures as LWRs. This caused the SNR-300 to become tangled in the German regulatory process, causing severe construction delays and financial problems. However, based on the present status of component manufacture, site work, and licensing schedules, commissioning will probably occur by late 1985. The primary system will then be filled with sodium, and experience will be gained in operating sodium systems, before nuclear commissioning in late 1986.

Britain has been working on the design of a Commercial Demonstration Fast Reactor (CDFR). This design takes advantage of experimental results obtained from the Prototype Fast Reactor (PFR) at Dounreay. The CDFR has many design features in common with the French SuperPhénix reactor (pool, superheat steam cycle, etc.), but differs considerably in the design of the steam generator and appears to have a somewhat more compact plant arrangement. Operation is tentatively scheduled for 1992.

Japan, after a slower start, is setting out to catch up. A 300-MWe unit, Monju, is under construction and is scheduled to begin operation in 1988. Like the French, British, and Russian breeders, Monju is of original, domestic design, helped by a bilateral treaty with France whereby technical data from the Phenix program is exchanged for R&D results from the Japanese breeder program.

LMFBR Technology

LMFBRs have characteristics that are basically different than LWRs. The principal ones are: the radioactivity of the primary coolant systems; flammability of sodium; the low vapor pressure of the coolant; and the vulnerability of thin walled, hot pipes to seismic loads. How these characteristics and others influence LMFBR plant design will be discussed below.

In an LMFBR, no effort is made to slow down the neutrons before they are captured by fissile material. In fact, the principal objective of such a reactor is the breeding of plutonium from ^{238}U which is possible only in a fast-neutron spectrum; consequently, slowing down must be minimized. In order to avoid slowing down and also to take advantage of the high temperatures which are possible in a fast reactor, sodium appears to be the most practical coolant at the present time. Because of the absence of moderator, the core is generally small and the power density, that is, power per unit volume, is high. This makes it essential to use a coolant with good thermal properties, for example, a liquid metal such as sodium. A high specific power, moreover, decreases both fuel charges and the doubling time for breeding. Because the macroscopic capture cross sections of fission products and other poisons is small in comparison with the macroscopic fission cross section of the fuel, there is more flexibility in the choice of construction materials, and the accumulation of fission products does not represent a limitation on burnup.

The power density of fast reactor fuel rods can be increased by using small-diameter fuel rods for fuel that has a high fissile material concentration. As is the case with thermal reactors, the limiting linear power density of a cylindrical fuel rod is relatively insensitive to fuel rod diameter. With mixed uranium and plutonium dioxide fuel, this limit is in the range of 50–60 kW/m. A factor of 2 reduction in fuel rod diameter, therefore, yields approximately a fourfold increase in specific power.

A basic difference between the various breeders is the design of their heat transport system. There are two possibilities. The first is a loop design, where the sodium coolant, after exiting the core, flows through an external piping loop, which contains a heat exchanger and pump. The second type is a pool design, where the primary sodium coolant never leaves the pressure vessel. In this variation, the sodium, after exiting the core, circulates through heat exchangers and pumps which are placed inside the vessel itself. This is accomplished by means of flow baffles and structures which channel its flow. An example of the former design is the U.S. Clinch River reactor, while the French SuperPhenix employs the pool arrangement. Both plants will be described later in some detail.

A pool-type pressure vessel, out of necessity, is much larger than that required for a loop design. It may be nearly 74 ft in diameter, compared to the 42 ft required for the loop-type pressure vessel.† However, the pool design avoids the external intermediate heat transport piping. Specially shielded compartments which contain the pumps and intermediate heat exchangers are required because the primary sodium is highly radioactive. These compartments greatly increase the size of the reactor containment building. The relative merits of the two designs is given in Table 13.11.

A typical sodium primary coolant loop is: a few hundred feet of 36-in.-diameter pipe; a very large pump (about 8 ft in diameter and 70 ft high); a large Intermediate Heat Exchanger (IHX); guard tanks for the pump and the IHX and other places where major leakage would be serious;

†Pressure vessels this large are possible because sodium has a low vapor pressure at operating temperatures, so that heavy thick-walled vessels are not needed.

Table 13.11. Comparison of Loop and Pool Designs

Advantages of Pool Design

Simpler, no need for external primary sodium piping.
Smaller reactor containment building required.
Neutron irradiation of pressure vessel is low, therefore, no neutron embrittlement and activation. As a result of the latter, the pressure vessel is accessible.
High Na inventory is an advantage in the case of an accident.
The pressure vessel sees low temperature of cold sodium (~400°C) uniformly. [Loop plants usually have cold sodium at bottom of pressure vessel, hot sodium (~510°C) at top.]

Advantages of Loop Design

Smaller reactor pressure vessel.
Seismic design is easier.
Pressure vessel does not have to support the pumps and IHXs.
Thermal and hydraulic design easier.

insulation; and hundreds of supports and snubbers.† This typical loop is housed in very large shielded cells which are lined with an "engineered safety" steel liner to protect the concrete walls from possible reaction with hot sodium and evolution of hydrogen. The supports and snubbers are fastened to structural steel braces that extend out into the cell to the required points. The braces themselves are anchored into the reinforced concrete which means that the braces penetrate the cell liner. These penetrations complicate the design and installation of the cell liner because the liner has to expand without buckling or tearing loose at these penetrations.

The primary coolant pipes in an LMFBR loop-type plant are hotter than the pipes in a pressurized water reactor plant. To obtain adequate flexibility, the LMFBR pipes must be much thinner walled. Fortunately, the low sodium pressure allows $\frac{1}{2}$–$\frac{7}{8}$ in. wall thickness to be used. A problem arises with the attachment of supports and snubbers to the hot thin walls of 36-in.-diameter pipes. The attachment rings are insulated from the hot pipe to avoid heat losses, variable temperatures along the pipes, and large temperature differences across the snubbers and supports.

The LMFBR pool advantages are atmospheric pressure inside and outside the reactor vessel wall (except for static head); primary vessel wall with no penetrations below the primary coolant level; retention of radioactive coolant within the reactor vessel; and passive shutdown cooling systems that do not require electric power, realignment of valves, pumps, or pressure control. The thermal inertia of the large pool of primary sodium provides a long period of time to operate safety systems. Even if a leak occurs in the wall of the tank, a guard tank surrounds it and keeps the primary sodium coolant from being lowered past a minimum safe liquid level in the primary tank (reactor vessel). This is a tremendous safety advantage that LMFBRs have relative to LWRs.

Thermal Design

The efficiency of any thermal plant, nuclear or otherwise, is determined by its peak operating temperatures. The temperatures of an LMFBR are typically 200°C higher than in a LWR; its thermal efficiency is correspondingly higher. The design temperatures of an LMFBR are limited by the fuel element cladding, the fuel assembly duct, and the temperature transients that the system can withstand. Table 13.12a compares operating conditions of LMFBR and LWR reactors. An important consideration is the creep strength of the materials used, particularly type-316 stainless steel. Most metals change "character" at about half their melting point (on an absolute temperature scale). For the 300 series of stainless steel, this occurs at about 1000°F (540°C). Above this temperature, intergranular failures and grain boundary sliding (creep) become important. As seen in Figure 13.14, the significant reduction in creep strength of stainless steel limits its use to below 950°F (510°C) or so. This material limitation can be very important at points in the system that undergo temperature cycling, such as hot leg pipes that undergo a transient when the plant's power level changes. Another important consideration is the effect of temperature on the allowable stress design of $2\frac{1}{4}$% Cr–1% Mo alloy used for steam generator tubes. Above 900°F (480°C) this material

†Piping supports which allow slow movement of pipes when they heat up or contract but are rigid supports otherwise.

Table 13.12a. Typical Temperature and Pressure Conditions LMFBR Versus PWR

	LMFBR	PWR
Reactor outlet temperature (°F)	1020	597
Reactor inlet temperature (°F)	740	553
Turbine inlet pressure (psia)	2200–3000	710
Steam saturation temperature (°F)	700	505
Turbine inlet temperature (°F)	910	500
Steam reheat temperature (°F)	455	453

Table 13.12b. Heat Transfer Properties, Na Versus H_2O

	Na	H_2O
Temperature (°F)	900	550
Velocity, $\frac{\text{sec}}{\text{ft}}$	30	13
Reynolds No., $\frac{\text{inertia forces}}{\text{viscous forces}}$	171,000	~200,000
Prandtl No., $\frac{\text{momentum diffusivity}}{\text{heat diffusivity}}$	0.0047	0.91
Peclet No., $\frac{\text{convection}}{\text{conduction}}$	804	~182,000
Heat-transfer coefficient, $\frac{\text{Btu}}{\text{hr-ft}^2 - °\text{F}}$	17,000	5,100

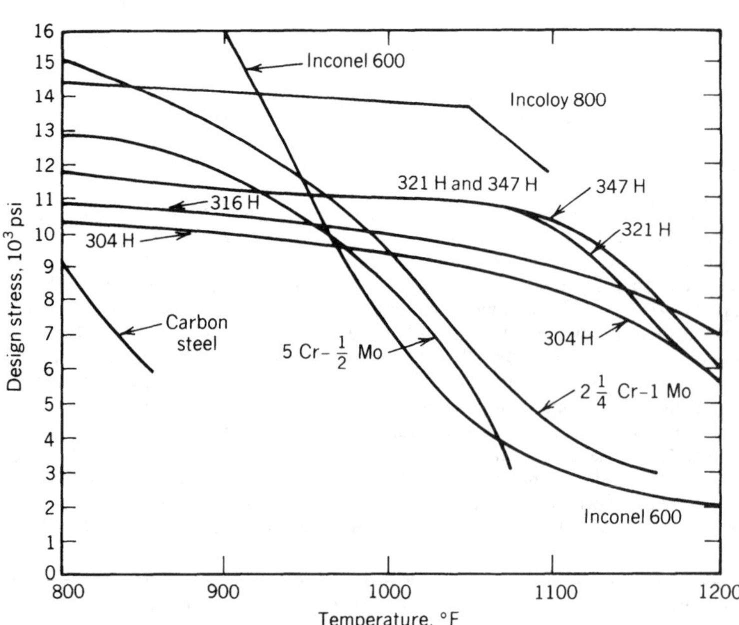

Figure 13.14. Candidate fast breeder reactor materials. (From Atomics International.)

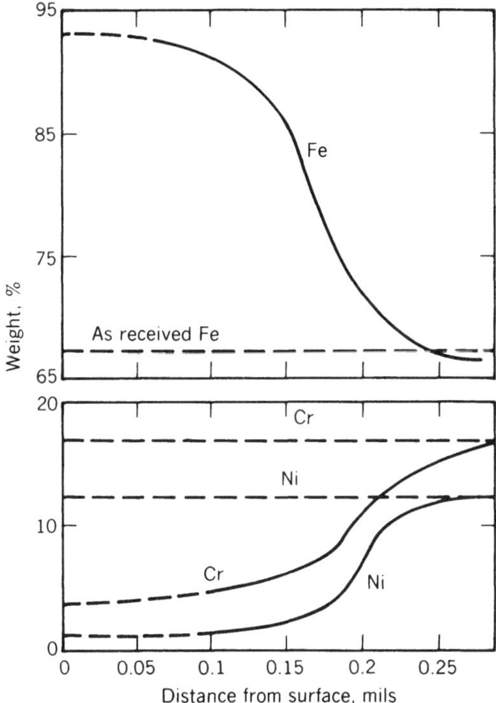

Figure 13.15. Compositional change in stainless steel associated with elemental leaching in sodium. (From Atomics International.)

degrades rapidly. Inconel alloy-800 can sometimes be used in place of $2\frac{1}{4}$% Cr–1% Mo for this application.

Sodium as a Coolant

In many ways sodium is an ideal coolant. It has a high thermal conductivity and low vapor pressure.† These properties, tabulated in Table 13.12b, allow a core with a high power density and system pressures much lower than for an LWR. Sodium freezes, however, at 208°F (97.8°C) so that piping and components must be heated to prevent its solidification when the plant cools down.

The properties of sodium give breeder operators an important ally for controlling reactor transients: time. For example, a breeder's liquid-sodium coolant can absorb a 300°C rise above operating temperature without boiling, giving operators up to several days to figure out a correct response. The sodium's natural circulation also would come in handy should pumps fail. This is because a breeder is designed so that sodium continues to flow naturally through the core via convection, even if all electric power fails. Thus during a shutdown, circulating sodium would continue to remove heat from the core. In a LWR, cooling water must be injected to remove decay heat.

Sodium is a metal in which some other metals are slightly soluble. Figure 13.15 shows the effect this solubility has on stainless steel in contact with sodium. The surface of the material is almost completely leached of its chromium and nickel alloying elements. Iron and carbon are also soluble in sodium. At 600°C, the solubility of iron is about 1 ppm, carbon 1.8 ppm. This can lead to the mass transport of iron, and the decarburization of steel when sodium, unsaturated in iron, passes over a hot component and iron or carbon start to go into solution. These elements are then carried through the system until they reach a cooler region where they deposit. Figure 13.16 suggests the mechanism that causes this mass transfer through the sodium solubility gradient. The solubility of iron in sodium is greatly increased by the presence of oxygen.

The purity of the sodium used in LMFBRs is very important. It is possible to obtain it 99.95% pure (i.e., 500 ppm impurities). About 200 ppm of the impurities are potassium, which represents

†At 900°C, the vapor pressure of sodium is only 1.2 atm (17.6 psi).

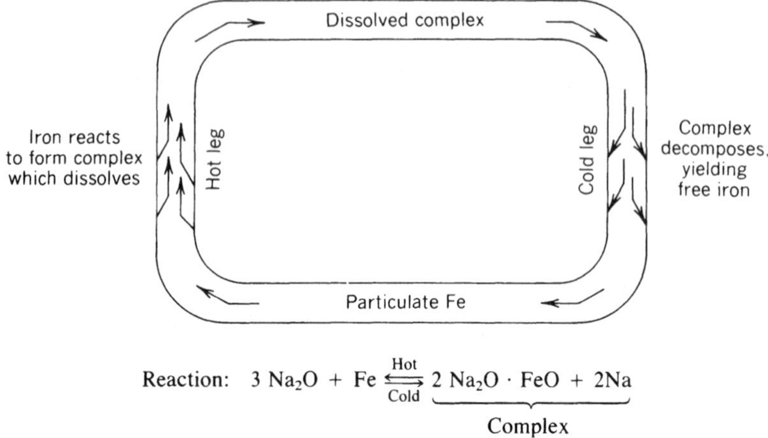

$$\text{Reaction:}\quad 3\ Na_2O + Fe \underset{\text{Cold}}{\overset{\text{Hot}}{\rightleftarrows}} \underbrace{2\ Na_2O \cdot FeO + 2Na}_{\text{Complex}}$$

Figure 13.16. Solubility-gradient mass transfer of iron. (From Atomics International.)

no particular problem. Oxygen impurities are important, however, because of oxygen's role in the mass transfer of iron and the corrosion of components. Carbon, at about 30 ppm, is an undesirable impurity since it can affect the mechanical properties of materials. For example, carbon added to, or removed from, the fueling cladding can weaken it.

When molten sodium is added to a system, it is usually passed through a sintered metal filter with a 10-μm pore size. This removes any scale and particulates picked up by the sodium from the transport containers. In the plant system, several filters are used to purify the sodium. These are either cold traps or hot traps that work on the temperature dependence of the solubility of various elements. When the solubility of carbon, oxygen, nitrogen, hydrogen, and so on, decrease they leave solution, leaving the sodium purified.†

Sodium does not chemically react with hot fuel cladding to produce hydrogen (as in an LWR Zr-H_2O reaction). This is a safety plus for the LMFBR. On the other hand, LMFBRs often have positive void coefficient of reactivity, a problem if the sodium ever boils in the core. (Void coefficients are negative in LWRs.) The positive void coefficient of a large "homogeneous" LMFBR core can be reduced a factor of 3 by using a well-designed "heterogeneous" core arrangement where blanket-type assemblies are inserted at strategic places within the array of fuel assemblies. This fuel arrangement, along with the Doppler effect and the time-space incoherence of coolant boiling in such a core, make the situation more manageable. However, because of this positive void coefficient, an LMFBR's scram system must shut down the reactor when needed.

Sodium is very active chemically; it burns in air and other oxidizing agents. Sodium smoke is strongly caustic, forming NaOH with the moisture of skin, eyes, and lungs, and with moisture in the atmosphere, and so on. Spilled sodium is a safety threat to people; burning sodium generates smoke that can damage equipment and instruments. The problem is compounded if the sodium smoke is radioactive. Hot sodium in contact with concrete can react and evolve hydrogen which in turn could pose a threat of exploding. Both sodium and sodium smoke must be carefully controlled to avoid hazards.

The possibility of a fire is always of concern in a power plant. Sodium ignites in air at 239°F (115°C), and burns at 1500–1600°F (840°C), producing no flame but a thick white smoke. Water, of course, is worse than useless in extinguishing the fire, as is CO_2 or CCl_4. The fire must be put out by excluding oxygen, so $CaCO_3$, sand, or products based on graphite are used. To prevent fires, any cell containing sodium equipment is usually inerted, and guard vessels‡ are provided to limit the amount of a sodium spilled. The guard vessels will also prevent the core from uncovering in the event of a pipe break, especially undesirable in an LMFBR because of its tendency to have a positive void coefficient.

The reactivity of sodium with water and organic materials has other ramifications in the design and operation of an LMFBR. One is in the design of the steam generators. Since a leak from the water to the sodium side of a steam generator will produce a rapid pressure buildup, rupture discs

†LMFBRs operate with less than 5 ppm oxygen in the primary coolant.
‡Catch vessels which surround a reactor vessel, pump, and so on.

must be provided on the shell side containing the sodium. The design must also provide for early detection of incipient leaks,† and be capable of preventing the catastrophic propagation of sodium leaks in the steam generator's tube bundle. For example, the Super-Phénix reactor has a double membrane safety device on the bottom of each steam generator. In the event of a leak, these membranes allow rapid evacuation of Na-water reaction products into a discharge circuit, limiting the pressure buildup. Any H^2 gas that might result is separately collected in N^2, not in air, to prevent an explosion.

LMFBR Stability

Uncontrolled power excursions are potentially dangerous in any nuclear reactor core. Like all other reactors, LMFBRs have inherent physical properties limiting the power level the core can attain. These properties are the core's temperature reactivity coefficients, which define the change in reactivity as the temperature changes. An LMFBR's stability is dependent on the following parameters:

1. *Sodium Void Coefficient.* A change in reactivity occurs when the sodium coolant changes density (or completely voids the core). This is because the neutron capture rate, spectrum, and leakage all depend on the amount of sodium present. The sodium void coefficient, which can be positive or negative, depends on the core size, geometry, and material composition.
2. *Doppler Coefficient.* The effective cross section seen by a neutron is a function of temperature: as the temperature increases, the probability of fission or capture in the fuel isotopes (^{235}U, ^{238}U, ^{239}Pu) increases in the energy region below 10 keV.‡ This temperature effect on fission resonances increases reactivity, while the capture resonances decrease it. For large LMFBRs, which have low fissile-to-fertile ratio,§ the Doppler coefficient is negative. The Doppler effect is prompt, since there is no mechanical or thermal delay as the fuel temperature increases.
3. *Mechanical Expansion.* As the power level in a core increases, thermal expansion of the fuel elements occurs. This effectively increases the size of the core, thereby decreasing its reactivity. Three types of expansion occur: axial fuel expansion, fuel element bowing, and radial core expansion. The expansion, however, is somewhat delayed in time as it is related to the structural material. It is, however, an important mechanism in the total reactivity feedback, both in normal operation and in accident situations.

Generally it is not desirable to have any of these reactivity coefficients positive. This is not always possible, particularly in the case of the sodium void coefficient. It is necessary that the overall reactivity coefficient¶ be negative and that any positive coefficient be made as small as possible. The characteristics of the reactivity coefficients as a function of core size are shown in Figure 13.17. It is evident from this figure that the larger the core size, the less negative the overall reactivity coefficient tends to be.

Radioactivity of Primary Coolant Systems

^{16}N is an activation product resulting from neutron irradiation of water in LWR cores.‖ ^{16}N has a 7-sec half-life, therefore, the activity is gone a minute or two after the reactor is shut down. The situation in LMFBRs is very different. ^{24}Na and ^{22}Na are the activation products resulting from neutron irradiation of the sodium primary coolant. The half-lives of ^{24}Na and ^{22}Na are 15 hr and 2.6 yr, respectively. As a result, the sodium primary coolant radioactivity is high for a considerable time after the reactor is shut down. Considering the ^{24}Na alone, four days or more are required after shutdown before a person can be in the vicinity of large amounts of sodium primary coolant. The 2.6-yr ^{22}Na builds up slowly with plant operation until the radioactivity reaches a level where it is

†Usually done by monitoring hydrogen in the sodium coolant. The hydrogen is produced as a by-product in the reaction: $Na + H_2O \rightarrow NaOH + \frac{1}{2} H^2$.
‡The Doppler effect as a reactor shutdown mechanism can be improved by using an oxide fuel such as UO_2-PuO_2. The slight moderating ability of oxygen increases the number of neutrons in the resonance region of the spectrum.
§Therefore low fission-to-capture ratio.
¶That is, the sum of all the reactivity coefficients.
‖^{16}N, produced when a neutron activates ^{16}O, has a very penetrating 7-MeV gamma ray. The hydrogen absorbs neutrons too, but the resulting ^2H is stable and does not contribute to the radioactivity in the water primary coolant. ^2H absorbs a neutron and produces ^3H (half-life 12.3 yr) but the cross section is low and there is not much ^2H present in the water.

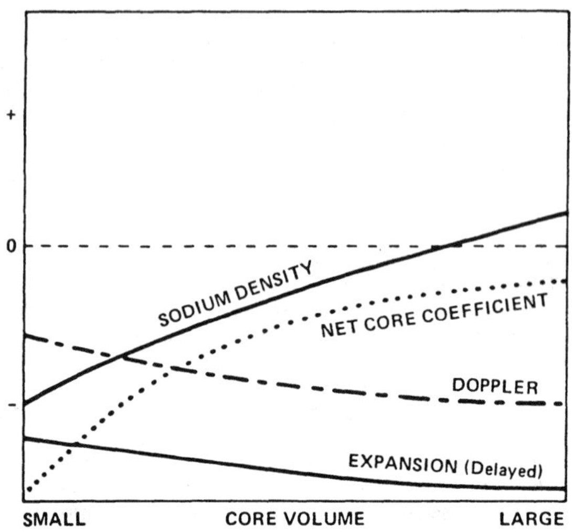

Figure 13.17. General characteristics of power or temperature reactivity coefficients in LMFBRs.

necessary to drain the sodium to shielded tanks before access into sodium primary coolant cells can be allowed. It would not be practical to wait 5–10 half-lives (13–26 yr) for the ^{22}Na to decay.†

LMFBR Systems Design

LMFBR systems requirements relate directly to the properties of the sodium coolant. For example, it is desirable for the steam generator to be higher than the IHX which in turn should be higher than the core. This arrangement allows natural circulation of coolant in the event of pump failure. The suction of pumps and the height between the centerline of the core and the top of an IHX is fixed by atmospheric pressure and the density of sodium. The maximum column of sodium is about 33 ft (10.1 m) high.

Inert gas, usually argon, is needed to cover all spaces above a free surface of sodium. If this cover gas is maintained slightly above atmospheric pressure, moisture is prevented from reaching the sodium, and sodium (vapor) from reaching the atmosphere. Both are undesirable, the former because of the formation of caustic (NaOH) and hydrogen gas, the latter because sodium that leaks into the atmosphere forms sodium peroxide which is highly corrosive.

IHXs have countercurrent flow with the hot fluid on the primary side flowing downward, the cooler secondary-side fluid flowing upward. Vertical mounting of the heat exchangers establishes flow patterns which complement natural convection forces, making flow reversals less likely in the event of a pump failure. Since coolant temperatures are high and can change rapidly, heat exchangers must accommodate thermal shock and differential expansion of its elements. Moreover, coolant velocities can be high, possibly leading to tube vibration and fretting problems, especially near the entrance of the component. Entrance plenums, therefore, are made large, thereby reducing coolant velocity and tube vibration.

Sodium Pumps

The large mechanical pumps for circulating primary sodium are high-cost items. Thermal transients in the sodium can cause pump problems. As pump size goes up, the shaft gets larger in diameter and the allowable clearance (between the shaft and the stationary housing of the bearing) becomes a smaller percent of the shaft diameter. When temperature differences around the shaft cause ovality (as well as increase the average diameter), interference between the stationary and the rotating parts can result. In addition, the thermal transients can cause bowing of the shaft with

†Historical note—This is one of the principal reasons why the U.S. Navy abandoned its otherwise successful sodium-cooled demonstration submarine propulsion system (USS Seawolf, SSN-575) and turned to PWRs—a decision that had far-reaching effects on commercial nuclear power programs.

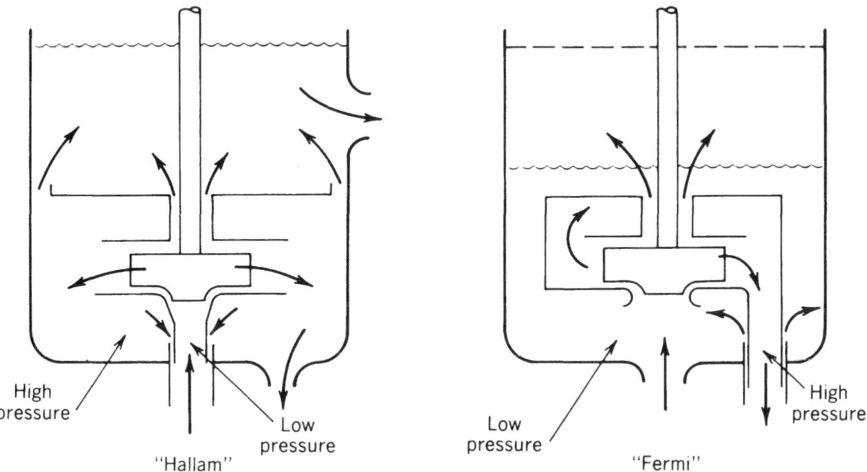

Figure 13.18. Key differences of Fermi–Hallam primary pumps.

similar results. Such problems are just a few of those that confront a mechanical designer of these critical components.†

The main difference between a sodium coolant pump and a water pump is the seal. A free surface (with a cover gas) is almost always used. For high-flow applications, centrifugal pumps are used. Sodium is not a good lubricant, so bearing designs are critical in preventing the pump shaft from rubbing against the casing. There are many variations of the following two basic designs (refer to Figure 13.18):

1. *The Fermi‡ Pump.* In this design, sodium enters on the side and is discharged out the bottom. An advantage of the Fermi pump is that it can be entirely removed from the top for maintenance. However, the sodium level in the pump barrel is determined by the sodium level in the reactor less the friction drop in the system. This requires the barrel to be sufficiently long to accommodate this level and the drawdown of the sodium as the pump reaches full speed. Long pump shafts cause bearing problems so that a sodium level control system is necessary.
2. *The Hallam Pump.* This is a bottom suction, side discharge design. In the Hallam design, the sodium level does not fluctuate as much as in the Fermi design. However, high pressure in the upper regions causes some leakage around the pump seals. An overflow line and holes in the pump's impeller are used to help stabilize the sodium level. The bottom inlet achieves a better flow distribution in the pump and is the only practical arrangement for an inducer/impeller pump blade.

An important design consideration is the location of the pump in the system. Several major factors must be considered when deciding whether the primary pump should be located in the reactor outlet pipe (hot leg) or in the reactor inlet pipe (cold leg). If the pump is in the hot leg, the pump must withstand thermal transients which occur when the reactor changes power level. A smaller pump is required, however, with less suction requirements, as the pressure drop through the IHX is eliminated.

When the pump is placed in the cold leg, the IHX protects the pump from a severe temperature transient. Almost all LMFBR designs use a constant ΔT across the core which means that pump speed is varied proportionally to the core power level. The required positive suction head is a function of the pump speed. There are obviously design trade-offs in the pump location. Most LMFBR designs to date, including CRBR, have the pump in the cold leg of the primary system. For pool reactors, including Phenix and Super-Phenix, the pump is also in the cold leg.

Primary system pumps need a large capacity. For a 1200-MWe plant, over 300,000 gal/min need to be circulated. Engineering trade-offs also are encountered in deciding the placement of pumps in the intermediate heat transport loop. Table 13.13 lists the various pros and cons. Most designs (including CRBR and Super-Phenix) have their secondary loop pumps in the cold leg.

†Another concern is that the lubrication of the upper ball bearings might possibly leak oil into the sodium, which could cause a "gunk" that might restrict the small coolant passages between fuel pins in the reactor core.

‡Fermi and Hallam refer to the plants where these designs were first used.

Table 13.13. Secondary Pump, Hot Leg Versus Cold Leg Location

Hot Leg		Cold Leg	
Pro	Con	Pro	Con
No additional piping to locate at loop high point	Higher cover gas operating pressure Higher sodium pressures throughout loop Higher operating temperatures Higher pumping costs	Lower cover gas operating pressure Lower sodium pressures throughout loop Lower operating temperatures Lower pumping costs	Some additional piping to locate at loop high point Greater possibility of contaminating pump with Na-H_2O reaction products after a steam generator leak

An entirely different type of pump is the Electro-Magnetic (EM) pump. It operates exactly opposite to the way a dc generator does. By inducing a field in a coil surrounding a pipe that carries highly electrically conducting sodium, a force is induced which pushes the sodium through the pipe. Direct current EM pumps have been used successfully for many years, but big ones were not so practical because to drive them a huge generator producing thousands of amperes at a few volts was required. Such a system would need huge busbars to carry the electrical current from the generator to the EM pump system.

An improved concept, called a flow coupler, is now possible. A flow coupler is a close-coupled electrical generator and an EM pump. Figure 13.19 illustrates the principles involved. The intermediate sodium is the moving conductor in the generator. A magnetic field is imposed across the duct in which the intermediate sodium is forced to flow. This causes an electrical current to flow perpendicular to the flux field. A parallel duct is located against the intermediate sodium duct such that the magnetic flux crosses it also. The electrical current from the first duct flows in series across the second duct (a necessary condition for the motor effect). The conductor in the second duct is primary sodium; the force pushes it countercurrent to the flow of the intermediate sodium. Thus, the second duct pumps primary sodium.

A flow coupler would be a tremendous simplification compared with the large mechanical pump

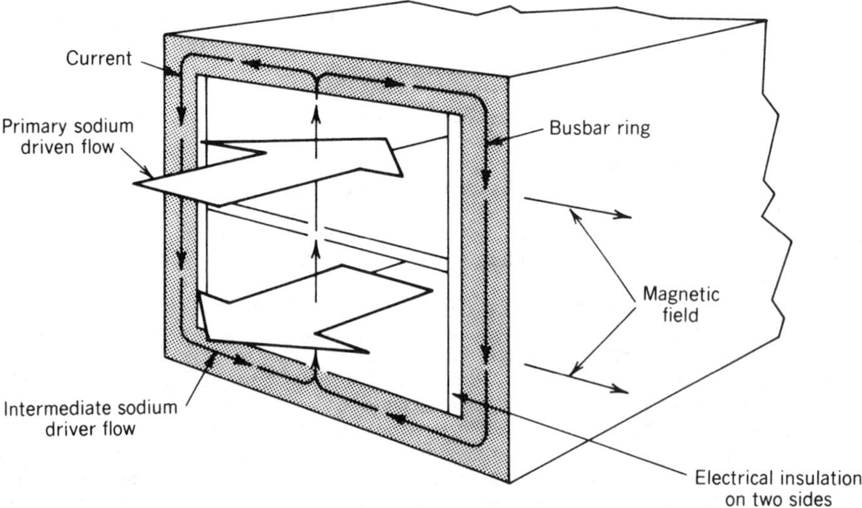

Figure 13.19. Principles of a flow coupler. (1) Magnetic field is across both ducts (horizontal). (2) Intermediate sodium flow forced along its duct (back to front) perpendicular to magnetic field—this produces electrical current (bottom-to-top direction). (3) Current flows through primary sodium and around busbar ring. (4) EM force pushes primary sodium counterflow to the driver intermediate sodium. (Courtesy EPRI.)

and drive motor that it would replace. The large hydrostatic bearing used on mechanical pumps is a source of concern to plant operators. The flow coupler derives its power from the intermediate sodium pump. The only system change required is that the intermediate sodium pump has to deliver a higher head. The overall efficiency of a flow-coupler system should be about the same as a mechanical pump. This is an important improvement over the older type of dc EM pumps and ac types as well.

LMFBR Plants

Two specific designs will be described as examples of the current state of the art in LMFBR design. The first, a loop plant, is the Clinch River Breeder Reactor under development until recently in the United States. Although the plant has been canceled, the CRBR design is described here because it represents one of the most advanced concepts in a loop-type plant, and may serve as the basis for future designs. The second, a pool design, is the French SuperPhénix reactor, under construction at Creys-Malville on the Rhône River. The latter is expected to be operational in 1984. Both designs incorporate advanced technological features that represent significant advances over previous LMFBR plants.

Clinch River Breeder Reactor (CRBR)

A prime example of advanced features in the CRBR was the heterogeneous core. Initial studies of this core configuration were made in 1975 by the CRBR design team. The original design had provided for a homogeneous core, like foreign breeders, in which fuel assemblies containing a mixture of plutonium and uranium oxide are surrounded by a blanket of depleted uranium oxide—that is, virtually pure in the isotope ^{238}U—assemblies. In the newer heterogeneous design, blanket assemblies of fertile ^{238}U not only surrounded the core, but were also interspersed within the core. The closer the blanket material is to the region of highest neutron activity, the greater is the rate of conversion of ^{238}U to plutonium. By selectively moving radial (outer) blanket assemblies into the high-flux (high-neutron activity) region of the core, a heterogeneous configuration with higher breeding gain could be achieved, without compromising safety. The major neutronic characteristics of homogeneous and heterogeneous core designs developed for CRBR is summarized in Table 13.14.

Table 13.14. Summary Comparison of Major Neutronic Characteristics of the CRBRP Homogeneous and Heterogeneous Cores

	Homogeneous	Heterogeneous
Breeding ratio		
Initial cycle, low ^{240}Pu fuel	1.15	1.29
Equilibrium cycle, low ^{240}Pu fuel	1.08	1.24
Initial cycle, LWR-Pu	1.21	1.34
Equilibrium cycle, LWR-Pu	1.14	1.29
Fissile plutonium inventory, initial core (kg)	1230	1502
Fuel enrichment, initial core, low ^{240}Pu fuel (wt/%)	0.174	0.328
Peak linear power, $3\sigma + 15\%$ overpower (W/cm)		
Fuel	469	525
Blankets	650	656
Peak flux (n/cm^2-sec)		
Total	7.4×10^{15}	5.4×10^{15}
Fast (>0.11 MeV)	4.2×10^{15}	3.4×10^{15}
Fuel burnup (cycles 1+2/3+4, MWd/kg)	63/104	77/110
Sodium void		
Maximum positive, BOC fuel assemblies ($)	3.90	1.51
Maximum positive, EOC fuel assemblies ($)	4.00	2.31
Doppler coefficient, start of life ($-T\,dk/dt \cdot 10^4$)		
Fuel	55.9	25.8
Internal blankets	—	44.0
Radial blankets	7.0	11.8
Axial blankets	4.4	2.6

Source: Courtesy of The Breeder Reactor Corporation.

In the heterogeneous core, the improvement in breeding is achieved by increasing the ^{238}U fraction through the introduction of blanket material in the fuel region. This improvement could also be achieved in a homogeneous core through the choice of a large (>0.30-in. in the case of oxide fuel) fuel pin diameter. However, with respect to the sodium void reactivity coefficient, the heterogeneous core showed a definite superiority.

From a neutronics perspective, the CRBR heterogeneous core had a lower core sodium void worth and lower fluence-to-burnup ratios than the homogeneous design. Moreover, doubling time, breeding gain, and reactivity swing were higher, whereas a lower fissile loading, improved Doppler coefficient, and lower flux-tilt sensitivity characterized the homogeneous concept. The division of the fuel region in the heterogeneous core into smaller regions separated by internal blankets led to a neutronic decoupling of the core. In general, the more loosely coupled a core, the larger the temperature rise during a transient, despite its much shorter duration because of more Doppler feedback.

Multiplexing was another example of design enhancement at Clinch River made possible by the research and development program. This is an electronic advance relatively new to the power industry, although it is widely used in aircraft and information processing. It permits thousands of signals to be transmitted simultaneously along one circuit. As a result, more than a million feet of electric cable would have been eliminated from the plant, substantially reducing costs, and at the same time making for more reliable plant operation.

Plant Design

The layout of the Clinch River Breeder (Figure 13.20) included two structural design categories: hardened and nonhardened. The hardened buildings contained those systems or equipment that had to remain functional under earthquake, tornado, or maximum possible flood-level conditions. The major hardened buildings which composed the "nuclear island"—that is, the nuclear steam supply system and other radioactive systems—was to be of reinforced concrete resting on a simple monolithic base mat of reinforced concrete 18 ft thick.

The reactor containment building, enclosing the reactor, primary heat transport systems, and their support systems, consisted of a building within a building. The inner containment was a steel shell $1\frac{1}{3}$–$1\frac{3}{4}$ in. thick, above grade, and a combination of the steel shell and concrete below grade. The outside confinement was reinforced concrete totally enclosing the inner containment, both above and below grade. An annular space between the two structures provided containment for any possible leakage from the inner containment.

The reactor containment building was divided in half horizontally by an operating floor. The lower level consisted of inerted, steel-lined concrete vaults housing the reactor, radioactive sodium piping, primary pumps (Figure 13.21), the intermediate heat exchangers (Figure 13.22), and the sodium overflow system. The upper level housed refueling equipment, reactor servicing equipment, and other primary components. A $44\frac{1}{2}$-ft-diameter hatch between the reactor service building and containment building allowed for movement of equipment between the two.

A steam generator building housed the steam generators (Figure 13.23), intermediate sodium systems, parts of the steam generator systems, and support systems. Two other hardened buildings were the control room building containing central plant control, protection, and instrumentation systems; and the diesel generator building containing two emergency diesels to provide the plant with independent power for instrumentation and control in case of loss of off-site power.

There were to be three primary sodium loops carrying heat from the reactor to the intermediate heat exchangers. Sodium entered the reactor vessel at 730°F and left at 995°F. The primary pumps moved in to the three IHXs at a rate of 33,700 gal/min and 175 psi pressure. The sodium then flowed back through a check valve and flow meter to the reactor. Primary piping was $\frac{1}{2}$-in.-thick welded stainless steel, 36-in. diameter between the reactor and the pump, and 24-in. elsewhere. Steam conditions at the turbine throttle were to be 906°F at 1550 psi pressure.

The 460-ton reactor vessel had an inside diameter of 20 ft, 3 in., and a height of 45 ft, 8 in. It was to be made of 304-type stainless steel (Figure 13.24).

The heterogeneous core design mentioned above contained 156 single-enrichment fuel assemblies having a mixture of plutonium and uranium oxide, arranged in a hexagonal geometry (Figure 13.25). There were 76 blanket assemblies interspersed within the fuel region, and 132 more completely surrounding it. Fifteen control assemblies were arranged within the core. These were divided into two independent systems, with independent instrument channels and associated electronics so that they are not subject to common-mode failure. Either system could achieve reactor shutdown with the other system completely inoperable, and even with the rod of most worth (i.e., the most powerful control rod) in the otherwise operable system stuck out of the core—even in the presence of the most severe reactivity fault event. Boron carbide was the control material for both systems. The rod drives were connected to the rods in differing ways in the two systems; in both, the rods were to fall by gravity into the core in case of scram, that is, emergency or fast shutdown, but with initial hydraulic assist in the secondary control system.

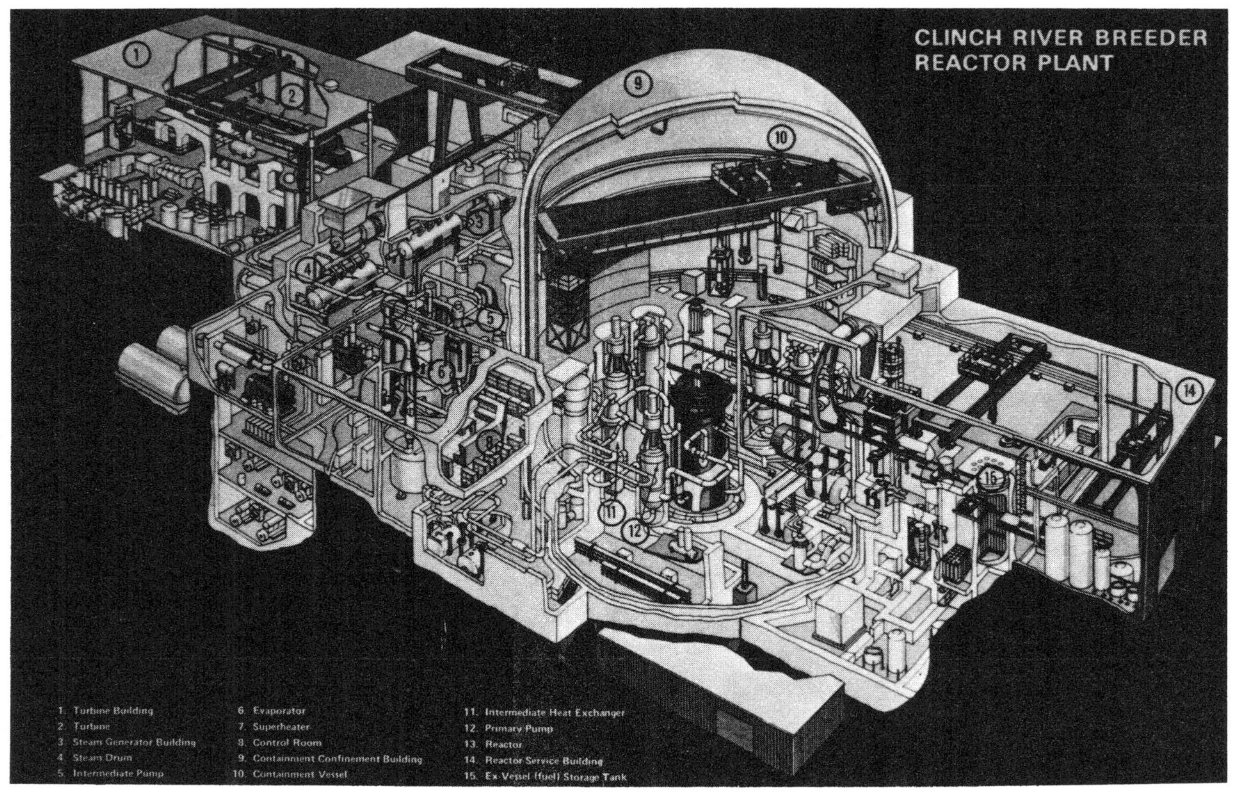

Figure 13.20. Clinch River breeder reactor plant. (Courtesy Breeder Reactor Corp.)

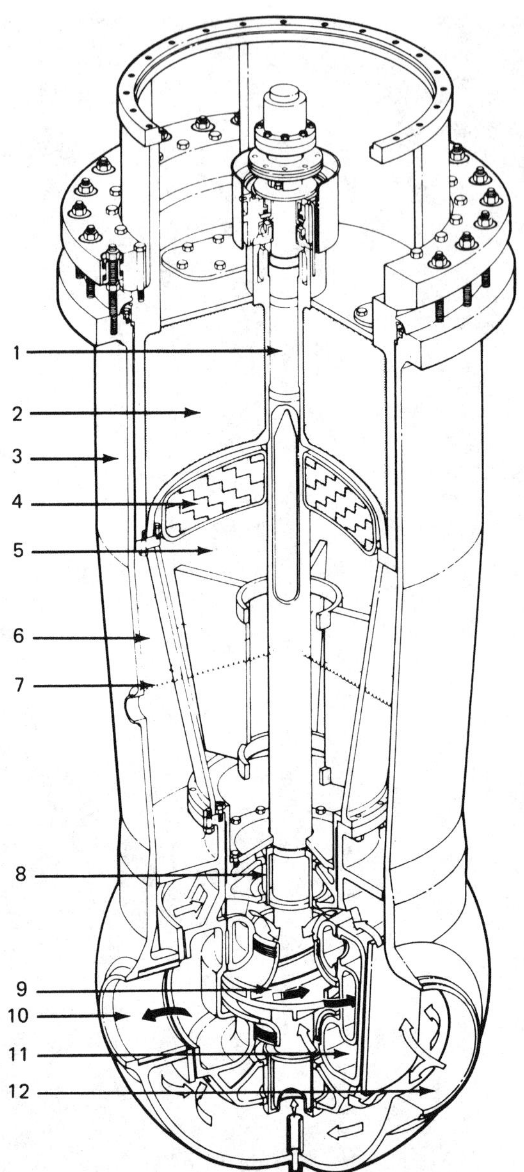

Figure 13.21. CRBRP primary and intermediate pump. *Features:* (1) Permits pressure boundary to be exposed to the plant transient duty cycle, made possible by multidimensional inelastic stress analysis and spherical lower tank geometry. (2) Eliminates the need for protective thermal barrier, eases bearing misalignment by minimizing creep and transient distortion effects. (3) Thrust bearing moved from pump to motor, reducing shaft length. (4) Shaft seal removable without motor hoist. *Key:* 1, drive shaft; 2, radiation shield (primary pumps only); 3, tank; 4, thermal shield; 5, argon cover gas space; 6, inner structural assembly; 7, sodium level; 8, hydrostatic bearing; 9, impeller; 10, outlet nozzle; 11, casing; 12, inlet nozzle. (From Project Management Corp.)

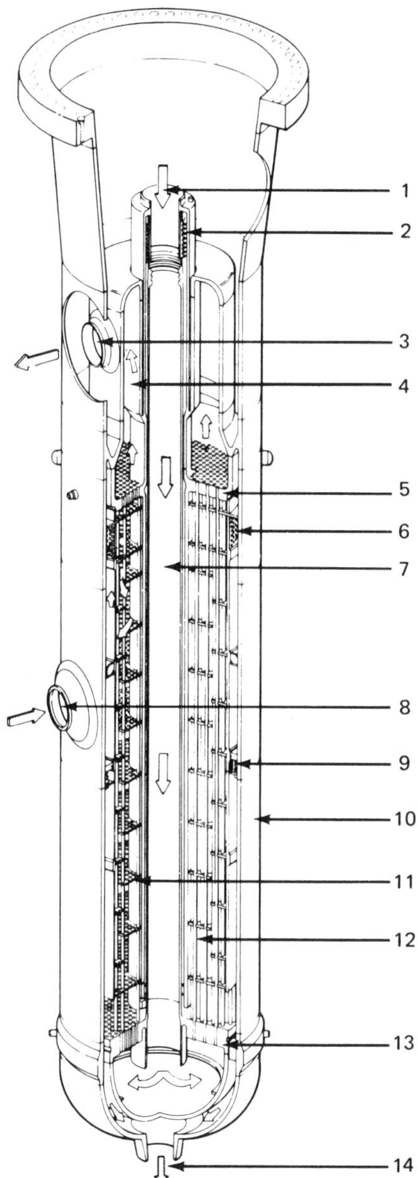

Figure 13.22. CRBRP intermediate heat exchanger. *Features:* (1) Straight tubes with bellows in inlet downcomer instead of bowed tubes, simplifying manufacture and reduces the tubesheet thickness. (2) Solid rather than segmented tube support plates. (3) Front Face tube-to-tubesheet welds. (4) Designed for in-place tube plugging. *Key:* 1, intermediate sodium inlet; 2, flexible bellows; 3, intermediate sodium outlet; 4, upper plenum; 5, upper tubesheet; 6, distribution cylinder; 7, downcomer; 8, primary sodium inlet; 9, bypass seal; 10, shell; 11, baffles; 12, tube bundle; 13, lower tubesheet; 14, primary sodium outlet. (From Project Management Corp.)

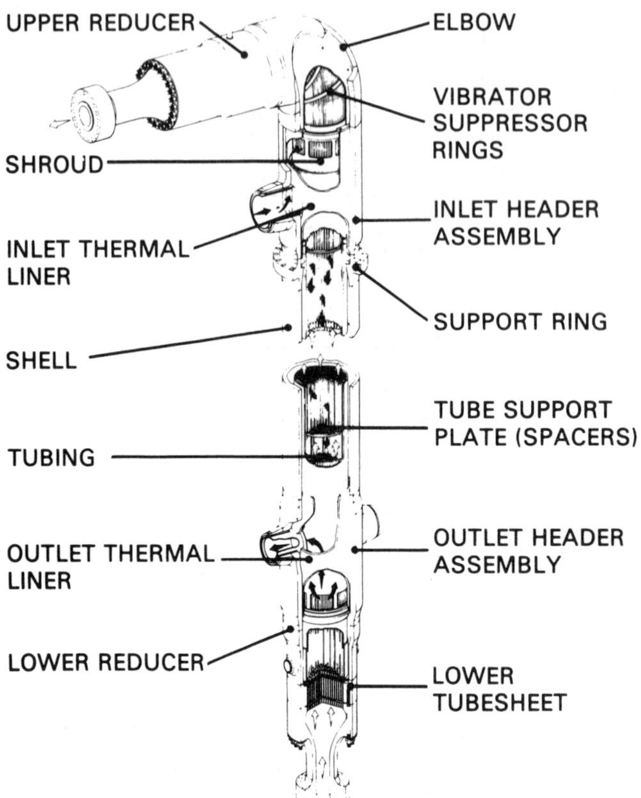

Figure 13.23. CRBRP steam generator. *Features:* (1) Water side of steam generator completely drainable. (2) Eliminates crevices on the sodium side, a classic site of caustic stress corrosion cracking. (3) Tubes fabricated from electroslag remelt $2\frac{1}{4}$ Cr–1 Mo steel to give least level of impurities in the metal—this alloy has demonstrated the best resistance to caustic corrosion. (4) Uses thick tubes (0.109 wall, full $\frac{5}{8}$-in.-diameter) to provide considerable margin for wastage or surface defects. (5) Uses recirculating superheat design with common superheat and evaporator units. (From Project Management Corp.)

SuperPhénix (Creys–Malville) Reactor

In the middle of the 1950s, the French Atomic Energy Commission (CEA) undertook the development of fast neutron reactors. To date this has been marked by three main stages, which evolved with a high degree of continuity, both as to the technique and the timetable.

The first one, Rapsodie, was an experimental irradiation reactor; it has been in operation since 1967 and was used as the first test bench for the fuel, materials, and equipment.

One year after the commissioning of Rapsodie, CEA and EdF† undertook the construction of a demonstration power station, 10 times more powerful and generating electricity. This was Phénix, with an electric power capacity of 250 MWe, commissioned in 1974. In the first 8 yr of its operation, this station generated more than 10 billion kWh, the equivalent of 40,000 hr operating at full power. It has worked very well and had very few "growing pains."

Encouraged by this success, France decided in 1976, 2 yr after the commissioning of Phénix, to construct a power station five times more powerful, of truly industrial size (1200 MW). This is the SuperPhénix station (Figure 13.26), installed at Creys–Malville; it will be commissioned in 1984.

The main feature of the SuperPhénix reactor is its pool design for the primary coolant circuit. The core [rated at 3000 MW(th)], four primary coolant pumps, and eight IHXs are placed in the main vessel (Figure 13.27). The reactor vessel is 21 m in diameter, containing 3200 tons of primary

†Electricité de France, the state-owned utility.

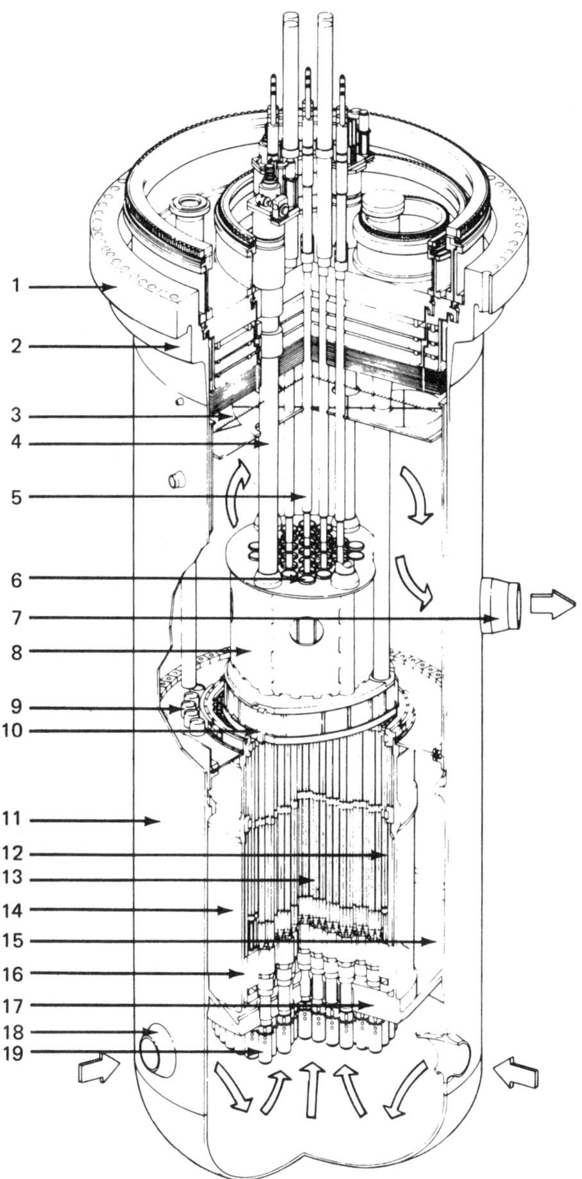

Figure 13.24. CRBRP reactor vessel and closure head. *Features:* (1) Uses austenitic stainless steel reactor vessel because of the high temperature. (2) Uses low-alloy carbon steel head to reduce cost and accommodate stainless steel forging limitations. (3) Uses Inconel-600 transition piece between flange and vessel wall to which ferritic and austenitic materials could be welded, possible because I-600 has thermal expansion midway between ferritic and austenitic steel. *Key:* 1, support ring; 2, upper flange; 3, cover gas; 4, support columns; 5, control rod driveline shroud tubes; 6, chimneys; 7, outlet nozzle; 8, upper internals structure; 9, fuel transfer and storage assembly; 10, locating key; 11, reactor vessel; 12, fixed shielding; 13, fuel assemblies; 14, core barrel; 15, support cone; 16, bypass flow module; 17, core plate; 18, inlet nozzle; 19, inlet module liners. (From Project Management Corp.)

Figure 13.25. Map of the CRBR core in which blanket assemblies are selectively interspersed with fuel assemblies in the high-neutron flux central core region. This core design dramatically improved the reactor's breeding performance and extended the lifetime of the fuel assemblies beyond that which would apply to the more conventional two-region core. (From Breeder Reactor Corp.)

sodium. Four independent loops (Figure 13.28) provide, by means of intermediate sodium circulation, the transport of heat to the steam generators (Figure 13.29). Each steam generator (one per loop) is of the once-through type, with an economizer, evaporator, and superheat section. The secondary loops are at 90° to each other in order to provide maximum separation between them. The main operating characteristics of the plant are given in Table 13.15.

The primary and secondary sodium pumps used at SuperPhénix are motor driven, centrifugal, free-level pumps. The sodium enters at the top of the pump, is driven by the impeller through the diffuser, and then to the discharge chamber. The pump shaft is supported at the top by a ball bearing, and at the bottom by a sodium hydrostatic bearing. Figure 13.30 shows one of the SuperPhénix pumps being tested.

The steam generators combine the evaporator and superheater into a single component. No sodium reheat is used. Each steam generator is a vertical once-through unit, with helically wound tubes. This design does not have a tube sheet, a thick plate that supports the heat exchange tubes that has often given problems in the past.† This arrangement mitigates thermal shocks during power transients.

†One particularly difficult problem has been crevice corrosion at the point where the tubes entered the tube sheet.

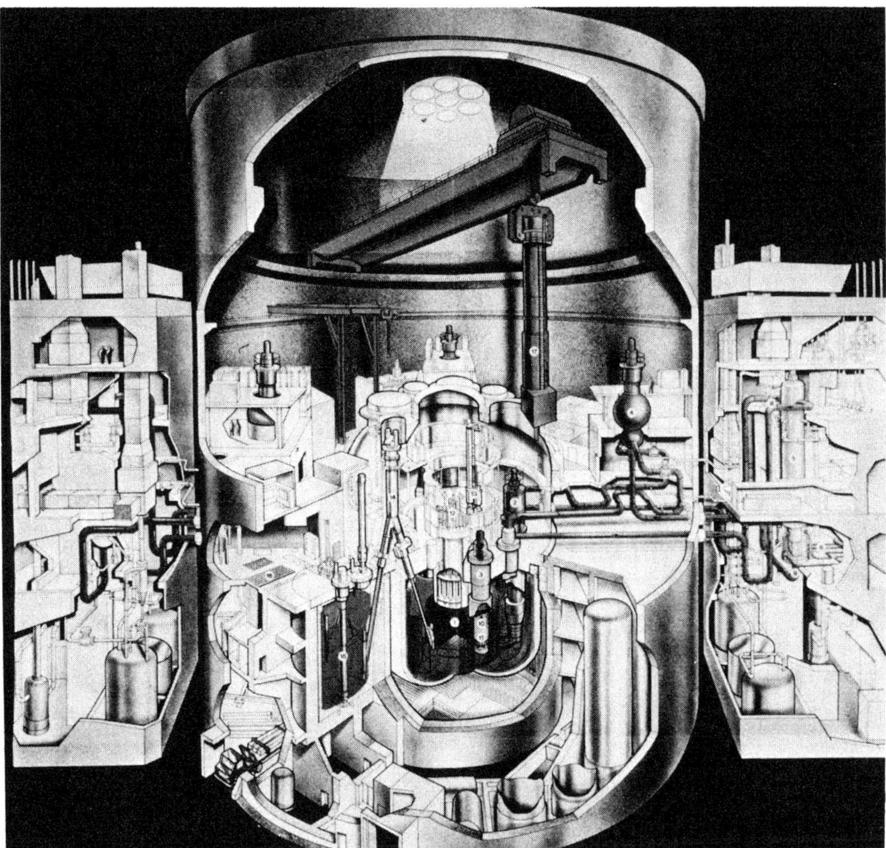

Figure 13.26. A cross section of the SuperPhénix reactor in France. (From Novatome.)

The core is formed by several radial zones of fuel elements. The central region, with 364 fuel assemblies, produces most of the power. It is subdivided into two radial regions to further improve the power distribution: the innermost contains MOX fuel with concentrations up to 15% Pu, and the outer region has 18% Pu. Each of the assemblies has an upper and lower axial blanket, 0.3 m high, which serves to reflect neutrons into the core region, and also breeds plutonium. The assembly itself is made of type 316 cold-worked stainless steel,† with a hexagonal channel to maintain cooling flow and prevent cross flow between assemblies (Figure 13.31). Each fuel pin, with a wire winding to increase heat transfer, contains the fuel pellets which are hollow.

Outward of the central core region lie 233 breeder assemblies of a similar design made of UO_2 where capture of neutrons leads to the production of plutonium. This region is followed by still another region containing steel assemblies used for reflecting neutrons and shielding purposes.

Two more exceptional items need to be mentioned about the SuperPhénix reactor: its construction method and its schedule. Because of the size of its sodium vessels (the main vessel is 21 m in diameter, 15.5 m high, and weighs 350 tons), transportation of these components by road or rail was impossible. To fabricate these vessels, an on-site workshop was used. This shop, considerably larger than a football field, performed the welding of the vessels and internal structures and the machining of the main vessel's top slab and rotating access plugs. These large components, after fabrication, were then moved from the shop to the reactor building by means of a gantry system and installed. The construction schedule itself is outstanding for a nuclear plant, let alone a first-of-a-kind unit. First started in 1977, commercial operation is expected in 1984, only 7 yr from issuance of the construction permit to finish of the construction project.

†316-stainless steel has good irradiation resistance.

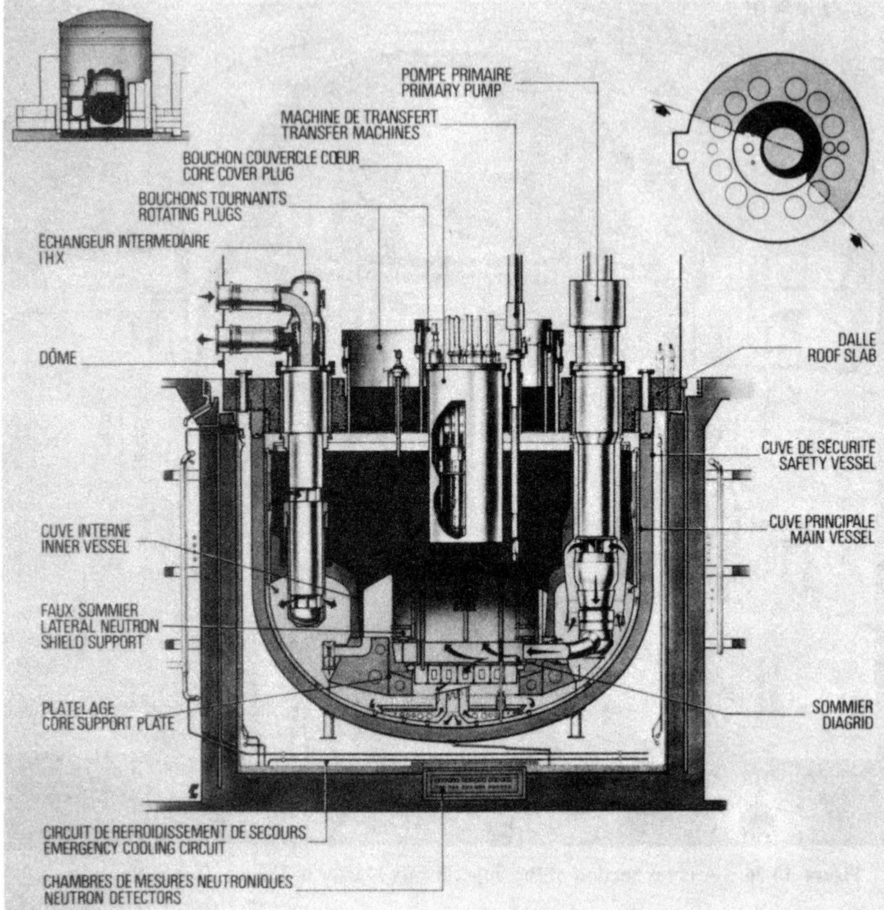

Figure 13.27. SuperPhénix reactor assembly: cross section through primary pump and IHX. (From Novatome.)

Availability of Plutonium LMFBR Fuel

Using reasonable estimates of LWR-installed capacity by 1985, the amount of plutonium being made yearly in the United States by that time will be in the range of 25–30 tons/yr. Against an initial plutonium requirement of 4–5 tons for a large breeder reactor, there appears to be no problem in attaining available plutonium from spent fuel, assuming that commercial reprocessing is a viable option. This is certainly the case in Europe, but may not be valid for the United States. It is unlikely that a breeder economy could be sustained without commercial reprocessing. Initial feed materials for the U.S. breeder program will consist of ^{235}U or plutonium (obtained from DOE stockpiles) and depleted uranium (which is a by-product of the enrichment of natural uranium).

13.4. THE CANDU

One successful reactor type that has stood the test of time for a quarter century is Canada's CANDU reactor (an initialism for CANadian Deuterium (moderated) Uranium (fueled) reactor). Not only has this reactor type been notably successful in Canada, but it has proved attractive in the international marketplace. Atomic Energy of Canada, Ltd. (AECL), the crown company that combines the roles of CANDU reactor manufacturer and vendor, with many of the functions of the Atomic Energy Commission or Department of Energy in the United States, has sold CANDU units abroad to four countries. Two 206-MWe units are in operation in India; one in South Korea came

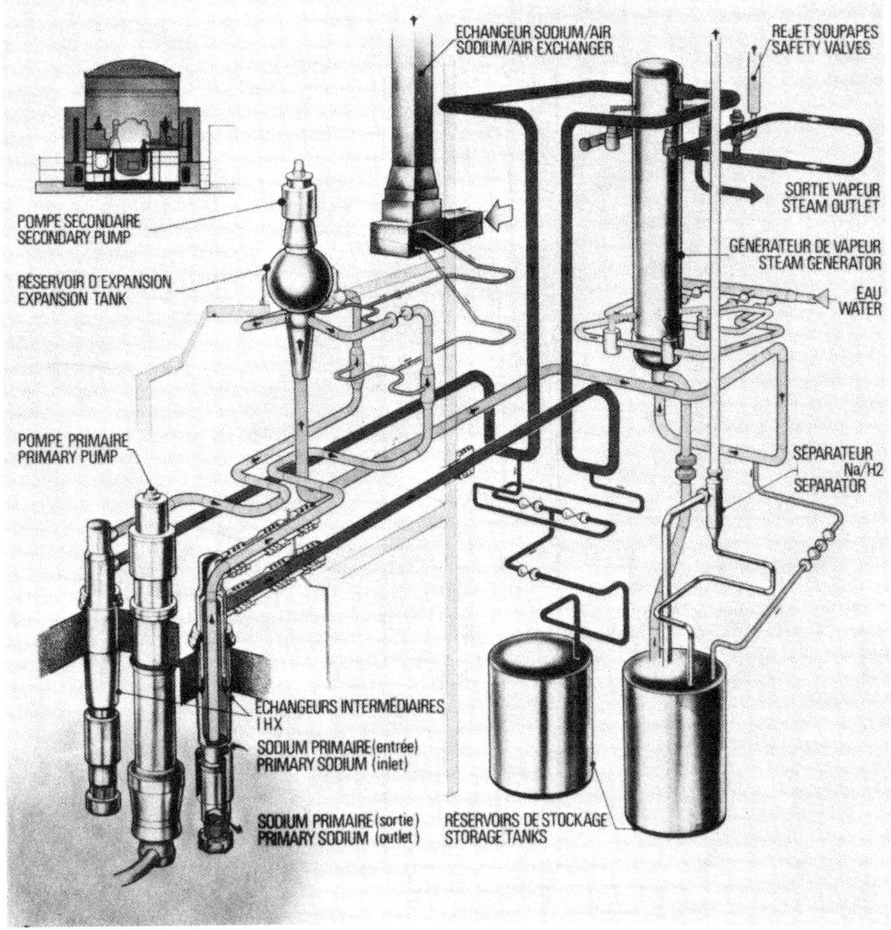

Figure 13.28. SuperPhénix main secondary sodium circuits. (From Novatome.)

on line at the end of 1982, with an output of 629 MWe; one 600-MWe unit in Argentina entered service in 1983; and two 700-MWe units have been ordered by Rumania, for operation toward the end of the 1980s.

At home, in Canada, following the 20-MWe Rolphton developmental CANDU plant and the 206-MWe Douglas Point commercial demonstration unit, there are four 515-MWe units at Pickering and four 740-MWe units at Bruce station, all in operation and all owned by Ontario Hydro. Another 630-MWe CANDU unit was started up in 1982 by the New Brunswick Electric Power Commission at Point Lepreau. These plants have proved so successful that Ontario Hydro is building twelve more: four 516-MWe units at Pickering, four 750-MWe units at Bruce, and four 880-MWe units at a new site at Darlington. Table 13.16 gives the evolution of the CANDU design, showing how the 208-MWe Douglas Point reactor was scaled up to the 514-, 600-, and 745-MWe units.

The Pickering station has posted net plant factors above 80% and in some years above 90%. Fuel failures have been relatively few, and experience with steam generator performance has also been very good.

In the CANDU system, heavy water acts as both coolant and as moderator. A good moderator, having a low-neutron capture cross section, heavy water yields an inherent advantage in neutron economy. This is seen in Table 13.17, where it can be seen that the moderating ratio (i.e., a measure of the ability of a moderator to slow down neutrons per neutron lost to capture in the moderator) is nearly 400 times greater for heavy water than it is for water. The low parasitic neutron capture in heavy water in turn permits use of natural uranium as fuel, meaning that no enrichment is necessary—that is, it obviates the need for Canada to build billion-dollar gaseous diffusion enrichment

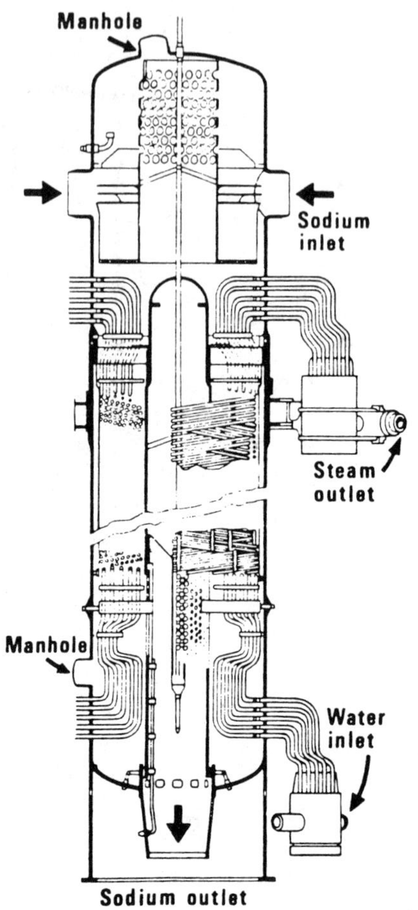

Steam Generator Characteristics

	Phénix	Creys–Malville
Number of units per secondary loop:	3 × 12	1
Rated Operating Data		
Thermal power [MW(th)]	186.3	750
Temperature:		
Sodium inlet (°C)	550	525
Sodium outlet (°C)	350	345
Feedwater temperature (°C)	246	237
Superheated steam temperature (°C)	512	490
Superheated flow rate (kg/sec)	70	340
Tube material	Chroloy + AISI 321	Incolloy 800

Figure 13.29. Cross section of one of the four SuperPhénix steam generators. [From *Nuclear Engineering International* (June 1978).]

Table 13.15. SuperPhénix

Power Circuit Characteristics	
Primary Circuits	
Total mass of sodium in primary circuits	3200 t
Nominal flow rate	4 × 4.10 t/sec
IHX outlet temperature	392°C
Core inlet temperature	395°C
Core outlet temperature	545°C
IHX inlet temperature	542°C
Secondary Circuits	
Total mass of sodium in secondary circuits	1500 t
Nominal flow rate	4 × 3.30 t/sec
Steam generator outlet temperature	345°C
IHX inlet temperature	345°C
IHX outlet temperature	525°C
Steam generator inlet temperature	525°C
Water–Steam Circuits	
Water temperature at steam generator inlet	235°C
Water pressure at steam generator inlet	210 bars
Steam temperature at turbine stop valves	487°C
Steam pressure at turbine stop valves	177 bars
Nominal flow rate	4 × 340 kg/s

Source: *Nuclear Engineering International* **23,** 43 (June 1978).

plants or to be dependent on imports of enriched uranium.† The result is an advantage in fuel cycle costs, although this is somewhat offset by the large capital investment in heavy water that is required.

Unlike the U.S. LWRs (both PWRs and BWRs) in which the primary coolant water circuit also acts as moderator, in the CANDU system the functions of moderation and cooling are separated. The smaller value of the slowing down power of D_2O, about 0.18 cm^{-1} as opposed to 1.28 cm^{-1} for H_2O, necessitates a small fuel-to-moderator ratio in the reactor lattice. This in turn leads to low power densities and large-volume cores. Since heavy-water cores need not be as closely packed as those using ordinary water as moderator, it is possible to utilize the pressure tube approach. This avoids the problem of large pressure vessels inherent in systems in which ordinary water is the moderator-coolant. To take advantage of the good moderating properties of heavy water, however, it is necessary to minimize neutron absorption in structural components. For this reason, Zircaloy, with its low capture cross section, is chosen for the pressure tubes and other structural members.

The CANDU core is contained in a large tank called a calandria, containing the unpressurized and relatively cool heavy-water moderator (refer to Figure 13.32). Through the calandria pass several hundred pressure tubes that contain the fuel and the circulating heavy-water coolant (Figure 13.33). These pressure tubes, of Zircaloy, are 6 m long and 10 cm in diameter, with a wall thickness of 4 mm (inset, Figure 13.34). The pressure tube design not only eliminates the need for the heavy-section pressure vessel, with its associated problem of brittle versus ductile fracture, but even more importantly, permits on-line refueling, that is, refueling without shutting down the reactor, while at full power. Because heavy-water reactors utilize natural uranium, not enough excess reactivity can be built into the core to compensate for the long-term effects of fuel depletion and fission product buildup. As a result, more or less continual fueling is necessary. Refueling is accomplished by means of mobile fueling machines that are attached to opposite ends of a pressure tube, which push new fuel assemblies into the tube at one end and push out the spent fuel assemblies into a shielded cask in the refueling machine at the other end of the tube (see Figure 13.35). Not having to shut down for several weeks each year to refuel obviously aids achievement of high capacity factor.

The natural uranium fuel is in the form of uranium dioxide pellets clad in 50-cm-long Zircaloy tube bundles, one of which is illustrated in Figure 13.36. The fuel bundle is composed almost

†However, plants to separate deuterium from water are required.

Pump Characteristics

Rated Operating Data	Phénix	Creys–Malville
Primary pump		
Flow rate (kg/sec)	1020	4100
Temperature (°C)	400	395
Discharge head (m·Na)	76	63
Secondary pump		
Flow rate (kg/sec)	737	3300
Temperature (°C)	350	345
Discharge head (m·Na)	38	28

Figure 13.30. SuperPhénix coolant pump undergoing testing. (From Novatome.)

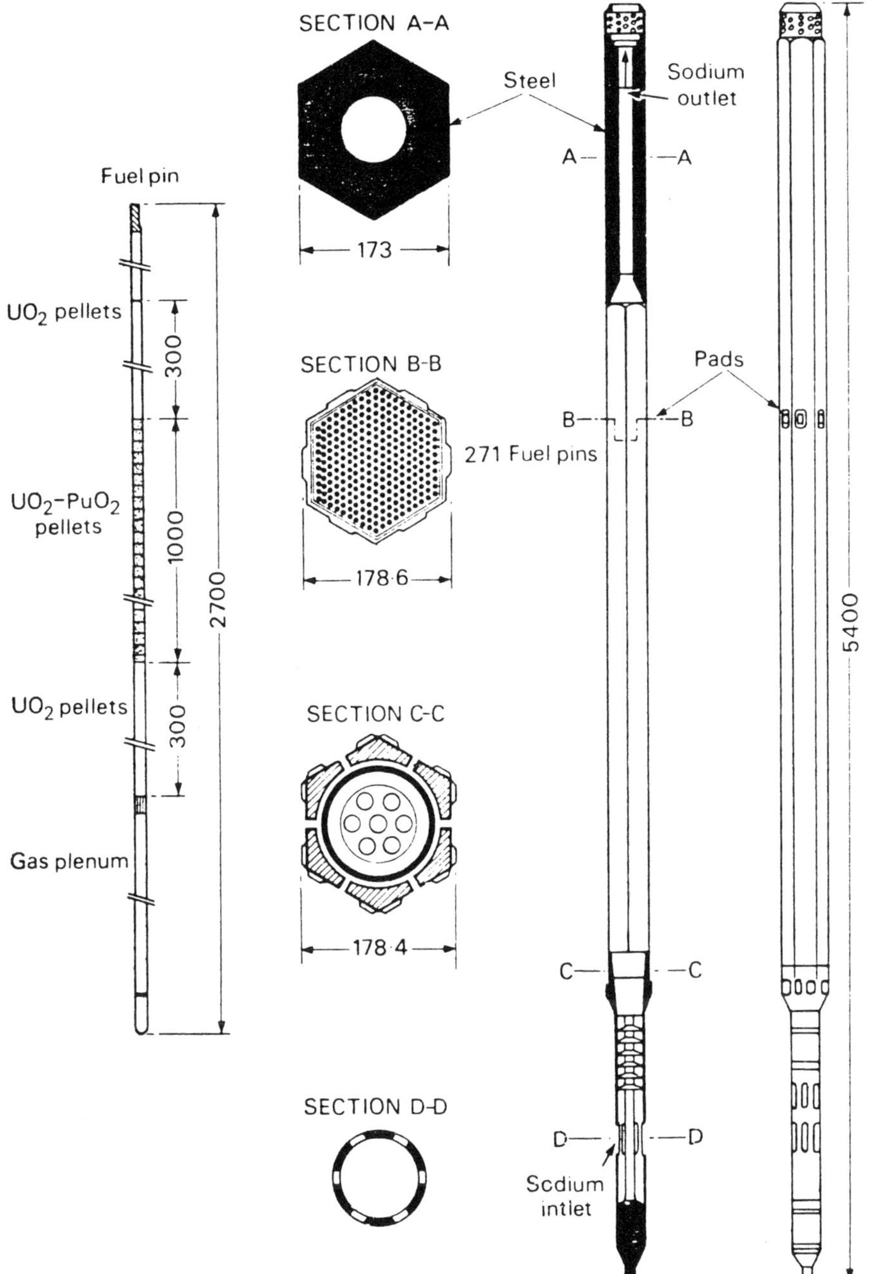

Figure 13.31. Sectional diagrams of fuel assembly and arrangement of pellets in SuperPhénix fuel pin. [From *Nuclear Engineering International* (June 1978).]

Table 13.16. Evolution of CANDU Power Reactors

	Douglas Point	Pickering A	Bruce A	Gentilly 2[a]
Net output (MWe)	208	514 × 4	745 × 4	600
Number of channels	306	390	480	380
Core length (cm)	500	594	594	594
Fuel inventory (Mg U)	41.5	92.3	114	95.8
Burnup (MWd/Mg U)	8400	8000	9600	7500
D_2O inventory (Mg)	179.5	403.69	568.1	467
Inlet temperature (°C)	249	249	252°C inner region 264°C outer region	267
Outlet temperature(°C)	293	293	299	312
Number of pumps	10	16 (12 active)	4	4
Number of boilers	8	12	8	4
Turbine				
Steam temperature (°C)	250 at throttle	250 at boiler	253	258
Throttle pressure (MPa)	4.05	4.02	4.13	4.54

Source: ANL-77-97.

[a]Typical of 600 MWe design.

entirely of Zircaloy. These assemblies, in a 600-MWe reactor, total 4560 and are arranged in 380 pressure tubes, 12 assemblies to the tube. The pressure tubes are nominally 4 in. in inside diameter and slip into close-fitting calandria tubes, with an overall length including end fittings of about 35½ ft. The control rods are inserted in the moderator through penetrations in the calandria, and the level of the moderator also can be varied to make fine power adjustments. In addition to the use of the control rods, pressure tube reactors can be rapidly shut down by dumping the heavy water from the calandria tank into a dump tank located beneath the core.

The use of natural uranium is permitted by the good neutron economy of the heavy-water moderator, and the maintenance of good reactivity level requires low burnups (750 MWd/t) and frequent on-line refueling from each end of the fuel tubes to keep neutron-absorbing poisons at a low level in the reactor core. As of the present, the CANDU fuel is discharged and stored; reprocessing and plutonium recycling have not been put into practice by the Canadians. The low burnup is a proliferation concern since the plutonium contained in the spent fuel is mostly all ^{239}Pu and very little ^{240}Pu. (Spent fuel from LWRs contains a much higher concentration of ^{240}Pu.) High ^{240}Pu content makes plutonium unfit for weapons use.

The objective of high neutron economy—permitting natural uranium fuel—was not attained without additional trade-offs other than the use of heavy water. An important factor is the reduced thermal efficiency compared to LWRs, which comes about because the pressure tubes are made with walls thin enough to be consistent with the neutron economy goal. The consequently lower allowable internal working pressure for the coolant results in poorer steam conditions for the turbine generator than a PWR would have. CANDU thermal efficiency is in the 28–30% range; corresponding values for LWRs are 32–34%. Neither type of reactor is exceptionally efficient compared to fossil power plants, breeder reactors, or HTGRs.

The on-line refueling procedure serves also as a means of coarse reactivity control, as the assemblies having the highest burnup (and therefore, highest accumulation of fission products that

Table 13.17. Slowing Down Properties of Moderators

Moderator	Slowing[a] Down Power	Moderating[b] Ratio
Water	1.28	58
Heavy water	0.18	21,000
Graphite	0.065	200

[a]Number of scattering collisions for a neutron to go from fission energy to thermal energy multiplied by the scattering cross section.

[b]Ratio of the slowing down power to the absorption cross section.

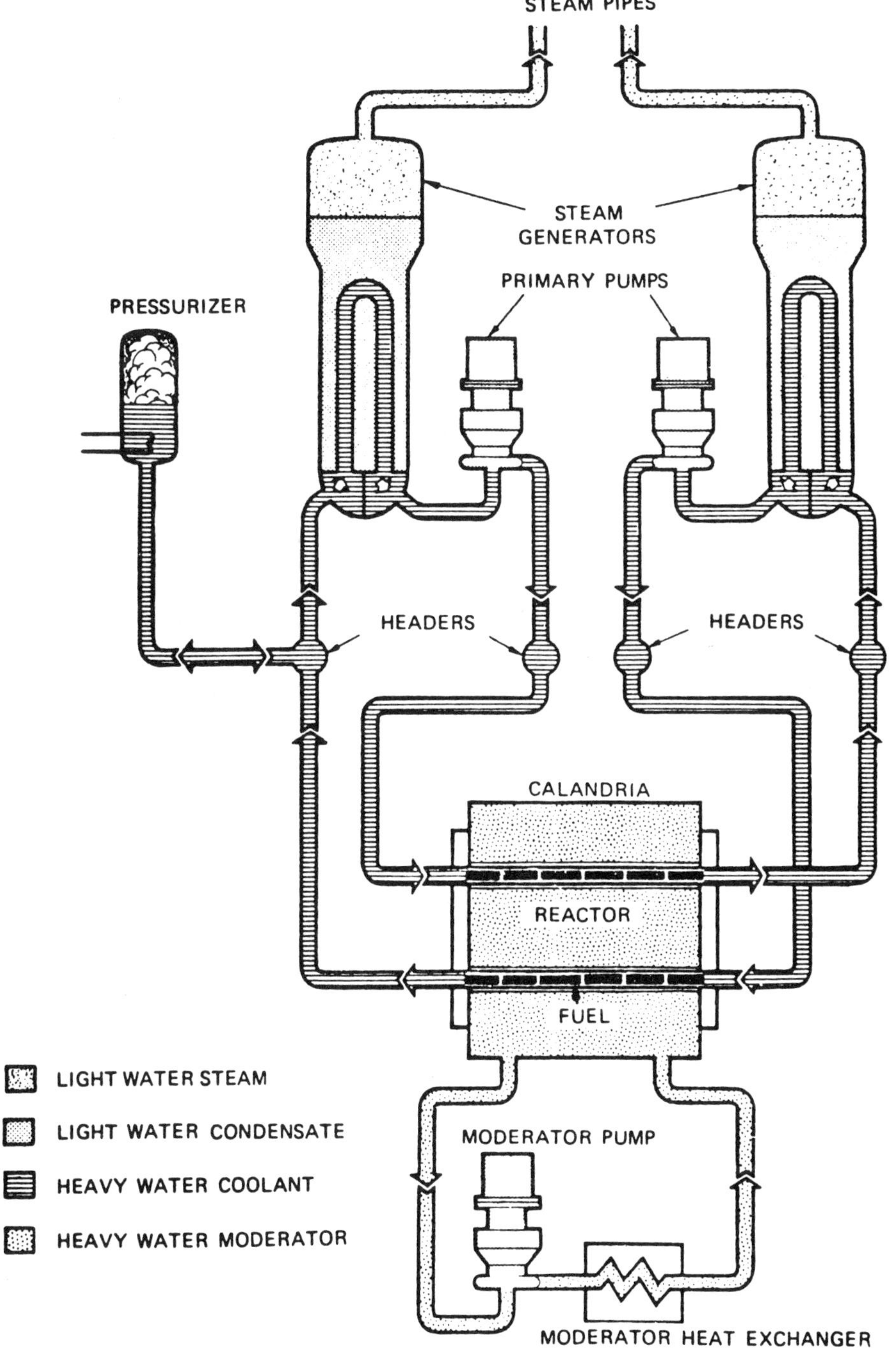

Figure 13.32. CANDU reactor simplified flow diagram. (From ANL-77-97.)

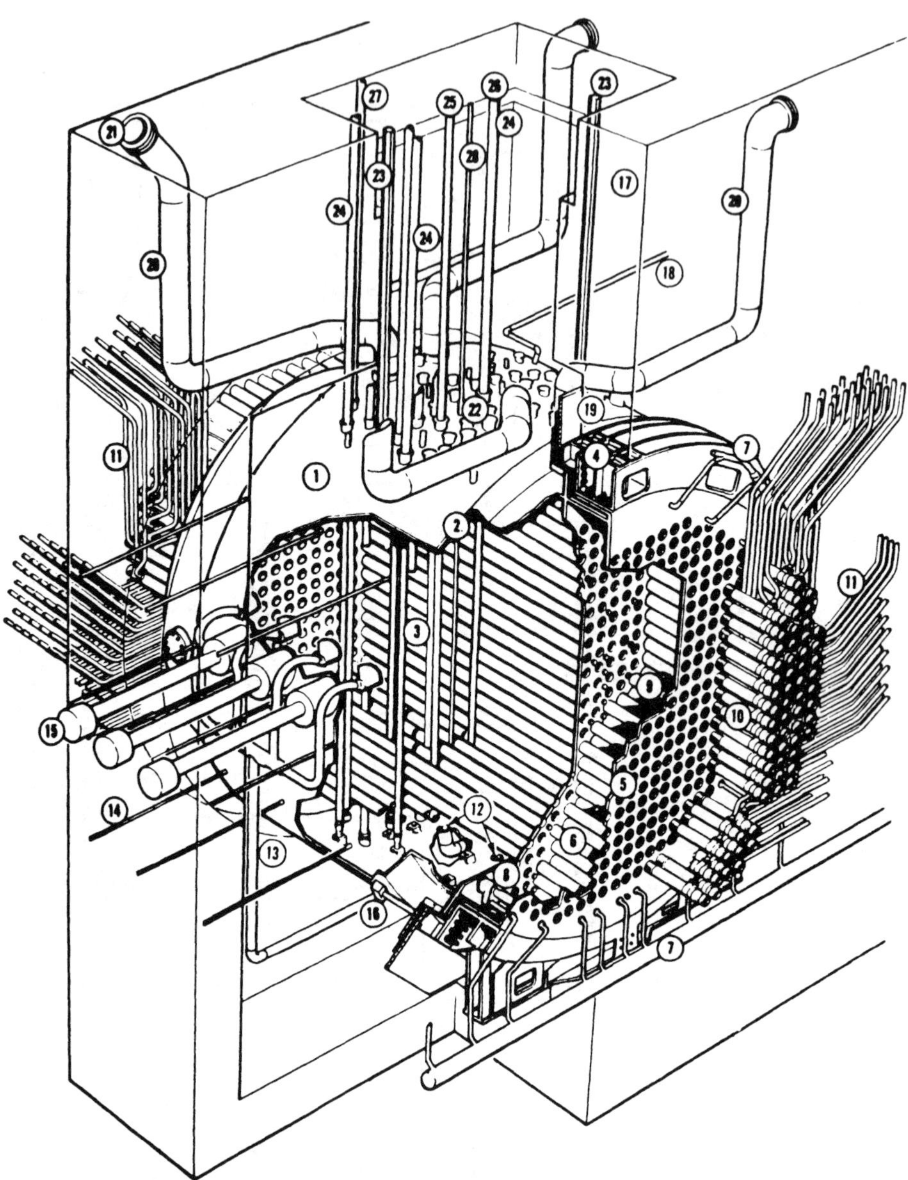

Figure 13.33. CANDU reactor assembly. *Key:* 1, calandria; 2, calandria shell; 3, calandria tubes; 4, embedment ring; 5, fueling tubesheet; 6, end shield lattice tubes; 7, end shield cooling pipes; 8, inlet–outlet strainer; 9, steel ball shielding; 10, end fittings; 11, feeder pipes; 12, moderator outlet; 13, moderator inlet; 14, flux detector and liquid injection nozzle; 15, ion chamber; 16, earthquake restraint; 17, vault wall; 18, moderator expansion to head tank; 19, curtain shielding slabs; 20, pressure relief pipes; 21, pressure relief disc; 22, reactivity control rod nozzles; 23, viewing port; 24, shutoff rod; 25, adjuster rod; 26, control absorber rod; 27, zone control rod; 28, vertical flux detector. (From ANL-77-97.)

Figure 13.34. The new generation of CANDU reactors, now being installed, is based upon the design of the Pickering Nuclear Generating Station of Ontario Hydro pictured above. The inset shows the calandria and associated pressure tubes prior to installation in the reactor. (From Atomic Energy of Canada, Ltd.)

usually have high parasitic capture cross sections) can be removed from the core forthwith and replaced with fresh fuel. This also means that low excess reactivity margins are required, an intrinsic safety feature. Table 13.18 lists some of the other important safety-related features of the CANDU system. An important difference from LWRs is that the CANDU's pressure boundary consists mainly of tubes. As a result, the primary coolant system has an ability to tolerate the rupture of any one of these tubes. On the other hand, CANDU reactors have a positive void coefficient. This is offset by the limited excess reactivity available due to the natural uranium fuel. By subdividing the primary cooling system into separate subsystems, the consequences of the positive-void reactivity-insertion during a LOCA is limited. The reactor containment building design (Figure 13.37) is another important safety characteristic of CANDU reactors. A separate vacuum building is used to effectively increase the containment volume in an accident. This assures subatmospheric conditions in the main containment building following a LOCA. The containment spray system, which draws water from a reservoir at the top of the structure, makes it possible to decouple the reliability of the system from the nuclear steam supply system.

The CANDU's high neutron efficiency permits operating at near-breeding conditions, with plutonium–thorium fuel and recycle of the ^{233}U produced in the thorium.

The on-line fueling mechanism also permits a leaky assembly to be traced and removed before it can release significant activity to the coolant.

The principal components of cost, capital cost, and operating cost, have opposing tendencies to

Figure 13.35. Installing CANDU fuel channels in Unit 6 at Bruce "B" Generating Station. (From Atomic Energy of Canada, Ltd.)

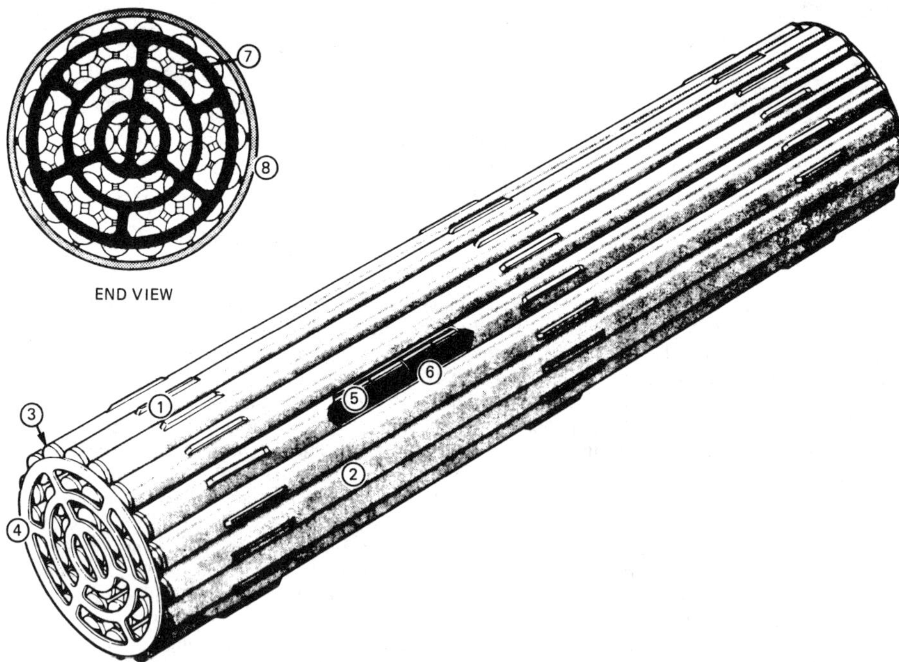

Figure 13.36. CANDU fuel bundle (37 elements). *Key:* 1, Zircaloy bearing pads; 2, Zircaloy fuel sheath; Zircaloy end cap; 4, Zircaloy end support plate; 5, uranium dioxide pellets; 6, Canlub graphite interlayer; 7, inter-element spacers; 8, pressure tube. (From ANL-77-97.)

Table 13.18. Some Important Safety-Related Intrinsic Characteristics of Heavy-Water-Moderated Pressure-Tube Reactors

Characteristics	Safety Implications
The pressure tubes (which are part of the primary coolant pressure boundary) traverse the active core region.	Stress-bearing components of the coolant pressure boundary are subjected to the full neutron flux.
The pressure tubes (having a relatively small wall thickness) have leak-before-break characteristic.	The probability of a sudden large-size break in a pressure tube is very small, because the tube will first develop a leak.
The pressure tubes are surrounded by calandria tubes, creating a gas-filled annular space between the tubes.	A crack in a pressure tube, resulting in primary coolant leakage, is easily detected.
The core is subdivided in separate fuel channels having individual coolant supply.	The primary cooling system can be subdivided into a number of subsystems, thus limiting complete blowdown to only a part of the core in case of a loss-of-coolant accident (LOCA).
Total excess reactivity is small for natural-uranium fueled equilibrium core.	Relatively mild power excursions due to accidental reactivity insertions.
Power-reactivity coefficient at nominal power level is close to zero, and may be slightly positive.	Power transients due to uncompensated reactivity insertions would not tend to be self-limiting.
Void-reactivity coefficient is positive.	LOCA leads to a reactivity increase.
Mean neutron lifetime is $\sim 10^{-3}$ sec, i.e., ~ 30 times larger than for LWRs.	Power transients tend to be, for the same reactivity insertion, less severe for CANDU reactors than for LWRs.
Inventory of tritium relatively large.	Requires special attention (however, the major part of the tritium inventory is in the low-pressure moderator region).

Source: Adapted from ANL-77-97.

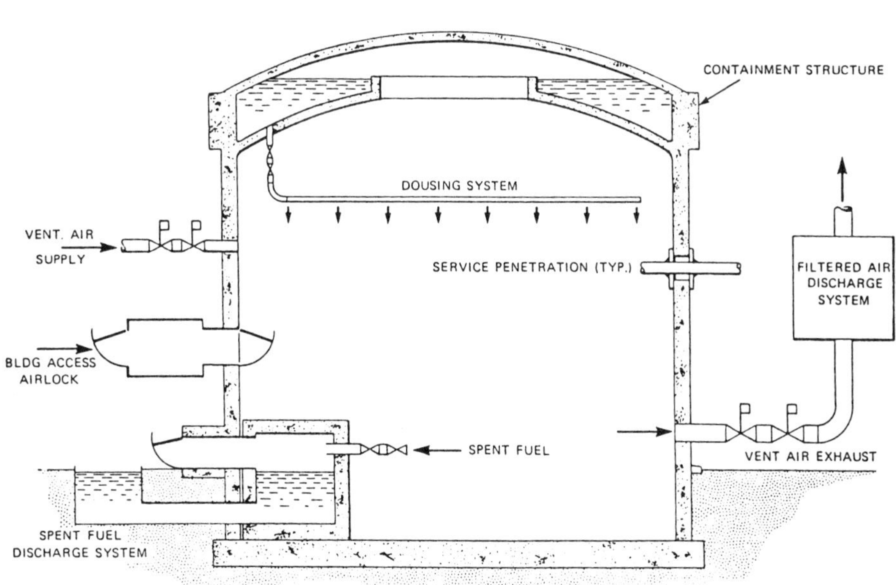

Figure 13.37. CANDU single-unit containment system. (From ANL-77-97.)

those of LWRs. Capital costs of the CANDU are estimated to be about 15 to 20% higher. On the other hand, use of natural uranium, continuous fueling without refueling shutdown, and good fuel performance experience result in fuel cycle costs tending to be low even in comparison with the low fuel cycle costs of LWRs.

Canada has one of the world's largest reserves of uranium and has been an exporter. Recently, however, the Canadian government placed a limit on the amounts that may be exported, expressed in terms of a percentage of the production above the needs of its own domestic reactors.

One of the few problem areas Canada encountered in establishing its line of CANDU reactors was in completing and debugging the large-scale, heavy-water extraction plants, notably the one at Glace Bay. Chapter 6 discusses the production of heavy water.

BIBLIOGRAPHY

Amorosi, A., Ed., *A Study of Basic Approaches to the Design of Loop Type LMFBR's*, ANL/A78-3 (1978).

Hill, E., "The Clinch River Breeder Reactor," *Power Engineering* **82**, 93 (August 1978).

Simon, R. H., *A History of and Prospects for Gas-Cooled Reactors in the U.S.*, GA-A16637 (1982).

———, "High Temperature Gas-Cooled Power Reactors," *Nuclear Engineering and Design Special Issue* **26** (1974).

———, *Sodium Technology*, North American Rockwell Corp., 1970.

———, "Creys-Malville Nuclear Power Station," *Nuclear Engineering International* **23**, 43 (June 1978).

Van Erp, J., *Preliminary Evaluation of Licensing Issues Associated with U.S.-sited CANDU-PHW Nuclear Power Plants*, ANL-77-97 (1977).

Winkleblack, K., *LMFBR Plant Design*, EPRI Report, September 1982.

CHAPTER 14
REPROCESSING OF NUCLEAR FUEL

14.1. INTRODUCTION

An important element of the nuclear fuel cycle is reprocessing the fuel discharged from the reactor. There are several reasons for doing this. The first is the recovery of fissile isotopes that remain in the fuel. After discharge, a fraction of the original ^{235}U in the fuel has not been depleted (i.e., fissioned), while a fair amount of plutonium has built up. After a burnup of 33,000 MWd/t, ^{235}U comprises about 0.83 wt% and fissile plutonium about 0.68 wt% of the fuel. In addition, many fuel elements have been discharged early. These discharged fuel elements represent an economic resource. The value of such elements, shown in Figure 14.1, comes from the uranium itself, the separative work of a given enrichment of uranium, and the amount of plutonium recoverable. Several billions of dollars' worth of unrecovered fissile material is now in spent fuel storage pools in the United States alone. Also shown in this figure is the enrichment of fuel discharged from U.S. reactors through 1979. Because many fuel elements were discharged early (because of leaks or their use in the first fuel loading), the ^{235}U isotopic concentration they contain is much higher than the 0.7% ^{235}U in uranium ore. For the uranium and plutonium to be utilized, however, they must be separated from the fission products and each other, the uranium reenriched, and new fuel elements fabricated.

A second reason for reprocessing is to safeguard the plutonium in the fuel so that it cannot be diverted for terrorist purposes, although the plutonium in spent fuel is not particularly desirable for bombs because of its ^{240}Pu content.

To a certain degree, fuel is self-protecting when first discharged from a reactor. The high radiation field makes it difficult to handle and therefore more diversion-resistant than fuel that has aged for some time. This radiation field decays over the years and consequently the fuel is self-protecting. Reprocessing would greatly reduce the amount of plutonium in an "unprotected" state available for diversion. This plutonium is needed for use in fast breeder reactors—about 130 t of fissile plutonium for those planned through the year 2020. This quantity of plutonium would be readily available from spent LWR fuel.

The third and perhaps most important reason for reprocessing is that it is an intermediate step to final waste disposal of spent nuclear fuel. While unreprocessed fuel elements can be disposed of safely, separating the long-lived actinides from the fuel significantly reduces the hazard of these wastes and reduces the volume of waste to be handled. The waste disposal problem would be simplified and the need for freshly mined uranium reduced at the same time. Figure 14.2 illustrates how the ingestion hazard for a PWR fuel cycle with reprocessing (labeled PWR-U/HLW) is much lower than for the fuel cycle without reprocessing (PWR-U), especially after a few hundred years following the reprocessing operation.

Reprocessing of spent fuel will result in a volume of solidified high-level wastes which is less than one-third of the volume of the initial spent fuel. There will also be significant quantities of low- and intermediate-level radioactive wastes produced during reprocessing, but these wastes contain low concentration of radioactive materials. Therefore, the size of a repository required for deep underground disposal of reprocessing wastes will be smaller than for spent fuel disposal.

There is a high degree of flexibility involved in treating waste materials resulting from reprocessing inasmuch as there are a number of processes available for compaction, volume reduction, and immobilization of the wastes produced. For example, reprocessing plants in the future will solidify high-level liquid fission product wastes into a calcine, vitrified product, Synroc, or metal–ceramic mixture; the actual form of the solidified waste will depend on the design of the disposal package, method of ultimate disposal, and other factors. The disposal of radioactive wastes is covered in Chapter 15.

Nearly 40 yr of reprocessing, in both government and commercial reprocessing plants, have

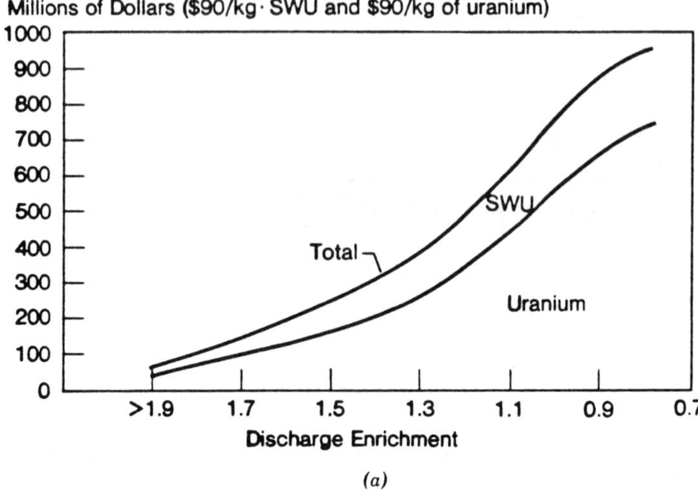

(a)

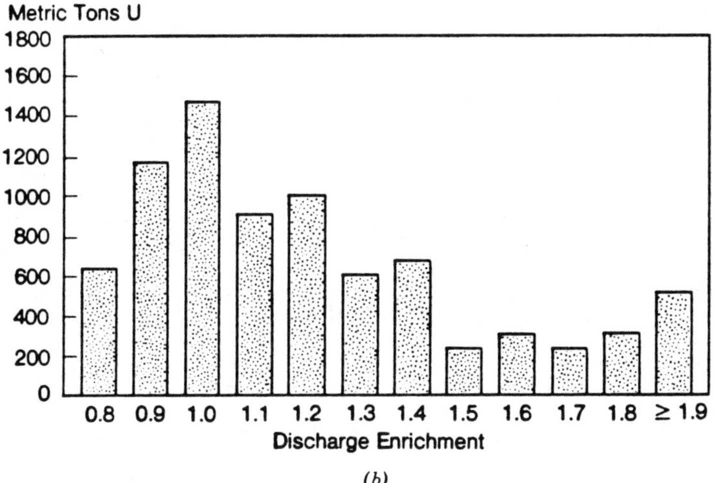

(b)

Figure 14.1. (*a*) Value of U and SWU's in spent fuel through 1979. (*b*) U resources (equivalent U) in spent fuel as a function of U_3O_8 enrichment.

demonstrated that such operations can be conducted safety and without a significant impact on the environment. About 99% of the uranium and 97.5% of the plutonium in spent fuel were recovered in commercial operations at the Nuclear Fuel Services plant in the United States. The technology of reprocessing has also been demonstrated on a routine basis in several foreign countries.

14.2. REPROCESSING NEEDS

The need for commercial reprocessing depends on the growth in the use of nuclear power. To a lesser degree, reprocessing needs are influenced by the fuel burnup achieved in reactor operation, the decisions about the merits of long-term fuel storage and once-through fuel cycles, and the introduction of breeder reactors.

Estimates are presented in Table 14.1 of the amount of spent fuel arising from LWR operation through the year 2000. Approximately 250,000 t of spent fuel will be in storage by that year, in addition to about 100,000 t which will have been reprocessed.† The average 1000-MWe LWR

†Most of this stored fuel will be in the United States. There is no reprocessing of commercial fuel in the United States today; the assumption in the table is that there will also be none in the year 2000. From 1976 through 1980, U.S. government policy discouraged reprocessing.

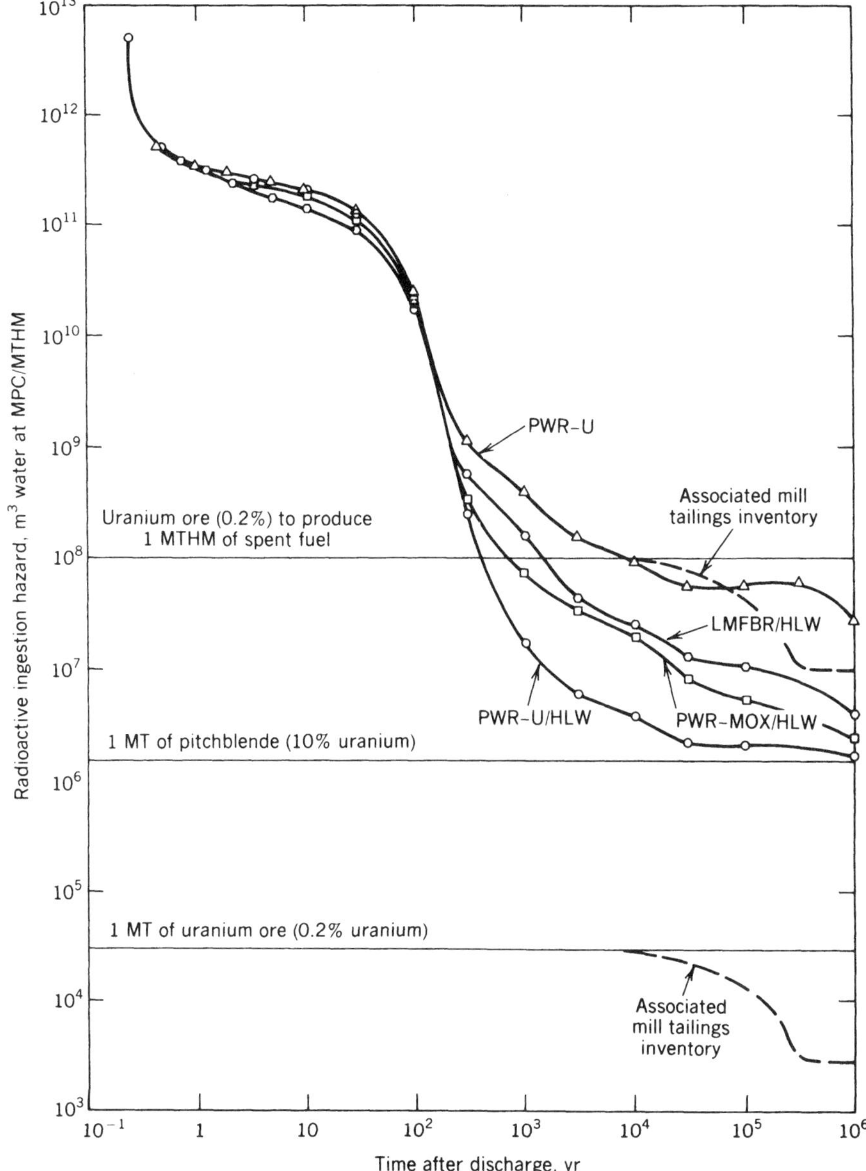

Figure 14.2. Ingestion hazard indexes of HLWs from various fuel cycles versus time. [From C. M. Malbain et al., *Nuclear Technology* **57** (1982).]

generates about 30 t of spent fuel per year; the 800 LWRs of this size expected by the year 2000 would therefore require 25,000 t/yr reprocessing capability. In 1980 there were 750 t/yr of worldwide reprocessing capability; this is estimated to grow to between 8000 to 10,000 t/yr by 2000 (Table 14.2).

Unlike LWRs, fast reactors require reprocessing to be closely tied to their fuel cycle. An LMFBR with fuel burnup of 100,000 MWd/t, for instance, would generate about 25 t/yr of spent fuel and blanket assemblies. Correspondingly less reprocessing is needed if higher fuel burnups are achieved for either LWRs or breeder reactors. Nevertheless, it is apparent from these tables that an increasing worldwide gap between spent fuel in storage and reprocessing capability will exist for at least two decades.

Table 14.1. Spent Fuel Arising from Thermal Reactors in the World Outside the Centrally Planned Economies (in Tons of Heavy Metal at End of Year)

	1985			1990			2000		
Region	Cumulative Spent Fuel Discharge	Spent Fuel in Storage at Year End	Cumulative Spent Fuel Reprocessed	Cumulative Spent Fuel Discharge	Spent Fuel in Storage at Year End	Cumulative Spent Fuel Reprocessed	Cumulative Spent Fuel Discharge	Spent Fuel in Storage at Year End	Cumulative Spent Fuel Reprocessed
European Economic Community	8,200	3,200	5,000	22,100	10,500	11,600	>57,000	>8,050	49,250
Total Europe	12,000	6,100	5,900	30,200	16,900	13,300	>70,200	>11,100	59,100
North America	27,100	27,100	600	56,450	56,450	600	166,700	166,700	600
Pacific	3,900	1,500	2,400	8,300	2,700	5,600	30,000	0	30,000
Total OECD	43,000	34,700	8,300	94,950	76,050	18,900	>266,900	>177,800	89,100
Non-OECD	4,100	3,850	250	11,600	9,950	1,650	>54,500	47,100	7,400
Total	47,100	38,550	8,550	106,550	86,000	20,500	>321,400	>244,900	95,500

Source: From F. Culler and R. Vogel, "Future Reprocessing of Spent Reactor Fuels," in publication.

Table 14.2. Estimated Reprocessing Capability in the World Outside the Centrally Planned Economies, t/yr

	Schedule	
Year	High	Low
1980	750	750
1985	1200	1200
1990	5900	4100
1995	9500	8100
2000	9500	8100

Source: INFCE, 1980.

14.3. HISTORICAL PERSPECTIVE

The reprocessing of spent fuel traces its origins back to the early days of the Manhattan Engineering District (when it was called "chemical processing" as there was yet no reprocessing of spent reactor fuel in prospect). The only objective at that time was to separate the plutonium, for weapons use, from the natural uranium that had been irradiated for the sole purpose of transmuting as much of it as possible into plutonium.

The Manhattan District scientists recognized early that separation of fissionable plutonium from fertile ^{238}U was a problem of a different nature than separation of fissile ^{235}U from ^{238}U. Whereas the latter, being isotopes of the same element, could only be separated by physical means based on their differences in weight, plutonium and uranium, being different elements, could be separated chemically.

The first steps toward developing such a process were taken in 1942 by Glenn Seaborg and his group at the Metallurgical Laboratory in Chicago (the seed of Argonne National Laboratory).

The Seaborg separation method was an oxidation–reduction process using lanthanum–fluoride carrier, but its scaling-up to industrial scale appeared only an incidental possibility. Seaborg then tried phosphate as a carrier, as the phosphates of many heavy metals are insoluble in acid solutions. This process worked. E.I. DuPont de Nemours Inc. agreed to be the contractor to build a chemical separations plant, for which the Hanford, Washington, site was chosen in January 1943.

At Hanford three separation plants were eventually built. Each consisted of a large canyon, or separation building; a concentration building where the separated plutonium would be freed of the solvent-extraction carrier (bismuth–phosphate) and other gross impurities; and a waste storage area where the often highly radioactive sludges of uranium, fission products, and process materials could be stored.

To carry out the remote operating requirement imposed by the high levels of radiation, new equipment was designed or invented. To avoid pumps and valves that would require servicing, steam jets were developed to transfer process materials from one tank to another. Rather than filters, centrifuges, considered more reliable, were designed to take their place. Liquid-level and density meters were developed to follow the progress of each operation.

Once the plant had been placed in operation, the only access to the cells was by means of the bridge crane which traversed the width of the building and traveled its whole length. A 70-ton hook could lift off the cell covers if necessary. From a heavily shielded crane cab, operators were able to look into the canyon cells with specially designed periscopes. With lighter weight crane hooks and specially designed tools, it was possible to remove and replace piping, the joints of which were designed to make this possible. Damaged equipment could be lifted out, placed in a storage cell, and substitute parts lowered into place and remotely reconnected. To accomplish this remote reconnection, "jumpers" were developed: pipe lengths with standard lengths, standard elbow bends, and standard mating end-fittings that could more easily be removed and replacements reconnected by a crane operator at a distance of 60 ft or more, without direct vision.

The first production runs through the bismuth–phosphate process were completed early in January 1945 with excellent results. Losses of plutonium in the process were much lower than had been expected. In the subsequent concentration step, using lanthanum–fluoride, some losses were encountered initially, but the problem was largely overcome quickly.

The Bismuth Phosphate Process

The bismuth phosphate process was the first widely used reprocessing method. It was a precipitation technique intended solely for the recovery of plutonium from uranium. The process depended on the solubility of plutonium in the +6 valence state, and its insolubility in the +4 valence state. Plutonium would be cycled through a series of changes of valences states until the desired purity was achieved. In particular, plutonium +6 is soluble in aqueous solution, while fission product phosphates and fluorides generally are not. Plutonium +4, however, could be precipitated from aqueous solution using bismuth as a carrier.

In the bismuth phosphate process, the irradiated fuel was first dissolved in nitric acid. Uranium formed the uranyl ion (UO_2^{2+}), while the plutonium ions were very much diluted in the solution. Bismuth nitrate and sodium phosphate were then added, the latter reducing the plutonium to the +4 valence state, causing plutonium phosphate, $Pu_3(PO_4)_4$, to coprecipitate with bismuth phosphate, $BiPO_4$. Sulfuric acid was added to prevent precipitation of the uranyl ions, since the uranyl sulfate complex turned out to be quite soluble.

The sequence was repeated several times: the $BiPO_4$ carrying the plutonium was redissolved in nitric acid; the plutonium raised to the +6 (soluble) valence state with $NaBiO_3$; and bismuth phosphate added to precipitate the fission products. Then plutonium was again reduced to the +4 (insoluble) valence state with sodium nitrate, coprecipitating it with $BiPO_4$. After adequate decontamination was achieved, the plutonium went through a similar cycle using lanthanum fluoride, LaF_3, instead of $BiPO_4$. This removed any fission products that still remained.

The very pure plutonium† fluoride that resulted was then converted to PuO_2. The bismuth phosphate process eventually became obsolete, suffering from the large amounts of $BiPO_4$ and LaF_3 required (which also greatly increased the waste volume) and the inability to recover uranium.

Solvent Extraction—and the Redox Process

The disadvantages of the bismuth phosphate process led to the development of various solvent extraction techniques that would recover uranium along with the plutonium.

The first solvent extraction process used on a large scale was the Redox process, so named because of the successive chemical *red*uction and *ox*idation steps involved. In many organic solvents, uranium in the +6 valence state and plutonium +6 and +4 are soluble, while fission products and plutonium +3 are not. As the solvents are essentially immiscible in water, if counterflowing aqueous and organic streams of the right acidity come in contact, the uranium and plutonium will tend to follow the organic fluid, leaving behind most of the fission products in the aqueous stream. The uranium and plutonium in the organic stream can then be partitioned: if plutonium is reduced to the +3 valence state, it then becomes insoluble and the organic solvent will contain only uranium. These steps can be repeated to obtain the fission–product purification desired.

The Redox process, which could be operated continuously, used hexone to extract uranyl (UO_2^{2+}) and plutonyl (PuO_2^{2+}) ions from an aqueous solution with a high nitrate ion concentration.‡ Aluminum or ammonium nitrate was used to supply the nitrate ions,§ as high concentrations of nitric acid will decompose hexone. An oxidizing agent, usually sodium dichromate,¶ was needed to produce the plutonyl ions. The large amounts of these reagents needed is a major disadvantage of the Redox process. They follow the fission product waste stream, greatly increasing the quantity of high-level wastes that need disposal.

Purex Solvent Extraction Process

Redox was supplanted in its turn by a newer solvent extraction process called *Purex*.|| The principal difference is use of a more efficient organic solvent, tributyl phosphate (TBP), and a recycleable salting agent. The process, like earlier processes, begins with the dissolving of the fuel. The salting agent is nitric acid instead of the ammonium or aluminum nitrate used in Redox; this reduces the amount of inert solids contained in the process wastes. The solute goes through five stages of solvent extraction and decontamination with a kerosene solution of TBP. As in Redox, the product uranium and plutonium are recovered as uranyl and plutonium nitrate solutions essentially free of fission products.

The Purex process is still the generally accepted method of treating irradiated material for the military program, as well as of reprocessing spent fuel from commercial power reactors.

Advantages of the Purex process over the Redox process, in addition to the reduction of the amount of inert solids in the wastes already mentioned, include these: TBP is less toxic, less

†Decontamination factors of 10^6 to 10^7 were achieved.
‡High-nitrate ion concentrations are needed to keep the uranyl and plutonyl ions in solution.
§When used in this manner, the $Al(NO_3)_3$ is referred to as a "salting agent."
¶$Na_2Cr_2O_7$ strongly oxidizes plutonium to the +6 state, which has the highest solubility in hexone.
||An acronym for Plutonium–URanium EXtraction.

flammable, and therefore more easily handled than hexone. Also, it is slightly more efficient as a solvent than is hexone.

In 1955, at the first United Nations International Conference on Peaceful Uses of Atomic Energy held in Geneva, there took place the first large-scale, general, declassification and dissemination of information about nuclear technology since the issuance of the Smyth Report in 1945 which explained the broad lines of the history of the Manhattan Engineering District.

It was at this conference that the existence of the Idaho Chemical Processing Plant (ICCPP) was disclosed. It is still being used to reprocess all the spent cores from U.S. Nuclear Navy ships. It was built at the National Reactor Testing Station (now Idaho National Engineering Laboratory) west of Idaho Falls. Unlike the Hanford canyon separation buildings, it was designed for direct maintenance. The cells are lined with stainless steel to facilitate decontamination, and the floors are slanted in such a way that should a major spill occur, the spilled liquids remain in subcritical configuration.

The process used is a combination solvent-extraction process. TBP is the first cycle extractant, followed by two further separation cycles using hexone. ICPP is a versatile plant. It was intended to handle nuclear fuel from a variety of research reactors, test reactors, and experimental or developmental power reactors, it has several alternative dissolver, or "head-end," facilities.

14.4. REPROCESSING TECHNOLOGY

There are at least 30 separation technologies applicable to nuclear fuel reprocessing that have been developed over the years. The predominant technology in use today revolves around variations on the Purex solvent-extraction process, which was, as we have seen, first developed in the 1950s. This process is thought to be the best and most reliable one available, and has been brought to technical maturation.

Reprocessing has been carried out on a large scale for about 40 yr.† The primary technical challenge now is in the design of a new reprocessing plant: the plant requires nuclear safety, and must be secure against proliferation threats and the diversion of nuclear materials. It must be able to operate remotely with special maintenance provisions as well.

As mentioned above, several processes for reprocessing nuclear fuel exist. They are usually classified as being either (1) an aqueous process, or (2) a pyroprocess. The principal difference between the two is that the former operate at a lower temperature (below 100°C) with the chemical elements from the fuel in an aqueous solution.

In the aqueous processes, the fuel is first dissolved in acid (usually HNO_3). Solvent extraction between streams of aqueous and organic liquids is the separation technique. (A similar process is used for purifying uranium: see Chapter 5.) Other techniques, such as ion exchange through resin beds, or photochemical separation using electromagnetic radiation in the visible part of the spectrum to excite certain chemical species selectively, are usually classified as aqueous processes.

The pyroprocesses, however, operate at elevated temperatures with molten metals or salts as the medium in which separation takes place. These are classified as either pyrometallurgical processes, or pyrochemical, although the distinction is not always clearcut. The pyrometallurgical processes included (a) fractionation techniques based on melting points (crystallization) or boiling points (distillation) of various compounds, and (b) partitioning techniques based on relative solubilities, or the precipitation from the liquid phase. The former includes a whole family of volatility processes, for example, fluoride volatility, that are quite important. Pyrochemical processes involve changing the valence states of the elements to achieve separation. A listing of the processes is given in Table 14.3.

The chemistry of reprocessing is dependent on the process, from fairly simple to highly complex. Most of the fission product isotopes are initially highly radioactive, although by the time reprocessing actually takes place, many have greatly decayed. Still, high radiation levels will be encountered because some of these radioisotopes have long half-lives. Under normal circumstances, spent fuel would be stored for about 3 yr before reprocessing. However, given the lack of availability of reprocessing services, it is realistic to assume that LWR fuels will be in storage for many years. High radioactivity is relatively more important in reprocessing LMFBR fuels, since storage prior to reprocessing is likely to be less than 1 yr.

Figure 14.3 shows the isotopes that are the main contributors to the spent fuel's radioactivity. For times less than 1 yr ^{144}Ce is prominent, as is ^{106}Ru. The latter can be troublesome, if very early reprocessing is necessary. For fuel elements that have been cooled for 5 yr or more, ^{137}Cs and ^{90}Sr account for most of the radioactivity. These two isotopes are also important when considering the long-term hazards of High-Level Waste (HLW). This is further discussed in the next chapter.

In addition to the highly radioactive fission products, spent LWR fuel contains about 1%

†Mostly in military weapons programs. There is currently no commercial nuclear fuel reprocessing in the United States, although other countries, notably France, offer this service.

Table 14.3. Spent Fuel Reprocessing Techniques

1. *Aqueous processes*	
Solvent extraction	Butex, chelation, Halex, Purex, Redox, Thorex
Ion exchange	
Photochemistry	
Electrolysis	Flurex
Precipitation	Bismuth phosphate
2. *Pyroprocesses*	
A. *Pyrophysical*	
Fractional distillation	Airox, Deboer, fluoride volatility, molten salt/fluoride volatility, nitrofluor, carbox, chloride volatility
Fractional crystallization	Hermex, hydride separation, pyrozinc, zone melting
Liquid–liquid partitioning	Fused salt/liquid metal
Liquid–solid extraction	DAP, tin-nitride
B. *Pyrochemical*	
Electrochemical	Electrorefining, molten salt electrolysis
Cyclic oxidation/reduction	Nitride carbide cycle
Selective oxidation	Melt refining

unfissioned ^{235}U, 0.5% plutonium isotopes, mainly ^{239}Pu, and the balance (around 95%) nonfissile ^{238}U.

Of the many chemical elements that enter into the chemistry of reprocessing, only about 10 prove troublesome, either in the reprocessing plant, or in their subsequent disposal. As the fuel waits in storage, it cools, evolving the decay heat left over from the fission process (Table 14.4), as some of the more troublesome radioisotopes decay. During the first year, both the power and the radioactivity decay by a factor of 200 from what they were at the time of discharge of the fuel from the reactor.

Particularly important are any gaseous radioactive wastes generated during reprocessing. Most of these decay quickly, but there are some isotopes that do not. For example, all the iodine isotopes† have half-lives of a few hours or days, with the exception of ^{129}I. Although the iodine radioactivity will decay a factor of a million or more by the time of reprocessing, it will still be a significant fraction of the total off-site dose. Radiation from iodine is controlled by ^{129}I with its 1.7×10^7 yr half-life, even though ^{129}I has only a 0.8% fission yield.‡ The other major gaseous wastes are ^{14}C (half-life 5500 yr), ^{85}Kr (3950 days), and tritium (12 yr). The handling of these waste gases will be covered later in this chapter.

The Purex Process

The Purex process, and its many variations, is the only process extensively used today in reprocessing nuclear fuel.§ Well over 30 yr old, the Purex process was first engineered at the Knolls Atomic Power Laboratory and developed at Oak Ridge National Laboratory where a pilot plant was first built. Its main advantages are (1) its high degree of development; (2) economical operating cost; and (3) low-waste volume. Specifications for the Purex process employed in various countries are given in Table 14.5, which shows that commercial reprocessing plants based on this process are designed to handle between 600 and 1500 tons of fuel per year and are remotely maintained.

The Purex process is similar in concept to the Redox process. It depends on changing oxidation states to separate uranium, plutonium, and fission products into three process streams. In the Purex process, tributyl phosphate, or TBP, is used as the organic solvent. It is dissolved in a kerosene-like hydrocarbon. When uranium and plutonium ions are in high valence states, they are more soluble in the TBP-hydrocarbon solution then in the aqueous solution, while the opposite is true of the fission products.

Since TBP is more stable than hexone, high-concentration nitric acid can be used. This elimi-

†Iodine is not normally gaseous in fuel, but can easily be oxidized by HNO_3, used in aqueous reprocessing schemes, to molecular iodine, I_2, which is a gas.

‡^{131}I, the iodine isotope having the second longest half-life (eight days) is one of the chief technical determinants of how long it is desirable to cool fuel before reprocessing.

§The one recent exception was at the Midwest Fuel Recovery Plant at Morris, Ill., where the Aquaflor process was used. The plant never operated as intended. During tests it was discovered that an additional solvent extraction cycle was needed, but could not be implemented because the design of the plant did not permit it.

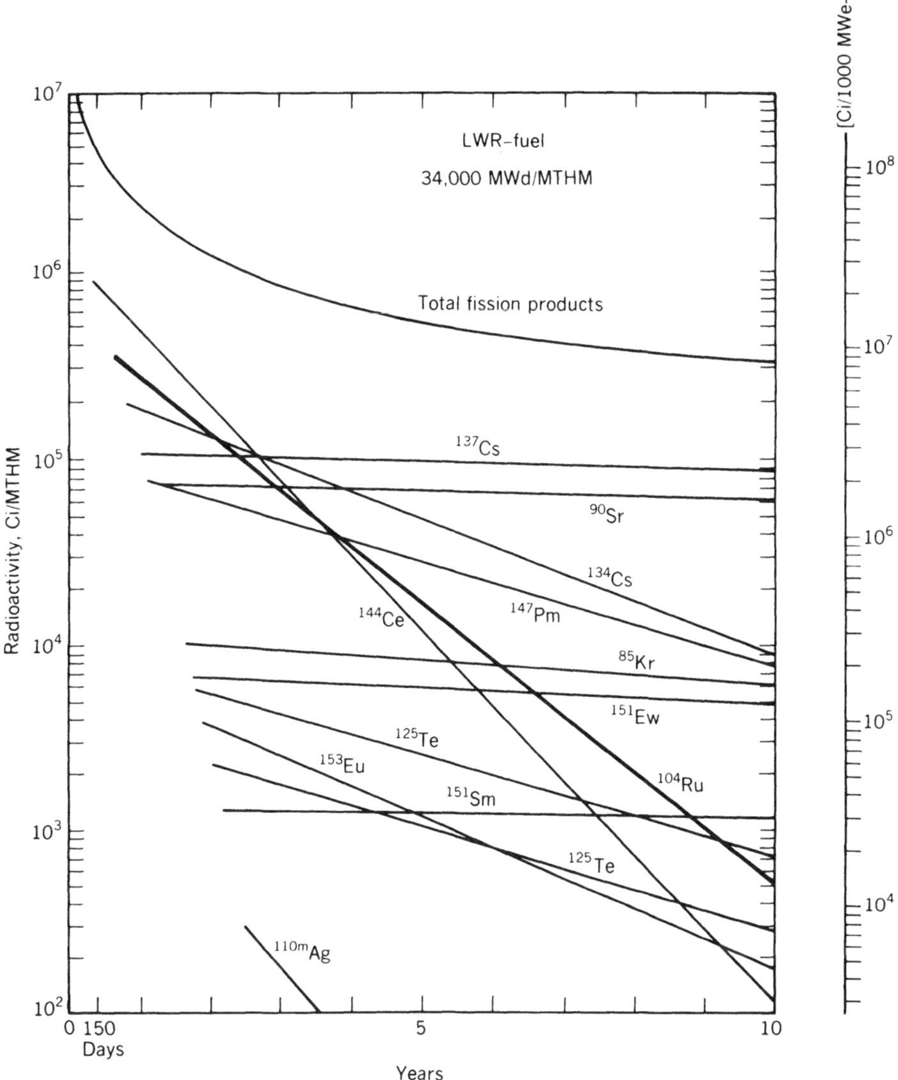

Figure 14.3. Fission product nuclide radioactivity of spent LWR fuel after reactor discharge. (From EPRI Report NP-2459-LD.)

Table 14.4. Decay of Power and Radioactivity in LWR Fuel (1 t Basis)

	Discharge	3 months	6 months	1 yr	3 yr	10 yr
Power (W)	1.9×10^6	2.7×10^4	1.9×10^4	9.8×10^3	3.0×10^3	9.0×10^2
Radioactivity (Ci)	1.6×10^8	6.6×10^6	4.4×10^6	2.3×10^6	7.9×10^5	3.0×10^5

Table 14.5. Comparison of Specifications of Industrial-Scale Reprocessing Plants

Topic	Japan	United Kingdom	France	Federal Republic of Germany	India
Process	Chop/leach solvent extraction	Chop/leach solvent extraction	Chop/leach solvent extraction	Chop/leach solvent extraction	Chop/leach solvent extraction
Design capacity	2 × 3 t/day	5 t/day		4 t U/day	0.5 t/day
Maximum fuel burnup	40 GWd/t	40 GWd/t	40 GWd/t	Up to 40 GWd/t (averaged over a campaign)	20 GWd/t
Fuel cooling time	1 yr (minimum)	~3 yr	1 yr (minimum)	~3 yr	0.5 yr (minimum)
Maintenance philosophy	Remote maintenance for highly active mechanical equipment. Contact maintenance for chemical process units.	Remote maintenance for highly active mechanical equipment. Contact maintenance for chemical process units.	Remote maintenance for highly active mechanical equipment and where the amount of sensitive materials is high. Contact maintenance in the other cases.	Remote maintenance for highly active mechanical equipment. Contact maintenance for chemical process units. Modular replacements	Remote maintenance for highly active mechanical equipment. Contact maintenance for chemical process units.
Selection of major equipment	Element bundle shear. Batch dissolver. Centrifuge clarification. Pulse column extractors.	Element bundle shear. 1st cycle pulsed columns. 2nd/3rd U cycle mixer settlers, 2nd/3rd Pu cycle pulsed columns.	Element bundle shear. 1st cycle centrifugal contactor and mixer settlers 2nd: U, Pu cycle 3rd: Pu cycle mixer settlers. 3rd cycle U centrifugal contactors.	As in UK, however, disassembly and single pin chopper are under consideration also.	Element bundle shear. Batch dissolver. Pulse column extractors. Mixer settlers for solvent treatment.

Ventilation philosophy	Areas classified and held under negative pressure. Pressure gradient ensures air flow from lowest contamination region to highest contamination region. Retain iodine and monitor krypton levels.	Areas classified and held under negative pressure. Pressure gradient ensures air flow from lowest contamination region to highest contamination region. Retain iodine and monitor krypton levels.	Areas classified and held under negative pressure. Pressure gradient ensures air flows from lowest contamination region to highest contamination region.	As in UK, in addition, krypton-85 will be retained.	Areas classified and held under negative pressure. Pressure gradient ensures air-flow pattern from lowest contamination region. Retain iodine and monitor krypton levels.
Safety philosophy	Radiation protection ICRP, ALARA physical barriers confinement system redundancy physical isolation backup Criticality control control of feed use of geometry use of poison use of monitors.	Radiation protection within ICRP guidelines Containment multiple barriers high level QA design basis accidents Criticality control administrative measures use of poisons use of geometry fuel parameters analytical measures.	Radiation protection within ICRP guidelines Containment multiple barriers design basis accidents Criticality control design technical and administrative measures	As in UK	As in UK

Source: Adapted from OECD Symposium on the Safety of the Nuclear Fuel Cycle.

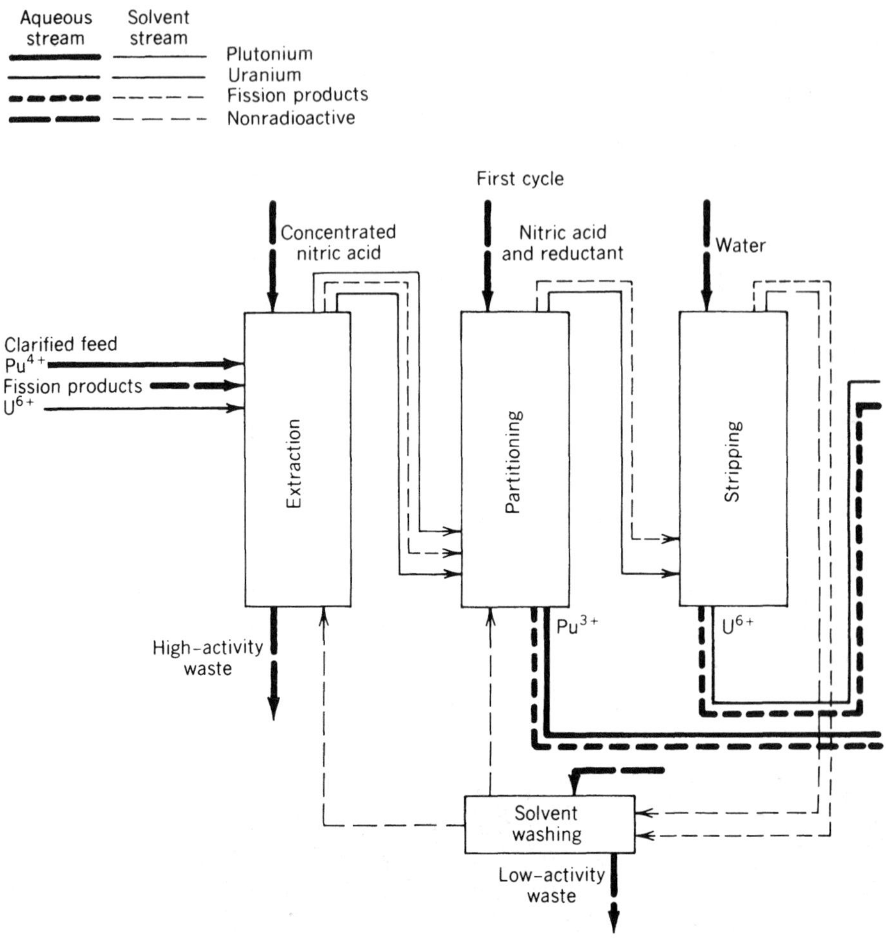

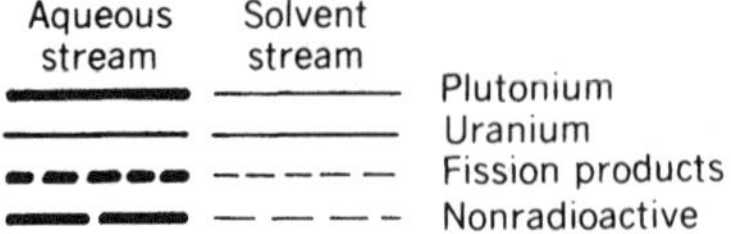

First cycle
Concentrated nitric acid
Nitric acid and reductant
Water
Clarified feed
Pu^{4+}
Fission products
U^{6+}
Extraction
Partitioning
Stripping
High-activity waste
Pu^{3+}
U^{6+}
Solvent washing
Low-activity waste

Figure 14.4. Purex solvent extraction process. This simplified diagram shows seven vertical columns in which organic and aqueous solutions are forced to travel countercurrently in intimate contact, so that substances more soluble in one solution than in the other can be efficiently separated. The feed mixture entering the first extraction column is the spent fuel in aqueous solution. The uranium ions are in a highly oxidized state, deficient in six electrons (U^{6+}); the plutonium ions are deficient in four electrons (Pu^{4+}). The aqueous feed enters the first extraction column near the middle; the TBP solvent enters at the bottom. The uranium and plutonium are extracted by the upflowing solvent; the fission products are "scrubbed" out of the solvent by the downflowing aqueous stream of nitric acid and leave from the bottom of the column. The uranium–

nates the need for $Al(NO_3)_3$, since the nitric acid is capable of supplying all the nitrate ions needed in the process.† As a result, the radioactive waste volumes are lower, since nitric acid can be evaporated from the waste product.

The principal steps of the Purex process are illustrated in Figure 14.4. It consists of two solvent extraction cycles for the separation of fission products: the first decontaminates and partitions uranium and plutonium, while the second further decontaminates the partitioned products. For complete separation, countercurrent extraction equipment is used.

The first step in reprocessing LWR fuel is to chop the fuel rods into small pieces. The uranium fuel matrix is leached in an aqueous nitric acid solution; the Zircaloy cladding does not dissolve but becomes part of the waste stream. Solutions from the head-end dissolvers can be centrifuged to remove any finely divided solids. To help clarify the solutions MnO_2 can be used: it precipitates,

†For this reason, the Purex process is sometimes referred to as "self-salting."

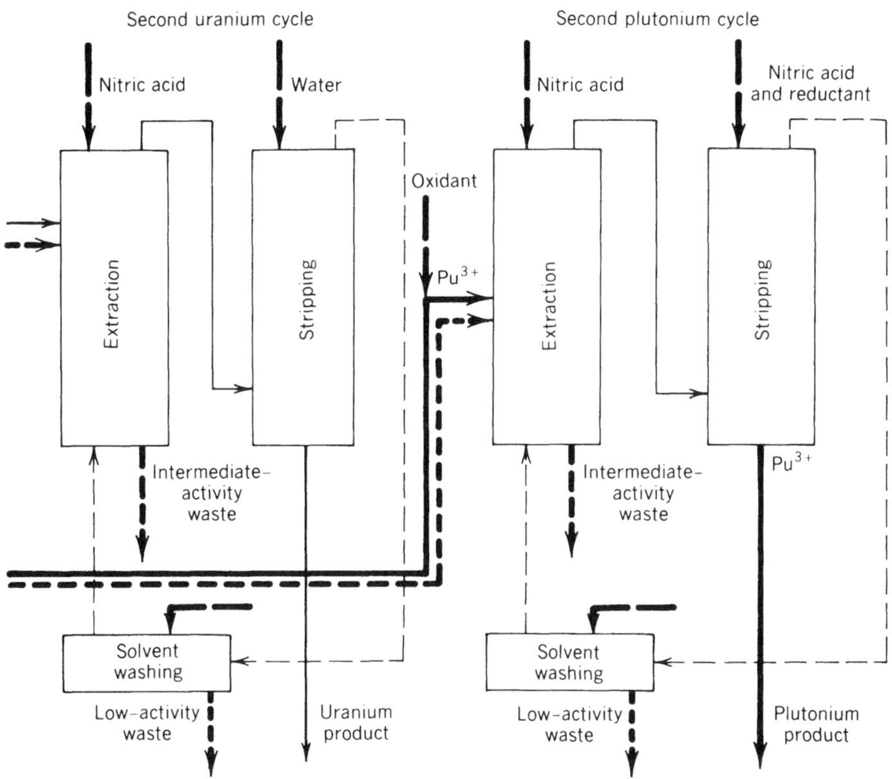

plutonium mixture passes to the second, or partitioning, column, where the plutonium is "stripped" out of the solvent by countercurrent contact with nitric acid that contains a reductant that reduces the plutonium to the 3+ state (Pu^{3+}), making it insoluble in the organic solvent. Simultaneously upflowing solvent scrubs the last traces of uranium from the aqueous solution of plutonium, which leaves from the bottom of the partitioning column. In the third, or stripping, column, the uranium is removed from the organic solvent by dilute nitric acid. In the second uranium and plutonium cycles the extraction and stripping are repeated separately. [From B. P. Bebbington, *Scientific American* **235,** 30 (1976).]

removing some of the fission products with it. As in the Redox process, the plutonium and uranium as nitrates are extracted into the TBP organic stream; then by changing the valence state of plutonium to +3, the separation from uranium is achieved. In this latter step, the plutonium returns to an aqueous stream, then is further purified in an additional extraction cycle (or ion exchange), and converted to PuO_2 by thermally decomposing, that is, calcining, the $Pu(NO_3)_4$. The uranium is likewise further decontaminated in another extraction cycle, and then converted to UO_2 or UF_6. The liquid wastes from the Purex process, which are strongly acidic, are stored in stainless steel tanks pending their ultimate disposal.†

†On the other hand, the wastes from the U.S. military reprocessing program are neutralized, so that they can be stored in carbon steel tanks. This was initially done during World War II, when stainless steel was unavailable. As a result, these military wastes contain a high level of sodium, which makes their conversion into an insoluble glass form more difficult.

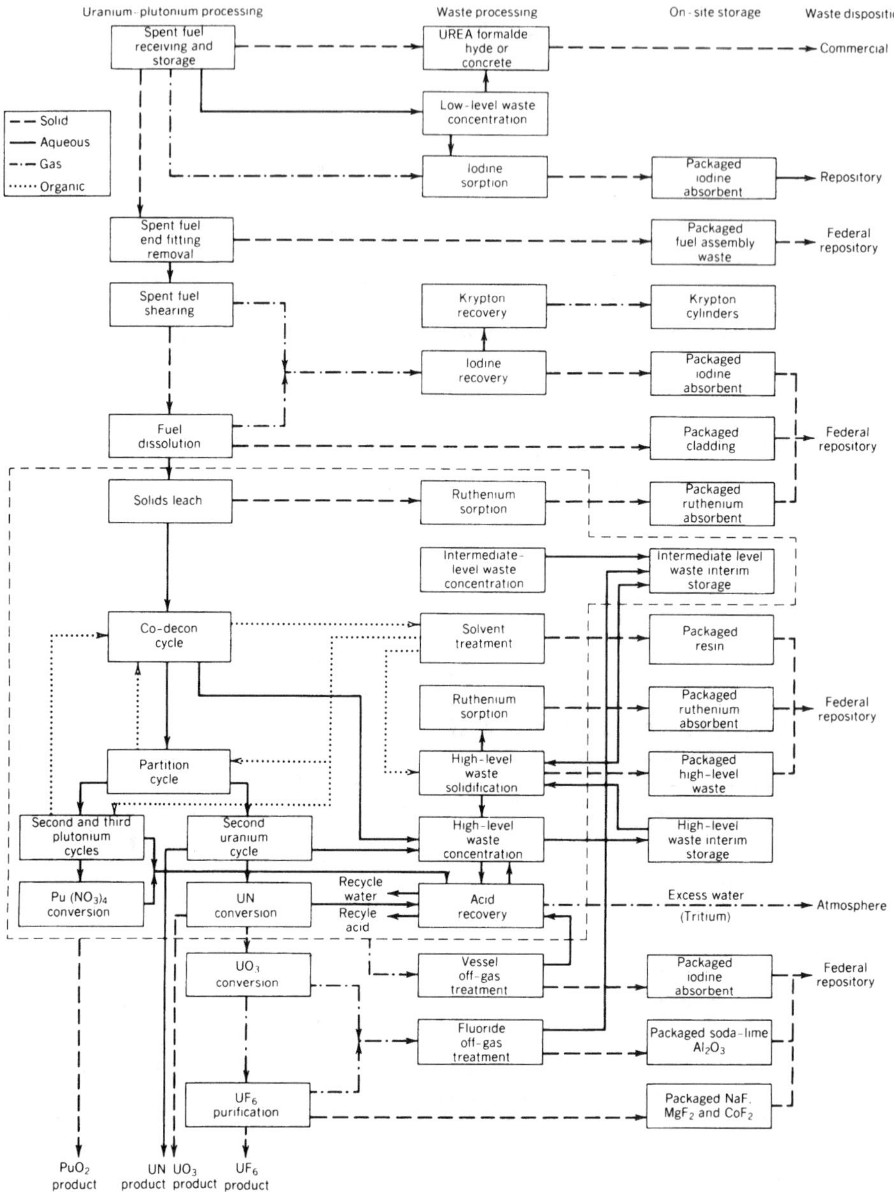

Figure 14.5. Source and handling of waste products from the Purex process. (From EPRI Report NP-2631.)

About 250 liters of concentrated waste results from reprocessing 1 ton of spent fuel. The handling of these and the other radioactive wastes are summarized in Figure 14.5, which shows the type of waste generated at each step of the process. The solid and liquid wastes are stabilized for disposal at a federal repository while the gaseous wastes are either stored (e.g., Xe), absorbed and packaged for disposal (e.g., I), or released directly to the atmosphere (e.g., tritium). The half-year or longer wait before spent fuel is reprocessed greatly reduces the waste problem since all gaseous fission products (except ^{85}Kr, ^{129}I, and tritium) have decayed to very low levels, the ^{131}I (with an 8-day half-life) is much reduced, and ^{239}Np (2.4-day half-life) has decayed to ^{239}Pu. In the United

States, the waste would be handled in accordance with the NRC and EPA regulations (see Chapter 15).

There are a number of important variations on the Purex process, including those for handling LWR fuels with high plutonium content (MOX fuel), LMFBR fuel, and thoria fuels. These are treated in subsequent sections.

Another possible modification is using the Purex process in conjunction with the sol–gel fuel manufacturing process. This offers the possibility of coprocessing and colocation of a facility with enhanced resistance to the diversion of plutonium. This feature is likely to be important in future reprocessing facilities.

Removal of Fuel Cladding

The first step in the Purex process is usually a shearing operation which chops the 12-ft-long fuel pins into short pieces from which the fuel can be leached. This can be easily accomplished with a mechanical shear. Ideally this operation requires no disassembly of the fuel elements, produces no fine clad particles, and uses equipment that can be easily maintained.

The fuel pin cladding can also be chemically dissolved, using either the Zirflex process or electrolytic dissolution in nitric acid. The former uses a boiling solution of ammonium fluoride to dissolve Zircaloy, and the latter produces nitrate as the only anion, and little hydrogen off-gas. A disadvantage of chemical decladding in general is that the metal cladding ions often end up in the high-level wastes, greatly increasing the volume. Sometimes, however, most of the zirconium in Zircaloy can be converted to hydrous ZrO_2 and filtered out before it enters the HLW stream.

LWR fuel pins contain He gas introduced in the manufacturing process (see Chapter 7) in addition to the fission product gases Xe and Kr. Gaseous iodine can also be evolved, either during the decladding or dissolution steps. These gases, and tritium and ^{14}C are released from the fuel and cycled to the off-gas treatment system.

Dissolution

In the Purex process, nitric acid is used to dissolve the fuel since the process is based on metal nitrates in aqueous solution. Oxygen is often added to the aqueous solution during dissolution to suppress the evolution of gaseous fission products. Nearly all of the fission products go into solution, although in high-burnup LWR fuel, the quantities of some elements present, such as molybdenum and ruthenium, may exceed their solubility limits and therefore they may not fully dissolve. The fission product, unlike uranyl and plutonyl, nitrates are not readily extracted by TBP. Iodine and ruthenium, however, can end up in any of a number of valence states, some of which can be extracted by TBP. This leads to a carry-over of these elements into the TBP solvent streams–an undesired event during the solvent extraction phase of PUREX. Preconditioning of the feed helps reduce the contamination of the product streams by keeping these elements inextractable.

After dissolution of the fuel is complete, the Zircaloy cladding hulls are checked for adherent fuel particles and then packaged as radioactive waste. The solution containing the dissolved fuel is centrifuged to remove fine particles, and then conditioned prior to entering the extraction columns. The conditioning brings the dissolved plutonium to its most extractable state, which is Pu^{4+}. This is necessary since the plutonium from the dissolution step is mostly either PuO_2 ions or Pu^{3+}. Hydroxylamine, N_2O_4, can be used for this purpose.

Solvent Extraction Process Equipment

Reprocessing of spent nuclear fuel requires specialized equipment. In solvent-extraction processes, a key component is the contactor which brings the aqueous and organic streams together so that separation of uranium and plutonium can occur. There are four types of contactors that have been developed: packed columns, pulsed columns, mixer settlers, and centrifugal devices. Each of these devices has its merits. It is important to successful commercial operation that whichever contactor is chosen, it be maintainable, easily operable, and flexible.

The packed column† is the simplest of the solvent-extraction contactors in use, but they are up to 15 m tall‡ and consequently require a large amount of radiation shielding. The packing forces the liquid streams to follow a tortuous path. Usually the liquids flow in opposite directions, increasing the extraction efficiency of the unit. Packed columns require no moving parts, and have the additional advantage of being able to operate efficiently over a wide range of conditions.

†So-called because stainless steel rings (about 2 cm in diameter) are used to effect the mass transfer between the solutes. The rings are allowed to settle by gravity in the column, forming a "packed" section. They increase the surface area for solute contact and facilitate mixing of the liquids.
‡In packed columns, flow rates are low and only gentle mixing occurs. This results in high columns.

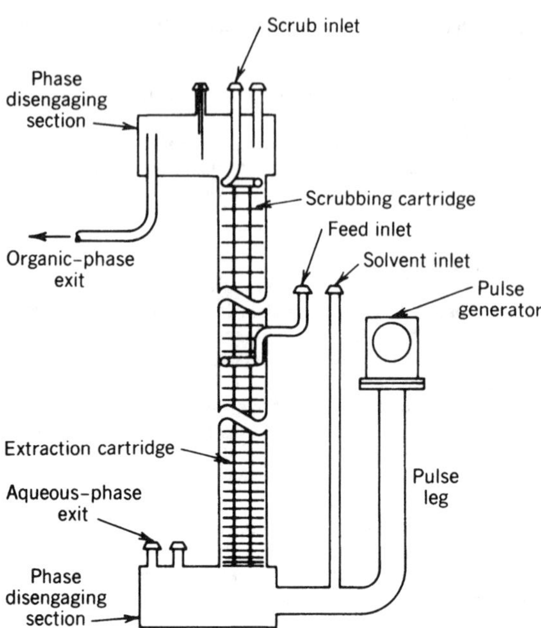

Figure 14.6. Typical solvent-extraction pulse column with extraction and scrubbing sections. Pulse columns have been built which have phase-contacting sections with inside diameters of up to 34 in. and with heights of greater than 33 ft. The pulse generator is attached to the column through a pulse leg, which ordinarily is combined with one of the streams entering or leaving the bottom of the column. The pulse leg extends high enough that the hydraulic head from the column is almost balanced. (From J. T. Long, *Engineering for Nuclear Fuel Reprocessing*, American Nuclear Society, 1978.)

A pulsed column (Figure 14.6) uses hydraulic pulsation to improve the contact of the liquid phases. Instead of packing rings, it usually contains perforated plates† which break up the liquids into small droplets as the column is pulsed. The pulse occurs when pneumatic or mechanical pressure is applied periodically to the liquids, or other packing devices, increasing the pressure, which then decays. This pulse causes droplets to form and then interact with the plates and each other, causing the liquid phases to mix. This mechanical agitation of the liquids allows pulsed columns to be built smaller than packed columns of equal efficiency. Consequently, less shielding is required and a smaller liquid inventory is needed. The operation of a pulsed column is optimized by adjusting the flow rate of the organic and aqueous streams, the pulse amplitude and frequency, and the geometry of the perforated plates. Pulsed columns were first used at the Purex plants at Hanford and Idaho Falls in the United States.

Mixer settlers (Figure 14.7) are a type of contactor that use an array of separate mixing vessels and settling vessels joined by piping. The flow is countercurrent between stages. A pump, impeller, or agitator in each mixing vessel brings the liquids into contact, effecting the extraction process. While the arrangement of vessels may be either vertical or horizontal, the latter is more common. By arranging the stages (usually about 10) head to toe, a compact design results and the piping required is greatly reduced. The flow patterns of aqueous and organic liquid can become complex in such an arrangement. Baffles can be used to minimize backmixing from the mixing stage to the preceding settler stage. Density differences between the liquids are important to the operation of a mixer settler. Workable density differences are obtained by altering the TBP density using a solvent (e.g., kerosene), and by altering the aqueous phase density by dissolved salts or acids. The use of a diluent with the TBP also helps to prevent emulsification of the phase.‡ The chief drawback of mixer-settlers is the large volume of uranium and plutonium that is held up in liquid inventory. Because of the large holdup the solvent is subject to considerable damage from radiation and

†Stainless steel is used because of its corrosion resistance to nitric acid, although plastics may also be used (in combination) if wettability of the organic liquid is desired.

‡Emulsification leads to thick, high-viscosity liquids, just as when oil and vinegar are beaten together with an egg to form mayonnaise.

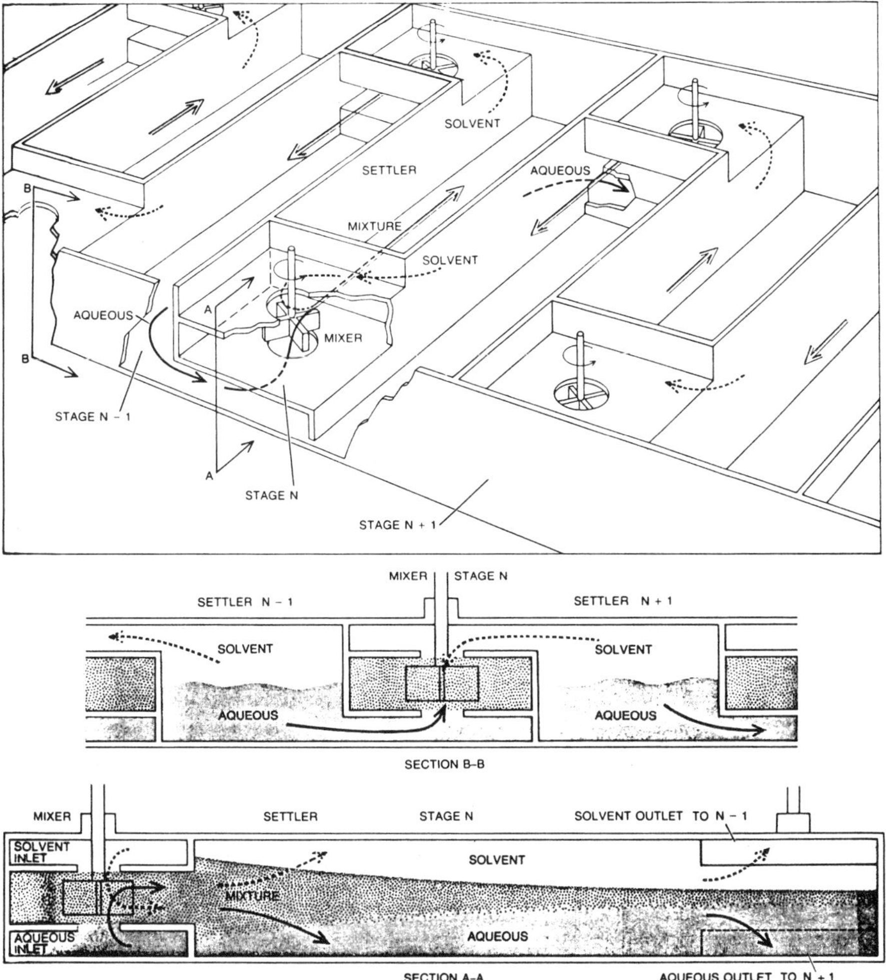

Figure 14.7. Mixer–settlers, in which flow is maintained by paddles rather than by gravity, were first used at the Savannah River Plant in the United States. Aqueous and solvent solutions flow countercurrently through horizontal "stages." Each stage consists of a mixing chamber and a settling one. [From W. P. Bebbington, *Scientific American* **235,** 30 (1976).]

chemical activity. Among the advantages of the system are that the contactor can be readily adapted to remote maintenance.

Centrifugal contactors have the advantages of being relatively compact and rapid. As a result residence times are low. This is important because radiation damage to the solvents is proportional to the time the two liquid phases are in contact—the shorter the better. The inventory of the solutions in process is small,† another advantage. Centrifugal contactors, although among the first tried, were the last to be employed because of reliability concerns, which have been overcome. Unlike that in the other contacting devices, flow is usually cocurrent in centrifugal contactors, although it is countercurrent between stages. The centrifugal contactor has a complicated array of rotating blades, stationary weirs, and baffles to mix and partition the flow. High accelerations‡ of the aqueous and organic phases are obtained. This allows efficient operation with liquids of smaller density differences than can otherwise be handled. Adjusting the nitric acid concentration in the aqueous phase prevents emulsification of the products obtained. Typical of centrifugal contactors is the French Robatel design (Figure 14.8), which has eight stages in a single unit. Robatel units were used for the plant at Barnwell.

†Centrifugal contactors have about one-fiftieth the volume of a mixer–settler unit.
‡Several hundred times the force of gravity.

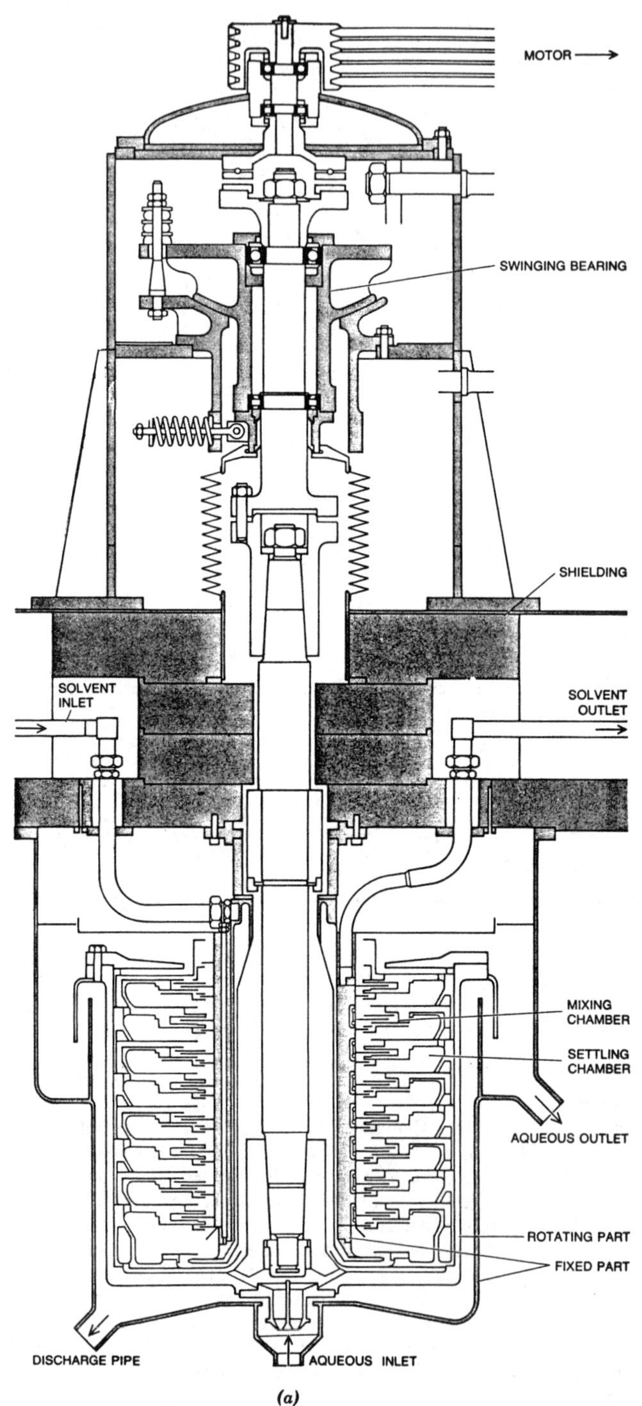
MOTOR
SWINGING BEARING
SHIELDING
SOLVENT INLET
SOLVENT OUTLET
MIXING CHAMBER
SETTLING CHAMBER
AQUEOUS OUTLET
ROTATING PART
FIXED PART
DISCHARGE PIPE
AQUEOUS INLET

(a)

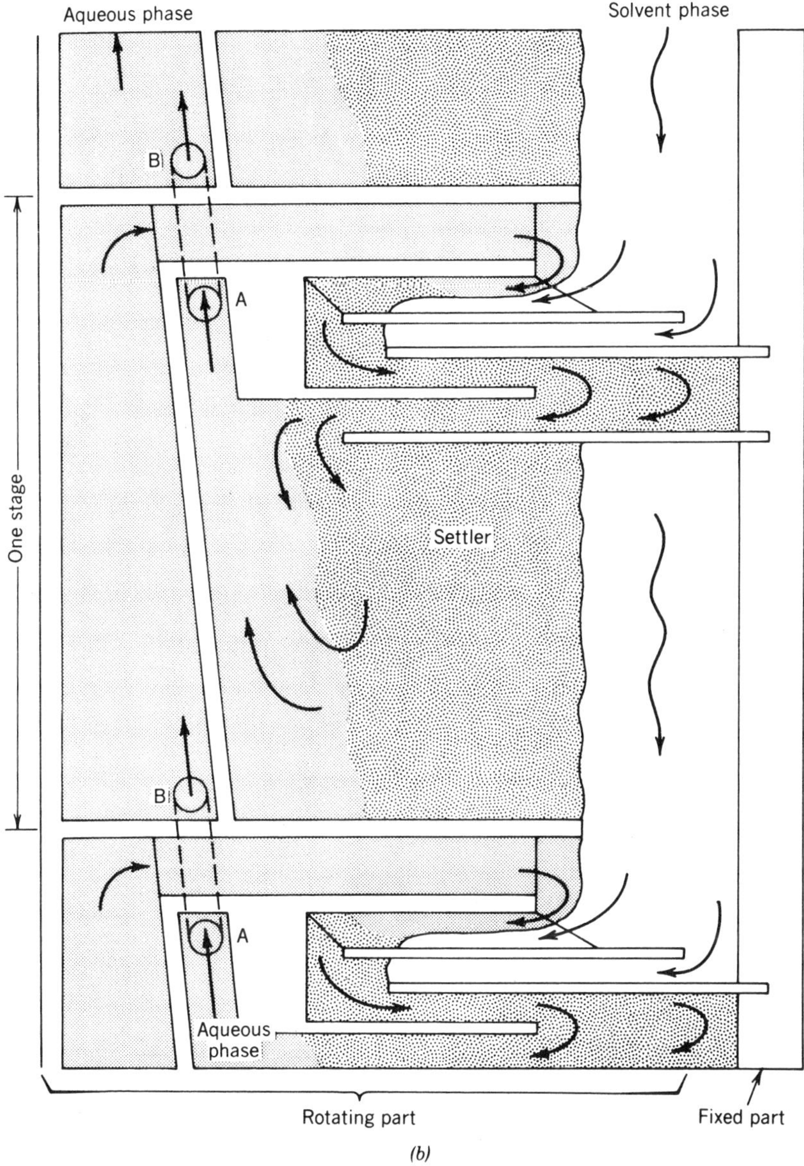

Figure 14.8. (*a*) Multistage contactor called the Robatel developed by the French firm Saint-Gobain Techniques Nouvelles. [From W. P. Bebbington, *Scientific American* **235,** 30 (1976).] (*b*) Flow scheme in the Robatel provides for eight stages of mixing and settling arranged one above the other. The schematic diagram shows the flow through a single stage. Briefly, the organic solution, traveling downward on the inside of the rotating bowl, is repeatedly mixed with the aqueous solution, which is conducted upward through a series of ports and baffles. Flow of organic solution is readily followed from diagram. At each stage aqueous solution leaves settler through ports labeled A and reappears in stage above ports labeled B. [From W. P. Bebbington, *Scientific American* **235,** 30 (1976).]

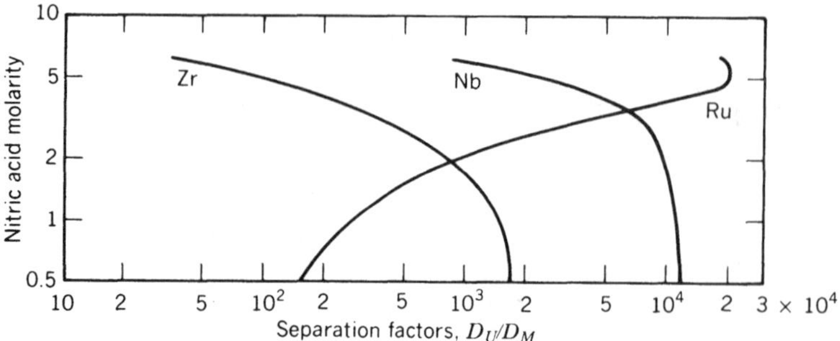

Figure 14.9. Separation factors for uranium from ruthenium, zirconium, and niobium. (From TID-7534.)

Extractants

Early solvent extraction was done using hexone,† which readily extracts U^{4+} and Pu^{6+} in the presence of a salting agent.‡ A complex between hexone, uranyl nitrate, and water forms which is the mechanism for the extraction. The hexone must be very pure, or the extraction of plutonium is impeded, or carry-over of some of the fission products occurs. Hexone can also degrade under certain conditions, and is particularly unstable in the presence of nitrous acid, high nitric acid concentrations, and poor heat transfer conditions. Hexone and water are nearly immiscible; the solubility of one in the other is about 2 wt%.

Tributyl phosphate (TBP) is the extractant used in most reprocessing work. TBP is more stable than Butex in nitric acid, is cheaper than hexone, and provides better separation than either. Its usefulness for the recovery of actinides was discovered in 1945. Like hexone, it forms complexes with metal salts, and is particularly effective with uranyl nitrate, $UO_2(NO_3)_2$ and plutonyl nitrate, $PuO_2(NO_3)_2$. The chemical reaction is

$$UO_2 + 2NO_3 + 2\ TBP \leftrightarrow UO_2(NO_3)_2 \cdot 2\ TBP$$

TBP is usually diluted with an organic solvent. This is done to control the density and viscosity of the organic phase and the relative concentration of the TBP. Numerous diluents are available, the most widely used being either kerosene or *n*-dodecane, a paraffin.§

TBP is particularly stable in the presence of nitric acid. This is advantageous, since the use of nitric acid as a salting agent¶ results in lower waste volume and smaller processing vessels. A disadvantage of nitric acid, however, is that it can carry over into the organic phase, changing the salt concentration in the aqueous stream. The effect of nitric acid on separating uranium from various of the more difficult-to-separate fission products is shown in Figure 14.9. This figure shows that some fission products separate better at low acid concentration, others at high concentration. For this reason, the acidity is often high in one stage of the process (say, 3.0*M*), and low in another (1.0*M*).

Deterioration of the TBP extractant leads to poor operation, including unsatisfactory separation and gumming up of the pipes. Degraded TBP also impairs the separation of plutonium from uranium in the partitioning column of the Purex process, and when the degradation is extensive, a highly explosive "red oil" results.

Radiation is one agent that causes TBP to deteriorate; hydrolysis is another. To prevent degradation of the TBP (and diluent), the solvent is periodically cleaned of radioactivity and degradation products.‖ Manganese dioxide can be used for this purpose, if the degradation is not too severe. It strips fission products from the liquid and prevents the buildup of impurities.

†Methyl isobutyl ketone.

‡Usually aluminum nitrate, $Al(NO_3)_3$.

§Carbon tetrachloride may also be used as a diluent for TBP. Its advantages are its nonflammability and its use of smaller process equipment. Because of the higher density of the organic phase when CCl_4 is used, the extraction column operates in the reverse mode from the Purex arrangement: the organic liquid enters at the top and the lighter aqueous solution at bottom. Carbon tetrachloride has never been widely used because of possible toxicity and radiation stability problems.

¶Aluminum nitrate $Al(NO_3)_3$ can also be used.

‖Any iodine carried over into the organic stream will also interact with TBP, forming iodine compounds that are difficult to remove.

Although hexone and TBP are the extractants most used to date, other extractants can be used. Any number of ketones (of which hexone is one), or organophosphorus compounds (TBP is one) may be used, but with less efficiency. Other possible extracting agents are from the ether family, or various chelating compounds. None of these are the basis of any commercial process. TBP is the extractant of choice because of its high extracting power and process compatibility.

14.5. REPROCESSING HTGR FUEL

HTGR fuel is made up of coated fuel particles that are formed into fuel rods, which are inserted into graphite moderator blocks (see Chapter 7). It differs from LWR fuel in three ways: (1) the fuel is contained in a graphite matrix rather than clad in Zircaloy, (2) thorium instead of plutonium must be separated from the uranium and fission products, and (3) design fuel burnup is two to three times as high, so that radiation levels and fission product concentrations are correspondingly higher. Unless the spent fuel has decayed for some time, it will contain appreciable amounts of ^{233}Pa (27-day half-life) which will have to be separately processed. The reprocessing scheme is designed to recover the unconsumed uranium in the fuel and ^{233}U bred from the thorium for further use. A pilot plant is in operation which employs simulated (i.e., unirradiated) fuel elements of the Fort St. Vrain type. The process is summarized in Figure 14.10.

The reprocessing of HTGR fuel starts with the crushing of the graphite blocks containing the fuel rods or "compacts" to reduce them to small fragments† suitable for fluidized-bed burning. The purpose of the burning is to remove the graphite moderator and BISO graphite coating of the ThO_2 particles by means of oxidation.‡ This prepares the fuel particles for the dissolution and leaching process. The burning leaves the fuel mostly in the form of oxide and silicon carbide particles. The TRISO-coated particles, which retain their silicon carbide coating, are separated from the denser BISO particles by elutriation with CO_2 gas. These are next leached with nitric acid to convert the fuel oxides to the nitrate solution required for solvent extraction. The BISO particles, which contain ThO_2, must be dissolved using a mixture of nitric and hydrofluoric acids. Aluminum nitrate, $Al(NO_3)_3$, must be added to the solution to slow corrosion of the process equipment. In contrast to LWR fuels which rapidly dissolve in hot nitric acid, ThO_2–UO_2 fuels do so only slowly and with great difficulty.

The solvent extraction system, illustrated in Figure 14.11, separates uranium from thorium as well as from other fission products. A modification of the Purex process called the Acid-Thorex process is used. A major difference in process variables results because TBP has less ability to extract thorium nitrate by complexing than uranium or plutonium. The equipment used, however, is similar to that used for LWR fuel reprocessing. It consists of a feed adjustment unit, several pulsed-column solvent extraction contractors,§ and a product concentrator. Preliminary operating data show that the process is of commercial importance. As seen in the figure, the feed adjustment step reduces the thorium nitrate solution, which enters at about 9 *M* in nitric acid, to being acid-deficient in nitrate ions. Otherwise thorium could not be satisfactorily decontaminated from some fission products, in particular, ruthenium and zirconium. Ruthenium can be made even less extractable by treating the aqueous solution with $NaHSO_3$.

The Acid-Thorex process separates the thorium, ^{233}U, and ^{233}Pa¶ from each other and from the fission products. It employs TBP; however, the nitric acid usually has to be catalyzed with fluoride‖ in order to dissolve the thorium. Thorium's only stable oxidation state is +4; moreover it is chemically similar to zirconium, the most troublesome of the fission products. Fission products and protactinium, which may follow the thorium and uranium streams, can be removed by an acid-deficient scrub solution containing aluminum nitrate salting agent.

Because of the weak complexing potential of thorium, the extractant used is 30% TBP diluted in *n*-dodecane (or kerosene). The thorium also presents problems when it precipitates out on equipment, a process caused by interaction with any degraded TBP present. To control this, extra fluoride is added. Up to this point, the uranium and thorium are both present in the organic phase. ^{233}U is usually separated from the thorium by contacting the organic stream with dilute nitric acid; then the ^{233}U is purified by ion exchange.

It is desirable to reprocess separately the fissile UC particles and the fertile THO_2 particles from

†About 0.5 cm in diameter, although very fine material and breakage of the TRISO-coated fuel particles are undesirable.

‡Considerable quantities of ^{14}C are contained in the graphite blocks. The CO_2 and CO coming from combustion must be treated as radioactive wastes. By contacting it with $Ca(OH)_2$ to form $CaCO_3$ a solid material forms which can then be stored as low-level radwaste.

§These units are fairly small, with diameters of only 5 to 10 cm on the pilot-plant scale.

¶^{233}Pa, the precursor of ^{233}U, has a 27-day half-life.

‖The Thorex reagent is usually 13 *M* nitric acid, 0.05 *M* hydrofluoric acid with 0.075 *M* cadmium nitrate for criticality control.

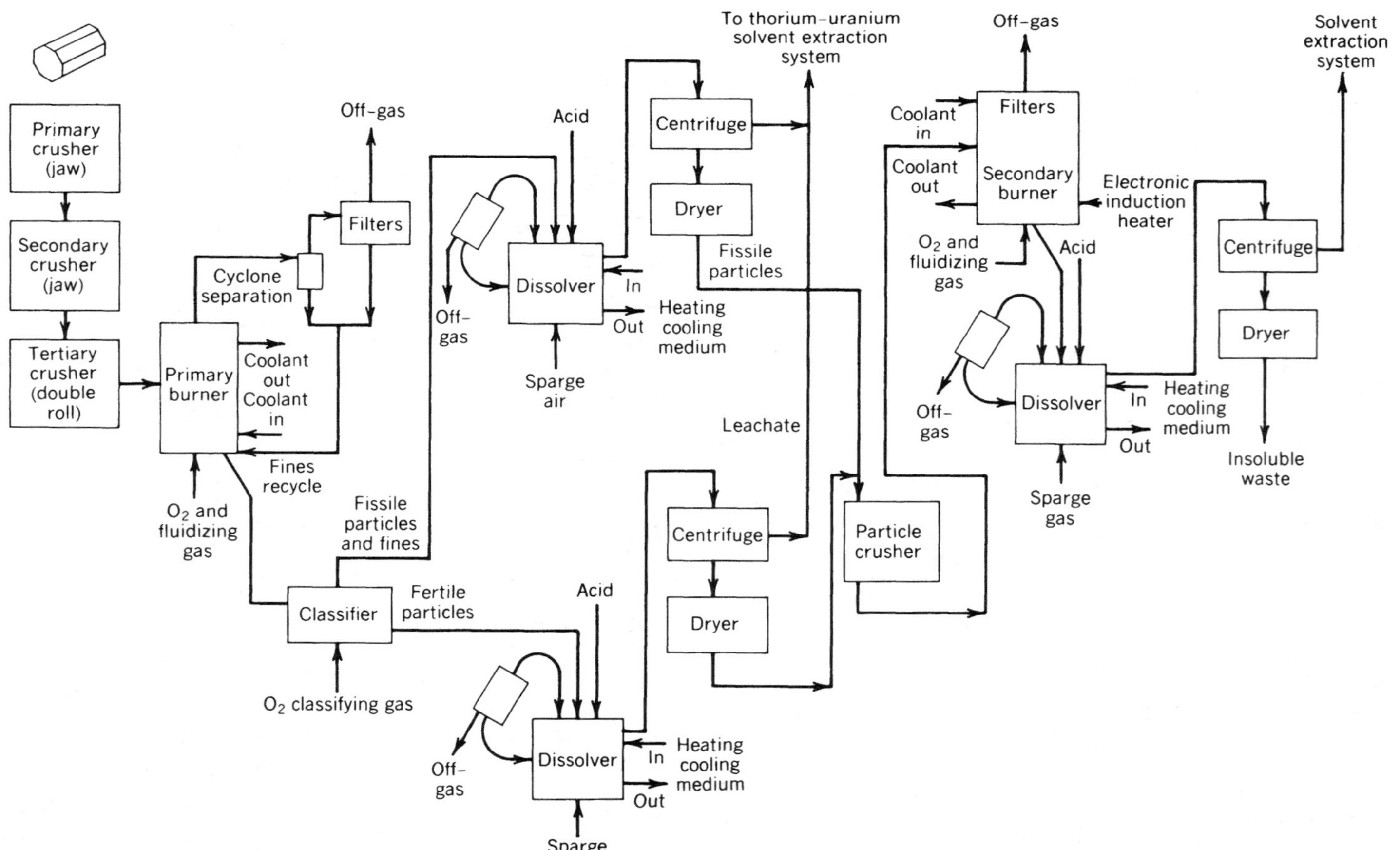

Figure 14.10. Simplified Triso-Biso reprocessing flow diagram for HTGR fuel. (Courtesy General Atomic Co.)

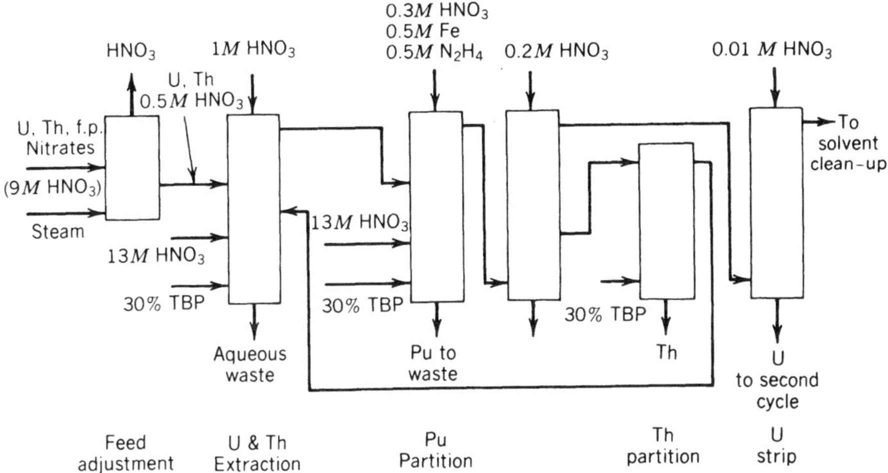

Figure 14.11. Solvent extraction partition cycle for thorium/uranium. (Courtesy General Atomic Co.)

HTGR fuel. This prevents the buildup of ^{236}U in the recycled fuel, caused by recycling uranium too often through the fuel cycle. ^{236}U absorbs neutrons and therefore acts as a poison in the reactor. Each time the uranium (which has a high enrichment in ^{235}U) cycles through the reactor, more ^{236}U is created. After a few cycles it may be desirable to discard the uranium to the waste stream. The uranium found in the fertile particles is predominantly ^{233}U, so separate reprocessing to avoid "mixing" the different isotopic concentrations is required. The fertile particles can be separated from the fissile ones either by size or by density. If this is done, the fertile particles could be handled by the Acid-Thorex process described, and the fissile particles, which contain no thorium, by the conventional Purex technology.

14.6. REPROCESSING MIXED-OXIDE FUEL

There is no fundamental difference in the Purex process for LWR fuel consisting of mixed oxides. The main variations arise from the composition of the fuel pellets, which is a consequence of substituting plutonium isotopes for ^{235}U in the fuel matrix. Table 14.6 shows the ^{235}U and plutonium content of UO_2 and MOX fuel with a burnup of 33,000 MWd/t. Roughly half as much ^{235}U and three times as much plutonium are encountered in reprocessing MOX fuel. Although MOX fuel is not widely used in LWRs, about 30 t of such spent fuel exist in western Europe today, and between 100 and 300 t may be available for reprocessing by 1995.

The high plutonium content of MOX fuel results in an increase in the amounts of ^{241}Am, ^{242}Cm, and other transplutonium isotopes in the spent fuel. The fission product yield for plutonium differs from uranium; as a result more ^{3}H, ^{95}Zr, ^{106}Rn, and ^{129}I are formed, but less ^{90}Sr and ^{85}Kr. The difference in fission yield, however, does not lead to major process modifications. More important in this regard is the high plutonium content of the fuel which leads to some adjustments, for instance, in the uranium-plutonium partition factors and criticality parameters. The physical characteristics of MOX fuel affect reprocessing in the following three ways:

Table 14.6. Comparison of UO_2, and MO_x Fuel After 33,000 MWd/t Burnup in an LWR

	Wt% Heavy Metal	
	UO_2	MO_x
^{235}U	0.9	0.4
Total Pu	1.0	3.4
Fissile Pu	0.7	2.1

Table 14.7. Comparison of Spent Fuel From an LWR and LMFBR

	Wt% Heavy Metal	
	LWR Fuel	LMFBR Core and Blanket
Uranium	86	95
Plutonium	10	1.0
Americium	0.4	0.1
Curium	0.001	0.005
Fission products	3.9	3.1

1. The dissolution of the fuel is difficult, even in boiling, highly concentrated nitric acid if the fuel matrix contains large particles of UO_2 and PuO_2. However, fuel manufactured from coprecipitated uranium and plutonium nitrates or from highly fragmented, well-mixed powders more readily dissolve and are therefore easier to handle.
2. The isotopic composition of MOX fuel does not lend itself to simultaneous processing with UO_2 fuel because of its high depletion of ^{235}U and higher content of nonfissile plutonium isotopes. Moreover, the much higher content of ^{238}Pu, ^{241}Pu, and ^{242}Pu in MOX fuel leads to much higher radiation levels, so that shielding and remote handling is required for even "pure" plutonium.
3. The TBP-organic solvent is more rapidly degraded by the higher alpha radiation due to the increased plutonium concentration. Special care is therefore required to maintain the purity of solvent streams.

The compositional differences of MOX fuel do not seem to present major technical difficulties to the Purex process, although this has not yet been demonstrated on a large scale.

14.7. REPROCESSING BREEDER FUEL

Breeder fuel cycles require reprocessing of spent fuel elements shortly after discharge from the reactor for best economic results. Because of high fission-product† content and plutonium content, spent oxide fuels are difficult to dissolve in nitric acid.‡ Fluoride§ may be needed to catalyze the nitric acid. Once the fuel is dissolved, a conventional Purex flow sheet could be used, although careful attention to criticality control is necessary because of the higher concentrations of plutonium. Because of the short cooling time between discharge and reprocessing of the fuel, high decay heat and radiation levels will be encountered, although when averaged over the total fuel and blanket inventory, the radioactivity levels are not that much higher (about 40%) than for LWR fuel cooled for the same period of time. The most undesirable aspect of the latter is the degradation of the TBP which interferes with the separations steps. Using centrifugal contactors, with their shorter residence times, will partly overcome this problem although other steps will probably also be required.

A less serious problem is the sodium coolant which may still adhere to the outer surface of LMFBR fuel assemblies. Because of the reaction of sodium with water or aqueous nitric acid solutions, it must be removed prior to the start of reprocessing. This is done by exposing the fuel to an inert gas such as argon containing a controlled amount of water vapor. After the sodium has been cleaned, LMFBR fuel could be stored under water like LWR fuel.

The burnup of LMFBR fuel is expected to be about twice that for LWR fuel. This leads to greater concentrations of fission products even after the blanket material is mixed with that from the core. Moreover, the initial high plutonium concentration of the fuel prior to irradiation leads to much greater concentrations of transplutonic isotopes in the spent fuel, and of course, the plutonium content is nearly 10 times that in LWR spent fuel. This is summarized in Table 14.7.

As covered in the previous section, mixed UO_2–PuO_2 fuel dissolves slowly in nitric acid. In some fuel, complete dissolution is impossible. A mixture of nitric and hydrofluoric acid can com-

†Particularly radioiodine.

‡Plutonium oxide *in solid solution* with uranium oxide, however, is readily soluble in nitric acid. Carbide and nitride fuels would present additional difficulties due to the formation of compounds that interfere with the solvent extraction process. They most likely would be first converted to an oxide before the start of reprocessing.

§Usually HF, which is very corrosive.

Table 14.8. Boiling Points of Fluorides, (°C)

TeF_6	−35.5
IF_7	4.5 (sublimes)
MoF_6	35
TcF_6	55.3
UF_6	56.2
NpF_6	56.4
RnF_6	62.2
PuF_6	62.3
IF_5	98
SbF_5	149.5
NbF_5	236
RnF_5	250

Source: From *Handbook of Chemistry and Physics,* 60th ed.

plete the dissolution, but corrosion of process equipment by the HF is a major problem. Fuel with low plutonium concentrations or which achieves microfine mixing of the plutonium and uranium during fabrication dissolves much more easily.

While the current Purex-based technology is believed to be adequate for breeder fuels, the applicability of the Purex technique has not yet been demonstrated on a large scale, although breeder fuel has been reprocessed for over 5 yr at EBR-II using a pyrometallurgical process.

14.8. NONAQUEOUS REPROCESSING METHODS

Of the numerous nonaqueous processes, none to date has found favor in the commercial reprocessing of spent fuel. Although they are not commercially important, several processes are briefly described to illustrate the different physical and chemical techniques that could possibly be used.

Most of the nonaqueous processes have been specially tailored for a particular fuel type or purpose. For instance, many of the pyroprocesses were developed to handle metallic fuel elements; when UO_2 became the fuel of choice in LWRs, their advantages became less apparent. Further development, or different fuel types, might restore their position, although today there is no serious challenger to the aqueous Purex process.

Several of the processes had a single design criterion, such as the recovery of plutonium from irradiated fuel. Other processes were capable of isolating various of the fission products, as is the fluoride volatility technique. This process was intensely studied, but never survived the pilot-plant phase of development. Most other processes never made it out of the laboratory.

The major advantage of nonaqueous processes is their ability to reprocess fuel after a very short decay because they use inorganic materials which are not sensitive to radiation. Moreover, they are often simpler than the Purex process and only produce small amounts of solid waste. On the other hand, these processes often require operation at high temperatures, which makes maintenance difficult, and generally yield low decontamination of fission products from the uranium and plutonium. This results in heavy shielding requirements during refabrication. The fluoride volatility process is an exception to the last disadvantage.

Two processes will be covered briefly: fluoride volatility, and pyrozinc. Further details on these or the other processes can be found in Benedict, Pigford, and Levi's *Nuclear Chemical Engineering;* Long's *Engineering for Nuclear Fuel Reprocessing,* or Selvaduray, Goldstein, and Anderson's *Survey of Reprocessing Techniques.*

Fluoride Volatility Process

The fluoride volatility method of reprocessing is a relatively low-temperature process that relies on fractional distillation to separate the elements. It can be used on most fuels, including metallic, oxide, carbide, and alloys. The process is based on the low-temperature volatility of uranium and plutonium fluoride. Most of the fission product fluorides volatilize only at relatively high temperature, with tellurium and ruthenium the notable exceptions. Table 14.8 gives some of the boiling points of fluorides of interest. Of special note in this table are that the boiling points of UF_6, NpF_6, and TcF_6 are within 1°C of each other, making their separation from each other by fractional distillation difficult. Purification of uranium is performed by distillation. Two distillation columns would be used, one for the low boiling point fluorides and a second for the high boiling point fission products.

Spent fuel is first oxidized to U_3O_8 and PuO_2. This accelerates a subsequent fluoridization process which is done in an alumina fluidized bed through which F_2 or BrF_5 gas is passed. UF_6 is readily separated. If the excess of F_2 gas is small and the filter temperature low, plutonium carry-over with the uranium is low.† Distillation results in the final product.

Neptunium and technetium fluorides, which have boiling points very close to that of UF_6, are removed by absorbing them on magnesium fluoride.

PuF_6 is more difficult to purify. Although volatile, it is not as stable as UF_6 and can decompose into F_2 and solid plutonium fluorides which can deposit in the equipment.‡ Plutonium is usually deliberately trapped in a filtering system at 65°C, revolatilized in a thermal decomposer, and then purified. The fluorine from the decomposer is recycled to reduce the cost of the reagents and the quantity of contaminated waste. The fluoride volatility process appears to be most useful for reprocessing fuels with low plutonium content.

A variation of the fluoride volatility process is the Aquafluor process developed by General Electric for use at the Morris reprocessing plant. In this variation most of the plutonium and fission products are first removed from spent fuel by conventional solvent extraction methods. The final purification of uranium is accomplished by converting the resulting still-contaminated uranyl nitrate to UF_6, then using fluoride volatility techniques to remove any impurities.

The Pyrozinc Process

The pyrozinc process is an example of a fractional crystallization separation technique. The fractional crystallization processes rely on the physical segregation of the elements in spent fuel by distributing them between a liquid metal and its solid form. By adding a large excess of a metallic solvent, such as zinc, the metallic phases and operating temperatures can be easily adjusted. The pyrozinc method works on the solubility difference of uranium and fission products in zinc. In liquid zinc the solubility of plutonium and fission products is high, but that of uranium is very low.

Intermetallic compounds§ coexist in equilibrium with uranium dissolved in molten zinc. The solubility of uranium in zinc decreases from 13 wt% at 910°C to almost zero at 500°C.

To reprocess spent fuel, the fuel elements are dissolved in zinc at about 700°C until the uranium concentration reaches about 0.3 wt% (Figure 14.12). The melt is then slowly cooled to 500°C, and the uranium crystals filtered away, leaving the fission products still in the liquid. This cycle can be repeated several times until the decontamination of fission products is satisfactory. The purified uranium can then be recovered by distillation from the zinc at 945°C.

14.9. SAFETY OF FUEL REPROCESSING PLANTS

As seen in Table 14.9, 1 ton of spent LWR fuel, cooled for 3 yr, contains 790,000 Ci of fission products. In addition, approximately 7 kg of plutonium is present. The in-process inventory is usually about five days of plant capacity, typically 10 tons of spent fuel. This corresponds to 8 million Ci and 80 kg of plutonium. Compared to what is in the storage area of the plant (where fuel is awaiting reprocessing), or the high-level liquid waste tanks (downstream of the plant), the inventory being processed is relatively low. Nevertheless, during this stage the materials are in easily dispersible forms (solutions, powders, or gases) while undergoing changes in mechanical and chemical form. Protective systems are therefore necessary to control the dispersal of these radioactive materials in the event of an accident. The two most important of these systems are the building containment and the off-gas cleanup equipment.

Reprocessing plants, like reactors, have a containment consisting of a series of physical barriers preventing the accidental release of radioactivity. The redundancy of these barriers greatly reduces the risk. Three barriers are usually provided: the process equipment and piping, thick-walled concrete cells, and the plant building. The equipment and piping are not usually accessible for maintenance,¶ so materials for these components must be carefully chosen.

The components are periodically inspected by TV cameras, ultrasonic devices, and pressure testing. Piping used to circulate liquids requires special attention. Water-tight conduit is often provided around the piping to provide additional safety. The equipment cells and plant building are of heavy construction to withstand natural phenomena (earthquakes or floods) and to provide shielding against radioactivity.

There are usually several gas cleanup systems in a reprocessing plant. Hot, moist gases must be

†NaF at 300°C can be used to further remove any traces of plutonium.

‡NpF_6 behaves in a similar manner, although it is not as unstable as PuF_6.

§U_2Zn_{17}, or UZn_{11}.

¶Fuel shear devices, dissolvers, high-level concentrators, and hull-handling equipment are the most difficult to maintain. (Hulls are the small sections of cladding tubing left over after the fuel has been dissolved out of them.)

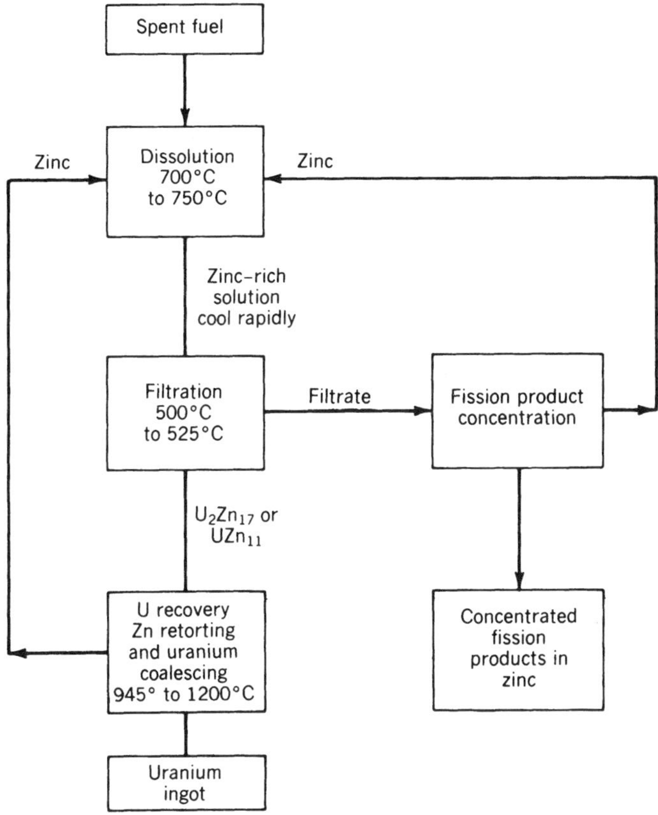

Figure 14.12. Flow diagram of the pyrozinc reprocessing scheme.

Table 14.9. Important Radionuclides in Spent Fuel[a] (1 t Cooled 3 yr)

	LWR	LMFBR[b]	HTGR
Uranium	960 kg	856 kg	85 kg
Plutonium	7 kg	103 kg	0.5 kg
Thorium	—	—	849 kg
		Fission Products	
Cesium	142,000 Ci	152,000 Ci	158,000 Ci
Strontium	70,300 Ci	162,500 Ci	105,000 Ci
Ruthenium	72,000 Ci	1,210,000 Ci	11,000 Ci
Rhodium	72,000 Ci	1,210,000 Ci	11,000 Ci
Krypton	9 kg	9 kg	5.6 kg

[a]The fission products in spent fuel range in atomic number from 30 (zinc) to 66 (dysprosium). The amounts of each vary with fuel type, burnup, and cooling time. Only some of the more important radionuclides are shown here.
[b]Cooled for 150 days.

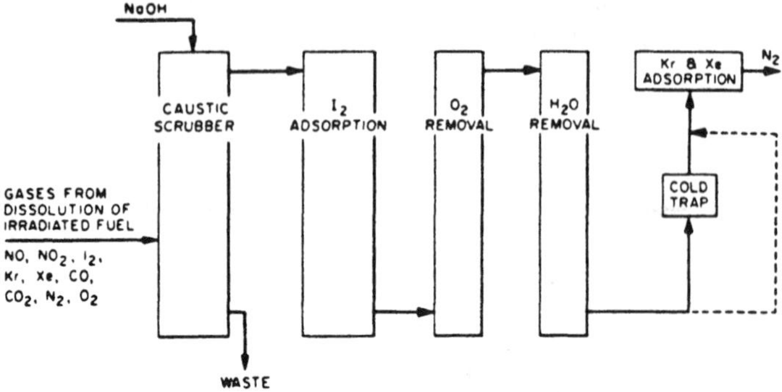

Figure 14.13. Schematic diagram of radioactive-gas separation. (From J. T. Long, *Engineering for Nuclear Fuel Reprocessing*, American Nuclear Society, 1978.)

handled. In some situations, for example in a dissolver unit, scrubbers are employed to clean these discharges, which often contain iodine. Where cooler off-gases are handled, dehumidifiers can be used. Aerosols carried in the gas (including PuO_2) are removed by high-efficiency particulate filters. The building ventilation system is designed to handle large volumes of basically clean air.

Figure 14.13 shows a schematic diagram of a radioactive gas separation train for use in a reprocessing plant. The first unit shown in the figure removes oxides of nitrogen that are liberated during various chemical reactions with HNO_3 occurring in aqueous solution. This is necessary to prevent corrosion of plant equipment and release of acid to the environment which would occur if these NO_x gases rehydrolyze to nitric acid. The caustic scrubber will also remove most of the iodine. Any iodine, including organic species, that survives the scrubber is absorbed in the second stage, which might use zeolites for this purpose. Following oxygen and water vapor removal in the next two stages, the noble gases are treated, leaving little besides nitrogen to be released to the environment.

In LWR fuel reprocessing, radioactive gases are released in the early stages of shearing and dissolving. The gases of greatest concern† are tritium, ^{14}C, ^{85}Kr, and ^{129}I. Tritium (^3H) is most easily handled as a gas. Once in solution, however, it is quite difficult to recover since it can replace one of the hydrogen atoms in a water molecule, forming tritiated water (HTO). Once in this form, the tritium quickly becomes diluted with aqueous streams and is very hard to concentrate and recover. ^{14}C releases from fuel are not well understood, and while expected, have not been measured in commercial reprocessing plants. ^{85}Kr, however, is present in large curie amounts. Although chemically inert, it (and Xe) can be removed from the off-gas stream by physical techniques such as cryogenic trapping. Once trapped, the krypton is concentrated and stored in metal cylinders. A holdup of about 100 yr would reduce its radioactivity to negligible levels. Alternately, the noble gases can be absorbed on charcoal beds. This would delay release of these gases sufficiently so that all isotopes except ^{85}Kr would decay to negligible levels.

As previously mentioned, iodine is usually removed by scrubbing the gas effluent with water streams. Additives to the water, such as NaOH, will improve its scrubbing efficiency. Other techniques for iodine removal include absorption onto zeolite molecular sieves, or onto silver nitrate coated surfaces at high temperature.

Another gas, ruthenium oxide, is also present in a reprocessing plant. It is created in the aggressive oxidizing environment of the aqueous HNO_3, and can be removed from the off-gas by absorption on a bed of ferric oxide. All gases purified of radioactive materials are passed through fiberglass filters before discharge to the environment.

14.10. MAINTENANCE OF FUEL REPROCESSING PLANTS

Many areas of reprocessing plants are intensely radioactive, and therefore can be approached only after the equipment has been decontaminated. There are three types of maintenance for such equipment: remote, direct, or underwater. The plant design is critical to the maintainability of the equipment. Good design places all equipment that may require repair or replacement outside of the highly radioactive areas. In early reprocessing plants, piping and equipment that carried radioac-

†Reprocessing plants are designed to handle 25,000 Ci of tritium, 40 of ^{14}C, 380,000 of ^{85}Kr, and 0.03 of ^{129}I for each GW-yr exposure in the fuel processed.

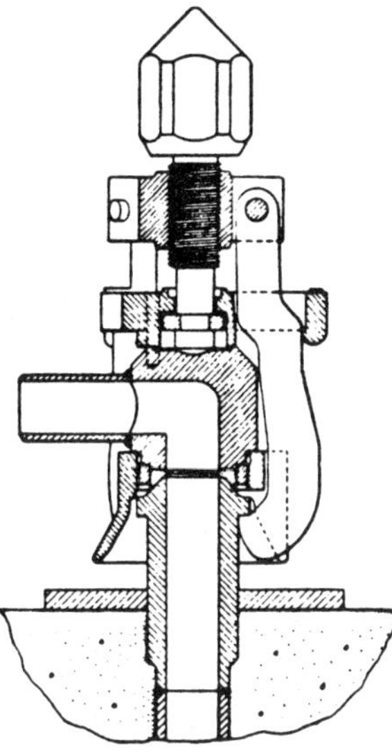

Figure 14.14. Cross-sectional diagram of a remote pipe connector. (From J. T. Long, *Engineering for Nuclear Fuel Reprocessing,* American Nuclear Society, 1978.)

tive liquids were grouped together in long, heavily shielded remote maintenance cells called "canyons." Rugged, but fairly simple piping connectors and highly specialized equipment were used. An operator, riding in a heavily shielded crane cab, could interchange specially balanced pipe sections. The equipment was designed so that the crane operator could fit the pieces together from some distance while remotely viewing the operation. Figure 14.14 shows a typical remote connector, which permits pipe connections to be made within a canyon. When the top nut is turned, the three connector jaws are loosened or tightened. During tightening, the jaws engage the underside of the nozzle flange and draw the two halves together.

Later designs employ improved manipulative capabilities, which permit simpler and smaller connectors, as well as remote cutting and welding of pipe systems. Remote maintenance is even more important in plants designed to safguard plutonium, where the removal of fission products from the spent fuel is deliberately incomplete. For such plants, unlike in earlier designs, the radiation levels are high in all equipment containing plutonium to render it unapproachable. The same is true of the fuel-fabrication part of the operation if it is colocated with the reprocessing plant.

Decontamination is first required whenever contact maintenance is required on radioactive equipment. There are various chemicals available to clean the surfaces of radioactive process equipment. These include many acids such as nitric, hydrofluoric, oxalic, and citric acid,† which are used to remove the thin corrosion layer containing the radioactivity. The acid solutions are usually used in combination with buffering and chelating agents for optimal results. The chelating agents, such as EDTA or NTA,‡ form complexes with the radioactive metal ions released by the acid, preventing them from redepositing on the surface. Various formulae exist to deal with specific requirements. In general, only mild reagents are necessary the first time equipment is decontaminated. As the corrosion proceeds over time, however, decontamination becomes progressively more difficult, and stronger combinations of reagents are used.

Underwater maintenance is often performed when decontamination is not feasible or desirable. The concept is simply to flood the equipment or cells with water, which provides radiation shielding. Special tools are used. As in any remote technique, equipment design is important so that maintenance operations may proceed smoothly and efficiently.

Significant improvements have been made since 1943 in the maintenance of equipment in reprocessing plants. There have been four basic approaches used to date: manned-crane canyons, contact cells, remote cells (windows), and remote cells (central aisle). The last concept was developed in the 1970s when electric master–slave manipulators became commercially available. Illustrations of these approaches are shown in Figure 14.15.

†Oxalic acid: HOOC—COOH; acetic acid: CH_3COOH.
‡EDTA: disodium ethylene-di-amine-tetra-acetic acid.
NTA: nitrilo-tri-acetic acid.

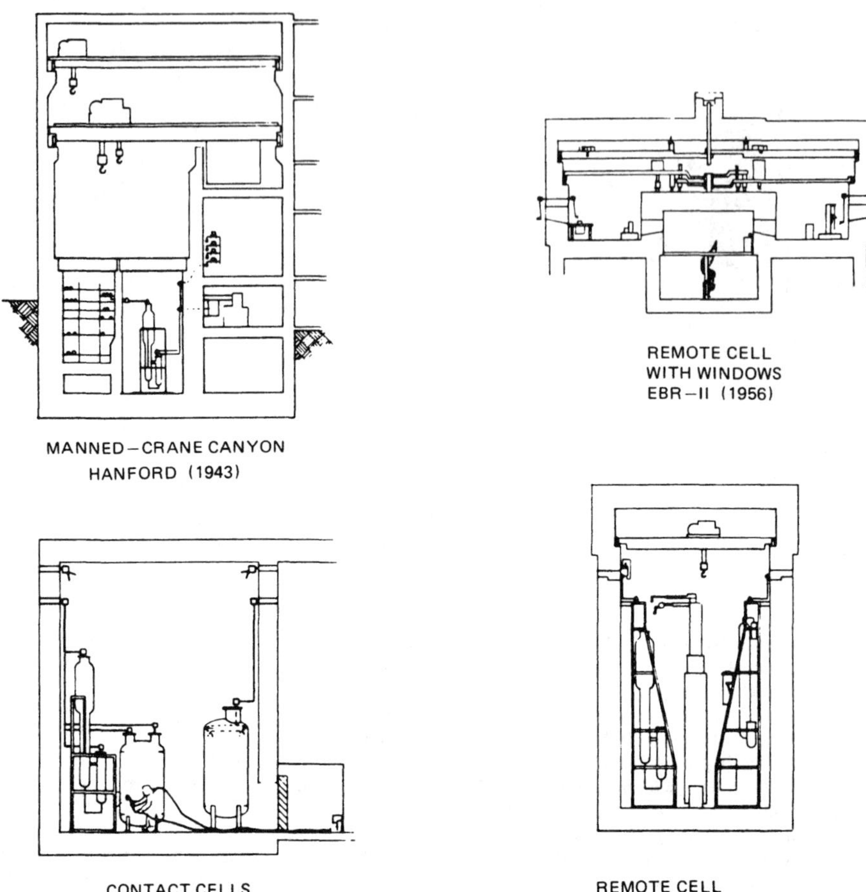

Figure 14.15. Process facility maintenance approaches. [From J. White, *Trans. Am. Nuclear Soc.* **43,** 735 (1982).]

The manned-crane canyon type has been used most frequently, including at the Savannah River and Morris facilities. However, the contact cell design has been used when low construction cost was a consideration, as was the case at the Nuclear Fuel Services (West Valley) and Barnwell plants. The most successful reprocessing plants used the manned-crane canyon or remote cell approaches. Availability factors between 80 and 90% were achieved over long periods of time in these plants.

Less successful were the plants having contact cell designs. The Nuclear Fuel Services plant—the design basis of many other reprocessing plants—operated for 6 yr, initially at 70% availability. However, less than 25% availability was achieved in the last 2 yr, during which time high occupational exposure rates exceeding 2000 person-rem/yr were encountered.

14.11. POTENTIAL ACCIDENTS AT REPROCESSING PLANTS

The operational safety record of reprocessing plants to date has been excellent. To maintain this record, reprocessing facilities are designed to handle several potentially dangerous situations, especially those involving a fire or explosion. The accidents of greatest concern in designing a plant are:

1. *Inadvertent Criticality.* This is prevented by several means, including use of a "safe geometry" (i.e., restricting the shape and volume of vessels so that a critical geometry is not

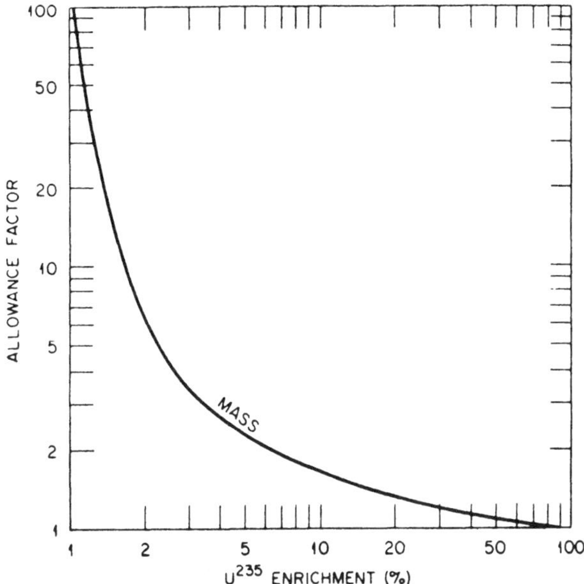

Figure 14.16. Allowance factors for safe limits of ^{235}U solutions as a function of enrichment. (From TID-7016.)

possible); addition of a neutron poison (e.g., boron) to the aqueous solutions; and maintaining concentrations of fissile materials at low levels. Close attention is paid to the design of the dissolver sections and the solvent-extraction process. Gamma ray† and neutron detectors are used to monitor the system for the inadvertent buildup of fuel that might lead to criticality.

2. *Explosions.* Many chemicals used in reprocessing are explosive. Early aqueous reprocessing techniques used hexone or Butex, organic chemicals that are very reactive with nitric acid. The Purex process now uses tributyl phosphate (TBP) diluted with kerosene, which is much less so. Formaldehyde is often used to destroy nitric acid, but this reaction must be closely controlled to reduce the chances of an explosion. Other chemicals, oils, even hydrogen produced by radiolysis of water, must be taken into account in the process design.

3. *Fires.* The Zircaloy cladding on LWR fuels can catch fire when in a nitric acid bath, such as occurs in the shear-leach section of a reprocessing plant. Safety rules are followed to prevent such a fire, such as limiting the Zircaloy concentration, and also keeping the Zircaloy fines, which are highly pyrophoric, covered with solution and mixed with other materials of high thermal capacity.

Criticality Accidents

Criticality accidents are prevented by controlling the geometry of the system and the mass and concentration of the fissile materials. All of these parameters are functions of the enrichment of the materials being reprocessed: the lower the enrichment, the less the chances of a criticality accident. Figure 14.16 shows a typical mass "allowance factor" for ^{235}U solutions as a function of enrichment. For instance, a 1% enriched solution would be safe with about 100 times as much ^{235}U as one with 100% enrichment.

Guidelines‡ exist for the designers of reprocessing plants. One widely used manual is *The Nuclear Safety Guide* (TID-7016). In addition to the factors cited above, two others are important: (a) moderators and reflectors, and (b) the use of poisons. The presence of water, either as a moderator or as reflector§ decreases the mass of material needed for criticality to occur. If a

†For instance, a gamma-ray detector might be set to monitor photon energies specific to certain isotopes. A high intensity of these gamma rays signal an unsafe situation.

‡In the United States, the American National Standard for Nuclear Criticality Safety in Operations Outside Reactors, N16.1, is used.

§If the water is mixed with the fissionable material it is considered a moderator; when external, it is a reflector. Other materials can also be moderators or reflectors, although not as efficient as water.

system is inadvertently flooded with water (or aqueous solution), it might go from a subcritical to a critical state, causing an accident. Equipment must be designed to handle such a contingency.

Neutron poisons are sometimes used to prevent criticality in process equipment. When poisons are used in this manner, care must be taken to assure that soluble poisons do not extract out of solution, or that fixed poisons do not erode or corrode away, resulting in an accident. In general, LWR fuels, having low enrichment, present less serious safety problems than do higher enriched fuels.

No reprocessing plant for low-enriched uranium fuels, and few that are authorized to process high-enriched uranium fuels, have been designed as completely geometrically safe. It would be impractical to do so, as the processing equipment would have very little throughput capacity. However, as discussed above, the use of geometrically safe equipment represents only one technique for protecting against inadvertent criticality. Control of concentrations, use of neutron poisons,† and administrative controls are all used in combination in reprocessing plants. Moreover, the design of the structures and ventilation systems in a reprocessing plant are such that the effects of an inadvertent criticality would be fully contained within the facility.

14.12. SAFEGUARDING REPROCESSING PLANTS

The goal of safeguards in commercial reprocessing plants is to assure that plutonium cannot be diverted to unauthorized uses. Two important aspects of the problem are: the quantities of plutonium that might be diverted without detection; and the timeliness of detection of such a diversion. A "strategic quantity"‡ of plutonium is about 8 kg. The IAEA§ has the responsibility for monitoring reprocessing plants (and other nuclear facilities) to detect any diversion of plutonium.

Accounting for all fuel material and controlling its movement within the plant are the two principal methods of safeguarding a plant. This requires that material balances be routinely made. Unfortunately, because of testing uncertainties, measured inputs and starting inventories rarely, if ever, exactly equal measured output plus ending inventory. The difference is called "Material Unaccounted For," or "MUF." Most of the MUF will be due to errors in estimating how much plutonium was left behind in the system's tanks, piping, scrap, and so on.

Ideally, the observed MUF should be zero. However, unless the MUF is clearly greater than the measurement uncertainties, no conclusion can be drawn about possible plutonium diversion. The goal of safeguards programs is to detect any significant amounts of missing plutonium over short-term and long-term periods. By short-term is meant the ability to do a complete plant inventory in a few hours' time, including draining all process tanks to the point where, taken together, they contain no more than a few kilograms, and thus to be able to achieve an on-the-spot materials balance of 1 or 2 kg. The long-term goal is to balance the inventory to within 8 kg (IAEA objective) or 2 kg (U.S. NRC objective) over a year's time. This is probably not achievable with today's technology, since it would require balancing throughput to better than 1 part in 10,000 for a 5 ton/day reprocessing plant¶—an exacting requirement indeed.‖ State-of-the-art permits sampling to about 1 part in 1000.

Other goals to strengthen the proliferation resistance of a reprocessing plant include:

1. Remote operation to limit personnel access to plutonium materials.
2. Material accountability performed by a separate organization.
3. Periodic and/or continual on-site inspection.
4. A plant layout that segments the facility into control areas, each of which is only open to specifically authorized personnel.

The above design objectives reflect IAEA and U.S. NRC philosophy for a recycle fuels plant that would have a high level of diversion resistance, and would be both licensable and commercially viable. Examination of existing reprocessing plants indicates that the most vulnerable areas are those where easy access to PuO_2 is possible: the PuO_2 conversion and rework areas.

Diversion Proof Designs

Reprocessing plants in operation today fall short of the safeguarding criteria described in the preceding section. Traditional methods of fabricating plutonium fuels, for example pelletizing, have

†For example, gadolinium can be used as a soluble poison in the solution, or built in as a permanent fixture in a process vessel.

‡That is, the minimum quantity necessary for a bomb

§The International Atomic Energy Agency, headquartered in Vienna.

¶Five tons/day of irradiated LWR fuel results in a yearly plant throughput of about 12,000 kg of plutonium.

‖Most of the problem comes from systematic errors in the sampling techniques.

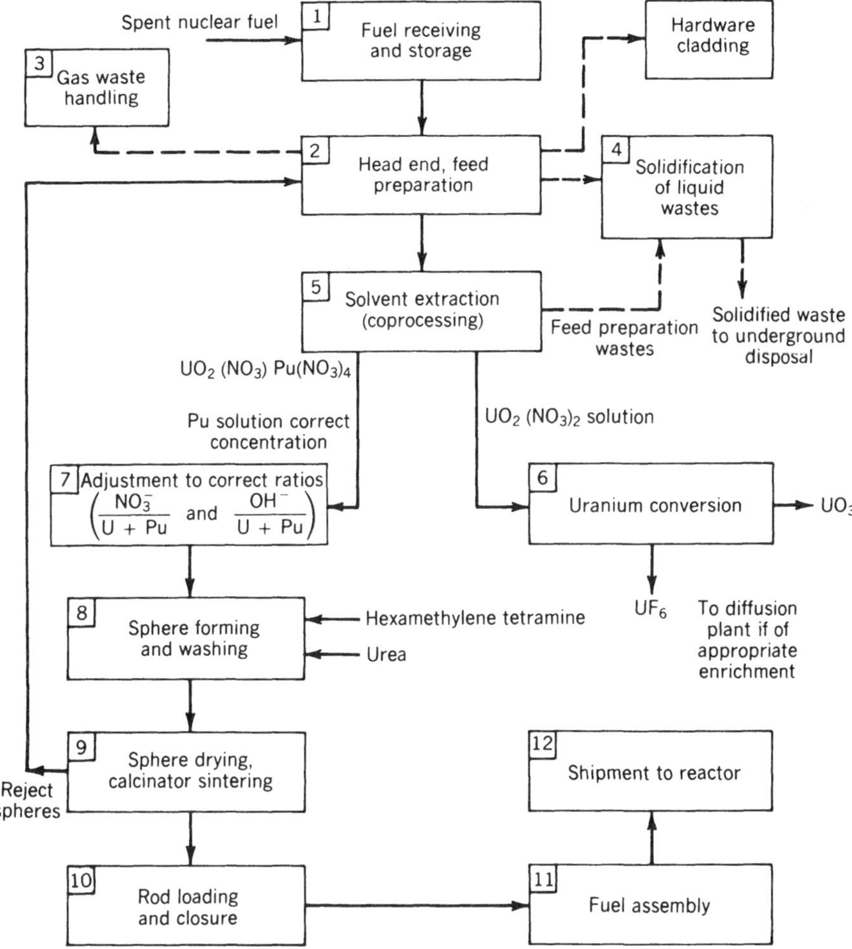

Figure 14.17. Generalized fuel-cycle flow sheet for the SAFAR process. (Courtesy EPRI.)

low diversion resistance because of hands-on access to PuO_2 and the difficulty of controlling personnel movement.

A number of advanced process designs exist that would offer considerable improvements. They are mostly variations of the Purex process that include the coprocessing of uranium and plutonium,† with immediate fabrication of fuel by the sol–gel process (see Chapter 7). This avoids the step of conversion to PuO_2. These processes go by various names, such as CIVEX, or SAFAR. As an example, the Exxon-developed SAFAR process will be described briefly. A flow sheet for the SAFAR process is shown in Figure 14.17. Notable in this figure are the coprocessing steps where uranium and plutonium exist together in solution as well-mixed nitrates. The other features of the SAFAR process to enhance safeguards against diversion are:

1. The solvent-extraction system can be rapidly emptied to permit frequent inventory measurements.
2. Remotely operated coprocessing is employed. Some uranium is mixed with the plutonium at all times. Some fission products are retained with the uranium–plutonium mixture, as only two cycles of plutonium decontamination are used.‡ These fission products result in a radiation field that "self-protects" the plutonium. This requires remote operation of the plant.

†The plutonium is diluted with uranium.
‡This leaves up to 1% of some fission products in the fuel, as complete purification takes three cycles in the Purex process.

Table 14.10. Relative Attractiveness of Process Materials

Material	Materials Attribute Factors			Relative Attractiveness
	Density	Gamma	Time	
Pure Pu metal	1	1	1	1
PuF_4, PuO_2	0.7	1	0.9	0.63
$(U,PU)O_2$	0.4	1	0.65	0.25
$Pu(NO_3)_4$ conc. soln.	0.25	1	0.8	0.2
$(U,Pu)(NO_3)_x$ conc. soln.	0.15	1	0.7	0.1
HAP solution[a]	0.04	0.04	0.7	0.001
UO_3 product	0.1	0.2	0.02	4×10^{-4}
Dissolver solution	0.06	0.004	0.35	8×10^{-5}
Fuel assembly	0.08	0.004	0.1	3×10^{-5}
HAW, concentrate[b]	0.025	0.001	0.35	9×10^{-6}
HAW, solid[b]	0.05	0.001	0.02	1×10^{-6}

Source: From EPRI Report NP-2631.

[a]The plutonium-carrying solvent exiting the first solvent extraction column in the Purex solvent extraction process.

[b]Materials associated with high-level waste.

3. The uranium–plutonium product, in the form of a nitrate solution, is converted to various-sized MOX spherical beads on a continuous basis.
4. The MOX spheres (along with UO_2 spheres) are loaded into fuel rods using a sphere-pac process (see Chapter 7), welded, inspected, and shipped.

In the SAFAR design, the plant itself safeguards the plutonium. For instance, the movement of Pu from one part of the plant to another is monitored accurately, with a minimum number of transfers taking place. Operations are also highly segmented, and under the supervision of a single organization. No direct access to plutonium exists. Physical protection, personnel access, and control and surveillance systems are used to prevent diversion for illicit purposes. And most importantly, plutonium never exists as a purified metal or solution, so that its attractiveness is highly reduced.

The relative attractiveness to a would-be diverter of plutonium-bearing materials depends on (1) the volume of material per gram of contained plutonium, (2) the gamma radiation of the material per gram of contained plutonium, and (3) the time required to convert it to an explosive device. These attributes are independent of plant design. The first two are a measure of the difficulty of obtaining the material, and the third is based on the chemical form, which is related to the time and difficulty of converting the plutonium to metallic form usable for a bomb. As seen in Table 14.10, metallic, oxide, and nitrate forms of plutonium present a high risk, while plutonium in fuel elements and coprocessed dissolver solution has small desirability. The reprocessing plants that coprocess uranium–plutonium with incomplete removal of the fission products, as described above, take advantage of the material form of the plutonium to limit its desirability.

Figure 14.18 shows the relative volumes per gram of plutonium which may exist at various points in a reprocessing plant. The higher this value the less quantity would have to be diverted to obtain a given amount of plutonium. Consequently, pure PuO_2 is relatively attractive, while concentrated HLW is not. Figure 14.19 shows the number of days a group of highly trained and competent individuals would need to convert various plutonium forms into bomb material, provided they had the proper facilities available. Again PuO_2 would be relatively attractive to obtain, and HLW is not so attractive.

14.13. STATUS OF COMMERCIAL REPROCESSING

In the United States, there are four large-scale reprocessing plants: Savannah River, Idaho Chemical Plant, West Valley, and Barnwell Nuclear Fuel Plant. The first two, owned by the DOE, are not commercial plants. West Valley, built by Nuclear Fuel Services, Inc., has a design capacity of 1 t/day of 93% enriched fuel with a maximum burnup of about 30,000 MWd/t. Barnwell, owned by Allied General Nuclear Services, is designed to handle 5 t/day of spent fuel with up to 5% ^{235}U content and 40,000 MWd/t burnup. Neither of these plants is currently operating. Another plant was designed and built at Morris, Illinois but was abandoned before being put into commercial operation.

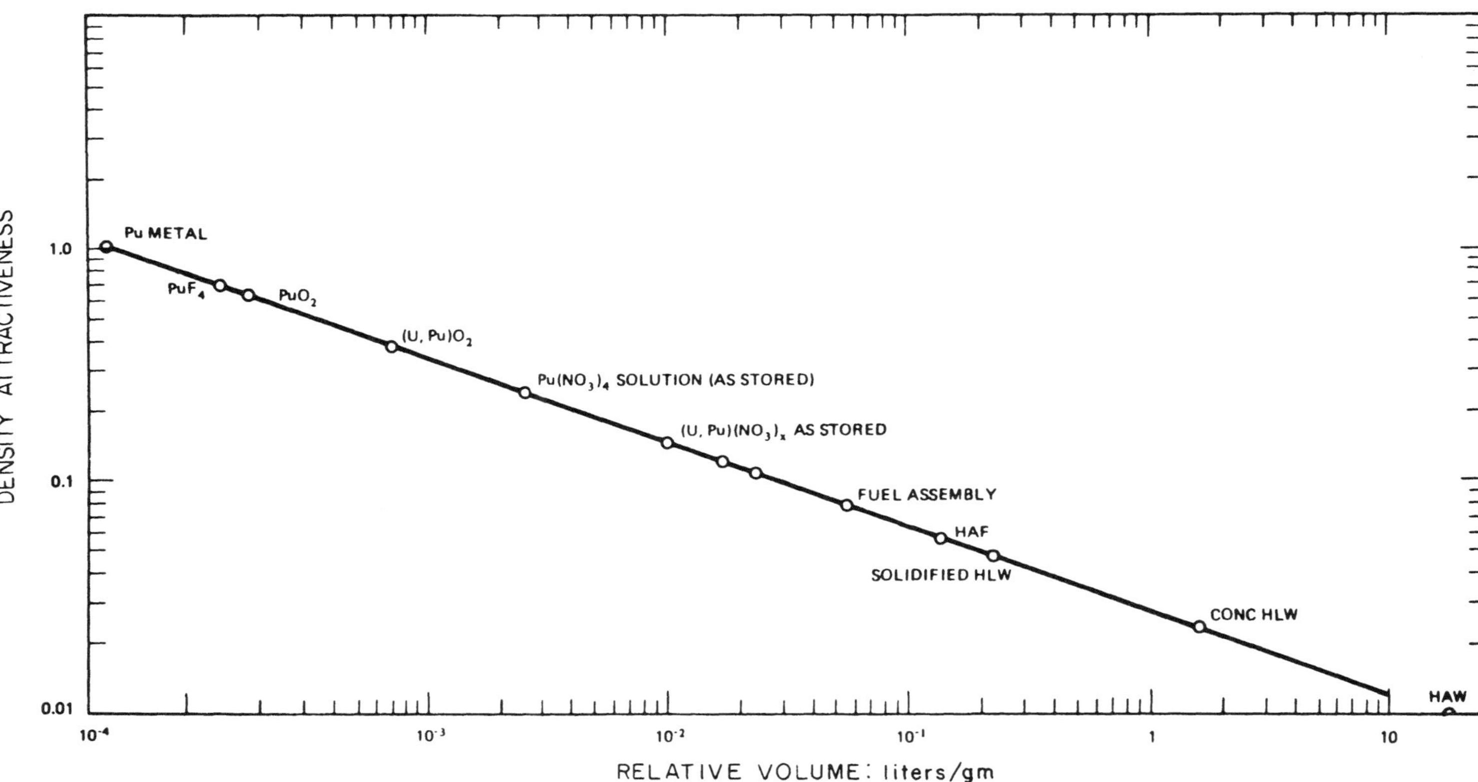

Figure 14.18. Pu density attribute factor. (From EPRI Report NP-2632.)

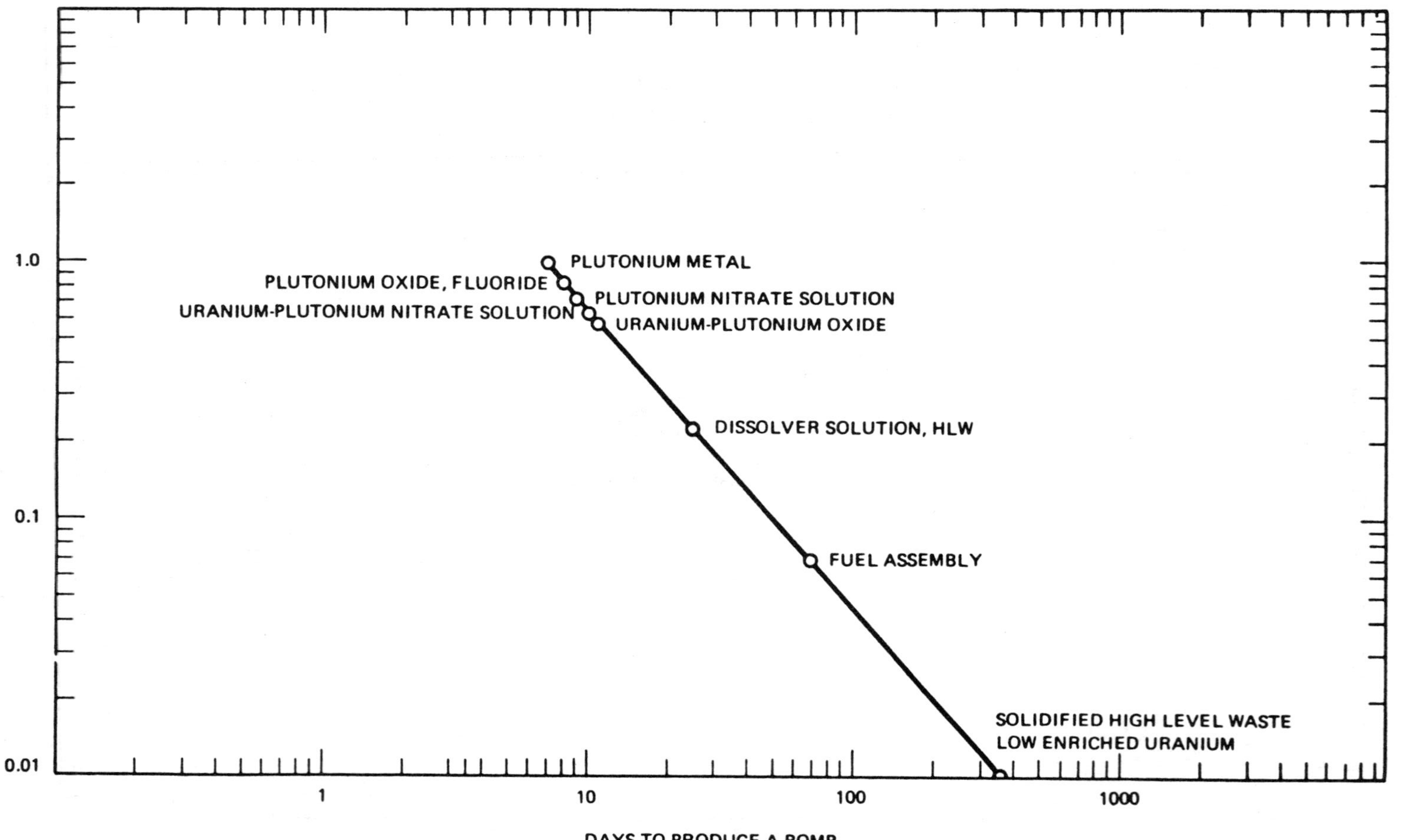

Figure 14.19. Time attribute factor. (From EPRI Report NP-2632.)

Historical Development of Commercial Activities

From the very earliest days of nuclear power planning, until the Carter administration, it had been an unchallenged assumption that commercial nuclear fuel would be reprocessed to recover the considerable amount of unfissioned ^{235}U and the plutonium left in the fuel when it is discharged. This material was viewed as a fuel resource valuable for reuse.

In January 1962, General Electric, operator at that time of the Hanford works for AEC, proposed to a number of firms in the industry that they lease one of the Hanford canyon separations plants not in use at the time for reprocessing of industrial fuel. This plan was eventually abandoned. The next month, February 1962, however, Davison Chemical, a division of W.R. Grace & Co., filed a formal letter of intent with AEC to seek licensing authority to build a plant to reprocess commercial power reactor fuel. For this purpose it established a subsidiary, wholly owned by Grace & Co., called Nuclear Fuel Services, Inc. The proposed plant was to be able to handle all types of power reactor fuel then in use, except graphite-matrix fuel.

This plant was built on a 3500-acre tract near West Valley, New York, about 30 miles southeast of Buffalo. It is the only U.S. privately owned facility that has actually performed reprocessing services. It was completed and started up in 1966. During a 6-yr period of successful operation, the West Valley plant reprocessed more than 600 t of uranium from nine different reactors.

In August 1972, however, Nuclear Fuel Services temporarily suspended nuclear fuel reprocessing operations, principally because of an AEC decision to require a construction permit for an expansion program already begun by NFS in 1969. NFS had planned to modernize and expand the plant from its capacity of 1 t/day, because it had become too small to operate economically with more nuclear power plants in service.

The target date of 1978 for completion of the expansion program kept slipping as the licensing approval became a matter of controversy and the construction permit was not forthcoming. Finally, Nuclear Fuel Services decided it could no longer afford the cost of maintaining the idle plant with no short-term prospect of obtaining the required construction permit. Accordingly, it abandoned the plant. Since the land it was built on was leased from the New York State Atomic Research & Development Authority, responsibility for the plant reverted to the state. The high-level wastes held in storage tanks were neutralized, to reduce their corrosive action on the steel storage tanks. The plant also has more than 900 fuel assemblies in storage.

In the meantime, two other reprocessing plants were built, neither of which has gone into operation.

One was a project of General Electric, which had begun work in 1959 to develop a reprocessing approach designed specifically to handle power reactor fuels. In September 1964 a decision was reached to begin a program to determine the feasibility of a new recovery process, and an engineer-contractor was selected. The process selected was named Aquafluor, which combines several of the features of the aqueous solvent extraction and the fluoride volatility technologies, although it is primarily based on the Purex (aqueous) process with a tail-end fluoride decontamination stage.

The advantages General Electric expected from this process were that the uranium product would be already in the hexafluoride state, eliminating the trip to a hexafluoride conversion plant prior to being shipped to a gaseous diffusion plant for reenrichment; also, that no liquid process wastes were planned to be discharged from the plant, and that the process was planned to be more economical than a conventional Purex reprocessing system.

Unfortunately, General Electric did not build a small-scale pilot plant since the process seemed to work well in the laboratory. General Electric went on to build a full-scale plant at Morris, Illinois, about 60 miles south of Chicago. The plant was designed to process 300 t/yr and was scheduled to begin operation in April 1974. General Electric's plans included expanding the capacity to 500 t/yr by 1976.

After $2\frac{1}{2}$ yr of unsuccessful test runs with nonradioactive simulant fuel, General Electric reported in July 1974 that the plant was inoperable as built, because the equipment installed in the cells for continuous operation would not work as designed at commercial scale. The problem—which had not been apparent at bench scale in the laboratory—was that the material agglomerated and jammed the automatic cell-to-cell transport mechanisms provided, and would not move continuously. The fundamental problem at the General Electric plant resulted from a design concept that called for final decontamination of the uranium by a series of calcination and fluorination processes that were to be carried out in a remote operation mode in fluidized solid reactors. Many of the problems of plugging, erosion, and caking normally encountered in fluidized-solids reactors were anticipated in the design of the facility; special equipment was developed. It was expected that these problems would be worked out during plant start-up. Plant tests showed, however, that all such problems were intensified by the properties of uranium compounds during the conversion process and that there was a high probability in regular plant operation of failure of the calciner and fluorinator reactors.

General Electric made a study of the possible options for putting the plant into operation, considering that new equipment would have to fit the existing concrete-walled cell sizes. The finding of the study was that it would cost too much to redesign and rebuild portions of the plant to make it operational. The company presently rents space in the tanks provided for waste storage to utilities requiring space for storing spent fuel assemblies.

The third reprocessing plant built in the United States is the Allied General Nuclear Services (AGNS) plant at Barnwell, South Carolina. The largest of the three, it was completed and scheduled to begin operation in 1976. Barnwell's initial start-up, like West Valley's expansion, was a victim of changing regulatory requirements. The operating license for the plant was challenged by intervenors who brought in a long list of contentions against the plant, which has since been sitting idle. There have been proposals to turn it into a demonstration to show that reprocessing plants can be made proliferation-proof, that is, impregnable against illicit diversion of fissionable material. Another suggestion was to make it an international joint demonstration of reprocessing technology.

Lastly, Exxon Nuclear Co., which fabricates fuel for LWRs, filed a construction permit application with NRC in January 1976 to build a 1500 t/yr plant. Exxon was working with ERDA (the successor agency to AEC and predecessor of the Department of Energy) to obtain use of a site in Oak Ridge, and in the meantime purchased a backup site near the TVA nuclear station at Watts Bar, Tennessee. The plant capacity was to be expandable to 2100 t/yr after demonstration of successful operation. Fuel storage capacity was to be 7000 t, considerably larger than that of the previous three plants. Estimates of completion date ranged from 1984 to 1986. However, when Barnwell failed to obtain its operating license, Exxon withdrew its construction permit application.

Reprocessing Overseas

A number of countries other than the United States have built spent fuel reprocessing plants and have been carrying on reprocessing activities for years. The principal foreign plants are listed in Table 14.11.

Britain, France, (West) Germany, and Canada have the longest established history and the most experience in chemical reprocessing of fuel; India and Japan have built plants and began operating them more recently. The Soviet Union certainly carries on reprocessing operations, but relatively little is known about them. Britain, France, Germany, Belgium, and Japan all use the Purex process or variants of it, and all employ TBP as the extractant.

France

France has operated a reprocessing plant, primarily to extract plutonium from spent gas–graphite reactor fuel, since 1958, at Marcoule—where the first two French power reactors were built. This plant has a capacity of about 2 t/day. An improved version—although of the same size and using essentially the same process—was started up in 1967 at La Hague, on the Cherbourg peninsula. Nine years later, in 1976, a third plant was placed in operation, this one to process oxide fuel from the PWRs that France had switched to building. This plant is also at La Hague, alongside the second reprocessing plant for gas–graphite reactor fuel. The third plant is of greater capacity than the first two; except for differences in the head-end (where the fuel is stripped from its cladding), it uses the same process. All three plants are operated by Cogema, the French national nuclear fuel company.

The present reprocessing is being carried out via the oxide head-end feeding into the main separation stages of the third (natural uranium) reprocessing plant, known as UP2, which is still being used for about six months of the year for parallel campaigns on some of the spent fuel from French gas-cooled reactors. The first completely new reprocessing line at La Hague will be the plant designated as UP3, for which preparation of the foundations has now commenced. This plant is being financed by reprocessing contracts from foreign customers, and it should provide a capacity of 800 t/yr by 1986.

Some Phénix reactor fuel has been reprocessed in the UP2 plant, mixed with the gas–graphite reactors fuel, since 1979. A total of 5 tons of Phénix fuel has so far been reprocessed, the average being 1.6 tons/yr. It was diluted to a factor of 1:17 with GCR fuel, to avoid criticality problems. This was done because the Phénix fuel pilot reprocessing plant in Marcoule cannot handle all the Phénix reactor spent fuel, and to demonstrate a completely closed operation of the Phénix FBR fuel cycle. A larger FBR fuel demonstration reprocessing plant—TOR—was completed at Marcoule in 1984.

Britain

Britain's reprocessing plant at Windscale, adjacent to the first British power reactors at Calder Hall, was started up in 1964. (Windscale is also the location of Britain's original plutonium production reactors.) The reprocessing plant is designed to handle gas–graphite reactor fuel. It is operated by British Nuclear Fuels Ltd., which—like Cogema in France—is the government's "chosen

Table 14.11. Principal Overseas Reprocessing Plants

Location	Marcoule, France	La Hague, France		Windscale, England		Karlsruhe, FRG	Hessen (WA 350) FRG	Mol, Belgium	Tokai-Mura, Japan
Owner	Cogema	Cogema		British Nuclear Fuels, Ltd.		KFK/GWK	DKW	Eurochemic	Power Reactor and Nucl. Fuel Devel. Corp.
Type of fuel	Magnox	Magnox	Oxide	Magnox	Oxide	Oxide	Oxide	Oxide or metal	Magnox or oxide
Year operational	1958	1967	1976	1964	—	1971	1992	1966	1975
Status	Operating	Operating	Operating	Operating	Planned	Operating	Planned	Shutdown	Operating
Capacity, t/day	~2	~2	1 (5 in 1985)	5	4	0.17	2	0.35	0.7
Maximum % ^{235}U	Natural	Natural	3.5	Natural to 1%	—	3	3.5	5	4
Maximum burn-up, MWd/t	—	3,000	39,000	4,000	37,000	39,000	40,000	17,000	28,000
Minimum cooling, days	120	140	—	130	360	250	2500	190	180

Source: Adapted from M. Benedict et al., *Nuclear Chemical Engineering*.

instrument" company for nuclear fuel activities. With the British considering building their first PWR, BNFL is planning to add a second reprocessing plant at Windscale, to process oxide fuel.

Germany

The Federal Republic of Germany has one reprocessing plant in operation and a second planned. One has been in operation at Karlsruhe since 1971, owned jointly by the Karlsruhe Nuclear Research Center and GWK, the German Nuclear Fuel Reprocessing Company. A small plant, on pilot-plant scale, it processes oxide fuel. First operated in 1971, it has been brought back on line after more than a 2-yr period of repair and refurbishment and has now processed a cumulative total of 120 t of oxide fuel with burnup levels as high as 39,000 MWd/t.

The ambitious plan in the Federal Republic of Germany for an integrated center at Gorleben to deal with the entire back end of the fuel cycle had to be abandoned for political reasons. The present status of proposals to build one or more reprocessing plants of 350 t/yr capacity in Germany is that formal licensing procedures have commenced for two prospective sites—one at Wackersdorf in the state of Bavaria, and the other at Dragahn, in Lower Saxony. A choice between these sites is expected in mid-1984. Deutsche Gesellschaft für Wiederaufarbeitung von Kernbrennstoffen (DWK) will operate the plant.

Eurochemic

In 1966, the Nuclear Energy Agency of the OECD (Organization for Economic Cooperation and Development) started up a small reprocessing plant called Eurochemic located at Mol, site of Belgium's national nuclear research center. This plant, also a Purex TBP process plant, was mothballed in 1974 because of political reasons and the reprocessing overcapacity that existed at the time. But with the expansion of nuclear power in Europe following the OPEC oil shocks, forecasts projected an undercapacity for reprocessing by the second half of the 1980s. The Belgian government took over responsibility for the mothballed plant in 1981, and currently plans to establish a new company to reopen the plant.

Italy

Italy's CNEN, or National Nuclear Energy Commission, has operated a small reprocessing plant called Eurex near Taranto, with the capability of reprocessing thorium fuel (since Italy had built a thorium-fueled demonstration reactor in the 1960s).

In the mid-1970s, CNEN and the industrial firm AGIP Nucleare were cooperating on design of a larger, industrial-scale reprocessing plant. This has not yet been built, however.

Japan

Japan's Power Reactor & Nuclear Fuel Development Corp. has operated a reprocessing plant at Tokai Mura since 1975. This also is a Purex TBP plant, but has a head-end that permits it to process both the magnox-clad fuel from Japan's first power reactor, a British gas–graphite unit, and oxide fuel from the LWRs that Japan has been building since.

14.14. FUTURE REPROCESSING STRATEGIES

Based on current trends, three types of fuel will require reprocessing in the future. They are standard uranium oxide fuel, LWR mixed-oxide fuel (i.e., mixed PuO_2–UO_2), and breeder fuel (again, a PuO_2–UO_2 mixture, although PuC–UC fuels may be introduced). The LWR fuels probably can be reprocessed at the same plant, as the processes used are nearly identical. Breeder fuels will require separate plants, not because of different technology, but due to differences in process optimization. If LMFBR fuel is to be reprocessed, then special provision is required for (1) cleanup of sodium on the fuel assemblies; (2) smaller fuel pins with stainless steel (as contrasted with Zircaloy) cladding; (3) shorter reprocessing times with higher radiation levels; and (4) more stringent criticality restrictions.

Variations on the Purex solvent-extraction process will be used for both LWR and breeder fuels (for example, refer back to Figure 14.17). Coprocessing of the uranium and plutonium will involve two product streams: a purified (U, Pu) $(NO_3)_x$ solution retaining a small fraction of some fission products, and a completely decontaminated $UO_2(NO_3)_2$ stream. The plutonium-bearing solution (about 4% by weight for LWRs, 15% for LMFBRs) would be formed into microspheres using a modification of the sol–gel process. The sphere-forming step will possibly mix the uranium–plutonium nitrate solution with HMTA† and urea.‡ The HMTA decomposes to form NH_3, pre-

†Hexamethylene tetramine.
‡A soluble basic compound, $CO(NH_2)_2$.

cipitating spherical ammonium diuranate droplets. The droplets are formed as the solution passes through a vibrating nozzle into a hot organic liquid, causing the HMTA to decompose.

The spheres are then washed, dried, and calcined. Unlike the pellet-sintering process now in use, no dust or wet grinding sludge is created, and rejected material can be easily recycled to the dissolver unit at the head-end of the reprocessing plant.

The uranyl nitrate stream is calcined to form UO_3. It is then converted to UF_6, purified, and sent to the enrichment plant (see Chapters 5 and 6). After enrichment, the uranium would be formed into spheres, as above. Three different sphere sizes (typically 1200 μm, 300 μm, and 30 μm) are fabricated so that when mixed, they will form a high-density LWR fuel.

For LWR–MO_x and for LMFBR fuel, plutonium-bearing spheres would replace some of the uranium ones. The smaller fuel rods characteristic of LMFBR fuels probably require a somewhat different sizing of the spheres. Once the fuel rods are loaded with fuel spheres and compacted, they are then assembled in the traditional way (see Chapter 7). Reestablishment of commercial reprocessing on a large scale will complete the nuclear fuel cycle.

BIBLIOGRAPHY

Bebbington, W. P., "The Reprocessing of Nuclear Fuels," *Scientific American* **235,** 30 (1976).

———, "Safety of the Nuclear Fuel Cycle," OECD Report Paris, May 1981.

Benedict, M., Pigford, T., and Levi, H., *Nuclear Chemical Engineering,* McGraw-Hill, 2nd ed., New York, 1981.

Campbell, M., and R. Tomlinson, *Safeguarding Fabrication and Reprocessing,* EPRI Report NP-2631 (1982).

Culler, F., and R. Vogel, "Future Reprocessing of Spent Reactor Fuels," in publication.

Long, J. T., *Engineering for Nuclear Fuel Reprocessing,* American Nuclear Society (1978).

Thomas, J. T., Ed., *Nuclear Safety Guide,* NUREG/CR-0095, U.S. NRC (1978).

U.N. International Conference on Peaceful Uses of Atomic Energy, *Proceedings, Chemical Reprocessing* **9,** New York, 1958.

U.S. Atomic Energy Commission, *Chemical Reprocessing and Equipment,* McGraw-Hill, New York, 1955, 302 pp.

U.S. Atomic Energy Commission, Wymer, Raymond G., Ed., "Thorium Fuel Cycle," Proceedings of Second International Thorium Fuel Cycle Conference, Oak Ridge, 1968, 839 pp.

White, J. R., et al., "The Evolution of Maintenance in Nuclear Processing Facilities," *Tran. Am. Nuclear Soc.* **43,** 735 (1982).

CHAPTER 15
RADIOACTIVE WASTE DISPOSAL

15.1. INTRODUCTION

Just as most human activities involve the creation of some by-product waste materials, so efforts to benefit from commercial nuclear energy involve the creation of some waste materials that are either radioactive themselves or contaminated with radioactive material. The nuclear fuel cycle is not the sole generator of nuclear wastes; they also come from medical procedures and defense weapons production.

About 39% of the radwaste in the U.S. commercial low-level burial sites is nonfuel-cycle in origin. This waste comes from the some 16,000 licensees for the use of radioactive materials in this country. These licensees are primarily in medicine, research, and industry. The medical waste volume is approximately 83% of nonfuel-cycle waste.

The objective of radioactive waste disposal is to deal with wastes in a manner that protects public health and the environment, while reflecting social and economic factors. Several choices are available:

1. *Dispersal Versus Containment.* Dispersal is the deliberate release of wastes into the environment, with its dilution by air or water to a level significantly below background levels. Containment is the other extreme, placing barriers around concentrated wastes to prevent their release to the environment.
2. *Passive Systems Versus Perpetual Care.* The former place no reliance on monitoring, while the latter requires continued administrative controls.
3. *Retrievability.* The ability to recover the wastes after disposal.

The options available do not have clear technical preferences that dictate the final choice, nor are they mutually exclusive. The final solution, therefore, will reflect societal and institutional values, modified by the economic consideration of the cost of a particular choice and the political consideration regarding the siting of a waste repository.

Waste Classification

Radioactive waste is classified into four categories: low level, intermediate level, high level, and transuranic, depending on the type and degree of activity of the waste. They are defined in terms of the concentration of radioactivity they contain, as given in Table 15.1. In recent years the "intermediate" category has become largely disused, and lumped together with "low-level" waste, while high-level wastes sometimes also contain transuranic elements.

The Department of Energy has responsibility for the receipt and disposal of radioactive wastes in the United States. Other federal agencies are also involved: the Environmental Protection Agency (environmental standards), the Nuclear Regulatory Commission (licensing and regulations), the Department of Transportation (transportation procedures), U.S. Geological Survey (repository geology), Corps of Engineers (property acquisition), and the Bureau of Land Management (access to public land). A summary of the responsibilities for radioactive waste disposal is given in Table 15.2.

The origins of high-level and low-level waste are quite different and distinct. High-level wastes are fission products produced when nuclei are fissioned in reactor fuel. This waste may take the form of separated fission products that are the waste stream from a spent fuel reprocessing plant, or, if the so-called throwaway fuel cycle (see Chapter 11) should be adopted, then the entire spent fuel assemblies become high-level waste, including their content of unfissioned ^{235}U and plutonium.

Table 15.1. Classification of Radioactive Wastes

	Ci/cm³	Ci/gal	Ci/g
Low level (LLW)	MPC[a] to 0.003 μCi	MPC to 10 μCi	Less than 10 nCi
Intermediate level	0.003–100 μCi	10 μCi to 0.4 Ci	—
High level (HLW)	Above 100 μCi	Above 0.4 Ci	—
Transuranic (TRU)	—	—	Greater than 10 nCi of transuranic elements

[a]MPC = Maximum Permissible Concentration of a radioisotope in water or air.

Table 15.2. Categories, Sources, and Responsibilities for Radioactive Wastes[a]

Type Waste/Source	Management	Disposal	Regulation	Standards
High-level wastes (spent fuel)—commercial sector	Industry	DOE	NRC	EPA
High-level wastes—defense disposal programs	DOE	DOE	NRC	EPA
Low-level wastes—commercial sector	Industry	Industry	Agreement states/NRC	EPA
Low-level wastes—defense programs	DOE	DOE	DOE	DOE
Transuranic wastes—defense program	DOE	DOE	DOE	DOE
Mill tailings (active)—commercial sector	Industry	Industry	NRC/EPA	EPA
Mill tailings (inactive)	DOE	DOE	NRC/EPA	EPA

Source: DOE.

[a]NRC—Nuclear Regulatory Commission; EPA—Environmental Protection Agency; DOE—Department of Energy.

High-Level Waste (HLW) is relatively small in volume, but remains highly radioactive for many years. As of 1981, there were about 270,000 m³ of military HLW, and 2300 m³ of commercial HLW stored in the United States.

Another type of radioactive waste is transuranic wastes (TRU). It can come from fuel reprocessing, although nearly all are from military weapons production. TRU wastes are primarily alpha particle emitters. About 766,000 m³ of TRU wastes are buried in shallow trenches at six U.S. sites. Table 15.3 shows these six sites and four others where TRU wastes have been produced. Wastes at these sites are commonly divided into three categories: buried wastes, retrievably stored wastes, and newly generated wastes. The Hanford site at Richland, Washington and Idaho National Engineering Lab at Idaho Falls are the two largest repositories of TRU wastes.

15.2. LOW-LEVEL WASTE

Low-Level Waste (LLW) is, generally speaking, everything else. It may, however, contain low quantities of fission products, as well as activation products. LLW is produced at the rate of 120,000 m³/yr in the United States, about half of which comes from the military. It includes a wide spectrum of items: uranium mine and mill tailings;† scrub water and decontamination solutions from all types of nuclear facilities; contaminated protective clothing, gloves, and shoe-covers; contaminated tools and burnt-out light bulbs from radioactive areas; pumps, valves, seals, bearings, and other components that have had to be replaced; scrap, fines, and dust from fuel fabrication operations; contaminated ion-exchange resins and gas filters; waste materials arising from use

†To date, 140 million tons of mill tailings have been produced in the United States.

Table 15.3. Estimated Volumes of Defense CH-TRU Wastes[a] as of June 1980

Site/Location	Contaminated Subsurface Volume,[b] 10^3 m^3	Retrievably Stored Wastes,[c] 10^3 m^3	Future Waste Generation,[d] 10^3 m^3
Hanford/ Richland, WA	290	28	28
Savannah River Laboratory (SRL)/ Aiken, SC	51	5.4	5.4
Los Alamos National Laboratory (LANL)/ Los Alamos, NM	23	16	16
Rocky Flats Plant/ Golden, CO	0	0	52
Argonne National Laboratory (ANL)/ Argonne, IL	0	0	2.6
Oak Ridge National Laboratory (ORNL)/ Oak Ridge, TN	170	1.9	1.9
Mound Laboratory/ Miamisburg, OH	0	0	7.3
Nevada Test Site (NTS)/ Mercury, NV	6	0.9	0.9
Idaho National Engineering Laboratory (INEL)/ Idaho Falls, ID	210	87	23
Bettis Atomic Power Laboratory/ Pittsburgh, PA	0	0	1.7
Total	766	139	139

Source: From W. B. Andrews et al. *Trans. Am. Nuclear Soc.* **39,** 226 (1981).

[a]TRU wastes with surface dose rates <200 mR/hr are called contact-handled TRU (CH-TRU) wastes.

[b]Buried waste and contaminated soil.

[c]Cumulative volumes through the year 2000 including future generation.

[d]Cumulative volumes through the year 2000.

of radioisotopes in nuclear medicine; exhaust ventilation air and off-gases from reactor containments.

Water effluent from reactor primary coolant systems and spent fuel storage pools is put through demineralizers until it is at the purity level of drinking water, then released to the environment; the demineralizer resins become low-level waste. Gaseous wastes are collected in holdup tanks, passed through charcoal filters or charcoal beds, and when safe, exhausted through a tall stack under controlled conditions for dilution and dispersion.

Shallow land burial is the accepted mode of disposal for low-level radioactive wastes. The long-lasting nature of some of the nuclides contained in the waste have necessitated restrictions on the Maximum Permissible Concentrations (MPC) for those nuclides. Of greatest concern are ^{90}Sr, ^{55}Fe, ^{14}C, ^{3}H, and plutonium because they do not emit easily detectable gamma rays characteristic of other radioactive nuclides. Radioactive waste for shallow land burial is classified according to the concentration of long-lived radionuclides (and their shorter-lived precursors) whose potential hazard will persist longer than the repository controls. There are several classes set out in the regulations. The lowest category is Class A waste whose radionuclide concentration does not exceed 10% of the values given in Table 15.4. This waste must meet the minimal restrictions on physical form and stability characteristics mandated by the NRC. The other waste classes defined in the regulations must meet more rigorous requirements on waste form to ensure stability, and, in some classes, require additional measures at the disposal facility to protect against inadvertent intrusion. With the exception of ^{90}Sr and ^{137}Cs, wastes with radionuclide concentrations exceeding the values in Table 15.4 are generally not acceptable for shallow land burial.

Table 15.4. Maximum Radionuclide Concentrations for Shallow Land Burial

Radionuclide	Concentration, Ci/m^3
^{3}H	400
^{14}C	8
^{14}C in activated metal	80
^{59}Ni in activated metal	220
^{90}Sr	0.4[a]
^{129}I	0.08
^{137}Cs	10[a]
Transuranic nuclides with half-lives greater than 5 yr	100[b]
^{241}Pu	3,500[b]
^{242}Cm	20,000[b]

Source: *Federal Register* **47,** 248 (1982).

[a] ^{90}Sr and ^{137}Cs can be accepted in some instances with concentrations up to 7000 and 4600 Ci/m^3, respectively.

[b] Units are nCi/g.

Since 1970, wastes containing plutonium concentrations greater than 10 nCi/g are placed in retrievable storage facilities pending ultimate disposal. These wastes have been produced and/or stored in significant quantities at 10 sites in the United States. Wastes at these sites are commonly divided into three categories: buried wastes, retrievably stored wastes, and newly generated wastes. Estimated untreated volumes of contact-handled TRU wastes in each category as of June 1980 were shown in Table 15.3.

In the United States, disposal criteria are based on the levels of naturally occurring radioactivity in the soil. NUREG-0456 has been proposed by the NRC as the basis for management of plutonium-contaminated waste. It lists different MPC values for each nuclide that are, in general, higher than 10 nCi/g. Radioactive wastes with plutonium concentrations below these values would be considered low-level wastes if NUREG-0456 were adopted. ^{239}Pu concentration in reactor wastes, however, are significantly below 10 nCi/g (Table 15.5) so would be considered low-level wastes under either criteria.

Other parts of the nuclear fuel cycle also produce substantial quantities of low-level radioactive wastes. Fuel fabrication facilities, enrichment plants, and reprocessing plants are all sources of such wastes. Decommissioning of nuclear facilities will produce contaminated and activated materials. The characteristics of the low-level radwastes expected from fuel cycle activities are given in Table 15.6. As seen in this table, however, nuclear plant operations are the largest source of low-level wastes, followed by reprocessing and fuel fabrication plants.

Solid wastes are usually subjected to one of several kinds of volume-reduction procedures, and then packaged by being encased in concrete in 55-gal drums, steel-lined boxes, or other special containers, and finally shipped to a federally licensed low-level burial ground for disposal.

In the United States, six such burial sites have operated, but four have been closed and only two remain open to the industry. The sites at Sheffield, Illinois; Morehead, Kentucky; West Valley, New York; and Beatty, Nevada, have been closed. Still in operation are burial sites at Barnwell, South Carolina, and Hanford, Washington. Figure 15.1 shows the location of these facilities.

Table 15.5. Plutonium Concentrations in Reactor Wastes

	Median Concentration of ^{239}Pu, nCi/g-dryed	
Waste Category	BWR	PWR
Resin	0.031	0.026
Filter sludge	0.63	—
Evaporator bottoms	0.09	0.015

Source: From EPRI Report NP-1494.

Table 15.6. Sources and Characteristics of Low-Level Radioactive Waste

Source	Original Waste Form	Major Radioisotopes	Activity, Ci/MTHM[a]	Final Waste Form
1. UF_6 conversion (fresh)	Liquid	U, ^{226}Ra, ^{230}Th	1.07×10^{-6}	1.3×10^4 liters of liquid waste per t U
	Solid	U, ^{226}Ra, ^{230}Th	9.40×10^{-3}	1.1 m^3 of solid waste (including CaF_2) per t U
2. UF_6 conversion (recycle)	Solid	Fission products	0.57	~1.3 m^3 of solid waste (including CaF_2 and carbonate-leached ash) per t U
		^{238}Pu, ^{241}Pu	4.12×10^{-5}	
		U	1.35×10^{-3}	
3. Enrichment (fresh)	Liquid	U	1.11×10^{-6}	675 liters of liquid waste per t U
4. Enrichment (fresh + 10% recycle)	Liquid	U	1.16×10^{-6}	675 liters of liquid waste per t U
		^{237}Np	1.67×10^{-9}	
		^{239}Pu	3.33×10^{-12}	
		Fission products	3.40×10^{-4}	
5. Fuel fabrication (fresh + 10% recycle)	Liquid	U, ^{234}Th, ^{234}Pa	1.20×10^{-3}	5.7×10^5 liters of liquid waste per t U
	Solid	U	7.34×10^{-3}	4.6 m^3 of solid waste (including CaF_2) per t U
6. Fuel fabrication (mixed oxide)	Solid	U, Pu, Am	3.47	~2265 (98.2)m^3 of solid waste per t of plutonium (uranium) processed
7. LWR Operation PWR (1000 MWe)	Liquid	Fission products and activation products	19.3	184 m^3 of resins, liquids and sludge typically solidified
	Solid		1.9	
BWR (1000 MWe)	Liquid	Fission products and activation products	100	326 m^3 of general trash
				807 m^3 of resin, liquid, and sludge typically solidified
	Solid		12.2	326 m^3 of general trash
8. Reprocessing	Solid	Pu, Am	0.53	~1586 (15.0) m^3 of solid waste per t of plutonium (uranium) processed
		Fission products		

Source: From NUREG/CR-2206.

[a]Metric ton of heavy metal.

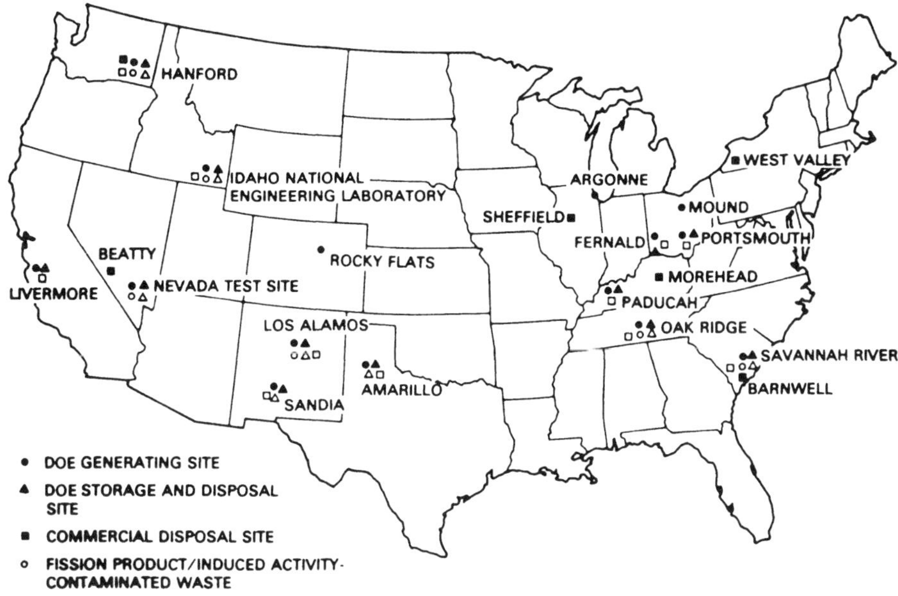

Figure 15.1. Major nuclear waste storage/disposal sites. (Courtesy DOE.)

In the 18 yr 1962 through 1980, 16,894,000 ft^3 of solid low-level waste was buried at these sites, at a rate gradually increasing from 36,000 ft^3 in 1962 to 2,000,000 ft^3 in 1980. If this 18-yr total were piled into a single cube, the cube would be about 250 ft on a side.

Low-Level Waste Disposal—The U.S. Approach

Recent U.S. federal legislation has made low-level waste disposal the responsibility of the states, to be handled on a regional basis. The first regional compact of Idaho, Washington, and Oregon has been formally chartered and should serve as a model for the other states.

Subsequently Montana, Wyoming, and Utah joined to complete what is now the Northwest Compact Region. The Southeast Compact Region was completed in 1983. It consists of the eight states south of Virginia and east of Mississippi. Four other regional compacts (Northeast, Midwest, Central and Rocky Mountain) are presently forming—spurred on by the 1986 target date for the regional compacts to take full control of waste burial. As of early 1984, two large radioactive waste producers, California and Texas, have not yet made a final decision as to which compact to join, or to go it alone.

The federal regulations embodied in 10CFR61 for establishing siting criteria have been issued in 1982. 10CFR61 provides a rational approach which is acceptable to industry. In the short term (5 yr) some nuclear facilities may experience problems in disposing of low-level waste as the regional compacts formally come to grips with the problem that they have been mandated to solve. However, in the long term the elements to provide a solution to this issue are at hand. Several technical issues require attention:

1. *Waste Form.* How to define an adequate waste form that is not unnecessarily complex or costly for utility use in conjunction with existing equipment.
2. *Volume Reduction.* What amount of volume reduction is technically and economically justified if a reasonable number of waste disposal sites are established?
3. *Administrative Control.* What is the duration of administrative control that should be required for low-level waste sites?
4. *Waste Package.* Development of waste containers for resins and evaporator sludges sufficient to meet the new 10CFR61 requirements.

Table 15.7. Average Plant Waste Activity

	Waste Activity, Ci/MWe-yr			
	Boiling Water Reactors		Pressurized Water Reactors	
Waste Type	Deep Bed CPS[a]	Precoat CPS	With CPS	Without CPS
Spent resins, filter sludges, and evaporator bottoms	4.48	0.517	0.93	0.356
Dry compressible waste and contaminated equipment	0.0052	0.0052	0.063	0.063
Irradiated components	0.397	0.397	—	—

Source: This table was taken from *A Waste Inventory Report for Reactor and Fuel-Fabrication Facility Wastes,* prepared for the U.S. Department of Energy.

[a]CPS = condensate polishing system.

Items (1) and (3) are dominated by policy and institutional concerns, although technical issues determine the boundaries of the solution. Item (4) is a straightforward problem of designing waste containers that meet the legal requirements. Item (2), however, is driven by technology with economics the incentive for improved techniques. We will consider it in some detail.

Contrary to conventional wisdom, the generation rate of dry radioactive waste is not related to reactor size. Rather, generation of dry waste is affected mainly by outages; current rates are consistent with an assumption that all stations undergo one refueling and repair outage each year. This assumption results in a weighted average production of dry radioactive waste of about 12,300 ft^3 (348 m^3) per unit per year, with lower and upper bounds of 7000 and 20,000 ft^3 (198 and 566 m^3) respectively, per unit per year. This is in addition to the 15,000 ft^3 (425 m^3) of liquid wastes produced. These wastes and their curie content are given in Tables 15.7 and 15.8.

It costs approximately \$55/ft^3 for off-site burial. Some disposal sites have allocations for each nuclear facility served. Every cubic foot in excess of the allocation must be shipped to another site. For example, a utility that would usually use the Barnwell, South Carolina disposal site would have to ship overallocation quantities to either Nevada or Washington, increasing the shipping distances several thousand miles. With transportation costs exceeding \$150/mile per truckload, an economic incentive exists to meet the volumetric allocation. Furthermore, large cost savings are possible if the waste volume can be reduced. Figure 15.2 shows that savings up to 75% are possible using volume reduction techniques.

To further explore the economics of waste disposal, it is interesting to look at the current price for disposal of low-level waste at the Barnwell burial site. All material shipped there must comply with (1) Department of Transportation packaging specifications, (2) the licenses of the operator of the site and of South Carolina state radioactive material licenses, and (3) site disposal criteria.

Table 15.8. Solidified Waste Volumes with Current Practices, m^3/MWe

	Boiling Water Reactors		Pressurized Water Reactors	
Waste Type	Deep Bed CPS[a]	Precoat CPS	With CPS	Without CPS
Spent resins, filter sludges, and evaporator bottoms	0.974	0.346	0.276	0.272
Dry compressible waste and contaminated equipment	0.22	0.22	0.326	0.326
Irradiated components	0.10	0.10	—	—

Source: This table was taken from *A Waste Inventory Report for Reactor and Fuel-Fabrication Facility Wastes,* prepared for the U.S. Department of Energy.

[a]CPS = condensate polishing system.

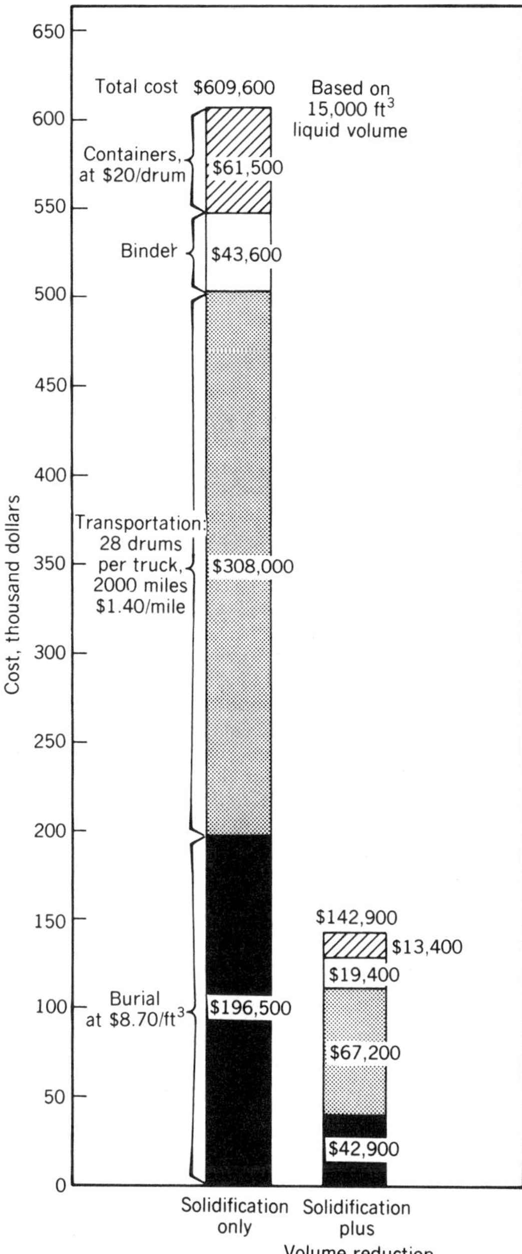

Figure 15.2. Solidification cost breakdown for liquid waste showing the value of volume reduction (Feb. 1981 prices). [From S. R. Beck, *Power* (February 1982).]

Disposal charges, excluding surcharges, are \$13.20/ft^3, but not less than \$300 per shipment. There are additional radiation surcharges depending on the maximum radiation level at the surface of the package—steel drums, boxes, and liners. There is no surcharge for 0 to 50 mrems/hr at the package surface. Beginning with a range of 51 to 100 mrems/hr maximum, the surcharge is \$5/ft^3; for 100 to 250 mrems/hr, the surcharge is \$8; and on up, stepwise, to 1000–5000 R/hr, \$400/ft^3, and anything greater than 5000 R/hr requires a special price on request. There are also weight surcharges based on the weight of the container which range up to a high of 50,000 lb, \$2000; and curie content surcharges that range up to a maximum of \$8000 for 5000-Ci content. Higher container weights or curie content likewise are priced by special request.

There are further surcharges. Drummed radioactive waste weighing less than 600 lb per drum *not* shipped palletized, on a flat bed trailer, incurs a surcharge of \$0.50/ft^3. For biological tissue there is a \$1/ft^3 surcharge. There is a "special handling surcharge" for unusually large or bulky containers. There is a cask-handling fee of \$500 per cask minimum. Finally, \$2.25/ft^3 is charged to be placed in a perpetual escrow fund.

Volume Reduction Techniques

Because of high transportation and burial costs, volume reduction has become a fundamental principle in management of low-level radioactive waste.

Beginning about 1978 there has been a shift in the economics of low-level waste management, with costs increasing almost exponentially. Consequently, there has been a research effort to develop new technology to achieve volume reduction (or VR, as it has come to be known). VR's importance grows with burial-site cost escalation and with waste volume and activity; when both are kept under reasonable control, inflation and interest rates take on significance. While dry-waste disposal benefits modestly from VR, the greatest savings are projected for wet-waste material.

Utility organizations have established consolidated and dedicated radioactive waste ("radwaste") groups. Plant and corporate management has become aware of radwaste problems and the need to support plant staff. The management techniques used include setting of radwaste minimization goals, performing periodic internal audits of radwaste activities, and establishing plant training and "radwaste awareness" programs. Also, "controlled areas"—that is, areas where radioactivity is or may be present—are minimized to the extent possible. Surfaces in controlled areas are properly coated to minimize the spread of contamination, contaminated-tool cribs are reused rather than added to the waste, color-coded containers in controlled areas collect different types of waste by levels of contamination, washable protective clothing is reused rather than daily disposal that adds to low level waste. These are a few of the strategies employed to minimize low level waste within the plant.

As already mentioned, a great deal of work is going on to develop improved techniques of VR. VR may be defined as the removal of nonradioactive material—primarily water, air, and combustible organics—from radioactive waste, to reduce the volume requiring ultimate disposal.

Four basic approaches are used: dehydration, crystallization, incineration, and compaction. As of the end of 1982, 21 U.S. nuclear stations were committed to the use of crystallizers (that is, either had them on site or on order), and 17 stations were committed to the use of other types of VR equipment.

The dehydration of evaporator bottoms has dramatic effects on the volumes requiring disposal. A study by an engineering firm showed, for instance, that for 100,000 lb of sodium sulfate (Na_2SO_4) waste† solidified in cement, about 2910 drums are produced if the waste is concentrated to 10 wt%. If the solution is further concentrated to 25 wt%, there are only 1024 drums, while a 50 wt% solution results in 400 drums. If the sodium sulfate is dried, there will be about 235 drums.

For comparison, if the same amount of resins were discarded without being regenerated, about 2570 drums of dewatered resins would be produced. If they were solidified in cement, about 3600 drums would result; if they were dried and solidified in asphalt, about 1720 drums would be produced. Figure 15.3 shows an extruder/evaporator used to remove water from radwaste feed while simultaneously mixing the dried waste product with a binder, normally asphalt.

A radwaste crystallizer is a specially designed forced-circulation evaporator consisting of a vapor body, recirculation pipe, large recirculation pump, and two-pass vertical heater (Figure 15.4). Steam is applied to the shell side of the heater where it condenses on the outside of the tubes and imparts heat to the liquid circulating inside the tubes. The steam condensate is then removed from the shell side of the heater and returned to the boiler or condensate storage tank. The liquor circulating through the tubes is not allowed to boil in the tubes due to proper layout of equipment and low-temperature rise across the heater. After the liquid passes through the heater it enters the vapor body where it releases water vapors to the condenser and subcooler system. The recirculation pump, the vapor body, and the heater are all designed to handle the undissolved solids which circulate throughout the unit.

†From a condensate polishing system.

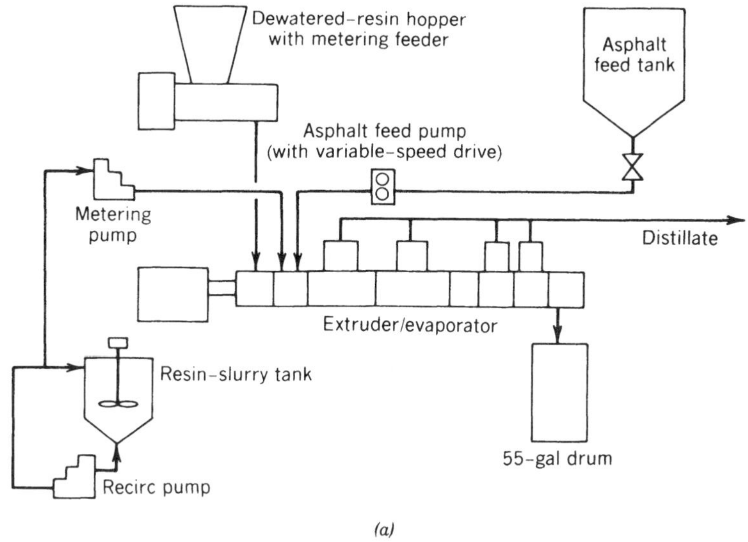

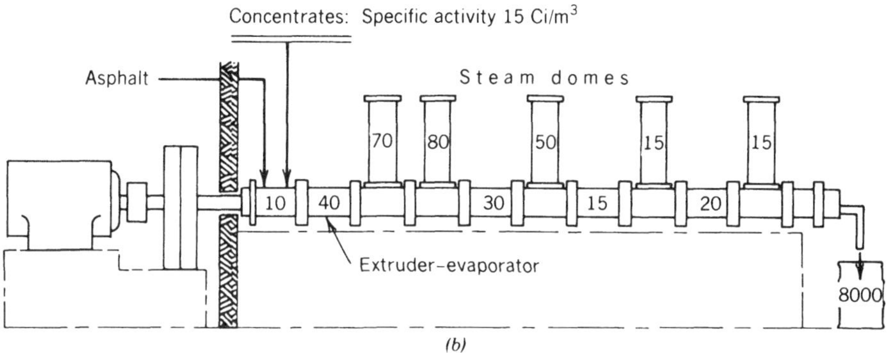

Figure 15.3. (*a*) Extruder/evaporator for removing water from radwaste. (*b*) Surface dose rates (mR/hr). [From D. Eggett and D. Enegess, *Power Magazine* (October 1982).]

New high-efficiency compactors have been introduced recently for low-level waste use. Some compact contaminated trash into 100 ft^3 (2.8 m^3) boxes, others into 55-gal (200-liter) drums. These compactors are able to compress clean trash from a bulk density of about 6 lb/ft^3 (0.1 g/cm^3) to densities in the range of 30–50 lb/ft^3 (0.5–0.8 g/cm^3).

One of the oldest methods of volume reduction is incineration. A radioactive waste incinerator is a sophisticated device that controls any off-gases bearing radioactivity. There are, in fact, about seven types of incinerators for low-level waste, including controlled-air, excess air, fluidized bed, pyrolysis, and other types of combustion chambers. The off-gases may be treated by wet filtration or dry filtration. There are also different ways of handling and treating the ash remaining in the combustion chamber. Further, there are batch-feed and continuous-feed systems.

Considerable experience has already been accumulated with the incineration method of VR in many countries. Different institutions in Austria, Belgium, Canada, England, France, Germany, India, Japan, Sweden, and Switzerland as well as the United States have experience with radwaste incineration in the past decade. The Yankee nuclear power station at Rowe, Massachusetts, had an incinerator for dry active waste in operation for more than 10 yr, until 1977 when its operation was terminated. The unit was quite simple but required excessive manual-contact operation by today's standards. Trash had to be manually sorted prior to incineration. This, together with the discomfort of working near the heat from the unit, placed demands on the operating staff such that when a need arose for new off-gas cleanup equipment, it was felt the investment in so old a unit was unjustified. The newer incinerators overcome these problems.

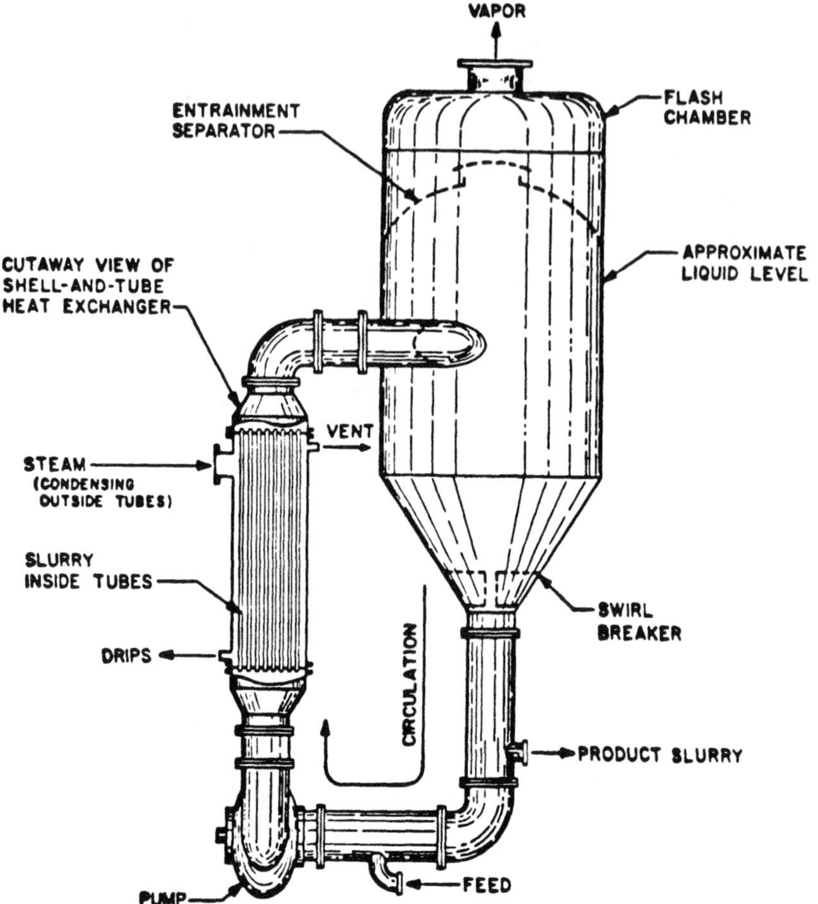

Figure 15.4. Evaporator/crystallizer. (From NUREG/CR-2206.)

New Volume Reduction Techniques

In addition to the traditional VR methods such as incineration, evaporation–crystallization, and other methods of dehydration and compaction, new and more advanced systems are in development. These include microwave drying, ultrafiltration, and hydrocycloning.

Microwave drying was developed at the Idaho Chemical Processing Plant where a fluid bed calciner had been in operation since 1963 to dehydrate the liquid waste stream. The calciner was fired with kerosene. This unit was designed for aluminum clad waste and aluminum oxide waste. When the plant began reprocessing zirconium clad fuel using hydrofluoric acid as a solvent, fluorine came into the calciner and quickly eroded the nozzles and ate away the calciner internals. Microwaves were suggested as an alternate heat source. The microwaves vibrate the molecules, producing friction; the friction heat vaporizes the water.

Subsequently, microwave heating was investigated for resins and evaporator bottoms from commercial nuclear power plants.

Early tests with small commercial microwave units showed that it is possible to reduce reactor-grade resins by a factor of 2 in volume. Boric acid (used to control reactivity in LWRs) can also be dried to "zero water."

UltraFiltration (UF) has been tried at the Ginna Nuclear Station near Rochester, New York. UF is a low-pressure membrane purification technology, used as pretreatment of liquid waste to an evaporator (Figure 15.5). The UF system was installed in parallel to an existing cartridge filter, and operated on an alternate basis from July 1979 through February 1981. In this period, 160,000 gal of liquid radwaste were processed. Volumetric concentration factors for the ultrafiltration system

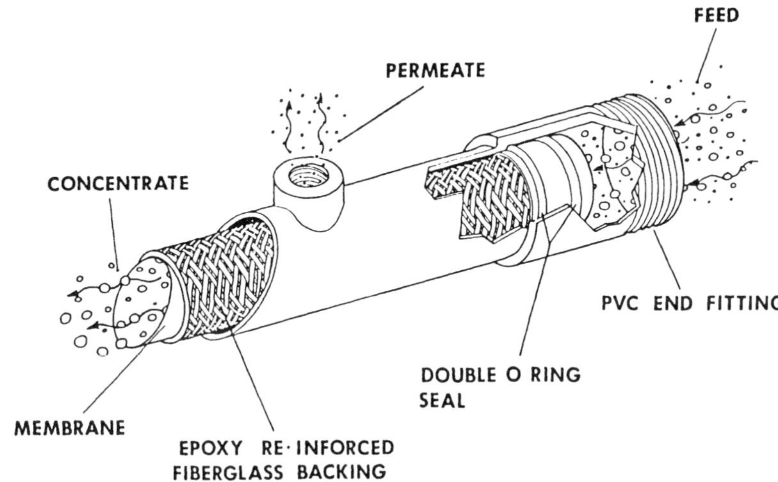

Figure 15.5. Ultrafiltration system. Cutaway view of ABCOR tubular membrane assembly. Each membrane assembly is 1-in. diameter by 10-ft long and has 2.2 ft^2 of active membrane area. The liquid suspension to be processed flows through the membrane tube at about 0.6 m/sec. (From EPRI Report NP-2335.)

ranged between 400 and 2000. Very little change was noted in the performance of the evaporator. However, significant reduction in evaporator maintenance, and associated radiation exposure, were clearly demonstrated. Reductions in evaporator radiation levels, and in repair, maintenance, and inspection activities were likewise noted.

A third volume reduction method still in the developmental stage is hydrocycloning. Hydrocyclones are static liquid separators. This type of volume reduction device has been tested at the Nine Mile Point Nuclear Station, between August and November 1981. Hydrocyclones of two different manufacturers were tested and evaluated. One type removed 95% of particles greater than 20 μm in size, and had a flow capacity up to 33 gal/min. The other removed 98% of particles greater than 74 μm in size, with a flow capacity up to 29 gal/min.

Thus, hydrocyclones are efficient for removing suspended solids from a liquid. The first type is essentially a long vertical cone into which the feed is introduced tangent to a short cylindrical section to establish a rotational flow pattern. As the liquid moves down the cone as the cone narrows, centrifugal forces move the suspended solids to the wall. Fines remaining near the center are carried out through the "vortex finder" at the top. This product is termed the "overflow." Larger particles spiral down the wall of the conical section and leave through an apex orifice at the bottom of the cone. This product is called the "underflow."

The second type of hydrocyclone tested, shown in Figure 15.6, has a spiral tube through which the feed enters and begins a circular flow. The feed is accelerated through tangential slots into a separation chamber, and solids are centrifugally forced to the inner chamber's perimeter, where they lose velocity and fall to the bottom of the collection chamber, whence they are periodically purged.

Several advantages are put forward for hydrocyclones. They have no moving parts, and are simple to operate. They are compact in size, ranging from 12 in. long and 1 in. in diameter, to 7 ft long, 2 ft diameter. They are also inexpensive, costing $300 to $500 per unit.

Performance characteristics include these: the higher the density, the lower the viscosity, the closer to spherical the suspended particles are, the better the performance. Determination of such characteristics makes it possible to tailor their use to situations for which they are best fitted.

As of the beginning of 1983, most nuclear plants were using—or had ordered—crystallizers, but the newer, more advanced devices for volume reduction had not yet penetrated the market to any marked extent.

15.3. SPENT FUEL STORAGE

In the United States, the ban placed on reprocessing spent fuel in 1976 upset plans to move spent fuel discharged from nuclear power plants to reprocessing plants. It placed a premium on storage space for spent fuel assemblies, and caused nuclear power plants to plan ahead to make certain that

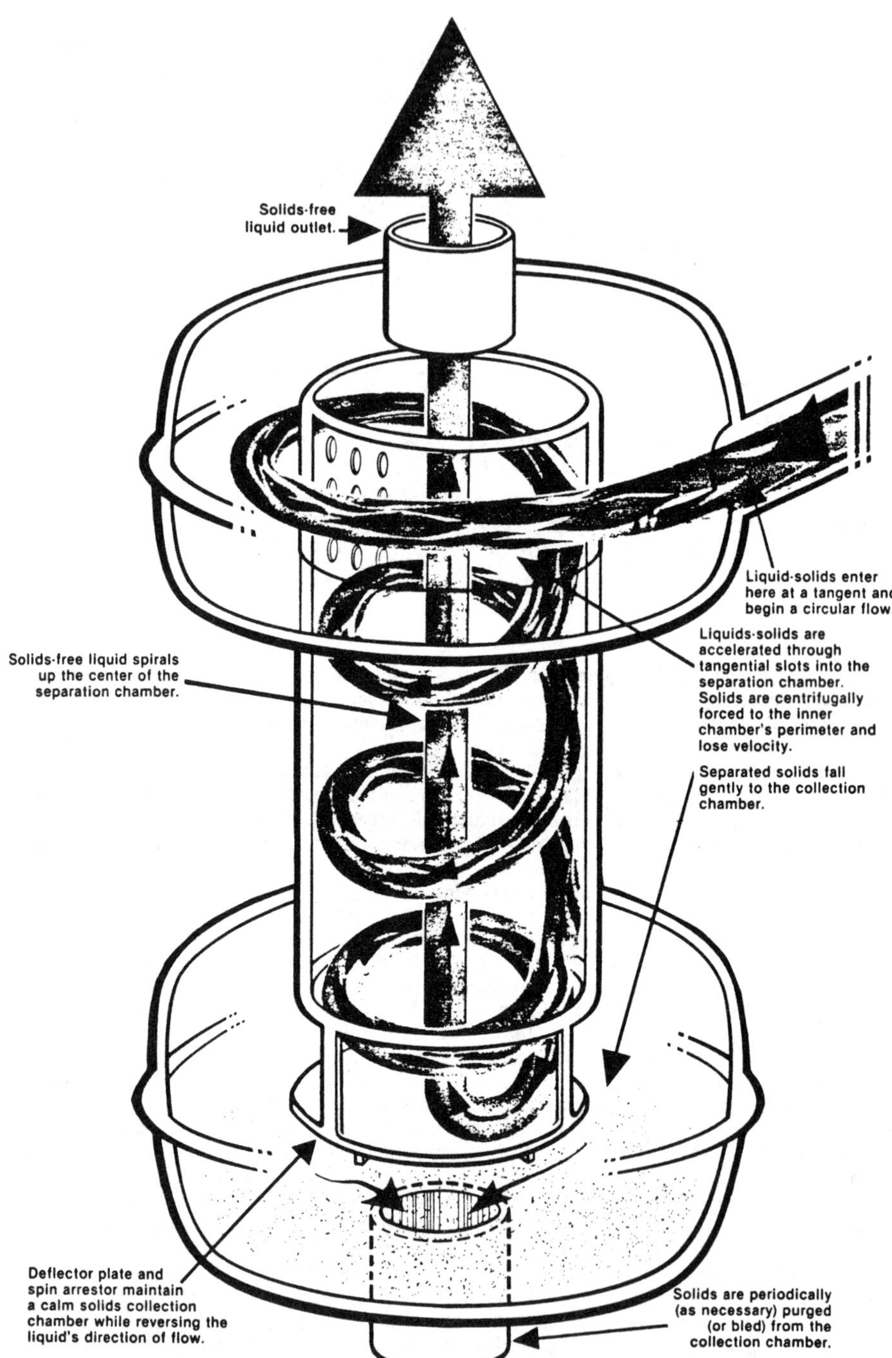

Figure 15.6. Hydrocyclones are mechanical classification devices which utilize centrifugal force to a separate denser particulates from a lighter liquid medium. The Lakos separator, shown above, also utilizes centrifugal force to separate higher density particulates from a fluid stream. (From EPRI Report NP-2338.)

Table 15.9. Estimated Spent Fuel Discharged from U.S. Reactors

End of Calendar Year	Uranium Accumulated, t	Number of Assemblies	Total Radioactivity, MCi
1980	6,700	25,000	10,400
1985	15,800	57,000	21,000
1990	32,000	111,000	35,000
1995	50,000	177,000	47,000
2000	72,000	252,000	55,000

Source: From DOE/NE-0017 (1981).

they would not be forced to shut down at some point in the future because there was no place in which to unload spent fuel when it became necessary to do so.

Because of decay, the tonnage and the number of assemblies increase at a faster rate than does the total radioactivity. Also, it has been estimated that the total energy content of the whole free world's spent fuel by the year 2000 will reach that of about 97 billion barrels of oil, or six times the free world's production of oil in 1975. By "energy content" is meant the latent energy in the unfissioned ^{235}U and plutonium in the spent fuel. The fissionable material that can be recovered by reprocessing from the spent fuel of four LWRs is sufficient to fuel a fifth one.

Table 15.9 which shows the buildup of discharged reactor fuel, refers exclusively to commercial electric power reactor spent fuel. The wastes on hand from national defense programs are in fact far greater. It has been calculated that accumulated military, or defense, nuclear wastes are at present between 70 and 100 times greater in volume than accumulated commercial wastes, although this ratio will rapidly diminish in subsequent years.

The Department of Energy's report on spent fuel and radioactive waste inventories and projections, published in September 1981, showed that as of the end of 1980, 6700 t of uranium had been accumulated from commercial reactors. This, of course, makes allowance for the spent fuel that had been reprocessed during the 6-yr period of operation of the West Valley reprocessing plant (see Chapter 14). Figure 15.7 gives a projection of the spent-fuel discharge rate from U.S. reactors through the year 2000.

Attempts to alleviate the situation took two routes. One was to increase the capacity of existing on-site spent fuel storage pools within their existing steel-lined concrete walls. Second were a number of tries in the United States to obtain contruction of a new, large, central facility for storing spent fuel. This gave birth to a new acronym, "AFR," meaning "Away From Reactor" spent fuel storage.

Two approaches toward construction of an AFR storage facility were followed. Some urged the government to undertake construction of an AFR facility; consideration was given to the idea in the Executive Branch and Congress, but no action was taken. The other approach consisted of efforts within the electric utility industry to put together a syndicate of utilities that would build an AFR facility. Similarly, these efforts never passed the preliminary stage. Probably the principal reason why these efforts remained unrealized was that the immediate crisis receded as on-site pool capacity expansion staved it off—for a while, at least. (It may return by the end of the 1980s.)

Several equipment manufacturers marketed new spent fuel racks for storage pools that increase capacity. These are not the conventional egg-crate supports that sit on the bottom of the storage pool, mate with the bottom-fitting of discharged fuel assemblies, and maintain them at distances sufficiently far apart to ensure that criticality is not possible in the fuel pool. Instead, they are boxlike sleeves extending the full height of the fuel assembly (Figure 15.8). They are made of alloys containing sufficient neutron poisons—boron, hafnium, or other—to prevent criticality. Consequently, they can be spaced much closer together, thereby permitting more assemblies to be accommodated in the pool.

Virtually every operating reactor in the United States has "reracked" its spent fuel pool in this manner, and reactors still under construction expanded the planned dimensions of their spent fuel pools.

Two other stratagems used to deal with the spent fuel problem have been: to use the receiving pools at the three nonoperational reprocessing sites—West Valley, Morris, and Barnwell; and to reduce the volume of each spent fuel assembly by disassembling it and storing the rods, packed tighter, in adequately poisoned containers.

Among the other alternatives are dry storage options that have potential economic and operational advantages. These options, however, are untested on a large scale, although dry storage of CANDU fuel in Canada, Magnox fuel in the United Kingdom, and some early LWR and LMFBR fuel in the United States has been tried with good results. Dry storage requires an initial period of

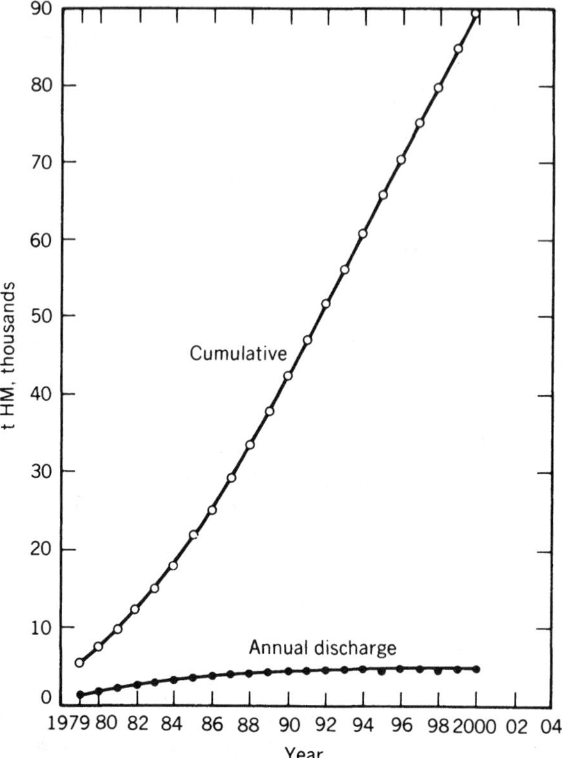

Figure 15.7. The planned commercial nuclear plants in the United States can be well defined until 1993 with minor alternations due to possible cancellations or deferrals of plants under construction. It is practical to assume that sudden changes in projected nuclear capacity through 1993 will not occur because few, if any, large nuclear plants will be retired by that time and no additional capacity can be installed beyond what is presently planned, due to a 10- to 12-yr lead time. [From U. Y. Park, *Trans. Am. Nuclear Soc.* **32,** 350 (1979).]

water basin cooling. Based on passive cooling, it utilizes fairly simple systems needing low maintenance. Dry storage can be added incrementally, that is, capacity additions can be made in small increments with a minimum of advanced capital expenditures.

Spent fuel storage in the United States is governed by 10CFR72 which specifies the conditions for independent storage facilities. The license conditions limit radiation releases and require monitoring, surveillance, and administrative controls. During storage the fuel cladding must be protected against degradation and rupture, thus the peak temperature buildup and the storage atmosphere must be controlled. Types of dry storage under consideration are illustrated in Figure 15.9.

The concept of using dry storage for spent fuel is being looked on with increasing favor by the United States utilities as the prospects for reprocessing or government AFR storage fade. The British and Germans have already licensed dry storage, and the Germans have announced their intent to use it as their national method of storing spent fuel.

15.4. HIGH-LEVEL WASTE

Disposal of high-level waste—that is, either the separated wastes resulting from operation of a reprocessing plant, or the spent fuel elements themselves if a throwaway fuel cycle is used—is a question overshadowing commercial nuclear power in the United States, causing some public anxiety, as this waste is potentially the most hazardous and the longest lived.

When fuel is discharged from a power reactor, it is stored in the spent fuel pool. Even with fuel reprocessing, the spent fuel resides in the power plant spent fuel pool before being placed in a cask for shipment, to permit the shorter lived radioactive material to decay. A year or two after unloading from the reactor, the total radioactivity level in the fuel is only about 12% of what it was when

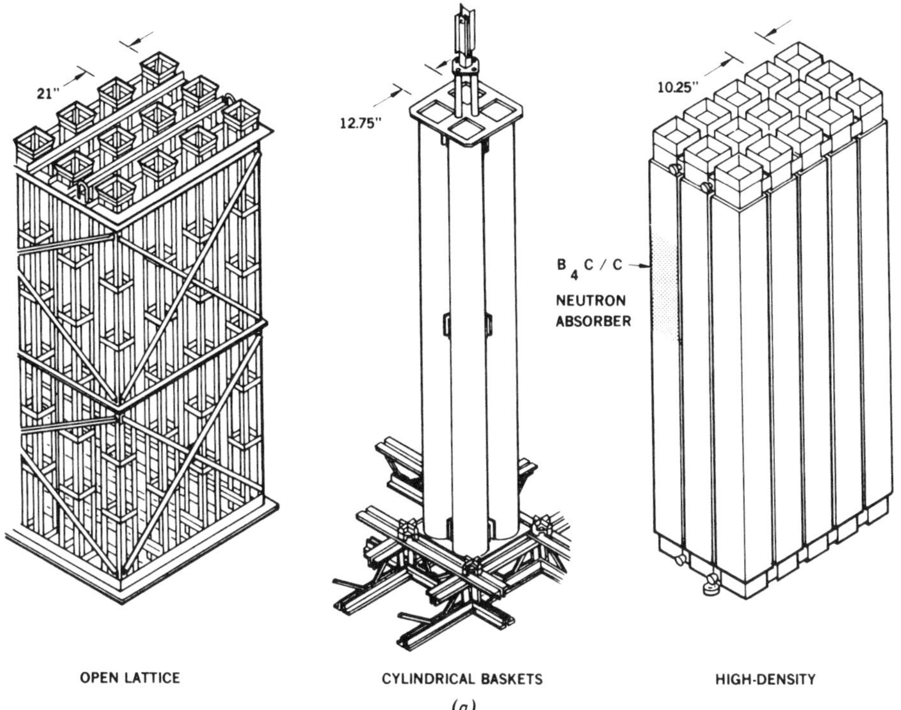

Figure 15.8. (*a*) Concepts of fuel storage racks. (*b*) High-density fuel storage rack.

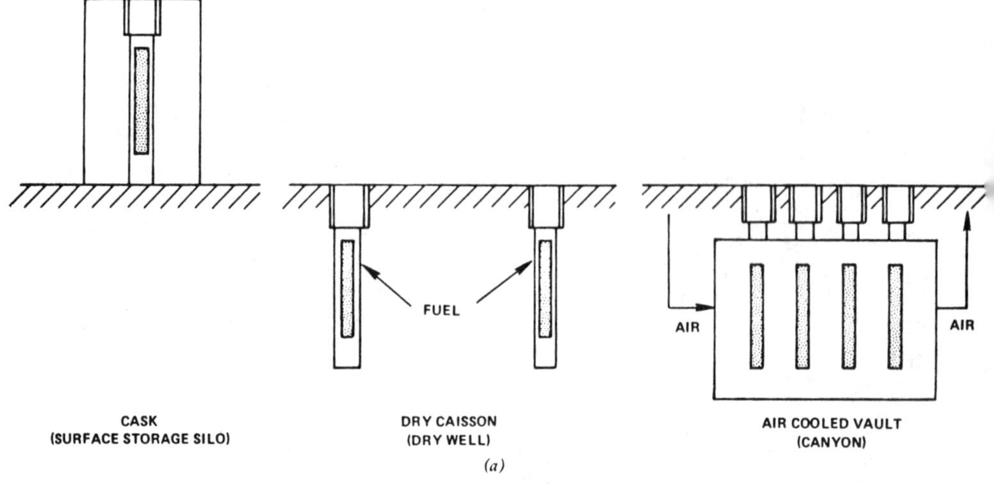

(a)

(b)

Figure 15.9. (*a*) Types of dry storage. (From EPRI Report NP-2735.) (*b*) Production model of a dry storage cask for spent nuclear fuel. It is comparable to casks being turned out by American and European producers. (Courtesy of Ridihalgh, Egger & Associates.)

discharged, and after 5 yr it is down to about 3% of the discharged level. The total activity of the fuel continues to decay slowly with time.

While a few radioisotopes have half-lives on the order of thousands of years, the hazardous components of nuclear waste rapidly decay to a radioactive toxicity level lower than that of natural uranium ore. For example, the strontium in waste becomes less toxic than natural uranium ore in 450 yr. The total waste, including plutonium, becomes less toxic in 500–1000 yr depending on the fuel history and the reprocessing plant's characteristics.

History of High-Level Waste Disposal

The question then is, what is to be done with the wastes during the time that they are hazardous.

When Congress passed the Atomic Energy Act of 1954, which permitted commercial activities using fissionable material including power generation, it was understood from the legislative history (the record of debates, speeches, and negotiations), although not spelled out in the language of the act, that dealing with the radioactive waste was the province and the responsibility of the federal government.

In 1957 the National Academy of Sciences recommended, as the best solution for ultimate disposal of high-level waste, deep geologic burial in salt formations. From that year through 1961 Oak Ridge National Laboratory conducted studies to investigate this concept.

In 1961, the National Academy of Sciences reviewed Oak Ridge's studies and recommended further work. The following year, the West Valley reprocessing plant began operation. Military high-level waste, as well as the plant's own waste by-product from processing of commercial spent fuel, were stored on site.

In 1963, calcining of liquid high-level waste to a dry powder was demonstrated at the Waste Calcining Facility built adjacent to the Idaho Chemical Processing Plant. Calcining reduces waste volume and reduces the danger of liquid leakage from tanks.

In 1965 AEC began a program of converting all liquid high-level waste to salt cake, by driving off the water in evaporators.

From 1963 through 1969 Oak Ridge continued its studies on ultimate disposal and the National Academy continued to advocate deep salt burial. In 1969 Oak Ridge completed development of a conceptual design for a prototype repository in deep salt for reprocessed high-level waste.

Finally, in 1970, AEC announced tentative selection of an unused salt mine near Lyons, Kansas, as the site for a demonstration waste repository—following several years of experimentation at the site to prove out the suitability of salt as a disposal medium. Congress directed AEC not to proceed with the Lyons project until its safety could be certified. The AEC meanwhile had dug galleries deep down in the salt, and taken the press down to see the proposed demonstration repository. After this, to its embarrassment, the AEC discovered in 1972 that although the Lyons salt bed had not been mined for a long period, solution mining of salt was still being carried on commercially a few miles away in the same salt stratum. This called into question the long-term dryness and integrity of the salt at the repository site. AEC subsequently abandoned the project.

During the decade following, the U.S. government has tried several approaches. The AEC turned then to the concept of a "Retrievable Surface Storage Facility" (RSSF) as an interim solution. This engineered storage facility might have been water cooled or air cooled; Hanford or the Nevada Test Site were mentioned as locations. In 1973, AEC declared it would announce the selection of a reference design and site for RSSF early in 1974, request funding in 1975, complete construction in 4 yr, and begin receiving waste about 1980.

In 1975, ERDA, the successor agency to the AEC, abandoned the RSSF concept. Instead it began developing plans for a system of deep geologic repositories. It initiated a comprehensive national waste terminal-storage program, with presidential backing; called on 36 state governors for cooperation and informed them of plans to conduct field investigations in their states. The ERDA plan was to have a repository in salt available by 1985, and a total of six repositories in salt, shale, and granite by 2000.

The program faltered, owing to federal–state communication problems and the political pressures generated during the 1976 presidential (Ford–Carter) campaign. During that time, President Ford deferred reprocessing, and upon his election President Carter continued the deferral.

In 1977, DOE, successor to ERDA, announced a plan for the government to accept title to and custody of commercial spent fuel, and store it in new AFR storage pools pending availability of deep geologic repositories. As has already been mentioned, the AFR project was also abandoned.

In 1978, a Federal Interagency Review Group on nuclear waste management published the report of its study, which favored deep geologic disposal, but pushed the date of earliest availability of a repository from 1985 to 1988. In the same year, five states passed laws prohibiting high-level waste disposal in their territories without the express consent of the legislature or other state authority.

In 1979 a DOE hearing board conducted public hearings in five major cities around the country on a draft Environmental Impact Statement on management of commercially generated radioactive waste. Then, in 1980, President Carter pushed the availability date of the first commercial high-level waste repository back from 1989 to the mid-1990s, and made utilities responsible for spent fuel, which was to be stored as spent fuel (i.e., unreprocessed).

On December 20, 1982, Congress passed—and on January 7, 1983, President Reagan signed into law—a landmark act that put an end to 25 yr of questions, debates, and political indecision about how the United States will dispose of its high-level radioactive waste. The long (63 printed pages) and comprehensive law, entitled the Nuclear Waste Policy Act of 1982, sets schedules and timetables to provide a permanent deep-underground geologic repository for such waste in the mid-1990s. It also provides for funding the disposal system by a user fee on nuclear power generation (a method that puts the nuclear industry in the forefront among industries that generate toxic wastes). The nation's nuclear utilities are paying a special tax (1 mill/kWh) yielding as much as $400 million/yr to pay for storage costs, in exchange for the government's promise to start taking waste off their hands by 1998.

Finally, the act also makes provision for temporary storage of spent fuel until the first repository is ready to receive waste.

The law authorizes early demonstration of the technology for geologic disposal of high-level radioactive waste in a "Test-and-Evaluation Facility" (TEF). The DOE had to identify three sites, in at least two different geologic media, for the TEF within 1 yr after enactment of the act, that is, by December 21, 1983. By April 1990, 76 months later, DOE is to begin a testing program at the site selected for the TEF.

In July 1984, DOE is to nominate five candidate sites for the first full-scale permanent geologic repository. By January 1, 1985, it must select and recommend three of the five to the White House. The president has a year and three months, until March 31, 1987, to consult and select one of the three. The NRC must then decide by January 1, 1989, whether to license it—although the deadlines could be extended by 1 yr provided Congress is notified.

Then, by July 1, 1989, DOE must nominate a "second tier" of five candidate sites for the second repository, and by March 31, 1990, the president must select one of the five to be another full-scale permanent geologic repository.

Although the bill focuses specifically on radioactive waste from commercial power plants, it also provides a mechanism through which defense wastes eventually might also be stored in the same repositories. Military wastes have been accumulating for about 13 yr longer than civilian wastes, and by 1976 were more than 600 times greater in volume than civilian wastes. It was estimated that civilian waste would not reach 10% of military waste volume until well into the 1990s, and possibly only into the next century.

States will have the power to veto site selections within their borders, and the veto will stand unless overridden by majorities of both House and Senate acting within 60 days.

Until the first repository is ready to receive waste, alternative storage is provided for by the act. Two kinds of interim surface storage facilities are authorized: (1) For utilities having reactors that are running out of on-site storage space for spent fuel, the government may provide temporary storage at existing federal facilities for a limited amount (up to 1900 t) of spent fuel. (2) Another type of AFR storage authorized is a "monitored, retrievable storage" facility to be built to permit spent fuel to be stored until a decision is made whether the fuel is to be reprocessed, or stored as spent fuel. The act requires DOE to propose to Congress by June 1985 from three to five sites where such a surface storage facility would be built. These provisions for interim storage are important because there has been concern in the industry that some reactors might have to shut down if all available on-site storage space becomes so choked that it becomes impossible to discharge fuel to permit loading fresh fuel.

A summary of how the U.S. high-level waste program evolved is given in Table 15.10.

Technical Aspects of High-Level Waste Disposal

In the mid-1950s, Brookhaven and other national laboratories were working to develop suitable processes for stabilizing and neutralizing high-level waste. The Brookhaven process—vitrifying the waste in borosilicate glass—has since been taken over by, and is being used in France. This process, as proposed for use in the United States is as follows (refer to Figure 15.10).

The waste is sprayed as a liquid into a heated chamber. The moisture and other volatile liquids are driven off. When the material reaches the bottom of the chamber, it is in the form of calcine. This calcine powder is mixed, as it continues to fall, by means of convergent funnels with glass-making frit (mainly oxides of silicon, boron, and phosphorus) and tumbled into a stainless steel canister about 10 ft high, 0.5–2 ft in diameter, with 1-in.-thick walls. The canister during loading is inside a melter furnace. The temperature of the canister is raised to 1100°C, at which temperature the frit turns to molten glass. It is then allowed to cool into a glass log, in which each atom of high-level waste occupies a fixed location that cannot change once the glass has solidified. Thus the radioactive atoms of the waste are chemically stabilized, a quality of the glass itself, which is a

Table 15.10. Evolution of the U.S. High-Level Nuclear Waste Disposal Program

1957	National Academy of Sciences panel recommends salt deposits be examined as possible repository sites
1963–1967	Project Salt Vault at Lyons, Kansas
1968	Evaluation of Hanford basalts in Washington state begins
1970	Proposed Pilot Facility at Lyons, Kansas
1972	Withdrawal from Lyons, Kansas Search continues in Kansas, expanded to New Mexico U.S. Geological Survey (USGS) begins reconnaissance of Gulf Coast salt domes USGS begins reconnaissance in Paradox Basin in Utah and Colorado
1974	Waste Isolation Pilot Plant (WIPP) facility for defense wastes proposed for site in New Mexico Evaluation of salt domes begins
1976	National Waste Terminal Storage (NWTS) program announced Evaluation of geologic formations at Nevada Test Site (NTS) begins Evaluation of Permian Basin in Texas, excluding Delaware subbasin, begins
1977	Evaluation of Salina Salt Basin in Michigan, New York, and Ohio begins Evaluation of Palo Duro subbasin (Permian Basin) begins
1978	Study areas recommended in Gulf Coast and Salina Salt regions
1979	Interagency Review Group on Radioactive Waste Management (IRG) publishes report Work at WIPP, NTS, Hanford basalts, and four salt basins proceeds Evaluation of other (nonsalt) rock types begins Draft Environmental Impact Statement (EIS) on Management of Commercially Generated Radioactive Waste issued U.S. Nuclear Regulatory Commission (NRC) commences Proposed Rulemaking on the Storage of Nuclear Waste (Waste Confidence Rulemaking)
1980	Final Environmental Impact Statement (FEIS)—Management of Commercially Generated Radioactive Wastes issued Preliminary Surveys of existing data in national files on crystalline rocks completed Department of Energy files Statement of Position on NRC's Proposed Waste Confidence Rulemaking Proceeding
1981	Intensive site investigations begin at three locations, leading to design and construction of exploratory shafts; design of a test and evaluation facility begins Broad national survey of geologic environments and geohydrological provinces in cooperation with USGS begins
1983	Nuclear Waste Policy Act permits the storage of military wastes in commercial facilities; establishes a timetable leading to the construction authorization for two commercial high-level waste repositories by 1992

Source: DOE.

fused substance. Even if the inch-thick stainless steel canister could be broken or corrode, the high-level waste is fixed in the borosilicate glass which has very low solubility in water.

The next step in the process is to move the canister remotely from the furnace to an automatic welding machine where an end-cap is remotely welded on.

In a replica of the defense-in-depth principle that governs reactor design, the canister is then placed in an overpack of cast steel for radiation shielding and physical durability. This also facilitates handling of the contained waste. Next, the canister with its overpack are placed inside a metal or ceramic corrosion barrier.

After being lowered into the hole prepared in the host material underground, bentonite and crushed basalt are first backfilled around the overpack to retard the penetration of water and to act as an ion-exchange material to absorb any radioisotopes and retard their migration. Then a second

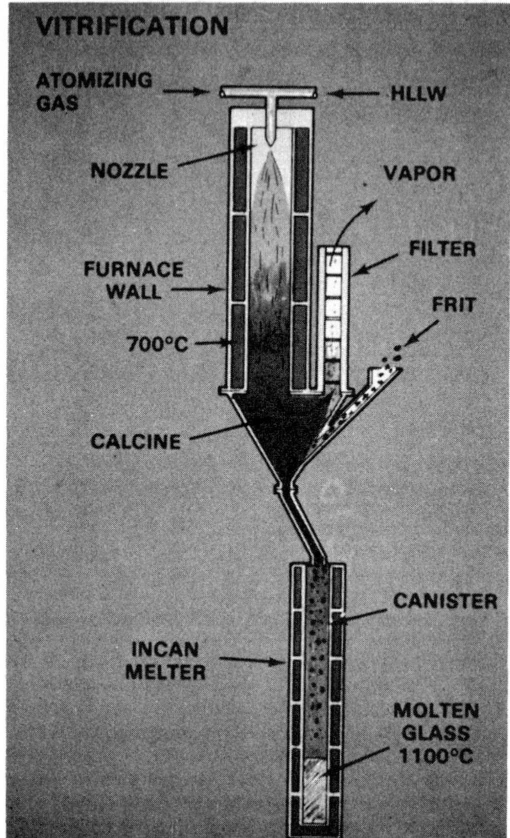

Figure 15.10. Vitrification step for HLW. (From Battelle PNWL.)

backfill of crushed rock is placed around the first, to facilitate heat transfer from the waste package and to ensure the integrity of the host rock.

The geology of the host material provides the last and major barrier. Candidate emplacement sites must show no water movement, and great geologic stability. Besides salt, other candidates presently being considered are granite, basalt, and tuff.

Scientific findings continue to accumulate regarding all the variants of the basic proposed technology for high-level waste disposal, and confirm and refine understanding of the mechanisms for waste-form corrosion and leaching, long-term behavior of engineered barrier materials, and the geology of specific sites.

Organization of the U.S. High-Level Waste Program

The National Waste Terminal Storage program (NWTS) was established in 1976 by ERDA, the precursor of DOE. Its mission is to provide storage facilities for commercial nuclear waste in geologic formations within the United States. Its program consists of investigating the properties of salt, granite, shale, and basalt to determine their suitability for terminal storage of high level radioactive waste, and to provide assurance that existing and future high-level radioactive waste from commercial activities can be isolated from the environment so as to pose no significant threat to public health and safety.

Lead responsibility in the NWTS is vested in the Office of Nuclear Waste Isolation (ONWI), a project management group established at Columbus, Ohio, and managed for DOE by Battelle Memorial Institute in Columbus. ONWI has oversight and coordinates all projects, development of the generic technology, and geologic exploration in all federal areas not managed by DOE. It directs and evaluates research and development studies carried out by national laboratories, universities, private R&D and engineering firms, and consultants.

These studies include work in waste packaging (waste form, engineered barriers and systems, design of package components); repository analysis and design (rock technology, near-term performance assessment, testing in situ and validation of models, repository equipment technology, instrumentation and monitoring, repository sealing); site qualification (long-term performance assessment, exploration, earth sciences investigations); and systems integration (criteria development, licensing and governmental environmental requirements).

ONWI's exploration and siting activities include studies of the feasibility of locating repositories in various types of geologic formations. Specific sites being investigated include salt formations in Mississippi, Louisiana, Texas, and Utah. Other areas, and other host materials such as shale and crystalline rock, are also under investigation.

Following the nationwide public hearings on the Draft Environmental Impact Statement on disposal of commercial radioactive waste, plans to use mined geologic repositories for such waste became the policy of DOE.

Such repositories will involve the sinking of vertical shafts 300–1000 m deep, development underground of a fishbone grid of horizontal galleries and chambers extending from the base of the vertical shaft, and placing the waste—in canisters with overpacks, as described earlier in this chapter—in holes drilled into the floor of the galleries.

From that point on, two alternatives present themselves: if the waste canisters are to be retrievable, only the holes around each canister will be backfilled, as described above; if, on the other hand, it is decided that retrievability is not necessary or desirable, then the chambers and galleries will be completely backfilled and sealed, and the vertical shaft itself backfilled and sealed.

In this connection, a retrievability consideration might some day come into play, but *prior* to vitrification. Oak Ridge National Laboratory has been working to develop an economic process for separating out of liquid high-level waste certain valuable fission products that are strategic metals, such as rhodium, ruthenium, and palladium. At 1982 prices for these metals—$225, $50, and $40 per troy ounce, respectively—there is an incentive to recover these metals present among fission products. They are essential because of their catalytic properties, electric conductivity, and resistance to chemical corrosion. The United States produces less than 2% of its requirement for these metals. By 1990, spent fuel discharged each year will contain approximately half our annual needs for these metals.

Recovery of these, and possibly other, strategic metals from reactor waste is technically and economically not yet a reality, but may be borne in mind.

Demonstration Projects

For the last several years, two experimental demonstration programs have been under way to test and observe the behavior of high-level waste canisters actually emplaced in holes drilled in geologic host rock: one at the Nevada Test Site, and one at the Hanford Nuclear Reservation. These locations were selected because they are both vast in size and federally owned, remote from population centers, and both already have radiological safety programs. Also both are arid regions with satisfactory groundwater conditions.

At the Nevada site, the geologic medium that is the focus of the work is tuffaceous rock—welded tuffs, that is, heat-fused volcanic ash. At Hanford, the geologic medium is basalt rock, of which there are thick dense layers. Both of these projects are in line with the emphasis of the Nuclear Waste Terminal Storage program to evaluate the suitability of potential repository sites, and potential geologic host materials.

The Nevada Nuclear Waste Storage Investigations (referred to as NNWSI) were formally organized in 1977. They are to determine whether selected underground rock on, or adjoining, the Nevada Test site is technically acceptable for a licensed commercial repository for spent reactor fuel or for high-level radioactive waste. The program is managed by DOE's Nevada Operations Office, and principal participants include the Los Alamos, Lawrence Livermore, and Sandia National Laboratories, the U.S. Geological Survey, and Westinghouse Electric Corp.

The studies also aim to develop or improve technology for safely handling, storing, and disposing of highly radioactive waste.

The Nevada Test Site (Figure 15.11) has a variety of potentially acceptable geologic media for disposal. The welded tuffs have been the subject of laboratory and field experiments for more than 2 yr. An interim status report for the National Academy of Sciences concluded in October 1980 that tuffaceous rocks are acceptable for a nuclear waste repository on the basis of present knowledge. One drill hole was continuously cored, logged, and hydrologically tested down to 6000 ft, near the center of the tuff block. A second stratigraphic hole is being drilled down to 6000 ft. Other holes have been drilled for hydrologic tests, to test for groundwater and permeability.

Underground radionuclide migration and rock mechanics experiments in tuff are also under

Figure 15.11. Spent fuel storage facility at a depth of 420 m in the Climax granite at the Nevada Test Site. Canisters containing the spent reactor fuel are lowered through an access hole into the white railcar cask shown at the far end of this drift. The railcar can then be positioned over any of the 17 storage holes in the floor of the drift. The canister is lowered by remote control into the storage hole, where it will remain for 5 yr. The purpose of the test is to evaluate the feasibility of storing spent reactor fuel in a typical granitic medium. Electrical heaters, which simulate the thermal field of a large nuclear waste repository, are located in drifts parallel to the one shown here. (Courtesy DOE.)

way, to develop accurate models of radionuclide migration and retardation, under both natural and man-made conditions, such as may be encountered in a commercial repository. The rock mechanics studies will determine the response in situ of tuffaceous rocks to stresses critical to a repository design.

A valuable resource at the Nevada Test Station is NASA's old E-MAD facility (Engine Maintenance, Assembly, and Disassembly)—a building designed and built for working with highly radioactive experimental nuclear engines for rockets. It is being used to develop the technology of handling and encapsulating spent fuel assemblies, in the event that the throwaway fuel cycle is adopted. As the building and its equipment were designed to work remotely with experimental reactors, it was relatively easy to adapt them for work with spent fuel and experimental storage canisters to contain it.

Temporary surface and near-surface methods for storing spent reactor fuel are being evaluated next to the E-MAD building. Such methods can serve to cool heat-generating radioactive materials before final disposal, or to provide overflow storage capacity for spent fuel should all existing storage locations become filled.

Two temporary storage methods are being tested. One holds spent fuel canisters in a surface, sealed concrete storage silo that is designed to eliminate external radiation, and to withstand being tipped over by an earthquake without significant damage. This reinforced concrete silo is 21 ft high and 9 ft in diameter, weighs about 95 tons, and is placed on a reinforced concrete pad 6 ft thick, and 14 ft square. The silo is instrumented to measure container temperatures and other parameters.

The second method of temporary storage uses near-surface dry wells to store spent fuel canisters. These 25-ft deep wells, spaced 20 ft apart, are in line in the center of railroad tracks laid especially for the equipment to lower canisters into the wells. The holes are 28 in. in diameter, fitted with 18-in.-diameter steel liners cemented in place. Figure 15.9*a* has already conceptually illustrated these two storage methods.

Besides the work in tuff, a new host medium has been under investigation at the Nevada Test Site since 1980. Lawrence Livermore National Laboratory has been conducting these tests, in granite. The test facility consists of three parallel galleries joined at each end, excavated in granite 1400 ft below the surface. In the spring of 1980, 11 spent fuel canisters were transported from the E-MAD building, where they had been encapsulated, to the top of the access hole in a special transport cask. They were lowered the 1400 ft to the gallery level into a remotely controlled vehicle which emplaced them in steel-lined storage holes in the granite floor one by one. Six other identical holes contain electrically heated canisters that match the thermal characteristics of the spent fuel canisters. This arrangement will permit determining if radiation causes any effect on the surrounding rock that could adversely affect its ability to contain nuclear waste. The two outer galleries also contain electric heaters that produce a thermal environment in the rock surrounding the storage gallery to simulate the center of a large repository. This will provide data on how an underground crystalline rock formation responds to heat loads such as may be generated in an actual radioactive waste repository. One of the outer galleries is also instrumented to measure any migration of radionuclides in granite.

The shipping casks developed to transport spent fuel or reprocessed high-level waste have also been actually put to the test at the Nevada Test Site. A cask placed on a railroad flatcar was deliberately struck head-on by a locomotive going at 80 mph. A film made of this impact shows the cask bouncing slightly in the air, and coming to rest with a minimal dent and some scratched paint.

Meanwhile, at Hanford, Washington, a near-surface test facility has been excavated in the basalt lava flows at Gable Mountain.

Battelle Pacific Northwest Laboratory, which has done much of the development work on fixing reprocessed fission-product wastes in borosilicate glass, has made several canisters of glass logs containing fixed radioactive waste. Two of these will be emplaced in one gallery 150 ft below the surface. Another gallery will contain electric heaters to simulate the thermal heat of the nuclear waste.

A transfer room is located at each end of the gallery that contains the canisters. Measuring 39 ft high and 32 ft wide, these transfer rooms will be used to transfer the canisters from the shipping truck to the bottom-loading transporter that lowers them into the prepared holes.

Data have already been obtained on the thermochemical behavior of basalt from the electrical heaters simulating real waste. It was reported that measurements of the magnitude and distribution of temperature and stress were within a few percent of calculations made prior to the tests.

Cost estimates have been made for radioactive waste disposal. DOE has estimated direct life-cycle costs for a repository in a salt dome at $9 billion (1981 dollars) over 24-yr life. This is for a repository containing 65,000 spent fuel packages, 60,000 drums of transuranic waste, and 23,000 packages of fuel end-fittings and hardware.

One expensive item where cost reductions are being sought is in the canisters. A titanium canister to contain a single spent PWR fuel assembly is estimated to cost from $30,000 to $50,000.

Other factors that have an impact on cost include the number of repositories required. It is now believed that two or three would be required; one large one would cost less, but political considerations and reduced transportation cost furnish incentives for regional repositories.

Another factor is the age of the waste. DOE currently plans that all waste be at least 10 yr old, but substantial reductions in cost could be achieved if the waste were allowed to age longer. For example, it is estimated that four times as much spent fuel can be placed in a single package if it is 100 yr old instead of 10.

It should be noted that the foregoing cost estimates are based on the throwaway cycle. If waste were disposed of as reprocessed, separated fission products, 16 times less volume would be required, and there would be other savings—for example, titanium canisters would not be required, stainless steel could be used.

The choice of host medium will have only a minimal effect on costs. Estimated construction costs in 1982 dollars for a 2000-acre repository with a capacity of 160,000 canisters holding 68,000 t of spent fuel is $2.17 billion in bedded salt, $2.49 billion in domed salt, and $3.15 billion for basalt and for granite.

High as these figures may appear, DOE declares that management costs for waste disposal will add only 3% to the total cost of nuclear power. The federal government will pay the initial costs, and has established a fund in perpetuity to recover these costs over time from the electric power companies. Regarding total volume of waste produced, a single large reactor running a full year produces about 2 m^3 (70 ft^3), the size of four standard filing cabinets; and that even if the U.S. nuclear program were to expand rapidly, the total volume of waste generated annually in the year 2000 could fit in a cube 12 m (40 ft) on a side.

To conclude this review of U.S. activities to develop secure storage of radioactive waste, it may be noted that the National Academy of Sciences, the American Physical Society, and the 40-nation International Nuclear Fuel Cycle Evaluation have all recommended that disposal of nuclear waste

Table 15.11. Solid Form Containment Options

Primary	Secondary	Container
Ceramic materials	Metals	Mild steel
Supercalcine	Cement	Stainless steel
Low-temperature ceramics	Glass	Titanium
High-temperature ceramics		Copper
Fuel pellets		Concrete
Glass		Alumina or other ceramics

Source: From NUREG/CR-0895.

in a mined geologic repository is a safe and acceptable approach. Likewise, the Interagency Review Group on nuclear waste management in its final report to President Carter stated that no scientific or technical reason is known that would prevent identifying a suitable site for a waste repository.

Solidification of High-Level Wastes

Solidification of liquid high-level wastes is required for nearly all proposed waste management schemes. The purpose of solidification is to minimize the migration of radionuclides, that is, provide a barrier to the release of the radioactivity to the environment. Many choices are available; the choice of a particular method, however, is dependent on the geologic medium into which the wastes will be placed and the other barriers that will be engineered into the waste repository.

A solid waste cask provides at least three levels of containment for radionuclides: (1) the primary phase, which contains the radioactivity at the molecular level, (2) a secondary phase, which binds the primary phase particles into a matrix, and (3) the tertiary level, the container itself. Some of the options for these three levels are listed in Table 15.11. Under consideration are glass and ceramic materials for the primary phase; metals, cement, and glass for the secondary phase; and highly corrosion-resistant metals for the container. The cask is the first of a succession of barriers that isolate the waste from the environment. This is shown in Figure 15.12, where the functions of the various barriers are explained. The last barrier to radioactivity release is the geologic formation itself, which eventually becomes the real container.

Intermediate Containment Forms

Some primary waste solid forms have excellent properties† for the final emplacement in the geologic medium; others are intermediate forms that do not necessarily have what is ultimately required. Further processing is required to convert the latter to final forms. The intermediate containment forms usually considered are:

1. *Calcine*—an unconsolidated powder (or granules) resulting from the evaporation and partial decomposition of high-level liquid wastes.
2. *Super calcine*—a crystalline assemblage made like calcine except aluminum and calcium nitrates are added to increase its thermodynamic stability and reduce its solubility.‡
3. *Super sludge§*—a solid/liquid slurry of high-level wastes converted by the addition of clay and aluminosilicates into a modified form with greatly reduced leachability.

Before final disposal, any intermediate form used would be further consolidated. Several means of consolidation are available; the ones most considered are ceramic and glass, although Portland cement or a metal could also be used. An evaluation of the various options is given in Table 15.12 which shows their degree of acceptability for manufacturing, flexibility of composition and physical properties. Some of the options, such as Supercalcine, have not been fully demonstrated.

Final Waste Forms

High-level waste forms (see Figure 15.13) considered for final repository are:

†Low leachability, low dispersability, high thermal conductivity, and so on.
‡By a factor of 10^4 or more.
§Pertains mainly to high-level military wastes.

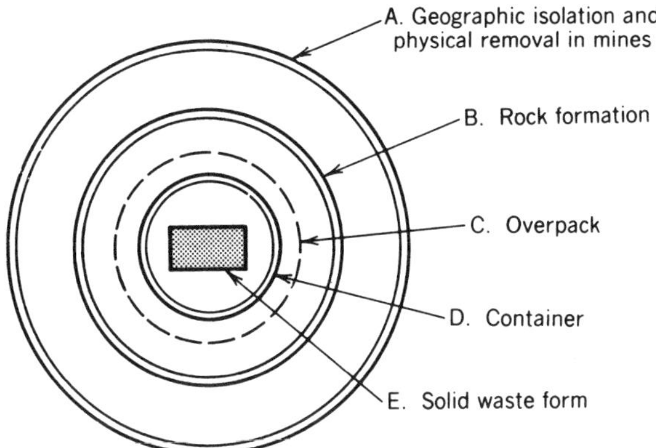

Figure 15.12. Multiple barrier concept for disposal of nuclear wastes. A. The outermost protection is provided by geographic isolation in mines or excavated vaults. B. The rock formation eventually will react chemically and physically with the waste to complete the long-term isolation. C. The waste is separated from the rock by an optional overpack, which can be a mineral powder that absorbs radionuclides. D. The container provides protection, particularly during shipping and during the retrievable phase after emplacement. E. The solid waste form is a major barrier during transportation, after emplacement, and after reaction with the host rock. (From NUREG/CR-0895.)

1. *Ceramics.* These are insoluble, nonmetallic materials composed of crystalline oxides. They are able to contain the hazardous isotopes, such as ^{137}Cs, in a thermodynamically stable phase. One ceramic candidate is SYNROC, an Australian developed material of specific natural minerals† that can hold up to 10% wastes. It is produced by hot pressing at 1200–1300°C. Supercalcine itself, or mixed with glass frit, can also be consolidated into ceramic at high temperature (1200°C) or by using a somewhat lower temperature (1000°C) and high pressure.
2. *Glass.* This is an amorphous material comprised largely of Si, B, and O (borosilicate)‡ when manufactured for radioactive waste disposal. A wide range of fission products can be accommodated because of the geometrical flexibility afforded by unordered glass structures.§ Also because of this unordered structure, glass has an intrinsic resistance to radiation damage. Glasses containing radioactive wastes can be produced by melting a mixture of calcine and glass-making components. In some cases, the melting vessel itself can form the waste container. Glass, however, can be difficult to process since the conversion of waste into the glass state requires handling of hot vapors and corrosive fluids.
3. *Spent Fuel Assemblies.* Unreprocessed fuel can serve as a final waste form since the nonvolatile fission products are retained by the ceramic UO_2 matrix. The cladding, if intact, provides an additional barrier.

The choice among the options is a trade-off between various economic and engineering parameters. The "best" choice may not be needed; what is required is an adequate solution to the waste problem. Each of the above can provide the desired waste isolation if properly engineered. Although in some instances additional testing to establish leach resistance, radiation stability, and long-term aging characteristics is needed before a final selection is made, several candidate waste disposal designs appear acceptable.

Size and Design of a High-Level Waste Repository

A typical repository design might call for a central area of about 400 surface acres. The central area will be within an inner controlled area of approximately 2000 acres, equivalent in dimensions to the

†Contains perovskite ($CaTiO_3$) which can dissolve rare earths and Sr; hollandite ($Ba(K)AlTi_3O_8$) which can dissolve Mo, Ru, and Rh; zirconia (ZrO_2), which can dissolve actinides; and calsitite ($KAlSiO_4$), which can dissolve Rb and Cs.
‡Borosilicate glass is used because it is much less leachable than other types of glass, although aluminosilicate glasses are sometimes considered.
§Crystalline minerals can only accommodate atoms of specific size and valence.

Table 15.12. Acceptability of Intermediate Radioactive Waste Forms

	Concrete Bitumen Plastics	Inorganic Materials	Glasses	Glass-Ceramics	Supercalcine	Synthetic Minerals (SYNROC)	Coated Particles	Metal Matrix Products
Manufacturing process	✓	✓	✓	✓	ND	ND	✓	✓
							Involves additional handling operations	
Maximum formation temp.	Low	?	✓	✓	✓	High	✓	✓
Flexibility of product composition	✓	?	✓	?	?	?	✓	✓
Waste content	✓	Low	✓	✓	Could be high	Low	✓	✓
Nature of additives	✓	✓	✓	✓	✓	✓	✓	✓
Leach resistance	X	✓	✓	✓	✓	NP	Could be very good	
Volatility	?	?	✓	✓	✓	?	✓	✓
Radiation stability	X	NP	✓	✓	NP	NP	✓	✓
Thermal stability	X	NP	✓	✓	NP	NP	✓	✓
Conductivity	X	Poor	✓	✓	✓	?	✓	High
Compatibility	✓	✓	✓ Provided not phosphate	✓	✓	✓	✓	✓
Mechanical strength	?	✓	✓ Provided it is devitrified	✓	✓	✓	✓	✓

Source: From DOE Report, *Radioactive Waste Management*, Vol. 1., 1980.

Key: ✓, acceptable; ND, not demonstrated; NP, not proven. X, not acceptable; ?, doubtful.

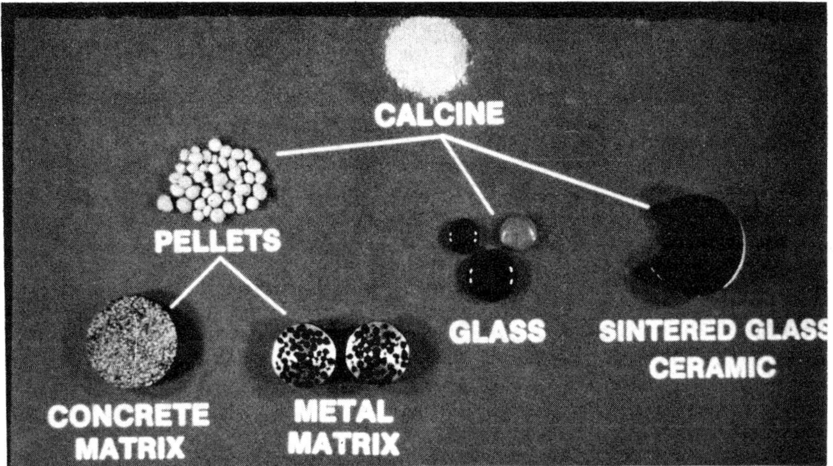

Figure 15.13. High-level waste alternatives. (Courtesy Allied Chemical Co.)

underground working repository plus a buffer zone of a minimum of 800 ft. There will be restrictions on surface and subsurface activities within the inner controlled area. The outer controlled area will extend a minimum of $1\frac{1}{4}$ miles beyond the outside perimeter of the inner controlled area. The outer controlled area will have restrictions on subsurface activities, including drilling and mining.

In the United States, the exact sizes of the outer and inner controlled areas at each repository site will vary depending on final criteria developed by the Nuclear Regulatory Commission, the site, the size of the repository to be constructed, the geometrical configuration of the repository, and other considerations.

The underground area of the repository will resemble a large mine, covering approximately 800 hectares (2000 acres), and be 600–1200 m (2000–4000 ft) below ground. A conceptual design of such a repository is given in Figure 15.14.

Engineered Repositories

Plans for high-level waste disposal in deep geologic storage include engineered barriers to prevent the migration of radioactive waste. These barriers provide varying degrees of protection in different time frames, as shown in Table 15.13. Dispersion of the radioactivity over time is prevented (or greatly retarded) by the following:

1. The radioactive elements are chemically bound in a matrix, such as glass.
2. The matrix is then enclosed in a canister which may consist of several successive metal layers, such as stainless steel or titanium.
3. A buffer material with high stability and low water permeability surrounds the waste canister. The buffer has an ion-exchanging capacity which would prevent the rapid dispersal of radioactivity (Tables 15.14 and 15.15 give some possible materials for this purpose).
4. The rock or salt formation has no, or only limited, amounts of groundwater motion.

One engineered repository system, developed in Sweden for use in granite, is shown in Figure 15.15. This concept for the final deposition of metal canisters with nuclear wastes uses drilled vertical holes with a spacing of about 6 m. The holes will extend from the floor of tunnels about 500 m deep in crystalline rock. The design for unreprocessed wastes shown in the figure would be modified if the waste was reprocessed. The canisters are surrounded by compacted bentonite,† while the tunnel is backfilled with a mixture of bentonite and sand.

†Bentonite is the geological name for a smectite-rich clay. The smectite gives the clay a large surface area, high ion-exchange capacity, and a strong affinity for water which causes it to swell (see Chapter 4).

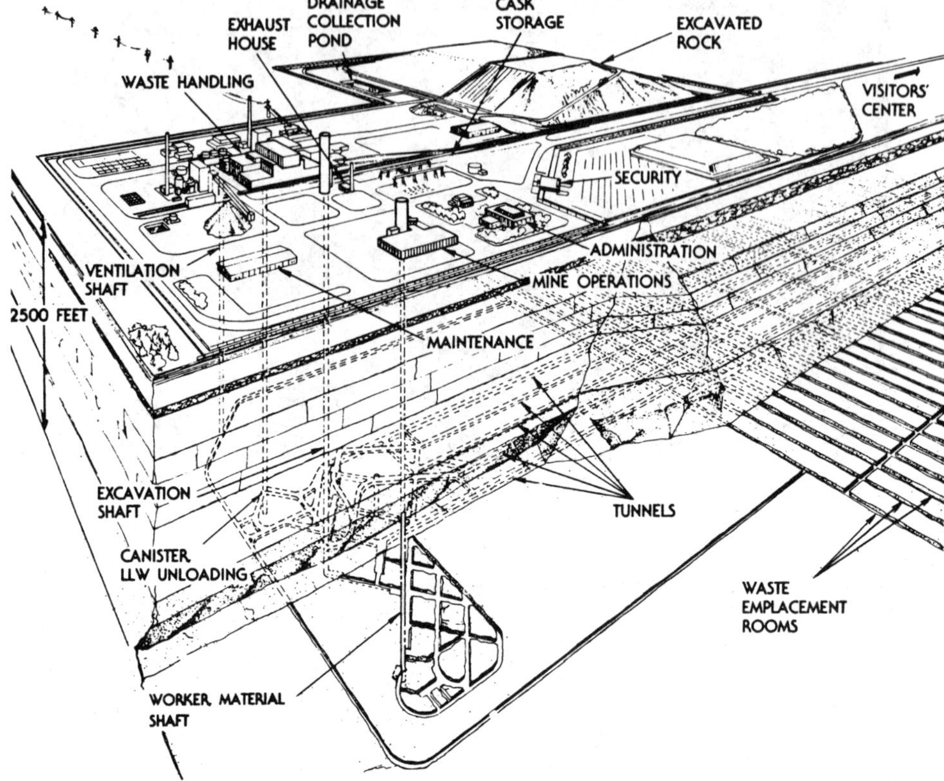

Figure 15.14. This artist's concept illustrates the surface support buildings and underground facilities of a high-level waste repository. (Courtesy DOE.)

Various combinations of containment and backfill materials are possible. Each combination has its advantages. The repository design, however, must consider the relative solubility of the key radionuclides given in Table 15.16, and the retardation values for each of these nuclides for various materials. As an example, the relative performance of basalt, illite, and bentonite as filler materials is shown in Table 15.17. As seen in this table, no one filler is best for every radionuclide. This is the reason why these filler materials are often used in combination. The engineering design goal is to provide multiple barriers *for each of the important nuclides*. Figure 15.16 illustrates an analysis for various combinations of materials in a repository design and how they perform relative to each other. Studies such as this are important in establishing an optimum design.

The engineered materials in a repository must be also capable of withstanding heat and radiation. Figure 15.17 gives the heat generation rate and radiation conditions for one particular canister design. The rate at which a repository's integrity diminishes depends on these parameters. For instance, if 350°C could exist in a repository, any glass used in the matrix would become completely altered in a few decades. The heat and radiation fields might also increase the thermal stress on the host geologic medium, leading to fissures. However, with proper repository design and operations, heat and radiation should not be a problem.

Transportation

Transportation is a necessary link in all fuel cycle activities, and is especially important in the disposal of high-level radioactive wastes. In the past, spent fuel has been moved with relative ease and only a few minor accidents. In the United States, transportation is subject to the rules of the Department of Transportation and the NRC. Similar rules have been developed by the IAEA for use throughout the world.

Spent fuel and high-level wastes are transported by truck or railroad in specially designed casks. Figure 15.18 shows one such cask. Another design specifically for rail transportation is given in

Table 15.13. Barrier Function Versus Time

Item	Barrier	Operating Period	Function
1	Geology (basalt)	1. Thermal period[a]	Supplementary chemical barrier to radionuclide migration
		2. Geologic control[b]	Primary chemical barrier to radionuclide migration
		3. Repository life[c]	Physical isolation of waste material from man
2	Backfill	1. Thermal period	Primary chemical barrier to radionuclide migration Inhibit groundwater intrusion
		2. Geologic control	Secondary chemical barrier
3	Overpack	Thermal period	Primary physical barrier to groundwater intrusion Aids in retrievability
4	Buffer	Thermal period	Chemically inhibit canister corrosion in event of failed overpack
5	Canister	1. Preemplacement[d]	Provide physical support and protection for waste form
		2. Thermal period	Supplement to overpack preventing groundwater intrusion Permit retrievability
		3. Geologic control	Primary physical barrier to groundwater intrusion
6	Waste form	Preemplacement and repository life	Retard release of radionuclides in the event of containment failure

Source: From B. J. Wood, *Nuclear Technology* **58,** 271 (1982).
[a]Time before 1000 yr of operation.
[b]Time after 1000 yr of operation.
[c]Thermal period + geologic control.
[d]Time from canister filling to emplacement in the repository.

Table 15.14. Possible Chemi-Sorber Minerals for Nuclear Waste Disposal Backfill Component

Mineral	Composition	Radionuclides Solved
Apatite	$Ca_5(OH,F)(PO_4)_3$	All actinides
Monazite	$(Th,\text{rare earth})PO_4$	All actinides
Vivianite	$Fe_3(PO_4)_2$	All actinides
Calcite	$CaCO_3$	Trivalent actinides
Dolomite	$(Ca,Mg)CO_3$	Trivalent actinides
Barite	$BaSO_4$	Strontium
Gypsum	$CaSO_4{\cdot}2H_2O$	Strontium
Cinnabar	HgS	I^-
Chalcocite	Cu_2S	I^-
Galena	PbS	I^-,IO_3^-

Source: From G. W. Beall and B. Allard, *Nuclear Technology* **59,** 405 (1982).

Table 15.15. Composition of a Backfill Material for Nuclear Waste Disposal

Mineral	Composition (%)
Quartz	60–70
Montmorillonite	15–20
Apatite or monazite	2–5
Barite	2–5
Chalcocite	2–5
Fe(II) mineral	2–5
Ellite and attapulgite	2–5

Source: From G. W. Beall and B. Allard, *Nuclear Technology* **59,** 405 (1982).

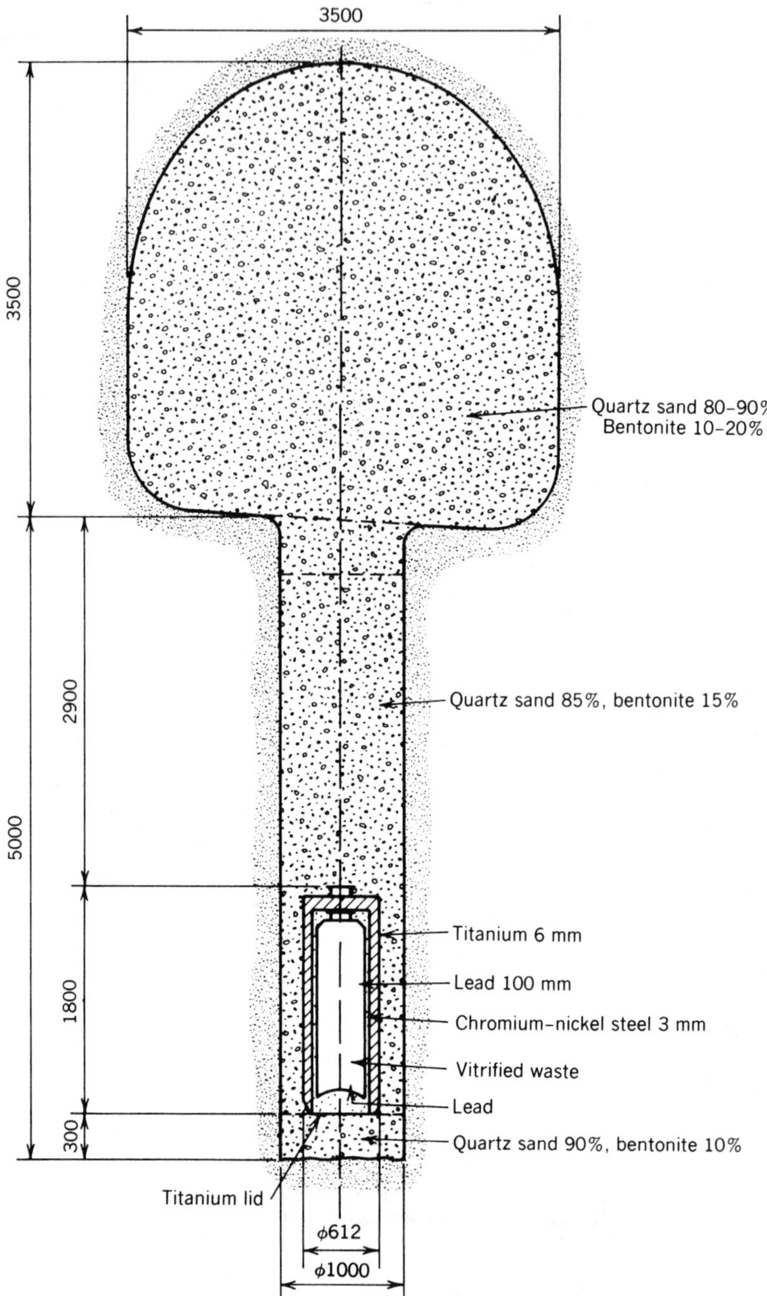

Figure 15.15. The Swedish KBS final repository. Tunnels and storage holes are completely filled with a buffer material consisting of quartz sand and bentonite. All dimensions are in millimeters. (From EPRI Report NP-1087.)

Table 15.16. Estimated Solubilities for Key Nuclides

Key Nuclides	Nuclide Half-Life, yr	Element Solubility-C_0, g/cm^3
^{231}Pa	3.28×10^4	1.0×10^{-9}
^{135}Cs	2.3×10^6	4.5×10^{-6}
^{129}I	1.6×10^7	1.3×10^{-4}
^{126}Sn	1×10^5	1.9×10^{-6}
^{99}Tc	2.1×10^5	1.0×10^{-8}
^{79}Se	1×10^4	1.0×10^{-5}
^{59}Ni	8×10^4	1.9×10^{-5}
^{14}C	5730	1.54×10^{-5}

Source: Adapted from S. G. Oston and D. M. Brown, TASC Report TR-3336-4 (1982).

Table 15.17. Relative Retention Time of Various Filler Materials for Key Nuclides

Key Nuclides	Crushed Basalt	Illite Clay	Bentonite Clay
^{231}Pa	16	250	250
^{135}Cs	900	2000	160
^{129}I	7	1	1
^{126}Sn	150	1	1
^{99}Tc	300	6	6
^{79}Se	34	1	16
^{59}Ni	150	1	1
^{14}C	7	1	1

Source: From S. G. Oston and D. M. Brown, TASC Report TR-3336-4 (1982).

Figure 15.19. These casks are designed to dissipate heat and to shield against radiation,† while being able to withstand any credible accident without losing integrity. The availability of transportation equipment is a problem. The current number of commercial casks available to move such wastes is limited.

Salt Versus Granite

Salt and granite are leading candidates as host media for high-level radioactive waste disposal. Large deposits of each cover vast areas of the United States (see Chapter 4). The selection of the host geologic structure is a key parameter in the engineering of a repository design.

Salt deposits conduct heat rapidly away from the waste containers. Moreover, salt beds are easy to mine. Since salt is highly soluble, intact salt beds are proof that no groundwater exists in the area. However, unresolved issues relative to using salt include long-term thermal stability of the deposits and the possibility that future groundwater intrusion might occur. The heat generated by the waste poses a problem because brine, which occurs naturally in salt deposits,‡ will migrate toward the heat source. This might lead to accelerated corrosion or movement of the canister. How the latter would operate is shown in Figure 15.20.

Granite, on the other hand, has a greater mechanical stability than salt, although the exclusion of groundwater is more difficult to guarantee because granitic rock is not monolithic, but contains fissures. Salt's higher thermal conductivity is balanced by the higher heat capacity of granite; in fact, the temperatures in granite may even be lower than in salt. Salt, because it is self-sealing and, unlike rock, does not suffer permanent cracks under the pressure of earth movements, is currently

†The radiation dose to a person living within 100 ft of the route of a vehicle containing spent fuel (or high-level waste) would be below 0.001 mrem per shipment.
‡Brine was trapped in the salt (0.5%) when it precipitated out of ancient seas.

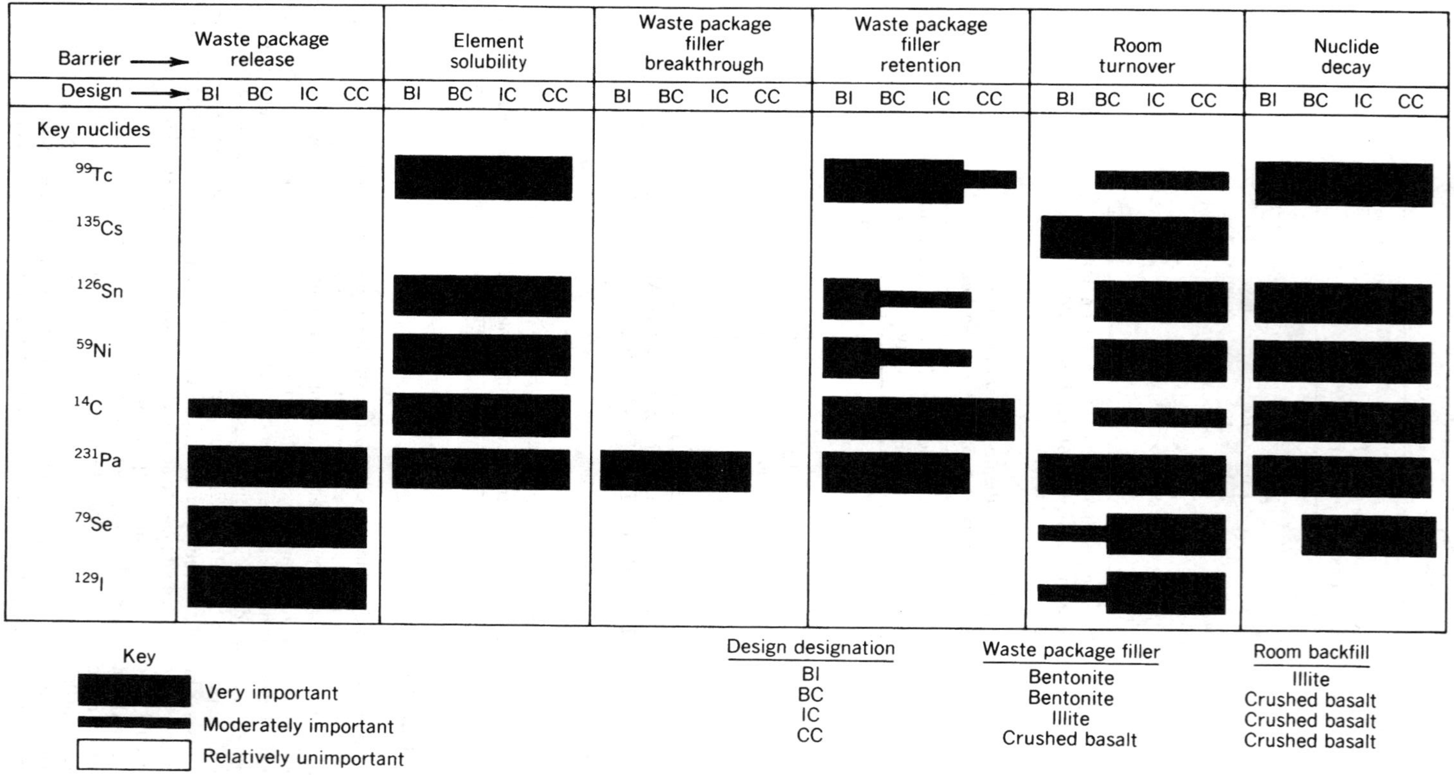

Barrier → Waste package release | Element solubility | Waste package filler breakthrough | Waste package filler retention | Room turnover | Nuclide decay

Design → BI BC IC CC | BI BC IC CC | BI BC IC CC | BI BC IC CC | BI BC IC CC | BI BC IC CC

Key nuclides

^{99}Tc

^{135}Cs

^{126}Sn

^{59}Ni

^{14}C

^{231}Pa

^{79}Se

^{129}I

Key

Very important

Moderately important

Relatively unimportant

Design designation	Waste package filler	Room backfill
BI	Bentonite	Illite
BC	Bentonite	Crushed basalt
IC	Illite	Crushed basalt
CC	Crushed basalt	Crushed basalt

Figure 15.16. Relative importance of basalt repository engineered barriers for key nuclides and disposal designs. [From S. G. Oston and D. M. Brown, TASC Report TR-3336-4 (1982).]

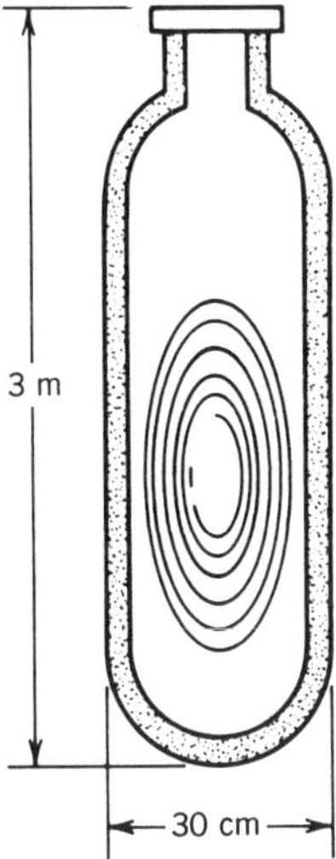

Decay Time, yr	Heat Generation Rate, kW	Cumulative α Dose/g	Dose-Rate 30 cm from Surface
1	22	1.0×10^{17}	1.1×10^{8} R/hr
10	3.1	2.5×10^{17}	6.2×10^{4}
100	0.36	7.1×10^{17}	5.8×10^{3}
1000	0.02	1.5×10^{18}	1.6
10,000	0.006	3.0×10^{18}	1.3
100,000	0.003	6.1×10^{18}	0.6

Can material—304L SS.
Volume—0.21 m^3.
Contents—2.5 t U equivalent.

Figure 15.17. Typical high-level waste canister. (From EPRI Report NP-1087.)

regarded as the best insulator for hot wastes. The best choice, however, is not clearcut and either may prove to be adequate. The United States and Germany intend to use salt deposits for their demonstration repositories, while Sweden is considering granite.

Glass Versus SYNROC

Glass in not a solid but a supercooled liquid. When glass hardens, it forms no set chemical pattern or structure—this is important for its stability and radiation resistance. All glass is a mixture of solids: sand-based silicates, modifiers such as sodium, and stabilizing compounds such as lime. Boron is used in place of sodium in glass used for radioactive waste disposal, because the glass then

Figure 15.18. Full- and half-size cast-iron spent fuel shipping storage cask. Note minor damage on lip of smaller cask caused by a 10 m drop test. (Courtesy Gesellschaft für Nuclear Service.)

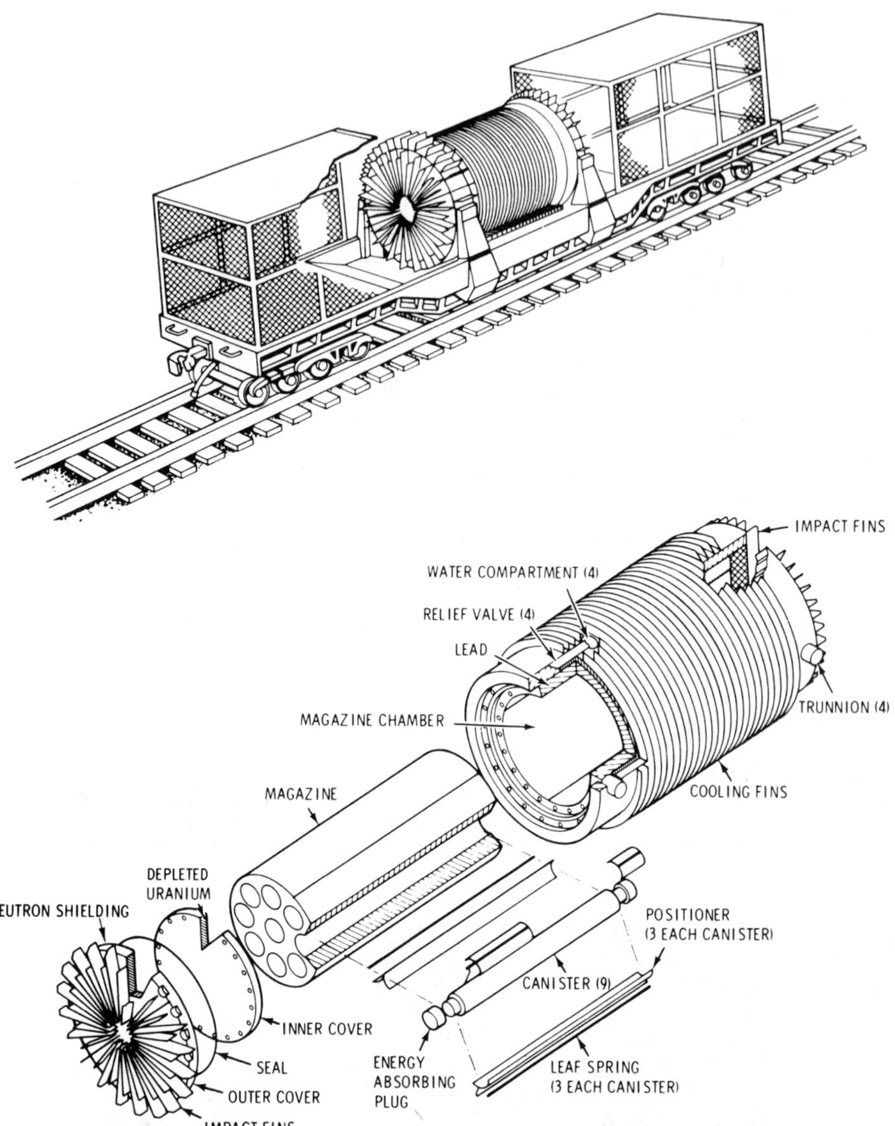

Figure 15.19. Conceptual solidified high-level waste shipping cask and railcar. (From EPRI Report NP-1087.)

melts at a lower temperature, reducing the amount of fission products volatilized by the process. One concern with glass is its ability to resist weathering, in particular, the leaching of the radioactivity by hot, high-pressure groundwater. The solution to the weathering process is the development of a low-leachable glass form, and the forming of glass in large blocks; with a low surface-to-volume ratio, only a small outer layer would be exposed. Although some glasses weather easily, others have survived 3000 yr in harsh conditions without extensive weathering. Nuclear wastes, buried deep in the earth, would not be exposed to as destructive environments as some of these ancient glasses have endured.

SYNROC is a synthetic rock material originally developed by A.E. Ringwood of Australia as an alternative to borosilicate glass. Some types of SYNROC retain strontium, cesium, actinides, and rare earth elements considerably more efficiently than glass. The concept borrows from nature—the minerals that comprise SYNROC are those that contain nuclear wastes and exhibit long-term

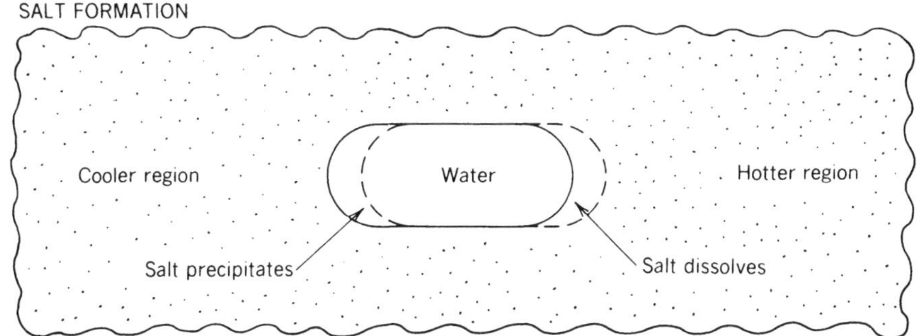

Figure 15.20. In salt, the heat from a waste canister would cause the migration of tiny pockets of water in the direction of the higher temperature, since the salt would tend to go into solution on the hotter side of the pocket (right) and to precipitate out of solution on the cooler side (left). [From B. Cohen, *Scientific American* (June 1977).]

stability. To synthesize SYNROC, the components of the minerals (titanium, zirconium, calcium, and aluminum oxides) are blended with an aqueous radwaste slurry and dried by spraying. The dried powder is then calcined at 800°C and hot pressed in a graphite die for about 1 hr at 15–30 MPa. Although more expensive than borosilicate glass, SYNROC can accept high radwaste concentrations, thereby requiring a smaller repository. However, it is more complex to manufacture and a consistently good product may be difficult to obtain. While the "best" waste form for radioactive waste disposal cannot yet be chosen, both borosilicate glass and SYNROC appear adequate; borosilicate glass is the near-term choice for most designs because it is more technologically mature, while SYNROC may perhaps prove to be an improved concept.

System Modeling

Licensing and siting criteria can be established using a systems approach referred to as the Retention Quotient (RQ) methodology. This approach establishes an acceptable radioactivity release rate to the environment rather than making each barrier in the migration path as formidable as possible, with no regard to cost or potential hazard. The RQ method is a simple, effective way of evaluating the safety performance of the overall repository system.

The ability of a geologic repository to contain nuclear waste material is evaluated in terms of the *multibarrier* framework. Barriers are impediments to the flow of radionuclides from their initial location in the repository to man. They have a number of important characteristics:

1. Barriers may be either *natural* or *man-made.*
2. They may be *consecutive* (in series) or *redundant* (in parallel).
3. Barriers may be *nuclide specific*, that is, effective against certain components of the waste, but not against others.
4. Barriers may be effective only in certain time periods.
5. They may act in such a way as to retard or slow the transport velocity of the various nuclides.
6. Barriers act independently, for the most part, although interactions among the various barriers are sometimes important.

In evaluating a nuclear waste repository, the total dose to man can be divided by an "allowable" dose consistent with health effects to obtain a dimensionless quantity, the RQ. To be more quantitative:

Q_i = Total inventory of isotope *i* in a body of waste material (Ci)
DF_i = The ingestion dose factor for isotope *i* that results in a 50-year dose commitment to an individual (rem/Ci-yr)
DC = Dose Criterion, a legislated allowable annual dose (rem/yr), for example, 1 mrem/year.

Then,

$$RQ = \frac{1}{DC} \sum_i Q_i(DF_i)$$

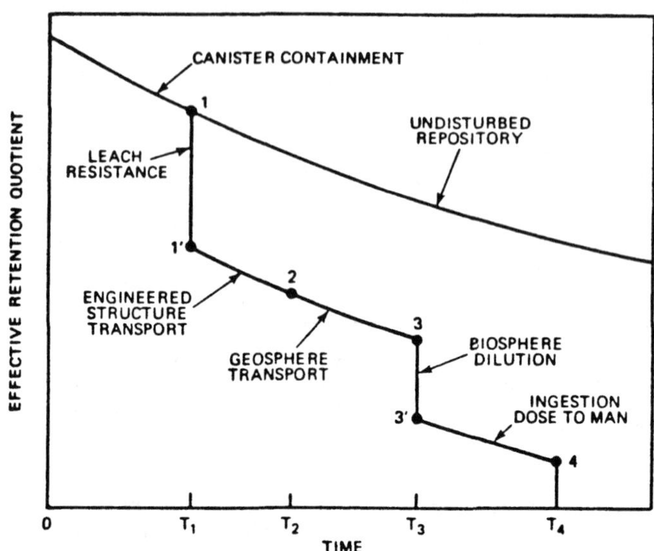

Figure 15.21. Generic effective retention quotient plot for a waste repository system. The effective RQ approach is best described by first considering contained waste in its canister after emplacement. A representation of a general waste/repository system behavior, the top curve labeled "undisturbed repository" depicts typical RQ versus time behavior. Up to point 1 is the *canister containment* period between times 0 and T_1. At T_1 the canister is assumed to fail, and the *leaching* of the waste form begins. The amount leached after canister failure, represented by line 1–1′, is the leading edge of the pulse of waste material that, through various pathways, will eventually reach the biosphere and be ingested by humans. Similarly, other failures of the repository can be represented. (From W. A. Rodger et al., EPRI Report NP-1655-IR.)

The RQ is a very large number, generally in the range of 10^{15}–10^{18}. Its reciprocal, namely 10^{-15}–10^{-18}, is the fraction of the waste in the repository which, if ingested, would just result in the allowable ingestion dose to an individual. RQ may also be viewed as the attenuation needed to reduce the hazard of the original waste inventory to allowable levels. An application of the RQ methodology is shown in Figure 15.21. This figure also shows how assumed sequential failure of the waste barriers would affect a waste repository's performance.

U.S. Federal Criteria

Table 15.18 summarizes the draft federal criteria (NRC and EPA) governing repository performance. It shows EPA cumulative releases over 10^4 yr after disposal per Metric Ton of Heavy Metal (MTHM) emplaced for eight selected key nuclides and the NRC release fraction limit of 10^{-5}/yr. This limit need not be imposed on nuclides whose inventories at 10^3 yr are less than 0.1% of the total nuclide inventory.

In general, the NRC standards are more difficult to attain than the EPA standards for all nuclides except ^{14}C. The gap is large for ^{129}I, ^{135}Cs, ^{231}Pa, and ^{79}Se, but these nuclides may not be subject to the overall NRC release criterion. The NRC criterion was intended to be applied to the boundary of an engineered structure, while the EPA criterion was intended to be applied away from the repository at the "accessible environment," a distance up to 10 km away.

Cost of High-Level Waste Disposal

The cost of disposing of commercial high-level nuclear wastes will be paid by the owners of nuclear power plants sending wastes to a waste repository facility. The cost will become part of the utility's overall expenses of providing the electricity, which will be passed back to the users. The cost to the consumer of electricity would be about a tenth of a cent per kilowatt hour. (The average cost of electricity is 6.3¢/kWh for residential users in the United States.) The cost of disposing of defense wastes is a federal responsibility.

Table 15.18. Summary of EPA and NRC Repository Performance Criteria for Key Nuclides

Key Nuclides	Existing Draft Criteria: EPA, Ci/MTHM[a]	Existing Draft Criteria: NRC, yr	Retention Time Criteria, yr: EPA	Retention Time Criteria, yr: NRC
^{231}Pa[b]	0.01	1×10^{-5}	3590	1×10^5
^{135}Cs[b]	2.0	1×10^{-5}	1960	1×10^5
^{129}I[b]	0.5	1×10^{-5}	670	1×10^5
^{126}Sn[b]	0.08	1×10^{-5}	7.20×10^4	1×10^5
^{99}Tc	2.0	1×10^{-5}	7.20×10^4	1×10^5
^{79}Se[b]	0.5	1×10^{-5}	7.78×10^3	1×10^5
^{59}Ni	0.5	1×10^{-5}	7.70×10^4	1×10^5
^{14}C	0.2	1×10^{-5}	1.34×10^5	1×10^5

Source: From TASC Report TR-3336-4 (1982).

[a]Integrated release over 10^4 yr. These numbers may be converted to Ci per waste package by multiplying by 0.9 MTHM per waste package.

[b]These nuclides have activities less than 0.1% of the total inventory of radionuclides for spent fuel at 10^3 yr. Depending on the interpretation of NRC's 10CFR60, they may be subject to less stringent standards, that is, higher release rates (Column 2) and lower retention times (Column 4) than those indicated above.

Toxicity of Repository Wastes

The hazard from high-level wastes is often assessed in terms of a "water dilution volume," a concept first used by Oak Ridge National Laboratory. This measure, in units of cubic meters, is the ratio of activity for each nuclide of waste to its corresponding maximum permissible concentration value for air or water, for inhalation and ingestion hazard, respectively. Tables 15.19 and 15.20 list the fission product and heavy-metal elements with the greatest hazard based on this index at various times after fuel reprocessing.

Ingestion toxicities are only measures of potential hazards since they do not consider the transport mechanism from a repository to the biosphere, or the probability of radionuclide release. To put the risk into perspective with the chemical risk from naturally occurring ores, Figure 15.22 shows the relative toxicity of nuclear waste over time compared with that of average mineral ores of toxic elements. Many ores, including those of mercury and chromium, have higher potential

Table 15.19. Selected Fission Product Elements and Nuclides in Decreasing Order of Ingestion Hazard

Years After Fuel Reprocessing					
1	3	10–30	100–300	10^3–10^5	10^6
Enriched U Fuel					
^{90}Sr	^{90}Sr	^{90}Sr	^{90}Sr	^{99}Tc	^{93m}Nb
^{144}Ce	^{134}Cs	^{137}Cs	^{137}Cs	^{93m}Nb	^{99}Tc
^{134}Cs	^{137}Cs	^{134}Cs	^{90}Y	^{135}Cs	^{135}Cs
^{137}Cs	^{144}Ce	^{90}Y			
Pu Recycle Fuel					
^{90}Sr	^{90}Sr	^{90}Sr	^{90}Sr	^{99}Tc	^{135}Cs
^{106}Ru	^{134}Cs	^{137}Cs	^{137}Cs	^{135}Cs	^{99}Tc
^{144}Ce	^{137}Cs	^{134}Cs	^{90}Y	^{93m}Nb	^{93m}Nb
	^{106}Ru	^{90}Y			

Source: From S. E. Logan, *Trans. Am. Nuclear Soc.* **19,** 204 (1974).

Table 15.20. Selected Heavy-Metal Elements and Nuclides in Decreasing Order of Ingestion Hazard

Years After Fuel Reprocessing									
1–3	10	30	100	300	1000	3000	10^4	10^5	10^6
Enriched U Fuel									
^{244}Cm	^{244}Cm	^{244}Cm	^{241}Am	^{241}Am	^{241}Am	^{243}Am	^{243}Am	^{226}Ra	^{225}Ra
^{242}Cm	^{241}Am	^{241}Am	^{243}Am	^{243}Am	^{243}Am	^{241}Am	^{241}Am	^{225}Ra	^{226}Ra
^{241}Am	^{243}Am	^{243}Am	^{242m}Am	^{242m}Am	^{242m}Am	^{240}Pu	^{239}Pu	^{229}Th	^{229}Th
^{243}Am	^{242m}Am	^{242m}Am	^{238}Pu	^{238}Pu	^{240}Pu	^{239}Pu	^{240}Pu	^{230}Th	^{237}Np
^{242m}Am	^{238}Pu	^{238}Pu	^{240}Pu	^{240}Pu	^{239}Pu	^{239}Np	^{237}Np	^{210}Pb	
^{238}Pu	^{241}Pu	^{240}Pu	^{239}Pu	^{239}Pu	^{238}Pu	^{237}Np	^{239}Np		
^{241}Pu	^{240}Pu	^{241}Pu	^{244}Cm	^{239}Np	^{239}Np				
^{240}Pu	^{239}Pu	^{239}Pu	^{242}Cm	^{237}Np	^{237}Np				
^{239}Pu									
Pu Recycle Fuel									
^{244}Cm	^{244}Cm	^{244}Cm	^{241}Am	^{241}Am	^{243}Am	^{243}Am	^{243}Am	^{226}Ra	^{226}Ra
^{242}Cm	^{241}Am	^{241}Am	^{243}Am	^{243}Am	^{241}Am	^{241}Am	^{241}Am	^{225}Ra	^{225}Ra
^{241}Am	^{243}Am	^{243}Am	^{242m}Am	^{242m}Am	^{240}Pu	^{240}Pu	^{240}Pu	^{210}Pb	^{229}Th
^{243}Am	^{242m}Am	^{242m}Am	^{244}Cm	^{245}Cm	^{239}Pu	^{239}Pu	^{239}Pu	^{239}Pu	^{230}Th
^{242m}Am	^{238}Pu	^{238}Pu	^{245}Cm	^{242}Cm	^{238}Pu	^{245}Cm	^{245}Cm		^{210}Pb
^{238}Pu	^{240}Pu	^{240}Pu	^{242}Cm	^{244}Cm	^{245}Cm	^{246}Cm	^{246}Cm		
^{241}Pu	^{241}Pu	^{241}Pu	^{238}Pu	^{246}Cm	^{246}Cm				
^{240}Pu			^{240}Pu	^{240}Pu					
				^{238}Pu					
				^{239}Pu					

Source: From S. E. Logan, *Trans. Am. Nuclear Soc.* **19,** 204 (1974).

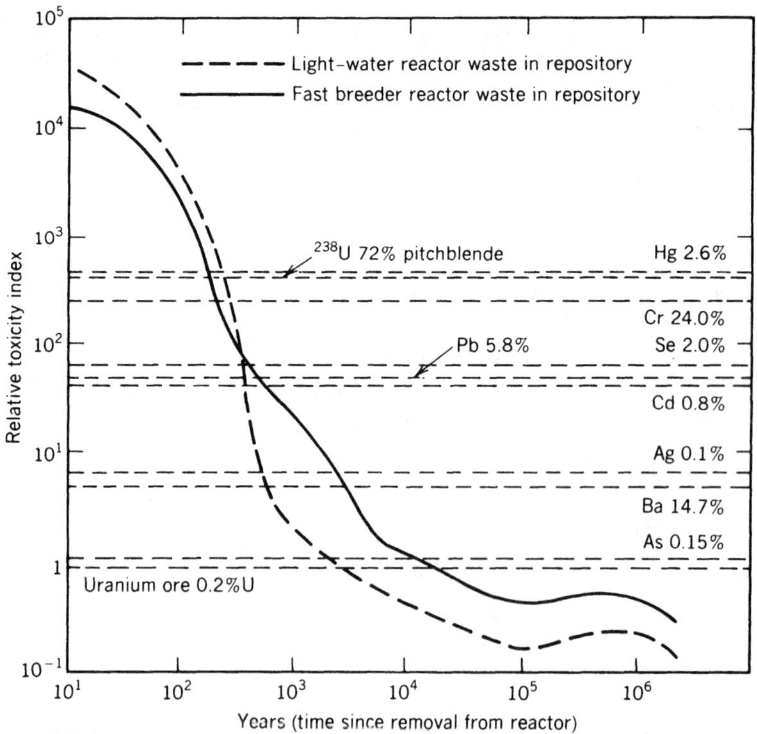

Figure 15.22. Relative toxicity of nuclear waste over time, compared with that of mineral ores of toxic elements. [From K. A. Tonnessen and J. J. Cohen, UCRL-52199 (1977).]

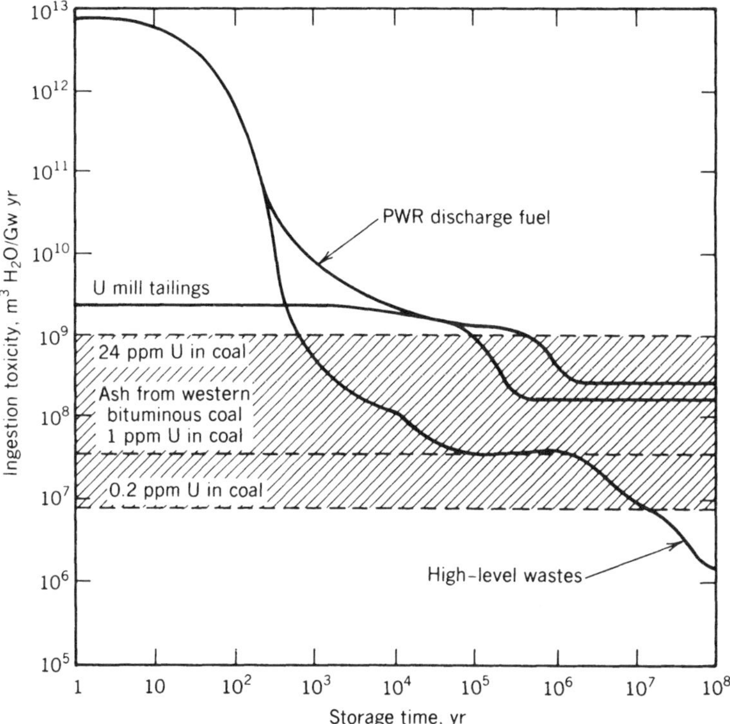

Figure 15.23. Comparison of ingestion toxicity in western coal ash, high-level reprocessing wastes, discharged fuel, and mill tailings. The ingestion toxicity is calculated by dividing the amount of radioactivity by its allowable concentration in drinking water. [From T. H. Pigford, *Trans. Am. Nuclear Soc.* **30** (1978).]

hazards than the radioactive wastes over most of the time that the radioactive wastes would be in the repository.

Coal ash and uranium mill tailings have small radioactive toxicities due to naturally occurring radioactive elements they contain. Their toxicity exceeds that of nuclear reactor high-level wastes after a thousand years. If, for instance, the radiological hazard of surface piles of coal ash is acceptable to society, then geologic isolation of nuclear wastes must provide about four orders of magnitude isolation during the first 100 yr, two orders of magnitude isolation during the next 400 yr, and very little isolation thereafter in order to reduce the potential hazard below that of coal ash. This is shown in Figure 15.23, which also suggests that after 300–500 yr of decay, the toxicity of high-level wastes from LWR reactors is less than the toxicity of the ore from which the uranium came.

Transmutation of Actinides

Irradiated fuel contains actinides with half-lives of many thousands of years. These actinides are the major contribution to the hazards of the high-level wastes after a thousand years and their hazard level does not decrease appreciably up to a million years. Recycling these actinides back into a reactor has the potential for decreasing their hazard level if they can be fissioned. Actinide recycle in thermal reactors is limited because of low flux levels and small thermal fission cross sections.

Actinides have a much higher probability for fissioning in an LMFBR than they do in a thermal reactor. The cross sections in Table 15.21 show that, except for ^{239}Pu and ^{241}Pu, absorption of a thermal neutron by an actinide essentially will only create another actinide. In contrast, an absorption of neutrons in an LMFBR fast-neutron spectrum will result in fission at least 25% of the time.

The production of actinide wastes in a LWR is given in Figure 15.24. The amount of actinides requiring disposal can be reduced by separating actinides from fission products during reprocessing, and by recycling them with fresh fuel in LMFBR reactors. The application of this concept

Table 15.21. Actinide Cross Sections

	Thermal		Fast	
Nuclide	σ_f	σ_c	σ_f	σ_c
^{238}U	0	2.7	0.04	0.29
^{237}Np	0.02	159	0.32	1.49
^{238}Pu	15	485	1.13	0.47
^{239}Pu	697	275	1.83	0.47
^{240}Pu	0.2	374	0.37	0.39
^{241}Pu	944	344	2.45	0.41
^{242}Pu	0.1	33	0.30	0.32
^{241}Am	2	446 + 86	0.39	0.99
^{243}Am	0.05	103	0.20	0.65
^{244}Cm	1.3	19.1	0.5	0.4

Source: From R. J. Breen, *Trans. Am. Nuclear Soc.* **21**, 262 (1975).

depends on the required chemical separation of actinides from fission products.† The conceptual model for the transmutation of actinides is shown in Figure 15.25. Continual recycling, however, will build up the higher actinides such as Am and Cm, as shown in Figure 15.26, although the total actinide inventory is reduced.

15.5. FOREIGN WASTE PROGRAMS

A number of European countries, France, England, West Germany, Sweden, and Belgium among them, appear to be ahead of the United States by varying distances in implementing methods for managing radioactive waste.

France placed a pilot waste-vitrification plant called PIVER in operation in 1970. It uses the technique of fixing reprocessed wastes in borosilicate glass logs that was originally developed at Brookhaven National Laboratory in the late 1950s. After years of successful operation of PIVER, a scaled-up prototype was placed in service in 1978, and it, too, has been operating successfully. It is known as AVM, for Atelier de Vitrification de Marcoule, the French nuclear research center where PIVER is also located. The AVM facility is shown in Figure 15.27. The process that it uses, given in Figure 15.28, has many steps in common with a U.S. vitrification process developed at INEL.

The canisters of glassified waste produced by PIVER were lowered into a concrete honeycomb below the floor of a large bay; each pit had a metal lid. Personnel could work on the floor above the waste without danger. No radiation overexposures occurred, according to the French.

AVM is capable of processing 150 m^3 of vitrified wastes per year. This not only satisfies the needs of the Marcoule Center, but will also absorb, within a few years, the backlog of liquid waste accumulated over the past 20 yr.

Between its commissioning in June 1978, and December 31, 1982, AVM has operated 15,016 hr. In this time it has vitrified 436 m^3 of calcined high-level waste, producing 200 t of glass. A total of 586 canisters of vitrified waste have been placed in storage vaults during that period, according to Cogema, the French nuclear fuel-cycle company that operates AVM.

A property of borosilicate glass taken advantage of at the AVM is that the proportions of its components can easily be modified to suit specific needs. The glass produced usually contains 35–50% silica and 14–20% boric oxide.

Fission product solutions from the adjacent reprocessing plant are fed to a metering unit that feeds a calciner at a rate of 36 liters/hr. The calciner is a continuously fed rotary kiln where the concentrated wastes are evaporated, dried, and partially calcined. The calcine flows continuously by gravity into a melting pot to which glass frit is also continuously injected. The mixture is melted at 1150°C. Throughout the process, off-gases are purified, condensed, and treated to remove radionuclides. Active secondary effluents are sent to the reprocessing plant, or to a waste treatment system.

The glass is periodically cast into stainless steel canisters. They are then subjected to radiological inspection, placed in a transfer cask, and routed to the storage vault by a traveling crane. Storage is in vertical concrete vaults in one of the AVM buildings. The storage building contains

†Several processes for actinide extraction from high-level wastes exist. TBP, tri-butyl phosphate, or DHDECMP, an organo-phosphorus bidentate compound, can be used to partition the actinides from the bulk fission products. Partition factors up to 10,000 have been achieved.

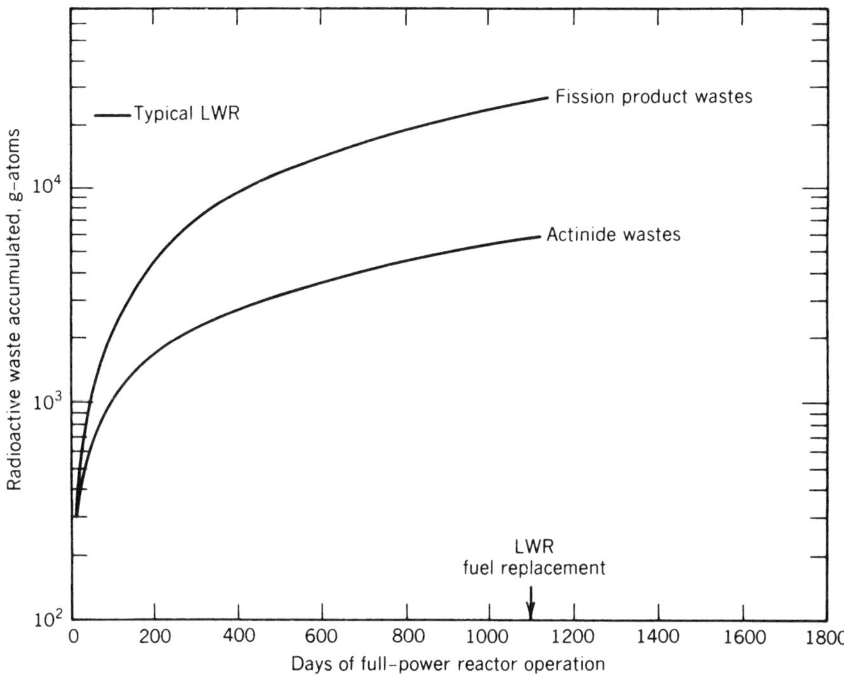

Figure 15.24. Radioactive waste production of 3425-MW(th) fission power reactor. [From R. Paternoster et al., *Trans. Am. Nuclear Soc.* **19,** 203 (1974).]

220 vaults each 10 m high, each with a capacity of 10 canisters. The vaults are cooled by forced-convection ventilation. The total capacity of 2200 canisters represents 10–15 yr of vitrification throughput.

Cogema has announced that the experience acquired at Marcoule with AVM will shortly be used to build two similar vitrification plants, AVH 1 and AVH 2 at the La Hague reprocessing plant on the Cotentin peninsula near Cherbourg. Where AVM has a capacity of processing 150 m^3 of liquid fission products annually, the two new plants will each have a capacity of 90 m^3 of fission products a year. AVH 1 will be installed at the first reprocessing plant at La Hague and will be able to work up in a few years all the backlog of liquid high-level waste accumulated since the start of

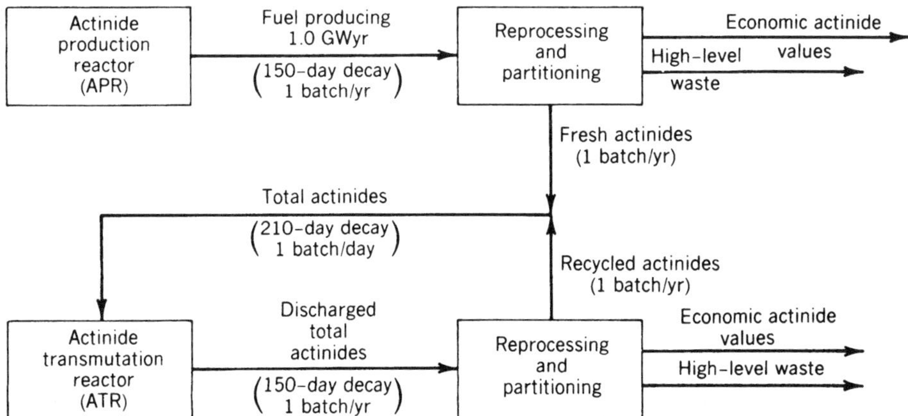

Figure 15.25. Actinide recycle model. [From A. G. Croff, *Trans. Am. Nuclear Soc.* **22,** 345 (1975).]

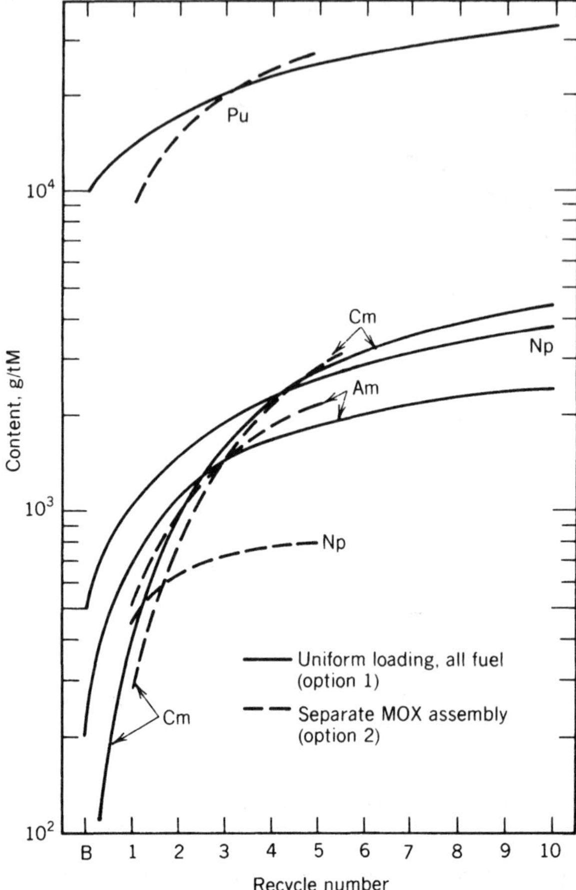

Figure 15.26. Transuranic content versus recycle number. [From T. C. Gorrell, *Trans. Am. Nuclear Soc.* **32,** 329 (1979).]

operations there, and thereafter to keep pace with the output of liquid waste from the reprocessing plant. The second vitrification plant will be installed at the second reprocessing plant at La Hague. Construction of AVH 1 began in 1981 and it will be completed in 1986. AVH 2 is to be operational by late 1988.

The cost of vitrification using the AVM process adds about 2% to the cost of electricity in France.

The French company has provided engineering services for the installation of four AVM-type vitrification systems in England, and one each in West Germany, Belgium and Italy.

In search of a permanent disposal site, the French have drilled a number of exploratory boreholes. One of them is more than 1000 m deep, into granite of the Massif Central, at Auriat.

Britain routinely discharges low-level liquid waste into the Irish Sea, but buries low-level solid waste. High-level waste from the Capenhurst reprocessing plant is stored in stainless steel, awaiting solidification, vitrification, and long-term storage. Meanwhile, exploratory holes have been drilled in northern Scotland and in Cornwall.

After several years of experimentation with their own methods of solidifying hot wastes, Britain has chosen the French process. British Nuclear Fuels Ltd. is building a $400 million AVM facility at Windscale that will go into operation before the end of the decade.

The British plan to relocate within the next few years the intermediate-level nuclear waste currently kept in hundreds of concrete silos on nuclear sites throughout Britain. The task will be handled by Nirex, a new agency jointly owned by Britain's four largest radwaste producers: CEGB, U.K. AEA, SSEB, and BNFL. Nirex is responsible for all but high-level waste, which remains the sole responsibility of BNFL. For long-lived intermediate-level wastes, Nirex is consid-

Figure 15.27. The Atelier de Vitrification de Marcoule (AVM) facility for the vitrification of high-level radioactive waste in France. (Courtesy COGEMA.)

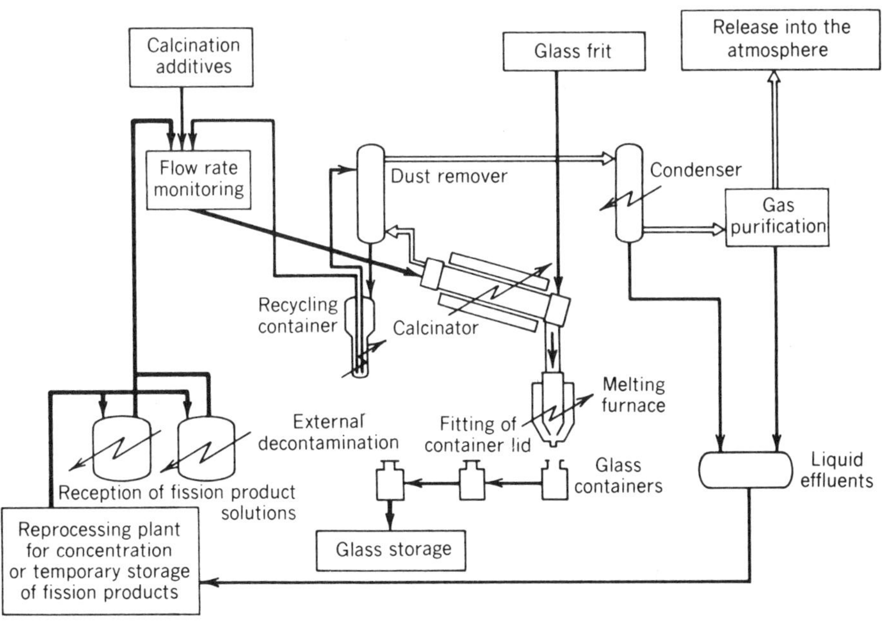

Figure 15.28. French AVM process at Marcoule. (From EPRI Report NP-1087.)

Figure 15.29. Asse, Germany salt mine used for radioactive waste disposal. The salt formation in this mine has been undisturbed for about 100 million yr. (Courtesy IAEA.)

ering using an abandoned anhydrite (calcium sulfate) mine in the northeast of England. The rock has three times the strength of concrete, and the rate of water seepage is very low. For short-lived intermediate-level wastes, Nirex is considering clay deposits which dominate the center of England, specifically a CEGB site near Bedford once earmarked for a power station.

West Germany originally planned to establish a single center for reprocessing and high-level waste disposal, at Gorleben, not far from the East German border. The plan became controversial and politicized, and was sidetracked. However, although deciding eventually in favor of smaller regional reprocessing plants, West Germany returned to its plan to build a waste repository at Gorleben. Drilling of shafts began early in 1982. The repository there would be in a salt dome. A review of the project by international specialists resulted in a finding in 1979 that the site was safe for a repository.

Low-level wastes in Germany are being buried in another salt mine at Asse in Lower Saxony near Braunschweig, pictured in Figure 15.29.

Belgium has an innovative approach, born of necessity. The country has no suitable salt or granite deposits. Consequently it is attempting to dig a repository in the homogeneous and impermeable clay that had been deposited millions of years ago on what was then a sea floor.

Some 525 ft under the Belgian national nuclear research center at Mol, this clay is 360 ft thick. A shaft has been drilled down 720 ft, penetrating this layer. A horizontal gallery is being excavated for tests of the suitability of the clay for the storing of medium- and low-level waste. A possible disadvantage, however, is the low thermal conductivity of clay. Thus heat might build up to unacceptable levels if high-level waste were stored there, unless it had been cooled a long time.

In addition, the Belgian government may soon give the go-ahead to the construction of an AVM plant at the Mol research center. But in order to neutralize some 65 m^3 of high-level waste still on the site as a result of previous reprocessing activities, Belgian specialists have come up with a variation of AVM that will produce borosilicate glass blocks and beads embedded in a lead-alloy matrix. The Pamela plant (named for the process) is now being built and should operate by 1986.

Sweden has dug a cavern in the bedrock under the temporary spent fuel storage facility built adjacent to the Oskarshamn nuclear power station. Four large pools are being carved in this cavern to hold spent fuel for cooling. This center is expected to be in service by 1985, and ultimately to accommodate 9000 tons of spent fuel and other reactor components.

High-level waste will be finally disposed of in granite, or comparably homogeneous rock. Problems of disposal in granite are being studied at the unused Stripa mine by an international group including Finland, Japan, Sweden, Switzerland, and the United States, with Canada and France as associates. Electric heaters are being used to simulate the heat of high-level waste. Sweden has also pioneered in the development of ceramic overpacks and canisters to hold waste.

Moreover, the Swedish government has issued the construction permit for a final storage facility for reactor waste (SFR) to be constructed in crystalline rock caverns some 50–100 m below the bed of the Baltic Sea, at a site close to the Forsmark nuclear power station. The repository will be used for all low- and intermediate-level wastes arising from the country's 12-reactor nuclear power program.

The location below the seabed is considered to offer several valuable safety factors. The hydraulic gradient in the rock mass underneath the sea is low, and therefore the groundwater flow is also very small. In the unlikely event of the radionuclides escaping, they would be diluted in the large volume of seawater. Finally, the risk of someone drilling a well through the repository is considered negligible.

The Swedish Nuclear Fuel Supply Company (SKBF) will build and operate the SFR facility, which will accept for final disposal all low- and medium-level reactor wastes from all Swedish nuclear power plants and the central interim storage facility for spent fuel. SKBF is a jointly owned company of the Swedish nuclear power utilities which, according to Swedish law, bear the primary responsibility for the safe handling and disposal of wastes from nuclear power production.

Australia has made a contribution to the technology of high level waste disposal with its development of SYNROC, or synthetic rock. This is a crystalline ceramic based on three titanate minerals (barium hollandite, perovskite, and zirconolite) which is being proposed as a substitute fixative for borosilicate glass.

The Australian Atomic Energy Commission's Lucas Heights Research Laboratories began the work in 1979, in association with the Australian National University. Current work is aimed at showing that SYNROC fabrication can be achieved relatively simply, and at demonstrating the key step in fabrication called "in-can hot pressing." Its major attraction is that it allows in situ densification of the SYNROC in the waste canister. Leach testing has thus far been successful. Only nonradioactive simulated waste has been incorporated into SYNROC until now, but fabrication and leach tests with tracer levels of transuranium actinide elements are planned. The effect of irradiation by fast neutrons on the structure and leach resistance of SYNROC is also being studied.

BIBLIOGRAPHY

Andrews, W. B., et al., "Impacts on Defense Waste Management Strategy," *Trans. Am. Nuclear Soc.* **39,** 226 (1981).

Beall, G. W., and B. Allard, "Chemical Aspects Governing the Choice of Backfill Materials for Nuclear Waste Repositories," *Nuclear Technology* **59,** 405 (1982).

Beck, S. R., "Law of Diminishing Returns Applies to Disposal of Nuclear Wastes," *Power* **126,** 109 (February 1982).

Breen, R. J., "Elimination of Actinides with LMFBR Recycle," *Trans. Am. Nuclear Soc.* **21,** 262 (1975).

Choi, J., and R. J. Tosetti, "Water Dilution Volume for High-Level Wastes Stored in Deep Geologic Media," *Trans. Am. Nuclear Soc.* **43,** 122 (1982).

Cline, J. E., et al., *Activity Levels of Transuranic Nuclides in Low-Level Solid Wastes from U.S. Power Reactors,* EPRI NP-1494 (1980).

Cohen, B. L., "Effects of ICRP Publication 30 on Hazard Assessment of High-Level Wastes," *Trans. Am. Nuclear Soc.* **38,** 84 (1981).

Cohen, B. L., "The Disposal of Radioactive Wastes from Fission Reactors," *Scientific American* **236,** 21 (June 1977).

Daniels, R. S., and B. D. Guilbeault, "Sources of Low-Level Radioactive Waste," *Trans. Am. Nuclear Soc.* **38,** 65 (1981).

Draper, E. L., "Nuclear Waste Management," *Trans. Am. Nuclear Soc.* **38,** 21 (1981).

Eggett, D., and D. N. Enegess, "Volume Reduction Offers Radwaste-Disposal Benefits," *Power* **126,** 57 (October 1982).

Kaplin, M. F., and J. E. Mendel, "Ancient Glass and the Safe Disposal of Nuclear Waste," *Archaeology* **35,** 4 (1982).

League of Woman Voters, *A Nuclear Waste Primer,* Washington, 1980.

McElroy, J. L., and R. E. Burns, *Nuclear Waste Management Status and Recent Accomplishments,* EPRI NP-1087 (1979).

Murray, R. L. *Understanding Radioactive Waste,* Battelle Press, Columbus, 1982.

National Academy of Engineering, National Academy of Sciences, *Solidification of High-Level Radioactive Wastes,* NUREG/CR-0895 (1979).

National Research Council, *Radioactive Wastes at the Hanford Reservation,* National Academy of Sciences (1978).

Oston, S. G., and D. M. Brown, *Repository Design and Regulatory Guidance Issues Analysis,* TR-3336-4, December, 1982.

Park, U. Y., and K. R. Yates, "Projections of Commercial Spent Fuel Accumulation in the United States," *Trans. Am. Nuclear Soc.* **32,** 350 (1979).

Pasupathi, V., and D. Stahl, *Expected Performance of Spent LWR Fuel Under Dry Storage Conditions,* EPRI NP-2735 (1982).

Rodger, W. A., et al., *Integrated Design and R&D Assessment of Nuclear Waste Disposal,* EPRI NP-1655 (1980).

Trigilio, G., *Volume Reduction Techniques in Low Level Waste Management,* NUREG/CR-2206 (1981).

Wheelwright, E. J., "Generation and Vitrification of High-Level LWR Liquid Waste," *Nuclear Technology* **58,** 271 (1982).

Wood, B. J., "Backfill Performance Requirements," *Nuclear Technology* **59,** 390 (1982).

———, *Answers to Your Questions About High-Level Nuclear Waste Isolation,* U.S. Department of Energy (1982).

———, *Disposal of Radioactive Waste,* OECD Nuclear Energy Agency, Paris (1982).

———, *Handling of Spent Nuclear Fuel and Final Storage of Vitrified High Level Waste,* Karn-Bransle-Sakerhet Report, Sweden (1978).

CHAPTER 16

DECOMMISSIONING OF NUCLEAR FACILITIES

16.1. INTRODUCTION

It is only in recent years that the decommissioning of overage reactors and other nuclear facilities has come forward as a public issue. Unlike overage ships, reactors obviously cannot simply be scrapped, because there is too much radioactivity in the innards of the plant's primary system. The two aspects of the issue of concern to the public are:

1. What to do with decommissioned nuclear facilities.
2. How to pay for their final disposal, by whatever means.

Decommissioning of facilities is not new to the nuclear industry. Worldwide over 70 licensed reactors have been or are in the process of being decommissioned. Most of these were demonstration, test, or research reactors; some were small power reactors. A significant number of other small fuel cycle facilities have also been decommissioned.

In the United Kingdom, the Fast Reactor Irradiated Fuel Reprocessing Plant at Dounreay was partly decommissioned and extensively modified to service the Dounreay Prototype Fast Reactor. This is the largest decommissioning/remodeling activity undertaken to date in the United Kingdom. Decommissioning required about 4 yr and resulted in about 700 m^3 of decommissioning waste.

In France, a total of eight reactors have been decommissioned to various states; of these, three have been dismantled, the largest being the 35-MW(th) Pegase reactor. The Chinon-I experimental power reactor was mothballed in about six months and will eventually become a nuclear facility of a different type. Of the other reactors shut down, one was dismantled, some were entombed, and others were mothballed.

Decommissioning activities have also been carried out in Switzerland, Belgium, Canada, Italy and India.

In 1976 the Atomic Industrial Forum (AIF) carried out a detailed study[1] of the alternatives. Three primary alternatives, and two combinations of those three, were proposed. These are:

1. Mothballing (the term comes from "mothballed" Navy ships that can be quickly put back into service in case of national emergency).
2. Entombing (filling the reactor vessel and other primary system parts with concrete).
3. Immediate dismantling and removal.
4. Combination of mothballing and delayed dismantling and removal.
5. Combination of entombing and delayed dismantling and removal.

The principal alternatives are shown in Figure 16.1.

The general estimate of the commercial life of a nuclear facility is 40 yr. No large commercial plant has yet reached that age, but starting in the year 2000, decommissioning of these units will begin in earnest. Thus the 158 reactors that began commercial operation in the 1970s may be expected to require replacement in the 2010s. Likewise, reprocessing plants will be replaced as the old plants become obsolete.

In the United States, about 10 small developmental plants, including Peach Bottom 1, the Enrico Fermi Fast Breeder, Humboldt Bay, and the pioneer Shippingport PWR, have already been declared shut down for good. Another one (Indian Point 1 in New York) is in limbo, awaiting a management decision on whether or not to invest the funds required to bring it up to post-TMI 2 more stringent safety standards, that is, whether or not it is economic to do so.

In addition to these 11 plants, a score of government-owned small experimental reactors have

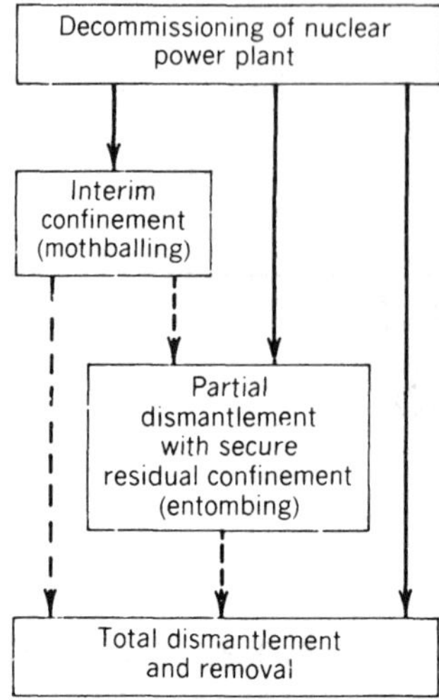

Figure 16.1. Possible combinations of decommissioning alternatives.

been dismantled and disposed of, including safety test reactors, the space propulsion program's experimental reactors, exotic power plant prototypes, and the like. These, however, were almost all laboratory-scale or mobile reactors, not embedded in deep, thick, concrete foundations.

Only one small commercial-type reactor has been dismantled: the 22-MWe Elk River (Minnesota) BWR owned by the Rural Cooperative Power Association. Much of the cost estimating and technology projections relating to decommissioning in the United States are based on that single experience. Although the deactivation of Elk River and other small reactors has provided experience in decommissioning nuclear facilities, even that experience is difficult to extrapolate realistically. The experience has, of course, been valuable, but it does not really address the problems involved in decommissioning large commercial plants.

The primary source of radioactive materials in all nuclear power plants is the fuel in the reactor core. Most of the radioactivity in a plant, therefore, leaves when the fuel is shipped for disposal prior to decommissioning. The residual radioactivity in a plant is of two types: (1) neutron-induced activation in metal components of the reactor primary system and (2) low-level surface contamination of various other components. The basic approach in disposing of the activated components is to cut them up into small pieces and ship them to a licensed waste burial site. Their radioactivity would be in the same range as material routinely disposed of today as low-level waste. The contaminated components are usually washed with various solutions that remove surface radioactivity, and the solutions themselves then are disposed of in a low-level waste burial site.

16.2. DECOMMISSIONING METHODS

The Atomic Industrial Forum's decommissioning study previously referred to differentiates the alternatives as follows (it adopted U.S. NRC definitions of decommissioning alternatives).

Mothballing

Mothballing consists of

> . . . *putting a facility in a state of protective storage. In general, the facility may be left intact except that all fuel assemblies and the radioactive fluids and waste should be removed from the site. Adequate radiation monitoring, environmental surveillance, and appropriate security procedures should be established under a NRC possession-only license to ensure that the health and safety of the public are not endangered.*

In contrast to the practice of mothballing naval vessels, it is not intended in the case of nuclear power plants that a mothballed reactor would be reactivated and returned to commercial service at a later date. Although the definition makes no mention of the duration that a deactivated reactor could or should remain in a mothballed state, permanent mothballing probably is not a cost-effective means of decommissioning.

The following procedures constitute the mothballing process. They are in approximate order of occurrence:

1. Loose contamination cleaned from accessible plant areas.
2. Radwastes processed and shipped off site.
3. Reactor vessel, its internals, and other radioactive components kept in place.
4. Entrances providing controlled access to radioactive areas locked.
5. Access to the site controlled by a 24-hr security force.
6. Possession-only license received from the NRC, if the plant is in the United States (for possession only, but not use, of radioactive materials).
7. Periodic, nonstructural and environmental surveys performed until termination of the possession-only license.

Because replacement of spent fuel and control rods is a routine procedure in operating nuclear power plants, fuel and control elements would be removed and disposed of prior to start of decommissioning activities.

Entombment

This usually consists of:

> *. . . sealing all the remaining radioactive or contaminated components, such as the reactor pressure vessel and its internals, within a structure integral with the biological shield, after having all fuel assemblies, radioactive fluids and wastes, and certain selected components shipped off site. The structure should provide integrity over the period of time in which significant quantities of radioactivity remain with the material in the entombment. An appropriate and continuing surveillance program should be established under a possession-only license.*

The steps to achieve entombment, in order of occurrence, were characterized by the AIF study as follows:

1. Loose contamination cleaned from accessible plant areas.
2. Radwastes processed and shipped off site.
3. The possession-only license and entombment order received.
4. The reactor vessel, its internals, and most other radioactive components that lie within the containment structure kept in place, and a reinforced concrete barrier constructed to enclose completely these components and systems (the AIF study does not suggest pouring concrete into the reactor vessel and cavity as some other entombment concepts do).
5. Intrusion alarms and other access control surveillance equipment installed.
6. Periodic minor maintenance (nonstructural) and environmental surveys performed until termination of the possession-only license.

The primary entombment barrier for a reference PWR from the AIF study incorporates the concrete shield wall of the reactor cavity. For a BWR it includes the drywell, and for a HTGR it includes the Prestressed Concrete Pressure Vessel (PCPV). In addition, PWRs and BWRs require construction of reinforced concrete covers over the top of the enclosure walls. In the case of BWRs, the entombment structure includes the primary coolant system components, but not the turbine and condenser systems that have only low levels of contamination.

AIF points out in its study that the entombing alternative that it describes does not correspond to the solid concrete structure usually associated with the concept of entombment. Rather, it is a form of protective storage of the residual high-activity sources, designed to permit removal of radioactive materials containing the very long-lived isotopes such as ^{59}Ni, ^{63}Ni, and ^{14}C at a time 100–150 yr after shutdown, with only limited demolition work on the structure being entombed. This is in contrast with the extensive work that would be necessary to remove these radionuclides from a solidly entombed structure.

Putting it another way, the entombment alternative in the AIF study lies between mothballing and the massive concrete-block type of entombment. It provides a greater degree of protective storage than does mothballing, and future removal of the materials still radioactive would not be as difficult as it would be in a massive concrete entombment structure.

Prompt Dismantling and Removal

This alternative is defined as follows:

All fuel assemblies, radioactive fluids and waste, and other materials having activity levels above accepted unrestricted activity levels should be removed from the site. The facility owner may then have unrestricted use of the site with no requirement for a license. If the facility owner so desires, the remainder of the reactor facility may be dismantled and all vestiges removed and disposed of.

Although in the United States the NRC does not require that the nonradioactive portions of a facility be dismantled and shipped off site in order to terminate a possession-only license, the prompt dismantling and removal alternative, as presented in the AIF study, includes the complete dismantling of the facility. The procedures for dismantling and removal were described as consisting of the following major activities, in approximate order of occurrence:

1. Loose contamination on buildings and components removed to reduce occupational radiation exposures during the dismantling process.
2. Radwastes processed and shipped off site.
3. Possession-only license and dismantlement order received.
4. All radioactive components and materials, including concrete, removed and shipped off site for licensed burial.
5. The possession-only license can be terminated upon removal of the radioactive materials.
6. All nonradioactive components, buildings, and structures, such as auxiliary buildings, cooling towers, and so on, cleared to below grade (this is not required by the NRC for termination of a possession-only license).
7. Appropriate landscaping or site preparation for other uses performed.

These activities are summarized in Figure 16.2.

Mothballing—Delayed Dismantling and Removal

This combination alternative is not specifically addressed by the U.S. NRC in its Regulatory Guide 1.86 on the decommissioning. However, that does not preclude its acceptability as a decommissioning method. In this alternative, a facility is placed in a state of protective storage according to the mothballing alternative, and then, after a period of time to permit the decay of radioactivity, the facility is dismantled and removed, as described above.

Although the duration of the mothballed period is not fixed either by regulation or by engineering considerations, the longer the mothballing the more likely it is that significant cost reduction can be realized because radioactive decay will permit the use of manual rather than remote removal procedures.

Entombing—Delayed Dismantling and Removal

This combination alternative similarly consists of sequentially following the procedures for entombing, and then after a period, those for dismantling and removal.

Of the 125 or more small U.S. reactors that have been deactivated—most of them research reactors, small reactor experiments, tests or prototypes—only 9 were commercial power generators. These are listed in Table 16.1. This table does not include the three reactors in AEC's 1954 five-reactor demonstration program which have been decommissioned:

Experimental Boiling Water Reactor (EBWR), Argonne, Illinois

Sodium-graphite Reactor Experiment (SRE), Santa Susanna, California

Homogeneous Reactor Experiment 2 (HRE-2), Oak Ridge, Tennessee

Of the other two units in this program, the Shippingport PWR was shut down for good early in 1983. The Experimental Breeder Reactor No. 2 (EBR-2) is still operating.

16.3. DECOMMISSIONING EXPERIENCE

As may be noted from the examples given in Table 16.1, of 15 of the highest powered U.S. reactors decommissioned thus far, 10 have been mothballed, 3 entombed, 1 partially dismantled (this is

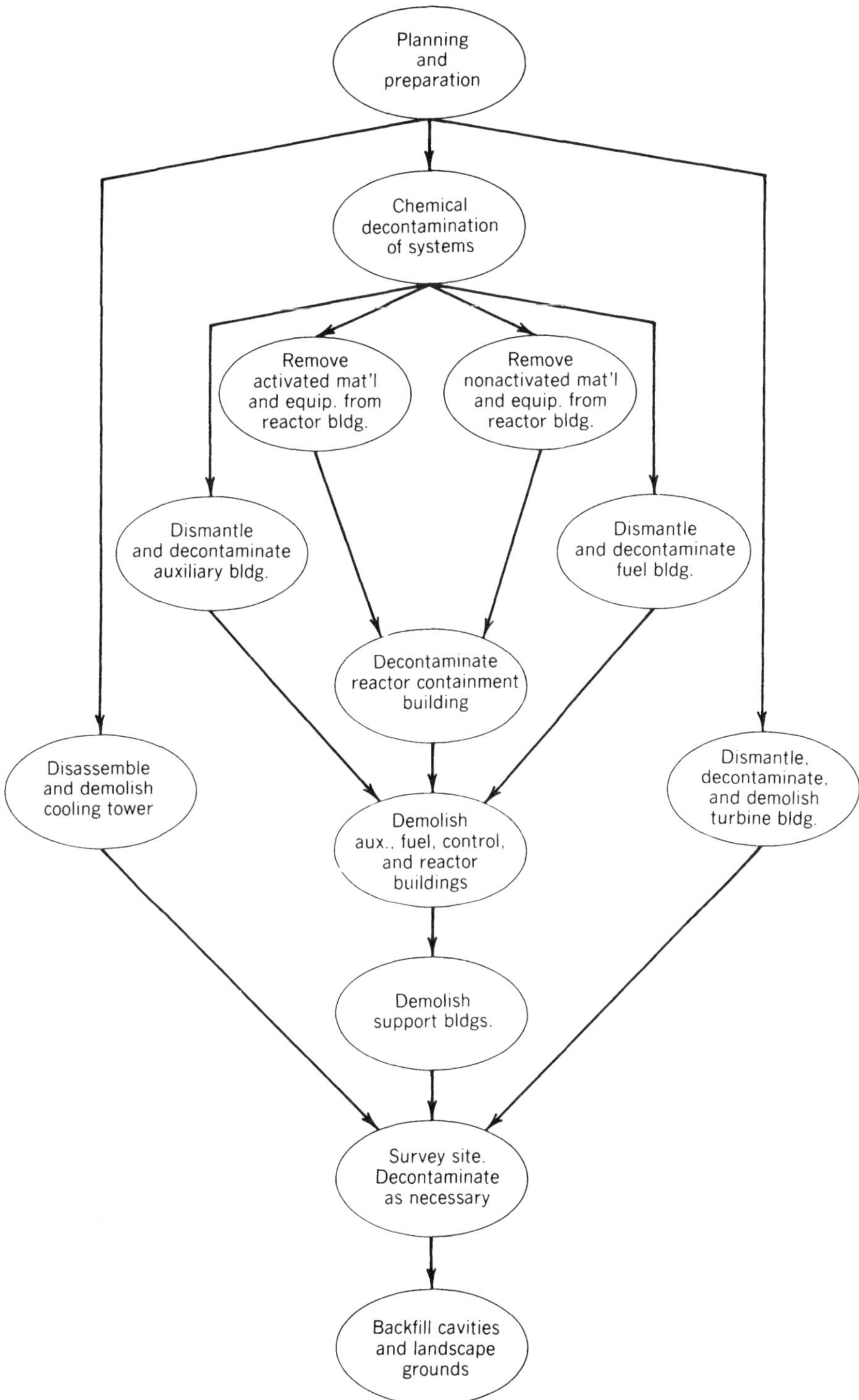

Figure 16.2. Sequence of major dismantlement activities. (From NUREG/CR-0130.)

Table 16.1. Decommissioned Power, Demonstration, and Test Reactors in the United States

Reactor	Decommissioning Mode Selected	Present Status of License	Location	Start-up	Shut down
Saxton	Mothballed	Possession only	Saxton, PA	1962	1972
SEFOR	Mothballed	By-product state of Arkansas	Strickler, AR	1969	1972
Westinghouse Test Reactor	Mothballed	Possession only	Waltz Mill, PA	1959	1962
NASA Plumbrook	Mothballed	Possession only	Sandusky, OH	1961	1974
GE EVESR	Mothballed	Possession only	Alameda Co., CA	1963	1967
B&W	Dismantled except for some concrete structures	By-product NRC	Lynchburg, VA	1964	1971
Hallam	Entombment	Operating authorization terminated	Hallam, NE	1962	1964
Piqua	Entombment	Operating authorization terminated	Piqua, OH	1963	1966
Elk River	Dismantled	Operating authorization terminated	Elk River, MN	1962	1968
Bonus	Entombment	Operating authorization terminated	Puerto Rico	1964	1968
VBWR	Mothballed	Possession only	Alameda Co., CA		
Fermi 1	Mothballed	Possession only	Monroe Co., MI	1963	1973
CVTR	Mothballed	By-product state parr, of South Carolina	South Carolina	1963	1967
Peach Bottom 1	Mothballed	Possession only	York Co., PA	1966	1974
Pathfinder	Conversion and mothballing	By-product NRC	Sioux Falls, SD	1964	1967
Shippingport			Shippingport, PA	1957	1983
Humboldt Bay			Eureka, CA	1963	1983

relatively easy for a pool-type research reactor), and only 1 dismantled and removed. That one, as already mentioned, is the Elk River, Minnesota, reactor.

That experience is of interest, and instructive, as the only U.S. case where the site of an operating power reactor was restored to preconstruction condition. The job took 2 yr, from 1972 to 1974. It was carried out by the United Power Association (successor organization to Rural Cooperative Power Association which built the unit), for $5.7 million. In 1972, United Power decided that it might be too expensive to return the reactor to operation. Under the terms of its contract with AEC, the utility could decide, and did insist, that the reactor be removed from the site.

The reactor containment building was 118 ft high and 85 ft in diameter. Following completion of an engineering study, United Power developed all the dismantling procedures. The utility co-op carried out its own radiological physics, all decontamination, and shipping of radioactive materials to burial grounds. The fuel, already discharged from the reactor, was stored under water in pools. The reactor vessel and its internals were cut up into large sections underwater using remotely controlled cutting equipment, and transferred to the spent-fuel storage pools. There, using remotely operated underwater cutting tools designed and fabricated at Oak Ridge National Laboratory, the pieces of the reactor vessel and internals were cut into smaller pieces and loaded for shipment to burial grounds.

These activities required less than a year. The manager of the dismantling operation reported that there had been "no exposure incidents that caused any problems."

About 1 ft of the concrete biological shield was removed with explosives, and shipped for burial. The uncontaminated portions were taken down with explosives and jackhammers. The biggest chore turned out to be the biological shield—more so than the reactor vessel.

Metal was removed from the outside of the containment shell. However, the concrete portions of the containment building survived attempts to reduce it by explosives, so a 900-lb wrecker's ball, swinging from a crane, had to be used. The rubble was buried nearby. The entire procedure took a little more than six months.

United Power used 52 workers on the job, most of them utility employees who had operated the plant and were familiar with the hazards. This turned out to be quite important in the reactor

Table 16.2. Dismantlement of the Elk River Reactor 1972–1974. Total Cost—$5.7 Million

Operation	% of Total Cost
Final planning	11.2
Removal of piping and equipment from containment	5.2
Removal of superheater and its building	1.5
Removal of passageway and equipment between superheater and containment	1.2
Removal and disposal of reactor pressure vessel internals	13.7
Removal and disposal of reactor pressure vessel	18.5
Removal and disposal of biological shield	21.7
Removal and disposal of containment building	7.0
Shipping costs	21.9
Closing-out operations	1.8

dismantling operation. The total $5.7 million cost of the dismantling was subdivided as given in Table 16.2. The total cost was $600,000 more than anticipated. The site of the nuclear plant was restored to preconstruction condition at grade-level, and a parking lot was installed where the reactor had once stood.

16.4. OCCUPATION EXPOSURE AND COST OF DECOMMISSIONING

Two aspects of decommissioning beyond the technological and the regulatory are important: namely, occupation radiation dose involved, and cost.

A controlling factor in determining how long a reactor is to remain mothballed or entombed is the time required for ^{60}Co to decay to levels low enough to permit manual removal rather than requiring remotely controlled equipment for removal. Minimum estimates for ^{60}Co decay to such levels are 108 yr for a PWR, 104 yr for a BWR, and 65 yr for an HTGR. (The differences are due to the amount of cobalt-containing steel used in an average plant of each type.) The total activity and dose rates from a reference PWR are given in Figure 16.3, while the effect of the length of reactor operation prior to shutdown is given in Figure 16.4. From these figures it is evident that the radiation dose rate from the internal components of an LWR will remain fairly high for many hundreds of years.

^{59}Ni in LWRs and ^{14}C in HTGRs pose special problems, as they would take thousands of years after reactor shutdown to decay to the 0.4 mrem/hr permitted by regulatory criteria for unrestricted contact work, and needed to terminate a possession-only license. For the sake of comparison, it might be recalled here that the average person receives about 200 mrem/yr natural background radiation.

^{59}Ni has not been considered a controlling radionuclide in decommissionings until now, because the periods of reactor operation have not been long enough to generate significant quantities of this isotope. However, as shown in Figure 16.5, commercial LWRs operated for 40 yr at 80% utilization will contain significant amounts of ^{59}Ni in certain reactor vessel internals.

The structural materials inside the pressure vessel of a reactor are exposed to neutron radiation which causes them to become radioactive. The elements most susceptible to activation are Fe and Ni, principal components of steel and Inconel alloys, and Co found in trace amounts in many reactor materials. As an example, the quantities, materials, and neutron fluxes to which they are exposed are given in Table 16.3 for the KRB-II BWR at Gundremmingen, West Germany. If the internal components are removed and shipped to licensed burial grounds, then ^{63}Ni becomes the controlling activated radioisotope, reducing the decay time to 0.4 mrems/hr in about 1000 yr.

Consequently, an attractive decommissioning strategy is the most cost effective: using the mothballing and entombing options in combination: mothballing about 100 yr and then removing the few remaining components that still contain hazardous quantities of ^{59}Ni and ^{63}Ni—or in the case of HTGRs, ^{14}C.

All the alternative decommissioning modes will result in some radiation exposure to the work force. This exposure is estimated in Table 16.4 for LWRs and the HTGR. A more detailed analysis of the occupational and public off-site risk from decommissioning in a PWR is given in Table 16.5, which presents both the radiological and nonradiological impact from normal decommissioning

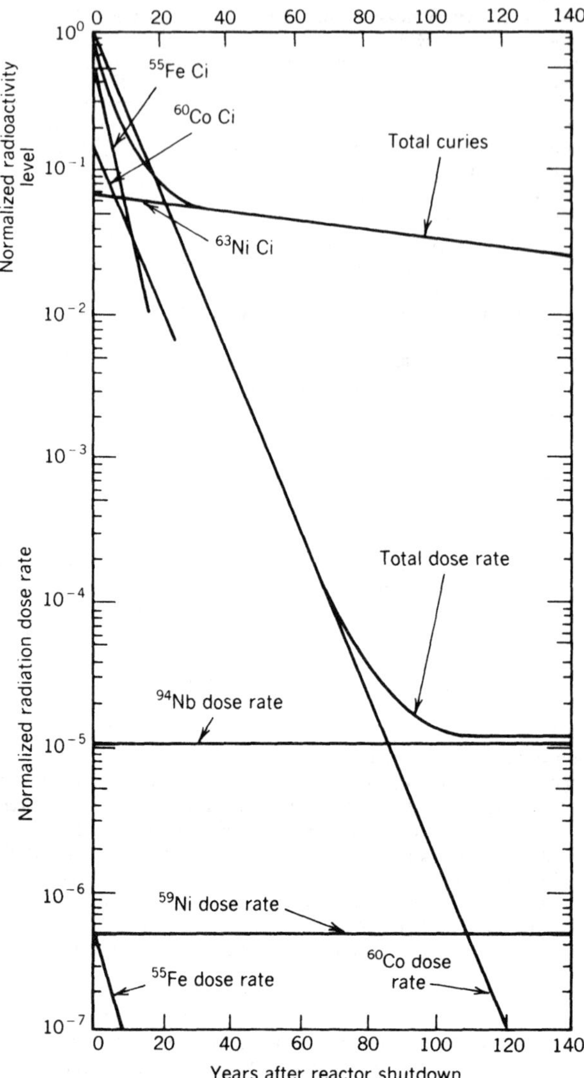

Figure 16.3. Time dependence of radioactivity levels and radiation dose rate in the activated reactor components of a typical BWR. (From NUREG/CR-0130.)

operations. As seen in this figure, between 400 and 1200 person-rems of exposure can be expected from the decommissioning operation itself, with transportation, which is about a factor of 10 lower, being the second most important source of exposure. The principal radiation doses to the public, which are generally small, occur during the transportation of activated materials from the reactor to the disposal facility (Table 16.6). The estimated radiation doses to the work force and public are primarily attributable to ^{60}Co.

In the case of mothballing or entombing, about 90% of the occupational radiation dose is attributable to draining, flushing, and securing contaminated systems. In the case of PWRs, the estimated dose for mothballing is somewhat larger than for entombing because more decontamination is required. For prompt dismantling and removal, the work activities that account for the doses are shown in Table 16.7. This estimate, from a different report, gives estimates a factor of 2 lower than those shown in Table 16.5. This is within the range of uncertainty for such estimates, which are difficult to make.

The dose estimates in Tables 16.5 and 16.7 are based on the assumption that extensive shielding

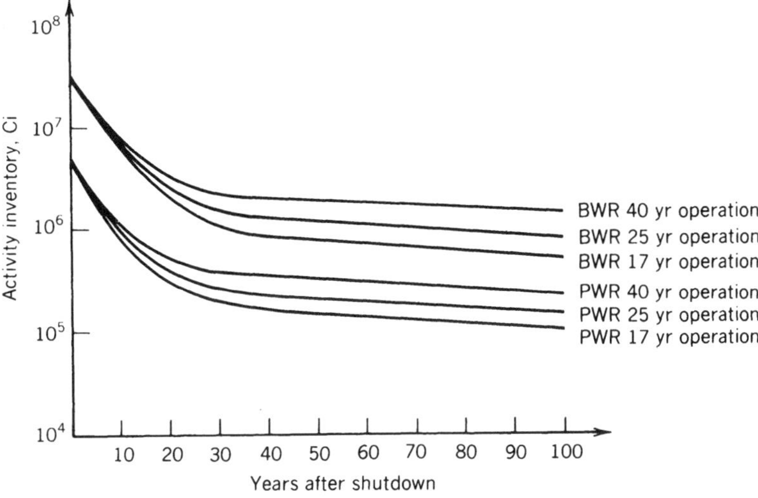

Figure 16.4. Activity inventory for a 1200-MWe LWR for different operating and cooling times. [From R. Bardtenschlager, *Nuclear Engineering and Design* **45**, 1 (1978).]

would be incorporated in the work platforms used to reduce dose levels. Otherwise the long duration of the removal activities—perhaps up to 50 months—would lead to significant exposures. The actual in-plant radiation levels at the time of decommissioning would be determined and evaluated in terms of the costs and benefits of implementing various personnel radiation protection measures, such as installing additional shielding.

In the case of the mothballing-and-delayed-dismantling-and-removal combination alternative, the estimated mothballed first-phase period of 108 yr for a PWR, 104 yr for a BWR, and 65 yr for an HTGR are based on the assumption that a peak contact dose level of 300 mrems/hr is acceptable for manual—that is, nonremote—dismantling of the most radioactive reactor vessel internals, provided the necessary personnel radiation monitoring is performed. Local shielding, such as lead skirts or water basins, would still be required, but manual cutting could be accomplished.

Nuclear plant operating and maintenance practices can mean large cost differences at decommissioning time. Most levels of radioactive contamination outside the pressure vessel fall under Class-A low-level wastes. That is the lowest category and the most economical to dispose of.

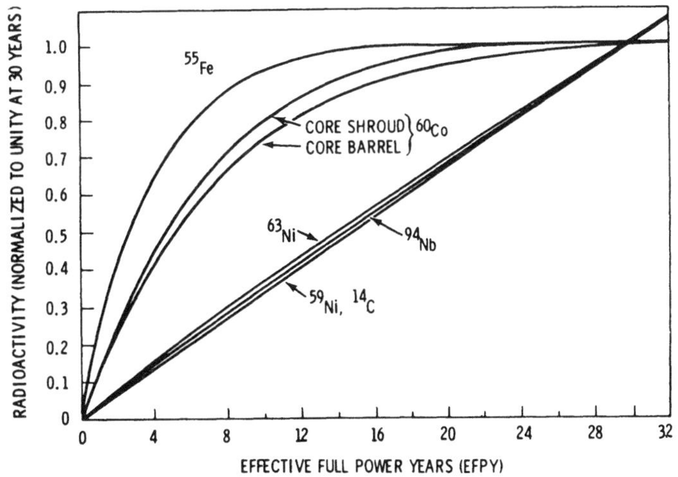

Figure 16.5. Buildup of activation products in PWR vessel internals as a function of reactor operation. (From NUREG/CR-0671.)

Table 16.3. Thermal Neutron Fluxes at Various Components of a Typical BWR

Component	Mass, kg	Material	Flux, $cm^{-2}\ s^{-1}$
Upper guide grid	7,000	X5 CrNi 189	9 (+13)
Emergency cooling spray ring	1,700	X5 CrNi 189	6 (+ 9)
PV cladding	9,400	Thermanit	1.4 (+ 9)
PV	47,800	22 NiMoCr 37	1.2 (+ 9)
Control rod guide tubes	1,930	X5 CrNi 189	4 (+13)
Control rod guide tubes	4,655	X5 CrNi 189	8 (+12)
Control rod guide tubes	10,743	X5 CrNi 189	6 (+10)
Core barrel, core zone	23,100	X5 CrNi 189	1 (+13)
Core barrel, bottom	18,750	X5 CrNi 189	1 (+10)
Lower guide grid	7,900	X5 CrNi 189	4 (+13)
Core fluxmeter housing	4,000	X5 CrNi 189	9 (+13)
Control rods	72.5	X5 CrNi 189	1 (+13)
Control rod guide rollers, upper	0.07	HS 3	1 (+13)

Source: Adapted from R. Bardtenschlager, *Nuclear Engineering and Design* **45,** 1 (1978).
8 (+5) means 8×10^5.

Table 16.4. Estimated Occupational Radiation Dose, person-rem

	Mothballing	Entombing	Dismantling-Removal
PWR	150	130	630
BWR	80	125	550
HTGR	25	30	1690

Source: AIF.

Table 16.5. Summary of Safety Analysis for Decommissioning a Reference PWR

Type of Safety Concern	Source of Safety Concern	Units	Immediate Dismantlement	Safe Storage with Deferred Dismantlement After 10 yr	Safe Storage with Deferred Dismantlement After 100 yr
		Public Safety			
Radiation exposure	Decommissioning operations	person-rem	0.0001	<0.0001	<0.0001
	Transportation	person-rem	22.	[a]	[a]
	Safe storage	person-rem	—	Neg.[b]	Neg.[b]
		Occupational Safety			
Serious lost-time injuries	Decommissioning operations	Total no.	4.0	4.9	4.9
	Transportation	Total no.	1.1	1.2	1.2
	Safe storage	Total no.	—	0.96	1.9
Fatalities	Decommissioning operations	Total no.	0.029	0.029	0.029
	Transportation	Total no.	0.068	0.075	0.075
	Safe storage	Total no.	—	0.00087	0.0087
Radiation exposure	Decommissioning operations	person-rem	1200	760	430
	Transportation	person-rem	100	[a]	[a]
	Safe storage	person-rem	—	10	14

Source: Adapted from NUREG/CR-0130.

[a]Not estimated.

[b]Neg. = negligible. Radiation doses to the public from normal continuing care activities but are expected to be significantly smaller than those from decommissioning operations.

Table 16.6. Radiation from Transport of Radioactive Materials from Decommissioning

	Radiation Doses from Transport, person-rem	
	Immediate Dismantlement	Preparations for Safe Storage
Occupational:		
Truck transport	99	10
Rail transport	3.5	3.5
Total	103	14
Public:		
Truck transport	21	2.1
Rail transport	1	1
Total	22	3

Source: Adapted from NUREG/CR-0130.

Higher levels of transuranics and fission products, much more costly to dispose of, may be found outside the pressure vessel in plants that have experienced extensive fuel failures.

In addition, studies of operating plants have shown that contamination of concrete is generally quite shallow, unless sealing paint is allowed to deteriorate or cracks develop. Unless the concrete is rough and cracked, contamination only affects the first two centimeters, while sealing paint generally keeps most contamination on the surface. Maintenance practices can therefore affect the costs of eventual decommissioning.

16.5. REGULATION

Decommissioning requirements were not directly addressed as part of a federal statute until 1978. Congress passed the Uranium Mill Tailings Radiation Control Act in November of that year. This act amended the Atomic Energy Act of 1954 to require a decommissioning plan and proof of financial ability to execute it as part of the license application for a uranium mine. As a result, abandoned mill tailings piles are now being stabilized and covered to protect the environment and eventually to restore the land area for other uses (see Chapter 5).

Firm requirements for decommissioning and decontamination of nuclear facilities, however, do not currently exist. The NRC staff is conducting some studies of its regulatory position with respect to decommissioning of facilities. NRC studies exist which cover the following: PWRs, BWRs, multiple reactor facilities, uranium mills, uranium fabrication, by-product utilization, fuel reprocessing, mixed-oxide fabrication, and low-level waste burial grounds, but the regulations for these facilities have not yet been formulated.

Because decommissioning of nuclear facilities in the United States is only specifically addressed by a few criteria, many of the requirements to be fulfilled in such an operation are not well defined. The only criteria that are legally binding are those in federal or state statutes or regulations. In most cases local regulations do not exist, but are likely to be enacted whenever decommissioning of a facility is imminent. Table 16.8 gives a matrix showing what regulations are binding in each situation. It shows that the individual states have a variety of regulations, most of which relate to the financial responsibility question. The principal federal guidance in the United States comes from NRC Regulatory Guide 1.86. It specifies the operational and procedural steps for decommis-

Table 16.7. Estimated Occupational Radiation Dose for Prompt Dismantling and Removal Option, person-rem

Major Activity	PWR	BWR	HTGR
Remove vessel internals	24	20	980
Remove reactor vessel	265	90	570
Remove activated systems	120	130	—
Decontaminate systems	220	310	140
Total:	630	550	1690

Source: AIF.

Table 16.8. Criteria, Regulations, and Statutes Pertaining to Decommissioning Nuclear Facilities

	(a) Federal Statutes	(b) Federal Regulations	(c) Administrative Orders	(d) Federal Court Decisions	(e) State and Local Requirements	(f) Regulatory Guides	(g) Industry Standards
A. Criteria that specifically address decommissioning							
B. Criteria that provide generic standards for entire fuel cycle (e.g., occupational radiation exposure).					"Grey area": may have legal force in some cases.		
C. Criteria that specify standards in an operational area applicable to decommissioning (e.g., waste transportation, SNM license, etc.).		Legally Binding					
D. Criteria that specify standards in a procedural area applicable to decommissioning (e.g., financial qualifications, transfer of license, etc.).							
E. Criteria pertaining to another point in the fuel cycle that could be extended or translated to apply to similar problems in decommissioning (e.g., plant security, inspection of facilities, etc.).							
F. Criteria pertaining to an operational step or a point in the fuel cycle that provide an analogy or example of standards needed in decommissioning (e.g., quality assurance standards in plant construction).						Legally not applicable, but worth some attention as examples of kind of requirement that may later be imposed.	
G. Criteria existing in an area unrelated to nuclear power that provide an analogy or example of standards or solutions needed in decommissioning (e.g., long-term monitoring in retired military facilities).							

Source: From NUREG/CR-0671.

Table 16.9. Operational and Procedural Steps Recommended by Regulatory Guide 1.86 for Four Acceptable Decommissioning Modes

	Decommissioning Modes			
Operational and Procedural Steps	Mothballing	Entombment	Dismantlement	Conversion
Submit request to amend operating license to possession-only license.	X	X	X	X
Submit dismantlement plan.		X	X	X
Fuel assemblies removed from site.	X	X	X	X
Radioactive fluids and waste removed from site.	X	X	X	X
Selected components removed from site.	?	X		?
All materials above unrestricted use radiation limits removed from site.			X	
"Sealing of all remaining highly radioactive or contaminated components (e.g., pressure vessel, reactor internals) within a structure integral with the biological shield."	?	X		?
"Surveillance and security for the retirement alternatives whose final status requires a possession-only license."	X	X		
Submit comprehensive radiation survey.	?	?	X	?
Release of site for unrestricted use.			X	
Optional dismantling of remaining structures.	?	?	X	?
License termination.			X	

Source: From NUREG/CR-0671.

sioning nuclear facilities. Table 16.9 summarizes these steps for the various decommissioning options.

An NRC reevaluation plan (NUREG-0436) was published in 1978, and subsequently revised several times. It redefines the decommissioning alternatives as follows:

DECON means to immediately remove all radioactive material to permit unrestricted release of the property.

SAFSTOR means to fix and maintain property so that risk to safety is acceptable for a period of storage followed by decontamination and/or decay to an unrestricted level.

ENTOMB means to encase and maintain property in a strong and structurally long-lived material (e.g., concrete) to assure retention until radioactivity decays to an unrestricted level.

The NRC issued a draft environmental impact statement on decommissioning (NUREG-0586) in 1981. This followed another draft report (NUREG-0590) which discussed the NRC "thoughts" on the subject. This report suggested that the primary goal of decommissioning should be DECON. However, since it may result in high occupational exposures, SAFSTOR, perhaps followed by ENTOMB to allow radiation levels to fall to unrestricted levels, should be considered.

The disposition criteria for decommissioning nuclear facilities are based on what are believed to be acceptable radioactive contamination levels of the facility and its site. These, in turn, are based on recommended dose-rate limits for the public, considering all potential exposure pathways. Regulatory Guide 1.86 sets these criteria according to surface contamination levels for particular

Table 16.10. Regulatory Guide 1.86 Acceptable Surface Contamination Levels

Nuclide	Acceptable Surface Contamination Levels, dpm/(dm)^2		
	Average	Maximum	Removable
Natural U, ^{235}U, ^{238}U, and associated decay products	5,000	15,000	1,000
Transuranics, ^{226}Ra, ^{228}Ra, ^{230}Th, ^{228}Th, ^{231}Pa, ^{227}Ac, ^{126}I, ^{129}I	100	300	20
Natural Th, ^{232}Th, ^{90}Sr, ^{224}Ra, ^{232}U, ^{126}I, ^{131}I, ^{133}I	1,000	3,000	200
Beta-gamma emitters (nuclides with decay modes other than alpha emission or spontaneous fission) except ^{90}Sr and others noted above	5,000	15,000	1,000

Source: Courtesy of PNWL.

radionuclides (Table 16.10). As seen from this figure, the restrictions on contamination from transuranic isotopes are the most severe. Equipment with higher radiation levels than given in this table must be decontaminated.

The radiation levels of the decommissioned site are due to the radioactivity accumulated over the life of the plant, as well as that deposited during the decommissioning operation. Although many isotopes will be present on site (Table 16.11), the dominant one will be ^{137}Cs which makes up 75% of the total activity—about 1.3×10^{-2} mCi/m^2—at the time of reactor shutdown. Because of its relatively slow decay (30-yr half-life), after 100 yr it constitutes almost all of the site activity. From the projected soil contamination levels, dose rates of 0.03 mrems/yr are estimated.

16.6. MULTIPLE AND ACCELERATED DECOMMISSIONINGS

Most of the decommissioning studies to date have considered single reactors on a single site. Many reactor stations, however, consist of multiple units on the same site. These units very often were built within a few years of each other, and consequently will require decommissioning at about the same time. While a detailed analysis of decommissioning costs is deferred until Chapter 19, the cost

Table 16.11. Calculated Isotopic Composition of Radioactive Surface Contamination in the Reference PWR. Fractional Surface Contamination at Decay Times

Radionuclide	Shutdown	10 yr	100 yr
^{51}Cr	6.9×10^{-4}	—	—
^{54}Mn	1.4×10^{-3}	—	—
^{55}Fe	2.2×10^{-2}	2.8×10^{-3}	—
^{59}Fe	8.7×10^{-4}	—	—
^{58}Co	7.5×10^{-3}	—	—
^{60}Co	7.5×10^{-2}	3.2×10^{-2}	—
^{89}Sr	1.2×10^{-3}	—	—
^{90}Sr	6.9×10^{-4}	8.8×10^{-4}	—
^{90}Y	6.9×10^{-4}	8.8×10^{-4}	—
^{95}Zr	2.5×10^{-4}	—	—
^{95}Nb	2.5×10^{-4}	—	—
^{129m}Te	3.1×10^{-4}	—	—
^{131}I	1.4×10^{-2}	—	—
^{134}Cs	1.2×10^{-1}	6.6×10^{-3}	—
^{136}Cs	1.1×10^{-3}	—	—
^{137}Cs	7.5×10^{-1}	9.6×10^{-1}	1.0
Total	1.0	1.0	1.0

Source: Adapted from NUREG/CR-0130.

Note: Inventories at each time period are normalized to 1 μCi/m^2.

Table 16.12. Estimated Cost Reduction for a Two-Unit Station over a Single-Unit Station

	Two Reactors on a Site but Only One, and No Shared Facilities, Decommissioned, % Cost Reduction			Two Reactors and Shared Facilities Decommissioned Simultaneously, % Cost Reduction		
	Mothball	Entombment	Dismantle and Remove	Mothball	Entombment	Dismantle and Remove
PWR	4	1	12	5	0.5	8
BWR	4	1	7	5	0.5	6
HTGR	4	1	10	8	0.5	10

Source: From AIF/NESP-009.

saving in terms of estimated percentage reductions are shown in Table 16.12 for a twin-unit station for each of the decommissioning modes.

A basic assumption in most studies is that all decommissioning work is carried out on a 40-hr work week. In the cases of entombing and dismantling-removal, some operations can be done on a two-shift basis. A cost-sensitivity analysis of this assumption, carried out for entombing or dismantling-removal of each of the three reactor types, is shown in Table 16.13. The estimated percent reductions in total costs for an accelerated (two-shift) work schedule compared to a single-shift schedule range between 16% and 22% for entombing, and 19% and 23% for the dismantling-removal option.

16.7. FINANCIAL ASPECTS OF DECOMMISSIONING

Financing the decommissioning of nuclear facilities is a major area of public concern. There are several financial approaches that can be used:

1. Pay the decommissioning costs when incurred, out of general revenue.
2. Treat decommissioning costs as a "negative" salvage value for the purposes of depreciation.
3. Establish a sinking fund to which contributions are made each year to cover estimated costs.
4. Establish a "perpetual care" trust fund.
5. The facility owner may enter into a bonding arrangement that assures the proper decommissioning of the facility.

Various combinations of these options are possible.

In the United States, 10CFR50 requires that "reasonable assurance" be provided by an applicant for a construction permit that the applicant is financially capable of paying decommissioning expenses. Several states have developed their own financial standards in this area. There is little uniformity among the state regulations, and a legal question exists as to whether decommissioning is essentially a federal or a state responsibility.

Presently, federal attention focuses on an operator's ability to meet the operating and decommissioning costs over the life of the facility. The concern with decommissioning is the "reasonable assurance" that funds will be available at the end of the 40-yr operating lifetime, although, also to be considered, are potential financing problems in the event of operator bankruptcy or premature end of a facility's operation.

The cost of the eventual decommissioning of a nuclear power station is as much a part of the

Table 16.13. Percent Cost Reduction for Accelerated Work

	Entombing	Dismantling-Removal
PWR	16	19
BWR	22	20
HTGR	16	23

Source: From AIF/NESP-009.

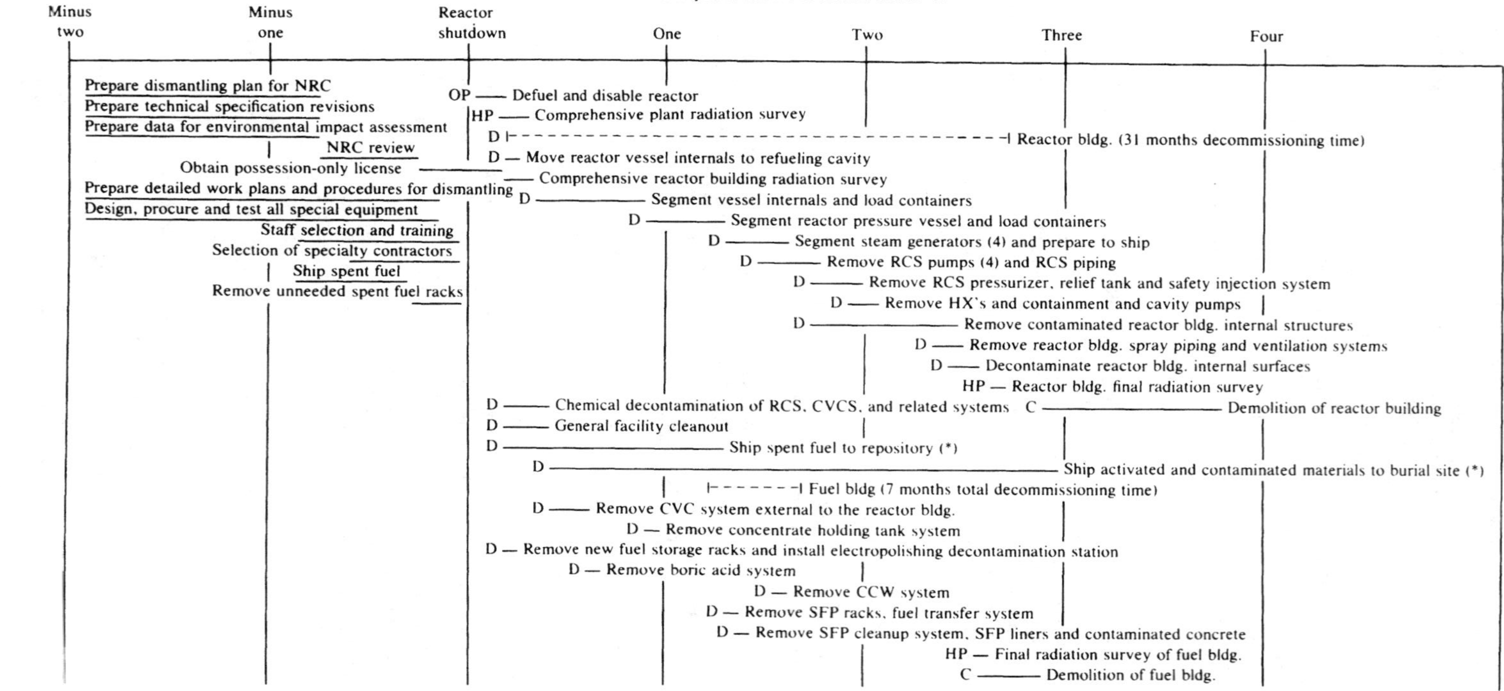
Time in years, relative to reactor shutdown
Minus two
Minus one
Reactor shutdown
One
Two
Three
Four
Prepare dismantling plan for NRC
Prepare technical specification revisions
Prepare data for environmental impact assessment
NRC review
Obtain possession-only license
Prepare detailed work plans and procedures for dismantling
Design, procure and test all special equipment
Staff selection and training
Selection of specialty contractors
Ship spent fuel
Remove unneeded spent fuel racks
OP — Defuel and disable reactor
HP — Comprehensive plant radiation survey
D — Reactor bldg. (31 months decommissioning time)
D — Move reactor vessel internals to refueling cavity
— Comprehensive reactor building radiation survey
D — Segment vessel internals and load containers
D — Segment reactor pressure vessel and load containers
D — Segment steam generators (4) and prepare to ship
D — Remove RCS pumps (4) and RCS piping
D — Remove RCS pressurizer, relief tank and safety injection system
D — Remove HX's and containment and cavity pumps
D — Remove contaminated reactor bldg. internal structures
D — Remove reactor bldg. spray piping and ventilation systems
D — Decontaminate reactor bldg. internal surfaces
HP — Reactor bldg. final radiation survey
D — Chemical decontamination of RCS, CVCS, and related systems
C — Demolition of reactor building
D — General facility cleanout
D — Ship spent fuel to repository (*)
D — Ship activated and contaminated materials to burial site (*)
Fuel bldg (7 months total decommissioning time)
D — Remove CVC system external to the reactor bldg.
D — Remove concentrate holding tank system
D — Remove new fuel storage racks and install electropolishing decontamination station
D — Remove boric acid system
D — Remove CCW system
D — Remove SFP racks, fuel transfer system
D — Remove SFP cleanup system, SFP liners and contaminated concrete
HP — Final radiation survey of fuel bldg.
C — Demolition of fuel bldg.

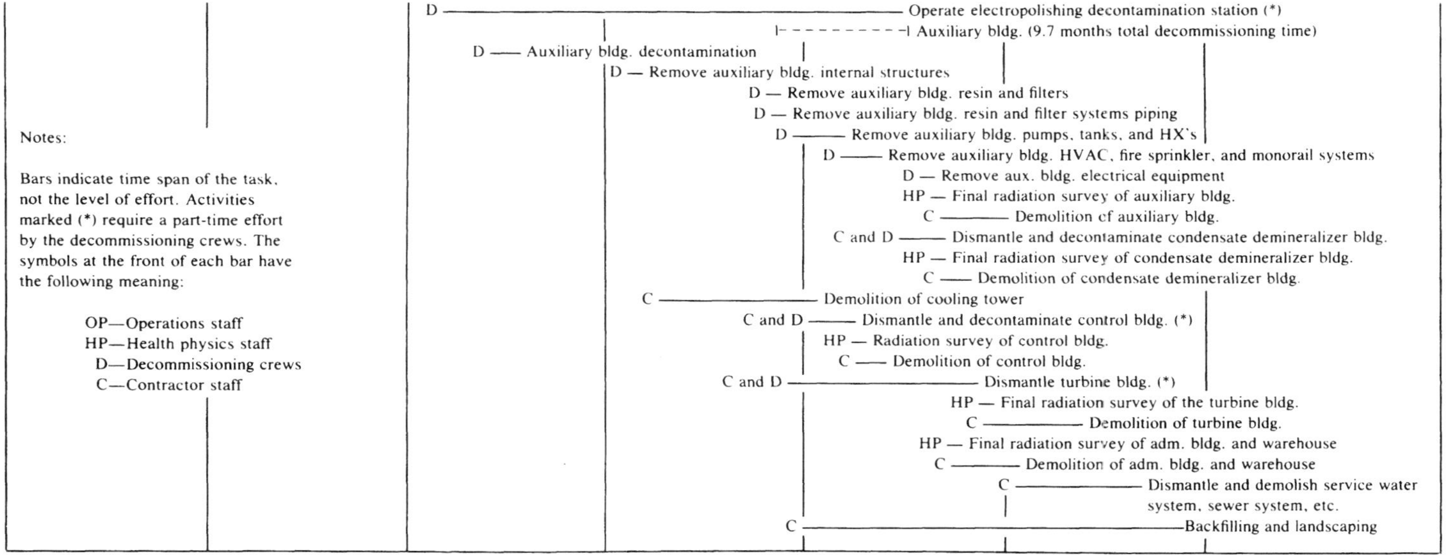

Notes:

Bars indicate time span of the task, not the level of effort. Activities marked (*) require a part-time effort by the decommissioning crews. The symbols at the front of each bar have the following meaning:

OP—Operations staff
HP—Health physics staff
D—Decommissioning crews
C—Contractor staff

D — Operate electropolishing decontamination station (*)
Auxiliary bldg. (9.7 months total decommissioning time)
D — Auxiliary bldg. decontamination
D — Remove auxiliary bldg. internal structures
D — Remove auxiliary bldg. resin and filters
D — Remove auxiliary bldg. resin and filter systems piping
D — Remove auxiliary bldg. pumps, tanks, and HX's
D — Remove auxiliary bldg. HVAC, fire sprinkler, and monorail systems
D — Remove aux. bldg. electrical equipment
HP — Final radiation survey of auxiliary bldg.
C — Demolition of auxiliary bldg.
C and D — Dismantle and decontaminate condensate demineralizer bldg.
HP — Final radiation survey of condensate demineralizer bldg.
C — Demolition of condensate demineralizer bldg.
C — Demolition of cooling tower
C and D — Dismantle and decontaminate control bldg. (*)
HP — Radiation survey of control bldg.
C — Demolition of control bldg.
C and D — Dismantle turbine bldg. (*)
HP — Final radiation survey of the turbine bldg.
C — Demolition of turbine bldg.
HP — Final radiation survey of adm. bldg. and warehouse
C — Demolition of adm. bldg. and warehouse
C — Dismantle and demolish service water system, sewer system, etc.
C — Backfilling and landscaping

Figure 16.6. Schedule and sequence of dismantlement events. (From NUREG/CR-0130.)

cost of electricity generated at the station as is the cost of fuel, and in theory should be borne by the consumers of that electricity. The money to pay for decommissioning has to be collected through charges for electricity, and these charges are controlled in the United States largely by the public utility commissions in each state.

The preferred approach appears to treat anticipated decommissioning costs as a negative salvage value added to the base for calculating the allowable rates for electricity. Whether or not the moneys so collected are required to enter an independent sinking fund varies from state to state.

Taxes paid on a nuclear facility are a factor that could help decide the timing and method of decommissioning. If, for instance, a shutdown plant is taxed based on its value as an operating unit, early dismantlement would become attractive because of the high cost of delay. If, on the other hand, the plant is taxed only on the value of the land comprising the site, then the financial pressure for early dismantlement is considerably less. In practice, the tax rate will be negotiated between the plant owner and the local tax assessor, although the latter approach is the more likely.

16.8. TIME REQUIRED FOR DECOMMISSIONING PLANTS

Mothballing is estimated to require 10 months for each type of reactor. This includes predecommissioning planning work, removal of all radwaste, decontamination, installation of security equipment, and issuance of the possession-only license. The schedule for mothballing is insensitive to plant size. It is not practical to accelerate the schedule by using a two-shift work force in the case of mothballing.

Entombing is estimated to require 36 months for a PWR, 34 months for a BWR, and 26 months for an HTGR. These schedules could be reduced to about 28, 26, and 20 months, respectively, if critical-path work activities were carried on with a two-shift work force.

Unlike the mothballing case, the duration of entombing work activities would be reduced for small reactors. The AIF study estimates 32 months for a 550-MWe PWR, 28 months for a 550-MWe BWR, and 21 months for a 770-MWe HTGR.

Dismantling and removal is estimated to require 76 months for a PWR, 72 for a BWR, and 79 for an HTGR. Figure 16.6 shows the timing of events required to dismantle a reactor. For this mode, as for the entombing mode, a two-shift work force could reduce these schedules to about 54, 47, and 51 months, respectively. Likewise, small reactors—using the same size reactors as cited in the previous paragraph—would require only 52, 58, and 67 months, respectively.

In conclusion, reactor sites are valuable resources, and may likely be wanted for another nuclear, or other, power plant. If that were the case, the combined mothballing-and-dismantling-removal alternative might be the mode of choice, for two reasons: the decommissioned reactor and the new one could be protected by the same security force, and this mode would be the most economical.

If on the other hand the site were not to be recycled, then entombment and dismantling-removal might prove the most economical.

16.9. FACILITIES OTHER THAN NUCLEAR POWER PLANTS

Many types of facilities that handle nuclear fuel require decommissioning at the end of their useful lives. These include uranium mills, uranium hexafluoride conversion plants, and fuel fabrication facilities at the front end, and reprocessing plants and low-level waste burial sites at the back end of the nuclear fuel cycle. For each of these facilities a spectrum of decommissioning options exist. These options, by and large, mirror those available for nuclear power plants. They consist either of dismantlement or of safe storage options, as shown in Table 16.14 and delineated in greater detail in Table 16.15. The option chosen for a particular case will be selected on the basis of a balance between safety and cost considerations, and will be consistent with federal and state regulations. As in the case of nuclear power plants, occupational exposure will be minimized by employing ALARA guidelines in the decommissioning work. The radioactive wastes will be properly disposed of: the high-activity and TRU† wastes will go to geologic waste repositories, while low-level wastes will be disposed of in shallow land burial sites.

The following types of fuel-cycle facilities require decommissioning:

1. *Uranium Mills.* More than 20 inactive uranium mills exist in the United States alone. The risk does not stem from the mills themselves, rather the mill tailings remaining after the uranium has been mostly removed. Mill tailings, generated at a rate proportional to uranium production, have reached 1,000,000 tons in some locations. Each ton of tailings contains about 0.6 mCi of ^{226}Ra, which releases radioactive ^{222}Rn to the environment. Under present U.S. policy, these tailings are required to be stabilized and controlled, as discussed in Chapter 5.

†TRU = transuranic wastes, consisting of the isotopes of plutonium, americium, and other elements heavier than uranium.

Table 16.14. Decommissioning Modes for Nuclear Fuel Cycle Facilities

	Dismantlement	
	Complete decontamination and removal of radioactivity No surveillance	Plant, unrestrictred use Site, unrestricted use
	Safe Storage	
Hardened (entombment)	Major decontamination and removal of radioactivity Hardened entombment of residuals Infrequent surveillance	Plant, conditional nonnuclear use Site, conditional nonnuclear use
Passive (protective storage)	Partial decontamination and removal of radioactivity Sealing of residuals Remote continual surveillance	Plant, nuclear use Site, conditional nonnuclear use
Custodial (Layaway) (Mothball)	Partial decontamination and removal of radioactivity Confinement of residuals Continuous surveillance	Plant, nuclear only Site, nuclear only

Source: Courtesy of PNWL.

Table 16.15. Summary of Activities for Decommissioning Fuel Cycle Facilities

Activity	Immediate Dismantlement	Hardened Safe Storage (Entombment)	Passive Safe Storage, Interim Continuing Care and Eventual Dismantlement	Custodial Safe Storage, Interim Continuing Care and Eventual Dismantlement
Planning and preparation	X	X	X	X
Chemical decontamination	X	X	X	X
Equipment deactivation	X	X	X	X
Equipment removal	X	X		
Mechanical decontamination	X	X	X	X
Immediate demolition and site restoration	X			
Fixing of residual radioactivity		X	X	X
Isolation of contaminated areas		X	X	
Interim continuing care, surveillance		Partial	X	X
Ultimate demolition and site restoration		Possible	X	X

Source: Courtesy of DOE.

Table 16.16. Information on LWR Fuel Fabrication Plants in the United States

Licensee	Plant Location	Plant Feed Material	Plant Product	Present Status
Babcock & Wilcox	Lynchburg, VA	UO_2 pellets	Fuel assemblies	Operating
Babcock & Wilcox[a]	Apollo, PA	UF_6	UO_2 powder or pellets	Operating
Combustion Engineering	Windsor, CT	UO_2 powder	Fuel assemblies	Operating
Combustion Engineering[b]	Hematite, MO	UF_6	UO_2 powder or pellets	Operating
Exxon Nuclear Co.	Richland, WA	UF_6	Fuel assemblies	Operating
General Electric	Wilmington, NC	UF_6	Fuel assemblies	Operating
General Electric	Pleasanton, CA	UF_6	Fuel assemblies R&D	Dismantled
Kerr-McGee	Crescent, OK	UF_6	UO_2 powder or pellets	In standby
Nuclear Fuel Services	Erwin, TN	UO_2 pellets	UO_2 powder or pellets	Shutdown
United Nuclear	New Haven, CT	UO_2 pellets	Fuel assemblies	Shutdown
Westinghouse	Columbia, SC	UF_6	Fuel assemblies	Operating

Source: From NUREG/CR-1266.

[a]Formerly Nuclear Materials and Equipment Corp. (NUMEC).
[b]Formerly Gulf United Nuclear.

Table 16.17. Specific Radioactivity of Residual Uranium Fuel Mixture at the Time of Shutdown and Various Times After Shutdown

	Specific Activity, μCi/g of Mixture[a]		
Radionuclide	Shutdown	10 yr	100 yr
^{230}Th	3.10×10^{-4}	4.58×10^{-4}	1.81×10^{-3}
^{231}Th	6.54×10^{-2}	6.54×10^{-2}	6.54×10^{-2}
^{234}Th	3.36×10^{-1}	3.36×10^{-1}	3.36×10^{-1}
^{231}Pa	2.93×10^{-5}	4.32×10^{-5}	1.73×10^{-4}
^{234m}Pa	3.36×10^{-1}	3.36×10^{-1}	3.36×10^{-1}
^{234}Pa	3.36×10^{-4}	3.28×10^{-4}	3.28×10^{-6}
^{234}U	1.72	1.72	1.72
^{235}U	6.54×10^{-2}	6.54×10^{-2}	6.54×10^{-2}
^{238}U	3.27×10^{-1}	3.27×10^{-1}	3.27×10^{-1}
Totals	2.85	2.85	2.85

Source: Adapted from NUREG/CR-1266.

[a]Based on average of 3% enriched uranium feed material.

Table 16.18. Radioactive Wastes from Decommissioning a Reference Fuel Reprocessing Plant

	Volume of Wastes as Packaged, m^3		
	Immediate Dismantlement	Placing in Passive Safe Storage	Placing in Custodial Safe Storage
Disposition of Waste			
Deep geologic disposal	4600	210	210
Shallow land burial	3100	180	180
Totals	7700	390	390

Source: Courtesy Battelle-PNWL.

Figure 16.7. The Elk River Reactor was completely dismantled and removed from its site in 1974. The operation is complete in the bottom photo. (Courtesy UNC Nuclear Industries.)

2. *UF_6 Conversion Plants.* To date, no UF_6 conversion plant has been decommissioned. No special problems are envisioned, however, as the main task in decommissioning such a plant will be the surface decontamination of process equipment.

3. *Fuel Fabrication Plants.* As shown in Table 16.16, four of the eleven U.S. LWR fuel fabrication plants have been shut down. One of the four plants has been decommissioned, the others have been decontaminated and released. Most of the radioactivity in such facilities comes from residues of the uranium fuel mixture, mainly from the uranium isotopes and their daughters (Table 16.17). The main task in decommissioning a fuel fabrication plant will be to decontaminate the surfaces where any residues may have deposited, and to dispose of unusable equipment.

4. *Fuel Reprocessing Plants.* Of the three commercial fuel reprocessing facilities in the United States (NFS at West Valley, New York; AGNS at Barnwell, South Carolina, and GE at Morris, Illinois), only the NFS facility has ever operated. In view of the uncertain status of the NFS plant, no plan presently exists regarding its decommissioning; however, DOE has awarded Westinghouse Electric Corp. a contract to study the alternatives with respect to returning it to service or decommissioning it, and to make recommendations. One particular problem is the relatively large quantity of neutralized liquid high-level wastes in storage in tanks on the NFS site. Their final disposal is made difficult and expensive because their high sodium content will make vitrification difficult—a problem not shared by future reprocessing plants where unneutralized wastes will be generated. The quantity of radioactive wastes to be handled from a reference fuel reprocessing plant is given in Table 16.18. The volume of high- and low-level radioactive wastes is smaller by a factor of 20 when removal of the waste is delayed.

5. *Low-Level Waste Burial Facilities.* Of the six commercial burial grounds in the United States, five are regulated by "Agreement States" (states that have entered into a regional agreement or compact on this subject). The sixth is regulated by NRC. The states have commitments for the perpetual care of any of the sites decommissioned, except for the Hanford low-level repository which is on federal land. None of these burial facilities is expected to be decommissioned in the foreseeable future.

16.10. DECOMMISSIONING SUMMARY

The basic approach to any mode of decommissioning is nearly invariable: that is, assembling a staff, a period of preparation, followed by chemical decontamination, and mechanical removal operations. The principal differences result from the design of the building and the design of the equipment to be decommissioned. In general, the technology available is adequate for the job, although remote-handling equipment, decontamination techniques, and waste volume-reduction methods can always be improved. Decommissioning is a costly, time-consuming job that usually involves millions of dollars and several years of effort. In the current regulatory and financial environment, options that defer dismantlement appear to be the most attractive option. Deferral of dismantlement also reduces the amount of radioactive wastes to be handled, and consequently the occupational radiation exposure. Nevertheless, this is a temporary state of affairs as, ultimately, any facility to be decommissioned will likely be dismantled. As shown in Figure 16.7, decommissioning operations are relatively straightforward.

REFERENCE

1. Manion, W. J., and T. S. LaGuardia, *An Engineering Evaluation of Nuclear Power Reactor Decommissioning Alternatives,* AIF/NESP-009 (1976).

BIBLIOGRAPHY

Bardtenschlager, R., et al., "Decommissioning LWR Power Plants," *Nuclear Engineering and Design* **45,** 1 (1978).

Elder, H. K., and D. E. Blahnik, *Technology, Safety and Costs of Decommissioning a Reference PWR,* NUREG/CR-1266, 1980.

Jenkins, C. E., et al., *Technology, Safety and Costs of Decommissioning a Reference Small Mixed Oxide Fuel Fabrication Plant,* NUREG CR-0129, 1979.

O'Donnell, F. R., et al. *Potential Radiation Dose to Man from Recycle of Metals Reclaimed from a Decommissioned Nuclear Power Plant,* NUREG CR-0134, 1979.

Schilling, A. H., et al., *Decommissioning Commercial Nuclear Facilities: A Review and Analysis of Current Regulations,* NUREG/CR-0671, 1979.

Smith, R. I., et al., *Technology, Safety and Costs of Decommissioning a Reference PWR,* NUREG CR-0130, 1978.

CHAPTER 17

THE SAFETY OF NUCLEAR POWER FACILITIES

17.1. INTRODUCTION

Nuclear power facilities present a potential hazard rarely encountered with other facilities: radiation. A major health hazard would result if, for instance, a significant fraction of the core inventory of a power reactor were released to the atmosphere. Such a release of radioactivity is clearly unacceptable, and steps are taken to assure it could never happen. These include use of engineered safety systems, various construction and design codes (e.g., ASTM standards), regulations on reactor operation, periodic maintenance and inspection, and so on. All these steps, however, are really designed to prevent faults of omission, because in the last analysis, the ultimate safety of any facility depends on the ability of its designers to use the forces of nature in such a way that a large release of radioactivity is not possible. To help them, various techniques are employed, including "conservative" design margins, the use of safety equipment, and reliance on various physical barriers to radiation release in case all else fails.

It is the current vogue that safety be approached on a probabilistic basis. This approach recognizes no absolute degree of safety—rather its implicit assumption is that at some (albeit extremely small) level of probability large accidents can happen. The methodology used in this approach (called Probabilistic Risk Assessment or PRA) is useful in many ways, but must be used with great care. One problem is many PRA analyses identify the high consequence events as having frequencies of occurrence of 10^{-7}/yr (i.e., one event in 10 million years); this seems to be contrary to our common experience that major accidents seem to be caused by rather common, unforeseen events (e.g., human error). The advent of PRA, however, has crystallized the long-held perception concerning nuclear safety: the worst accident, a major release of radioactivity from the core to the atmosphere, is only possible if both a core meltdown *and* containment building failure occur.

Less well appreciated, however, are the safety study results which show that even a moderate release of radiation is highly improbable, and then only as the result of major damage to the plant. Consequently, the economic penalty for even a "small" accident (in terms of released radiation) is likely to be high—high for consumers whose extra cost for replacement power would probably be measured in the hundreds of millions of dollars, but even higher for a utility whose investment in a billion dollar plant would be at risk. A case in point is the Fermi incident (described in Chapter 13), or the accident at Three Mile Island. The incentives for safety are therefore large. Moreover, the public interest and that of a nuclear plant's owner are the same—the prevention of accidents. This common interest is an important factor in assuring the health and safety of the public.

It is the practice, in the United States and elsewhere, for regulatory bodies to establish licensing procedures for nuclear facilities. These procedures set design requirements, construction practices, operational limits, and the siting of such facilities. While regulations are a necessary part of nuclear safety, it is important not to confuse the regulatory aspects (i.e., licensing) with safety itself. Meeting all requirements does not mean a plant is safe. The regulatory process itself is legislated, semijudicial in nature, and relies upon many judgmental aspects. Therefore, the discussion of regulation is (mostly) postponed to Chapter 18, while this chapter concentrates more on the technical aspects of safety. The two, however, are not completely separable; as a result, the reader should be conscious of some overlapping in the following material.

17.2. HISTORICAL ASPECTS OF REACTOR SAFETY

The first nuclear reactor was built under the West Stands at the University of Chicago. Its designers, well aware of the potential dangers, provided crude but effective shutdown measures to be used in the event of an accident. For example, they stationed a man with an axe to cut the rope holding a shutdown rod and assigned another man to break a large bottle of boric acid placed on top of the pile. The few new reactors built were located in unpopulated areas, in recognition of the dangers of radioactive contamination if a serious accident occurred. As these activities took place during World War II, it is not surprising that location of reactors at remote sites was the means chosen for protection of the population and that containment was not considered.

After World War II, reactors were enclosed in a containment building of one sort or other. Very often these were steel vessels that contained the reactor and varying amounts of its heat transport and electrical generating systems. These containment buildings were deemed necessary for reactors to operate in less remote, more highly populated areas. The relationship of plant site and population density was first addressed by the first Safeguard Committee set up by the U.S. AEC. It issued a report that set forth for the first time an exclusion-distance rule. It recommended that "the general public be excluded from a certain area in the vicinity of each reactor. This area, which would represent a region of maximum hazard, would be a circle of radius in miles equal to one one-hundredth of the square root of the normal thermal operating level of the reactor in kilowatts ($0.01 \sqrt{kW}$)." This formulation, which would imply an area of 18 miles for a 1000-MWe reactor, did not assume the use of effective containments and was only meant to apply to the relatively small research and production reactors of the time.

Although containment building design has since evolved to a highly refined form, and the extent of exclusion areas have been modified at various times, these two concepts have survived as important parts of reactor safety. All power reactors built in the United States (and overseas) have a containment building and are sited in generally low population areas with exclusion areas defined by regulation.

17.3. GENERAL SAFETY CONSIDERATIONS

When considering the safety of nuclear power, potential effects of concern include:

1. Immediate deaths and injuries (both occupational and to the general public).
2. Latent deaths and illnesses in the present or future generations.
3. Damage to property or the contamination of land and ecosystems with radioactivity.
4. Damage to society and its institutions.

All but the last are concerned with the potential release of radioactivity which may cause the damage; the last includes a concern for the weapons potential of nuclear fuels, which is treated in Chapter 20. The risks posed by the entire nuclear fuel cycle are illustrated in Figure 17.1.

The front end of the fuel cycle poses relatively small risk since the fuel is only slightly radioactive until it is irradiated. At that point, it becomes intensely radioactive, and a potential hazard. To be hazardous, however, a substance must not only be toxic (i.e., radioactive), but a means must exist for it to enter the biosphere. From this point of view, the nuclear power plant represents the largest risk, since the radioactivity levels in the core are high, a proximity to the biosphere exists, and the energy needed to violate safety barriers may be available. On the other hand, waste disposal is a small risk in comparison; although the radioactivity levels are high, the path to the environment is not direct and the energy level in the spent fuel is low. Most of this chapter, therefore, deals with power reactor safety. Other aspects of safety related to the fuel cycle have been already covered: Chapter 5 deals with the mine safety, Chapter 6 with enrichment plant safety, and Chapter 15 with waste disposal.

Figure 17.1 also suggests alternatives if some part of the fuel cycle becomes unacceptable from a safety point of view. For example, alternatives to the LWR reactor are gas reactors or liquid-metal fast breeder reactors. These may eventually prove superior to LWRs. Safety, however, should not be put on a relative basis; rather one needs to know if a particular technology is safe. Not considered in Figure 17.1 are nonradiation related safety concerns, for example, job related injuries or waste heat damage to the environment. The risk associated with nonradiation types of personal injury turns out to be quite small, while the risk of ecological damage due to waste heat† is not unique to nuclear power and can be controlled by proper plant design.

In 1979, an attempt to assemble the knowledge of radiological risks to humans was made by the National Academy of Sciences. Table 17.1 summarizes their evaluation of the risks of nuclear power on a radiation-dose basis, radiation for each reactor-year of electricity produced, and for accidents expected per reactor year of operation. Converting these estimates to fatalities is very uncertain; one very conservative estimate widely used is that, on average, one eventual excess cancer death will occur per 5000 person-rems of radiation.

†All thermal power plants reject waste heat to the environment. This heat can damage the environment, if not properly controlled. For example, fish in a river may be harmed if the temperature increase of the water is too high.

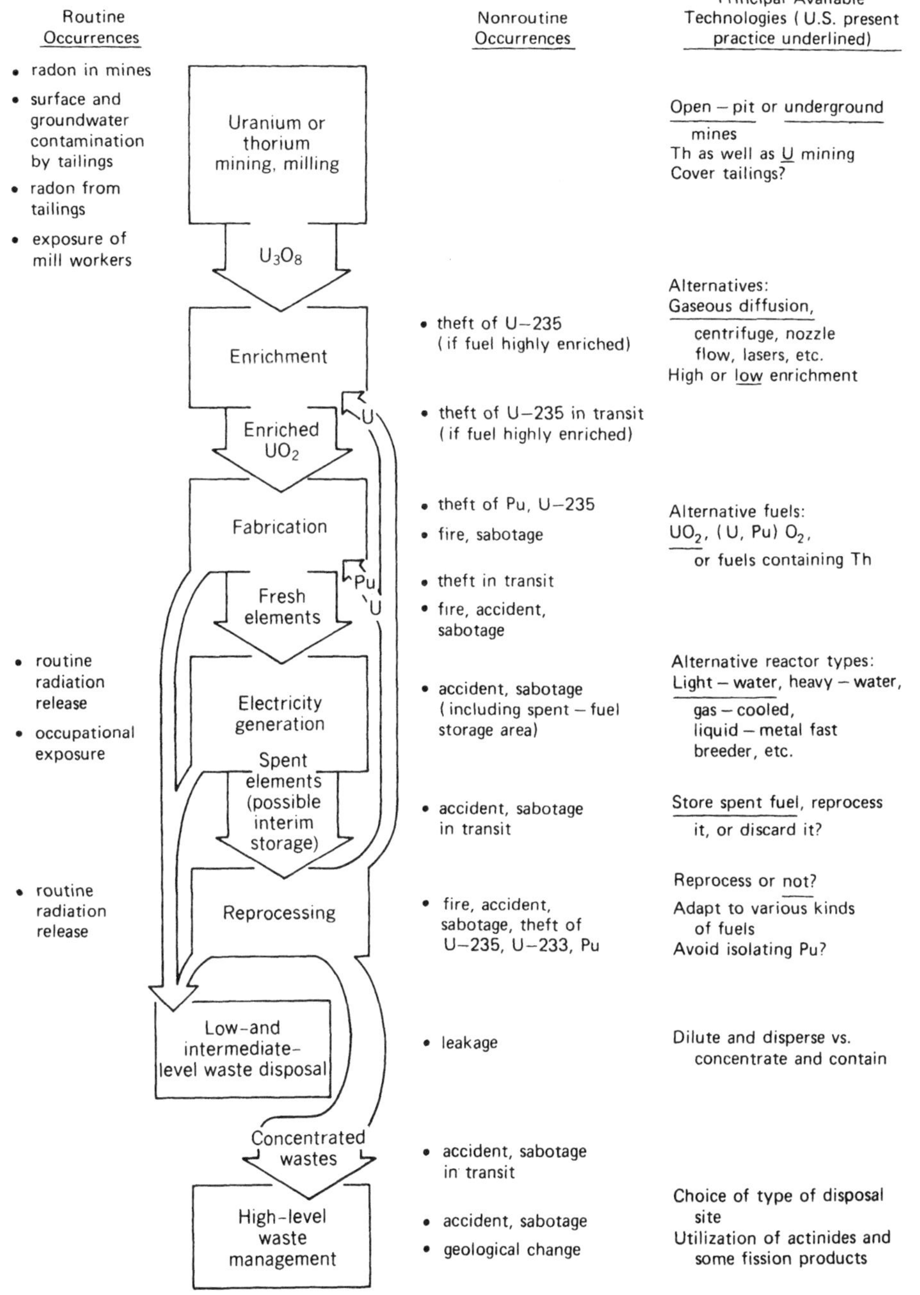

Figure 17.1. Principal risks and relevant alternatives in the nuclear fuel cycle. [From W. C. Herring, *Nuclear Safety* **20,** 666 (1979).]

Table 17.1. Summary of Risks Associated with Low-Level Radiation Exposures Attributable to the Production of Nuclear Electric Power

	Expectation of Population Dose, in person-rems/GW(e)-yr Electricity Produced, with Present Technology				
Source of Risk	Present Generation	Future Generations	Degree of Uncertainty for a Given Technology	Opportunities for Modification	Remarks
Occupational exposure	~1600[a]		Probably only a fraction of the value given	Probably modest, but data on variation with types of reactors and their ages are scanty	Mostly from reactor operation; some from mining
Public exposure from normal effluents	~{1100[a,b], 1350[a,b]}	~{1700[b], 6000[b]}	Probably only a fraction of the value given for the case of no reprocessing; a little more uncertain with reprocessing	Larger if escape of xenon[c] or ^{14}C (footnote *d*) is allowed to increase. Future-generation doses severalfold smaller if ^{14}C is captured in reprocessing[e]	Future-generation dose dominated by ^{14}C (half-life 5570 yr)
Public exposure from tailings piles	Very small	Estimates for perpetually uncovered piles range from 1.5×10^5 to 2×10^6; actual values much less	Very uncertain, as result dependent on future population distribution, weather, and geology, especially with covering by transport of dust	*May* be greatly reduced by covering; surely greatly reduced by reburial, reduced by a factor of ~50 in a breeder economy	Incremental *dose rate* at all times a minute fraction of background; may be compensated at *very* long times by removal of uranium[f]
Reactor accidents	*Reactor Safety Study*[g] estimates ~120; absence of major accidents[h] to date gives inequality $<10^4$	Much less than "present generation"	Conceded to be quite uncertain, with most qualified judgments favoring values a fraction of the *Reactor Safety Study* value	Might be appreciably reduced for light-water reactors; probably substantially less for at least some of the other reactor types	

Other accidents	Very small, according to most studies	Much less than "present generation"	All literature is in reasonable agreement, except for a few workers who speculate on the possibility of higher releases for some transportation accidents[i]	Reprocessing plant accidents can occur only if there is reprocessing; transportation accidents can be decreased by "nuclear parks"	Accidents in reprocessing and perhaps in transportation, although rare, have the greatest possibilities to deliver sizable population doses
Leakage from waste repositories	Small[j]	Few attempts at quantitative estimation have been made; these have usually indicated small dose expectations even if leakage occurs[j]	Although active acceptance of the conclusions to the left is limited, there seem to be no specific dose and probability analyses disagreeing with them; some unresolved issues concerning likelihood of leakage	Although many of the proposed modes of disposal would yield low dose expectations, very careful site selection might make the expectation far lower still	Most important desideratum is to minimize chance of escape to the environment in the first few hundred years

Source: Adapted from W. C. Herring, *Nuclear Safety* **20**, 664 (1979).

[a]Figures given are whole body doses, that is, doses delivered at about the same level to all organs of the body.

[b]The upper figure is for the case of no fuel reprocessing; the lower for the case in which all fuel is reprocessed and plutonium as well as uranium is recycled.

[c]Figure tabulated assumes that short-lived xenon isotopes are held up in BWRs until most of their activity has decayed.

[d]Some foreign reactors seem to produce considerably more ^{14}C than do U.S. reactors, possibly because of the presence of nitrogen.

[e]It is likely that future reprocessing plants will sequester ^{14}C and store it as waste rather than discharging it to the environment.

[f]Time scale for the population dose from tailings is $\sim 10^5$ yr; that for the decrease in natural ^{222}Rn due to consumption of uranium is $\sim 10^6$–10^8 yr.

[g]*Reactor Safety Study*.

[h]"Major accidents" defined as those releasing significant radioactivity to the environment.

[i]It seems agreed that transportation accidents in which spent-fuel casks are ruptured will be very rare.

[j]These conclusions assume waste to be placed somewhere where its probability of escape in the next few hundred years will be extremely small; the feasibility of this is not seriously disputed.

Table 17.1 suggests that:

1. ^{14}C from reprocessing plants may represent a serious risk, mainly to future generations. The technology for reducing ^{14}C emissions exists.
2. ^{222}Rn emitted from abandoned ore tailings has a large total dose, although the dose per person is quite small. This risk would be greatly reduced with the large-scale introduction of the LMFBR or the covering over of the tailings with an impervious layer.
3. The risk with the greatest commonly perceived uncertainty is from reactor accidents.

Analyzing the public impact of reactor accidents can be relatively complicated. A frequency versus severity estimate for nuclear power plants can be obtained by interpolating data from operating experience and the estimates of core melt accidents, such as those in the *Reactor Safety Study* (WASH-1400) or other risk studies. The risk estimated from these methods all show the probability of a large number of people (say 1000) being killed or injured in a reactor accident is orders of magnitude lower than for an accident in which a few (i.e., below five) people are so effected. However, as noted, the uncertainties are quite large as the estimates are often based on an incomplete understanding or ability to model the very complex nature of a reactor accident. The concern of a large accident is valid, however, since, as we have already mentioned, the factors toxicity, proximity and energy are all present, and the a priori assumption must be that a severe (i.e., catastrophic) reactor accident is possible. That reactors are safe, that is, that barriers and mechanisms exist that will attenuate the radioactivity to acceptable levels, must be determined from a given reactor design.

17.4. SEVERE ACCIDENTS AND THEIR CONSEQUENCES

In the event that an accident leads to an extensive failure of fuel in a reactor core, it is probable that fission products will be released. These fission products may be partially or totally trapped in the primary reactor system, or they may be released to the containment, or they may escape from the containment. The quantities of fission products existing in a given reactor core at a given time can be accurately estimated from the power history of that core. However, the fraction of fission products that will be released under a given set of circumstances cannot be estimated in any easy way. Therefore, in early evaluations of safety of nuclear reactors, it was assumed that 100% or, at least, a very large percentage of the fission products would be released from the fuel to the containment. Clearly, this assumption was overconservative.

The main radioactivity in a reactor lies inside the core region in the form of fission products. Fission products include many atomic species in varying amounts with very different physical, chemical, and biological properties. Some are definitely more volatile than others; some may deposit or, by chemical interaction, may be selectively trapped in their immediate environment before they can escape into the containment proper. Others, even if they escape both the core and the containment, are relatively nonhazardous. Of the many fission products that exist in the core, most safety analyses agree that the most important contributors to off-site risk are iodine, cesium, and tellurium.

The amounts of fission products in the core vary with the power and operating history of the reactor, but are quite substantial. An average LWR contains about 10^{10} Ci of radioactivity. For example, up to 200 kg of Cs and I are present, of which some 61 kg would be radioactive. From these two elements alone, several hundred million curies of radioactivity exist at the time of core shutdown, although this level would immediately start to decay. The total radioactive core inventory is given in Table 17.2. Also shown on this table are the half-lives of the radionuclides. Some nuclides, such as ^{134}I, have such short half-lives (in this case 0.036 day) that they are of no real concern. Other nuclides, notably those of tellurium, decay rapidly, but in doing so transmute to other isotopes of equal or greater hazard, for example, tellurium decays into iodine. Special note of ^{239}Np should be made since it contributes 30% or more of the total gamma-ray activity in a core at shutdown.

Although the radioactive quantity in the core is large, the real quantity of concern when assessing hazard is the release fraction, that is, the quantity of fission products that can escape from a damaged reactor. The fraction released depends on many variables including chemical form, environment, temperatures, and flow conditions, but is usually classified according to element volatility. Three classes are usually considered: (1) inert, including the noble gases; (2) volatile, including the halogens, alkali metals and tellurium group, and (3) nonvolatile, including the alkaline earths, noble metals, rare earths and refractory oxides. This is summarized in Table 17.3, which lists the elements in each group.

The following groups are of greatest concern:

1. *Noble Gases.* Although chemically inert, they are gaseous and therefore easily transported throughout the reactor system, containment building, and environment. When contained, as

Table 17.2. Activity of Radionuclides in a Reactor Core at 3560 MW(th)

Group/Radionuclide	Radioactive Inventory in Millions of Curies	Half-Life, Days
A. *Noble gases*		
Krypton-85	0.60	3,950
Krypton-85m	26	0.183
Krypton-87	51	0.0528
Krypton-88	73	0.117
Xenon-133	183	5.28
Xenon-135	37	0.384
B. *Iodines*		
Iodine-131	91	8.05
Iodine-132	129	0.0958
Iodine-133	183	0.875
Iodine-134	204	0.0366
Iodine-135	161	0.280
C. *Alkali metals*		
Rubidium-86	0.028	18.7
Cesium-134	8.1	750
Cesium-136	3.2	13.0
Cesium-137	5.1	11,000
D. *Tellurium–antimony*		
Tellurium-127	6.3	0.391
Tellurium-127m	1.2	109
Tellurium-129	33	0.048
Tellurium-129m	5.7	34.0
Tellurium-131m	14	1.25
Tellurium-132	129	3.25
Antimony-127	6.6	3.88
Antimony-129	35	0.179
E. *Alkaline earths*		
Strontium-89	101	52.1
Strontium-90	4.0	11,030
Strontium-91	118	0.403
Barium-140	172	12.8
F. *Noble metals and cobalt*		
Cobalt-58	0.84	71.0
Cobalt-60	0.31	1,920
Molybdenum-99	172	2.8
Technetium-99m	151	0.25
Ruthenium-103	118	39.5
Ruthenium-105	77	0.185
Ruthenium-106	27	366
Rhodium-105	53	1.50
G. *Rare earths, refractory oxides, and transuranics*		
Yttrium-90	4.2	2.67
Yttrium-91	129	59.0
Zirconium-95	161	65.2
Zirconium-97	161	0.71
Niobium-95	161	35.0
Lanthanum-140	172	1.67
Cerium-141	161	32.3
Cerium-143	140	1.38
Cerium-144	91	284
Praseodymium-143	140	13.7
Neodymium-147	65	11.1
Neptunium-239	1800	2.35
Plutonium-238	0.061	32,500
Plutonium-239	0.023	8.9×10^6
Plutonium-240	0.023	2.4×10^6
Plutonium-241	3.7	5,350
Americium-241	0.0018	1.5×10^5
Curium-242	0.54	163
Curium-244	0.025	6,630

Table 17.3. Groupings of Radionuclides That May Contribute Significantly to Radioactive Releases from Nuclear Power Plants

Xe, Kr	Noble gases	I Inert
I, Br	Halogens	II Volatile
Cs, Rb	Alkali metals	
Te, Se, Sb	Tellurium group	
Ba, Sr	Alkaline earths	III Nonvolatile
Ru, Rb, Pd, Mo, Tc	Noble metals	
Y, La, Ce, Pr, Nd, Pm, Sm, Eu, Np, Pu	Rare earths	
Zr, Nb	Refractory oxides	

in a Reactor Containment Building (RCB) following an accident, they represent a very potent source of radiation, both for personnel and for damaging equipment. If they leak from the RCB, they generally dissipate quickly in the environment, and therefore are a transient public health hazard.

This is seen in Figure 17.2 which gives the atmospheric conditions expected around U.S. reactors using the atmospheric dispersion models discussed in Chapter 4. The figure presents annual average χ/Q data† as a function of distance for 42 actual nuclear power plant sites in the United States. The cloud immersion and inhalation doses decrease roughly in proportion to the curves presented, that is, the dose decreases with decreasing χ/Q.

Figure 17.3 shows the maximum dose to a person off-site due to a total release of the noble gases in the core of a damaged reactor. The consequences of such a release are sensitive to the time of release and atmospheric conditions. Using the atmospheric data from Figure 17.2, and a start of release $2\frac{1}{2}$ hr after the accident starts, no early deaths would be expected, since the dose projected in this figure is below the fatality threshold.

2. *Halogens.* These are very reactive chemical species whose release particularly depends on the conditions prevailing during the accident. Of greatest concern is iodine, which has a high radiotoxicity in the body, since it collects in the human thyroid. However, iodine is not released as a gas, I_2, but as a salt, CsI. It therefore has a high solubility in water, and if released will generally follow the water pathway, that is, to the sump in the RCB, the building walls, and so on.

The chemistry of iodine is summarized in Table 17.4. Particularly important points in this table are the tendency of iodine to combine with cesium and the fact that tellurium decay is one way to form iodine. The aqueous behavior of iodine is shown in Figure 17.4, where iodine species are plotted for various pH and Eh conditions. Only in very low pH and highly oxidizing environments does I_2 form. Such conditions do not normally exist in LWRs. Moreover, expected iodine concentrations would be very low. If the entire core inventory of iodine (about 15 kg) were to be dissolved in the water of the primary coolant system, iodine concentrations would be about 4×10^{-2} g/liter (3×10^{-4}M).

3. *Alkali Metals.* The alkali metals are highly chemically reactive. Some of their properties are given in Table 17.5. They react with water to form hydroxides (e.g., CsOH) or with other elements to form salts (CsI). Also, they are highly soluble and like iodine generally follow the water released in an accident. The principal concern is ^{137}Cs. Because of its long half-life (27 yr), ^{137}Cs remains persistent in the environment and can be a long-term ground contamination hazard.

4. *Tellurium and Ruthenium.* Tellurium‡ has an intermediate volatility. Its health hazard is due mainly to external radiation. Ruthenium has a high melting point, but under special conditions one of its oxides is highly volatile. It can be an internal hazard to the kidneys and gastrointestinal tract.

Tables 17.6 and 17.7 summarize the chemistry of these elements. Apart from what appears on

†Analyses of doses received by individuals near the site of a postulated accident are calculated for various atmospheric release assumptions. The most important meteorological parameter used in such analyses is the term χ/Q, which has units of sec/m^3. When this parameter is multiplied by the release rate Q, in units of Ci/sec, the downwind concentration is calculated in units of Ci/m^3 of air at the off-site location of interest.

‡Tellurium and ruthenium were once expected to be released from the core of a damaged reactor in significant quantities. However, recent experimental work at Argonne National Laboratory, Oak Ridge National Laboratory, and other places does not support this assumption. As a result, risk studies may be conservative with respect to the health effects of these elements, which are major contributors to calculated off-site consequences.

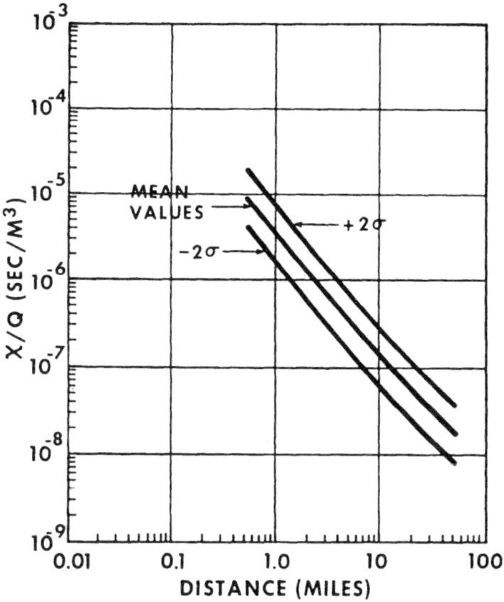

Figure 17.2. Annual average χ/Q values for each of 42 nuclear sites. (From E. A. Warman, Stone and Webster Engineering Corp.)

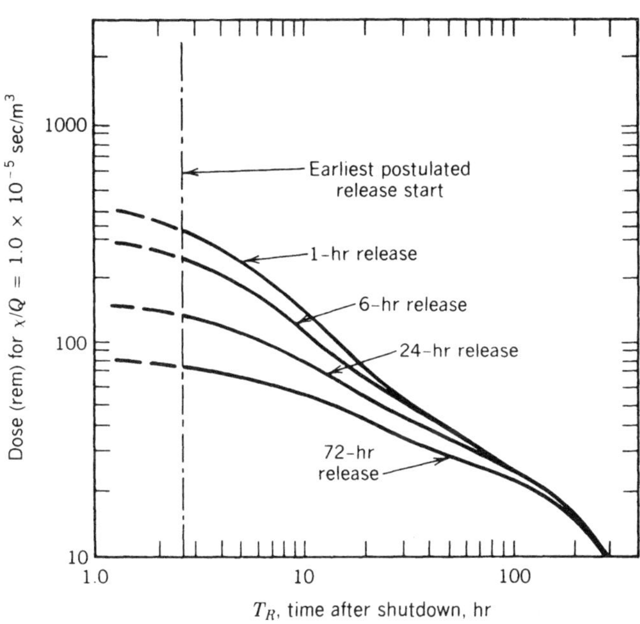

Figure 17.3. Whole body gamma dose from 100% release of noble gases occurring at time T_R after shutdown. (From E. A. Warman, Stone and Webster Corp.)

Table 17.4. Iodine Chemistry

1. I_2 sublimes at 184°C.
2. Forms compounds with alkali metals (Cs, rubidium).
3. Probable formation of Zr compounds ZrI, ZrI_2, etc. (vapor pressure of these compounds low).
4. Oxidation of CsI by O_2 at high temperature yields I_2.
5. All important iodine isotopes (there are 23) spend significant time (25 min to 78 hr) as Te.

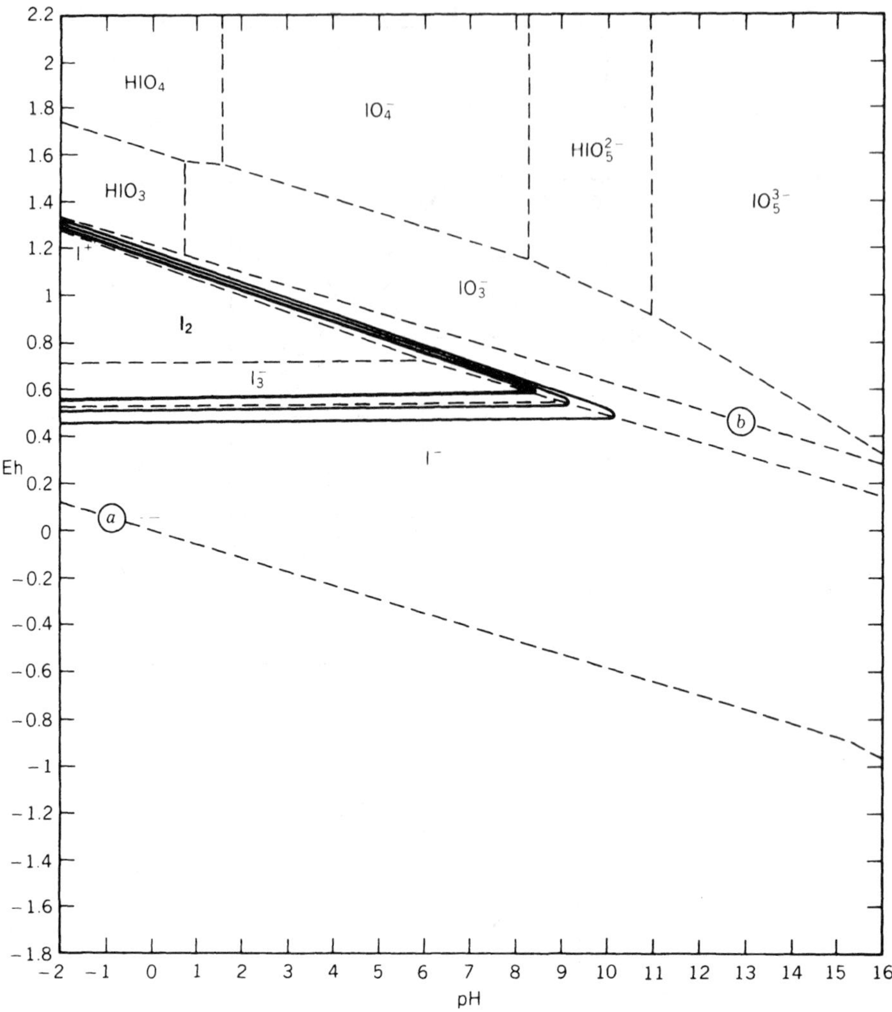

Figure 17.4. Iodine species as a function of oxygen potential (Eh) and hydrogen ion potential (pH). (From M. Pourbaix, *Atlas of Electrochemical Equilibria*, Paris, 1963.)

Table 17.5. Chemistry of Cs and Rb

1. Hydroxides, soluble in water.
2. No solid compounds form in aqueous solution.
3. In "dry" accidents Cs, Rb are expected to vaporize and condense as particulates (as hydroxides, carbonates, etc.).

Table 17.6. Tellurium Chemistry

1. Group VI semimetal (oxygen, sulfur, selenium group).
2. Te formed and trapped in UO_2 matrix until 1300°C.
3. Te_2 vapor is very reactive with Cs, forms Cs_2Te.
4. Te_2 surviving Cs reaction plates out at 450°C as solid Te.
5. Cs_2Te dissolves in water Cs^+ and HTe^- ions.
6. TeI_4 is known and insoluble.

Table 17.7. Ruthenium Chemistry

1. Relatively noble metal (platinum group), b.p. ~4150°C.
2. Can react with oxygen to form RuO_x at high temperature.
3. Inside fuel rod, oxygen potential too small for *any* oxides to form.
4. Is trapped in UO_2 matrix.
5. Although RuO_4 is volatile, its vapor pressure is low and it condenses on cool surfaces, dust, and aerosols.

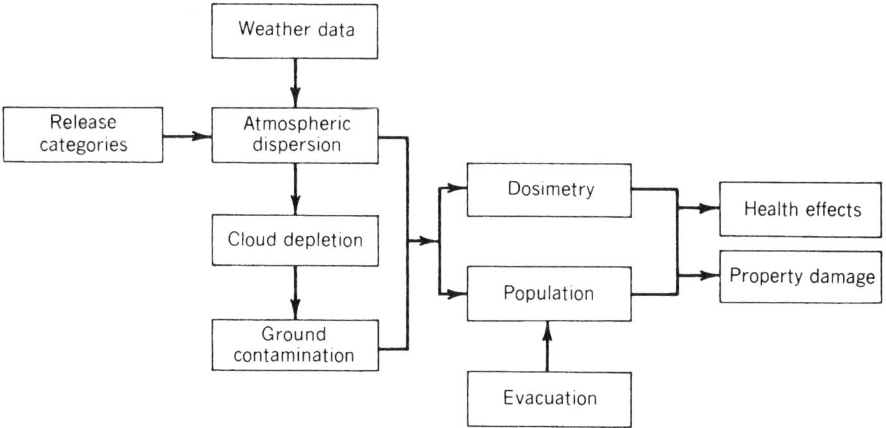

Figure 17.5. Schematic outline of consequence model. (Adapted from WASH-1400.)

these tables, relatively little is known about the chemical behavior of tellurium (and to a lesser extent, ruthenium). This is especially true concerning its interaction with other materials, although it appears to react rapidly with those found in a reactor.

The preceding was a brief, somewhat simplified, view of important chemical species behavior. When considering severe accidents, potential consequences to be evaluated include early fatalities and illness, latent effects (cancers and genetic effects), and land contamination. Each of the radionuclides do not contribute in the same proportion to these consequences. Factors affecting the hazard posed by a particular radionuclide are:

1. The total core inventory.
2. The half-life of the isotope.
3. The volatility of the dominant chemical species.
4. The chemical reactivity with various materials and its solubility in water.
5. The atmospheric transport properties.
6. The biological effects of the radionuclide.
7. The type of the emitted radiation.

Proper evaluation of these factors requires a consequence model. Figure 17.5 shows how such a model could be put together. Since many of the boxes shown in this figure require extensive analysis, a detailed estimate of reactor accident consequences can be a formidable undertaking. The safety of reactors, however, does not rely on the designer's ability to model consequences.

As an example of which radionuclides are important, Figure 17.6 shows one analysis from WASH-1400 for off-site radiation doses to the bone marrow.† The first year after a reactor accident, the early and continuing somatic effects would be directly related to the radiation dose received by an individual. The figure shows (1) the external dose from the passing cloud, (2) the

†Dose to bone marrow is related to early fatality.

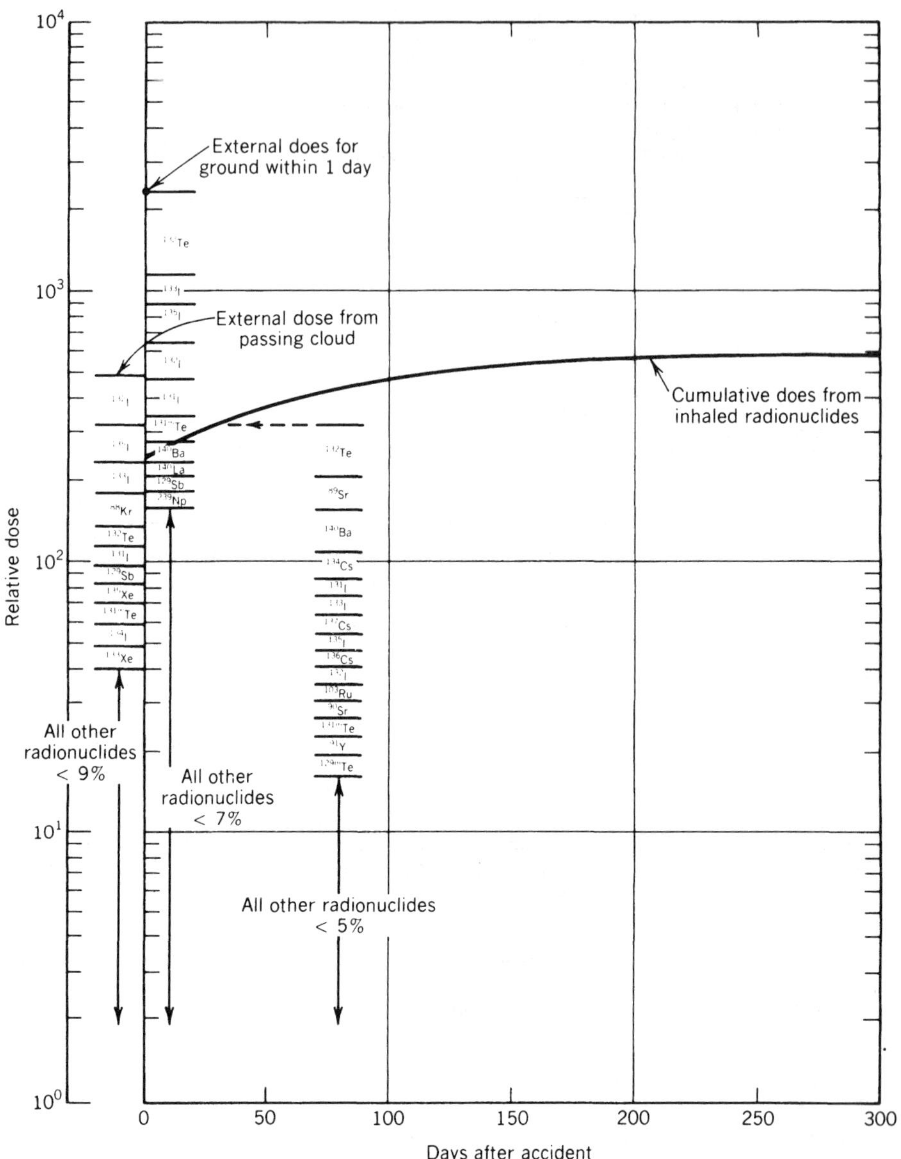

Figure 17.6. Relative doses to bone marrow at 0.5 mile from reactor. (From WASH-1400.)

external dose from ground contamination, and (3) the dose, as a function of time, from internally deposited radionuclides to the bone marrow. As expected, the isotopes of iodine and tellurium are responsible for most of the consequences calculated in this example.

17.5. CONTROL AND STABILITY OF REACTORS

Accidents that can occur in a nuclear plant are much less catastrophic than what is often imagined. The rate of energy release is limited by the physics of the reactor itself, the enrichment of the fuel, the geometry of the core, and the properties of the moderator, all of which make it literally impossible for a plant to go up in a "puff of smoke."

A reactor is protected from damage by its scram system and various reactivity feedback mechanisms if the scram system fails to operate. If an overpower situation occurs, the reactor quickly

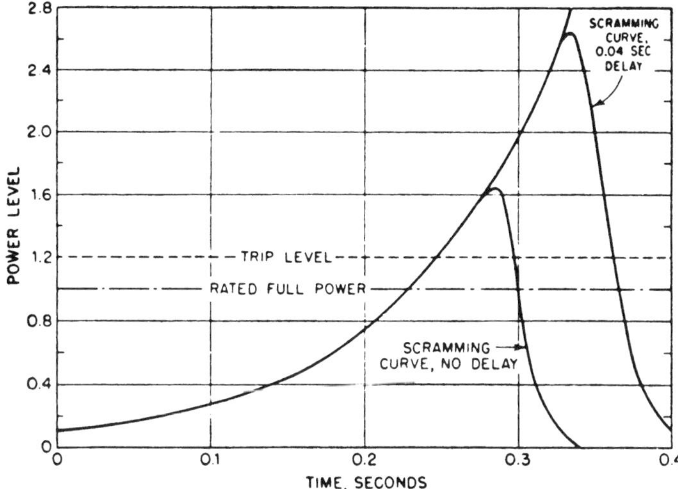

Figure 17.7. Overpower scram operation. Reactor on 0.1-sec period, and trip level at 120% full power. (From M. A. Schultz, *Control of Nuclear Reactors and Power Plants*, McGraw-Hill, New York, 1955).

goes through the power range up through rated full power to an arbitrary trip level. The trip level is usually 120% of full power, but this level may be set at any convenient point. Figure 17.7 illustrates an example of a power excursion. A small delay, even a mere 40 msec, is sufficient to cause a tremendous difference in peak power. Actually, however, it is not the peak power that is destructive but rather the energy that is involved. The energy in this case is the area under the curve in watt-seconds. When the energy exceeds a given amount, the plant is damaged. The reactor protection system, including the insertion rate of the control rods, is engineered to prevent such damage.

Reactivity Feedback

A reactor's kinetic behavior during normal operation is the result of the delayed neutrons in the fission process. A few percent of the neutrons released during fission are delayed from a few seconds to a few tens of seconds. This allows sufficient time for the control rods (and other processes affecting reactivity) to stabilize the power level and prevent a runaway reaction. The factors that counteract reactor instability form a feedback loop with the reactor.

There are two distinct types of feedback loops: external loops and internal loops. The internal loops are caused by the temperature coefficient and by poisoning. The external feedback loop is associated with the external reactor plant. It is related to the circulation of the primary coolant through the reactor. A discrete amount of time (a few tens of seconds) is involved in the process of circulating the coolant from the reactor through the heat exchanger and back into the reactor.

The reactor responds to changes in reactivity. The reactivity k depends on the ratio of neutron production rate to the rate of neutron loss, which in turn depends on the geometry of the reactor and on variables that effect the absorption and leakage of neutrons. These variables include the temperature and pressure of the coolant, and the concentration of neutron-absorbing poisons. Since reactivity depends on plant variables, which in turn depend on reactor power, the plant contains inherent feedback.

There are four main feedback loops in a reactor:

1. *Poison Concentration.* This includes the effect of control rods, xenon buildup, burnable poisons, and changes in the boron concentration in the coolant (PWRs). The role of poison concentration was discussed in Chapter 12.

2. *Doppler Coefficient.* When operating at power, the temperature of the fuel is much higher than the moderator. The temperature coefficient of the fuel is negative, due almost entirely from the random thermal motion of the ^{238}U atoms broadening the shape of the neutron capture cross section (the Doppler effect). If an uncontrolled power excursion were to occur, this additional neutron capture would self-limit the event.

3. *Average Coolant Temperature.* As the power of the reactor increases, so does the temperature of the coolant. The coolant density, therefore, decreases, along with its ability to moder-

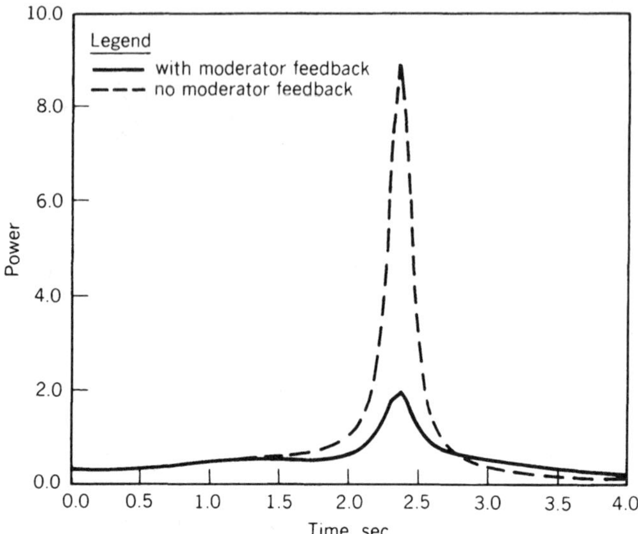

Figure 17.8. Transient behavior of reactor power. [From H. S. Cheng and D. J. Diamond, *Trans. Am. Nuclear Soc.* **33,** 474 (1979).]

ate neutrons. This leads to a decrease in the power. An example is shown in Figure 17.8, which gives core power as a function of time for a hypothetical control rod withdrawal accident. Two calculations were made, one with and one without moderator feedback.

The dramatic effect of moderator feedback during the accident is clearly seen. Reactor scram was never initiated throughout the accident when moderator feedback was included in the calculation since the reactor never reached 120% of rated power, the point where the reactor protection system would activate. In both cases, the reactor power reached its peak at the time (2.4 sec) the rod moved fully out of the core. In the case without moderator feedback during the transient, the reactor would have to scram to terminate the accident.

4. *Coolant Pressure.* In BWRs especially, a rapid increase in power is accompanied by more boiling (i.e., void formation) in the core. As the voids expand, less moderator is in the core limiting the power excursion.

These mechanisms limit the power a reactor can produce before it automatically shuts itself off. As long as excess power can be removed from the core, a reactor accident is a relatively benign event. Only when a means of cooling the core is lacking can fuel melting and a major release of radioactivity occur. This underscores the importance in reactor safety of the so-called Loss-Of-Coolant Accident (LOCA).

Excess Reactivity

The criticality parameters that prevent an uncontrolled chain reaction are listed in Table 17.8. Particularly important are the Doppler reactivity coefficient and the overall power coefficient. As seen in the table, both of these are sufficiently negative to ensure that rapid power excursions are quickly terminated.

Table 17.8 also gives the effective multiplication constant of the core (k_{eff}) for various conditions. The different k_{eff} values indicate the amount of excess reactivity needed to go, for example, from cold, zero-power to hot, zero-power (termed the temperature defect) or to go from hot, zero-power to hot, full-power (called the power defect). As a core burns up, fission products are generated which capture neutrons. Neutron losses to these fission products also require a core to have excess reactivity. In sum, a reactor must have sufficient excess reactivity such that it can operate through the end of its lifetime. However, large amounts of excess reactivity are undesirable for safety.

A fundamental requirement in reactor operation is that there must always be sufficient control poison available to bring the reactor subcritical with some margin to spare. This negative reactivity following the trip of the reactor is referred to as the shutdown margin. Usually the even more stringent requirement is made that shutdown be obtainable even though one or more control rods

Table 17.8. Reactivity Parameters for a PWR, BWR, and HTGR

	PWR, Indian Point-2	BWR, Browns Ferry	HTGR, Fort St. Vrain
k_{eff}	1.275—Cold, no power, clean 1.225—Hot, no power, clean 1.170—Hot, full power, Xe and Sm equal	1.25—Cold, no power, clean 0.96—With all control rods in <0.99—With strongest control rod out	1.143—80°F Initial core 1.110—400°F Initial core 1.03—Operating 0.923—All control rods in (80°F) 0.934—Max worth rod pair stuck out
Doppler coefficient ($\Delta k/k$/°F)	-1×10^{-5} to -2×10^{-5}	Cold: -1.3×10^{-5} Hot: -1.2×10^{-5} Operating: $\leq 1.3 \times 10^{-5}$	Equil. core, beginning of cycle, with Xe and Sm -2.8×10^{-5} (80°F) -2.3×10^{-5} (400°F) -1.1×10^{-5} operating
Moderator void coefficient ($\Delta k/k$/% void)	1×10^{-3} to -3×10^{-3}	Hot: -1.0×10^{-3} Operating: -1.6×10^{-3}	—
Moderator temperature coefficient ($\Delta k/k$/°F)	$+1 \times 10^{-4}$ to -3×10^{-4}	Cold: -5×10^{-5} Hot: -39×10^{-5}	Isothermal coeff. equil. core, BOC, with Xe and Sm -2.9×10^{-5} (80°F) -2.3×10^{-5} (400°F) -5.7×10^{-6} operating
Coolant temperature coefficient (per °F)	Same as above	Same as above	$\Delta\rho$ due to the loss of all the helium from the reactor $= 5 \times 10^{-5}$ $\Delta k/k$
Pressure coefficient ($\Delta k/k$/°F)	-1×10^{-6} to $+3 \times 10^{-6}$ BOC 2170 ppm boron; EOL no boron	—	Negligible
Power coefficient	$-0.02 \dfrac{\Delta k/k}{\Delta p/p}$ at the beginning of core life	$-0.04 \dfrac{\Delta k/k}{\Delta p/p}$ at the beginning of core life; $-0.02 \dfrac{\Delta k/k}{\Delta p/p}$ at end of core life	$-0.037 \dfrac{\Delta k/k}{\Delta p/p}$
Other reactivity coefficients	Boron worth; Hot → 1% $\dfrac{\Delta k}{k}$/150 ppm Cold → 1% $\dfrac{\Delta k}{k}$/120 ppm	—	—

Source: Adapted from T. Thomson and J. Beckerley, *The Technology of Nuclear Reactor Safety*, MIT Press, Cambridge, Massachusetts, 1973.

BOL = Beginning of core life.
EOL = End of core life.

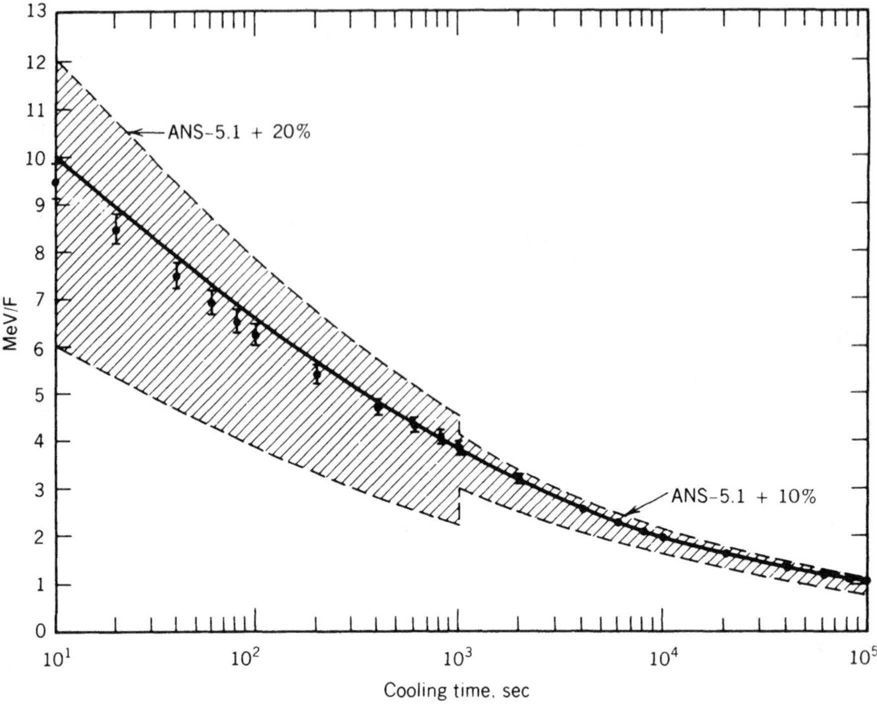

Figure 17.9. The decay heat versus time after reactor shutdown. (Courtesy American Nuclear Society.)

are stuck outside of the core. The negative reactivity obtainable following trip is then referred to as the stuck-rod shutdown margin.

Although criticality accidents have not occurred in commercial nuclear plants, in the last 30 yr at least 12 such accidents have occurred in government facilities (see Chapter 6). Of these, five were in chemical processing plants or laboratories. Because of the geometry and rapid dispersal of the fuel, the maximum energy released in these accidents was quite low (equivalent to $\frac{1}{2}$ to 5 liters of gasoline). The instantaneous burst of radiation can be quite high, however, and one fatality occurred.

Decay Heat Considerations

This does not mean, however, that severe accidents cannot occur. The largest credible accident is one where loss of reactor coolant causes the core to overheat and melt down, releasing its inventory of radioactivity. This is possible because after a reactor is shutdown, heat is still evolved from fission product decay. Initially about 8% of the core's pre-shutdown power, this heat source rapidly decays as shown in Figure 17.9. For a typical 1000-MWe reactor, after a few hours, 50 MW of heat is still evolving. If this heat is not removed from the core, severe damage could occur and radioactivity could be released. Decay heat levels are about 2% of initial power after 15 min, 1% after $2\frac{1}{2}$ hr, 0.5% after one day. A major safety goal is to keep the reactor core covered with water at all times, so that excess heat can be removed.

17.6. ENGINEERED SAFETY SYSTEMS

All reactors have engineered safety features, both active and passive, designed to prevent serious accidents and mitigate them if they occur. A nuclear plant's safety is achieved through the concept of defense in depth. This provides a series of protective barriers, with redundancy at each level, for each active component.

Every reactor has four main barriers to radioactivity release in the event of an accident:

1. *Fuel Matrix.* The exceptionally high melting point (2760°C) and chemical stability of UO_2 prevents the escape of fission products except in extreme accident conditions. Although the fission

process creates large amounts of radioactivity in the fuel rods, the ceramic pellets of uranium dioxide fuel retain more than 98% of this radioactivity. About 2% of the radioactivity, chiefly gaseous krypton, xenon, and iodine, diffuses into the gas plenum between the fuel pellets and the sealed Zircaloy cladding. Without fuel melting and subsequent release of fission products, a nuclear reactor accident would involve no more hazard to the general public than any conventional power plant accident of a similar nature. Thus, melting, followed by the release of fission products, is one of the unique features of a serious nuclear reactor accident.

2. *Fuel Cladding.* The Zircaloy clad surrounding the fuel pellets retains any radioactivity released from the UO_2. Fuel cladding behavior is important to the safety of a nuclear plant primarily because the fuel contains the major part of the radioactive products in the plant. The cladding is protected through use of design criteria which limit the nucleate boiling ratio (see Chapter 12) and maximum amount of Zircaloy oxidation (see Chapter 7).

3. *Reactor Primary Coolant System.* Boundary integrity of the primary coolant system is assured by thick steel vessels and piping up to 20 cm thick, and the continual inspection of these components for leaks and cracks. One of the major bases for coolant loop and pressure vessel integrity is design, manufacture, test, and inspection to the requirements of ASME code, Section III (Nuclear Vessels) and Section XI (In-Service Inspection). The plant's license requires protection against ruptures in the reactor coolant loop and connected pipework, including a double-ended guillotine break of the largest coolant pipe. This constitutes the design basis for loss-of-coolant accidents.

4. *Reactor Containment Building (RCB).* The RCB generally consists of a 4-ft thick concrete shell lined with steel and is heavily reinforced with steel bars. Figure 17.10 shows one containment building under construction; particularly note the size, thickness, and density of the steel reinforcing bar. This steel, embedded in concrete, gives a RCB great strength to withstand forces that might occur in a reactor accident. Chapter 9 covers the design and integrity of containment buildings.

Each of these barriers is capable of retaining the hazardous radioactivity contained in a reactor core. Only if all were breached would a release to the environment be possible. To prevent breaches, and to attenuate any radioactivity, various safety features are employed. Their objectives are threefold: shut down the reactor (in the event that the normal scram mechanisms fail), cool the core (to prevent overheating and meltdown), and safeguard the integrity of the barriers (such as reducing any pressure in a containment building).

Active Safety Systems

To limit the consequences of an accident, engineered safeguards systems are provided. The main engineered safeguard features are as follows:

The Residual Heat Removal System (Figure 17.11)

Its main function is to transfer thermal energy from the core after plant shutdown. This system operates typically at 400 psi. It has two large-capacity pumps and two heat exchangers. This system can typically handle up to 84 MW, roughly the decay heat of a core at a few hundred seconds after shutdown. Operation of the RHRS is initiated after the control rods have been inserted into the core and the RCS has been partially cooled and depressurized. Initial reactor cooling is achieved by dissipating heat through the steam generators† and discharging steam to the condenser by means of the turbine steam bypass system.‡ When the reactor coolant temperature has dropped to 350°F and pressure has been reduced to 400 psig or less, the RHRS equipment is placed in operation. This reduces the reactor coolant temperature to 140°F within 20 hr after shutdown, if both the residual heat removal pumps and heat exchangers are in operation, with 95°F cooling water supplied to the system.

Safety Injection System (SIS)

The primary function of the SIS is to supply borated water to the core in order to limit fuel rod cladding temperature in the event of a LOCA. The SIS consists of several independent subsystems characterized by equipment and flow path redundancy inside of the missile protection boundary. This redundancy assures complete reliability of operation and continued core cooling, even in the event of a failure of any single component to respond actively in accordance with its design function. Although details differ, safety injection systems for PWRs typically resemble the system

†In PWRs.

‡Boiling of water in the primary system removes thermal energy at the rate of 1130 Btu/lb or about $\frac{1}{8}$ gal/sec-MW. (1 MW-sec = 10^6 J = 950 Btu.)

Figure 17.10. View of construction underway on the containment holding one of the two GE-supplied reactor systems at Carolina Power & Light Company's Brunswick nuclear power station. (Courtesy Brown & Root.)

shown in Figure 17.12. The initial operation is passive: accumulator tanks (one per loop) rapidly inject borated water, stored at about 650 psig, into the cold legs of the primary system. Each tank contains about 7200 gal of water. This alone can remove about 10^8 Btu of heat, approximately the decay heat evolved in the first 70 min after shutdown.

Following the emptying of the accumulators, cooling water is pumped from a large refillable reservoir, such as the refueling water storage tank. After some period of time, the reservoir is depleted and large volumes of water—from both primary system boil-off and the containment spray—will collect in the containment sump. The core-cooling and containment sprays can then be

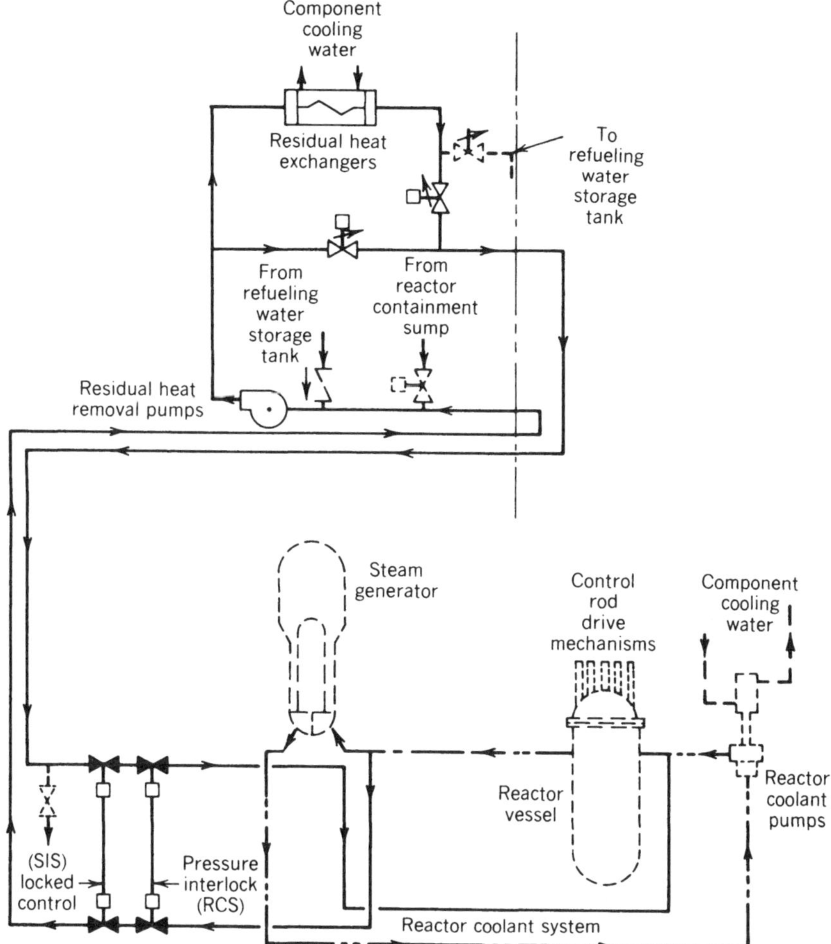

Figure 17.11. Residual heat removal system, flow diagram. (Courtesy of Westinghouse Electric Corp.) *Key:* CVCS—chemical and volume control system. RCS—reactor coolant system. SIS—safety injection system.

switched to a recirculation mode in which water is pumped from the containment sump, through a heat exchanger and into the primary system. The decay heat is thus removed through the heat exchanger and dissipated in the environment. In all these systems, redundancy is provided to increase reliability. The High-Pressure Injection (HPI) system typically uses three pumps capable of removing 70 MW of heat, while Low-Pressure Injection (LPI) turns on when the system pressure falls below 300 psi. There are typically two pumps in the LPI system; each one can remove 470 MW.

In a BWR, Figure 17.13, the reactor core is enclosed in a barrel and jet pump shroud arrangement in such a way that even if one of the pipes used to recirculate coolant through the core were broken at its lowest elevation, the core could be reflooded. In one current BWR design by ASEA-ATOM, the recirculation lines are eliminated entirely by placing the recirculation pumps inside the vessel. Consideration of recirculation line breaks then becomes unnecessary. Emergency core cooling in BWRs is provided by high- and low-pressure systems for spraying water onto the top of the core and by injecting water at low pressure to fill the vessel.

Other core damage preventatives are also available, including operator action and alternate means of heat removal. In actuality, the amount of water required to remove decay heat is quite small. A 1000-MWe plant, shutdown $2\frac{1}{2}$ hr, requires a coolant flow rate of 12 liters/sec (at 20°C). This is about the water flowrate necessary to fill a bathtub in a minute.

CONTAINMENT SPRAY
REFUELING WATER-STORAGE TANK
CONTAINMENT VESSEL
CONTROL RODS
MAIN STEAM LINE TO TURBINE
STEAM GENERATOR
REACTOR
CORE
MAIN FEEDWATER LINE FROM TURBINE
N_2 PRESSURE
ACCUMULATOR TANK
HIGH-PRESSURE INJECTION SYSTEM
BORON-INJECTION TANK
CIRCULATING PUMP
"HX"
RESIDUAL-HEAT-REMOVAL SYSTEM
CONTAINMENT SUMP

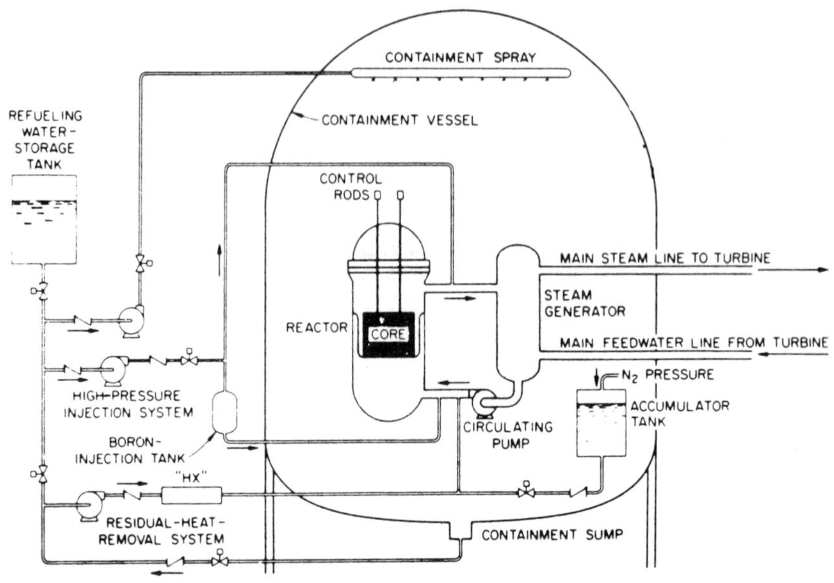

Figure 17.12. PWR emergency cooling system. [From W. B. Cottrell, *Nuclear Safety* **15,** 30 (1974).]

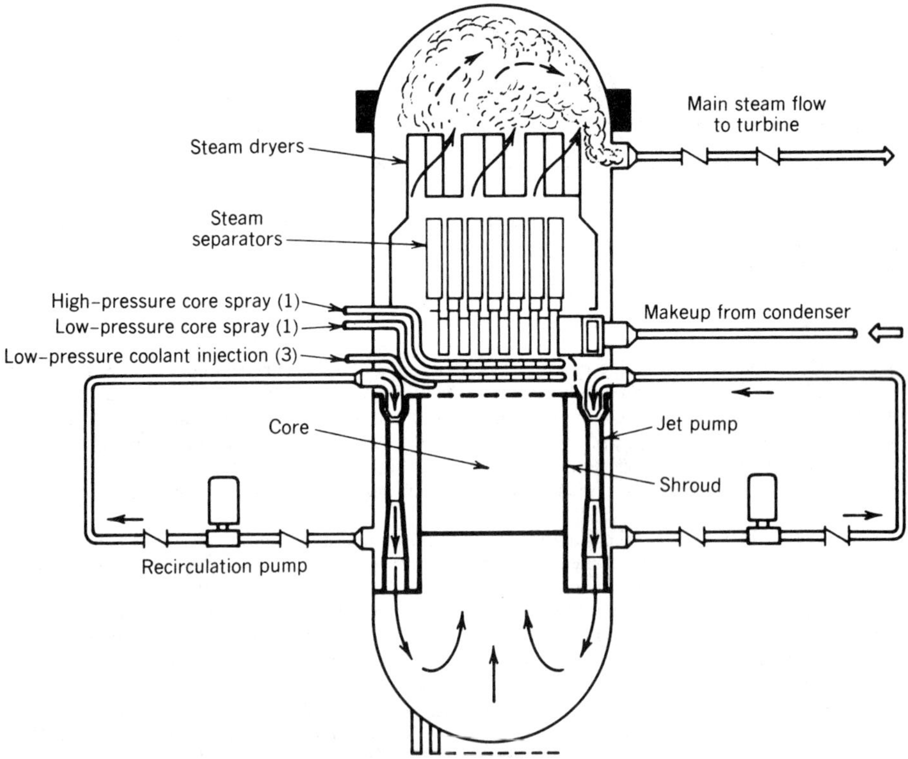

Main steam flow to turbine
Steam dryers
Steam separators
High-pressure core spray (1)
Low-pressure core spray (1)
Low-pressure coolant injection (3)
Makeup from condenser
Core
Jet pump
Shroud
Recirculation pump

Figure 17.13. Typical U.S. BWR system. (Courtesy General Electric Co.)

Containment Spray System (CSS)

This system has two purposes: to condense steam (relieving internal pressure in the containment building) and to remove any radioactivity that might leak into containment. The containment pressure is maintained at a low level by condensing the steam with a spray system. The spray water is also supplied by a reservoir, as was shown in Figure 17.12.

The CSS is made up of two independent spray trains located high in the containment building. Each puts out 3200 gal/min of cooling water, capable of removing 4×10^8 Btu/hr. The water contains sodium hydroxide or other chemicals to accelerate iodine removal from the air via wash-out mechanisms. As a result, the containment building will always be wet and humid, a condition that also helps deplete any other airborne radioactive species. A final heat sink is the Containment Heat Removal System (CHRS). This consists of fans blowing over heat exchangers fed by water from outside containment. The heat removal capacity of the CHRS system is about 65 MW.

Pressure Suppression Pool

In BWRs, these are designed to condense steam following loss of coolant accidents, thereby reducing containment pressure. Three types of BWR containment designs exist. Each design involves the use of a large water pool to provide pressure suppression in an accident. The layout of the Mark III design is shown in Figure 17.14.

The wetwell is in an annular region at the periphery of the containment. The vapor space of the wetwell actually forms the upper containment compartment. In the Mark III concept, the volume is somewhat greater than for the other two BWR containment designs and the design pressure is substantially lower.

In addition to condensing steam in an accident, the BWR suppression pools would remove fission products from the flow of gases passing from the drywell to the vapor space of the wetwell. Spray systems are also included in these designs but would not necessarily be activated in an accident.

BWRs are further surrounded by a relatively leak-tight building. An annular space of 10,000 m^3 exists between the containment shell and the leak-tight building. In this annular space is a Standby Gas Treatment System (SGTS). It is comprised of high-efficiency particulate and charcoal filters that trap airborne radioactivity before it can be released.

Containment Isolation and Heat Removal

In the event of an accident, abnormally high pressure (usually about 4 psig) in the RCB will cause its isolation valves to be closed. Emergency coolers are actuated to provide postaccident heat removal from the containment atmosphere. These coolers have sufficient capacity to return the containment building pressure to atmospheric levels within 24 hr. In addition, blowers collect leakage from the reactor building, filter it, and discharge it through the station vent. These blowers are concentrated in the penetrations rooms of the auxiliary buildings, since leakage is more likely at places where pipes and electrical cable penetrate the containment.

Emergency Power

Electrical power for the engineered safeguard systems is supplied from batteries and emergency diesel generators. Like the other safeguard systems, redundancy is provided. For instance, a plant normally has three separate diesel generators, each capable of supplying the power needed for all the safeguards equipment. In addition, at least one of the emergency feedwater pumps is a turbine driven by steam pressure, so that even if electrical power is lost, water can still be provided to cool the core.

Passive Safety Features

Although many active engineered safeguards systems exist in nuclear plants, real plant safety is due to passive aspects of the design. A major accident would require gross core melting, which in turn would release radioactivity in gaseous and aerosol forms. However, there are many natural phenomena operating which greatly reduce the amount of radioactivity actually released. Some of these are listed in Table 17.9. Risk studies which include all these natural phenomena suggest that few public fatalities are likely to result from any reactor accident, no matter how severe.

17.7. DESIGN BASIS ACCIDENTS

For the purposes of plant design and accident evaluation, the accidents that might occur in a nuclear reactor are grouped in nine classes of increasing severity, ranging from lesser accidents

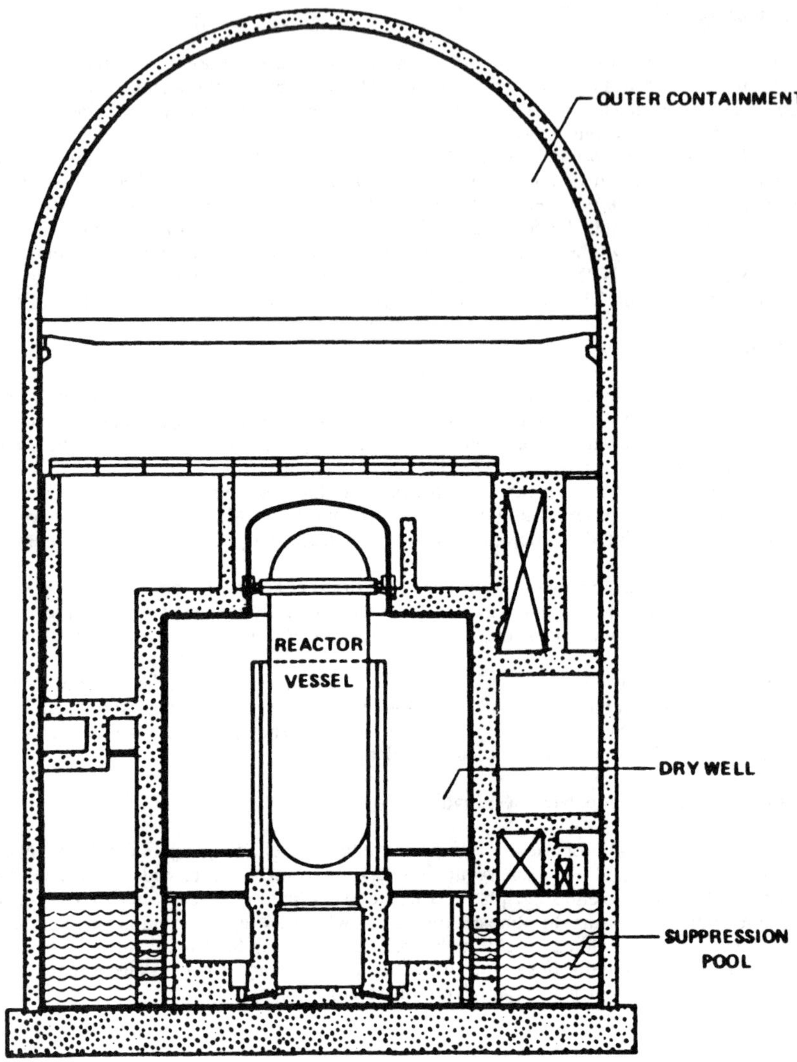

Figure 17.14. BWR Mark III containment design. (From NUREG-0772.)

such as small spills (Class 1), to very serious occurrences such as a break in the primary coolant loop (Class 8), to hypothetical accidents more severe than those in Class 8, grouped in Class 9. Accidents through Class 8 are Design-Basis Accidents (DBAs). They provide the conditions that the reactor and associated structures must be designed to withstand, and are the subject of Preliminary and Final Safety Analysis Reports (PSAR and FSAR) which must be submitted by a utility seeking a construction permit.† Class 9 hypothetical accidents need not be considered; their probability of occurrence is thought to be extremely small.

Among the DBAs of Class 8, the safety analyses must consider the possibility that, despite all the measures taken in the design, construction, testing, and operation of the plant, a large break in the primary coolant loop will occur. The most severe PWR break case‡ is the double-ended guillotine severance of the reactor inlet section of the piping (also called the "cold leg"). If this occurs, the reactor coolant would be rapidly expelled from both ends of the broken pipe. Since the primary coolant system is under high temperature (550°F) and high pressure (1000–2500 psi), the

†See Chapter 18. DBAs have a dual role in the safety design and licensing of a plant.
‡In some accident scenarios, a small break in the system may be actually more difficult to handle.

Table 17.9. Natural Phenomena that Mitigate Reactor Accidents

1. Stable, dispersible aerosols are difficult to create. Highly concentrated aerosols coalesce rapidly. Low density aerosols increase their effective density extremely rapidly in the presence of water vapor, serving as condensation nuclei. The effective size of the particle becomes that of the water droplet.

2. Aerosols agglomerate and tend to be trapped when passing through cracks and penetrations, whether in pipes, compartment walls, or containment buildings.

3. Agglomerated aerosols formed at high concentration are physically dense, and settle out close to their source. The original mass of particulates, although it may be large, is not significant, because only a small proportion survives this settling process and remains airborne.

4. Iodine in its many forms is chemically and physically reactive. Since nearly all of the surface area inside containment is covered with paint, plastic, or organic films, iodine retention is high. In addition, iodine is adsorbed on the surface of aerosol particles, which themselves are rapidly agglomerating and falling out. In either instance, much of the iodine is quickly immobilized.

5. The reactor containment building and the equipment in it present a large amount of surface area for fission product plateout and adsorption. The compartmentalization of the building and the complexity of piping and hardware means that any escaping material passes multiple surfaces prior to escape.

6. The moisture conditions in the reactor containment building cause most of the soluble fission products that become airborne to go into solution. A core melt accident will always be accompanied by large amounts of steam and water because coolant loss from the primary system is the *sine qua non* of core melting. "Rain" or "fog" will exist in the building even if the containment spray system is never used. This is due to the heat capacity of the building and equipment causing condensation and dripping from all the surfaces. Such a condition would wash out large fractions of the various fission products prior to atmospheric release. As mentioned earlier, moisture further tends to agglomerate aerosols and enhance their density.

7. The earth itself acts as a filter and effectively sequesters any escaping fission products in the event of a "melt-through" accident or an "atmospheric release" accident (which, in spite of its name, would likely result from a below-grade failure of the containment building in many cases). If the overpressurization in an accident blew out the penetrations or seals in the reactor containment building, the path for escaping radioactive materials usually would be through other buildings. This would provide further opportunity for plateout and fallout of radioactivity.

8. The presence of large amounts of water and vapor plus the heat capacity of the containment building and debris would be sufficient to immobilize a large fraction of the radioactivity in the event of a postulated massive reactor building failure.

Source: From M. Levenson, *Nuclear Technology* **53,** 98 (1981).

sudden pressure drop causes the coolant to flash to steam. It is possible that, in a short period of time, the entire inventory of coolant would be discharged through the break. This is known as a loss-of-coolant accident (LOCA).

This sudden loss of core coolant, which also acts as a neutron moderator, causes a shutdown of the neutron chain reaction. However, the fuel elements in the core contain stored energy and continue to generate heat from the decay of the fission products accumulated during the operation of the reactor. The stored energy is quite large and plays the dominant role in the first few seconds after the break, during blowdown. At later times, the heat generated by fission products is the dominant factor.

Prevention of LOCAs

Loss of reactor coolant can be a serious event. It could result from any misoperation, malfunction, or failure of equipment, such as a stuck open relief valve, which allowed uncontrolled discharge of water or steam from the reactor coolant system. It also constitutes a failure of a primary barrier to the escape of radioactivity from the plant.

The first and obvious approach to this problem is to take the necessary steps to minimize the probability of such an accident; namely, to prevent a rupture of the primary system. This approach was taken by the nuclear industry with the adoption of an industry-wide code (Section III, Nuclear Vessels, of the ASME Boiler and Pressure Vessel Code and a similar code for pressure piping) with which all constructon materials, design criteria, fabrication methods, testing procedures, and quality control must comply. A second line of defense uses instrumented leak detection systems as protective devices to detect quickly abnormal conditions, such as the opening of small cracks. These systems are complemented by inspection and in-service testing.

Despite these measures, it is generally recognized that there exists a finite probability for a sudden large pipe break to occur and hence for a LOCA. These probabilities cannot be calculated on the basis of past experience since nuclear systems have never failed in this way. Estimates by people experienced in high-pressure systems put this probability in the range of 10^{-4} to 10^{-6} per reactor-year. With some hundreds of reactors expected to be in operation in the year 2000 in the United States, the probability of a LOCA, using the high end of the probability range, would be a few percent per year or one every 20 or 40 yr. This figure is considered unacceptably high, and further measures are required to mitigate the consequences of a LOCA, which could be very severe. All present-day nuclear reactors are, therefore, provided with auxiliary systems to cool the reactor in the event of loss of coolant. These are the emergency core-cooling systems previously described.

Small LOCAs

LOCAs are classified according to the size of opening through which the fluid is discharged. In a small-break accident, the water and steam would be expelled from the reactor coolant system relatively slowly and the system would remain at a pressure of several hundred psi until almost empty. The accident would evolve much more slowly than for a large break. The fuel rods might be uncovered and the cladding might melt before water could be added at low pressure, so a High-Pressure coolant Injection System (HPIS) is provided. The HPIS maintains sufficient inventory in the reactor vessel to cool the fuel rods until the system is depressurized and at low temperature. A small-break LOCA puts great reliance on the HPIS to operate; if it fails, the accident would be more serious then in a large (low-pressure) break situation.

Loss of Cooling Capability

In principle, there is only one way for the fuel to melt: it must generate more heat than is being removed from it. There are three ways for this to happen: the heat generation can rise due to an overpower situation, the coolant can be lost from the reactor core (LOCA), or the cooling capability can decrease. The first two situations have been already covered; the last might result from what is known as loss of the ultimate heat sink.

Every reactor relies on a river, lake, or ocean to provide the ultimate cooling for the turbine condenser. It is possible to postulate a combination of rare events where loss of the ultimate heat sink might happen: loss of all electrical power at the reactor plant, stuck open secondary system relief valves, and so on. If the heat sink is lost, the decay heat in the core has nowhere to go, therefore, it causes the water in the primary system to overheat, eventually leading to core melting. This is a relatively slow process. Since many hours would elapse before the core would be in danger of melting, ample time is available to restore the system's cooling capability.

17.8. HISTORICAL REACTOR ACCIDENTS

In reactor accidents, the point of interest is the fractional inventory release; that is, the amount of radioactivity escaping relative to the radioactivity in the core. This fractional release is called the "source term," and is the major determiner of the consequences of a reactor accident and the public perception of the risks associated with nuclear power plants.

Since the first reactor started up in 1942, there have been a number of serious accidents at reactors involving major core damage, but where no significant amounts of radioactive material were released to the environment. These accidents, summarized in Table 17.10, occurred at Detroit Edison's Fermi-1 reactor, the Experimental Breeder Reactor in Idaho (1955), the Sodium Reactor Experiment facility in California (1959), the NRX reactor at Chalk River (1952), and the Westinghouse Test Reactor (1960). There have also been at least three major reactor accidents that resulted in radioactive releases to the environment: at Windscale, at the SL-1 reactor, and at Three Mile Island (TMI). Both the Windscale and SL-1 accidents occurred in noncommercial reactors, neither of which had containment buildings. Nevertheless, the radiological releases were limited. More recently, in September 1983, an accident occurred at a research reactor in Argentina which resulted in the death of one of the operators. No radiation was apparently released to the environment in this case.

Windscale

In October 1957, a major fire occurred in the Windscale No. 1 reactor on England's western coast. Windscale was an air-cooled reactor used for plutonium production, and was not typical of commercial reactors. The burning of its graphite and uranium core, and the lack of a containment system, allowed the radioactive fission products to escape from the reactor's 400-ft stack to the surrounding countryside. The reactor burned for more than two days. Large amounts of radioactive iodine existed in the core, and much of it was released from the fuel during the fire. Yet, only a small fraction exited the stack. The highest radiation level reported off-site was approximately 4 mR/hr. This reading was reported at a single location approximately 1 mile from the reactor. The areas surounding Windscale, and the locally produced milk, were monitored. In certain areas, the consumption of milk was temporarily halted as a precautionary measure.

The burning uranium heated the graphite, which burned releasing CO and CO_2. The released iodine represented 12% of the available inventory. The stack filter removed much of the particulate iodine (20,000–50,000 Ci), but gaseous iodine (20,000 Ci) was released from the stack along with about 7.5% of the tellurium and 0.03% of the strontium in the core. The relatively low off-site radiation levels were due to the low release of the core's radioactivity, and the rapid dilution of what reached the atmosphere. From a public protection point of view, this was the worst reactor accident recorded to date. The radioactive plume was detected as far away as Germany and Norway.

SL-1 Reactor Accident

On January 3, 1961, the SL-1 reactor at the Idaho National Reactor Testing Station experienced a reactivity accident, caused by the sudden removal of a control rod during maintenance. This reactivity insertion led to a power excursion and extensive core melting. Three employees were killed.

The SL-1 was a small, natural-circulation, 3 MW(th) boiling water reactor. It was a prototype military reactor operated by military personnel. Its metallic fuel elements were constructed of highly enriched uranium–aluminum alloy, surrounded by aluminum alloy cladding. Few engineered safety features, such as a containment building, existed. In these respects, it differed appreciably from a modern power reactor. The reactor building is shown in Figure 17.15.

At the time of the accident, the reactor had been shut down for 11 days. The vessel head was on, but there was access to the core through the shield plugs. The rapid withdrawal of the central control rod led to the reactivity insertion accident. The subsequent power excursion resulted in fuel vaporization and melting. There was considerable steam formation and some metal–water reaction. There was a prompt 130 MW-sec nuclear energy release and another 24 MW-sec release from the metal–water reaction. The steam void terminated the power transient, but it created a high-pressure region in the core. Consequently, the water column over the core was accelerated upward, impacted on the upper head, and blew out several shield plugs. The water hammer caused the vessel to rise ~9 ft out of the cavity, shearing off coolant piping before falling back into the cavity. During this process, water, steam and core debris were expelled through the openings in the vessel head and into the operating room space. The whole process apparently occurred in a time span of only 2–4 sec.

SL-1's melted fuel contained approximately 19% of the total core fission product inventory. However, less than 0.01% of the radioactive inventory† actually reached the atmosphere following the event, in spite of the fact that the sheet metal building that housed the reactor was "drafty" and vented to the atmosphere. For instance, environmental sampling results indicated that only approximately 80 Ci of ^{131}I had escaped, out of an initial core inventory of 28,000 Ci. Further sampling indicated releases of approximately 0.5 Ci of ^{137}Cs (core inventory 3100 Ci) and approximately 0.1 Ci of ^{90}Sr (core inventory 3070 Ci) following the accident. As shown in Figure 17.16, the release to the environment was rather slow; for instance, only 50% of the radioiodine was released in the first three days. In total, 0.01% of the fission products escaped from the leaky reactor building, although 5–10% had escaped from the pressure vessel.

In comparing this accident to what might happen in a commercial nuclear plant, the latter's reactor containment building (required for all power reactors), and the multicompartment nature of such a building, would further decrease the amounts of radioactivity released. Nevertheless, except for the noble gases, the radioactive releases in the SL-1 accident were quite small because of the physical and chemical laws‡ governing fission product behavior, not because of the existence of engineered safety features or a containment building.

†The noble gases, particularly xenon and krypton, were almost totally released. Because of their chemical inertness, they pose a less serious threat per Ci to the public than most of the other radioisotopes.

‡For example, many of the more hazardous fission products such as iodine are attenuated when they come in contact with water.

Table 17.10. Reactor Accidents

Facility	Dry/Wet	Contained (C)/ Uncontained (U)	Release			Plume Distance to Bkg., Miles	Contaminated Area	MW(th)	MWd	Off-Site Person-rems	Individual Whole Body Dose (Maximum)	Maximum Thyroid Dose
			Iodine	Fission Products	Noble Gas							
Windscale-1	Dry	U	2×10^4 Ci (12%) in atmosphere	1600 Ci tellurium 600 Ci ^{137}Cs 80 Ci ^{89}Sr 9 Ci ^{90}Sr (in atmosphere)	3.4×10^5 Ci in atmosphere	200+ (estimated)	200 miles^2	~250 (estimated)	4000 (150 channels)	*a*	4.5 rems on-site; <20 mrems off-site	Adult: 9.5 rems; Child: 16 rems (off-site)
SL-1	Wet	C−	80 Ci (<0.5%) in atmosphere	~0.1 Ci ^{90}Sr ~0.5 Ci ^{137}Cs (on ground)	10^4 Ci in atmosphere	50 [ground measurement (GM)]	75 acres	3	932	0	Three fatalities; 27 rems on-site	Off-site; 0.035 rad Adult: 5.5 rads on-site
NRX[b]	Wet	C	*a*	10,000 Ci in 10^6 gal water (in containment)	*a*	¼ (GM)	Reactor building	30	*a*	0	16.1 rems on-site	0 off-site
TMI-2[c]	Wet	C+	17 Ci in atmosphere	Not detected in atmosphere	10×10^6 Ci in atmosphere	20 [air measurement (AM)]	Reactor containment building (RCB) and auxiliary building	2720	2.42×10^5	2000	4.18 rems on-site; 70 mrems off-site	0 off-site
WTR[d]	Wet	C	0 Ci in atmosphere	10 000 Ci in 1.6×10^6 gal water in containment	<800 Ci in atmosphere	1 (GM)	RCB		One element	0	2.1 rems on-site; 0 off-site	0 off-site
CR-3[e]	Wet	C+	70 Ci in 4×10^4 gal containment water; 2 Ci in containment air	*a*	1000 Ci in containment air	0	RCB	2452		0	0	0

PRTR[f]	Wet	C	205 Ci (27%) containment water; 7 Ci (0.9%) in containment air		~50% in containment air	0	RCB			0	*a*	*a*
HTRE-3[g]	Dry	U	34 Ci (~14%) in atmosphere	~0.1 Ci ^{91}Sr ~400 Ci gross in atmosphere	*a*	>6 miles	*a*	0.12	0.001	0	0	0
ORR[h]	Wet	C	0.15 to 0.2 Ci in atmosphere	~1000 Ci in primary system (~300 Ci iodine)	*a*	*a*	RCB	24	1.66	*a*	*a*	*a*
MTR[i]	Wet	C	*a*	~15 times normal in primary system	*a*	*a*	RCB (slight)	40	491	0	*a*	*a*
ETR[j]	Wet	C	*a*	6.4 Ci in atmosphere; 42 Ci to leach pond	*a*	*a*	RCB (minor)	90	*a*	*a*	*a*	*a*
NRU[k]	Wet	C	*a*	Large amount released to coolant and building. Small amount to environment.	*a*	*a*	100 acres	200	*a*	*a*	19 rems on-site	*a*

Source: From H. Morewitz, *Nuclear Technology* **53,** 120 (1981).

[a]Not available.
[b]NRX = the NRX natural uranium, heavy-water-moderated research reactor in Chalk River, Ontario.
[c]TMI-2 = Three Mile Island Unit 2, Metropolitan Edison Co. in Middletown, Pennsylvania.
[d]WTR = Westinghouse Testing Reactor in Waltz Mills, Pennsylvania.
[e]CR-3 = Crystal River Unit 3, Florida Power Corporation, in Crystal River, Florida.
[f]PRTR = Plutonium Recycle Test Reactor in Hanford, Washington.
[g]HTRE = Heat Transfer Reactor Experiment.
[h]ORR = Oak Ridge Research Reactor.
[i]MTR = Materials Testing Reactor.
[j]ETR = Engineering Test Reactor.
[k]NRU = the NRU natural uranium, heavy-water-moderated and -cooled test reactor in Chalk River, Ontario.

Figure 17.15. The SL-1 reactor prior to the accident. (Courtesy DOE.)

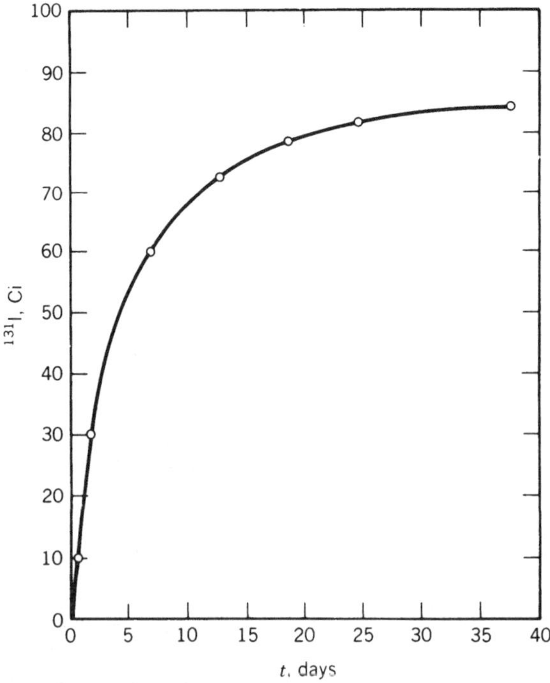

Figure 17.16. Cumulative iodine release to the environment from the SL-1 accident. [From H. A. Morewitz, *Nuclear Technology* **53,** 120 (1981).]

Three Mile Island—Unit 2

The accident at Three Mile Island occurred on March 28, 1979. The sequence of events is summarized in Figure 17.17. The accident began during attempts to unclog a pipe leading from the demineralizer in a secondary loop of the reactor. A combination of malfunctioning valves in the demineralizer and blocked valves in a backup safety system stopped the flow of feedwater to the steam generators. The turbine tripped automatically, and the reactor scrammed shortly thereafter. With no heat removal through the steam generators, the primary system pressure rose. The pilot-operated relief valve opened to reduce this pressure, and, unbeknownst to the operators, it stuck in the open position and remained in that state, undetected, for about 150 min.

The loss of coolant was finally halted, but the damage continued until about 200 min into the accident when the emergency cooling pumps were turned on at full throttle and reflooded the core. At that time the core was severely damaged, and the primary system contained large quantities of steam and hydrogen that impaired the flow of coolant through the core. The operators realized that the core may have been uncovered, and throughout the first day they struggled to establish stable conditions.

The seriousness of what had occurred was not generally realized until late the next day when a pressure spike on the monitor printout from the previous day gave evidence that hydrogen had burned inside the containment building. Evidently, severe overheating of the core had caused the cladding to react with steam and produce large amounts of hydrogen, some of which escaped to the containment through the open relief valve.

The accident at TMI resulted in the release of approximately 15 Ci of ^{131}I to the environment. This was less than 1 part in 10 million of the iodine in the core. Negligible amounts of ^{140}Ba were also released. A much larger quantity of the noble gases xenon and krypton was released (approximately 2.5 million Ci or 2% of the noble gas inventory). This noble gas release was quickly dissipated. Radiation levels outside the reactor site were quite low, mostly below 1 mR/hr. The fractional releases of the radioactive core inventory are given in Figure 17.18. As seen in this figure, with the exception of the noble gas, many factors of 10 reduction occurred during the transport of the fission products from the core, to the containment building, and through the auxiliary building before they were released to the environment.

At TMI, there was no failure of the reactor containment building during the accident. As a result, there were no direct releases from the containment. The releases that did occur were secondary leaks from auxiliary systems. With the exception of the noble gases xenon and krypton, most of the radioactivity was retained by the water in the reactor's containment building. The amount of material leaking from the containment building was further attenuated in the auxiliary building prior to escaping to the atmosphere.

RA-II Reactor Accident

An obvious violation of fundamental safety procedures resulted in a sudden excursion at an Argentine research reactor. The incident occurred September 23, 1983 when a technician, described as a qualified operator with 14 years' experience, was changing the core configuration of the RA-II reactor at the Constituyentes Atomic Center near Buenos Aires. The reactor is a zero-power, light water, tank-type reactor designed and built by the Comision Nacional de Energia Atomica which achieved criticality in 1966. The U.S. supplied the plate-type fuel. The standard approved safety procedure for changing fuel in the reactor is to drain the water from the tank, but the operator attempted to make the changes without draining the moderator water. In addition, two cases of unloaded fuel were placed on the outside of the graphite reflector instead of being removed completely and an error was made in setting up the final configuration of the fuel.

Prompt criticality occurred in milliseconds at 10–15 megajoules, the equivalent of $3\text{–}4.5 \times 10^{17}$ fissions, and was stopped automatically by reduction of moderation (plate expansion, expulsion of water/steam) and because the safety systems opened the moderator dump valve. The operator received an estimated dose of 1,400 rads of fast neutrons and at least 500 rads of gamma radiation. He died two days later of radiation effects. No equipment damage resulted, nor was any radiation apparently released to the environment.

Radiation Releases from Controlled Experiments

Three series of destructive reactor experiments were carried out to examine the effects of core melting, and even more severe, accidents. The tests studied fission product dispersal to the environment and fission product retention in the fuel, coolant, and structural surroundings. The experiments included: the Boiling Reactor Experiment (BORAX-I), 1954; Special Power Excursion Reactor Test (SPERT-I), 1962; and Systems for Nuclear Auxiliary Power Transient Reactor test series (SNAPTRAN). The SNAPTRAN series included test number 2/10A-3, 1964, and SNAPTRAN-2,

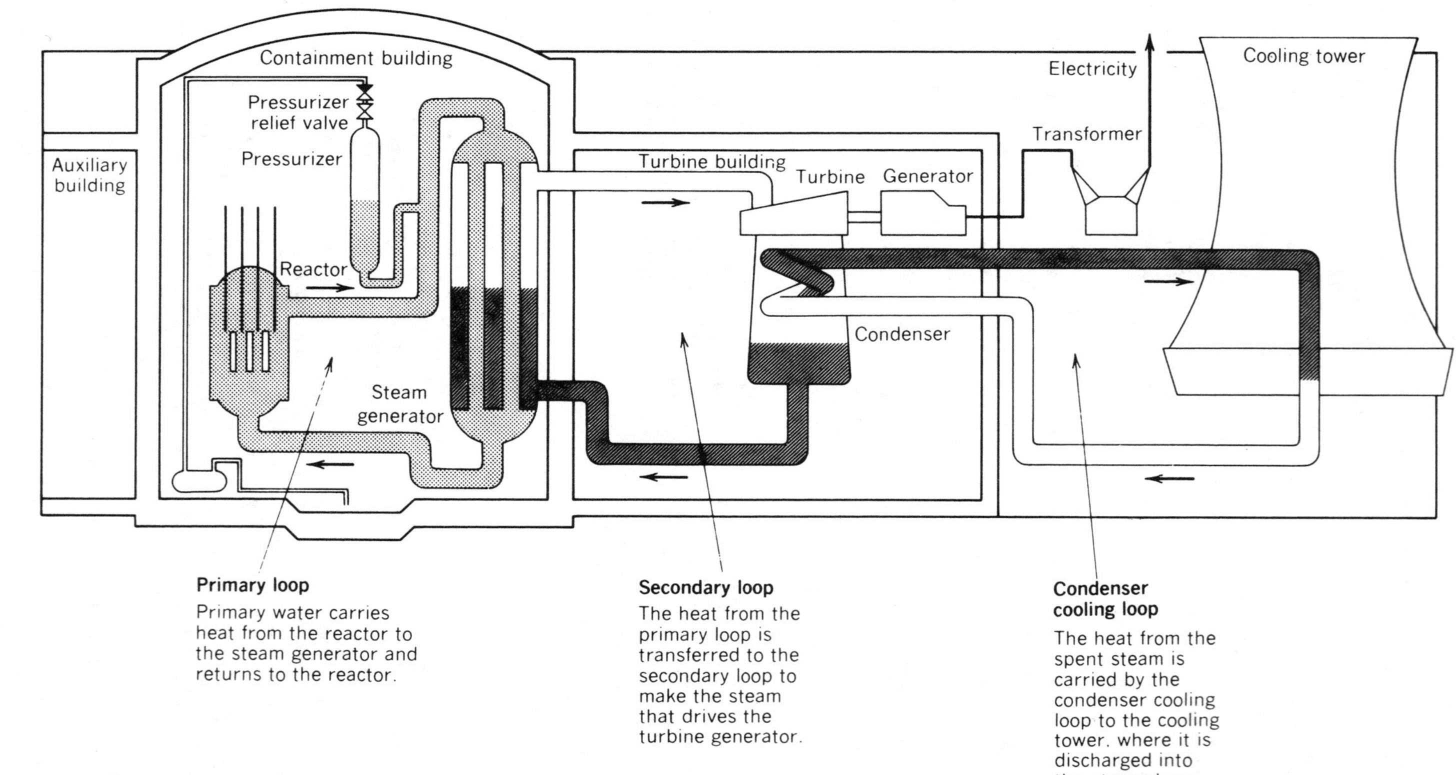

Figure 17.17. Analysis of the Three Mile Island accident. [Courtesy *EPRI Journal* (June 1980).]

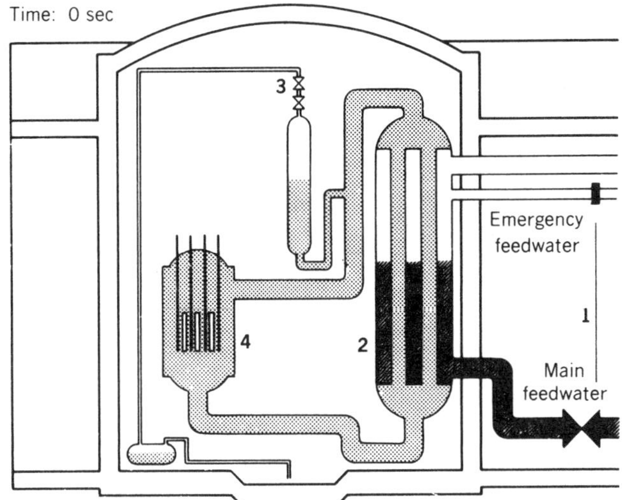

1 As a result of maintenance work, the main feedwater pumps trip. Emergency feedwater flow is blocked by two valves that inadvertently had been left closed sometime during the previous two days.

2 When feedwater flow stops, heat removal from the primary system decreases.

3 At 3 sec, relief valve on the pressurizer opens to reduce momentary overpressure but fails to close when pressure drops. Operators are unaware valve is open.

4 Reactor shuts down at 8 secs.

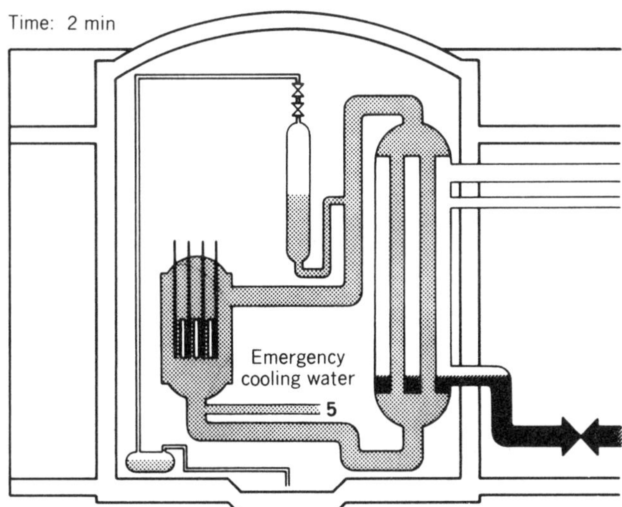

5 Pressure in primary system continues to fall and triggers automatic injection of emergency cooling water into the core. At 5 min this is throttled by operators, who believe the system is overfilled with water because the pressurizer is full.

Figure 17.7 (*Continued*)

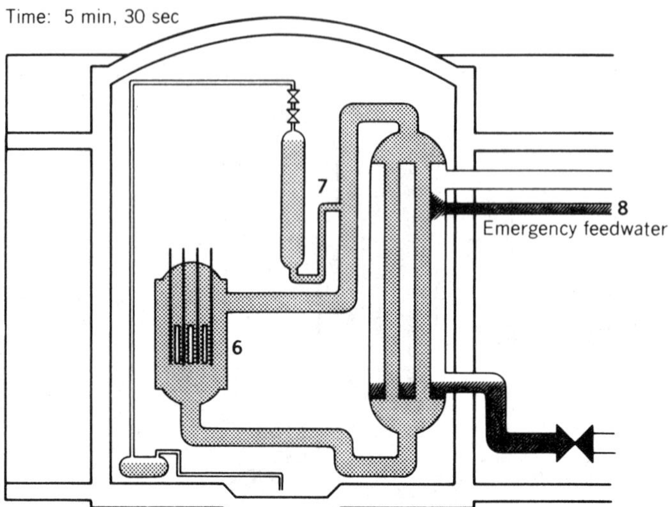

6 Water begins to boil in the core.

7 Increasing steam volume forces water into the pressurizer. The high water level in the pressurizer continues to mislead operators into believing the primary system is overfilled.

8 Operators discover the closed valves in the emergency feedwater lines and open them at 8 min.

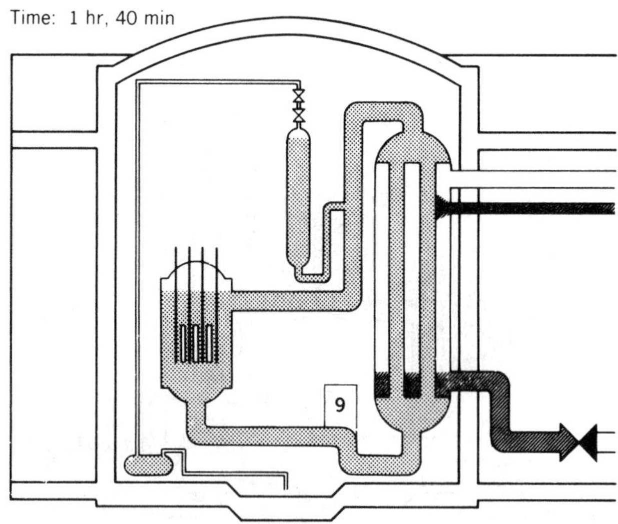

9 Insufficient water remains for proper operation of reactor cooling pumps. Pumps begin to vibrate excessively. Last two pumps are shut off at 1 hr, 40 min.

Figure 17.7 (*Continued*)

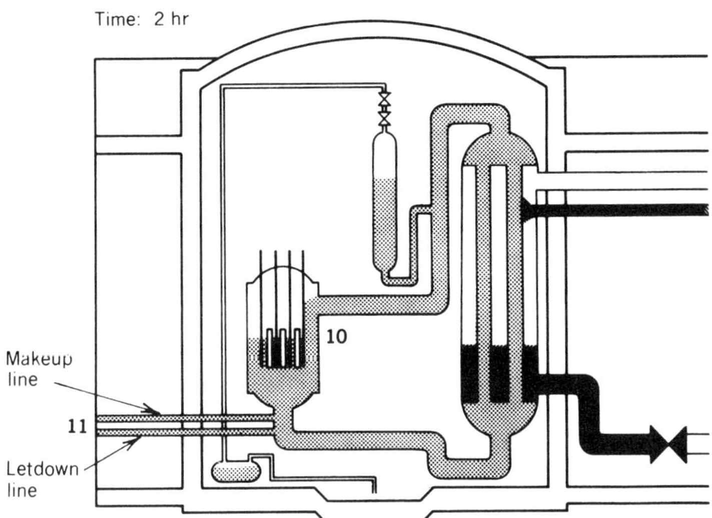

10 After the pumps are shut off, the core begins to overheat. Fuel cladding begins to fail.

11 A small fraction of the radioactive gases from the fuel travel with the primary system water to the auxiliary building through the piping (letdown line) of the level control and purification system.

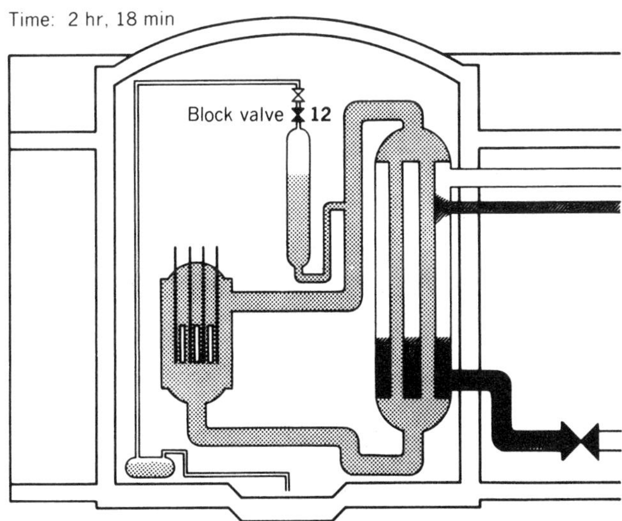

12 Operator closes the block valve to stop flow through the stuck-open pressurizer relief valve. The loss of primary system water is stopped.

Figure 17.7 *(Continued)*

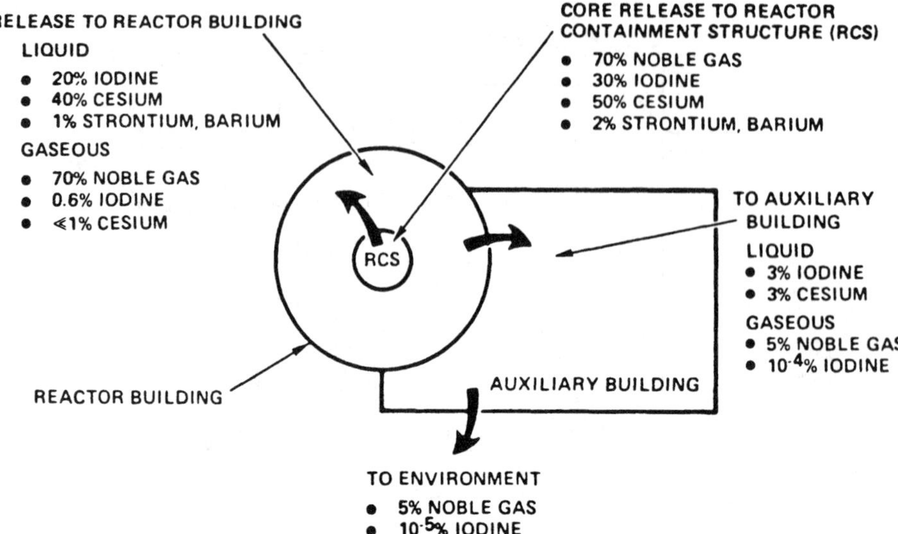

Figure 17.18. Release fractions at TMI-2. [From NSAC-1 (1979).]

1966. All but SNAPTRAN-2 were carried out in water. Particular emphasis was placed on the release behavior of iodine fission products since these have the highest radiological toxicity.

A review of these destructive tests, given in Table 17.11, shows that the availability of water played a powerful role in limiting the amount of fission products released and in delaying the release of radioiodine. In all destructive tests, no more than 0.5% of the available iodine has ever been released to the atmosphere and only very limited quantities of the other fission products have been detected in the environment. The iodine has always been released over a period of days. However, in the case of fuel damage in air (SNAPTRAN-2), 70% of the radioiodine was released to the atmosphere. It was then dispersed and carried down wind as it gradually settled out.

Release fractions for the noble gas fission products were also evaluated. These ranged from a low of 3% to 4% in SNAPTRAN-2/10A-3 (water medium) to a high of 75% in SNAPTRAN-2 (air medium). These data, along with those for radioiodine, show the effectiveness of water in limiting fission product release to the environment from damaged fuel.

The role of water in limiting iodine release is explained by iodine's chemical form which is cesium iodide (CsI). One of the most stable iodine compounds, CsI easily dissolves in water. The only ways to obtain gaseous iodine from a CsI water solution are by slow processes: either contacting the solution surface with air or by reacting the solution with oxidizing materials, such as hydrocarbons (paint, etc.). Most of the other volatile fission products also dissolve in water. This includes rubidium, strontium, barium, cesium, and their oxides, which dissolve after first reacting to form their respective hydroxides. Arsenic and selenium oxides are directly soluble in water. However, tellurium and its compounds (except the alkali metal tellurides, the acid and the hydride) are largely insoluble in water.† In reactor accidents and destructive tests where water was absent, up to 45% of the tellurium was released to the atmosphere in the form of fine particles (less than 1 μm in diameter), yet in cases when water was present, no tellurium was released. This result may be related to the fallout of the fine particles due to growth caused by condensation of water vapor or to the solubility of Cs_2Te, since there is some evidence for this compound in the intact fuel.

Vaporized fission product compounds form aerosol particles as they condense. The aerodynamic sizes of these aerosols increase as the aerosol concentration is increased; this has been confirmed by several experiments that indicate a size dependence with the cube root of concentration. Above approximately 30 g/m^3 concentration, experiments show the aerosol size depends more strongly on the concentration; this leads to the rapid formation of very large agglomerates. In addition, when aerosols are released into a saturated steam atmosphere, steam condenses on them and causes them to grow to still larger sizes. Such large aerosol particles fall out in a short time. As a result, the aerosol mass available for leakage is greatly reduced. Furthermore, in saturated steam atmospheres, leak paths are rapidly plugged with water so that the leakage of aerosols to the

†Another mechanism, the "gettering" of tellurium by hot stainless steel and zirconium, appears to be responsible for greatly limiting the quantity of tellurium that might escape the core region.

Table 17.11. Destructive Tests

Facility	Dry/ Wet	Contained (C)/ Uncontained (U)	Atmospheric Release: Iodine	Atmospheric Release: Fission Products	Atmospheric Release: Noble Gas	Plume Distance to Bkg., Miles	Contaminated Area	Energy, MW-sec
KIWI-TNT	Dry	U	6.45%	67%	~100%	250 at 9000 ft (AM)	380 acres	10^4
SNAPTRAN-2[a]	Dry	U	70%	21%	6×10^5 Ci (75%)	18 at 500 ft (AM)	<32 acres	54
SNAPTRAN-3[a]	Wet	U	0	0	3.2×10^4 Ci (<4%)	21 at 1200 ft (AM)	<1 acre	45 ± 4
SPERT-1[b]								
U-Al	Wet	U	<0.01%	<0.79%	7%	*c*	Very small	31
UO_2	Wet	U	<0.01%	*c*	0.06%	*c*	0	165
UO_2	Wet	U	<0.01%	*c*	0.06%	*c*	0	155
BORAX-1	Wet	U	*c*	*c*	*c*	<1 (GM)	<9.2 acres	135

Source: From H. Morewitz, *Nuclear Technology* **53,** 120 (1981).

[a]SNAPTRAN = Systems for Nuclear Auxiliary Power Transient reactor test series.
[b]SPERT = Special Power Excursion Reactor Test.
[c]Not available.

environment is even further restricted. All of the above conditions are present in reactor environments.

The presence of moisture during LWR accident scenarios cannot be overemphasized since it would greatly accelerate aerosol depletion processes and aid in the removal of radionuclides escaping a damaged core. Thus it plays an important role in LWR safety.

17.9. HYPOTHETICAL ACCIDENTS AND THEIR CONSEQUENCES

A severe accident is one that results in fission product release from the core, breaching some of the engineered barriers which are supposed to prevent their release. Such an accident can occur from loss of core coolant, as happened in the accident at Three Mile Island. If a loss-of-coolant accident were to occur and the emergency core cooling system failed to work properly, the core would go through a process in which steam is boiled off from the core. As the water evaporates, the core heats up. As the temperature continues to rise, various parts of the core would fail structurally, leading to release of fission products.

Releases of radioactive fission products are not possible unless the barriers preventing release are breached. The first two barriers, the fuel matrix and cladding, require the core to overheat before they become ineffective. The residual decay heat is sufficient to cause the core to melt once the core is no longer covered with water. A key event in any postulated accident scenario is the time when the coolant level in the pressure vessel reaches the top of the core. The progression of the accident past this point is more or less independent of the prior evolution of the accident.

As the core starts to heat up, it reaches a temperature where zirconium–water reactions become important (around 1400°C). Above these temperatures, this exothermic reaction gives off heat very rapidly and hydrogen is evolved in substantial quantities, according to the reaction

$$Zr + 2H_2O \rightarrow ZrO_2 + 2H_2 + 140 \text{ kcal/mole}$$

The water comes from steam from the pressure vessel bottom rising through the core. There are 20,000 kg of zirconium in a typical core. Oxidation of this material could release 2×10^5 MW-sec of energy, producing hydrogen at a rate of 10 kg/sec. This hydrogen can pose an explosion hazard in the RCB.

During the rapid core heatup period, fission products are being released. The release would probably occur more or less continuously until the system finally cools. Release rates vary over wide limits depending on fission product properties, system temperatures, and the surface-to-volume ratio of the molten material. However, it is possible to identify four conditions at which major releases would occur:

1. *Gap Release.* Occurs when the cladding experiences initial rupture. It consists mostly of activity that was released to void spaces within the fuel rods during normal reactor operation.
2. *Meltdown Release.* Occurs when the fuel first heats to melting. High gas flows in the core during this period are expected to sweep the activity out of the core region.
3. *Vaporization Release.* Occurs after large amounts of molten core material fall into the reactor cavity from the pressure vessel. The hot core material would cause the concrete base mat to start melting and gas such as CO_2 to be released, sparging the melt of fission products.
4. *Oxidation Release.* Occurs just after, and as a result of, a postulated steam explosion event. Finely divided fuel material would undergo extensive oxidation, liberating specific fission products.

Chronology of a Core Melt

The process of core melt would take roughly 1 hr once the coolant water level started uncovering the top of the core.† Elevated fuel-rod temperatures during core uncovering would cause the Zircaloy fuel-rod cladding first to balloon, then rupture, and finally oxidize. The cladding would balloon because of the pressure difference between the gas inside the fuel rods and the steam outside. The cladding balloons until neighboring fuel rods come in contact with each other and coolant flow is impeded. However, ballooning probably has little effect on the time and extent of fuel-rod rupture. The next stage of damage, rupture of the cladding, would lead directly to release of gaseous fission products to the primary coolant.

Because of local decay heat power variations, the core does not heat up uniformly; rather some

†The process is not, however, inexorable; the core could be prevented from further degradation at any time by a resumption of coolant flow.

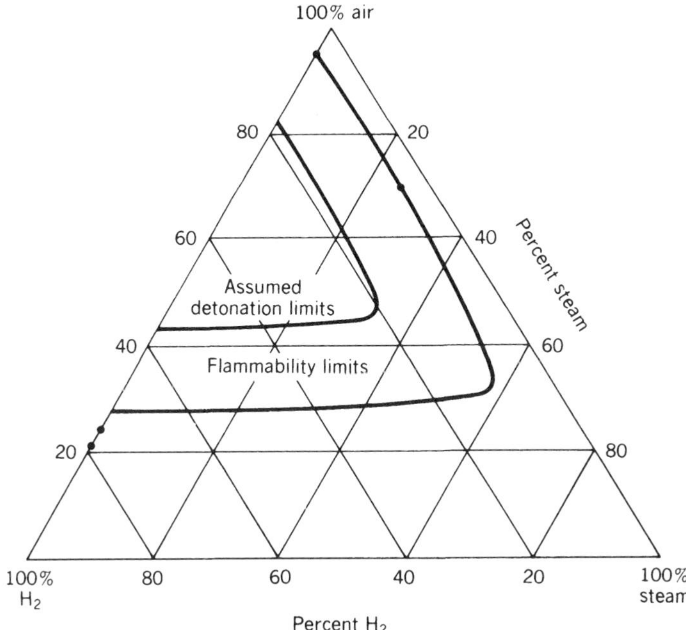

Figure 17.19. Flammability limits of hydrogen/air/steam mixtures. (From NUREG-0205.)

parts are much hotter than others. Eventually some of these areas would reach a temperature at which the Zircaloy–water reaction begins in earnest. This exothermic reaction increases temperatures at an ever more rapid rate. Large amounts of radioactive aerosols might be produced during this time. Eventually, if core cooling is not restored, the core can melt though its structural supports and the pressure vessel, and fall onto the concrete base-mat of the containment building.

If the hot core reaches the concrete of the base-mat, the high temperatures will cause it to decompose and produce more aerosols. The reaction would proceed until sufficient heat was dissipated to solidify the melt. Penetration of the base-mat into the underlying bedrock could occur in some instances. Interactions with the bedrock would not be significantly different from those with concrete. The site's geology would then determine the release of radioactivity. Generally, release of fission products through a penetration in the base-mat is not a high consequence event because the radioactivity is trapped in the ground.

Containment Failure

Of concern is a pressure buildup in the containment building that could lead to its failure. Containment buildings are designed to handle the full loads due to the primary coolant system steam blowdown. However, other gases, such as noncondensable CO_2 and H_2 generated during the course of an accident, might increase the RCB's internal pressure to the point of failure. Such a condition, however, is unlikely until many hours after the start of an accident. A late failure of a containment is a relatively benign event since most of the radioactivity released in the accident would have settled from the RCB's atmosphere and, therefore, could not be released to the environment.

Of greater concern is hydrogen buildup and combustion in the RCB. The pressure generated from a hydrogen burn is a possible mechanism for causing the early failure of the RCB itself. The flammability limits for H_2 in a steam environment are given in Figure 17.19. Below about 4 vol.% in air, hydrogen will not burn; nor is detonation possible below about 18 vol.%. As seen in the figure, however, the hydrogen concentrations must be considerably higher when steam is present.

Depending on the extent of the zirconium–water reaction and the volume of the containment building, various H_2 concentrations might exist. Figure 17.20 shows the hydrogen concentration that would be reached in various types of reactors for a given amount of metal–water reaction. In general, BWRs, especially Mark I and II designs, can reach concentration levels where hydrogen burning might be a problem.

A hydrogen burn at TMI created a pressure spike in containment of ~2 bars, well below the

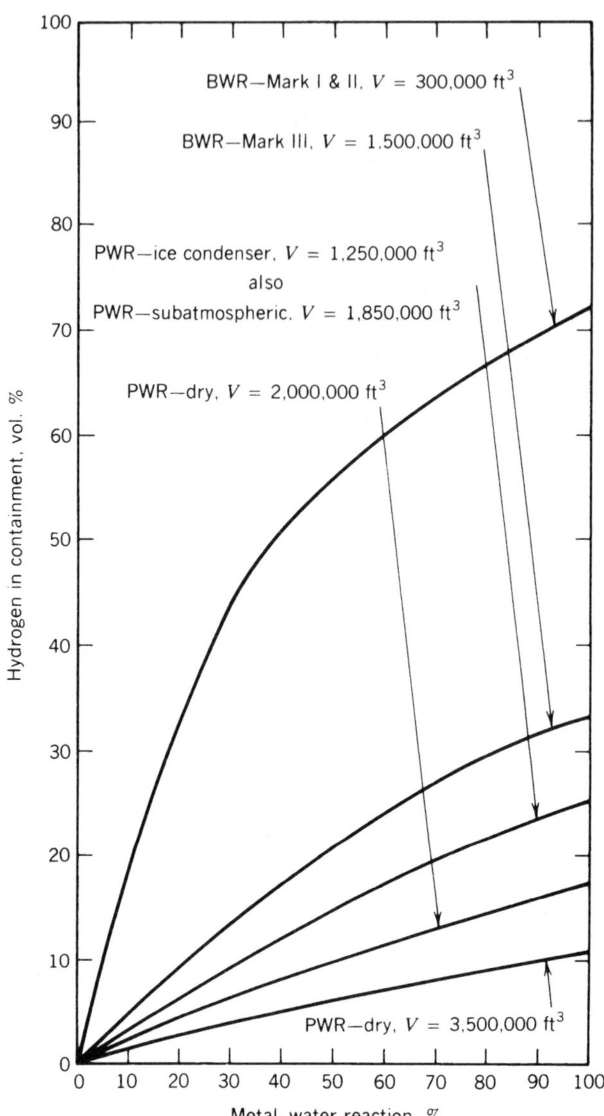

Figure 17.20. Vol.% hydrogen in containment versus % metal–water reaction. (Courtesy NSAC.)

containment design pressure of ~4 bars.† The hazard of H_2 explosion in an LWR depends on the containment design. In designs where hydrogen buildup becomes a threat to containment integrity, ignitors can be installed to burn the H_2 in a controlled manner before it would reach explosive concentrations.

Radioactivity Depletion Mechanisms

During an accident's meltdown–fission product release phase, several mechanisms operate to reduce the amount of radioactivity that can escape into the environment. The timing of radioactive release is important. Even a few minutes between core melting and containment failure would be extremely important. For example, consider a postulated early penetration of the RCB. The time

†The actual failure pressure of the TMI reactor containment building has been estimated at 10 bars.

Table 17.12. Possible Fission Product Reactions, Degraded Core Accident

Reaction Process—Iodine/Cesium	Product
Iodine with cesium in fuel	Cesium iodide
Cesium iodide with water	Dissolved cesium iodide
Dissolved cesium iodide with oxygen from air	Iodine
Iodine with water	Hypoiodous acid
Iodine with organic material (e.g., paints)	Organic iodides
Iodine with metals in reactor building	Nonvolatile iodides
Iodine with dust and dirt	Nonvolatile iodides
Gravitational settling of solid iodides	Nonvolatile iodides
Adsorption/plate out of airborne iodides on surfaces	Nonvolatile iodides
Filtration of airborne particulates	Immobilized iodides
Removal of nonvolatile iodides by water scrubbing	Iodide solutions
Reaction Process—Tellurium/Cesium	**Product**
Tellurium with cesium in fuel	Cesium telluride
Plate out of cesium telluride in fuel	Adsorbed cesium telluride
Cesium telluride with water	Cesium–tellurium solution
Precipitation of tellurium from solution	Solid tellurium
Oxidation of tellurium (solution) by air	Nonvolatile tellurium
Reaction Process—Particulate Fission Product	**Product**
Particulate becomes airborne after fuel clad rupture	Airborne particulate
Airborne particulate settles out due to gravity	Plated/adsorbed material
Airborne particulate scrubbed out by water	Water suspension or solution of fission products

Source: From R. C. Vogel, private communication.

between fission product release from the fuel and the RCB failure allows time for chemical reactions, condensation phenomena, and the effects of moisture to occur. Aerosol agglomeration effects would also occur in both the primary coolant system and the containment building.

If an accident progresses at a modest rate, the time gained thereby helps in three ways: the residual decay heat decreases, the energetics of core damage diminishes, and the radioactive inventory decays. More importantly, time elapses before the last engineered barrier—the containment building—is in danger of being breached. A failure of the containment building due to steam overpressurization would take several days to occur. In the meantime, depletion phenomena would have been functioning to reduce the source term available for release. Physical/chemical reactions, many of which lead to high attenuation of fission products released from the core, are quite numerous. Some of these are given in Table 17.12.

To obtain realistic estimates of the consequences of severe core damage accidents, careful modeling is required. Consequence analyses of such events often tend to be very conservative. An example of how consequence modeling can affect estimated risk is shown in Table 17.13 which examines the Reactor Safety Study. The table shows fission product attenuation mechanisms which were not well understood at the time of the study and, therefore, were not included in it. These are marked with a dot in the table, indicating that a more realistic calculation would lead to predicted off-site consequences at least two times lower. Since each of the important accident sequences have five or more such areas of conservatism, one could reasonably expect the results of the Reactor Safety Study to be too pessimistic by a factor of 10 to 100 in its prediction of early fatalities, latent fatalities, and other consequences.

17.10. SAFETY, RISK, AND PERCEPTION

The inherent and perceived safety of nuclear power affects its commercialization. Although most questions about nuclear safety can be answered yes or no, safety criteria must be set by a standard which, by its nature, is difficult to define and often subjective. Such a standard must incorporate the public's view of how safe is safe enough. A central aspect of safety standards is the known carcinogenic and mutagenic properties of radiation. Public policy often reflects the position that whatever *can* cause cancer, *will* do so (and, implicitly, the reasoning that if you are not exposed to radiation, you will not get cancer). Policy based on this premise ignores the reality that some level of risk is inherent in every activity known to humans.

Table 17.13. WASH-1400 Conservatisms Impacting Consequences for Dominant Accident Sequences

	Accident Sequence				
	PWR			BWR	
Area of Conservatism	V	TMLB′	S_2C	TW	TC
Lack of FP retention in primary system	•	•	•	•	
No FP deposition in containment leak passages		•	•	•	•
No FP trapping in saturated water pools	•	•		•	
No FP retention by auxiliary buildings	•	•	•	•	•
Total release of "volatile" FP's from the fuel	•	•	•	•	•
Uninhibited fuel oxidation and Ru release in steam explosions		•	•	•	•
Iodine assumed I_2 rather than CsI		•	•	•	•
Incomplete aerosol behavior modeling	•	•	•	•	•
Puff discharges upon containment overpressure failure		•	•		•

Source: From I. Wall, private communication.
• in the table indicates a factor of 2 (or greater) reduction in consequences by including a particular phenomena in the modeling.
FP = fission product
V = LPIS check valve failure
TMLB′ = High-pressure failure of relief valve
S_2C = Small-break LOCA
TW = Transient with failure to remove core heat
TC = Transient with failure of reactor protection system

Public policy is frequently rooted in individual attitudes toward risk. These attitudes are largely psychological, and are, by nature, nonrational (not irrational). Acceptance of any risk is governed by three preferences which seem to determine a person's willingness to accept a given level of risk in society:

1. *Control of Risk.* A person may feel he controls the risk when he drives a car or skis down a hill, whereas a nuclear power plant in his area is an imposed risk.
2. *Potential for Disaster.* People seem to be adverse to a risk that kills 100 passengers in one airplane accident, but will accept 50,000 individual traffic fatalities a year for the convenience of an automobile.
3. *Familiarity.* Familiar risks, such as the danger of electrocution from power tools, appear easier to accept than the unfamiliar ones from a nuclear reactor.

The setting and enforcing of acceptable risk levels is the province of various regulatory agencies. This process is, however, tempered by public insistence that government set much lower risk levels for the public than persons are willing to set for themselves. Often overlooked is the fact that a utility which owns a nuclear plant has a billion dollar investment to protect—and only by operating a safe plant will its investment be secure. Moreover, risk decisions are not absolute, but must incorporate alternatives and benefits. The questions to be considered are: Is nuclear power safer than alternate sources of electricity such as a coal plant? And, does a nuclear plant's benefit to society exceed its risk? This section will examine the risks associated with the use of nuclear reactors, with the understanding that absolute risk is not necessarily the only criteria to be considered when answering the question: How safe is safe enough?

Financial Impact of Accidents

Accidents bring large financial costs to a utility and its customers; a short outage might cost $1 million per day. Longer outages of a year or more (including those resulting from accidents that would ruin a plant) have decreasing costs per diem, but a minimum loss for a ruined plant would be several billion dollars. Probability distributions for the costs of reactor accidents are given in Figure 17.21, which compares public risks to utility financial risks. The risk to the utility is partially

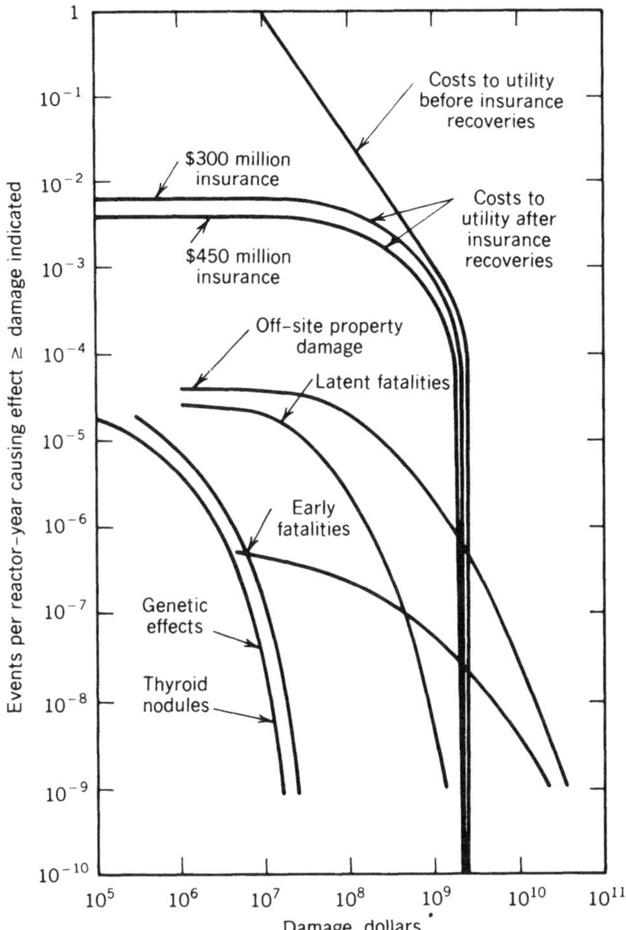

Figure 17.21. Probability distributions for costs arising from reactor accidents and outages. Accident costs were calculated from report WASH-1400 based on: $\$10^5$/genetic effect, $\$3 \times 10^3$/thyroid nodule, $\$10^6$/latent fatality, $\$5 \times 10^6$/early fatality, and property damage two times the WASH-1400 estimate. [From C. Starr and C. Whipple, *Nuclear Safety* **23,** 1 (1982).]

mitigated by insurance coverage. At the time of the TMI accident, nuclear plant operators carried property damage coverage of \$300 to \$375 million per site. Coverage has recently been increased to \$375 to \$450 million, and plans to raise the limit to \$1 billion are underway.

NRC-estimated costs to the public in terms of health risks are about 1/50 of the financial risk to a utility. This conclusion, which is confirmed in Figure 17.21, is insensitive to the social cost assigned to a fatality, given that the ratio of utility risk to the social cost of early fatality is roughly $10^4:1$. This result is also insensitive to any uncertainties in the probability estimates, since if new information suggests that a particular accident is more or less likely to occur than previously thought, then both the public and utility risk will change in response by the same amount. However, many recently revised analyses suggest that radioactive fission product releases from damaged reactors are lower by a factor of 10 or more than indicated in the WASH-1400 study. Because of the "threshold" effect for acute death from radiation, a tenfold reduction in risk would imply no early public fatalities even in the most severe accident.

17.11. CALCULATION OF RISK AND RELIABILITY

Risk assessment techniques for nuclear power plants begin where reliability analysis leaves off, estimating the risk to the public of accidents or abnormal operating conditions. It was started in a

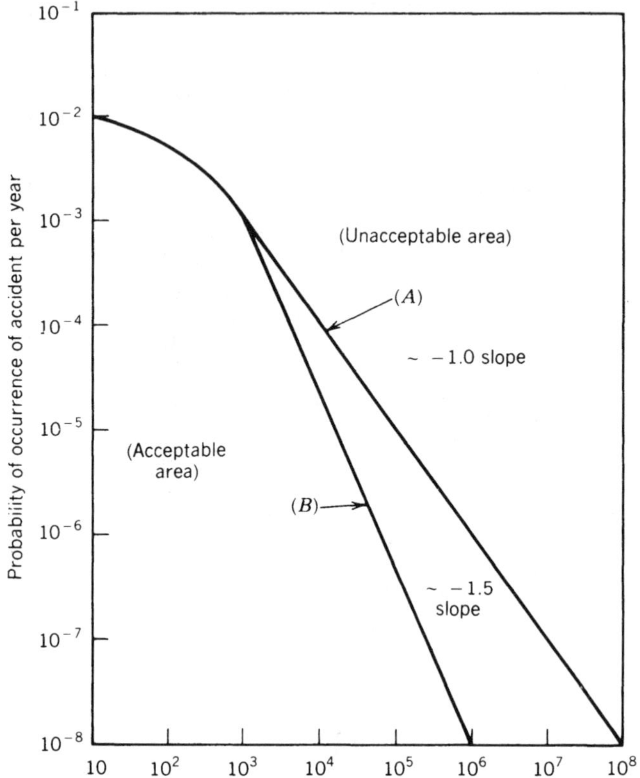

Figure 17.22. Equivalent ground-level release of iodine-131 in curies. (From EPRI Report NP-79-LD.)

quantitative way by F. R. Farmer in 1967. He proposed a criterion whereby an accident exceeding a certain probability for a given consequence (e.g., acute fatalities or latent cancers) would be judged unacceptable to society. Engineering modifications to the plant would then be made to reduce an accident's probability, consequences, or both. The criteria he proposed assumed a societal aversion toward large accidents.

Farmer proposed a limit line for accidental releases. When potential accident sequences were found to fall below the line, they were considered acceptable. When potential sequences were found above the line, they were considered excessive and measures were instituted to move such sequences below the limit line. Figure 17.22 shows two Farmer-type lines. Either line can be used as a limit line, depending on the acceptance criterion used. Line (A) has a slope of −1, indicating an equal risk acceptance for large as well as small incidents. Line (B) has a slope of −1.5, indicating some form of societal aversion toward the large accidents. To fix the limit line, the point at 1000 Ci with a probability of 10^{-3} yr was selected. Small accidental releases would be considered unacceptable above a frequency of 10^{-2}/yr.

The subsequent development of Probabilistic Risk Assessment (PRA) techniques reached a major milestone with the issuance of the Reactor Safety Study (WASH-1400) in October, 1975. Its objective was to provide a *realistic* estimate of the consequences of a reactor accident. This study superceded WASH-740, the 1957 study which deliberately chose pessimistic values for calculating reactor accidents in order to bound the risk; the detailed information necessary for a precise calculation was not available at the time. The 1957 study was limited by its inability to estimate probability of accident sequences, and to quantify physical mechanisms for fission product release. WASH-1400 used event and fault trees† to define important accident sequences. The results were considerably improved and much more descriptive than WASH-740.

†Fault tree analysis is a technique that can be used to determine failure sequences and probabilities for complex systems. The event trees provide a mechanism for systematically analyzing what follows an initiating event, such as the failure of a system component.

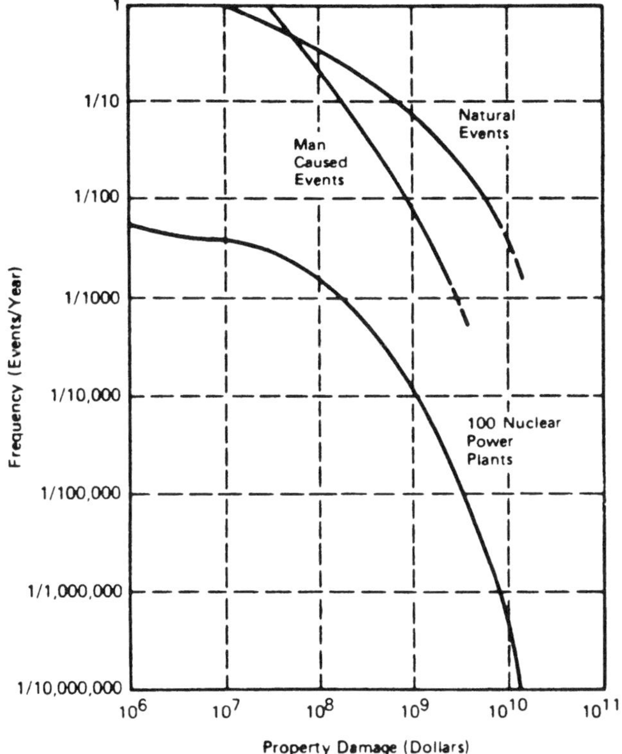

Figure 17.23. Frequency of property damage due to natural and human-caused events. (From WASH-1400.)

A major output of WASH-1400 was a curve (Figure 17.23) that showed the number of fatalities versus frequency for nuclear accidents. This curve was later used to justify an approach to licensing which emphasized large accidents. The perception in 1975 was that nuclear safety would be best served by concentrating on the accidents with the greatest consequences. (This approach was proved wrong at TMI.) Another result was that only accidents involving core melt contributed significantly to public risk. This was an important, still valid, conclusion. The WASH-1400 study estimated the probability of core melt to be 5×10^{-5} per reactor year, or about 1 chance in 10 of a core melt in the United States within the next 15 yr. Even though the risk of a public fatality given such a core melt is still quite low, these estimates impact the nuclear industry in many ways. They affect many licensing issues, the perceived financial risk of owning a reactor, and the public's opinion of nuclear power.

Although the advent of the PRA methodology has proved to be of great benefit in quantifying risk, more troublesome aspects are how to assign acceptable risk and how believable are the results. Some of the benefits of PRA and some of the criteria for its use are listed in Tables 17.14 and 17.15.

The method itself is relatively straightforward. Figure 17.24 shows the steps required. Analysis begins with an understanding of the plant and equipment. Because "defense-in-depth" is used in all aspects of nuclear power, and multiply–redundant equipment is used in safety systems, accident scenarios are complex; they require chains of failure of active and passive barriers to the release of radioactivity.

A plant's calculated risk is arrived at by a summation of the risks of individual postulated accident scenarios:

$$\text{risk} = \sum_n (\text{probability of event } n) \times (\text{consequences of event } n)$$

which in turn is composed of two parts: (1) the probability (likelihood) of an accident occurrence, and (2) the effects (consequences) of this accident to the public. This risk can be mitigated by corrective actions taken during an accident to reduce its severity.

Table 17.14. Some Benefits of a Probabilistic Risk Assessment

1. Identifies the dominant risk sequences, and factors that differ from plant to plant which significantly change the risk.
2. Permits evaluation of proposed changes in safety related systems, including the justification of expenses to improve plant safety.
3. A valid fault tree can be a valuable operational guide, and can be used to train personnel and plant operators.
4. Proper use can:
   a. Uncover unexpected areas of risk, including safety risks to the public and financial risks to the utility.
   b. Define what the precursors of major accidents are.
   c. Reveal oversights in design, construction, and operating procedures.
5. Once into an accident, a preexisting analysis can give the probability that serious consequences will result, and the new dominant risk sequences to be guarded against.

Table 17.15. Criteria for the Credibility of the PRA Method

1. The numbers are verifiable, there is general agreement as to what they mean and how to use them.
2. The results are "scrutable."
3. Adequate data bases exist and the events portrayed are not low-frequency ones that fall outside the tails of the distributions.
4. A confidence estimate and sensitivity analysis of the results exist.
5. "Short circuits" and common mode failures are either accounted for, guaranteed not to exist, or are unimportant to the result.
6. The scenarios modeled fall within our everyday experience, or we have a subjective "feel" for them.
7. We are willing to emotionally accept the results.
8. The methodology has been used successfully in other areas to assess the risk arising from active, complex systems (e.g., the transportation of LNG).

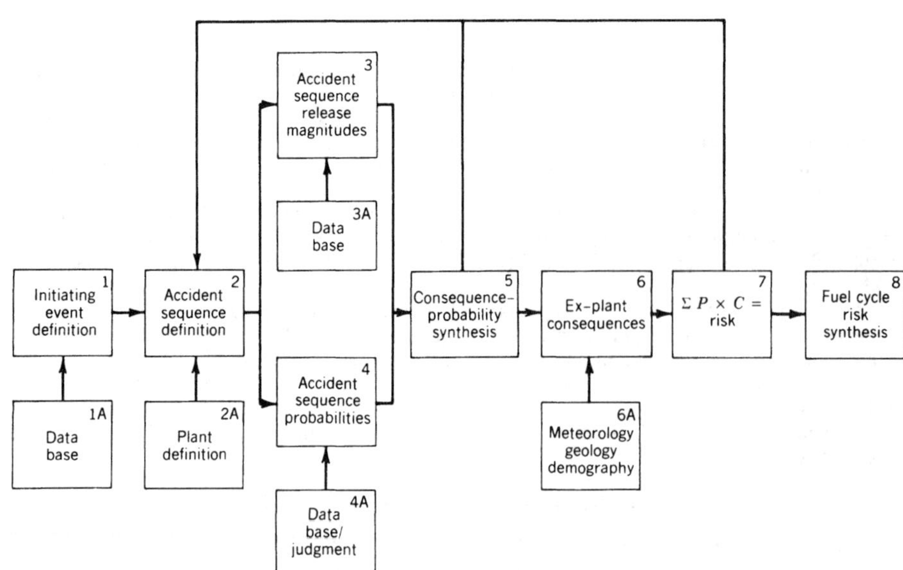

Figure 17.24. Steps in constructing a probabilistic risk assessment.

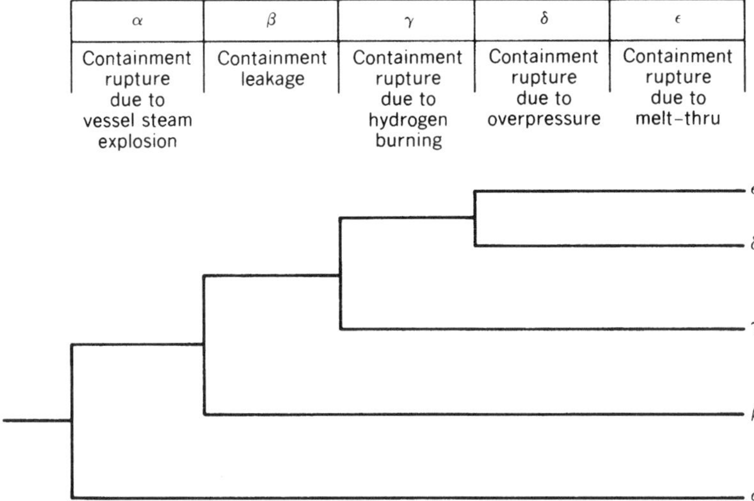

Figure 17.25. PWR containment event tree. (From WASH-1400.)

The probabilities of component failure can be found in reliability studies; these in turn have a direct input to overall risk assessment. Reliability analysis is a fairly new development, with both qualitative and quantitative methodologies used only recently. In a qualitative-only analysis, numerical evaluations are not done and few conclusions are reached. Rather, qualitative study is used in the design phase to make sure that hazards are identified and addressed in the design.

Reliability studies in the 1950s were based on single-failure analysis: determining that no single failure should have unacceptable consequences. This type of analysis was often done by modeling the whole system and then studying the effects of a failure, component by component. Included in this type of study were methods to detect failed units, secondary effects on nearby units, and specifications of failure types that needed to be considered.

The set of circumstances that make an accident possible is called an accident sequence, which may be drawn as an event tree. Event trees try to evaluate risk by answering the questions: What undesirable events can happen? Can they lead to radiation release? What are the probabilities of occurring? These questions can be answered by analyzing potential accident sequences. Sequences are traced by starting with an initiating event and adding up events until an accident either occurs or does not occur. A complete picture of nuclear plant risk is an analysis of all possible initiators and every possible sequence.

Figure 17.25 illustrates an event tree. Its logic is very similar to decision tree logic (used in business, economics, etc.). An event tree is usually drawn from left to right and begins with an initiator. This initiator is any event that could lead to a shutdown of a system or component. In the event tree, the initiators are connected to other possible events by branches; each scenario is a path of these branches.

By defining all of the initiators and organizing them into logical sequences, one ends up with a large number of potential accident scenarios. Event tree analysis can identify the paths whose higher probabilities or release magnitudes cause them to be major risk determinants. Analyzing the branches and paths can lead to design and operational modifications along those paths. The event tree methodology can:

1. Define accident scenarios with various outcomes from various initiators.
2. Show relationships of system failures to accident consequences.
3. Reduce the initial set of potential accidents to those logically meaningful.
4. Identify top events for fault tree analysis.

Event trees work well for single-failure situations, but multiple failures are a challenge to the current state of the art.

Each step in the event tree sequence is analyzed by fault tree analysis, using data obtained from a failure data base. The fault trees try to quantify risk by a deductive process. They identify a risk event or situation, and then ask the question: How could this come about? The answer, of course, is that the event can come about in a variety of ways. A fault tree analysis is the description of all

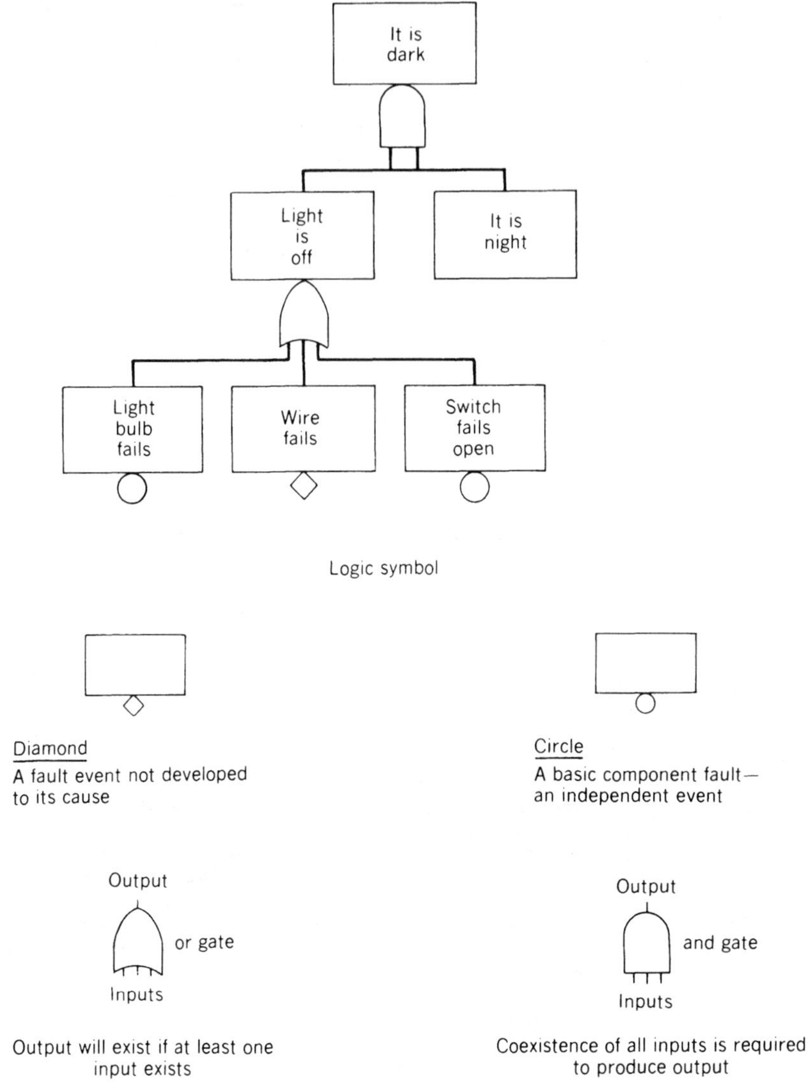

Figure 17.26. Example of a fault tree. (From EPRI Report NP-79-LD.)

possible causes of each event. Pictorially, the tree is drawn from top to bottom. The specified event is located at the top of the tree, and thus is called the top event. A fault tree's validity depends on the top event being very accurately evaluated. These top events have causes; a fault tree analysis looks for root causes. In fact, most direct causes of top events can themselves be examined as if they were top events. This deduction could be theoretically carried down many levels, but for tractability, must soon stop. The most easily examined root causes are components that have a well-recorded failure history. Pumps are a good example. While a pump failure could be a top event, with causes such as hose breakage, bearing disintegration, and so on, pump failure data by itself might be sufficient to allow it to be treated as a root cause. No further analysis would be necessary to determine risk of failure. Since the deductive stopping place is arbitrary, it makes sense to stop at components which have (or could have) enough historical data to accurately develop a probability of failure of that component.

Figure 17.26 is an example of a fault tree analysis of a lighting system which consists of a light bulb, a wire, and a switch. Two circles and one diamond are shown in this example. In the case of the circles, the components' (light bulb and switch) failures are modeled as independent events.

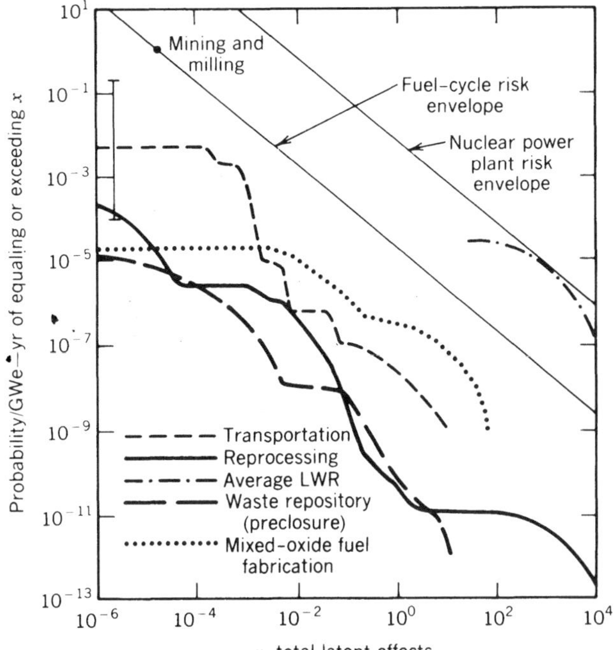

Figure 17.27. Health effects risk of the nuclear fuel cycle compared with that of nuclear power plants. The risk envelopes are lines where the product of probability and consequences is constant. (From WASH-1400.)

There is no outside agent involved in the component failure. It is implied in the analysis that there is no concern over the root cause of the failure. For example, the light bulb may fail due to a leak in the glass or to the element burning out. In the case of the diamond, it might be significant if the wire fails open or shorted. Therefore, the diamond is used. If a concern about sabotage existed, a diamond describing a rock (an outside agent) thrown at the light bulb might be shown on the tree.

An Application—Fuel Cycle Risks

The traditional nuclear fuel cycle includes the reprocessing of nuclear fuel, and recovering and reusing both uranium and plutonium from the spent fuel. Alternate fuel cycles include an option to recycle uranium only, and one with no recycling at all. In assessing the benefits of the various options risk, quantification is important. This can be done by using a probabilistic risk assessment.

For example, in the recycle option, preliminary work showed that conversion, enrichment, and uranium-only fabrication resulted in only small contributions to the risk. They were therefore excluded from the risk analysis, subject to later verification. Mining and milling were chosen for detailed study because they appeared to be the largest contributors to routine risk. Waste disposal was included because of the potential impact on future generations. Reprocessing, mixed-oxide fuel fabrication, and transportation were also examined.

The analysis result appears in Figure 17.27. The fuel cycle is seen to pose a small fraction of the risk compared with the power plant; the highest risk steps of the fuel cycle are transportation of plutonium-bearing wastes and the fabrication of mixed-oxide fuel. More significantly, the results show that the fuel-reprocessing fuel cycle contributes less than 1% of the total risk from nuclear power. The partial-recycle and once-through fuel cycles contribute even less. For perspective, the analysis showed that even for a very large nuclear industry (685 plants), the incremental radiation exposure to the public would be less than 1/200 of that received from normal background radiation.

The Uses of PRAs

After the TMI accident, much emphasis was focused on the use of PRA techniques, since WASH-1400 had considered an accident sequence quite similar to what happened at TMI. As of 1983, four

Table 17.16. Proposed NRC Safety Goals

1. Individual members of the public should be provided a level of protection from the consequences of nuclear power plant accidents, such that no individual bears a significant additional risk to life and health.

2. Social risks to life and health from nuclear power plant accidents should be as low as reasonably achievable and should be comparable to or less than the risks of generating electricity by viable competing technologies.

The numerical guidelines consist of the following:

1. *Individual and Societal Mortality Risks*
   a. The risk to an individual or to the population in the vicinity of a nuclear power plant site of prompt fatalities that might result from reactor accidents should not exceed 0.1% of the sum of prompt fatality risks resulting from other accidents to which members of the U.S. population are generally exposed.
   b. The risk to an individual or to the population in the area near a nuclear power plant site of cancer fatalities that might result from reactor accidents should not exceed 0.1% of the sum of cancer fatality risks resulting from all other causes.
2. *Benefit-Cost Guideline.* The benefit of an incremental reduction of risk below the numerical guidelines for societal mortality risks should be compared with the associated costs on the basis of $1000 per man-rem averted.
3. *Plant Performance Guideline. Large-scale core melt:* The likelihood of a nuclear reactor accident that results in a large-scale core melt should normally be <1 in 10,000 per year of reactor operation.

Source: From F. J. Remick, *Trans. Am. Nuclear Soc.* **43,** 50 (1982).

major PRA studies on nuclear plants had been completed,† with 11 additional studies underway. Some of these studies were in response to the U.S. NRC Reactor Safety Study Methodology Applications Program (RSSMAP) and Interim Reliability Evaluation Program (IREP). RSSMAP was intended to study how reactor and containment design differences affected risk, while IREP emphasized accident sequences that dominate core melt and tried to standardize risk assessment procedures. The latter led to the development of the PRA Procedures Guide in 1982. Parallel to the NRC programs, many utilities in the United States have sponsored their own plant-specific studies. The results will provide guidance in designing systems (i.e., to help select components with lowest risk or highest reliability) and help analyze the safety of systems already built. Further, PRA is being applied to plant operations, helping select operating procedures that reduce the risks.

PRA techniques are also being used outside the United States with greater frequency. One notable example is the German Risk Study, commissioned by the German Ministry for Research and Technology. Phase A of the study, started in 1976 and now complete, largely used the methodology of the RSS. Phase B, still underway (as of 1984), is using advanced methodology and concentrates on some specific problems. The United Kingdom used PRA methodology for the hearing on their first PWR, the Sizewell B plant. Other countries are also making greater use of the techniques.

Safety Goals for Nuclear Power Plants

A difficult task in any risk analysis is deciding what indeed is a reasonable risk, and what constitutes adequate protection against the risk of nuclear accident. The answers to these questions are basic to any coherent regulatory process. In the United States, the NRC issued, in 1982, a proposed policy statement on the safety goals for nuclear power plants (NUREG-0880). These safety goals are summarized in Table 17.16. They are intended to provide a basis for regulatory rules in the United States. The safety goals are also meant to express the NRC's view to both the nuclear industry and the public as to how decisions over safety/cost can be resolved. Since no single parameter describes the entire set of safety requirements, NUREG-0880 specifies several performance criteria including core damage frequency, and individual and societal risk.

The NRC has long utilized probabilistic arguments in parallel with more deterministic criteria such as design basis events. As early as the mid-1960s, the AEC required utilities to consider low-probability events in siting inquiries and has accepted probabilistic arguments on some of these issues. In 1973, as part of its assessment of anticipated transients without scram, the AEC first

†Included were the RSS study on Surry Unit 1 and Peach Bottom Unit 2, the studies on the Limerick Generating Station, Zion Station, and Indian Point Units 2–3. The latter two were companion studies, and are sometimes collectively referred to as the Z/IP study.

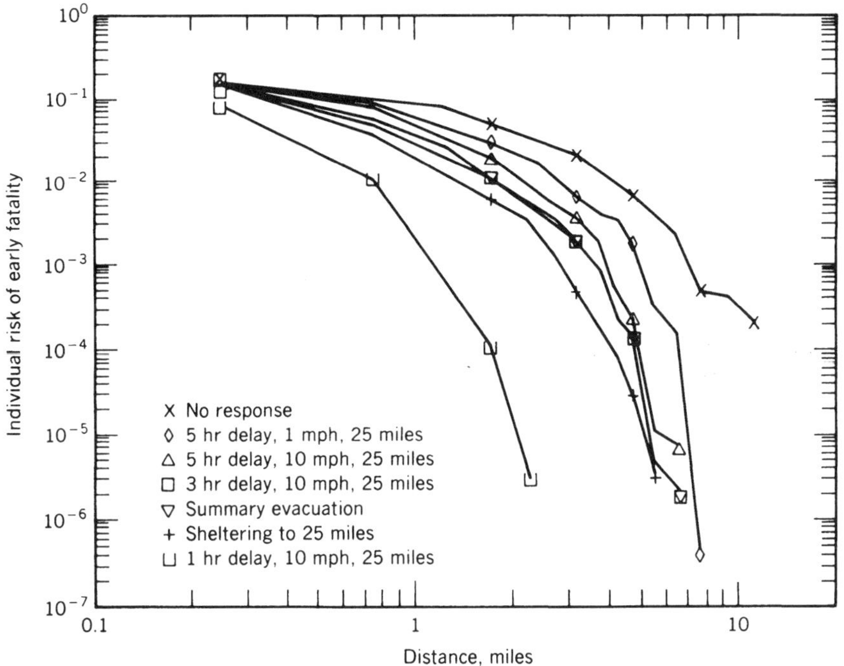

Figure 17.28. Fatality risk versus distance for six emergency response scenarios. (Courtesy S. Levine, NUS Corp.)

defined a safety goal that assumed a population of 1000 LWRs, and proposed that the frequency of a serious reactor accident should be less than 1 in 1000 per year. A serious accident was defined as one which leads to doses exceeding those in 10CFR100 guidelines.

17.12. EVACUATION PLANNING

If a reactor accident were to occur, those charged with the health and safety of the public would have to decide how to protect the public. Various factors would influence their decision, including the risks of evacuation, traffic accidents and psychic trauma brought on by the stresses of evacuation, relative to radiation risks. To model the effects of a given emergency response, detailed sheltering and evacuation models exist that consider the dynamics of radioactive plume dispersal and that of population movement. The results of one such calculation, based on the WASH-1400 release fractions, is given in Figure 17.28. It shows how various delay times, sheltering strategies, and evacuation rates will reduce risk.

The U.S. Environmental Protection Agency (EPA) Protection Action Guide currently establishes levels of 500 mrems whole body dose and 1500 mrems to the thyroid as "action" threshold doses (see Chapter 18). If projections indicate that these levels will be exceeded, then protective action should be considered. For core melt accidents, the off-site doses would probably exceed those specific in the Protective Action Guides only within a very limited area outside of a reactor site boundary. Only within this area would it appear that evacuation might be prudent to consider, although not necessarily more effective than sheltering in mitigating the radiation dose to the population. The time before such a threat would evolve is relatively long. However, if a threat were to materialize very early in an accident, sheltering would be the only real option. While evacuation plans must be developed, the decision to implement such a plan is based on actual conditions that exist at the time. One of the key parameters during a reactor accident is meteorological conditions. Every U.S. reactor is required to have a meteorological information system (see Figure 17.29) for emergency preparedness per NUREG-0654.

The relative merits of evacuation versus sheltering depend greatly on the particulars of a given accident. Parameters to be considered are severity, site location, meteorological conditions, and so on. Precise answers to the questions of whether to evacuate particular individuals, when to evacuate them, how far, and in which direction, are site- and accident-specific. Relatively simple procedures may be quite effective in mitigating the potential consequences of an accident in a

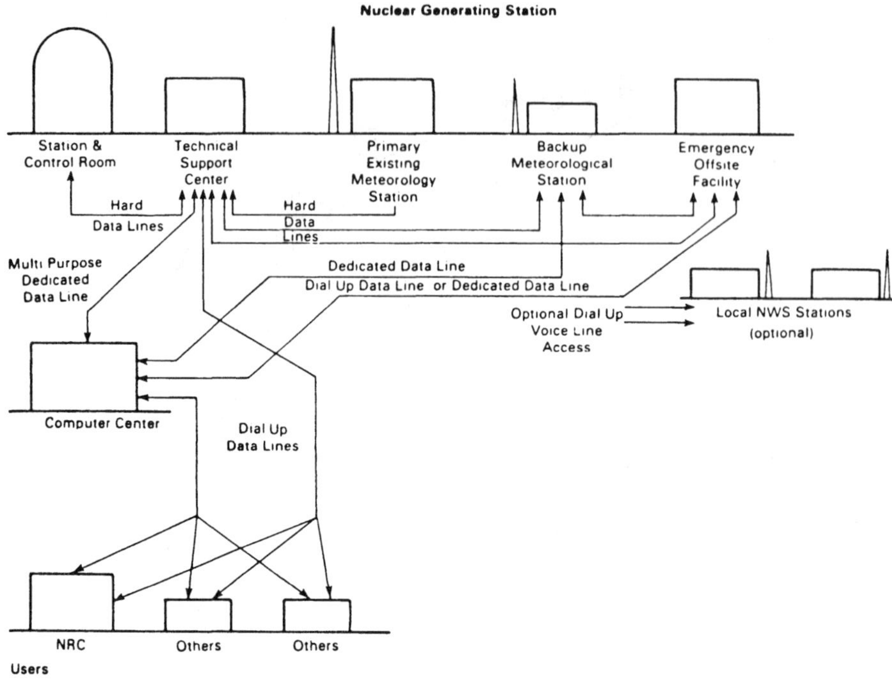

Figure 17.29. Schematic diagram of enhanced reliability meteorological information system. [From D. G. Smith et al., *Trans. Am. Nuclear Soc.* **39,** 121 (1981).]

nuclear facility. For example, closing the windows greatly reduces the potential inhalation dose. The concentration of noble gases is not as strongly reduced as the concentration of particulates by such measures, although factors of 2 or 3 are likely. Precise estimates depend on the ventilation rate. If the ventilation rate were high, however, due to the presence of windy meteorological conditions, such conditions would also considerably shorten the time of passage of any radioactive cloud that existed and rapidly disperse it.

The shielding ability of structures also offers substantial protection. A simple wood frame house reduces the dose rate from a passing cloud by a factor of 2. A masonry structure can give dose rate reductions up to a factor of 10 on the first floor, 50 or more for a person staying in the basement. These shielding factors are for gamma sources with mean energies close to 1 MeV. For sources containing primarily noble gases released a day or two after the accident, the actual shielding offered by such structures is considerably greater because of the much lower average energy of the radiation. In general, the radioisotopes emitting the most penetrating radiation decay quickest.

17.13. SAFETY RELATED OPERATING EXPERIENCE

In the United States, Licensee Event Reports (LERs) record abnormal events that have occurred in nuclear power plants. Over 2000 of these reports are filed with the NRC each year. They cover trivial to very serious events. Serious events, that is, potential accident precursors, are relatively rare (Table 17.17). The leading cause of concern is loss of the off-site power needed to operate safety systems.

Figure 17.30 shows the forced outages reported by PWRs in the United States. The average number of reactor protection system scrams was 9.3 per plant-year, based on 192 plant-years of commercial operation. About 77% of the scrams were attributed to systems and component failures, resulting in an average annual unavailability of 13%. In light of this data and the TMI-2 accident, the Advisory Committee on Reactor Safeguards (ACRS)† has recommended several new safety concepts for future plants. These are listed in Table 17.18. Foremost among these recommendations is improvement in a plant's ability to deal with extended loss-of-power situations.

†The ACRS advises the U.S. NRC on important matters related to nuclear safety.

Table 17.17. More Significant Potential Accident Sequence Precursors[a,b]

Events	Number of Occurrences
Pressurized Water Reactors	
Loss of off-site power	12
Safety-related power failure	5
Auxiliary feedwater failure	6
Safety/relief valve failure	6
Valve failure (other than safety/relief valves)	1
Reactor-coolant-pump seal failure	1
Steam generator tube break	1
Reactor-coolant-pump shaft failure	1
Incorrectly utilized instrumentation calibration signals	1
Boiling Water Reactors	
Loss of off-site power	5
Safety-related power failure	1
Loss of feedwater and failure of safety-related equipment	4
Failure of high-pressure coolant injection function	1
Major blowdowns or small-break loss-of-coolant accident	2
Failure of automatic depressurization system	3
Fire in instrumentation cable room	1
Plugged service water strainers	1

From NUREG/CR-2497.

[a]Data were compiled over an 11-yr period.
[b]Human error was involved in 36% of these events.

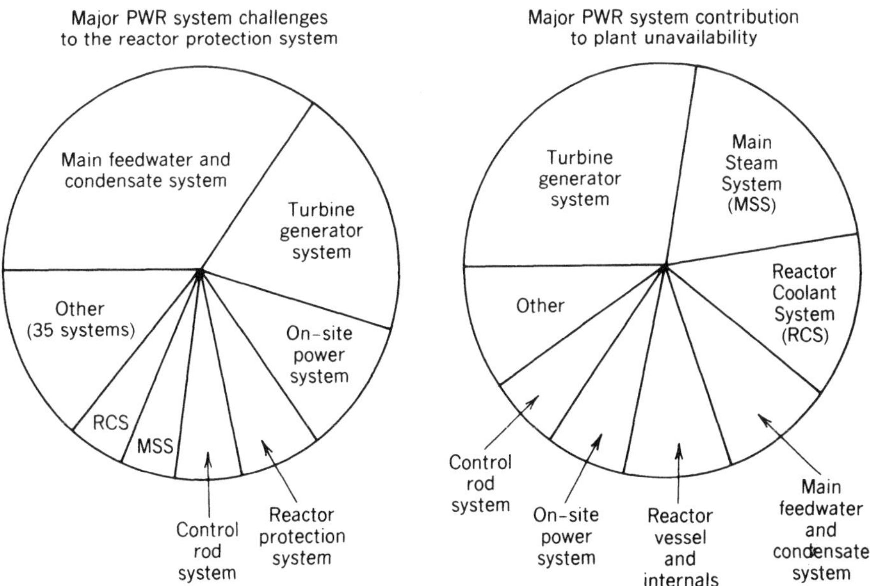

Figure 17.30. Forced outages and scrams in PWRs from inception of commercial operation to the end of 1978. [From DOE Report ALO-74 (1980).]

Table 17.18. New Safety Concepts for Future Reactor Designs

Improvements in the reliability of ac and dc power supplies and in the capability of the plant to withstand an extended loss of power.
Design features to mitigate accidents involving severe core damage or core melt.
The inclusion of consideration of industrial sabotage in design.
Design measures to improve control system reliability and control room functionability.
The incorporation of a bunkered, dedicated system for shutdown heat removal (or otherwise improved shutdown heat removal system) into the design.
The use of probabilistic methodology in design to ascertain the means and the need, if any, to go beyond the single-failure criterion.
The more effective use of separation to reduce the likelihood of certain common-mode failures.

Source: From M. S. Plesset, unpublished.

Loss of Off-site Power

The unlikely, but possible loss of ac power from both the off-site source and from the on-site source is referred to as a station blackout. In such an event, the capability to cool the reactor core would be dependent on the availability of systems that do not require ac power and on the ability to restore ac power in a timely manner. The concern is that a prolonged station blackout might result in a severe core-damaging accident.

Station blackout is an issue because there have been instances where a nuclear power plant became disconnected from all off-site power. The reliability of the on-site emergency diesel generators that are supposed to start up automatically in such an event has not always been as favorable as hoped for. The combination makes station blackout an important factor in any overall plant risk assessment.

At most plants, when the connection to off-site power is lost, the main turbine-generator is also lost as a source of plant power and the plant is dependent on the diesel generators for ac power. A few BWRs and PWRs have been supplied with sufficient turbine bypass-line and condenser capacities to make it possible to lose the plant connection to the outside grid without tripping the turbine and reactor. But most plants have only about a 40% turbine bypass capability. In practice, essentially all plants automatically trip the turbine and reactor on load loss, and many call for a manual scram as well.

There are a number of recent developments that are tending to diminish the consequences of a station blackout. All BWR plants have steam turbine-driven or diesel-driven high-pressure injection pumps, and most BWRs now have some means of routing water from the diesel-driven fire pump to the reactor. The ability of BWRs to depressurize the reactor helps to assure that water from the fire pump will enter the reactor. All PWR plants have, or are installing, steam-turbine-driven or diesel-driven auxiliary feedwater pumps.

The reliability of offsite power is highly plant-specific. Reliability is improved by having: (1) multiple interties, (2) strong interties, (3) other power plants nearby, (4) multiple switchyards, (5) good lightning protection, and so on. Experience has shown that nuclear power plants have an off-site power unreliability in the general range of 0.03 to 0.3 per year (they can expect a total loss of off-site power somewhere in the range of every 3 to 30 years depending on the above factors). The historical average for the United States had been thought to be about 0.12, representing a loss of offsite power about once every eight years per nuclear unit.

However, recent investigations have revealed that in reality, offsite power was actually available in a substantial fraction of these reported losses. Many plants start their emergency diesel generators automatically and only close onto their backup off-site source (manually) if the diesels fail to start. The availability of the backup off-site source had seldom been mentioned. It is known that the history of the past several years is favorable: There were only two losses of off-site power in 1982.

Experience shows that the probability of restoring at least one source of off-site power is good. A recent EPRI report on this subject (NP-2301) indicates the following recovery-time probabilities for offsite power:

Recovery takes longer than:	
	2 hours—28%
	4 hours—23%
	8 hours— 9%
	24 hours— 5%

It should be emphasized that the data base for these statistics is small. Individual plants may differ significantly from these values depending on the number, length, and strength of their transmission ties.

Like the reliability of offsite power, the probability that the required number of diesel-generator units will start on demand and keep running is highly plant-specific. Plants may have anywhere from two to four diesel generator sets (depending principally on the number of nuclear units and when the plant was built.) If it is a multiunit station, means usually exist also to switch one or more diesels to either unit. Moreover, temporary cables can be used to power one unit's house load from the diesels of the other unit.

Operating Experience Feedback

In most countries with nuclear power plants, an organization exists for systematically analyzing all significant incidents, for drawing lessons, and for taking timely corrective actions. The objectives of these organizations are: detecting precursor incidents of more severe accidents; assessing strong and weak points of the nuclear plants; and validating system reliability studies from operating experience. The screening process involves:

1. Events that do not require corrective actions. These are just filed.
2. Significant events that go through a rapid review to verify that the corrective actions proposed by the licensee are acceptable.
3. Incidents that are accident precursors, or are deemed to be rich in interesting lessons. These are submitted to an in-depth analysis.
4. Trends or pattern studies.

A typical content of an in-depth analysis is: incident sequence; consequences, actual and potential; causes; operator reaction; assessment of licensee proposed corrective actions; general lessons; and recommendations.

The mechanism for performing this type of analysis differs from country to country. In the United States, many of these functions are performed by the Nuclear Safety Analysis Center (NSAC), while others are performed by the Institute for Nuclear Power Operations (INPO). INPO also has a systematic training and evaluation program to continually upgrade the quality of plant operations.

17.14. THE SAFETY OF GAS-COOLED REACTORS

Gas-cooled reactors have inherent and design safety features that are significant and unique, requiring safety criteria that differ markedly from other reactor types. Many of these aspects have been already discussed in Chapter 13.

The coolant gas has the advantage of being a single-phase fluid; therefore, a sudden reduction of primary coolant system pressure cannot cause loss of all coolant or prevent coolant circulation because of change of phase. The use of gas as a coolant means that the core's reactivity is relatively insensitive to changes in coolant density, particularly so when helium is used. Control of the reactor is inherently easier than in reactors where the coolant functions as the moderator. Helium, used in HTGRs, is particularly desirable as a reactor coolant since it is chemically inert and noncorrosive, is chemically and radioactively stable, and has excellent heat transfer characteristics.

All major components for the primary coolant system, including the steam generators, are housed in a steel-lined PCRV. At maximum credible pressure, the prestressing elements of the PCRV are not stressed above levels experienced during their installation. As a result, sudden loss of coolant due to prestress failure is not credible. Since the entire primary coolant system is contained within the PCRV, external coolant piping, which might be subject to sudden rupture, is eliminated. The fact that the PCRV is in turn housed in a conventional reinforced concrete secondary containment building means that an extra safety dimension is provided.

Three ways of shutting down a gas reactor are: the control rods, gas injection (such as nitrogen), and boron bead injection. Heat can be removed from the system in several ways: via the coolant, through the decay heat system, or through the main steam generators. A postscram cooling system exists whose main function is to circulate sufficient gas to transfer heat from the fuel (and graphite) to the steam generators while providing the latter sufficient feedwater so that the heat can be transferred to the site's heat sink (river, ocean, etc.).

An important safety feature of a gas reactor is that, in the event of failure of forced circulation, natural circulation would prevent overheating of the core. This, combined with graphite's very large heat capacity, adds considerably to the inherent safety of gas reactors.

The high heat capacity of the large mass of graphite [about 3 million lb for a 3000 MW(th) HTGR] ensures that any core temperature transients resulting from reactivity insertions or interruptions in cooling will be slow and readily controllable. Moreover, graphite is ideally suited to high-temperature operation, since, unlike most materials, its strength increases at higher temperatures, reaching a maximum at about 4500°F, well above the reactor operating range. It retains usable strength at all conceivable accident temperatures.

Potential Accidents in Gas Reactors

Loss of external electrical power and loss of coolant pressure are severe accidents for some gas reactors because of their probability of occurrence and possible radioactive releases due to some fuel failure. A loss of external power shuts down the gas circulators, causing an automatic reactor scram to occur. To provide power for the plant in such an event, emergency diesel generators are provided. Should the diesels fail to start, however, the core could not be cooled by forced circulation, but natural circulation would be sufficient to keep the temperature of the fuel well below the allowable limit. Natural circulation flow would maintain fuel integrity by an ample margin.

Depressurization accidents involve a primary coolant system failure, the subsequent coolant gas release (He or CO_2), and a reduction in pressure. In these accidents, the coolant density would fall, necessitating an increased gas velocity through the fuel channels to keep temperatures within safe limits. For British AGR plants, which use clad fuel, the gas pressure may at some time during the transient fall below the cladding's internal pressure.† This leads to fuel failure and radioactivity release. To cope with a depressurization accident, the circulator speed would be increased above the normal postshutdown rate. This provides adequate cooling as the gas pressure falls. The emergency feedwater supply starts and additional gas is injected into the system to prevent air ingress. The latter is necessary to prevent a chemical reaction of the air with the graphite moderator, which would increase the heat to be removed.

Other possible accidents do not have consequences as serious as those already described. The accidents usually considered in a safety analysis for a gas reactor include: feedwater failure, main steam line failure, and water ingress into the primary coolant system. Certain other accidents are not credible, and therefore are not considered. One example is a major failure of the prestressed concrete pressure vessel, which is precluded by its design, construction, and amount of redundancy in the prestressing tendons.

17.15. LIQUID-METAL FAST BREEDER REACTORS

Breeder reactors have many safety aspects in common with LWRs, especially equipment reliability and balance of plant systems. They also differ in many respects. The main differences derive from the core configuration and the coolant used. In general, breeder reactors pose less off-site risk than an LWR would. The German Birkhofer Enquete (1982), for instance, estimated the risk of core destruction as 2×10^{-6}/yr.

A breeder reactor's core is significantly more compact than an LWR core of equal power rating. It is about the same diameter as an LWR core, but much shorter. The efficient sodium coolant properties allow a high power per unit core volume.‡ Because the core operates in the "fast neutron" part of the spectrum, the time between neutron birth and absorption is very short, about 10^{-6} sec or less.§ Hence, the core response to changes in reactivity is very rapid¶ once prompt-critical is reached. Since, however, reactors are not designed to operate in the prompt-critical regime, the short neutron lifetime is of concern only during criticality accidents. For reactivity changes within the delayed neutron regime, the transient behavior of fast and thermal reactors is similar.‖

In a criticality accident, a major mechanism limiting the peak power level is the Doppler effect. As the fuel heats up, the atoms' thermal motion widens the capture resonances that a neutron sees, in effect, changing the self-shielding and causing more neutrons to be absorbed without fission. This effect limits the power, terminating the excursion. (The resonances occur in a part of the neutron spectrum containing only a few neutrons, even in a large core. The geometry and materials

†This is not the case, of course, in ceramic HTGR fuel.

‡Up to 400 W/g of fuel, 10 times higher than for LWRs.

§That is, neutrons have undergone only a few scattering collisions before being absorbed by the fuel, while in a thermal system, several thousand scattering collisions are expected at very slow neutron speeds, resulting in long lifetimes (10^{-4} sec).

¶Like LWRs, control of breeder reactors relies on delayed neutrons. As long as the reactor requires these delayed neutrons to be critical, the power transients are slow and the reactor is easily controlled. The excess reactivity needed to become prompt-critical varies with the fissile isotopes in the fuel, so is different for a plutonium-fueled reactor. The delayed neutron fraction is 0.2% for ^{239}Pu, 2.2% in ^{232}U, 1.5% for ^{238}U, and 0.65% for ^{235}U.

‖Reactivity changes are expressed as a proportion of the delayed neutron fraction, for which the unit is the dollar. For small changes, each cent (100 cents = 1 dollar) of reactivity produces an immediate power change of 1% due to the prompt neutron increase. Reactivity insertions exceeding one dollar result in rapid transients.

in a LMFBR core determine the spectrum. Small LMFBR cores may have no Doppler effect of consequence.)

Another contributor to breeder reactor safety is its coolant. For LMFBRs, the coolant is sodium, a low vapor pressure, high boiling point liquid.† As a result of the low vapor pressure, sodium systems operate at a few tens of psi (a few bars). Therefore, pipe rupture is not a problem, since the system is essentially unpressurized, and the pressure loads on a containment building in the event of an accident would be small. The chemical reactivity of sodium reduces the fission product release. For example, any molecular iodine released from the fuel would combine with sodium to form NaI, a salt. Using sodium, however, leads to a positive void coefficient. (See Chapter 13 for a more detailed discussion of reactivity shutdown mechanisms.)

In an LMFBR, if the scram system fails while the coolant pumps are turned off, an accident could occur. In an LWR, such a loss of flow would reduce coolant density, ending the chain reaction. In an LMFBR, this would lead to an excursion. An LMFBR core is not in its most reactive geometry. As the sodium density decreases, the reactivity increases, an undesirable situation.‡ The larger the core, the bigger the positive void coefficient. It is less of a problem, however, with newer core designs. As more of the fertile blanket material (^{238}U) is brought inside the central regions,§ the core acts as if it has more edges; since the fertile fuel assemblies capture neutrons, this results in improved safety margins. The division of the fissile region into smaller regions separated by fertile regions decouples the neutronic behavior of the core. Core design is a trade-off between breeding performance and the various safety considerations involved. Figure 17.31 shows that by rearrangement of the mixed-oxide fuel and the blanket material within the core, it is possible to reduce the magnitude of the positive sodium void reactivity change while maintaining or improving the breeding gain. Another advantage of such a rearrangement is that the temporal and spatial incoherence of the sodium voiding increases, thereby reducing the magnitude of the reactivity ramp rate.

After reactivity excursions, the next most serious LMFBR accident involves a sodium fire (see Chapter 13). Also of concern is the possibility that a leak in a steam generator will bring water in contact with sodium. This would lead to a propagation of the leak,¶ a rapid pressure buildup, and a violent reaction. To mitigate such an occurrence, steam generators are designed to handle the pressure surge and to prevent the rapid propagation of the leak site. Since hydrogen is produced in a sodium/water reactor, the coolant is monitored for H_2 gas as an early indication of a leak. Leaks less than 0.1 mm can be found in this manner.

17.16. FUTURE IMPROVEMENTS TO LWR SAFETY

Design changes have been proposed at various times to improve LWR safety. Some of these safety concepts are listed in Table 17.19. They mostly increase the reactor water inventory, thereby increasing the system's thermal inertia, or improve the heat removal systems needed to keep the core cool. The latter concentrates on auxiliary feedwater and safety injection system reliability in PWRs and the residual heat removal systems for BWRs.

A recent Swedish modification of the basic LWR design addresses this problem. The Swedes call the concept PIUS (Process Inherent Ultimate Safety). The stated purpose of this relatively small (1600-MWt) reactor is to create an intrinsically safe light-water power reactor that will simplify plant design by eliminating need for add-on engineering safety systems, will make smaller unit output economic, will provide for combined heat and power schemes, will improve safety under adverse conditions (e.g., in Third World countries), and will alleviate public concerns by relying "on the laws of nature rather than failure prone equipment and human intervention." The design philosophy is to make the plant independent of any failure from mechanical or electric components, insensitive to human error, and possessive of a high degree of immunity to destructive human intervention. The achievement criteria require that the core must remain submerged at all times and that core power level must not rise above the cooling capacity of the contained water.

This design puts all of the major components, along with the piping that connects them, inside a single, large, prestressed concrete vessel filled with borated water. A relatively small core is positioned near the bottom. There are no control rods. The steam generator is located within the vessel. An internal enclosure system and a submerged pump provide pressurization and forced circulation through the core and the steam generator. If the forced circulation stops, the reaction stops, and the contained water cools the core with natural circulation. The long-term nuclear fuel cooling is provided in a fashion that is not dependent on switches and pumps. Instead, the cooling comes from natural circulation of a large pool of water contained inside the concrete vessel itself.

†Gas-cooled fast reactors use He or CO_2; see the last section for their safety aspects.
‡This is mitigated by other effects, such as the Doppler coefficient and thermal expansion of the core. As long as the overall reactivity change with temperature or coolant void is negative, the reactor is safe.
§This is referred to as a heterogeneous core.
¶Due to caustic stress corrosion cracking in steel.

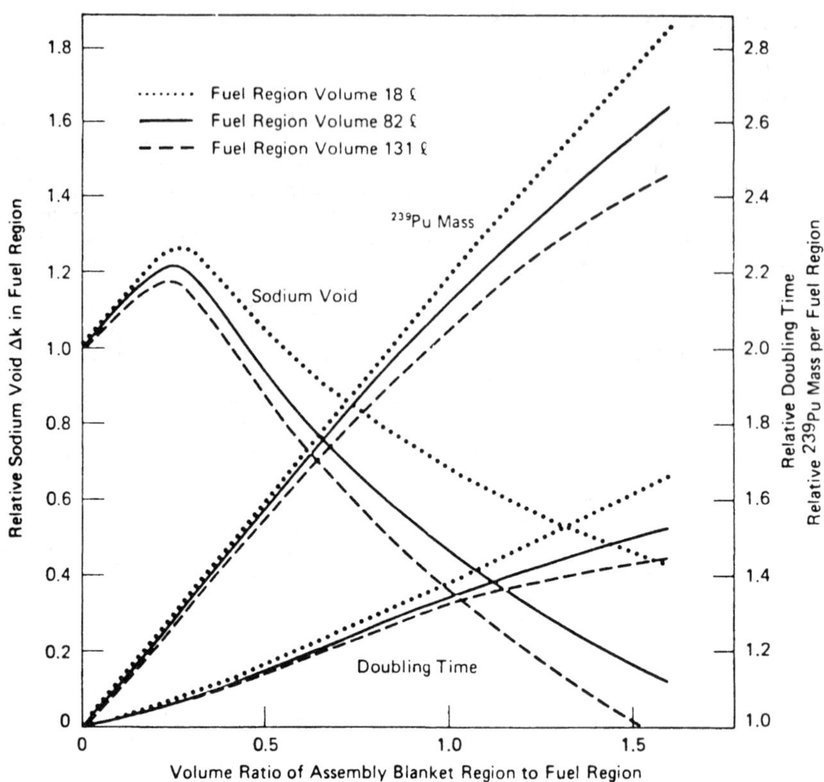

Figure 17.31. Variation of LMFBR physical parameters with volume ratio. [From B. R. Sehgal et al., *Nuclear Technology* **57,** 149 (1982).]

Table 17.19. Alternate Shutdown Decay Heat Removal Concepts

Concepts Proposed by	Concept Name	Objectives of the Concept
Nucledyne Engineering Corporation	Alternate Decay Heat Removal System	To provide auxiliary feedwater through a passive steam jet injection; quench steam flow from steam generator, lowering secondary loop pressure
	Engineered Safety System for LOCA	To feed water inventory to the primary reactor coolant system by passive steam jet injection at high pressure and by gravitational feed from deluge tank at low pressure
	Main Steam and Feedwater System	To provide main feedwater through the quench tank
	Postaccident Decay Heat Removal System	To transfer heat from containment through a natural-circulation loop to an outside cooling pond
Sandia National Laboratories	Passive Makeup or Circulation Pump	To provide auxiliary feedwater to steam generator through a passive steam jet injection
	High-Pressure Residual Heat Removal System	To provide additional feed-and-bleed to the primary loop at high pressure
	Passive Feedwater System	To provide feedwater to the steam generator by passive gravitational feed
	BWR Add-on Decay Heat Removal System	To provide in a BWR an additional circulation path for cooling at high or low pressure by means of an add-on pump and a heat exchanger

Source: From L. S. Tong, *Nuclear Safety* **23,** 127 (1982).

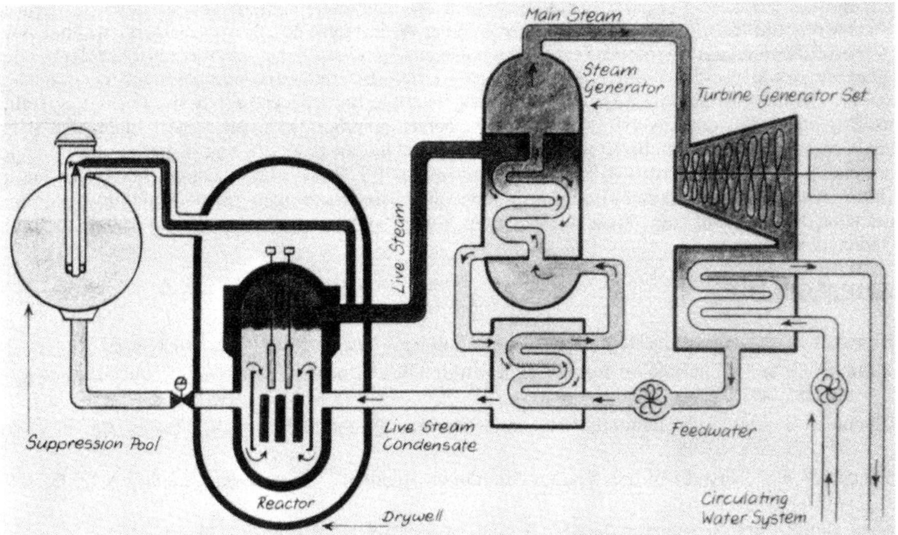

Figure 17.32. KWU design for a 200/400 MWe nuclear power plant. (Courtesy KWU.)

This "passive" approach eliminates the need for conventional electrical and mechanical "active" safety systems and the reliance on operators to prevent an accident. It can provide cooling for about two weeks without external emergency cooling systems, without the use of electricity, and without operation action.

Based on its design concept, the plant should be able to tolerate operator error and multiple failures of almost all the active systems. Other designs based on similar ideas are under consideration in the United States, Japan, and elsewhere. Figure 17.32 shows one such design by KWU in Germany, where simplicity, reliability, and uncomplicated safety technology are the characteristic features of the plant. The heart of the plant is an indirect-cycle BWR with natural circulation and thus no pumps are required for coolant recirculation. The containment is of the pressure suppression type, that is, it consists of a drywell and a pressure suppression pool which are connected by vent pipes. The pressure suppression pool is located at a higher elevation than the reactor and contains the water which in the unlikely event of a loss-of-coolant accident flows into the reactor pressure vessel by gravity and ensures emergency cooling of the core. If implemented, such designs would lead to an increase in the safety of what appears to be an already safe plant design.

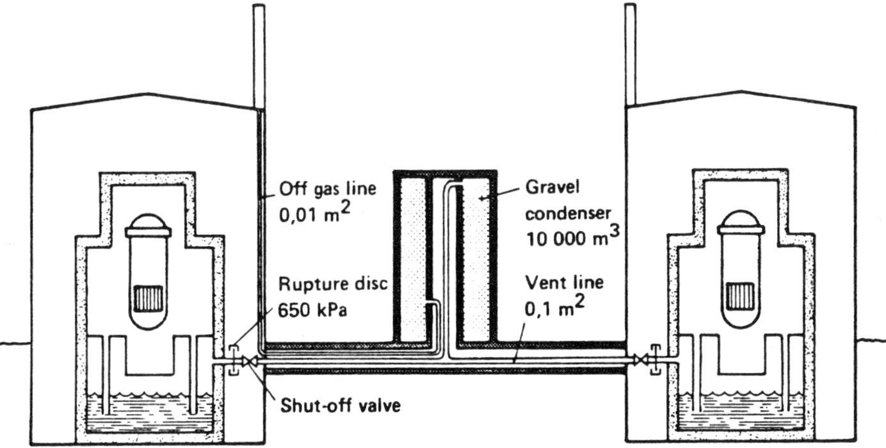

Figure 17.33. FILTRA vented–filtered plant arrangement. (Courtesy Swedish State Power Board.)

Another innovation is a RCB modification using a filtered, vented system shown in Figure 17.33. It would use a reinforced concrete chamber 40 m high and 20 m in diameter to filter out 99.9% of the radioactive isotopes (excluding noble gases) released in a major reactor accident. The chamber would be filled with crushed granite to absorb radioactive particles and to condense steam. The first installation of such a system will be at the Barsebaeck unit in Sweden. The system itself is somewhat controversial in the reactor safety community; some experts claim that it is unnecessary, while others believe that it may actually increase off-site risk if, by increasing containment system complexity, it reduces overall reliability. There is no question, however, that a Filtra system would attenuate fission products, since it relies on many of the same physical phenomena (water scrubbing, large surface area, etc.) that are effective inside the plant to limit radioactive releases.

BIBLIOGRAPHY

Breen, R. J., "Defense-in-Depth Approach to Safety," *Nuclear Safety* **22,** 561 (1981).

Bunz, H., et al., "The Role of Aerosol Behavior in LWR Core Melt Accidents," *Nuclear Technology* **53,** 141 (1981).

Cheng, H. S., and D. J. Diamond, "Effects of Thermal-Hydraulic Feedback," *Trans. Am. Nuclear Soc.* **33,** 474 (1979).

Cohen, B. L., "Physics of the Reactor Meltdown Accident," *Trans. Am. Nuclear Soc.* **38,** 459 (1981).

Core Meltdown Experimental Review, Sandia Report No. NUREG-0205, March 1977.

DuPont, R. L., "The Nuclear Power Phobia," *Business Week,* Sept. 7, 1981.

"EPRI Nuclear Fuel-Cycle Accident Risk Assessment," *Nuclear Safety* **22,** 300 (1981).

Erdmann, R. C., *Risk Methodology,* EPRI Report NP-79-LD (1979).

Herring, W. C., Chairman, National Academy of Sciences, "Risks Associated with Nuclear Power," *Nuclear Safety* **20,** 664 (1979).

Levenson, M., and F. Rahn, "The Realistic Consequences of Nuclear Accidents," *Nuclear Technology* **53,** 99 (1981).

Lewis, E. E., *Nuclear Power Reactor Safety,* Wiley, New York, 1977.

Lewis, H. W., "The Safety of Fission Reactors," *Scientific American* **242,** 53 (1980).

Maxey, M. N., "Richer is Safer," *The Public Interest* (June 1980).

Mendoza, Z. T., et al., "Radiation Releases from the SL-1 Accident," *Nuclear Technology* **53,** 155 (1981).

Morewitz, H. A., "Fission Product Behavior Following Degraded Core Accidents," *Nuclear Technology* **53,** 120 (1981).

"Nuclear Safety After TMI," *EPRI Journal Special Issue* (June 1980).

"Reactor Safety," *Los Alamos Science Special Issue* **2,** (1982).

Reactor Safety Study, WASH-1400, October (1975).

Smith, R. R., "Radiological Consequences of BORAX/SPERT/SNAPTRAN Experiments," *Nuclear Technology* **53,** 147 (1981).

Starr, C., and C. Whipple, "Coping with Nuclear Power Risks," *Nuclear Safety* **23,** 1 (1982).

Thomas, G. R., and E. L. Zebroski, *Detection and Control of Potential Core Damage,* EPRI Report WS-81-201, pp. 1–59 (1981).

Technical Basis for Estimating Fission Product Behavior During LWR Accidents, NUREG-0772 (1981). Also NUREG-0956 (1984).

Tong, L. S., "Issues Concerned with Future LWR Designs," *Nuclear Safety* **23,** 127 (1982).

CHAPTER 18
NUCLEAR POWER REGULATION

18.1. THE REGULATORY PROCESS

United States' nuclear power plants and their fuel cycle infrastructure are governed by laws enacted by Congress, and carried out by the Nuclear Regulatory Commission. The NRC evolved from the old Atomic Energy Commission, which in 1954 was given the regulatory authority from Congress to protect the public from radiological hazards and to license all facilities using radioactive materials. Since the AEC had the dual objective of fostering the evolution of nuclear technology and providing for public safety, its licensing reviews with industry were often informal and subjective. During the 1960s, nuclear power became economically competitive with fossil fuel power. This was followed by a rapid scale-up of nuclear plants, both in size and number of plants ordered. The sudden and large increase of nuclear capacity on order, led to the need for a more formal and objective review process for licensing. About this time, the Congress passed a large number of environmental laws, one of the most significant being the National Environmental Protection Act (1969), and the number of institutions involved in power plant regulation increased (Figures 18.1 and 18.2).

In the late 1960s the nuclear industry grew rapidly, but outside the industry there was a growing dissatisfaction with the AEC's dual objective of both promoting and regulating nuclear technology. This was seen by many as a conflict of interest. In 1971, a federal district court ruled that the AEC's environmental standards were not consistent with the National Environmental Protection Act (NEPA). This court case was known as the Calvert Cliffs decision, and it reduced public confidence in the AEC's ability to regulate nuclear power. Hence, the Energy Reorganization Act of 1974 abolished the AEC, and divided its research and licensing responsibilities between ERDA (Energy Research and Development Administration) and the NRC (Nuclear Regulatory Commission). The NRC was given the responsibility for regulating and licensing all aspects of nuclear energy, and for carrying out inspections to ensure compliance with nuclear regulation. Figure 18.3 depicts the current structure of the NRC, including the realignment of April 1981, wherein the office of Nuclear Regulatory Research and the Office of Standards Development have been consolidated into a newly reorganized Office of Nuclear Regulatory Research.

At the top of the NRC's organization are the five commissioners (commission) who are appointed by the president, confirmed by the Senate, and serve a 5-yr term. From among the commissioners, the president appoints a chairperson. The commission and the NRC staff are independent of other executive departments and agencies. Under the commission is the Executive Director for Operations (EDO) who has responsibility for the day-to-day functions of the NRC.

The regulatory staff, under the EDO, is organized to carry out the legislative and policy mandates of the NRC and is divided into four offices (Figure 18.3) as follows:

1. Nuclear Regulatory Research.
2. Nuclear Material Safety and Standards.
3. Inspection and Enforcement.
4. Nuclear Reactor Regulation.

Each of these offices has various divisions under it, each charged with specific responsibilities. The Office of Nuclear Reactor Regulation (NRR), whose functions cover the topic of this chapter, has the following responsibilities:

1. Perform licensing functions associated with the construction and operation of nuclear reactors and with the receipt, possession, ownership, and use of special nuclear and by-product material used at reactor facilities.

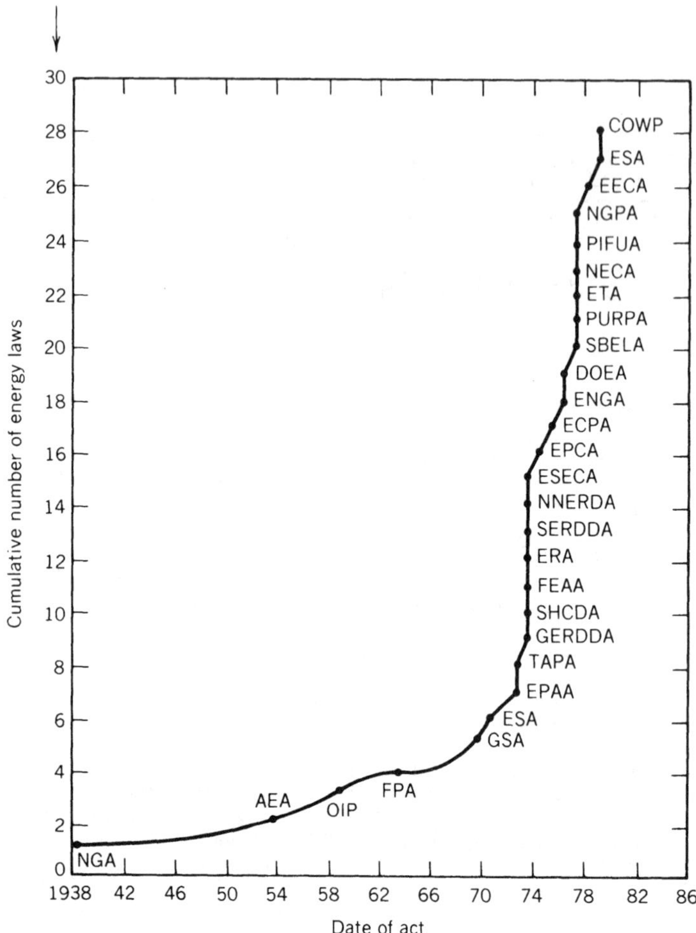

Figure 18.1. United States federal energy legislation from 1938 to 1980. [From *Power Engineering* **5**, 5 (May 1981). Permission obtained from Fred Olds, senior editor.]

2. Review applications and issue licenses for reactor facilities.
3. Evaluate the health, safety, and environmental aspects of facilities and sites.
4. Develop and administer regulations.
5. License reactor operators.
6. Provide assistance to other agencies in matters involving reactors or critical facilities exempt from licensing.
7. Analyze reactor design concepts.
8. Evaluate methods of transporting nuclear materials and radioactive wastes on reactor sites.
9. Monitor and test operating reactors, recommending upgrading of facilities and modification of regulations as appropriate.

In addition to the NRR, an independent Advisory Committee on Reactor Safeguards (ACRS), a three-person Atomic Safety and Licensing Board (ASLB), and an Atomic Safety and Licensing Appeal Board (ASLAB) may also become involved in the licensing process.

The Atomic Safety and Licensing Boards (ASLB) are empaneled to conduct public hearings and make decisions with respect to granting, suspending, revoking, or amending any NRC authorized license. Each three-person board generally consists of an attorney and two technical members (with knowledge of reactor safety and environmental impacts, respectively). Separate Atomic

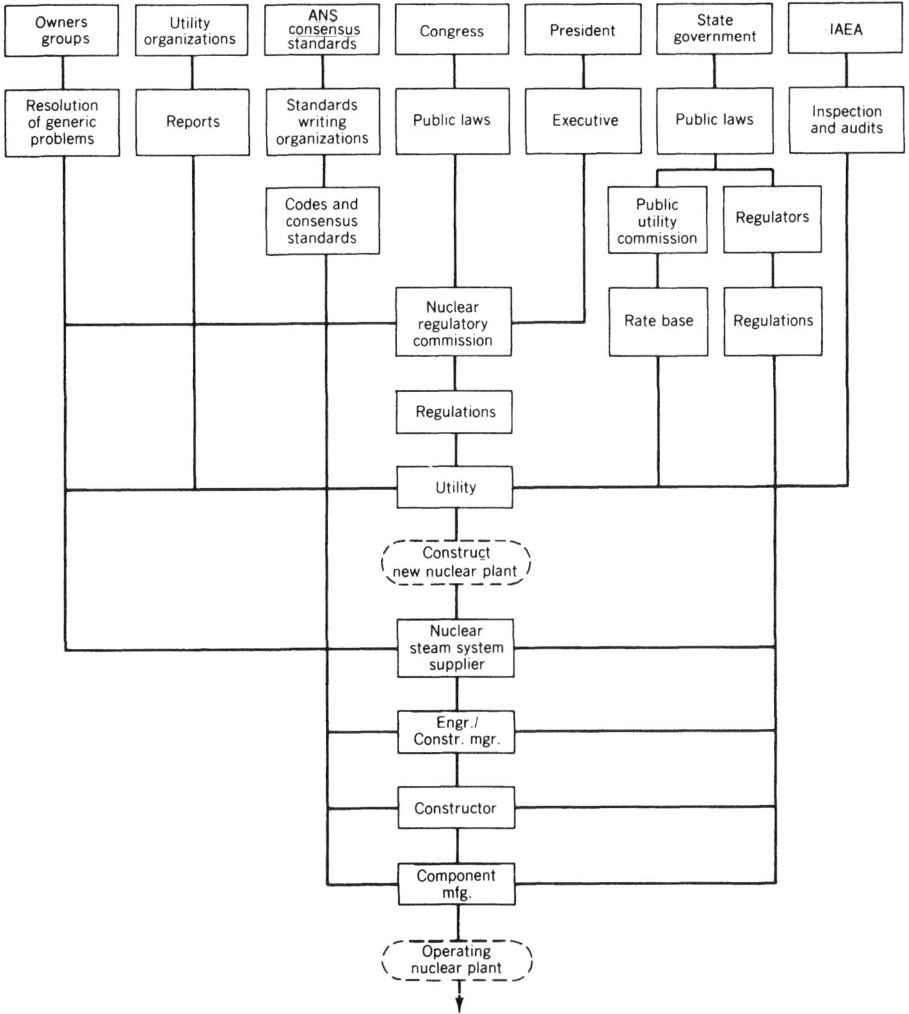

Figure 18.2. Contributing organizations to regulations and standards.

Safety and Licensing Appeal Boards (ASLAB) are similarly constituted for the purpose of handling appeals of ASLB decisions.

The Nuclear Regulatory Commission's function is to set standards for radiological safety, environmental protection, and antitrust conformity which the applicant must satisfy to obtain a license, and to ensure the applicant's subsequent compliance with those standards through audit-type inspections and other enforcement activities. The commission must coordinate its activities with other federal agencies which dictate environmental and health standards that the licensee must meet, and with state and local governments which have regulatory oversight for nonradiological matters in plant siting, construction, and operation. It is, of course, clear that although the NRC has plenary regulatory responsibility on all matters of radiological health and safety, the primary responsibility for the safe design, construction, and operation of a nuclear power plant ultimately rests with the operating utility.

The authority of the NRC is established by Title 10 of the Code of Federal Regulations (CFR). Title 10 covers the entire field of energy; chapter one defines the NRC and sets forth general policy and procedures. The NRC chapter, more than 500 pages long, is divided into 200 parts, which define the conditions under which nuclear power plants can be built and operated. In particular, part 50 (10CFR50) is concerned with the "Licensing of Production and Utilization Facilities." One

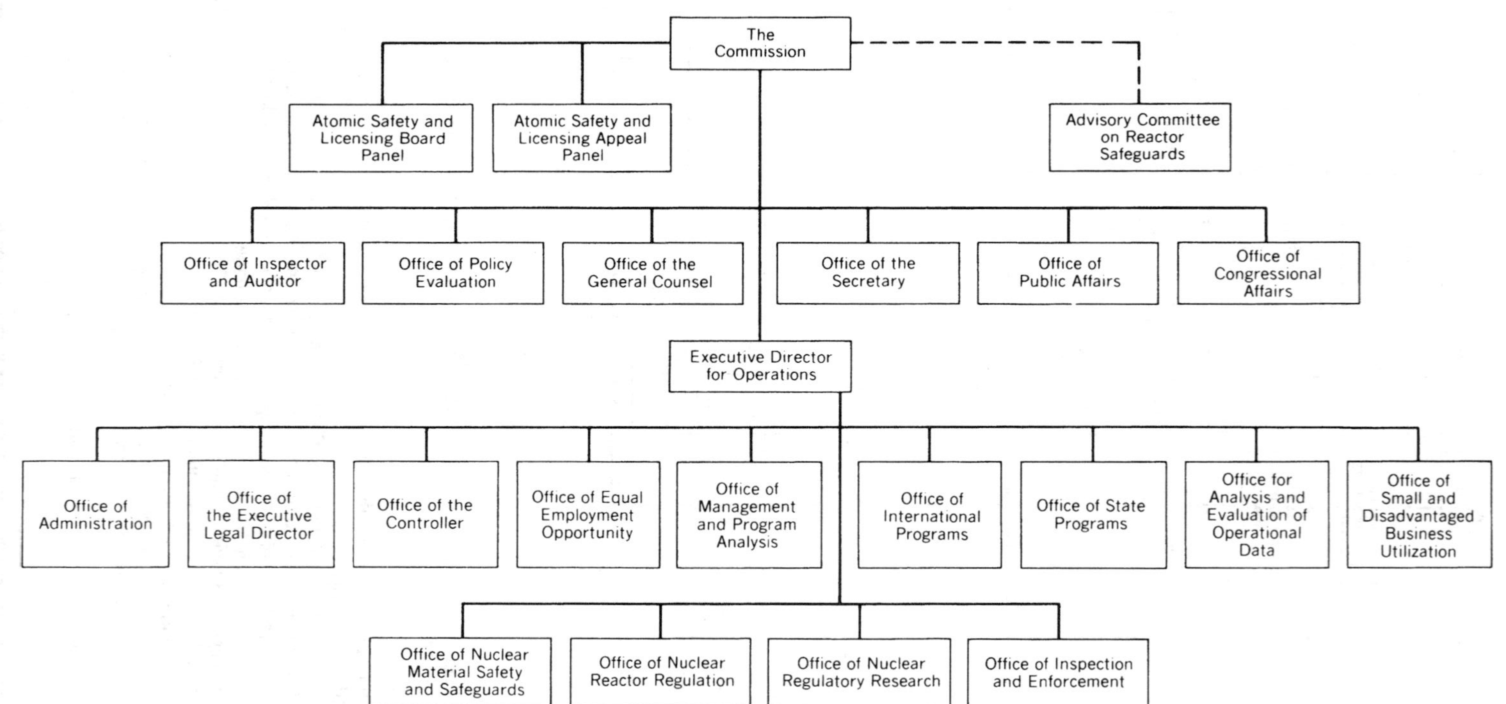

Figure 18.3. U.S. Nuclear Regulatory Commission organization chart.

of the most important provisions of 10CFR50, from the point of view of nuclear power plant construction, is the following:

> *50.10(b) No person shall begin the construction of a production or utilization facility on a site on which the facility is to be operated until a construction permit has been issued. As used in this paragraph, the term "construction" shall be deemed to include pouring the foundation for, or the installation of, any portion of the permanent facility on the site, but does not include: (1) site exploration, site excavation, preparation of the site for construction of the facility and construction of roadways, railroad spurs and transmission lines; (2) procurement or manufacture of components of the facility; and (3) construction of non-nuclear facilities (such as turbine buildings) and temporary buildings. . . .*

The 200 parts are often supplemented by regulatory guides intended to clarify regulatory interpretations and help the prospective operator satisfy the regulations. The regulatory guides suggest approaches to overcoming technical and procedural obstacles, or propose alternative solutions. However, the alternative solutions can be quite complicated and are thus generally avoided by industry.

Many of the regulations and their numerous appendixes are often revised after NRC rulemaking hearings. The NRC's regulations are a mixture of specifics and generalities which the license seeker must meet by submitting to the NRC a specific set of descriptions, systems, drawings, models, and response predictions. From these, the NRC can judge the impact on public safety and rule on the license application.

18.2. THE LICENSING PROCESS

The NRC uses a two-step licensing approach, involving a safety evaluation and mandatory hearing prior to the issuance of a construction permit, and another complete safety evaluation and a nonmandatory hearing prior to the issuance of an operating license. This two-step process requires issuance of a construction permit before major work can begin on a nuclear facility, and thereafter, the granting of an operating license before the unit can actually begin producing power with nuclear fuel. A schematic of the overall licensing process is shown in Figure 18.4.

An applicant must submit information to the NRC at each stage of licensing proceedings, as required. If construction is completed in accordance with this previously issued permit and the completed plant meets NRC standards, an operating license will be issued.

A regulatory reform proposal submitted in 1982 to Congress by the Department of Energy would move toward a one-step licensing approach with prior approval of power plant sites and standardized plant designs. The licensing review and hearing process would then address only site specific issues related to modifications of the plant design required by local conditions as well as the basic issues of need for power and utility capabilities in undertaking a nuclear power project. Licensing reform issues are discussed in a later section of this chapter.

Construction Permit (CP)

According to the Atomic Energy Act of 1954, construction of a nuclear power plant may not begin until a CP (or a Limited Work Authorization) has been issued by the NRC. The CP application to the NRC is a two-part process. First, the applicant must prepare an environmental report. This report must contain sufficient data on the proposed site and its environmental effects, and it must also show that alternative sites and power sources have been evaluated and considered. The NRC then evaluates the report and prepares its own environmental statement. The purpose of this document is to evaluate the potential environmental impact of the proposed plant, as well as to provide comparisons between the benefits to be derived and the possible impact to the environment. After completion of this review, a Draft Environmental Statement (DES) is issued. The DES is circulated for review and comments by the appropriate federal, state, and local agencies as well as by individuals and organizations representing the public. After receipt of all comments and resolution of any outstanding issues, a Final Environmental Statement (FES) is issued.

In addition, an analysis is made of the utility's technical and financial qualification to construct and operate the plant. The commission's review of technical qualifications involves an analysis of the utility's organizational structure, including the depth of its engineering and nuclear expertise. The financial analysis constitutes an effort to determine if the utility can afford to safely construct the plant, operate it, and decommission it at the end of its useful life.

The Atomic Energy Act also requires that antitrust aspects of a nuclear power plant license application must be considered in the licensing process. The antitrust information submitted by the applicant is sent to the attorney general for his advice on whether activities under the proposed license would create or maintain a situation inconsistent with the antitrust laws. In any event, the

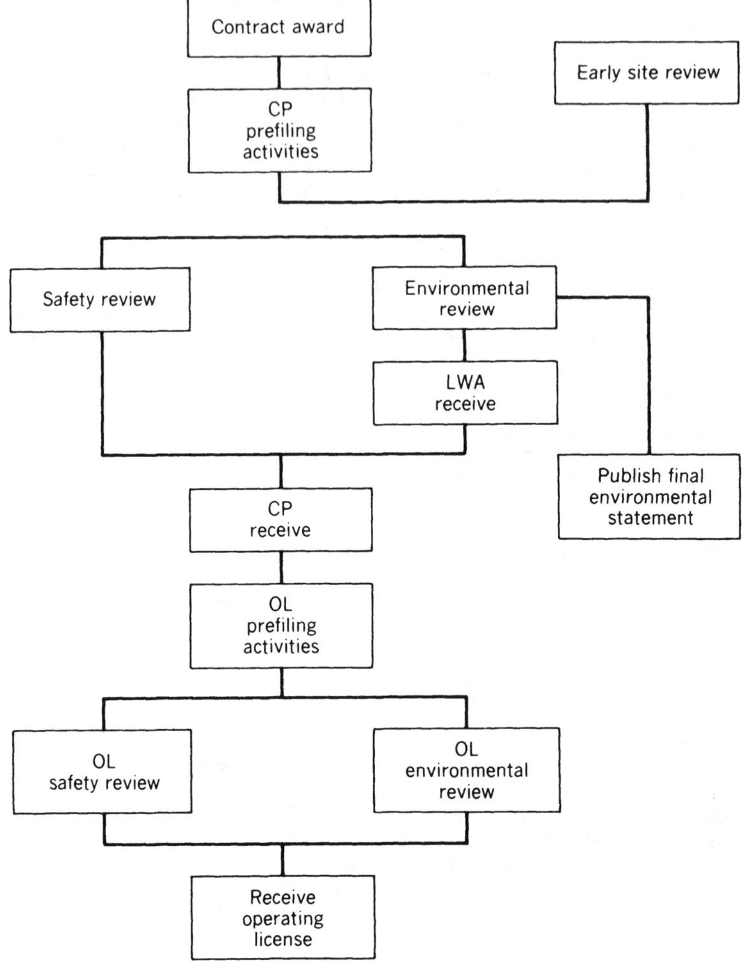

Figure 18.4. Licensing process overview.

NRC must make a finding on antitrust matters in each case where the issue is raised. Antitrust hearings are held separately from hearings on environmental and safety matters.

After a waiting period and a review, conferences, and hearings, the NRC will issue their environmental statement and a public hearing will be conducted by the ASLB. Both the applicant (usually a single utility or a lead utility of a consortium) and the NRC must be present at the public hearing. The applicant is expected to be knowledgeable and able to answer all questions raised, although utility personnel may be aided at the hearings by nuclear system suppliers, architect/engineers, and consultants. After the hearings are completed, the ASLB issues its conclusion, and, if affirmative, the NRC will issue a Limited Work Authorization (LWA) which permits groundbreaking. The regulations provide for the authorization of two types of LWA. Under one type, the applicant may be authorized to begin site preparation work, and carry out installation of temporary construction support facilities, excavation, construction of service facilities, or certain other construction not subject to the quality assurance requirements. Under the second type of LWA, the applicant may be authorized to install structural foundations. Any LWA may be granted only after the hearing board has made all of the National Environmental Policy Act (NEPA) findings required by 10CFR Part 51 for the issuance of a construction permit and has determined that there is reasonable assurance that the proposed site is a suitable location, from a radiological health and safety standpoint, for a nuclear power reactor of the general size and type proposed. The second type of LWA may be granted if, in addition to the findings described above, the hearing board determines that there are no unresolved safety issues relating to the work to be authorized.

The second part of the construction permit application requires the applicant to prepare a Preliminary Safety Analysis Report (PSAR). The PSAR must contain information on the site and its suitability for the proposed unit; a summary of the facility itself, including safety considerations; preliminary design information related to the NRC's General Design Criteria; the Quality Assurance Program needed to meet NRC established requirements; an assessment of the risks of the plant's operation to the public; identification of additional research into safety issues necessary before the plant can be granted an operating license; an emergency plan to cope with potential emergencies; and the technical and financial qualification of the utility to build and operate the facility.

The NRC staff reviews the PSAR and either dockets it or requests more information. During the staff's PSAR review, the applicant is required to provide such additional information as is needed to complete the evaluation. The principal features of the staff's review can be summarized as follows:

1. A review is made of the population density and use characteristics of the site environs as well as the physical characteristics of the site, including seismology, meteorology, geology, and hydrology, to determine whether these characteristics have been evaluated adequately and have been given appropriate consideration in the plant design.
2. A review is performed of the facility design and of programs for fabrication, construction, and testing of the plant structures, systems, and components important to safety to determine that they are in accord with the current regulations, regulatory guides, and other requirements, and that any departures from these requirements have been identified and justified.
3. Evaluations are made of the response of the facility to various anticipated operating transients and to a broad spectrum of design basis accidents. The potential consequences of these design basis accidents are then evaluated conservatively to determine whether the calculated potential offsite doses that might result, in the very unlikely event of their occurrence, would not exceed the guidelines for site acceptability given in 10CFR Part 100.
4. A review is made of the applicant's plans for the conduct of plant operations including the organizational structure, the qualifications of operating and technical support personnel, the measures taken for industrial security, and the planning for emergency actions to be taken in the unlikely event of an accident that might affect the general public. An important aspect of this review includes an assessment of the applicant's programs for quality assurance and quality control to assure compliance with the commission's requirements.
5. Evaluations are made of the design of the systems provided to control the radiological effluents from the plant, to determine if these systems can control the release of radioactive wastes from the station within the limits specified by the regulations. Moreover, the evaluation ensures that the applicant will operate the facility in such a manner as to reduce radioactive releases to levels that are as low as are reasonably achievable.

When the evaluation of the application progresses to the point where the staff concludes that acceptable criteria, preliminary design information, and financial information are adequately documented in the application, a safety evaluation report is prepared. This report represents a summary of the evaluation of the application by the staff relative to the anticipated effect of the proposed facility on the public health and safety. After the applicant and the NRC have each submitted their own safety reports, another hearing is conducted, this one by the Advisory Committee on Reactor Safeguards, an independent technical group within the NRC.

The ACRS is a statutory independent group of experts in fields relevant to reactor safety, selected by the NRC for advice in reactor safety matters. It was established by a 1957 act of Congress which mandates the ACRS to conduct independent safety reviews for all power reactor license applications. In addition, the ACRS advises the commission regarding hazards of proposed or existing nuclear facilities and the adequacy of proposed reactor safety standards. Although the ACRS reports to the commission, it is not a part of the NRC. The committee's independent analysis of the safety of each proposed plant is recorded in a written letter to the NRC chairman. The ACRS conducts a separate review of the two safety reports and then submits a report of its own to the NRC. It is for the NRC staff, intervenors, or, in some cases, the Atomic Safety Licensing Board to raise any safety issues regarding the application which might be identified in the advisory committee's report.

The NRC and ACRS reports are distributed, and a public hearing is held near the proposed plant site. At the hearing the applicant must present and justify all aspects of its proposal. The Safety Evaluation Report, its supplements, and the Final Environmental Statement are offered as evidence by the staff at the public hearing(s). The hearing(s) may be a combined safety and environmental hearing, or separate hearings can take place even if the application is not split. After the hearings are completed, the ASLB will issue its conclusion based on the evidence submitted. The difference between uncontested and contested construction permit hearings is significant. In an uncontested hearing, the ASLB does not conduct a detailed review of the application; it only

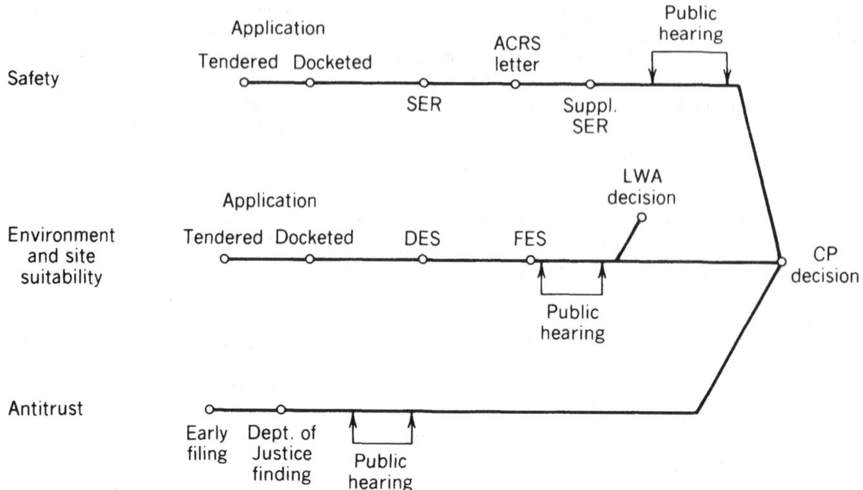

Figure 18.5. Parallel tracks in construction permit review process. *Key:* SER—safety evaluation report. DES—draft environmental statement. FES—final environmental statement. ACRS—Advisory Committee on Reactor Safeguards. LWA—limited work authorization.

decides generally whether the staff's review of the applicant's proposal is adequate. In a contested proceeding, by contrast, the ASLB must resolve the specific contentions raised by the parties concerning the application, although it has limited authority to consider other matters not put in issue by the parties. The NRC may then issue a construction permit. The total time from filing to construction permit averages 3 to 4 yr. No new construction permits have been issued in the United States following the Three Mile Island plant accident, and thus current estimates of this licensing lead-time are somewhat academic. With the granting of the construction permit, the applicant assumes the responsibility of informing the NRC of any deficiencies it finds in the design or construction of the plant or in any breakdown in the Quality Assurance Program. Any change in the "principal architectural and engineering criteria" must be authorized by amendment to the construction permit, and an application for such an amendment must satisfy the same procedural requirements and standards described above. A schematic representation of the CP licensing process is shown in Figure 18.5.

Operating License (OL)

When construction of the plant is nearing completion, the applicant must prepare another environmental report and a Final Safety Analysis Report (FSAR) in order to apply for an operating license. The purpose of the second environmental report is to evaluate any possible changes the construction of the nuclear plant has produced, and the possible effects on the environment. The same general sequence of reviews and public hearings follow this second report; eventually, the ASLB must grant or withhold its approval.

Likewise, the FSAR follows the same general procedures as the PSAR. The FSAR sets forth the pertinent details on the final design of the facility, including final containment design, design of the nuclear core, and waste-handling system. The FSAR also supplies plans for operation and procedures for coping with emergencies. The staff again prepares a Safety Evaluation Report (re: the operating license) and, as during the construction permit stage, the ACRS again makes an independent evaluation and presents its advice to the commission by letter. This second Safety Evaluation Report and its supplements, the ACRS meeting, and its letter to the commission are available to or may be attended by the public. Although a public hearing on the FSAR is not mandatory, the NRC must allow for one if the public so desires. At the completion of the environmental and safety hearings, the ASLB will advise the NRC, and the NRC may then issue an operating license for the nuclear plant.

The procedural steps required for obtaining an OL are shown in Figure 18.6. The standards used by the NRC in determining whether to grant a construction permit or an operating license are different. The standards for issuing a construction permit provide that the permit can be issued even without all of the technical information that will eventually be necessary for an operating license if "the principal architectural and engineering criteria" have been described; further infor-

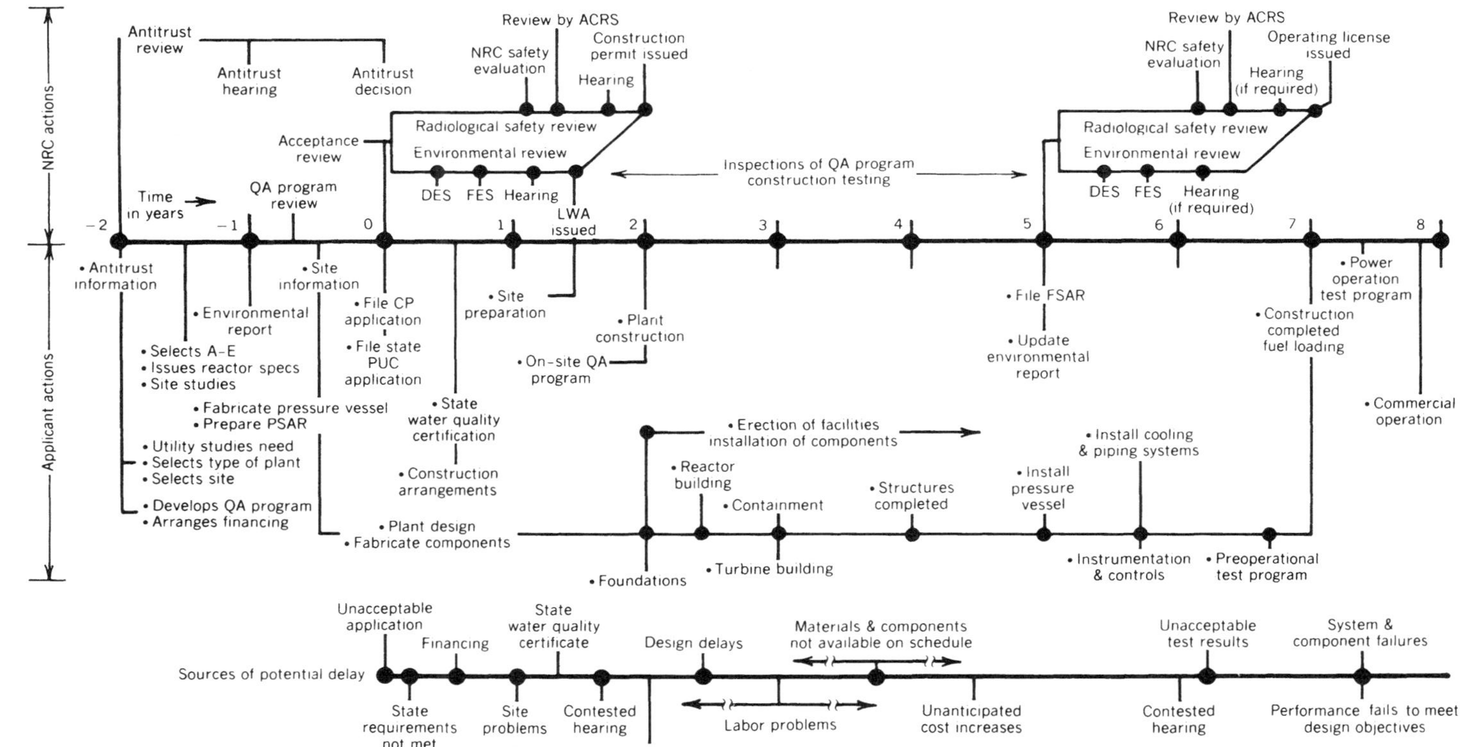

Figure 18.6. Nuclear power plant licensing process (operating license). *Key:* A–E—architect engineer. QA—quality assurance. CP—construction permit. PUC—Public Utility Commission. DES—draft environmental statement. FES—final environmental statement. LWA—limited work authorization.

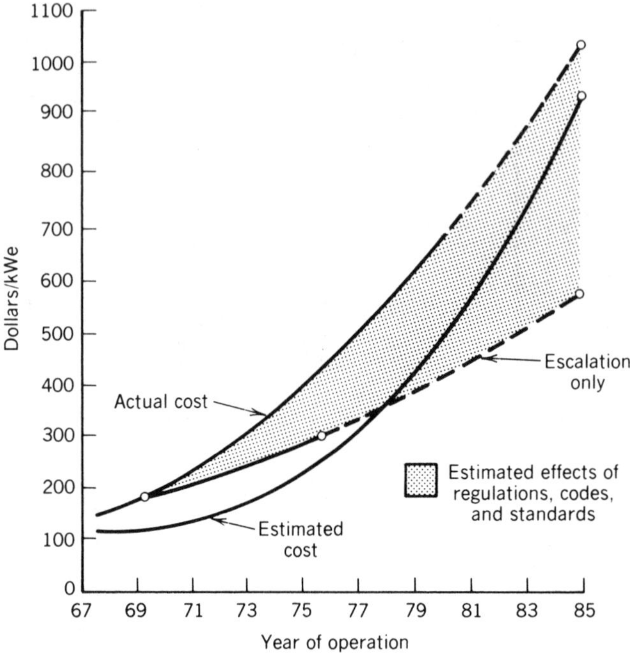

Figure 18.7. Effect of regulations, codes, and standards on nuclear power costs.

mation will eventually be supplied; research into safety issues is promised; and there is "reasonable assurance" that all safety considerations will be resolved before completion of construction, and that the proposed nuclear plant "can be constructed and operated at the proposed location without undue risk to the health and safety of the public."

There are built-in limitations in "converting" a construction permit to an operating license. For example, issuance of a construction permit normally does not indicate approval of safety systems unless such approval has specifically been requested. NRC regulations provide, however, that the Final Safety Analysis Report must be submitted before an OL can be granted, and the OL is not granted unless the NRC is satisfied that the safety systems are adequate. An OL will be issued if the plant was constructed in conformity with the construction permit application, the Atomic Energy Act, and the commission's rules and regulations; if it will operate in conformity with all of the above; and, finally, if there is reasonable assurance that the licensee's activities will not endanger the health and safety of the public. The applicant also must show his technical and financial qualification to operate the nuclear facility and must demonstrate that granting the license will not be "inimical to the common defense and security."

During the 1970s the added number of regulations, reports, reviews, and public hearings have lengthened substantially the period between the perception of a need for a nuclear power plant and its commercial operation date. This length of time is now about 12 yr; in the 1960s it was about 5 yr. The added expense to meet all the regulations, together with increases in construction costs and inflation, has been a major factor in escalating the unit capacity cost of a nuclear plant. By 1978 this cost was approaching 10 times what it was in 1969. The effects of the various codes and regulations on nuclear plant capital costs have been quantified, as seen in Figure 18.7. The increasing labor requirements associated with nuclear projects design and supervision are shown in Table 18.1. Additional cost increments related to backfitting expenditures (direct costs), and engineering person-hours requirements (indirect costs) are further discussed in Chapter 19.

Reporting

The operating license is good for an initial period of 40 yr from the date the construction permit was issued. However, the NRC may revoke, suspend, or amend the license at any time during the 40-yr period. The licensee is also subject to compliance with future rules and regulations which might be promulgated, and the license is conditioned upon having operators at the controls who are licensed by the NRC. Just as the *design* of the plant system has to meet certain codes and standards adopted

Table 18.1. Annual Increase in Labor Requirements for Design Supervision and Construction of Coal-Fired and Nuclear Power Plants

	%/yr Increase over Inflation (1978–1982)	
Category	Coal Plant	Nuclear Plant
Craft labor costs	3	15
Home office engineering costs	8	17
Field office engineering and services costs	16	33

by the NRC, so must *performance* of those systems meet adopted codes and standards. Further, new technical specifications, rules, and regulations and directives can modify the operation of any specific unit.

When the operator is finally issued a license to run a nuclear plant, it must keep the plant within the maximum power level and technical specifications prescribed in the license. Any deviations from these license specifications must be reported immediately to the NRC. These reports, called Licensee Event Reports, are applied to systems, components, and procedural breakdowns connected with safety. Operators who fail to report such events face severe fines and jail sentences.

Also subject to the reporting regulation are all primary and secondary suppliers of equipment and services to the nuclear plant. Regulation 10CFR21 states that both the licensee and its plant suppliers must report immediately to the NRC any hardware or software condition that may result in a lessening of protection to public health and safety. The regulation also requires that the licensee and its suppliers enact procedures to assure such reporting and that both the regulation and the method of reporting be posted and made accessible. Regulation 10CFR21, though, leaves unclear how far safety liability extends to manufacturers and suppliers of equipment for nuclear plants. The difficulty of complying with the reporting regulation and the risk of liability has, together with the projected size of the market, limited the number of nuclear plant suppliers.

The NRC attempts to ensure compliance with the standards it has set for the design, construction, and operation of the plant through inspection and enforcement. NRC regulations place a duty on the applicant to retain and make certain information available to the NRC Office of Inspection and Enforcement (IE). Regional inspection offices conduct announced and unannounced visits to plants to ensure compliance with license, the related technical specifications, the Atomic Energy Act, and the promulgated rules and regulations thereunder. All plants also may have "resident" IE inspectors. Finally, when requested, the holder of a construction permit or an operating license must also undertake studies and make reports to the NRC.

Enforcement of these provisions is provided for in both the Atomic Energy Act and in NRC regulations. Sanctions include revocation, suspension, or modification of a license, and the commission is also authorized to seek injunctions in the federal courts and to impose civil penalties for violation of license requirements. In appropriate cases, the directors of the Office of Nuclear Reactor Regulation (NRR) and Inspection and Enforcement (IE) have the authority to require immediate corrective action, subject to the right of a licensee to challenge it later.

The NRC imposes substantial responsibilities on a utility when it becomes an applicant for a license or a licensee. Conditions on design, construction, and operation are imposed in the license or construction permit itself, as well as through the technical specifications. In spite of the formidable regulatory structure described above, the fact remains that the primary responsibility for the actual design, construction, and operation of a nuclear power plant rests with the applicant—the utility that seeks to sell the power to its customers. Finally, the utility has the responsibility to properly decommission the nuclear facility. This includes filing and following an NRC-approved decommissioning plan and terminating a license only with NRC approval.

18.3. NUCLEAR REGULATION BY OTHER ORGANIZATIONS

Additional authority in various aspects of nuclear power regulation rests with federal and state agencies other than the NRC. These organizations are also directly responsible for the licensing procedures of fossil fuel fired power plants, discussed below.

Federal Agencies

Other federal agencies with statutory or regulatory authority over some aspects of nuclear power plants include: the Environmental Protection Agency, Army Corps of Engineers, National Oceanic and Atmospheric Administration, Department of Energy, Department of the Interior, U.S. Geological Survey, Department of Agriculture, Department of Housing and Urban Development, Advisory Council on Historic Preservation, Department of Transportation, Federal Aviation Agency, Department of Defense, Council on Environmental Quality, River Basin Commissions, and the Great Lakes Basin Commission. Almost all of these agencies review and comment on the Environmental Impact Statements for each plant, and administer specific issues under their jurisdiction.

Federal Emergency Management Agency (FEMA)

After TMI, the president shifted the lead in off-site radiological emergency activities from NRC to FEMA, which codified its procedures regarding state and local plans into 44CFR350. This, and the agency's Memorandum of Understanding (MOU) with NRC, define the duties of the two regarding evacuations and emergency procedures. FEMA is charged with reviewing site emergency planning and preparedness, in cooperation with state and local authorities. This is referred to as the FEMA 350 review process. FEMA prepares an evaluation on off-site preparedness at nuclear units, which is then provided to the NRC and Atomic Safety and Licensing Boards. In addition, FEMA requires a utility to sponsor an evacuation exercise every two years to test emergency procedures. It is developing a computerized system, called the Exercise and Simulation Facility (ESF), to analyze radiological releases, estimate dose to population, and predict evacuation dynamics.

State Regulatory Responsibilities and Agencies

A wide range of state legislation and regulations affect the licensing, construction, and operation of nuclear power plants. During the 1970s, the states have moved to a more thorough consideration of need for power and choice of technologies, environmental policy, and energy facility siting. In addition, several states (e.g., California, Oregon, Vermont, Wisconsin) have legislated special restrictions on the construction of nuclear power plants on radiological health and safety grounds, or until waste disposal issues are resolved. In most cases, required state approvals must be obtained before the NRC can take any action on a permit or license application.

Primary responsibility for regulating electric utilities has been vested for many years in state Public Utility Commissions (PUCs). The PUCs approve investments for new facilities deemed necessary to supply service, and issue a Certificate of Public Convenience and Necessity (CPCN), which certifies that when the facility goes into service the capitalized cost will be added to the rate base.

Although the procedures for determining need for power and issuing a CPCN vary from state to state, no utility will proceed beyond engineering to construction without a CPCN or an equivalent guarantee that it may earn a return on this investment. Furthermore, it is unlikely that a utility would apply to the NRC for a construction permit without already having obtained a CPCN or at least being confident of receiving it. Thus, in effect, the states have a veto over any facility on economic or need for power grounds.

Traditionally the states have been responsible for land use, and many states have comprehensive land use planning programs. The comprehensive land and water use planning processes for coastal areas were developed and implemented by coastal states under the Coastal Zone Management Act. Once a Coastal Zone Management (CZM) program is approved by the federal government, the state can have considerable leverage over federal activities that might affect land and water use within coastal zones. Thus a utility must obtain a state verification of consistency with its CZM program before the NRC can issue a permit or license. Federally approved state CZM programs also must include certain planning elements that will affect the siting of nuclear facilities, including a boundary delineation of the coastal zone, definitions of permissible land and water uses, and guidelines for the relative priority of uses.

The state water management agencies also must approve a proposed nuclear power plant, including issues related to both the quality and quantity of cooling water supply and the effluent discharge limitations. The states have programs to review water withdrawals from streams and structures placed in water, and issue Water Quality Certificates under the Clean Water Act. The state certification of water quality includes any effluent limitations, monitoring, or other requirements necessary to assure that the applicant will comply with applicable federal and state water quality standards, and these conditions become part of the NRC permit or license. In addition, if a nuclear facility will discharge into navigable waters, it must obtain a National Pollutant Discharge Elimination System (NPDES) permit. The Clean Water Act establishes special procedures for NPDES permits dealing with thermal discharges.

Twenty-five states currently have siting laws. These might include "multistop" regulation by a variety of state agencies, each concerned with a separate aspect of the construction or operation of a plant; state licensing through a "one-stop" agency charged with determining the suitability of all aspects of a particular site on behalf of all state regulatory bodies; or state ownership of the site, with a single agency empowered to administer the terms of lease with the utility or consortium that owns the plant.

18.4. REGULATORY PRACTICE IN OTHER COUNTRIES

A comparison of regulatory organizations and practices between the United States and other nuclear power nations is now presented. After discussing in some detail the regulatory policies of seven countries, a summary evaluation of the differing practices is made. Such comparison is useful in highlighting potential improvements to the current U.S. regulatory climate, based on the applicable good examples of foreign licensing experience.

Canada

The licensing process in Canada is the responsibility of the Atomic Energy Control Board (AECB), but because of obvious provincial concerns in many aspects such as health and environment, the AECB has evolved a "joint regulatory process" that enables all concerned federal and provincial agencies, ministries, and departments to participate. The AECB acts as the lead agency. When issued, licenses may include a reference to requirements to meet provincial regulations as long as they are compatible with federal requirements.

The Canadian licensing process involves three major phases, which include: site acceptance, construction approval, and operating license.

The AECB receives an application for site approval which is accompanied by a Site Evaluation Report. This report contains information on the proposed power plant to be constructed, the meteorology, hydrology, seismology, and geology of the site and on the demographic data around the site. The information obtained at this phase should enable the AECB to determine the acceptability of the proposed site. At this point, the applicant is required by the AECB to publicly announce his intention to construct the plant and to conduct a program which permits the expression of public opinion. The AECB also requires that the applicant prepare an environmental impact assessment and submit it to appropriate provincial or federal agencies for review and acceptance. Following the satisfactory recommendation of the AECB staff and provincial authorities, site acceptance is issued.

Subsequent to site acceptance, application for a construction license (see Figure 18.8) is made. Primary documentation supporting the application consists of a Preliminary Safety Report (which includes site characteristics, design description, and preliminary safety analyses), a Quality Assurance Program, and preliminary plans for generation (including staffing and training plans).

The AECB staff reviews the supporting documents and, if satisfied, recommends the board issue a construction license. This review normally includes consultations with the provincial authorities and the applicant so as to obtain any additional information which may be required. Near the completion of construction, the applicant files an application for an operating license. The application is supported by documents which include a Final Safety Report (with as-built design description and completed Safety Analyses), Commissioning Reports, Operating Policies and Principles, Radiation Protection Procedures, and Operating Procedures and Emergency Plans. Following the satisfactory recommendations of the AECB staff, an operating license is issued.

It is generally considered that Canadian licensing practices have less of an impact on design and construction when compared to licensing practices in the United States. The intervenor and appeals process used in the United States to revise site and design requirements or potentially block or delay construction or operation of nuclear plants once governmental approval has been given, does not exist in Canada.

As to operation of nuclear plants in Canada, nothing comparable to the I&E Bulletins used in the United States to address newly identified safety issues for operating plants, has been developed. To a considerably greater extent in Canada than in the United States, the responsibility for nuclear power plant safety in construction and operations appears to be placed on the utility operator rather than on federal governmental agencies.

Federal Republic of Germany (FRG)

The FRG licensing procedure differs from other national regulatory processes in that each ruling that is handed down by the FRG Licensing Authority is essentially a final decision. The licensing process consists then of obtaining a series of partial licenses, each of which deals with a specific aspect of the plant. The generalized licensing procedure is schematically shown in Figure 18.9. The first Partial License (PL) is particularly important because it deals with obtaining approval for both the site and the overall plant concept. In addition, the first PL normally includes a request for partial construction of building structures.

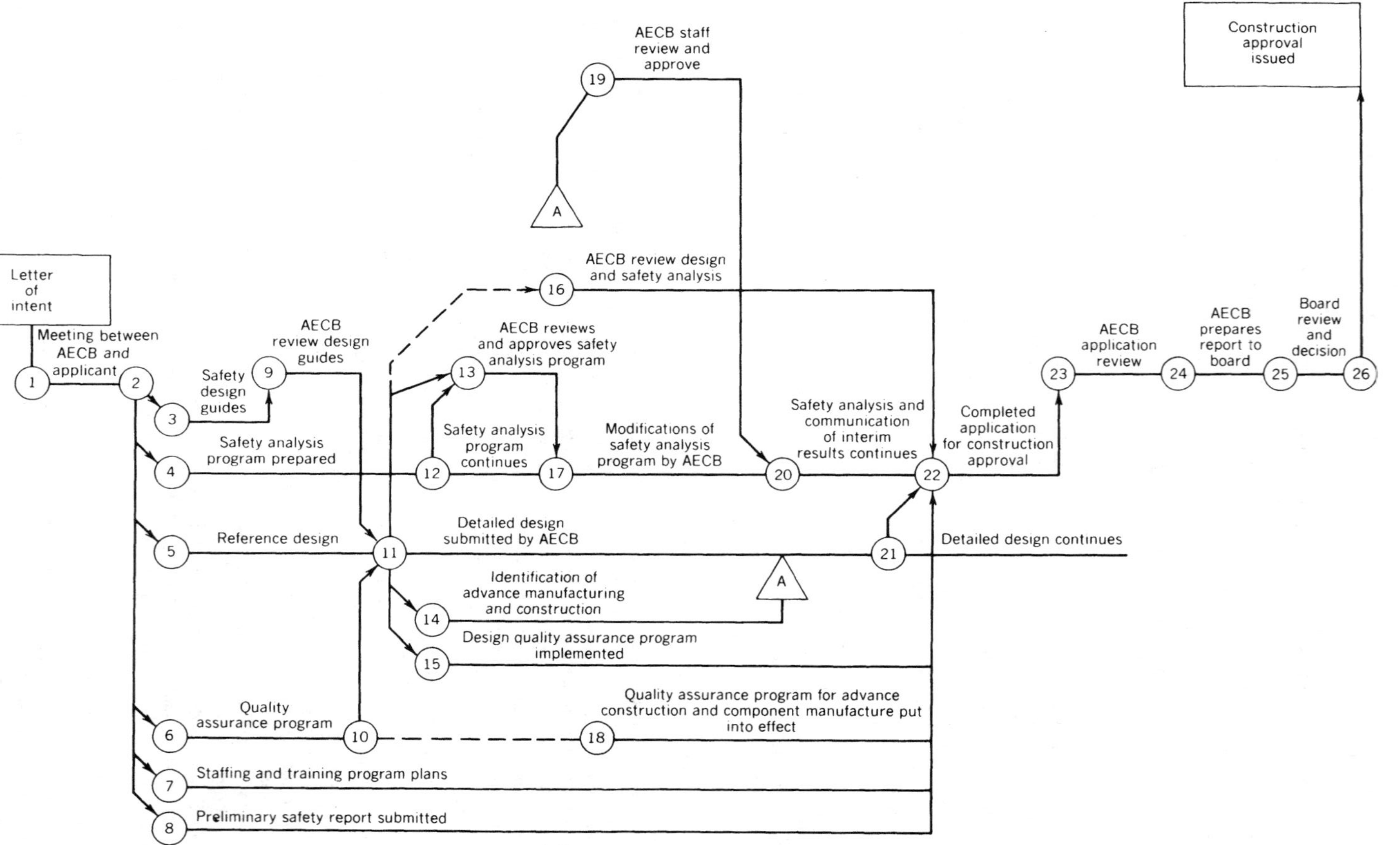

Figure 18.8. Canada: schematic of activities leading to construction license.

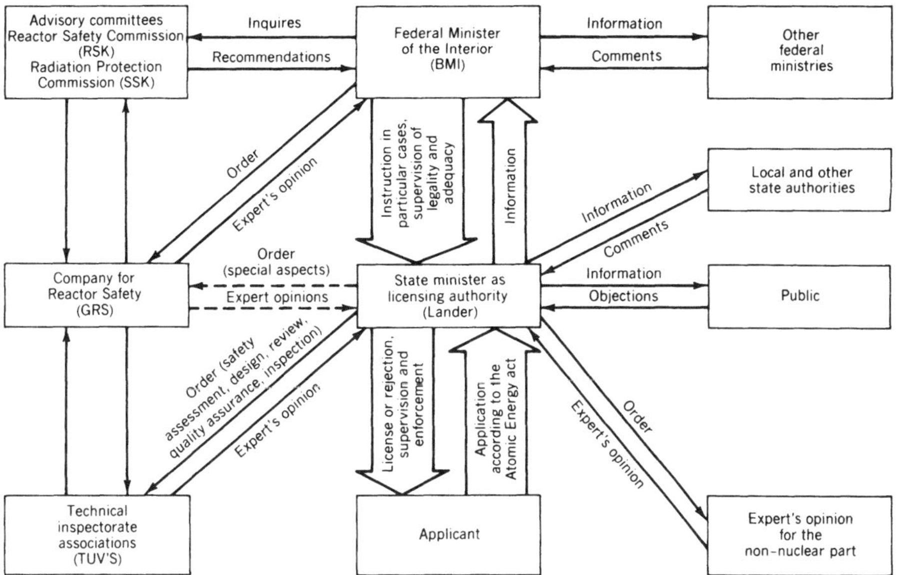

Figure 18.9. Federal Republic of Germany: participants, their responsibilities and interactions in the licensing procedure.

All application documents have to be submitted to the State Licensing Authority. The original application must be accompanied by the following documents:

1. Explanatory plans, drawings and descriptions.
2. A safety report describing the installation and its operation, specifying all hazards involved as well as the planned safety measures.
3. Data enabling the examination of the reliability and expert knowledge of the persons responsible for the erection of the installation and the management and control of its operation.
4. Data concerning the physical protection of the installation and its operation.
5. Proposals concerning the financial security for third party liability for nuclear-related damage.

Once the application is accepted as complete by the licensing authority, it contracts with technical experts to conduct an evaluation, consults other affected state authorities, and involves the Federal Ministry of the Interior (BMI). The BMI has been assigned the responsibility for the overall supervision of the states' licensing procedures by the federal government. At the same time as the state's licensing authority is conducting its review, the BMI coordinates reviews at the federal level (involving all federal ministries concerned), the Reactor Safety Commission (RSK), the Commission on Radiation Protection (SSK), and others, if further studies or opinions are necessary.

When granting a license, the authority must either expressly reject interventions or impose corresponding conditions upon the licensee. The decision has to be served on the applicant as well as the intervenors who may challenge it in the administrative courts. The administrative courts concerned are state courts and the federal administrative court which have jurisdiction over many areas other than nuclear power. The FRG appears to be one of the few countries where nuclear power plant licensing questions may be under the jurisdiction of the regular judiciary. Furthermore, the judiciary in question is at both the state and the federal level.

The receipt of the first PL allows the utility to begin work on foundations and lower structures as specified in the particular application. Even more important, it provides formal approval of the site and the design concept, which allows the utility to proceed forward into the next PL with some confidence that the rules will not be changed on what has already been approved.

A positive decision implies that the licensing authority cannot reject an approved site or design concept later on. In fact, the licensing authorities impose conditions upon the license, which must be complied with in the following licensing steps.

The procedure is repeated for the follow-up on PLs which relate to stages of construction in the plant. During review of these additional PLs, only the subject at hand can be evaluated, which means that items approved in previous PLs are not open to discussion. However, before granting the operating license, the licensing authority has to examine if the plant is in accordance with the current state-of-the-art.

Eventually the licensee applies for an operating license. Technical specifications have been approved for each aspect of the plant during the preceding PL approvals. When applying for an operating license, the following general documents are required:

1. Final safety analysis report.
2. Program for initial fuel loading and commissioning the plant.
3. Operational organization.
4. Protection and safety rules.
5. In-service inspection program.
6. Physical security precautions.

Although complex and rigorous, the FRG licensing system appears to offer the applicant the guarantee needed to risk capital on such a major investment as a nuclear plant. It appears to be the only system where financial compensation is offered to the utility if a design and safety related concept once approved is subsequently modified or changed by the licensing authority, given that the system originally proposed was not inherently unsafe.

France

The first step in the French licensing process shown in Figure 18.10 is the filing of an application with the Minister for Industry (MI). This application includes the principal characteristics of the facilities, a site plan, and a preliminary safety analysis report (PSAR). The application is then forwarded by the MI, through the Service Central de Sureté des Installations Nucléaires (SCSIN), to any other government ministry involved (Interior, Health, Equipment, Agriculture, Environment, and Transportation) and to the prefect of the department where the plant is to be built.

The second step is, in effect, a two-directional effort whereby all parties concerned are consulted. This two-directional effort includes, on the one hand, a public inquiry held by the prefect and, on the other, a study by the SCSIN of the PSAR.

The local inquiry is opened by the prefect of the department in which the installation is to be sited. The file submitted to inquiry must contain information about the identity of the applicant, the purpose of the inquiry, the nature and essential specifications of the installation and a plan of the latter, a map of the area, and so on. At the positive conclusion of a public inquiry a declaration is issued that the proposed facility is in the public interest.

At the same time as the consultations with the public and local authorities are being carried out, one of the Advisory Committees of the SCSIN, with the technical assistance of the Institute for Protection and Nuclear Safety (IPSN) of the Commissariat à L'Energie Atomique (CEA), will examine the PSAR submitted.

The opinion of the advisory committee, together with the results of the public inquiry and the comments of the other ministries concerned, are used by the MI to determine if a construction license should be issued. Provided no obstacles exist as a result of these reviews, the MI then prepares a draft decree authorizing construction. This draft is submitted to the Interministerial Committee (CIINB) which has two months to communicate its opinion. The draft decree, as amended (where necessary) by the CIINB, is then submitted to the Ministry of Health, which has three months to give its opinion.

The decree, signed by the prime minister and countersigned by the minister for industry, fixes the perimeter of the installation and the requirements with which the operator must comply. It also lays down the conditions to be met by the operator for his installation to be brought into operation. In addition to the conditions relating to the safety of the installation, the decree may include instructions on other aspects, for example, disposal of waste heat and climatic effects.

The final commissioning step schematically outlined in Figure 18.11 comprises two phases:

Submittal of Provisional Safety Report

Six months prior to the loading of a reactor, the operator must send the Ministry for Industry a provisional safety report together with proposals for provisional general operating instructions. The report and instructions are referred to the responsible standing group for its opinion. In the light of this opinion, the minister may, as appropriate, give his approval for the loading of fuel and for start-up testing.

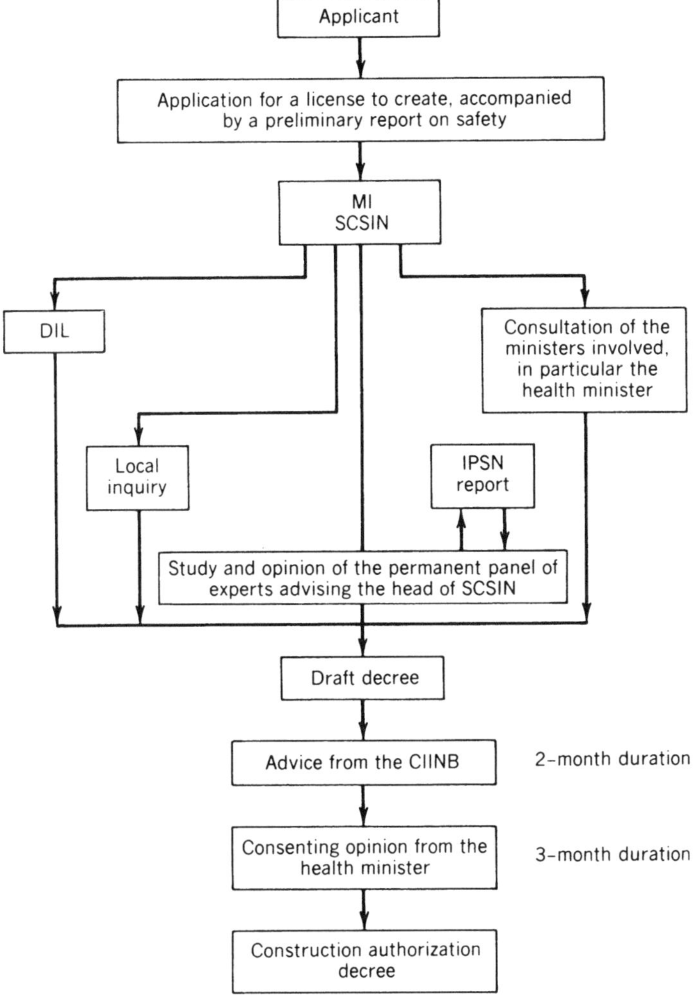

Figure 18.10. France: licensing procedure for basic nuclear installations.

Submittal of Final Safety Report

Before approval can be given for a reactor to be brought into commercial operation (a decision that must be made within the time limit specified in the licensing decree), the operator must submit a final safety report to the Ministry for Industry accompanied by his proposals for operating instructions. At the request of the head of the SCSIN, the responsible standing group studies these documents and delivers its opinion. Based on this opinion the minister for industry will—if appropriate—decide in favor of the installation being brought into operation, subject to making any modifications to the installation or to the general operating instructions which may be required.

Design and construction of nuclear power plants in France is now standardized around 900-MWe, 1300-MWe, and eventually 1500-MWe PWRs. The formalized Quality Assurance Program requirements that exist in the United States are not applied in France. While definitive cost and manpower estimates are not currently available, it would appear that the standard plant concept, the use of the more traditional quality assurance procedures, and no need for an extensive backfit program result in engineering and construction manpower requirements at least half the typical figures now found in U.S. nuclear construction projects.

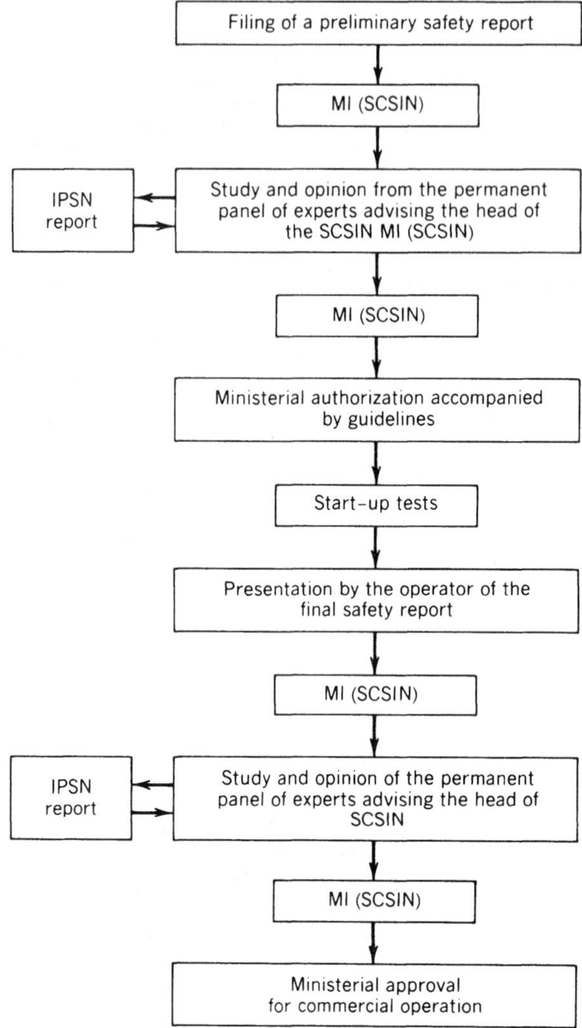

Figure 18.11. France: operating license.

Japan

Only the prime minister has the authority to issue licenses for the construction and operation of nuclear power plants in Japan. All government and regional organizations involved in the licensing process, for example, the Ministry for International Trade and Industry (MITI), either directly or indirectly provide the required information necessary for making that determination. The preparation of a Safety Analysis Report is the responsibility of the MITI and not that of the applicants (electric utility). It should be understood that the role of local government and environmental public hearings are extremely important to nuclear power development. The lack of suitable sites and local opposition to siting of nuclear power plants have been the most important factors in restraining nuclear power development in Japan.

The procedures for obtaining a license to construct and operate a nuclear power plant are schematically shown in Figure 18.12 and include the following stages:

1. Reactor installation license.
   a. Filing the application.

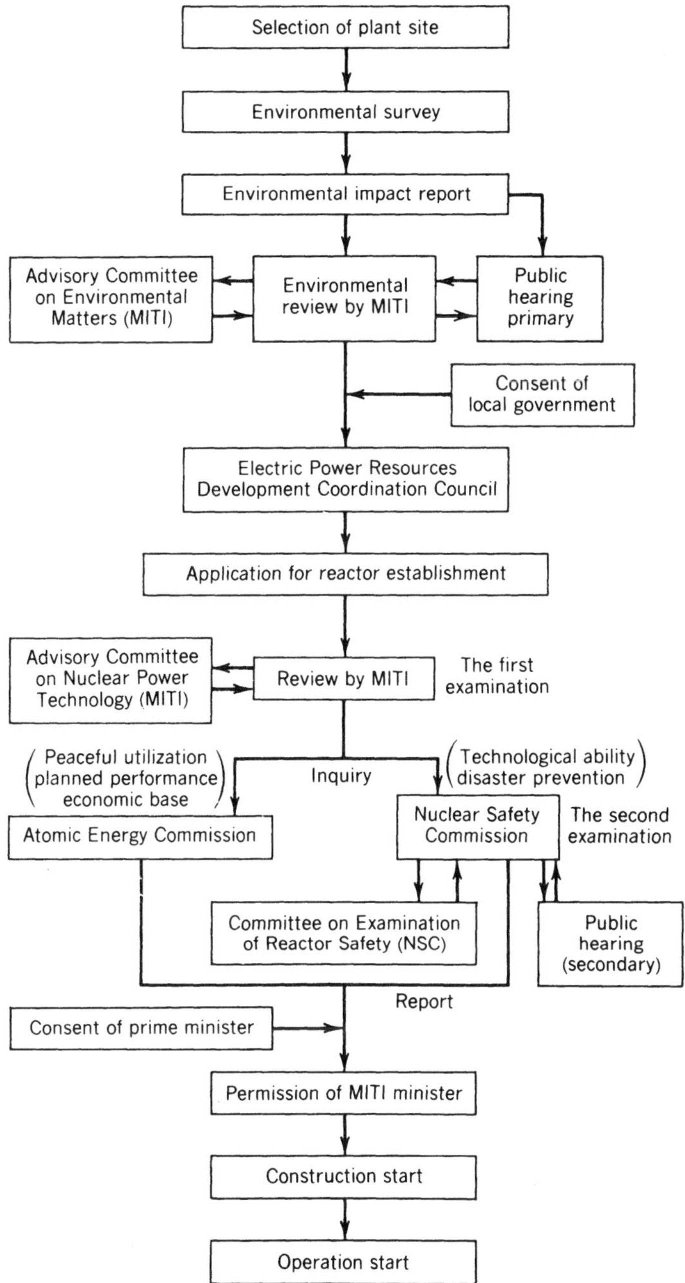

Figure 18.12. Japan: simplified outline of licensing procedure for nuclear power plants.

b. Examination and consultation.
c. Granting the license.

2. Authorization before construction.
3. Authorization before operation.

A description of these stages now follows.

Under the Electricity Utility Law (Law No. 170 of 1969), applicants for a commercial nuclear reactor must first submit siting data to MITI so that an environmental impact review may be performed. The siting data furnished must include both an environmental survey and an environmental impact statement. This information is submitted to MITI who, reviewing it with the help of the Advisory Committee on Environmental Matters, then holds a public hearing. After the hearing, consent of the local government is obtained. The construction project is then submitted to the Electric Power Resources Development Coordination Council for its coordination and approval.

MITI examines the safety aspects of the proposed reactor and prepares the Draft Safety Analysis Report with the help of the Technical Advisory Committee, and seeks the opinion of the Nuclear Safety Commission (NSC) (with respect to safety) on the Draft Safety Analysis Report. The NSC examines this document and ascertains if it conforms with the various safety standards, guides, and so on, prepared by the NSC, as well as with relevant laws and regulations. Although there are no legal procedures that require public consultation, in practice the NSC holds public hearings to consider the public's opinion concerning the safety of the planned installation.

The license for a commercial nuclear reactor is then granted by the prime minister based on the recommendations of MITI and other cognizant organizations. When determining whether or not to issue a license, the prime minister appears to be extremely sensitive to the concerns of local government and citizen groups as to the siting of nuclear power reactors. A negative response from a local government or a significant group of local citizens will normally cause the project to be abandoned at a particular site. It appears that the Japanese requirements for a single license would help reduce the licensee's concern over the financial risks involved in constructing a nuclear power plant installation. Since a single license with additional intermediate permits is all that is needed to operate the installation, once site approval has been granted, the chances for unwarranted delays or stoppage of the installation in the construction or start-up stages are minimized.

Sweden

The Swedish licensing procedure is basically a five-step system which involves the following phases:

1. The plant owner prepares a PSAR and applies for an approval license. An approval license covers site permit, construction, and plant commissioning. Both construction and operation are subject to granting of permits by the Swedish Nuclear Power Inspectorate (SKI) and the National Institute of Radiation Protection (SSI). This license is basically a government go ahead for the nuclear project.

2. Within six months of starting construction, and after obtaining a license approval, the plant owner must transmit to the SKI data demonstrating that he is able to meet conditions laid down in the license. As the plant is constructed, the various components and systems are tested. Before the reactor is loaded with fuel, comprehensive preoperational testing is carried out both with cold systems and up to full coolant pressure and temperature in order to verify the functioning of the various systems and the combined functioning of all the systems. The results of the testing are compiled and submitted to SKI for review.

3. Before fuel may be brought into the plant, permission is required from SKI and SSI. SKI issues regulations for the systems that are required for handling fuel, for monitoring nuclear materials, and for guaranteeing physical protection. SSI issues radiation protection regulations which specify requirements on certain systems, including monitoring, ventilation, and waste systems. Regulations are also issued on dosimetry and the reporting of discharged radioactivity. The procedural requirements of Phase II are shown in Figure 18.13.

4. At least six months before the scheduled fuel loading, the applicant must submit a Final Safety Analysis Report (FSAR). After SKI approves the FSAR, a fuel-loading and reduced-power operating permit is issued.

5. After the applicant has obtained the fuel-loading and reduced-power operating permit (which the SKI authorizes in stages), the SSI studies radiation protection arrangements, makes pertinent recommendations, and informs SKI of its approval. If satisfied, SKI issues an operational license which is accompanied by a set of rules and conditions, established by the SKI, which must be observed in order to continue operation.

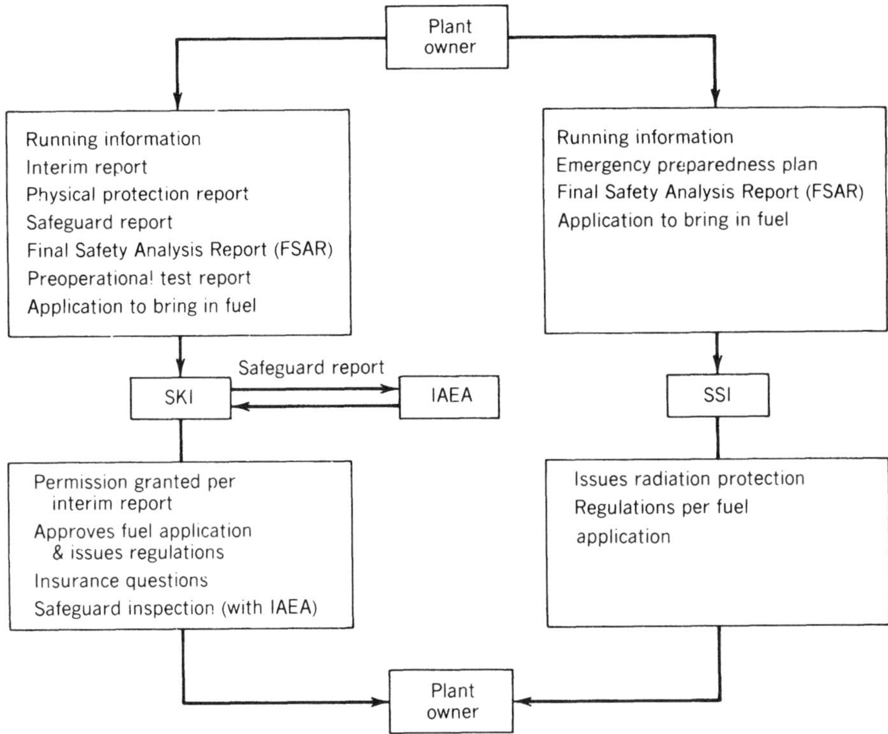

Figure 18.13. Phase II Swedish licensing procedure.

It should be noted that Swedish legislation makes no special provisions with regard to public inquiries. However, the application, through the Ministry of Housing, is transmitted to the County Council and the Commune Council. Under Swedish law (Urban Planning and Building Act), the commune may veto the siting of the first nuclear reactor within its area.

Finally the Swedish referendum on nuclear power held on March 23, 1980 should be mentioned. One month after the referendum the government presented an energy bill to the parliament. The minister of energy declared that the long-term objective of the energy policy would be "to abandon nuclear power at a rate which may be possible considering the need for electric power to maintain employment and welfare." At most the 12 reactors in the program were to be used during their technical lifetime, estimated at 25 yr from the start of the operation. Measures to improve reactor safety such as venting filter systems were under study. The safety analysis of each reactor was to be intensified; the Nuclear Power Inspectorate was to be reorganized and get increased personnel and economic resources. This bill obviously will affect the licensing of future nuclear plants in Sweden.

United Kingdom

In the United Kingdom, a single "site license" is necessary to site, construct, and operate a nuclear power plant. This license sanctions the use of a particular site for a specific reactor type, after a preliminary assessment of the proposed installation is combined with the requirements laid down by the siting policy. All subsequent checks and controls during final design, construction, and operation phases are exercised via the conditions incorporated or by conditions that can be further attached to this license.

The procedure consists essentially of three stages:

1. Filing the application.
2. Consulting the parties concerned.
3. Granting the license.

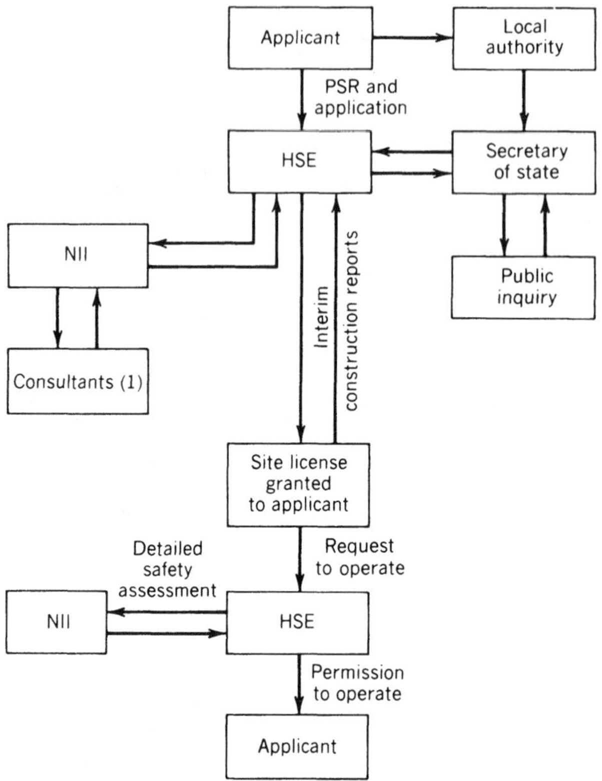

Figure 18.14. Licensing procedure in the United Kingdom. NII can obtain assistance from: (1) other parts of HSE; (2) outside consultants; (3) UKAEA; (4) universities; (5) Department of Energy; (6) Department of the Environment; (7) Ministries of Agriculture, Fisheries, and Food.

Figure 18.14 demonstrates the flow of the United Kingdom's licensing procedure. The application must contain sufficient information to enable the Nuclear Installations Inspectorate (NII) to satisfy itself regarding the safety of the proposed plant and the suitability of the site. For power reactors, applicants are required to submit details of the basic safety principles on which the design is based and indicate how these principles are to be incorporated in the plant. This information is included in the Preliminary Safety Report (PSR). Information must also be given on the main pressure containment system and cooling arrangements both in normal and in accident conditions. In addition, the layout of the site, the expected radiation contours, and arrangements for dealing with radioactive effluents, waste storage, and irradiated fuel elements must also be furnished.

The Health and Safety Executive (HSE), or secretary of state, may also require that the applicant publicize the proposal and give notice to pertinent local authorities who will have three months to comment. At this time, the secretary of state will determine if a public inquiry is necessary and whether or not the proposal is acceptable. Once approval of the secretary of state is obtained, the HSE may proceed to obtain the advice of the NII and make a decision with regard to the acceptability of the application. An extensive public inquiry on the first PWR to be constructed in the United Kingdom—the Sizewell B plant—and on the generic safety issues concerning PWRs was started in late 1982 and is expected to continue till 1984 or even early 1985, before approval for plant construction is granted.

It appears that the procedures used in the United Kingdom for licensing nuclear power plants would serve to substantially reduce the period of time involved in going from the point of application to initial plant start-up. The all-encompassing "site license" appears to give the applicant the definitive criteria with which the project will be judged. While this procedure has performed satisfactorily in the case of the UK Magnox and Advanced Gas Reactor (AGR) plant series, its effectiveness has yet to be demonstrated regarding the new PWR plant series. The experience to date of the Sizewell licensing process points to a prolonged licensing process for the first UK PWR.

It is expected that future licensing lead times for the next series PWRs will be shorter, as the generic PWR safety issues were extensively covered in the current hearings.

Nuclear Regulation in the USSR

In the USSR, the state regulation of nuclear power safety is accomplished by:

1. The State Committee on Supervision of Safe Operations in Industry and Mining under supervision of the Council of Ministers of the USSR, which supervises engineering safety in design, construction, and operation of nuclear power plants.
2. The State Nuclear Safety Inspectorate which supervises nuclear safety in design, construction, and operation of nuclear power plants.
3. The State Sanitary Inspection of the USSR under the Ministry of Public Health which supervises radiation safety.

These three supervisory bodies largely regulate the nuclear power industry by issuing various regulatory guides.

The main regulatory document on nuclear power plant safety in the USSR, General Regulations to Ensure the Safety of Nuclear Power Plants, was enacted in 1973. This document covers all types of commercial reactors in operation and under construction in the USSR. Requirements are presented in a general way in this document without concrete details. In most cases the general regulations only prescribe necessary tasks to ensure safety (what must be done); they do not determine the solutions (how it should be done).

The basic document of the State Nuclear Safety Inspectorate, Nuclear Safety Regulations for Nuclear Power Plants, was introduced in 1975. In regulates nuclear safety, not only in reactor operation, but also refueling, transportation, and waste storage. It contains the main technical and organizational requirements to ensure nuclear safety in the design, construction, and operation of nuclear power plants, and the training requirements for personnel associated with reactor operation.

In the field of radiation safety, the basic document is Radiation Safety Standards (RSS-76). These standards were worked out on the basis of recommendations of the International Commission on Radiological Protection (ICRP) and establish the system of dose limits and principles of their application. The Health Regulations for Design and Operation of Nuclear Power Plants, issued in 1978, further develop and specify the basic RSS-76 document to include siting, monitoring, and inspection problems.

Comparison of National Licensing Practices

In summary it appears that the U.S. regulatory agencies have less trust in the ability of the utility applicants or licensees and their agents to carry out rigorous and safe nuclear power plant design or construction programs than regulatory agencies in foreign countries. Conversely, the electric utilities in the United States tend to see the NRC as an organization overly concerned with political pressure groups rather than true technical safety issues. Possible reasons for these different perceptions are identified as follows:

1. In the United States there are approximately 65 nuclear utilities employing 14 different nuclear power plant architect/engineer design agents which interact with four major nuclear steam system suppliers, as seen in Table 18.2. This large group tends to lead to impersonalized contacts between the regulatory body technical personnel and those of the utility, their design agents, and nuclear steam system suppliers.

2. For various reasons amplified by recent U.S. history, there is a strong mutual suspicion and lack of candor fostered by a legalized decision process between government regulatory agencies and the regulated electric utilities and their design agents. Even in purely technical matters, there is a tendency in the United States during the licensing process for both the regulator and the utility to present extreme positions in anticipation of bargaining for a compromise. Technical safety decisions in the United States as compared to other countries tend to be made more on the basis of adjudication rather than on pure merit.

3. Other countries tend to make much greater use of existing state and local regulatory or inspection agencies set up to monitor conventional heavy construction. Examples of these agencies are the Provincial Pressure Retaining Component Safety Departments in Canada, the Ministry of International Trade and Industry (MITI) in Japan, the Swedish Plant Inspectorate (SA) in Sweden, and the TUV in the FRG. These agencies essentially perform on a more local level many of the functions performed by NRC staff and I&E inspectors in the United States. It should be noted such independent agencies generally do not exist in the United States.

Table 18.2a. Nuclear Reactor Suppliers

Manufacturer	Commercial Plants		Under Construction		On Order	
	Number	MWe	Number	MWe	Number	MWe
Westinghouse	27	20,063	38	41,454	3	2,590
General Electric	24	17,758	28	30,101	7	8,304
Combustion Engineering	8	6,361	15	17,893	6	7,490
Babcock & Wilcox	9	7,885	8	7,947	3	3,790
Other	3	1,230	—	—	—	—
Total	71[a]	53,297	89	97,396	19	22,174

Source: U.S. Department of Energy.

[a]Does not include Indian Point 1 or Humboldt Bay.

Table 18.2b. Architect/Engineering Responsibility for Nuclear Power Plants

Architect/Engineer	Commercial Plants		Under Contruction		On Order	
	Number	MWe	Number	MWe	Number	MWe
Bechtel	27	20,099	21	22,564	6	7,494
Burns & Roe	4	3,184	2	2,163	1	350
Black & Veatch	—	—	—	—	2	2,300
Brown & Root	—	—	2	2,500	—	—
Ebasco	4	2,676	8	8,003	1	1,150
Gilbert/Commonwealth	—	—	3	3,310	—	—
Gibbs & Hill	1	457	2	2,222	—	—
Gilbert Associates	3	2,114	—	—	—	—
Fluor Power Services	3	1,595	—	—	—	—
Sargent & Lundy	8	5,626	13	13,310	2	2,240
Stone & Webster	9	5,859	11	10,797	4	4,800
United Engineers	4	3,480	4	4,836	—	—
Tennessee Valley Authority	4	4,343	13	15,896	—	—
Utility owner[a]	4	3,864	10	11,795	3	3,840
Total	71[b]	53,297	89	97,396	19	22,174

Source: Office of Technology Assessment.

[a]Includes Niagara Mohawk Power Corp., Public Service Electric & Gas Co., American Electric Power Service Corp., Pacific Gas & Electric Co., and Duke Power Corp.

[b]Does not include Indian Point 1 or Humboldt Bay.

Table 18.2c. NSSS/AE Combination of Light Water Reactors Under Construction or on Order

	Westinghouse	General Electric	Combustion Engineering	Babcock & Wilcox
Bechtel	6	10	6	5
Burns & Roe	—	1	1	—
Black & Veatch	—	2	—	—
Brown & Root	2	—	—	—
Ebasco	4	1	4	—
Gilbert/Commonwealth	1	2	—	—
Gibbs & Hill	2	—	—	—
Gilbert Associates	—	—	—	—
Utility Owner	7	—	6	—
Fluor Power Services	—	—	—	—
Sargent & Lundy	8	7	—	—
Stone & Webster	5	6	2	2
United Engineers	2	—	—	2
Tennessee Valley Authority	3	6	2	2

Source: Office of Technology Assessment.

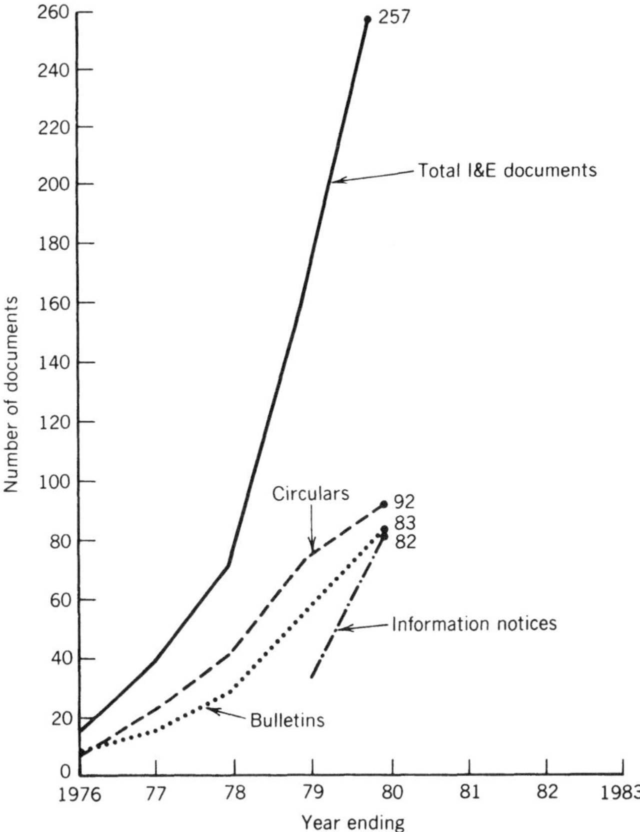

Figure 18.15. Number of NRC inspection and enforcement documents issued from 1976 to 1980.

4. As a result of the extremely rapid expansion of the nuclear power industry in the United States in the period between 1965 and 1973 (e.g., a doubling of engineering manpower occurred every 9–12 months), there were many instances of inadequate design and construction documentation and, in some instances, lack of technical experience. As a result, in the United States, a massive, independent, and largely administrative project management Quality Assurance Program, or "management by the numbers," was mandated by the NRC in 10CFR50 Appendix B. In foreign countries, the greater use of plant standardization, the later start, and the somewhat slower buildup in nuclear plant design and construction activities permitted a more traditional project and engineering-management responsibility for quality assurance. While all countries to some extent have expanded their nuclear quality assurance program, the strong dependency on formal documentation and administrative controls has not been repeated to the same extent outside the United States. This has significantly affected engineering manpower requirements, costs, and schedule in the United States as compared with other countries.

It is interesting to note that, except for the United States and the United Kingdom, there is an outside agency inspection or review of plant design as well as the other aspects of construction and manufacture associated with nuclear power projects. This fact may to some extent account for the relatively high incidence of design reevaluations identified in I&E bulletins for U.S. plants as compared to plants in the other countries. The increase in the number of I&E documents issued since 1976 is shown in Figure 18.15. There does not appear to be anywhere near the reevaluation of design effort on operating plants in foreign countries as in the United States. Even Canada, which generally uses the provisions of the U.S. ASME Boiler and Pressure Vessel Code in its nuclear plants, mandates a design review requirement by the equivalent of the code authorized inspector—a requirement that is missing in the United States.

Of the countries discussed above, the United States is second only to the FRG in the complexity of its licensing and regulatory process, in the number of regulatory personnel per megawatt of installed capacity, and in the potential for licensing delay. The FRG process is particularly complicated by the joint licensing and regulatory role played by both the federal and state governments with the state government having supreme licensing authority as well as having the potential for legal challenge in the regular state administrative courts. The FRG regulatory impact on plant costs and schedule is tempered somewhat, at least as far as the utility is concerned, by a provision in the law whereby the government reimburses the utility for costs of any additional, regulatory-imposed safety requirements which are imposed during the licensing of the plant.

Finally, it should be pointed out that on any given project the existence of formal and expensive quality assurance programs may actually lead to less quality. The goal of any quality assurance program should be a reliable and safe facility. This end would seem better served by direct assurance in the form of independent peer review of the project design and analysis procedure. Foreign experience appears to favor the use of independent up-front technical evaluations, design reviews and audits prior to commitment to construction, with less formal quality assurance administrative controls during construction.

18.5. JUDICIAL DECISIONS AFFECTING NUCLEAR POWER

Various issues affecting nuclear power have proceeded through the regulatory process and have then been turned over to various levels of judicial review in order to influence the outcome of those issues. The number of cases litigated before the courts, especially over the last two years, underscores the magnitude of the nuclear power debate in the United States, and reflects the growing tensions between the federal policies and state and local attempts to regulate nuclear power.

One of the earlier and most famous court cases which affected nuclear power generation was the "Calvert Cliffs" case of 1972, which resulted in the imposition of the National Environmental Policy Act (NEPA) requirements on the nuclear plants regulatory process. The inclusion of a detailed Environmental Impact Statement (EIS) in the regulatory process was one of the results of that court case. A set of important issues was litigated before the courts during the 1976–1978 time period. Several representative cases from that period are discussed below.

The Midland Case

Aeschliman et al. v. U.S. Nuclear Regulatory Commission et al. (Consumers Power Co., Intervenor); *Saginaw Valley Nuclear Study Group, et al. v. U.S. Nuclear Regulatory Commission, et al.* (D.C. Cir. 1976)

It was claimed in this case that the Midland plant's EIS did not adequately consider "alternatives to the proposed action" since it failed to examine energy conservation as an alternative to the plant. It was ruled that intervenors need not show some "threshold" of evidence of reasonability of alternatives but need only draw "sufficient attention" to the potential alternative to stimulate the commission's consideration of it. As a result, the ACRS report had to be returned to ACRS for clarification, and on remand, the fuel cycle issues had to be examined in light of *NRDC v. NRC (Vermont Yankee).*

The Vermont Yankee Case

Natural Resources Defense Council, Inc. (NRDC) et al. v. U.S. Nuclear Regulatory Commission, et al. (Vermont Yankee Nuclear Power Corp., Intervenor), and *Natural Resources Defense Council et al. v. U.S. Nuclear Regulatory Commission et al.* (Baltimore Gas & Electric Company et al., Intervenors), (D.C. Cir. 1976)

It was claimed by the NRDC that procedures used in rule-making proceedings to assess incremental environmental contribution of a hypothetical LWR fuel cycle were, in the aggregate, inadequate to sufficiently ventilate the issues in that proceeding. The NRC thus relied on conclusory testimony of staff scientists without itself critically questioning or permitting any meaningful challenge by intervenors, according to the NRDC. The court remanded the rule for further proceedings to develop a sufficient record with the general mandate to the commission to adopt procedures that could provide for meaningful intervenor participation.

The court also remanded the Vermont Yankee license to the NRC for consideration of fuel cycle impacts. It ruled that in the absence of an effective generic proceeding, these issues must be dealt with in individual licensing proceedings. Both decisions left it open to the commission whether to decide the fuel cycle issues on a case-by-case basis or in a generic proceeding.

The Vermont Yankee Case is one of the first manifestations of the fight over the S-3 table in the NRC's Generic Environmental Survey of the Nuclear Fuel Cycle of 1972. At issue is whether the NRC violated NEPA in adopting a "fuel cycle" rule, including the controversial Table S-3, which specifies environmental releases from high-level waste disposal and other uranium fuel cycle operations for use in nuclear power plant environmental impact statements. The Generic Environmental Impacts Summary Table fails to permit reconsideration in individual licensing proceedings if new uncertainties in the prospects for safe high-level waste disposal are discovered.

The Natural Resources Defense Council started its fight against Table S-3 in 1972 when the AEC began to develop a procedure to handle environmental effects of the complete fuel cycle. In its first effort, the NRDC took the Yankee Atomic Electric Co. to the Supreme Court, claiming long-term waste storage uncertainties were ignored in the licensing of the Vermont Yankee plant. The matter was returned to a lower court. The NRC has since revised the table twice, but the NRDC has continued to protest its alleged inadequacy, stressing primarily that, being generic, the table cannot be properly applied to individual plants. In April 1982 the U.S. Court of Appeals for the District of Columbia (D.C.), which had sided with the NRDC in the Vermont Yankee case, found again in the NRDC's favor. It ruled that "the original and interim versions of the (NRC's) fuel cycle rule forbade consideration in individual cases of health, socioeconomic, cumulative and similar effects from the (radioactive) releases specified in the rule, and were subsequently invalid."

One of the three plaintiffs in the combined case heard before the Supreme Court was Baltimore Gas & Electric Co. which represented in its brief a group of 18 utilities. They argued that a finding invalidating the S-3 table could conceivably invalidate many of the 90 operating licenses and construction permits issued since 1974. The NRDC countered in its brief that this was an exaggeration and insists its only objective was to get the NRC to develop a more adequate table. The D.C. court's decision to invalidate Table S-3 could have led to case by case licensing review of waste disposal for each nuclear power plant, thus significantly increasing the nuclear regulatory burden. The Supreme Court decision of July 1983 came down on the side of the NRC, ruling that the NRC was acting properly when it cited the Generic Table S-3 to fulfill certain environmental impact requirements in specific individual licensing proceedings.

The Generic Environmental Statement on Mixed-Oxide Fuels (GESMO) Case

National Resources Defense Council, Inc. et al. v. United States Nuclear Regulatory Commission et al. (2nd Cir. 1976)

The plaintiff in this case—the NRDC—claimed that the NRC interim commercial licensing of mixed-oxide fuels facilities prior to completion of a generic impact statement violated NEPA. The Court ruled that the NRC decision to bifurcate the GESMO hearings was well within agency discretion. NRC's decision to hold primarily legislative-type hearings was within agency discretion with the expectation that procedure would be designed to allow for "meaningful participation" of public interest groups.

The entire issue of the GESMO hearings and of the mixed-oxide fuel recycling in LWRs was made moot by President Carter's decision of April 1977 to indefinitely postpone spent fuel reprocessing and fissile materials recycling in U.S. nuclear power plants in order to demonstrate opposition to the plutonium economy and the related nuclear proliferation concerns. The GESMO hearings were thus terminated in 1978, and this subject has not yet been formally reopened, despite President Reagan's lifting the ban on fuel reprocessing.

The Supreme Court decisions in 1976–1978, especially the Midland and the Vermont Yankee cases, have resulted in a 5-yr period of reduced litigation activity. The Court had admonished all litigants, stating that the U.S. legal system was not intended to be the arena for an open-ended debate about the need for nuclear energy within the framework of a national energy policy. "Nuclear energy," the Court's opinion read, "may some day be a cheap, safe source of power or it may not. But Congress has made a choice to at least try nuclear energy, establishing a reasonable review process in which courts are to play only a limited role. The fundamental policy questions appropriately resolved in Congress and in the state legislatures are not subject to reexamination in the federal courts under the guise of judicial review of agency action."

In the years immediately following that directive, the center of gravity in the nuclear debate shifted, variously, back to Congress, NRC, the Department of Energy, the Transportation Department and other federal agencies, or to state levels. In 1982, though, the Supreme Court had agreed to review several nuclear cases, some of which were decided in 1983. One of the more important cases under review in 1983 was *The Pacific Gas and Electric (PGE) Case.*

Pacific Gas and Electric Co. v. California State Energy Resources Conservation & Development Commission, 1976.

Oral arguments before the court were held on January 1983. In this case, two California utilities challenged the constitutionality of provisions of the state's Warren–Alquist Act, which created and empowered a state energy commission to prohibit the construction of new nuclear power plants. Initially, separate U.S. district courts found in favor of the utilities, but the U.S. Circuit Court of

Appeals for the 9th District reversed these decisions and found that the state statutes were not preempted, as had been argued, by the Atomic Energy Act of 1954.

In accepting the case, the Supreme Court limited the dispute to two statutes, one banning construction of new plants until there is a finding by the California Energy Commission that there are adequate arrangements for storage of spent fuel rods, and a second requiring commission approval of an acceptable disposal method for high-level radioactive waste.

PG&E, and those filing briefs in its support, all argued that the statutes are preempted by Congress and that this preemption was upheld by a circuit court decision involving Northern State Power Co. v. the State of Minnesota. The California Energy Commission's position was supported by a brief filed by the states of Alaska, Arizona, Arkansas, Hawaii, Kansas, Louisiana, Minnesota, Mississippi, Montana, Nevada, New York, Ohio, Oklahoma, South Carolina, Vermont, West Virginia, and Wyoming. In essence, these states argued that the statutes in question are economic in intent and that "states have ample authority to regulate public utilities for protection of the ratepayers and the effectuation of other state policies." The Supreme Court in its decision of July 1983 sided with the position of the California Energy Commission that the nuclear regulation laws passed by that state (as well as other states) are valid, as they aim to protect state ratepayers on the basis of economic issues related to nuclear power generation.

The TMI or the Psychological Stress Case

NRC v. People Against Nuclear Energy; Metropolitan Edison Co. v. People Against Nuclear Energy, 1980

On November 1, 1982 the Supreme Court announced it would consider the issue of whether NEPA requires the NRC to consider psychological stress, and accompanying physical symptoms, allegedly induced in persons residing in the vicinity of Three Mile Island (TMI) Unit 1, before ruling on a request to authorize restart of the facility. The oral arguments brought to a head the 3-yr effort of a small organization of residents in the area around TMI, People Against Nuclear Energy (PANE), to make psychological stress testing a means of preventing the restart of TMI-1. Once again, it was the U.S. Court of Appeals for the District of Columbia that was responsible for the matter reaching the Supreme Court. In a 2–1 decision in January 1982, it ordered the NRC to begin assessments of both psychological stress and community deterioration as factors which may need to be evaluated. In an amended decision in April 1982, the district court softened its order somewhat through new wording that left any final decision as to whether to actually proceed with the testing up to the NRC. Even this attempt at moderation, however, was seen by plaintiffs as opening the door to the use of the psychological stress issue in any licensing action. The counsel for PANE has argued, however, that the issue is limited solely to TMI-1 because of its unique relationship to the crippled TMI-2 facility.

In its decision of July 1983, the Supreme Court ruled for the NRC and the Metropolitan Edison Company, and against PANE. The issue of psychological stress and the attendant regulatory and administrative work loads need not be considered in future nuclear licensing cases.

The Silkwood Case

Silkwood v. Kerr-McGee Corporation, 1982

In May 1982 the Supreme Court agreed to review the case of Karen Silkwood, the former employee of the Kerr-McGee corporation. Silkwood was killed in a single car accident in November 1976. At the time of her death she was said to be en route to Oklahoma City to meet with a union official and a newspaper reporter to hand over alleged evidence of negligence on the part of her employer, Kerr-McGee Corp., in the handling of plutonium at its Cimarron, Oklahoma plutonium facility where she worked as an analyst.

Her father brought suit in federal district court against Kerr-McGee, claiming the corporation's negligence resulted in plutonium escaping from its plant and subsequently led to the death of his daughter. A jury awarded the father $505,000 in actual damages and punitive damages of $10 million.

Kerr-McGee took the case to the U.S. Court of Appeals for the 10th Circuit, which reversed the district court on its award of punitive damages. In its 2–1 decision, the appellate court let stand an award of $5,000 for property damage to Silkwood's apartment.

In the appeal of the reversal to the Supreme Court, plaintiffs restated the issue, making it a question of whether federal law preempts an award of punitive damages provided under state law for exposure to radiation in the course of employment. An *amicus curiae* filed on behalf of Silkwood by the State of Minnesota removed the radiation element, and argued that the reversal would in effect nullify a state statute, one which allows Minnesota to award punitive damages in civil actions where the court has found that the defendant's acts show a willful indifference to the rights or safety of others. The issue, however, was far more narrow, in the view of the U.S. Department of Justice. In its brief it argued that "the court of appeals was clearly correct in holding that punitive damages may not be awarded in the circumstances of this case." In 1984, however, the Supreme Court decided that federal law does not prohibit juries from awarding punitive damages against companies regulated by the NRC, reversing the appeals court decision that threw out the $10 million award against Kerr-McGee. The $505,000 compensatory damages, reduced to $5000 by the appeals court on grounds they were limited by Oklahoma's workers compensation law, were not part of the Supreme Court decision. The 5-4 decision held that Congress, in enacting the Price–Anderson Act, "assumed that state-law remedies were available to those injured by nuclear incidents, even though Congress was aware of the Nuclear Regulatory Commission's exclusive authority to regulate safety matters." The effect of upholding the Silkwood award and allowing state punitive damage awards is to enable states to enforce standards more exacting than the federal standard. The case was remanded to the appeals court for reconsideration of the punitive damage award.

18.6. STANDARDIZATION

Power Plants

The nuclear industry that has developed in the United States since 1959 has grown up with a surprising degree of technical diversity. All but a handful of the 83 plants that are currently licensed for operation have been custom designed and custom built. A result of this practice is that the plants must also be individually licensed, since the safety analysis of each is inevitably different. When a utility decides to build a plant, it usually first hires an architect/engineering (AE) firm, then contracts with a reactor manufacturer (one of the four existing "nuclear vendors") to build the nuclear core, vessel, and cooling and control mechanisms, which represent about 10% of the total plant investment. Each vendor has a different design for its nuclear system, so there are four different options. Then the AE designs the Balance Of the Plant (BOP), which includes the cooling systems, feedwater systems, steam supply systems, control room, and turbine/generator systems. The various vendor/AE combinations responsible for most of the plants now under construction are shown in Table 18.2.

There are about 12 AEs presently designing nuclear plants in the United States, and each has its own preferred approach to these various systems. The AE's approach will be tailored by past experience to be consistent with one vendor's nuclear system, but not necessarily compatible with the systems of all four. In addition to the diversity due to the different architect–vendor combinations, there is also a degree of variability due to the different meteorological, seismic, and hydrological conditions at different plant sites.

Further variability is introduced by the length of the process (12 yr) and the piecemeal approach that is taken, both to plant design and to licensing. Because safety standards have grown up with the nuclear industry rather than being formulated in full and fixed fashion when the industry began, plant builders and designers have taken a "design-as-you-go" approach to new plants in order to be able to meet upgraded safety standards that might be adopted during the period a plant was under construction. For some years, the industry's practice has been to start plant construction with the design about 15% complete. Even among units of the same plant intended to be identical, but started at different times, significant design differences have occurred.

In 1972, the AEC announced a goal of nuclear plant standardization. The advantages of plant standardization are expected to be many: lowered construction costs, increased safety (since a potential problem discovered in one plant can be corrected in all plants), and theoretically an increased efficiency and effectiveness of the licensing process. In 1975, the NRC reaffirmed the belief in the efficacy of standardization by establishing a reference system, in which, according to the NRC, "A generic design of an entire facility or a major portion thereof can be reviewed once and utilized repeatedly by reference without further review in individual applications for licenses."

Under the reference plant concept there has been quite a lot of vendors' activity on standardizing NSSSs designs, but this is of marginal value for the complete reactor systems because the vendors' NSSS are a relatively small part of the nuclear station design. Five AE firms have submitted BOP designs under the reference system concept, but none of these have yet been used. Under the duplicate plant concept, two major projects have been undertaken. With two units being planned at each of three sites, Duke Power Co. and the Commonwealth Edison Co. have more experience with this concept than other utilities. Duke is also unusual in that it serves as its own AE. A consortium of utilities is also making considerable use of the duplicate plant concept [Standardized Nuclear Unit Power Plant System (SNUPPS)]. Originally planned for six plants, the group now envisions two plants under this concept. Four other applications for pairs of plants under the concept have been made. Two major extensions of the duplicate plant concept are the "convoy system" prepared in the Federal Republic of Germany, and the series production of identical PWRs installed in France.

Despite the NRC's intentions, the licensing process in the 1980s is markedly longer and more complicated than it was in 1975. Complete plant standardization appears unlikely in the current regulatory environment nor is it necessarily desirable. A plant constructed on a river site in Nebraska needs to be different in many respects from a nuclear plant situated on the Florida Gulf Coast. The specificity required in the PSAR and the various environmental reports makes it impractical to design generic plants. Component and construction drawings now required by the NRC must be finely detailed. Time for front-end work is thus lengthened, and changing regulations often create a need for backfitting and redesign. As for environmental reports, specific inclusions and emphasis necessary are essentially site specific and must be addressed in great detail. While the plant in Nebraska has to be evaluated for its effects on Nebraska wildlife, the seawater-cooled plant in Florida must be evaluated differently. Similarly, the technical specifications for dealing with the cooling water supply and discharge are different.

Efforts to encourage standardization have thus met with slow acceptance. It can be argued that the many deviations from original designs that now occur before plants operate indicate that neither the technology nor the licensing process is sufficiently stabilized to support standardization. Furthermore, the nonstandardization that now exists in the industry is a direct result of the diversity that exists in the marketplace, and a substantial move toward standardization could result in some restructuring of the nuclear industry.

Currently two licensing reform packages proposed by the DOE and the NRC are before Congress, and are discussed below. Both proposals involve some degree of plant standardization as an integral complement to a streamlined regulatory process. Various standard reactor island and balance of plant packages are expected to be combined with preapproved sites. These measures are expected to reduce the required review process, so as to deal mostly with site specific issues. Passage of the proposed regulatory reform legislation in the Congress is yet uncertain.

Systems

A trend that will likely develop in the 1980s and 1990s is the standardization of systems within the power plant. A low-level waste disposal system, for example, might have a few standard designs produced by the major vendors. Customers could select from among such standard systems the options they wanted, and builders could efficiently assemble the systems into a completed plant.

Another trend likely to occur will be standardization of the Nuclear Steam Supply System (NSSS). Although the NSSS is one of the major systems of a power plant, it is still a system, and vendors can thus standardize the hardware and still offer optional core loadings and power densities to meet the customers' needs. This is particularly significant in nuclear power plants, where the costs of analyzing and engineering changes in design are a major fraction of the total cost. The potential savings of a standard plant construction would be lost if many regulatory and geographical changes had to be made.

Standards

The NRC often uses industry standards in its regulations and guidelines. In order to provide guidance in the interpretations of these regulations and criteria, the nuclear power industry supported voluntary consensus standards. Consensus standards are the industry tools for accomplishing tasks of varying degrees of difficulty in a uniform and logical manner. In the United States, the American National Standards Institute (ANSI) coordinates, provides management leadership, establishes a national consensus, and provides effective participation in international standardization. ANSI does not formulate standards, and does not write standards, but determines that standards written by the various societies have been developed in accordance with ANSI procedures, and that consensus among interested and affected parties has been achieved. Nuclear standards are administered by the Nuclear Standards Management Board (NSMB) of ANSI.

Figure 18.16 depicts the various voluntary standards-writing organizations coordinated by the NSMB. For example, for the design, manufacture, operation, and repair of pressure vessels, the NRC has adopted in total the American Society of Mechanical Engineers Pressure Vessel Code. The N45 standards of the American National Standards Institute are referenced for quality assurance programs. The Institute of Electrical and Electronic Engineers standards for components have also been adopted, as have the American Nuclear Society fission product decay tables. In many instances, the referenced standards have been judged incomplete by the NRC, and supplementary regulatory guides have been issued.

Nuclear standards have an average preparation time of 2 yr. This is accomplished through bypassing the normal standards writing, testing, and updating process, and by moving directly from the state-of-the-art to a standard. In effect, the voluntary standards effort is often writing regulations without the benefit of accumulated experience to allow convergence of practice. Future regulatory reform measures are aimed at fostering better communication between the code and

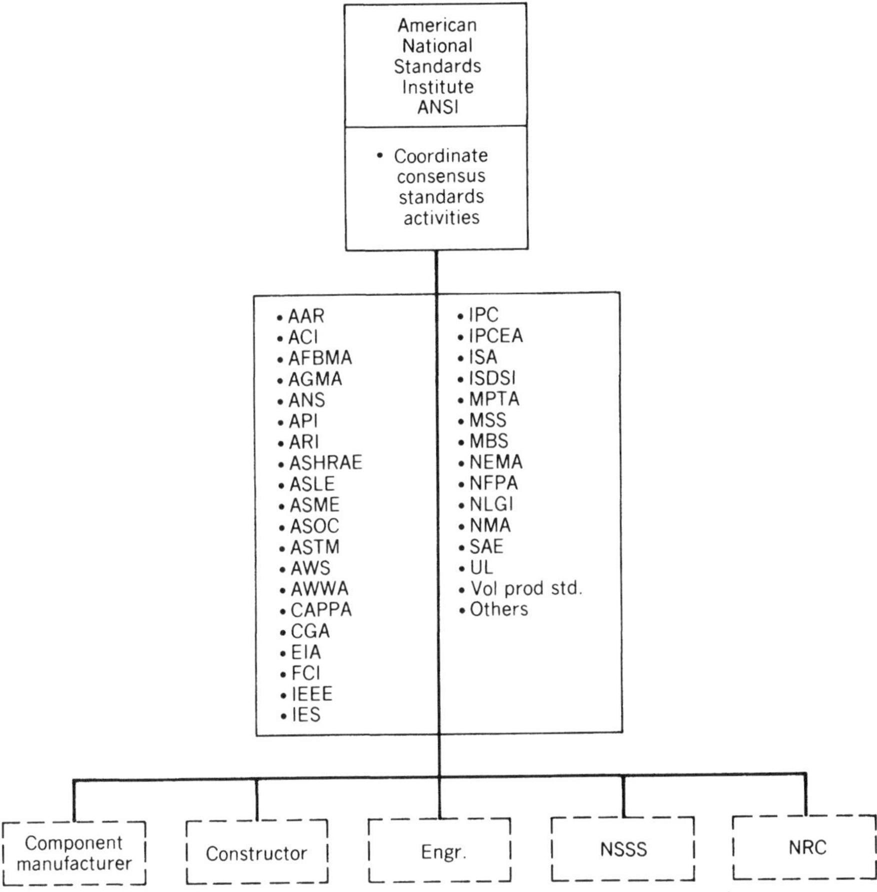

Figure 18.16. American National Standards Institute.

standards committees, designers and constructors concerning the real intent of the codes, hopefully eliminating extreme conservatisms.

18.7. GENERAL SITING GUIDANCE

Since 1962, Regulation 10CFR100, "Reactor Siting Criteria," has provided guidance for site selection based on the safety and protection of human health and welfare. Regulatory Guide 4.7 discusses the site characteristics related to safety, public health, and the environment. The guidelines are intended to be used in a screening process to identify suitable candidate sites. The safety issues of concern in site selection are primarily the relation of the population, geologic/seismic, and environmental characteristics of proposed sites.

Population

According to the NRC, a nuclear power plant site must be isolated from major population areas. The immediate area around the plant is defined as a population Exclusion Area (EA). This area must, in turn, be surrounded by a Low Population Zone (LPZ). The population in the LPZ must be low density and distributed in such a way that appropriate evacuation measures could be taken in the event of a serious accident. A proposed site will also have a "population center distance," defined as the distance from the nuclear reactor to the nearest boundary of a densely populated center of more than 25,000 residents. The edge of the population center must be at least $1\frac{1}{3}$ times the distance to the outer boundary of the LPZ. A schematic of the various distance and zoning requirements is

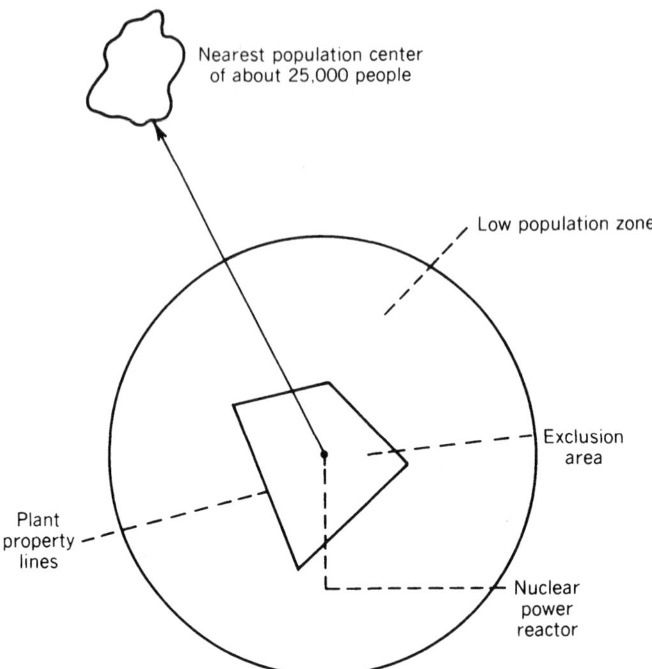

Figure 18.17. Part 100 distance requirements (typical plant). (1) At boundary of exclusion area, no member of public may exceed 25 rems whole-body dose for design basis accident. (2) Timely evacuation of low population zone must be planned. (3) Population center must be at least $1\frac{1}{3}$ times farther away than LPZ boundary.

shown in Figure 18.17. The NRC also requires that the boundaries of the EA and LPZ be sufficiently large so that a potential release of fission products in an accident will not endanger anyone outside these boundaries.

The new safety goal proposed by the NRC (see Section 17.3) addresses the risk to individuals within 1 mile of the plant (plant vicinity) from the consequences of a major reactor accident. If there are no individuals residing within a mile of the plant boundary, then the vicinity of the plant is defined as a 1-mile-wide annulus measured outward from the location of the reactor.

The safety goal defines population at risk from latent cancer fatalities as the entire population within 50 miles of the plant site. A substantial fraction of exposures to radiation would be concentrated within this distance. The safety goal requirements are formulated such that if the design objective for prompt fatalities is met for individuals in the immediate vicinity of the plant, the estimated risk of delayed cancer fatality to persons within 50 miles of the plant would generally be much lower than the limit set by the design objective. Thus, compliance with the design objective applied to individuals close to the plant would generally mean that the aggregated estimated societal risk for a 50-mile radius area would be a number of times lower than it would otherwise be, if compliance with just the design objective applied to the population as a whole were involved.

The general trend of the NRC regulations following the Three Mile Island accident favors remote plant siting, significantly away from population centers. This general requirement was the basis for the safety reevaluation of the Zion and the Indian Point plants which are older plants operated near the Chicago and the New York City metropolitan areas, respectively. Such a remote siting requirement is feasible in the United States, even though it might raise the cost of nuclear-generated electricity due to longer transmission distances. The situation is, however, different in the European context where smaller countries with large uniform population densities do not allow for remote reactor siting. Acceptance of the NRC siting philosophy may thus clash with the European nations' desire to increase nuclear electric capacity so as to displace imported oil use.

Geological and Seismic Criteria

The NRC adopted its geological and seismic criteria as a result of input from the U.S. Geological Survey, the National Oceanic and Atmospheric Administration, the Advisory Committee on Reac-

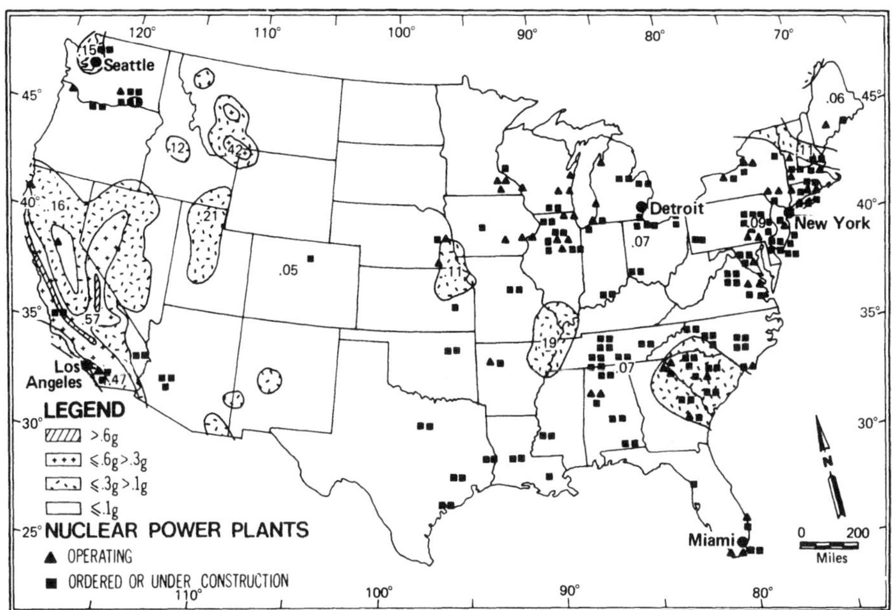

Figure 18.18. U.S. seismic zone map. Seismic data adapted from *EERI*, July 1976, Vol. 10, No. 4, Algermissen and Perkins, U.S.G.S., p. 78. Nuclear power plant data from *Nuclear News*, August 1979, Vol. 22, No. 10.

tor Safeguards, and numerous independent consultants. The principal NRC requirements for the siting of nuclear power plants are found in the regulations in 10CFR Part 100 and its Appendix A, Geologic and Seismic Siting Criteria for Nuclear Power Plants. The siting reviews carried out by the staff in implementing this regulation play an important role in assuring that the likelihood of severe reactor accidents due to siting considerations is very low. For example, the requirements of this regulation, supported by the independent evaluations of seismic and geologic conditions at a reactor site by the NRC staff and its consultants, provide the basis for establishing the seismic design parameters for a plant. The seismic design parameters are required to be conservative enough so that the likelihood of an earthquake more severe than the design basis earthquake is very low, and the possibility of a severe accident resulting from such an earthquake is even lower.

A nuclear plant today must be designed to withstand the type and level of earthquake that might be expected in the exact site being used. Figure 18.18 shows the distribution of seismic zones used for design and siting in the United States. Two levels are generally specified: the Operating Basis Earthquake (OBE) and the Safe Shutdown Earthquake (SSE). The SSE has about double the ground motion of an OBE. Ground motions in three coordinates are required, within the spectrum of a composite of several dozen previously measured earthquakes. The response of all safety-related systems and components must be predicted, and their ability to survive the earthquake must be demonstrated. This generally involves vibration testing and the construction of a detailed mathematical model which approximates the three-dimensional interaction of the soil, basemat, building, and components. Ratios are established between motion of the soil and subsequent motion of each safety-related component. Components are then shake-table tested to demonstrate their capability versus plant design requirements. Where the combination of seismic and other responses are appropriate, a choice of root sum of the squares, sum of the absolute values, or some other method must be made. No single choice has been agreed upon yet by the NRC or the components suppliers.

Similarly, NRC regulations require evaluation of other environmental considerations, such as flooding, tornadoes, industrial accidents at nearby facilities, that have the potential to cause a severe reactor accident. Common-cause failures are the single most significant aspect of earthquake-induced risk for nuclear power plants. Components of a plant critical to its safe operation have a designed redundancy. During an earthquake, however, all parts of a plant are simultaneously stressed and if damage occurs, the redundant features may also fail. In contrast to random failures, such common-cause failures can compromise a redundant safety system by damaging all of its components. Most people in the United States regard severe earthquakes as being a serious hazard only in the western part of the country. This is not the case, however (Figure 18.18). The massive earthquakes that occurred in Missouri in 1811 and 1812 were felt from New York through Florida. The magnitude of earthquakes is also difficult to predict. Until the El Centro (California) earthquake of 1980, which registered a ground acceleration of 1.7*g*, most geologists believed that a ground acceleration of about half this value was the maximum possible.

Early Site Approval Proposals

NRC review of site suitability is not initiated until the CP application is docketed. This places site review on the critical path for reactor licensing. The existing NRC regulations permit review of site suitability prior to filing of the CP application, but the outcome of this review is not binding in the final CP decision.

In the NRC legislative regulatory reform proposal, an advanced site approval (without reference to a particular nuclear plant) would be granted for up to 10 yr, with renewal possible for 5–10 yr. Federal, state, regional, and local agencies as well as utilities could apply for site approvals, thus encouraging broader planning. A site approval would not preclude the use of the site for an alternate or modified type of energy facility or for any other purpose.

The public would have an opportunity for public hearings on the site approval, but issues related to the site would be excluded from further licensing proceedings unless matching the site with a particular plant design raises issues that were not considered at the time of the site approval.

The Department of Energy (DOE) regulatory reform proposal is similar to the NRC's, except the site approval would not allow alternate uses, but would allow CP applicants to perform limited construction activities before issuance of the permit. Early site approval could contribute to shorter construction leadtimes because it would take siting out of the critical path entirely. As long as the site approval process still allows adequate opportunity for public participation, and ensures consideration of issues related to the marriage of a site and a design prior to issuance of a CP, then binding early site approval should not be a controversial reform. However, the selection of particular sites—whether they are matched with a plant or not—will remain controversial, and utilities and the NRC may devote more consideration to the addition of units at existing sites, rather than trying to gain approval of new sites.

18.8. OTHER CONSIDERATIONS

Fire

In March 1975, a fire occurred in Unit III of TVA's Brown's Ferry nuclear power plant in Alabama. The fire started when a worker, using a candle to check for air leaks, accidentally ignited a rack of electrical cables near the control room. The fire destroyed most of the cables of Unit III as well as those of another 1000-MWe unit on site, thus disrupting significant portions of the emergency core cooling systems of the two units. Protecting the core became a concern when the water level in one reactor core almost dropped below the tops of the fuel rods. The fire burned for 7 hr until firefighters extinguished it with water.

The Brown's Ferry fire investigation renewed the emphasis on the defense-in-depth principle to improve the fire safety of nuclear reactors. The governing criteria in the United States are NRC Regulation Guides 1.75 and 1.120. These guides incorporate the safety philosophy of redundancy and separation, especially in regard to the performance of plant safety functions. One of the problems during the Brown's Ferry fire was that the electrical cables came together in the so-called cable spreading compartment underneath the control room of the plant. The fire not only knocked out the instruments for Unit III, but threatened those of the other two units.

All of the studies and reports issued since that fire have investigated the required combination of causes for a fire: initiating heat source, amount and distribution of the combustibles, and the source of oxygen. Elaborate analyses were made regarding fire propagation, transmission between compartments, detection and suppression, and whether fire fighting systems should be manual or automatic. The conclusion reached is that the plant withstood 7 hr of fire without causing a hazard to the public. The problem, therefore, was that although the plant was constructed to withstand a fire, there remained inadequate procedures to put the fire out. Since the Brown's Ferry fire, there has been increased emphasis on early detection, immediate direct action, increased redundancy of emergency cooling systems, and early liberal use of water as a fire extinguisher.

In addition to the immediate steps that can be taken to detect and extinguish fires, further tests have been made on the combustibility of electrical cables and construction materials. From these tests, steps have been taken to reduce the likelihood of fire ignition and also to lessen the amounts of combustibles available and of the smoke generated in the event of a fire. Experiments have also been performed to determine the best location for fire detection sensors.

Plant Damage from Missiles

Missiles refer to potentially hazardous projectiles that may penetrate the reactor's buildings. Missiles can originate from tornadoes outside the containment building or from steam turbine blade failures inside the turbine building. Current regulation requirements (General Design Criteria 4, 10CFR50) protect all safety-related structures, systems, and equipment from such missiles. Design criteria for safety barriers are usually based on limited testing of full-scale projectiles of the expected largest object with the highest predicted velocity and the most unfavorable impact angle.

The probability of a missile accident is extremely low. The potential hazard of most concern is the stress corrosion cracking of discs in large steam turbines. A projectile hurled from a large turbine spinning at 1800 rpm can do considerable damage. The first two discs in the Yankee Rowe low-pressure turbine failed in this manner, although the reactor containment was not challenged. Protection of essential systems from turbine missiles is required by the NRC unless the combined generation, strike, and damage probability is very small. For most plants, adequate protection against turbine missiles is provided by favorable turbine placement and orientation, and adherence to the guidelines of Regulatory Guide 1.115, Rev. 1, "Protection Against Low-Trajectory Turbine Missiles."

Sabotage and Terrorism

For reasons of drama and media publicity, nuclear power plants are claimed to be potential targets of sabotage. Technically, a nuclear plant would be difficult to sabotage and the result would present less of a public hazard than sabotage of many other facilities. Yet events in the past indicate that the perceived hazard of a sabotaged nuclear plant would be large. There would be widespread press and media coverage, and people would feel threatened. Acts of terrorism are often performed to create such hysteria. Therefore, a motive for terrorist sabotage exists.

Currently, the NRC requires that plant licensees take measures to protect against sabotage. These include such deterrents as fences, guards, and quick access to local law enforcement officials. The greater deterrent to sabotage, though, is the nuclear plant itself, which to great lengths has been designed to protect the public in the event of a major accident. Inherent protection around a nuclear power plant exists, because the intense radioactivity inside the reactor requires massive shielding, usually several feet of concrete. Moreover, to protect the public against radioactive leaks, the reactor and the primary coolant loops are enclosed in a containment building of steel and concrete. Access to the reactor for terrorists would thus be difficult, although feasible in case of a strong and well-mounted attack. However, even a successful attack would not likely create a real public hazard.

Radiation Protection Standards

Protection standards set forth by the NRC take the form of (1) maximum permissible dose levels for on-site (worker) and off-site (public) populations, and (2) the design objectives for exposure levels that are "As Low As Reasonably Achievable" (ALARA). Numerical standards are set for individuals, but no numerical levels are set for a collective dose to the public or for design objectives.

Radiation exposure is estimated off-site by use of mathematical models applied to radioactive emissions, and verified by sampling air, water, soil, and so on. The NRC leaves the methods of measurement and verification to the operator, but these are still subject to NRC regulation and inspection. The operator is required to report to the NRC all emissions of radiation that exceed natural background.

On-site radiation exposures are measured by air samplings taken throughout the restricted area, and in certain locations in the nuclear plant, such as stack monitors. Maximum permissible dose limits for workers are to ensure that the probability of harm is negligible. These dose limits pertain to single exposures as well as quarterly, annual, and occupational lifetime exposure to a worker. The current limit for workers is 3 rems/quarter and 5 rems/yr. However, the NRC must be notified whenever any one worker receives even 25% of the maximum permissible dose. The average nuclear plant worker receives about 600 mrems/yr; 95% of the workers receive less than 2 rems/yr.

Radiation exposures to workers in nuclear power plants come from two basic sources. The first is from direct radiation caused by the fissioning of fuel during the operation of the reactor; this amount is negligible. The second source is from radiation due to products or materials that pass through the reactor core and are activated by the neutron flux. Many products that pass through the core are thus converted to radioactive isotopes with varying half-lives. Some of these are short-lived, whereas others have long half-lives and have potential hazards. An example of the latter is cobalt-60, formed by the neutron capture in cobalt-59, a trace element in many steels and a major alloying element in most hardfacing materials. Radioactive cobalt-60 has a half-life of 5.26 yr and emits penetrating gamma rays. During reactor operation, cobalt-60 is produced in the core region

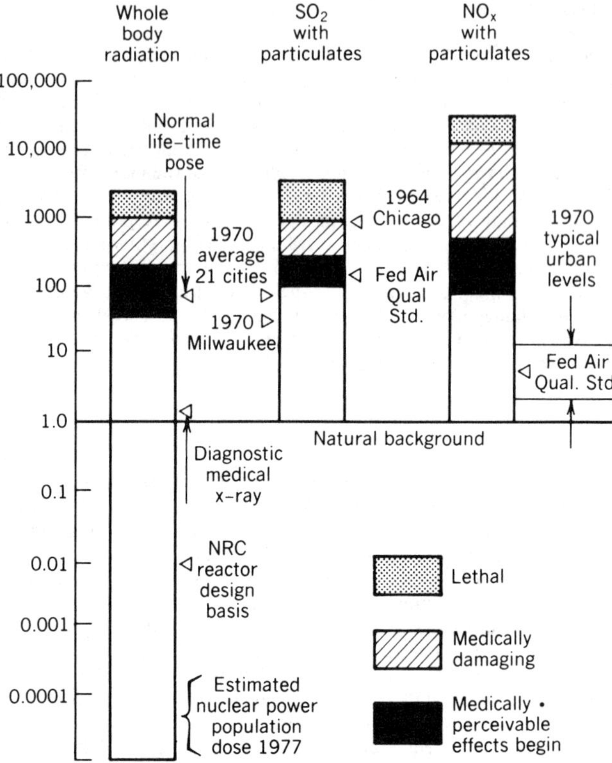

Figure 18.19. Comparison of standard and biological effects of radiation and air pollutants.

and eventually is carried by the coolant through the water loops. Dose due to cobalt-60 is usually the largest source of radiation to workers in nuclear plants.

Recent methods of compacting, disposing, and filtering radioactive effluent have reduced the total cobalt-60 dosage to the workers. Also, careful planning of work, the training of workers, and the monitoring of work locations have been successful in limiting total plant exposure to cobalt-60 and other isotopes. The application of the ALARA principle to nuclear plant operations is discussed in greater detail in Chapter 3. The relation of radiation protection standards to various levels of biological effects is shown in Figure 18.19. A similar comparison for fossil fuel emissions is also shown in that figure.

18.9. TECHNICAL ISSUES

Technical Approach to Safety and Licensing

For many years the NRC has regulated nuclear plants using a safety review process mandated in Appendix K of 10CFR50. Many countries throughout the world followed the U.S. NRC approach which was based on an analysis of the plant's ability to cope with a small number of Design-Basis Accidents (DBA). The set of DBAs considered was grouped according to severity and it contained Class 1 (small spills) through Class 8 events, with Class 8 (a break in a primary coolant loop) being the most severe. Siting of a plant, governed by 10CFR100, did not require the assumption of radioactive releases much larger than the DBA limits, referred to as Class 9 releases. The Class 9 accidents included complete core melt scenarios, which were not considered to be credible events. The argument advanced at the time was that the most severe credible accident was a large-pipe break Loss-of-Coolant Accident (LOCA). This accident was a specifically covered Class 8 DBA. Plant systems, such as the Emergency Core Cooling System (ECCS), existed to mitigate the consequences of such an accident. What was not realized was that a small-pipe break LOCA could be more difficult to cope with, and could lead to core melting, a Class 9 event.

The safety of nuclear power plants is based on the defense-in-depth concept, augmented by good management, quality assurance, and conservative design, construction, and operations. The intent is the prevention of accidents and mitigation of consequences. To complete this approach, nuclear plant regulation mandates:

1. Emergency plant shutdown and core cooling systems based on the single failure criterion.
2. Engineered safety systems to contain fission product releases.
3. No plant sitings in populated areas.
4. On-site and off-site emergency response plans.

By and large, the defense-in-depth concept and the use of DBAs to evaluate plant safety were critical factors in the safety record of the nuclear industry, and the guiding principles in reactor safety systems design.

As the nuclear industry matured, operating experience has formed a data base from which safety guidance can be drawn. One major function of the Institute for Nuclear Power Operations (INPO) is to review significant operating events and to report on their safety implications. This is done by immediately analyzing any operating transient with obvious safety deficiencies, and by scanning the Licensee Event Reports (LERs, see Chapter 17) that all plants must periodically submit to the NRC. The LERs concern system failures that might have important, but not obvious, safety consequences.

The stylized approach based on Appendix K is changing as a result of this operating data, new insights from PRA analyses, and an improved understanding of the processes controlling radioactive releases. The Appendix K approach has a number of advantages, however, including simplicity and a rigid format for safety assessment. It also results in technical overspecification (which is costly and sometimes counterproductive to real safety) and in impediments to technical advances. An example of the latter is the use of advanced computer techniques in control rooms. These were delayed because of licensing problems. The Appendix K approach to licensing, however, is now being modified to include more operating experience and a wider spectrum of accidents identified in the PRAs.

Loss of Coolant Accidents (LOCAs)

Among the DBAs of Class 8, the safety considerations and analysis must include the possibility that, despite all the measures taken in the design, construction, testing, and inspection of the piping and in the operating and maintenance of the plant, a large break in the primary coolant loop will occur. It turns out by calculation that the most severe PWR break case is the double-ended guillotine severance of the reactor inlet section of the piping (also called the "cold leg"). If this were to occur, the reactor coolant would be rapidly expelled from both ends of the broken pipe.

This sudden loss of core coolant water, which acts also as a neutron moderator, causes an almost instantaneous shutdown of the neutron chain reaction inside the core. However, the fuel elements in the core contain stored energy and continue to generate heat from the decay of the fission products accumulated during the operation of the reactor. The levels of decay heat present in the reactor core at various times after shutdown are shown in Figure 18.20.

The first approach to countering this problem is to take the necessary steps to minimize the probability of such an accident; namely, to prevent a large rupture of the primary system. This approach was taken by the nuclear industry with the adoption of an industry-wide code (Section III, Nuclear Vessels, of the ASME Boiler and Pressure Vessel Code and a similar code for pressure piping) with which all construction materials, design criteria, fabrication methods, testing procedures, in-service inspection, quality assurance, and quality control must comply. A second line of defense was established by providing instrumented leak detection systems as protective devices, meant to detect quickly abnormal conditions, such as the beginning of small cracks, and to arrest or fix them. These systems are complemented by inspection and in-service testing.

Despite all these measures, it is generally recognized that there exists a finite, nonzero probability for a sudden large pipe break to occur, and, hence, for a LOCA. All present-day nuclear reactors are, therefore, provided with auxiliary systems to cool the reactor in the event of loss of coolant. These systems are known as Emergency Core Cooling Systems (ECCS) and are described in Chapter 17.

Assumptions for Safety Criteria

The calculations used by NRC in siting nuclear plants and determining evacuation policy stem from the source term mandated in 10CFR100. The "Part 100" source term, developed in technical document TID-14844, was originally for siting purposes only and was not intended to be realistic. Developed over 25 yr ago, the source term specified the release of radioactivity to the atmosphere in a nuclear accident as determined by the NRC staff for the licensing of nuclear plants. Although

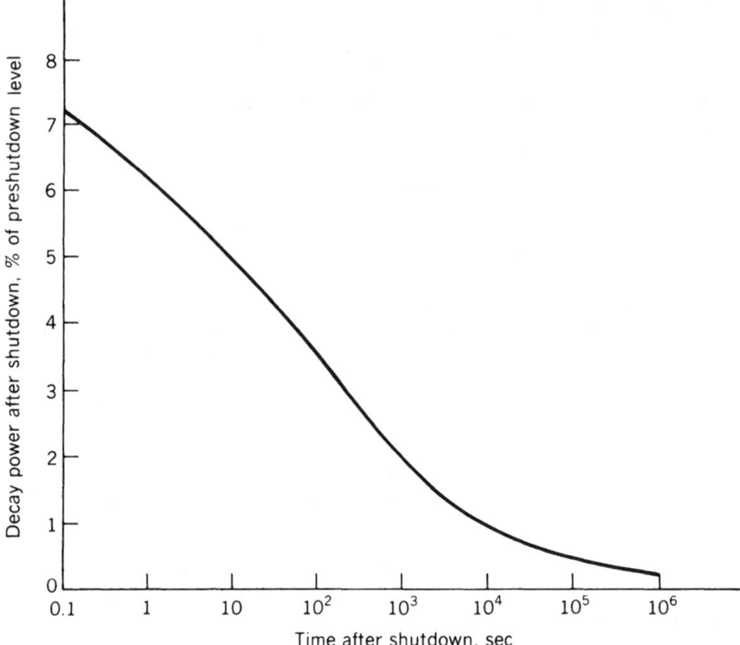

Figure 18.20. Thermal power after reactor shutdown.

the NRC rule-making hearings in the 1960s led to the adoption of ECCS systems in all plants, the licensing source term has not changed. As a result, its present value does not take into account successful ECCS operation, nor the improved technical information that has accumulated on the behavior of fission products since TID-14844 was first developed. The NRC has maintained the Part 100 source term as a basis for regulation (a) to ensure stability in the regulatory process and (b) to maintain continuity of acceptability from one design to the next.

This policy of maintaining the Part 100 source term is undergoing a reevaluation at NRC. The trend is to go from the fixed release fractions presented in Part 100 to a spectrum of accident scenarios which are defined from risk and consequence modeling, which treat mechanistically the release of radioactivity in an accident (see Chapter 17). Risk and consequence modeling is now becoming an integral part of the NRC approach to criteria for (a) system design, (b) siting, and (c) emergency response planning. Class 9 accidents are now specifically included in setting these criteria. The NRC licensing source term serves as the basis for emergency response planning on both the federal and state level. The general distribution of responsibilities and planning relationship in emergency situations is shown in Figure 18.21.

Emergency Response Planning

The origin of emergency planning requirements and the regulatory programs devoted to their establishment stem from an initial effort to define the potential consequences of a severe accident at a commercial nuclear power plant (WASH-740), followed by an attempt to define the most severe reactor accident that could reasonably be expected to occur and to place limits on the need to consider the consequences of such accidents in plant design and siting (10 CFR Part 100, TID-14844, Regulatory Guides 1.3 and 1.4). The nonmechanistic, conservative approaches taken in these efforts were improved upon by use of a mechanistic quantitative probabilistic risk assessment approach in the *Reactor Safety Study* (WASH-1400) to predict fission product releases from severe reactor consequences and their potential off-site consequences. The accident sequences, release source terms, containment behavior factors, transport mechanisms and parameters, and dose conversion assumptions from these studies and regulatory documents form the basic assumptions used as the bases for defining estimated severe reactor accidents and the requirements for their management. Since various documents were developed over a span exceeding 10 yr, it is not surprising that the concepts, data, and analytical approaches vary among them, leading, in turn, to

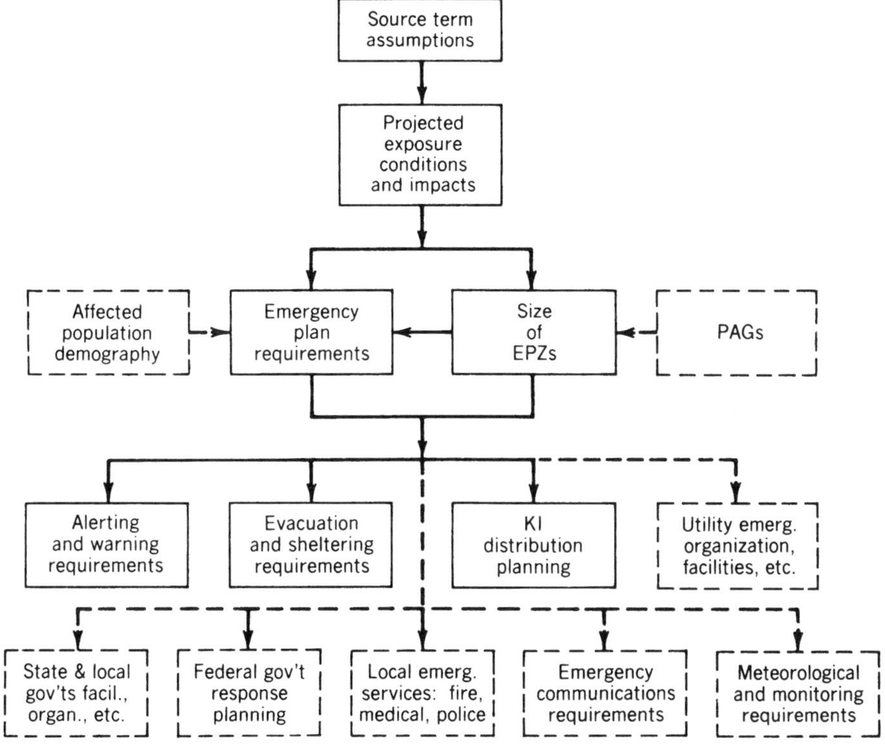

Figure 18.21. Generalized emergency planning relationships.

variance in the emergency planning requirements and guidance which are in large measure based upon them.

In 1976, the NRC began a more substantive review of emergency planning requirements, starting with a recommended planning basis for state and local emergency plans for LWRs (NUREG-0396), followed closely with draft emergency action level guidelines (NUREG-0610) and criteria for preparation and evaluation of radiological emergency response plans (NUREG-0654, Rev. 1). These documents depended heavily on studies encompassing such subjects as consequence modeling and efficacy of protective measures (NUREG/CR-1131 and NUREG/CR-1433), all of which obtained data and assumptions from the reactor safety studies discussed above. On the licensing side, NRC established regulatory requirements for accident consequence analysis and for emergency planning and management through its regulations (10 CFR Parts 100 and 50, Appendix E), regulatory guides (including Regulatory Guides 1.3 and 1.4) and policy statements (e.g., 44 *FR* 61123). Other federal and quasifederal agencies also developed companion requirements and guidance in the areas of radiation protection standards and protective action guidance (RFC, EPA, and FDA), emergency planning requirements (FEMA), and guidance to public health authorities (FDA, EPA, and NCRP). These ancillary requirements, which are to some degree locked into NRC's regulatory requirements by cross reference, also are based largely upon data, technical approaches, and analytical assumptions from both the basic safety studies and the secondary requirements and guidance derived from such studies in the NRC emergency planning methodology, as shown in Figure 18.22.

18.10. UNRESOLVED SAFETY ISSUES

The NRC continually evaluates safety requirements used in its reviews. As license applications have been scrutinized in the past several years, general categories of problems have emerged. These problems usually have low probabilities but their occurrence could have significant undesirable effects, such as a LOCA.

Generic issues are general technical matters relating to safety, safeguards, or environmental

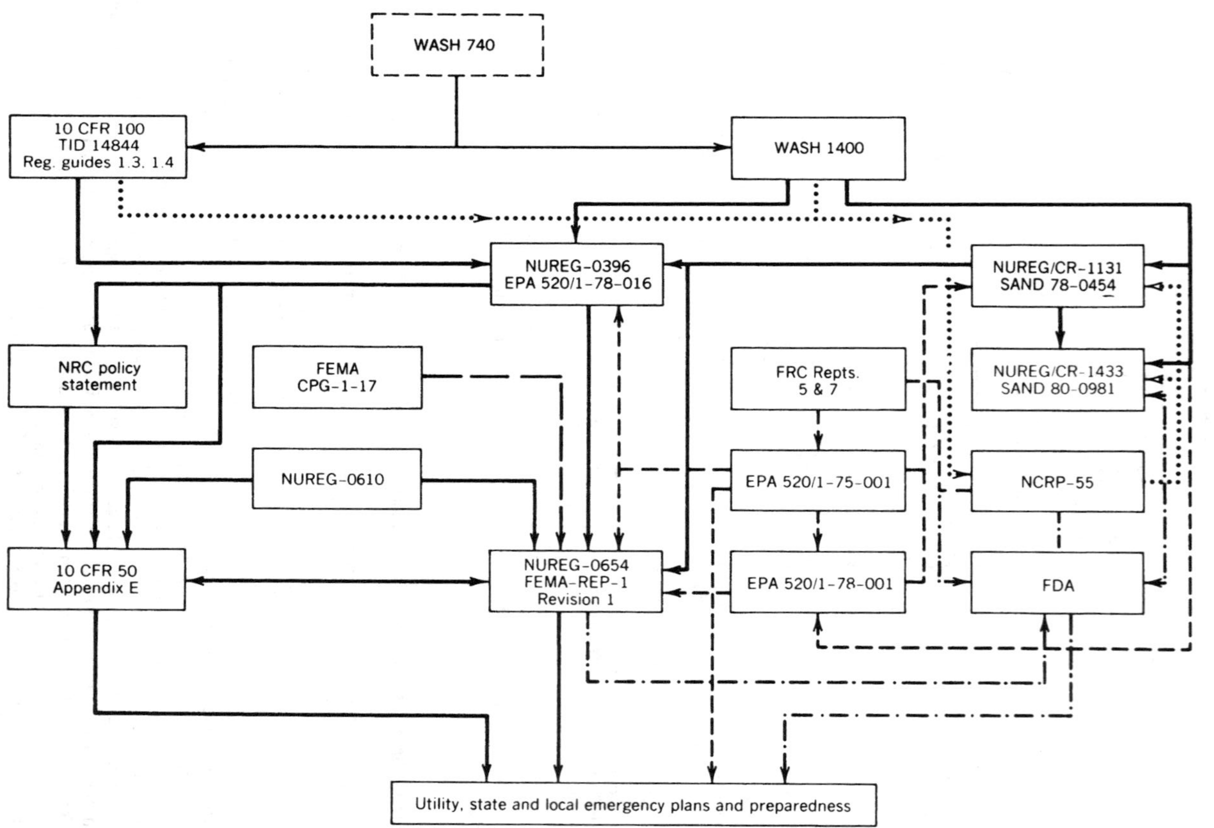

Figure 18.22. Interdependence of emergency planning requirements and guidance. (Courtesy of G. Sauter.)

aspects of nuclear power plant design, construction, or operation which are applicable to all or to a subset of all plant types. Most generic issues are identified in the review of individual applications. However, because generic issues are not limited to a specific plant, they are not handled as part of an individual licensing case. Categorization of an issue as generic typically delays its resolution. Because these issues are treated on a general basis and are not regarded as impediments to individual plant licensing, little incentive exists for their prompt resolution.

Impetus for addressing generic issues comes primarily from the Advisory Committee on Reactor Safeguards, which since 1972 has identified these issues during its review of utility applicants to construct or operate nuclear power plants.

As the various generic problems are identified, the NRC assesses the need for action to assure safe operation of nuclear power plants. In some cases, immediate correction of the safety problem is required. In other cases, the plant operating procedures may be modified until the problem is studied and resolved. In still other cases, the NRC may decide that the problem is not serious enough for immediate action, but may want to study the problem further to determine whether additional safety requirements are needed. The NRC defines this last group as "Unresolved Safety Issues." To address these issues, the NRC initiates programs and studies aimed at publishing governing regulatory guides. NUREG-0510 was published in January 1979 and is a report to Congress on the 17 identified "unresolved safety issues" of that time.

Although the precise number of generic issues has fluctuated as some are redefined or recategorized and others identified for the first time in licensing actions or elsewhere, some progress has been made in this area. The current listing of unresolved safety issues, which appeared in the February 1983 issue of the *NRC AQUA Book*, includes 12 items. These are:

1. Water hammer.
2. Steam generator tube integrity.
3. Fracture toughness of steam generators and reactor coolant pump supports.
4. Systems interactions in nuclear power plants.
5. Seismic design criteria.
6. Containment emergency sump performance.
7. Station blackout.
8. Shutdown decay heat removal requirements.
9. Seismic qualification of equipment in operating plants.
10. Safety implications of control systems.
11. Hydrogen control measured and effects of hydrogen burns on safety equipment.
12. Pressurized thermal shock.

A short description of these issues now follows:

Water hammer (or steam hammer) incidents have involved steam generator feed lines and piping, emergency core cooling systems, and containment spray, service water, feedwater, and steam lines. The incidents have been attributed to such causes as rapid condensation of steam pockets, steam-driven slugs of water, pump start-up with partially empty lines, and rapid valve motion. Most of the damage reported has been relatively minor, involving pipe hangers and restraints; however, there have been several incidents which have resulted in piping and valve damage.

The steam generators tube integrity problem involves the PWRs steam generators tubes, whose integrity can be degraded by corrosion-induced wastage, cracking, reduction in tube diameter (denting), and vibration-induced fatigue cracks. The primary concern is the capability of degraded tubes to maintain their integrity during normal operation and under accident conditions (LOCA or a main steam line break) with adequate safety margins.

Fracture toughness of steam generators and pump supports was discovered as an issue during the course of licensing action for North Anna Power Station Units 1 and 2. A number of issues regarding the potential for lamellar tearing and low fracture toughness of the steam generator and the reactor coolant pump support materials were raised. In the case of the North Anna Station, auxiliary electrical heat will be supplied as necessary to supplement the heat derived from the reactor coolant loop to obtain the required operating temperature of the support materials. However, since similar materials and designs have been used on other nuclear plants, the concerns regarding the supports for the North Anna facilities are applicable to other PWR plants. It was therefore necessary to reassess the fracture toughness of the steam generators and reactor coolant pump support materials for all operating PWR plants and those in CP and OL review. Lamellar tearing may also be a problem in those support structures similar in design to North Anna. This possibility will be investigated on a generic basis.

Systems interactions in nuclear power plants involve questions regarding the interaction of various plant systems, both as to the supporting roles such systems play and as to the effect one system can have on other systems, particularly with regard to whether actions or consequences could adversely affect the presumed redundancy and independence of the safety systems.

The seismic design process required by current NRC criteria includes the following sequence of events:

1. Define the magnitude or intensity of the earthquake which will produce the maximum vibratory ground motion at the site (the Safe Shutdown Earthquake or SSE).
2. Determine the free-field ground motion at the site that would result if the SSE occurred.
3. Determine the motion of site structures by modifying the free-field motion to account for the interaction of the site structures with the underlying foundation soil.
4. Determine the motion of the plant equipment supported by the site structures.
5. Compare the seismic loads, in appropriate combination with other loads, on structures, systems, and components important to safety, with the allowable loads.

While this seismic design sequence includes many conservative factors, certain aspects of the sequence may not be conservative for all plant sites. At present, it is believed that the overall sequence is adequately conservative. The objective of the seismic design criteria program is to investigate selected areas of the seismic design sequence to determine their conservatism for all types of sites, to investigate alternate approaches to parts of the design sequence, to quantify the overall conservatism of the design sequence, and to modify the NRC criteria in the standard review plan.

The concerns regarding containment emergency sump performance have to do with the sequence of safety systems operation following a LOCA in a PWR. The principal concerns are somewhat interrelated but are best discussed separately. One deals with the various kinds of insulation used on piping and components inside of containment, the concern being that break-initiated debris from the insulation could cause blockage of the sump or otherwise adversely affect the operation of the pumps, spray nozzles, and valves of the safety systems.

The second deals with the hydraulic performance of the sump as related to the hydraulic performance of safety systems supplied therefrom. Preoperational tests have been performed on a number of plants to demonstrate operability in the recirculation mode. Adverse flow conditions have been encountered, requiring design and procedural modifications to eliminate them. These conditions, air entrainment, cavitation, and vortex formation, are aggravated by blockage. If not avoided or suppressed, they could result in pump failure during the long-term cooling phase following a LOCA. The concerns relative to debris, blockage, and hydraulic performance also apply to boiling water reactors during recirculation from the suppression pools, and will also be addressed in the related research program.

The problem of station blackout involves the unlikely but possible loss of ac power, both from off-site sources and from the on-site source. In the event of a station blackout, the capability to cool the reactor core would be dependent on the availability of systems which do not require ac power supplies, and on the ability to restore ac power in a timely manner. The concern is that the occurrence of a station blackout may be a relatively high-probability event and that the consequences of this event may be unacceptable, for example, severe core damage may result.

Issues regarding shutdown decay heat removal requirements were raised following the Three Mile Island Reactor accident. The unresolved safety concerns under this grouping will require an evaluation of the adequacy of the current licensing design requirements, in order to ensure that nuclear power plants do not pose an unacceptable risk due to failure to remove shutdown decay heat. The objective will be to develop a comprehensive and consistent set of shutdown cooling requirements for existing and future LWRs, including the study of alternative means of shutdown decay heat removal and the study of diverse "dedicated" systems for this purpose.

The design criteria and methods for the seismic qualification of mechanical and electrical equipment in nuclear power plants have undergone significant change during the course of the commercial nuclear power program. Consequently, the margins of safety provided in existing equipment to resist seismically induced loads and perform the intended safety functions may vary considerably. The seismic qualification of the equipment in operating plants must, therefore, be reassessed to ensure the ability to bring the plant to a safe shutdown condition when it is subject to a seismic event. The objective of this unresolved safety issue is to establish an explicit set of guidelines that could be used to judge the adequacy of the seismic qualification of mechanical and electrical equipment at all operating plants. This guidance will concern equipment required to safely shut down the plant, as well as equipment whose function is not required for safe shutdown, but whose failure could result in adverse conditions which might impair shutdown functions.

The issue of safety implications of control systems concerns the potential for accidents or transients being made more severe as a result of control system failures or malfunctions. These failures or malfunctions may occur independently or as a result of the accident or transient under consideration and would be in addition to any control system failure that may have initiated the event. Although it is generally believed that control system failures are not likely to result in loss of safety functions which could lead to serious events or result in conditions that safety systems are not able to cope with, in-depth studies have not been performed to support this belief.

The hydrogen control measures and the effects of hydrogen burns on safety equipment relate to postulated reactor accidents which result in a degraded or molten core and in generation and release to the containment of large quantities of hydrogen. The hydrogen is formed from the reaction of the zirconium fuel cladding with steam at high temperatures and/or by radiolysis of water. Experience gained from the TMI-2 accident indicates that more specific design provisions for handling larger hydrogen releases than currently allowed by the regulations particularly for smaller, low-pressure containment designs, may be required.

The unresolved safety issue for a pressurized thermal shock arises out of the fact that neutron irradiation of reactor pressure vessel welds and plant materials decreases the fracture toughness of the materials. The fracture toughness sensitivity to radiation-induced change is increased by presence of certain materials such as copper. Decreased fracture toughness makes it more likely that, if a severe overcooling event occurs followed by or concurrent with high vessel pressure, and if a small crack is present on the vessel's inner surface, that crack could grow to a size that might threaten vessel integrity. Severe pressurized overcooling events are improbable since they require multiple failures and improper operator performance. However, certain precursor events have happened that could have potentially threatened vessel integrity if additional failures had occurred and/or if the vessel had been more highly irradiated. Therefore, the possibility of vessel failure due to a severe pressurized overcooling event cannot be ruled out.

All of these safety issues are concerned ultimately with the prevention of unsafe levels of radiation exposure to the public. The technical concern always comes down to one fundamental requirement: to remove heat from the fuel with water at least as fast as the heat is being generated. To that end, a defense-in-depth design philosophy is employed. This seeks to assure the cooling rates required by providing a diverse, redundant, and separate mix of cooling methods which can cope with any realistic scenario envisioned. The result is a set of systems that can effectively cope with all of the postulated failure situations not specifically enumerated. Efforts expended solely on the biggest problems that can be foreseen can be self-defeating if not enough effort is also spent on the many smaller events that can grow into major problems. For this reason, many items, including the steam generator tube integrity, systems interaction, and containment emergency sump reliability items deserve special attention.

Technologically, the safety issues can be divided into three groups: (1) limit of the required duty unknown (issues 1, 12, 8, 5, 6, and 7); (2) environmental life of equipment (issues 3, 2, 10, and 9); and (3) system capabilities unknown (issues 11 and 4). The first group addresses design basis criteria now used by suppliers of systems and components. It has not been resolved whether certain systems and components can withstand all combinations of operating "duties" during the life of the plant. The range and severity of these duties is a combination of operational experience and speculation.

In the second group, it is known that plant equipment can successfully withstand the combination of duties (normal and abnormal). However, there remains doubt that the component in question can survive a long period in a given environment. Resolution of these safety issues can be accomplished only after lengthy environmental tests of the components in question. The third group is concerned with accidents that could result from combinations of systems and component failures. It is resolved that certain degraded combinations, which could result in a LOCA, are safeguarded. The solution now used is massive redundancy, diversification, and separation of functions.

The NRC annually evaluates the unresolved safety issues, and assesses the risk. From these studies, the NRC determines what action is needed, if any. Further work is done to determine whether existing requirements should be modified for new plants, and if backfitting is needed for plants already under construction or in operation.

18.11. POST-THREE MILE ISLAND CONCERNS

Technical Modifications

The accident at Three Mile Island 2 has shed a new and urgent light on a number of issues. Although not entirely new to the safety R&D community, these are now being pursued with greater intensity and a sense of purpose. Risk assessment activities have accelerated in a large number of plant-specific applications in order to obtain a better evaluation of risk trends as designs, locations, and other related parameters change. The methodology is being scrutinized at several levels in order to obtain reliable and widely acceptable results. The older fault and event tree methodologies are now being supplemented by other methodologies in full-scale applications.

The ability to process data in nearly real time so that the trends can be observed as they take place is an objective that has emerged to prominence recently. A considerable body of work related to real time analysis and display, which was initiated at EPRI before the TMI-2 accident, exists today. An example is the Power Shape Monitoring System (PSMS), already installed at the Oyster Creek plant. The system, with a number of fast predictive and display capabilities, has already provided its usefulness during a transient in that plant. Another current example is the Disturbance Analysis and Surveillance System (DASS) now under development. This work will initially focus on the installation of a safety panel that will assist the operator to understand the status of important safety functions at the plant during transients and to take appropriate measures to avert further deterioration. The ultimate goal of the system would be to alert the operator to the onset of disturbances and to help prevent them altogether. Core uncovery possibly occurred at TMI-2. To understand the phenomena, particularly heat transfer, during such an event, tests are being conducted at various facilities throughout the world.

Degraded core cooling was investigated in a small-scale facility using a bed of debris to simulate a severely degraded core. Hydrogen is a combustible gas that may be produced from water decomposition by zirconium at elevated temperatures. To understand the details of hydrogen combustion, detonation, and deflagration, and the effect of moisture and sprays, large-scale tests are being planned. They are expected to yield additional data for anticipating and predicting hydrogen behavior and to assist in providing means for its effective management. In this connection, containment studies are also being conducted to provide a more solid quantification of safety margins built in the containment designs used in nuclear plants.

Emergency Response Risks

Recent work has suggested that the WASH-1400 study is incomplete in assessing all aspects of accident risk. When accident consequence estimates lead to actions (such as evacuation of an area) that pose significant safety, health, and economic risks, these estimates must be consistent with what is likely to occur. In addition, the risks posed by a nuclear accident and the mitigating action should be evaluated on the same basis. If the risks of the mitigating action are treated less conservatively than the accident risks, incorrect conclusions will be reached and faulty emergency strategies may result.

To model the effects of a given emergency response, detailed sheltering and evacuation models exist which consider the dynamics of radioactive plume dispersal and population movement. Even with the models and source terms used in the WASH-1400 study, the technical basis for widescale evacuation is marginal. For core-melt accidents, the off-site dose would probably exceed those specified in EPA's draft Protective Action Guides only within a very limited area outside a reactor site boundary. It is only within this area that it might be prudent to consider evacuation, although it is not necessarily more effective than sheltering, in mitigating the whole body dose to the population. The time before such a radiation exposure threat would evolve is relatively long. However, it should be recognized that if a threat were to materialize very early in an accident, sheltering would be the only real option. Also, it should be recognized that although it may be prudent to develop evacuation plans, the decision to implement such a plan should be based on actual conditions that exist at the time.

Considerable safety margins are provided by sheltering and controlled air supply; these mean nothing more complicated than staying indoors, closing the doors and windows, and shutting off ventilation fans. The relative merits of evacuation versus sheltering depend greatly on the particulars of a given accident. Parameters to be considered include severity, site location, and meteorological conditions. However, only in a few instances, and only for a few individuals, does it appear that evacuation will be better than sheltering. Precise answers to the questions of whether to evacuate particular individuals, when to evacuate them, how far, and in which direction are site- and accident-specific. The concept that evacuation of very large areas is desirable or necessary for public safety is probably wrong on both counts.

In estimating the real risk to the public from an accident at a nuclear power plant, several quantities are important: the probability and consequence of the accident itself and the risk resulting from any mitigating action taken. The uncertainties of the risk associated with the accident seem to be dominated by the uncertainties of the consequence estimates. The current procedure of using "conservative" assumptions (usually at each stage) in the calculations produces an estimate of the risk that is likely to be much too high, by an order of magnitude or more.

18.12. SAFETY GOALS POLICY AND DEVELOPMENT PLAN

The Need for a Safety Goal

A major concept related to changes in the NRC technical regulations is the use of safety goals to establish regulatory requirements and gauge the need for changes in those requirements. In its simplest form, a safety goal could be just a statement of NRC safety philosophy that clarifies the commission's policy toward safety. At the opposite extreme, safety goals could place quantitative limits on the risks from nuclear power plants to which workers and the public are exposed.

It is noted that the absence of a safety goal is a major concern with the NRC regulatory base, because of the lack of standards that systematically address the question of acceptable levels of risk for overall plant operation. As a result, it can be argued, decision making tends to be focused on a case-by-case basis, thereby affording those in the process little in the way of certainty and predictability. Rather, the lack of a safety goal has led the NRC to promulgate conservative criteria that have caused the analysis of lower and lower probability events and the inclusion of additional features in plants to mitigate the consequences of such events. Thus this lack has detracted from concern for less severe accidents that are more likely to occur from the same initiating event. A related concern stems from the current reliance on methodologies which are used primarily because they can generate a documentable record and can calculate theoretical analyses of safety impacts, but require designers to reject design choices which cannot be documented so clearly but instead rely on judgment and experience gained from actual nuclear plant operation. These concerns, articulated in the several studies and analyses of the TMI accident and its aftermath, have eventually resulted in the new Safety Goals Proposal made by the NRC.

NRC Safety Goals Proposal

The NRC published in March 1983 a policy statement titled Safety Goals for the Operation of Nuclear Power Plants. This policy statement contains preliminary safety goals and preliminary numerical design objectives that are intended to be consistent with the goals (see Table 17.6). The goals and objectives are preliminary in that they are subject to change at the end of a 2-yr evaluation period. The commission has also published the staff's plan for the 2-yr evaluation period, which is an initial description of the activities to be performed during this period. The evaluation plan stresses caution in making comparisons or safety inferences because such analyses may not have been performed on a consistent basis, and because there may be large uncertainties inherent in the existing probabilistic risk assessments. In particular, there are uncertainties in the source term that represents the amount of radioactive material that may be released from the reactor containment in a severe accident, as discussed above. Therefore, during the evaluation period, NRC will strive to set forth more consistent analytical bases and improve the treatment of uncertainties in the calculations, *including use of a new source term which is currently being developed.* NRC will also reassess the probabilistic risk assessments that have already been performed and compare the results to the preliminary safety goals and design objectives.

The NRC's policy statement focuses on the risks to the public from nuclear power plant operation. These are the risks from release of radioactive materials from the reactor to the environment related to normal operations as well as to reactor accidents. The potential risks from the nuclear fuel cycle, which have been considered in their own right and determined to be quite small, are not considered in the Safety Goals Proposal; neither are the possible effects of sabotage or diversion of nuclear materials, which cannot be properly quantified.

The NRC's first qualitative safety goal is that the risk from nuclear power plant operation should not be a significant contributor to a person's risk of accidental death or injury. This goal formally states that individual members of the public should be provided a level of protection from the consequences of nuclear power plant operation such that individuals bear no significant additional risk to life and health. The risks of nuclear power plant operation should be comparable to or less than the risks from other viable means of generating the same quantity of electrical energy. Thus, the commission's second safety goal is:

> *Societal risks to life and health from nuclear power plant operation should be comparable to or less than the risks of generating electricity by viable competing technologies and should not be a significant addition to other societal risks.*

The comparative part of this goal is to be interpreted as requiring that the risks from nuclear power plant operation are comparable to or less than the risks of the operation of competing electricity generating plants, particularly coal-fired plants.

The commission has decided to adopt the following two design objectives:

1. The risk to an average individual in the vicinity of a nuclear power plant of prompt fatality that might result from reactor accidents should not exceed one-tenth of one percent (0.1%) of the sum of prompt fatality risks resulting from other accidents to which members of the U.S. population are generally exposed.
2. The risk to the population in the area near a nuclear power plant of cancer fatalities that might result from nuclear power plant operation should not exceed one-tenth of one percent (0.1%) of the sum of cancer fatality risks resulting from all other causes.

The commission has adopted that 0.1% ratio of the risks of nuclear power plant operation to the risks of mortality from non-nuclear plant origin to reflect the first qualitative goal, which would provide that individuals bear no significant additional risk. The 0.1% ratio to other risks is low enough to support an expectation that people living or working near nuclear power plants would have no special concern due to the plant's proximity.

In applying the design objective for individual risk of prompt fatality, the commission has proposed to define the vicinity as the area within 1 mile of the nuclear power plant site boundary since calculations of the consequences of major reactor accidents suggest that individuals within a mile of the plant site boundary would generally be subject to the greatest risk of prompt death attributable to radiological causes.

In applying the design objective for cancer fatalities, as a population guideline, the commission has proposed that the population generally considered subject to significant risk be taken as the population within 50 miles of the plant site. A substantial fraction of exposures of the population to radiation would be concentrated within this distance. This design objective would ensure that the estimated increase in the risk of delayed cancer fatalities from all potential radiation releases at a typical plant would be no more than a small fraction of the year-to-year normal variation in the expected cancer deaths from non-nuclear causes.

The commission has also adopted a benefit-cost guideline for use as one consideration in decisions on safety improvements. It has decided that a guideline of $1000/person-rem averted be adopted for trial use. This value is to be in 1983 dollars, and should be modified to reflect general inflation in the future.

This guideline is intended to encourage the efficient allocation of resources in safety-related activities by providing that the expected reduction in public risk that would be achieved should be commensurate with the costs of the proposed safety improvements. The benefit as measured by an incremental reduction of societal mortality risks in terms of person-rems averted should be compared with the reasonably quantifiable costs of achieving that benefit (e.g., design and construction of plant modifications, incremental cost of replacement power during mandated or extended outages, changes in operating procedures and manpower requirements).

To assure emphasis on accident prevention, the commission has decided to adopt a limitation on the probability of a large-scale core melt as an objective for NRC staff use in the course of reviewing and evaluating probabilistic risk assessments of nuclear power plants. The design objective for large-scale core melt is subordinate to the principal design objectives limiting individual and societal risks. Thus, the commission has selected the following design objective:

The likelihood of a nuclear reactor accident that results in a large-scale core melt should normally be less than 1 in 10,000 per year of reactor operation.

The commission has also recognized the importance of mitigating the consequences of a core-melt accident and continues to emphasize features such as containment, siting in less populated areas, and emergency planning as integral parts of the defense-in-depth concept. The basic impediment to adoption of regulations requiring risks to the public to be below certain quantitative limits, as exemplified by the quantitative design objective for large-scale core melt, is that the techniques for developing quantitative risk estimates are complex, and have substantial associated uncertainties. This raises a serious question whether, for a specific nuclear power plant, the achievement of a regulatory-imposed quantitative risk goal can be verified with a sufficient degree of confidence. For this reason, the commission has decided that, during the evaluation period, implementation of the policy statement should be limited to uses such as examining proposed and existing regulatory requirements, establishing research priorities, resolving generic issues, and defining the relative importance of issues as they arise.

It is expected that during the evaluation period familiarization may be gained with the techniques of risk estimation and sufficient data may be collected and analyzed so that the commission can decide whether to expand the use of the policy statement or to propose a rule-making process that would incorporate quantitative risk limits as design objectives in the regulations.

18.13. FOSSIL-FUEL-FIRED POWER PLANTS—ENVIRONMENTAL REGULATIONS

This section deals briefly with the evolution of emissions control regulations on fossil-fuel-fired power plants from the 1960s on. While not directly related to the topic of this chapter, the discussion nonetheless may provide interesting insights into the development of a parallel body of environmental and safety regulations.

Environmental legislation in the United States and regulations implemented at federal and state levels have historically resulted in imposition of increasingly stringent emissions limitations for fossil-fuel power plants. This situation has led to requirements for the utility industry to reduce emissions to the extent capable with existing, and in some cases, relatively unproven, technology.

Table 18.3. Trends in Environmental Regulations

Legislation	Emissions	Control Technology
1960s		
Clean Air Act	TSP, SO_2, NO_x	Tall stacks ESPs Low-sulfur fuels
Clean Water Act	Thermal	Cooling towers
Solid Waste Disposal Act	Open burning	Sanitary landfills
1970s	SO_2, TSP, NO_x	Scrubbers
Clean Air Act		ESPs Fabric filters Coal cleaning NO_x control
Clean Water Act	Thermal Blowdown	Cooling towers Intake structures Water treatment
Resource Conservation and Recovery Act	Hazardous wastes	Groundwater monitoring Liners for disposal ponds
Toxic Substances Control Act	PCBs	Substitution Incineration Sanitary landfills
1980s		
Superfund	Toxic/hazardous substances	Cleanup of abandoned waste disposal sites
Risk Assessment Criteria and Procedures	Consolidation of environmental regulations	Prioritization of control strategies
Alternative Marketplace Legislation	Air, water, solid waste	IEC Env. Auditing, multimedia bubbles and banking
1990s		
Treaty requirements	CO_2	IEC
Toxic substances control	Fine particulates Priority pollutants Hazardous wastes	IEC, visibility control IEC, zero discharge IEC, resource recovery

TEC = Total Suspended Particulates
ESP = ElectroStatic Precipitators
IEC = Integrated Emissions Control

Further, controls have historically been implemented in media-specific fashion with less than full regard for overall impacts on the functioning of the entire environmental control system.

To provide a framework for this discussion, four time periods have been proposed as shown in Table 18.3. For each period, distinct environmental issues appear to predominate. Each major issue area is described by examples of the primary legislation and regulations of the general time period and by the primary emissions or media regulated. Finally, the discussion focuses on how these regulations and legislation have impacted and may influence environmental control system design.

The 1960s demonstrated a discrete approach to environmental regulations. Each environmental media (air, water, solid waste) developed its own sense of history, a unique constituency, and separate regulatory frameworks. Inter-relationships between and among the media were given a low priority in both control agency planning and organizational structure.

The 1970s began with the formation of the Environmental Protection Agency which combined the separate emission control disciplines and constituencies. Although the EPA began integration strategies to create interrelationships between emission control efforts, the progress was hindered by the growth of legislation and regulations in each discrete area. When the Toxic Substances Control Act and the Resource Conservation and Recovery Act became law, a toxic perspective began to link environmental media more closely. Throughout this period environmental instrumentation was undergoing revolutionary change with vastly more sensitive instrumentation and testing methodologies. By the end of the 1970s, this sensing revolution was adding great strength to the growing consensus on integration of toxic substances control.

The major environmental issue of the 1980s is toxic substances control. Concern over hazardous chemicals in air, water, and solid waste has further pierced the individual emission control barriers, creating a consensus in the separate constituencies that future control includes integration. The emerging alternative policy mechanisms such as environmental auditing and emission trading (individual and multipollutant) contain environmental integration within their policy structures.

The 1990s can be expected to see Integration of Emission Controls (IEC) for fossil-fuel power plants recognized as the accepted approach for both new and existing plants. Forcing functions such as water conservation requirements, toxic substances concerns, and energy conservation sensitivities are likely to foster federal and state IEC technology policies. Alternative control options such as marketable emissions (obtained through "fine-tuning" an IEC system) could add a powerful economic incentive to the spread of IEC designs.

The impact of the changes in environmental regulations occurring during these four time periods on power plant design is significant. In the 1960s, environmental control requirements were a small part of the overall plant design. Today's regulatory requirements for air, water, and solid-waste discharges are a dominant factor in the design and operation of new coal-fired power plants. By the 1990s, integration of environmental control technology may be advanced by cost savings in energy and resources as well as by a greater focus on reducing the risks associated with potentially toxic substances.

18.14. CONCLUDING REMARKS

The TMI accident's related investigations have revealed an over-reliance by the regulatory agencies on detailed written regulations that seem to specify how a reactor should be designed and operated for safety. Writing these regulations and evaluating nuclear plants design and construction against these regulations have been the preoccupation of the regulatory agency. Developing the massive written responses required of each plant by these regulations has occupied much of the best talent within the nuclear industry. Complacent and erroneous attitudes of the industry and the NRC that safety is assured, once these regulations are complied with, have resulted. It is now recognized that the most effective function of the regulator is to specify overall performance criteria for safety and to review and evaluate the success of the industry in achieving this necessary safety performance. This joint approach to safety, utilizing the complementary skills of regulators, designers, and operators, earmarked the early development of safety systems. It placed the greatest and ultimate responsibility for achieving safety on the designers and operators. This fundamental approach to safety is no longer followed in present regulatory practice.

There are other problems with the current U.S. regulatory approach. The regulations themselves have not been developed with an adequate focus on what the most important elements of safety are and how they can be achieved. These regulations and guidelines have been developed without quantified safety goals and objectives; many safety concerns have been postulated and acted upon without adequate evaluation of their importance to safety. A disproportionate effort on the part of government and industry has been required for some relatively minor issues. Many of the requirements are arbitrary, having neither a valid technical basis nor value-impact analysis. Without any criteria or yardstick for "how safe is safe enough?" no clear means exist for the NRC to set priorities according to risk and degree of safety achieved. Lack of such criteria invites overly zealous demonstration of concern for safety by regulators, particularly under the scrutiny of public criticism, with little or no balancing of the safety benefits against the cost of achieving them. The recently approved NRC Safety Goal Policy Statement and the Evaluation Plan for this policy go a long way toward rectifying this problem.

Another problem in the present approach to nuclear safety is its adversarial nature. What is mainly a process of technical specification, design, and review for safety has often become submerged in the adversarial legal process of the NRC. The process inhibits the interchange of technical information between the NRC and industry. Lack of such interchange was a contributor to the TMI accident. Also, the regulatory system suffers because it is not based upon a comprehensive approach to the entire plant. A large proportion of the regulatory staff specializes in narrow topics; relatively few systems engineers possess the experience needed to integrate individual safety features into an overall concept and to place issues in perspective.

Management of nuclear safety requires a competent regulatory approach which is aimed at identifying the main goals and problems of safety, specifies and evaluates safety performance, and is implemented by realistic analysis and diagnosis.

Even the most competent of regulatory agencies cannot, however, assure nuclear safety. The primary responsibility rests with the operating company, together with the engineering firms and equipment suppliers that design and build the plant. The operating company must expend sufficient manpower and energy to go beyond fulfilling the requirements of the regulatory agency. It and its suppliers must have qualified manpower to attend to all problems of nuclear safety, whether or not they are required by regulations. They must take the initiative in innovating ideas and procedures to maintain and enhance nuclear safety, for the ultimate benefit of the utility, its customers, and society in general.

CHAPTER 19
NUCLEAR POWER ECONOMICS

19.1. INTRODUCTION

This section covers the commercial nuclear power plants operated in U.S. electrical systems today, and similar plants that will begin operation in the next 10–12 yr.

The economic comparisons in this chapter are made in the context of the U.S. electric utilities' economic conditions. For all practical purposes, general costs from pressurized water reactors (PWRs) and boiling water reactors (BWRs) are equal. Both may be referred to as light-water reactors (LWR) electricity production costs, and compared with similar coal-fired plant costs in various regions in the country. Whereas nuclear plant costs are to some degree regionally dependent due to varying plant construction expenses, coal plant costs vary widely with the kind of coal used, the pollution control method, and the distance between the mine and the power plant. Thus regional cost differences are much more pronounced in the case of coal-fired versus LWRs. A recent regional comparison of current coal and nuclear plants generation costs is shown in Figure 19.1.

In order to cost compare generating units scheduled to be installed in a decade or more hence, whose service lives may extend to 2020 or 2030, one must express all costs in one of two ways: (1) in constant dollars, using carrying charge rates which exclude the inflation component of the cost of money, and include only real escalation rates above inflationary effects; or (2) in current dollars, projecting the course of inflation and making sure that the options compared have comparable service dates and lives. Examples of cost comparisons in this chapter use either of these two methods, as stated. Constant-cost comparisons are usually preferred by R&D organizations that evaluate various future technology options and by government organizations that have to justify large-scale multiyear projects. This method is used in the European countries and in centrally planned economies. Current-cost comparison methods are preferred, on the other hand, by business organizations or by electric utilities, where the exact computation of the actual annual expenditures is essential for proper budgeting and business planning. A comparison of generation costs with and without inflation is shown in Figure 19.2.

Power plant electricity generation costs are usually broken down into three major categories: capital, fuel, and operating and maintenance.

Capital-related expenses include all investments in the construction of the power plant. This includes the real materials, labor, and construction expenditures, as well as interest charges during the construction period and the front-end costs of preparing detailed designs and environmental review documents. This stream of expenses is then converted to an equivalent stream of levelized annual capital charges which form a significant portion of the total generation costs. Two additional cost items recently added to the annual nuclear capital charges are the costs of eventual plant decommissioning and the cost of periodic cleaning or extensive maintenance. Both cost items are considered as a form of annual carrying charge payments which accumulate over a specific period to the total sum required, and are thus treated as equivalent annual capital charges.

Fuel costs include all expenses related to fuel mining, preparation, burning, and waste disposal—the entire set of fuel cycle expenditures. The nuclear fuel cycle is, in general, more complex than the coal cycle. It involves a larger number of steps along the entire cycle, and each of these steps has to be accounted for separately. The coal fuel cycle exhibits a more pronounced regional variation, as mentioned before. The nuclear fuel cycle both before and after use in the power plants extends over a much longer time period than the coal cycle.

Operating and maintenance (O&M) costs include all other expenses related to the annual operation of the power plant. These expenses usually include a fixed portion (independent of the plant's actual capacity factor), which is comprised mostly of materials costs, and a variable costs portion, which is directly related to reactor operation. O&M costs are the smallest component of

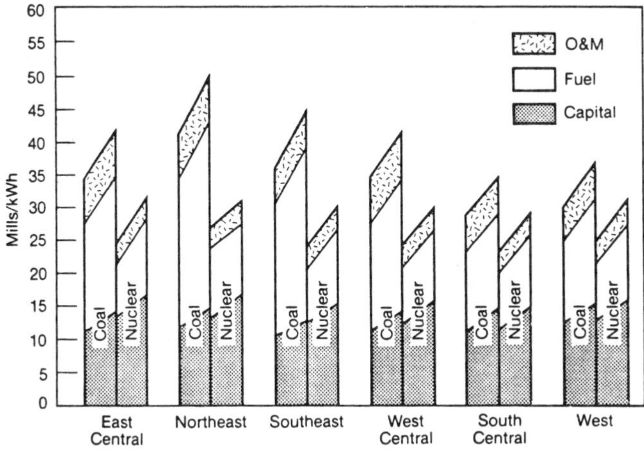

Figure 19.1. Levelized generation costs of nuclear and coal-fired plants. (From Reference 1.)

	Generating Cost,[a] Mills/kWh Inflation Rate, %/yr				
	0	6	8	9	10
Nuclear, 2 × 1200 MWe	30.2	87.0	119.8	140.7	164.2
Fossil,[b] 3 × 800 MWe					
Coal, Hi-S w/FGD	34.8	94.0	128.0	148.8	172.4
Coal, Lo-S w/o FGD	30.6	82.5	112.2	130.5	151.2
Coal, Lo-S w/FGD	35.2	95.3	129.9	151.0	175.0
Oil, Lo-S w/o FGD	76.7	189.5	251.6	289.0	331.3

[a]Costs for O&M and fuel are 10-yr levelized; all costs are in 1991 $ except 0% inflation case results which are in 1981 $.
[b]Hi-S = High Sulfur. Lo-S = Low Sulfur. FGD = Flue Gas Desulfurization.

Figure 19.2. Levelized plant generating cost summary. (From Reference 2.)

the total nuclear electricity generation costs, though they have significantly increased in recent years.

The levelized electricity generation costs of nuclear and coal-fired power plants are shown in Table 19.1. The total costs are computed both on a current and on a constant-dollar basis, and are broken down into capital, fuel, and O&M costs. Four other kinds of coal–nuclear cost comparisons are shown in Figures 19.3 to 19.6. These demonstrate the various forms of presenting future nuclear–coal generation cost differentials. The computations relate mostly to future power plants to be commissioned within this decade. Table 19.2 shows a 6-yr comparison of coal and nuclear generation costs in a large midwestern utility. A national average power production cost comparison for 1981 is shown in Table 19.3.

In all cases, nuclear power production is found to be cheaper than coal electric generation by 7 to 28%. The apparent economic advantage of nuclear electricity production for baseload generation is, however, regional and time dependent. A detailed analysis of the various cost components may show specific regions in the Central and Midwestern parts of the United States where low coal price escalation rates may result in an economic advantage to coal electric power plants over LWRs. The overall conclusion, though, is that in some regions of the United States nuclear power plants continue to be the most economic choice for baseload generation. A detailed analysis of all the relevant cost factors is, however, essential in comparing power plant alternatives at each specific site.

The dramatic reversals in the ambitious plans to expand nuclear electric capacity which was recently manifested in the cancellation of many nuclear plants,† is attributed to five major underly-

†See Appendix A.4.

Table 19.1. Total Power Generation Costs (1982 Dollars)

	Levelized Cost, Mills/kWh		
	LWR Once-Through	LWR Recycle	Eastern Coal
Capital	29.5	29.5	22.2
O&M	6.3	6.3	5.4
Fuel	10.7	10.2	29.0
Decommissioning	0.4	0.4	0.0
Total (constant $)	46.9	46.4	56.6
Total (current $)	192	190	232

Source: From Reference 3.

ing causes: lower forecasted load growth, constraints on the ability to finance construction, reversals in the cost advantage of nuclear power over coal-fired generation, a changing and uncertain regulatory climate, and denials of plant certification by some state power plant siting authorities. Of these, the first three factors appear to be responsible for most of the cancellations.

Six to fifteen years ago, when utilities made initial commitments to construct the nuclear units that they subsequently canceled, both industry and federal government studies gave nuclear power a significant cost advantage over coal-fired generation in most regions of the country. In the intervening years, this cost advantage has narrowed to the point where today, in most regions, nuclear power no longer offers a clear cost advantage over coal and additionally involves a greater degree of uncertainty. One consequence of this is that many utilities, and their regulators, are reexamining ongoing nuclear projects from the perspective of whether they should be canceled, and whether less uncertain options, such as coal-fired power plants, be constructed instead.

	Nuclear	Coal
Assumptions:		
Plant life (yr)	30	30
Capacity factor (%)	65	65
Fuel cost escalation (%)	2	2
Plant size (MWe)	1000	600
Fixed-charge rate	18	18

Results are life-cycle levelized costs in 1982 dollars (¢/kWh)

Year of Initial Operation	Capital Cost: Base[a]	Capital Cost: Time-Related[b]	Fuel-Cycle Cost	O&M Cost	Total Power Cost
Coal					
1982	0.61	1.13	2.42	0.63	4.79
1984	0.64	1.17	2.52	0.63	4.96
1986	0.66	1.22	2.62	0.63	5.14
1988	0.69	1.27	2.72	0.63	5.31
1990	0.72	1.32	2.83	0.63	5.50
Nuclear					
1982	0.80	1.50	0.82	0.67	3.78
1984	0.83	1.56	0.84	0.67	3.89
1986	0.86	1.63	0.85	0.67	4.00
1988	0.90	1.69	0.87	0.67	4.12
1990	0.94	1.76	0.88	0.67	4.24

[a]Base costs include direct, indirect, and contingency costs.
[b]Time-related costs include escalation and interest during construction.

Figure 19.3. Projected generating costs for coal and nuclear plants. (From Reference 4.)

	Nuclear[a] (6 Largest Units)		Coal (6 Largest Units)	
	1976	1981	1976	1981
Capital cost ($/kW)	$199	$229	$163	$280
Net capacity factor (%)	57.1	64.1	44.7	45.1
Cost of power (mills/kWh)				
Carrying charges[b]	8.2	8.2	8.3	14.2
O&M	2.5	4.2	1.7	5.0
Fuel[c]	3.4	7.2	8.0	27.4
Total	14.1	19.6	18.0	46.6
Cost of power (mills/kWh) Adjusted to a 60% net capacity factor	13.6	20.5	15.6	41.5
Nuclear advantage (%)	12.8	50.6	base	base

[a]Nuclear data excludes 25% ownership interest of Iowa–Illinois Gas and Electric Company in Quad Cities Station.
[b]Carrying charges are calculated using a 20% annual fixed-charge rate on the total investment in the plant. Carrying charges on fuel inventories (coal) and investment (nuclear) are included in the fuel expense.
[c]Nuclear fuel costs include a provision for spent fuel disposal that equaled 0.5 mills/kWh from October, 1976 through August, 1978, and 1 mill/kWh from September, 1978 through June, 1981, and 2.0 mills/kWh from July, 1981 through December, 1981.

Figure 19.4. Commonwealth Edison Co. actual costs. The cost for all years are not calculated on the same basis. Please note the difference between years in note *c*. (From Reference 5.)

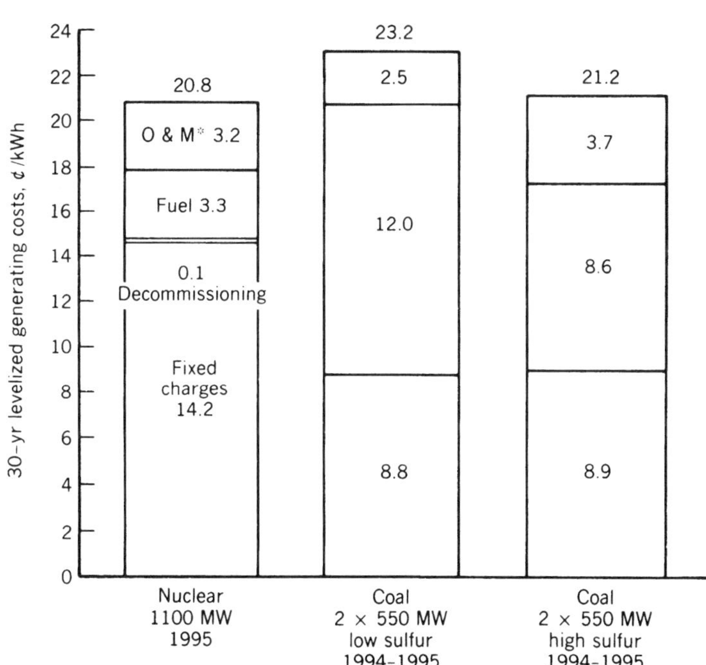

Figure 19.5. Nuclear versus coal—30 yr levelized generating costs from 1995—base case. (From Reference 6.)

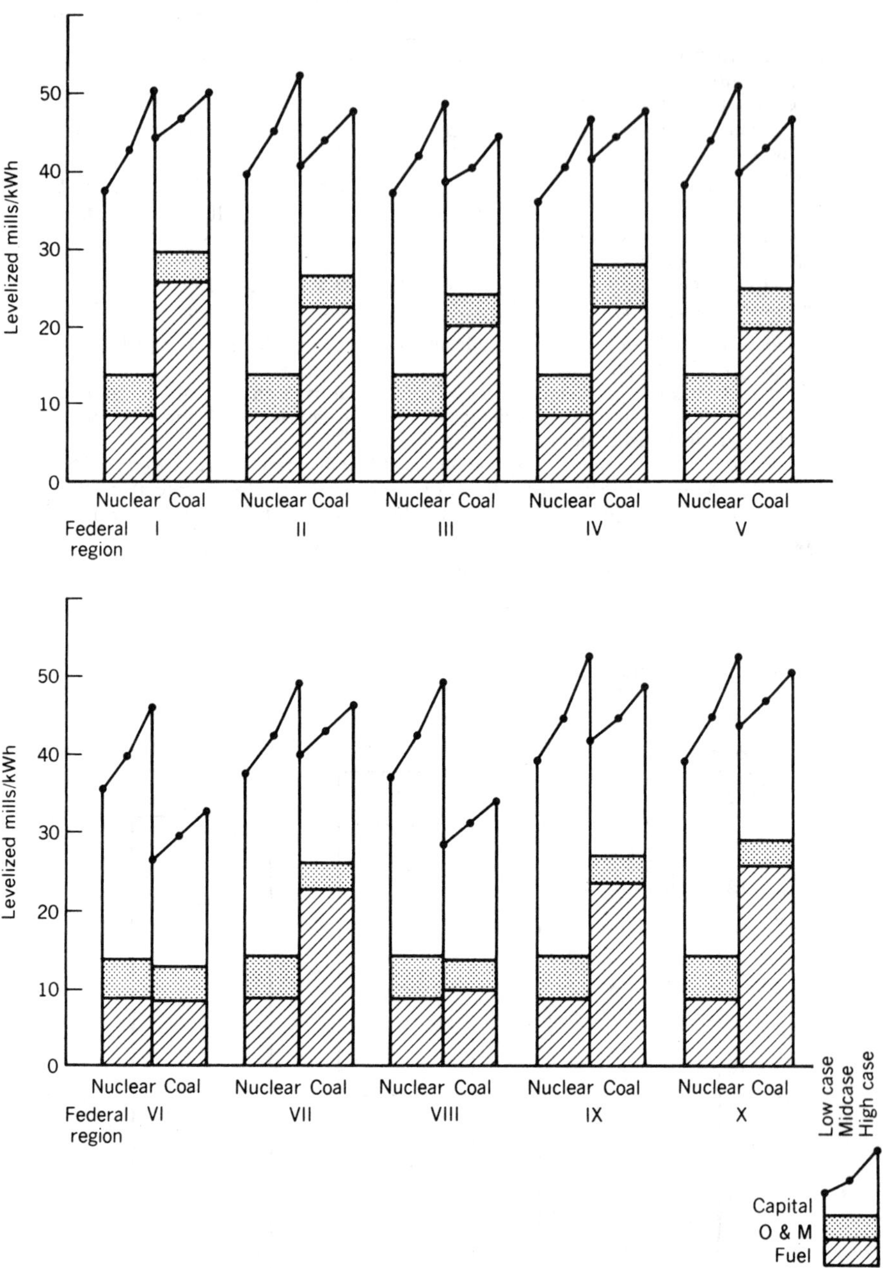

Figure 19.6. Comparative bus-bar costs for low and high construction and financial conditions. Nuclear and coal fired power plants operational in 1995, levelized mills/kWh. All costs are in equivalent 1980 dollars levelized over 30 yr of plant operation at an average annual capacity factor of 60%. Results are based upon the low, middle, and high assumptions for licensing and construction leadtimes, labor productivity, and AFUDC rates. (From Reference 7.)

Table 19.2. Six-Year Comparison of Coal and Nuclear Generation Costs in a Large Midwestern Utility[a]

	Fuel	Total	Adjusted to 60% Capacity Factor[b]
1974			
Nuclear	3.9	15.3	
Coal	5.1	12.3	
Nuclear advantage	1.2	−3.0	N.A.
1975			
Nuclear	4.0	17.2	
Coal	6.8	15.6	
Nuclear advantage	2.8	−1.6	N.A.
1976			
Nuclear	5.0	15.7	
Coal	8.0	18.0	
Nuclear advantage	3.0	2.3	N.A.
1977			
Nuclear	4.5	14.1	14.2
Coal	10.1	20.9	19.0
Nuclear advantage	5.6	6.8	4.8
1978			
Nuclear	4.7	13.6	15.1
Coal	14.0	25.3	22.7
Nuclear advantage	9.3	11.7	7.6
1979			
Nuclear	5.2	16.9	16.8
Coal	18.0	30.2	27.3
Nuclear advantage	12.8	13.3	10.5

Source: From Reference 8.

[a]Comparisons are for 12 nuclear and coal-fired units, except for 1974 and 1975, which exclude coal-fired Powerton Unit 5, which did not come in service until Dec. 1975. Prior-year data have been revised from earlier published data to reflect fully a 2-mill allowance for spent fuel disposal.

[b]N.A., not available.

19.2. CAPITAL COST

Cost Components

Nuclear plant total capital costs can be divided into engineering expenses and time-related expenses. The total investment up to the time of operational start-up is then divided by the plants' electric output and expressed in the form of \$/kWe. Computation of capital costs is complicated by the effects of escalation during construction; this is partly related to inflation. It is thus required to specify whether the capital costs are expressed in constant dollars (all inflationary effects excluded), in dollars of the year of completion, or in mixed-year dollars as accrued during the construction period.

A recent capital-cost breakdown for nuclear and coal-fired power plants is shown in Table 19.4a and in Figures 19.7 and 19.8. As seen in Table 19.4a, the engineering costs are broken down into three major components: direct, indirect, and contingency expenses. A generic breakdown of the various capital cost components is shown in Table 19.4b.

Direct investment costs are related to the actual construction of the power plant. They are further broken down into a very detailed list of accounts initially promulgated by the Federal Power Commission, and then somewhat modified for the specific categories of nuclear power plant designs. The major cost categories are listed in Table 19.4a. It is of interest to note that the nuclear steam supply system is less than one-third of the total direct costs, and about one-tenth of the total plant investment.

Table 19.3. U.S. Average Electrical Generating Costs and Power Plant Performance in 1981 for Units Entering Commercial Service in the Years Listed[a]

Initial Year of Commercial Operation	Number of Units	Generating Capacity, MWe	Total[b] Generating Cost, ¢/kWh	Capital Cost, ¢/kWh	Fuel Cost, ¢/kWh	O & M Cost, ¢/kWh	Other[c] Cost, ¢/kWh	Capacity[d] Factor, %	Availability[e] Factor, %	Forced[f] Outage Rate, %
					Nuclear					
1976	5	4,710	3.1	1.8	0.5	0.8	0.0	62.4	71.9	17.0
1977	5	4,042	4.1	2.6	0.5	1.0	0.1	55.1	61.8	20.5
1978	3	2,839	3.5	2.5	0.5	0.4	0.0	61.9	67.7	13.3
1979	1	755	3.4	2.1	0.5	0.8	0.0	66.0	78.5	7.9
1980	2	1,748	3.2	2.1	0.7	0.4	0.0	65.0	71.0	16.1
Totals or weighted averages	58	45,617	2.7	1.4	0.5	0.6	0.1	61.0	68.8	11.8
					Coal					
1976	3	2,279	3.1	1.0	1.6	0.4	0.0	65.7	86.6	7.9
1977	3	1,607	3.5	1.4	1.7	0.4	0.0	66.4	89.1	3.8
1978	4	2,247	3.1	1.2	1.7	0.2	0.0	63.1	89.1	3.0
1979	2	1,214	2.8	1.4	1.2	0.3	0.0	55.3	88.5	2.4
1980	6	4,317	4.7	2.3	2.1	0.3	0.0	60.4	82.9	10.8
Totals or weighted averages	48	35,099	3.2	1.1	1.8	0.3	0.0	58.6	79.7	10.2

Oil										
1976	1	783	5.9	1.0	4.8	0.1	0.0	50.9	87.3	3.3
1977	3	2,221	7.9	2.0	5.6	0.4	0.0	25.7	65.6	13.2
1978	1	511	5.1	0.7	4.3	0.1	0.0	59.5	95.2	0.5
1979	0	—	—	—	—	—	—	—	—	—
1980	1	783	9.1	3.5	5.5	0.1	0.0	30.0	85.0	10.9
Totals or weighted averages	15	8,103	6.9	1.6	5.1	0.2	0.0	35.7	80.3	7.1

Source: From Reference 9.

[a]Baseload units of 400 MWe or larger capacity, entering commercial operation from 1970 through 1980 and in commercial service during all of 1981. All utilities having at least a 10% interest in one or more nuclear units are included.

[b]Total cost includes capital, fuel, operation, and maintenance, carrying charges, insurance and taxes as well as costs incurred while any unit was not on-line but remained in commercial service during the year. For nuclear units "total cost" includes present allowances for decommissioning and waste management, where permitted by state regulatory authorities.

[c]Other cost represents generating expenses not recorded by the reporting utilities in capital, fuel, or operation and maintenance categories.

[d]Capacity factor is the percentage of electricity produced compared with the amount which could have been produced at continuous full power.

[e]Availability factor is the percentage of time during which the unit was capable of producing power at some level, whether or not it was actually in service.

[f]Forced outage rate is the percentage of time during which the unit was not available to produce power when required for service, due to component or other failure.

Table 19.4a. Power Plant Capital Investment Cost Estimates for the Northeastern U.S. for Commercial Operation in 1995 (Millions of Dollars)[a]

	LWR Nuclear	High-Sulfur Bituminous Coal	Low-Sulfur Sub-bituminous Coal	Residual Oil	Natural Gas
Direct Costs (January 1982 Dollars)					
Land and land rights	5	5	5	5	5
Structures and improvements	200	85	90	85	75
Reactor/boiler plant equipment	280	470	390	295	175
Turbine plant equipment	220	165	165	165	165
Electric plant equipment	75	70	65	60	55
Miscellaneous plant equipment	25	20	20	20	15
Main heat rejection system	40	35	35	35	35
Subtotal (direct costs)	845	850	770	665	525
Indirect Costs (January 1982 Dollars)					
Construction services	130	85	75	65	40
Home office engineering and services	195	25	20	20	15
Field office engineering and services	95	25	25	20	15
Owner's costs	125	95	85	75	60
Subtotal (indirect costs)	545	230	205	180	130
Total Costs					
Direct and indirect costs (January 1982 dollars)	1390	1080	975	845	655
Contingency allowance (January 1982 dollars)	210	160	145	125	65
Total direct and indirect costs (January 1982 dollars)	1600	1240	1120	970	720
Allowance for escalation (as spent dollars)	1440	1380	1255	1130	840
Allowance for interest (as spent dollars)	1580	895	815	640	470
Plant capital investment cost at commercial operation (as spent dollars)					
Millions of dollars	4620	3515	3190	2740	2030
Dollars per kilowatt	3850	2930	2660	2280	1690
Rounded dollars per kilowatt	3900	2900	2700	2300	1700

Source: From Reference 3.

[a]Direct average of Boston, New York, and Philadelphia.

Indirect investment costs relate mostly to engineering, design, and supervisory expenses, and to specific owner's costs. The engineering services costs are divided between the office and site expenses throughout the project's lifetime. The owner's expenses relate to administrative and legal costs incurred in launching a power plant construction program. In recent years, the indirect costs have increased faster than the direct construction costs. This is largely due to the increased paperwork required, greater emphasis on documenting quality control, and responses to regulatory questions. Contingency funds are those set aside to cover underestimation in component costs or unexpected increases in construction or labor costs. This cost item is quite important in view of the significant cost of backfittings and rework recently required in most nuclear projects.

The direct costs are about 65% of the total cost of a nuclear power plant completed in the 1980–1983 period. This cost fraction is, however, decreasing. Figure 19.9 indicates that for plants completed in 1988, the direct costs will be less than 50% of the total plant costs.

Table 19.4b. Components of Capital Cost

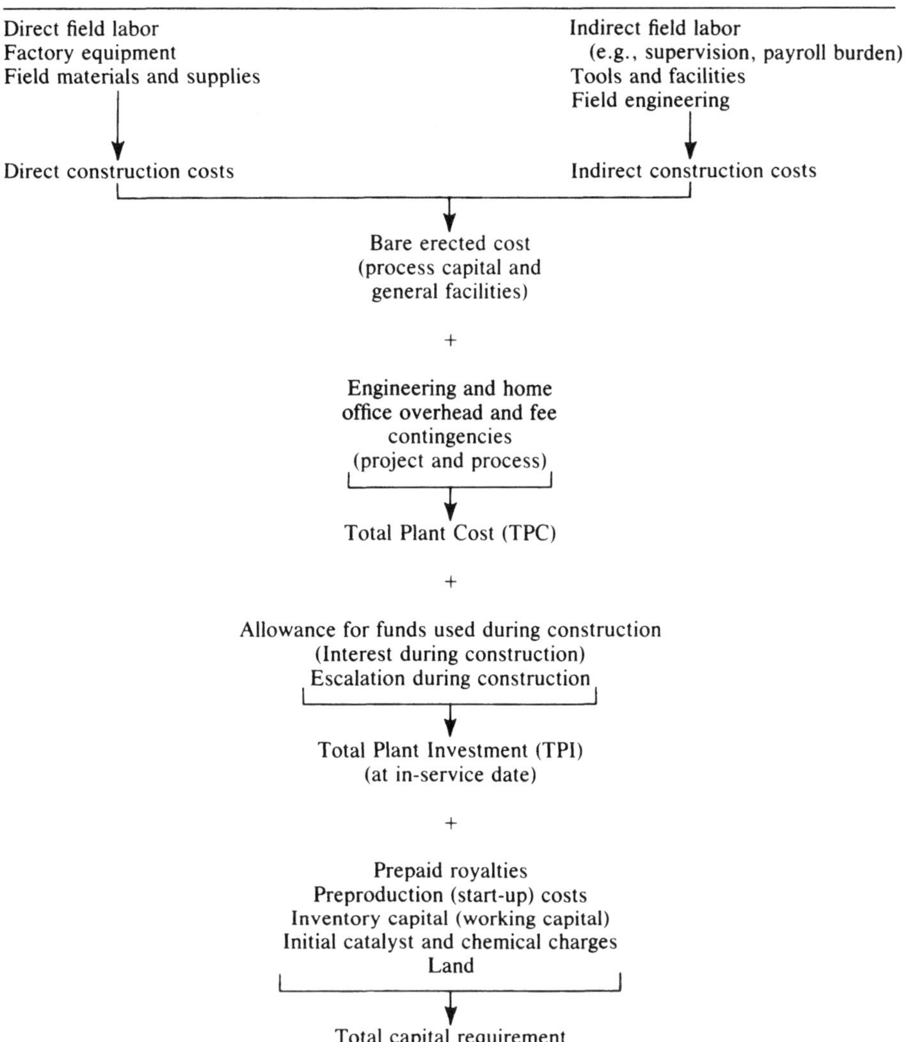

Source: From Reference 1.

The time-related expenses of nuclear plant capital costs include two major components: allowance for funds during construction (also referred to as interest during construction) and escalation expenses. Escalation during construction has increased at the fastest rate of all the nuclear capital cost components. With the increase in inflation rates, escalation expenses, which account for about 20% of the total cost of a plant completed in 1982, will account for more than 33% of the cost of a reactor operated by 1988, as seen in Figure 19.9. A constant dollars comparison of power plant capital costs would, however, result in much lower escalation components, as only the real cost increases would be considered. The contribution of both the escalation and the interest components to the total investment cost will depend on the length of the construction project. The longer the lead time, the greater the contribution of the time-related charges to the total cost. Figure 19.9 shows the change that has occurred since the mid-1970s in the breakdown of the nuclear plant capital costs. Today time-related charges are significantly greater and construction expenses contributed a smaller fraction of the total plant cost. By 1988 more than 50% of the total plant cost will be time charges, and the nuclear island will cost only 10% of the total investment.

During the late 1980s and 1990s the total (as spent) capital cost of a 1000-MWe nuclear or coal-fired plant will be in the range of 2–5 billion dollars. Such capital cost figures for a single power

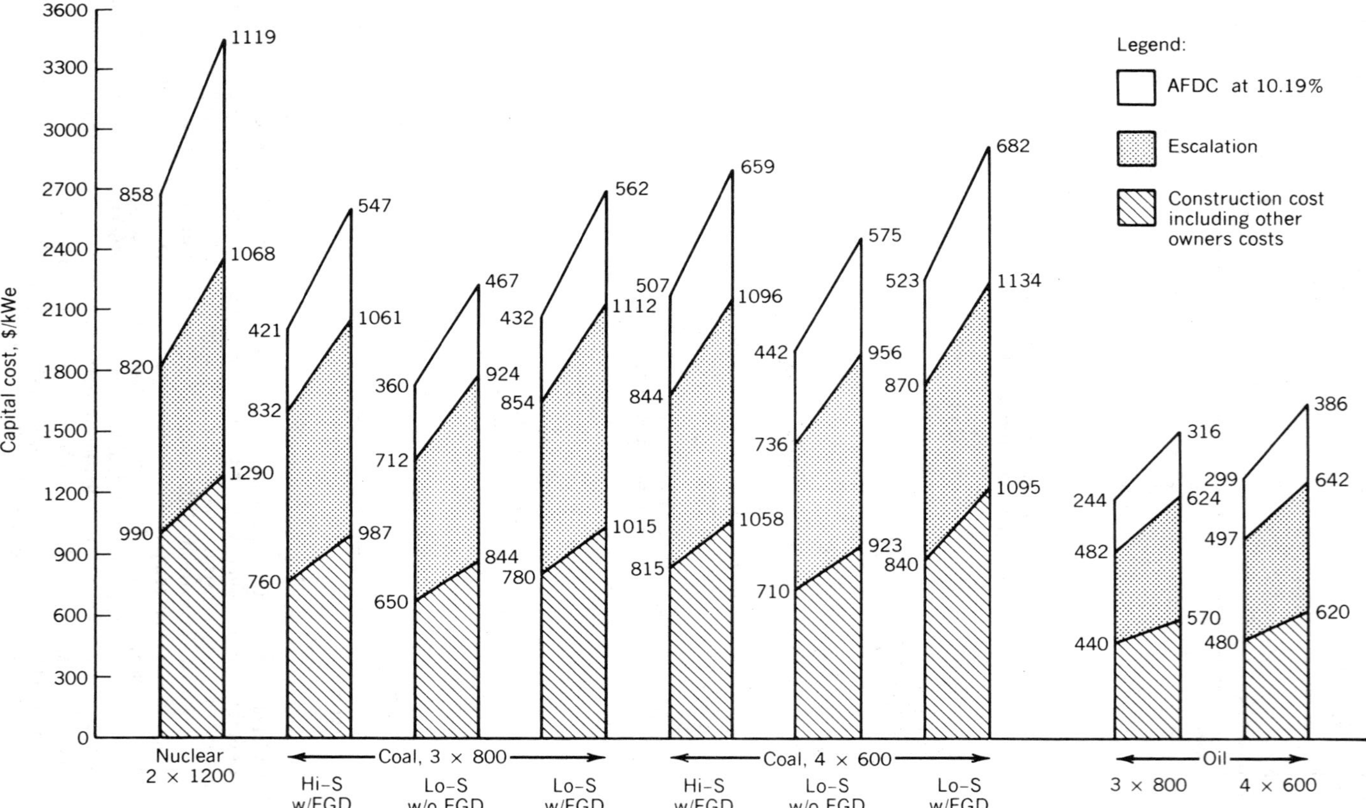

Figure 19.7. Plant capital costs at 9% inflation. *Key:* Hi-S, high sulfur coal plant. Lo-S, low sulfur coal plant. FGD, flue gas desulfurization. (From Reference 2.)

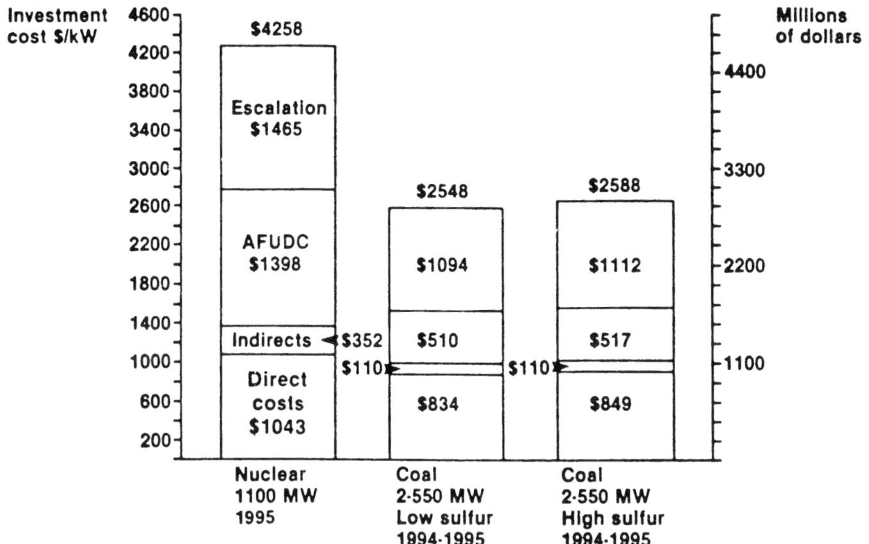

Figure 19.8. Nuclear versus coal projected midwestern capital investment costs. Date of operation 1995. (From Reference 6.)

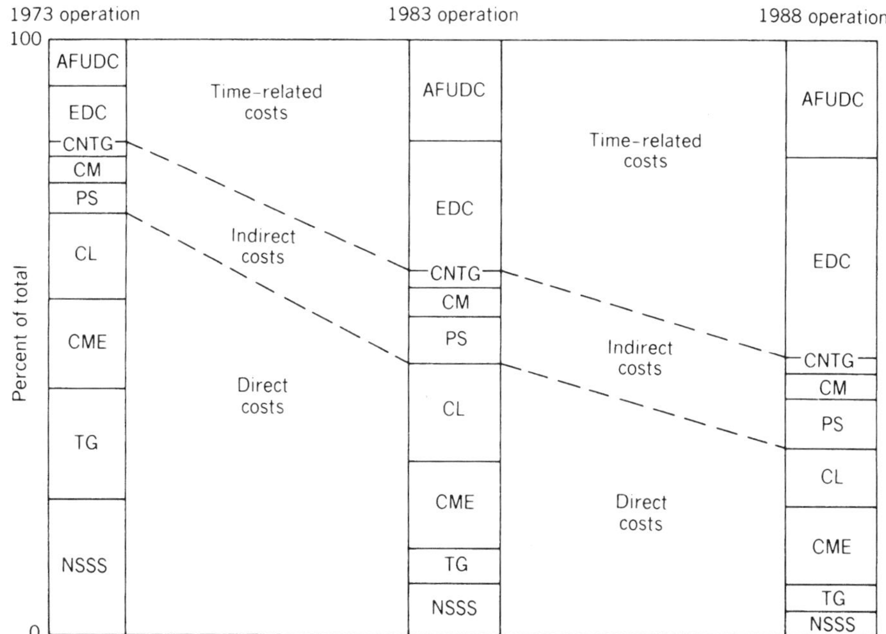

Figure 19.9. Shifts in distribution of nuclear power plant capital costs. *Key:* NSSS—nuclear steam supply system. TG—turbine generator. CME—construction material and equipment. CL—craft labor. PS—professional services. CM—construction tools and material. CNTG—contingency. EDC—escalation during construction. AFUDC—interest during construction. (From Reference 11.)

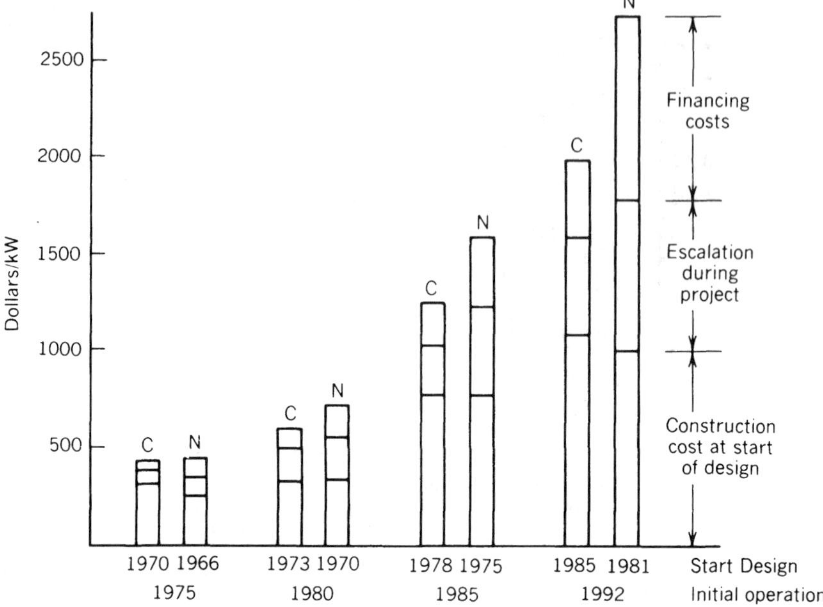

Figure 19.10. Capital cost components, typical U.S. generating plants. (From Reference 12.) N—nuclear; C—coal with sulfur removal.

plant may equal or exceed the total equity value of the owner utility. Inclusion of such capital investment figures in the allowed utility rate base will significantly increase the rate payers' monthly bills, at least during the first few years of operation of these power plants. Various reviews of increase in rate bases due to the commissioning of large nuclear projects are now in progress, for example, in the cases of the Shoreharm plant, New York, the Commonwealth Edison Co. nuclear program in Illinois, and the Limmerick and Susquehanna plants in Pennsylvania. Various schemes for reducing the initial rate increase to the utility customers, and stretching the large annual capital charges over a larger time period, are being considered. These schemes can be divided into measures taken while the plant is under construction, that is, inclusion of construction work expenditures in the rate base directly as they are accrued, and measures taken after the plant started operating, that is, "trending the rate base" or graduated payback of borrowed construction capital through the lifetime of the plant.

Historic Evolution of Capital Costs

Historic data on nuclear power plant costs are shown in Figures 19.10 and 19.11. A projection of the expected trend in capital costs over the next 10 yr is shown in Figure 19.12. All three studies point to the fact that nuclear power plant capital costs show time-related escalation above the rate of inflation. Figure 19.11 shows 15-yr cost estimates made for the Department of Energy based on experience of architect/engineering firms. Figure 19.12 estimates the costs of nuclear plants to be completed in the next 9 yr by making a linear fit through the cost figures provided by the electric utilities. Figure 19.13 attempts to project future costs by making a logarithmic fit to the existing data on plant construction costs, as completed.

The record clearly indicates an increase in plant capital costs above inflationary trends. This correlates with increased construction and planning periods and increased average nuclear plant capacity. Commonwealth Edison's (CE) experience is a case in point. CE's four reactors in the Dresden and Quad Cities stations were contracted for in 1965 and placed in service in the early 1970s. They ranged in capacity from 210 to 790 MWe and in costs from \$150 to \$160/kWe. Today, CE's four Byron and Braidwood reactors, at 1120 MWe, are estimated to cost about \$1500/kWe when completed in the mid-1980s, and total plant lead times will exceed 10 yr. These upward cost trends have averaged 15%/yr over the last 8 yr, or about 8%/yr above inflation. The United Engineers and Construction Company's updated study[13] indicates a 20% increase in inflated cost or 12% annual increase in constant dollars. Similar changes were found in studies conducted by the RAND Corporation. A recent RAND study indicates than an annual capital-cost increment of 140

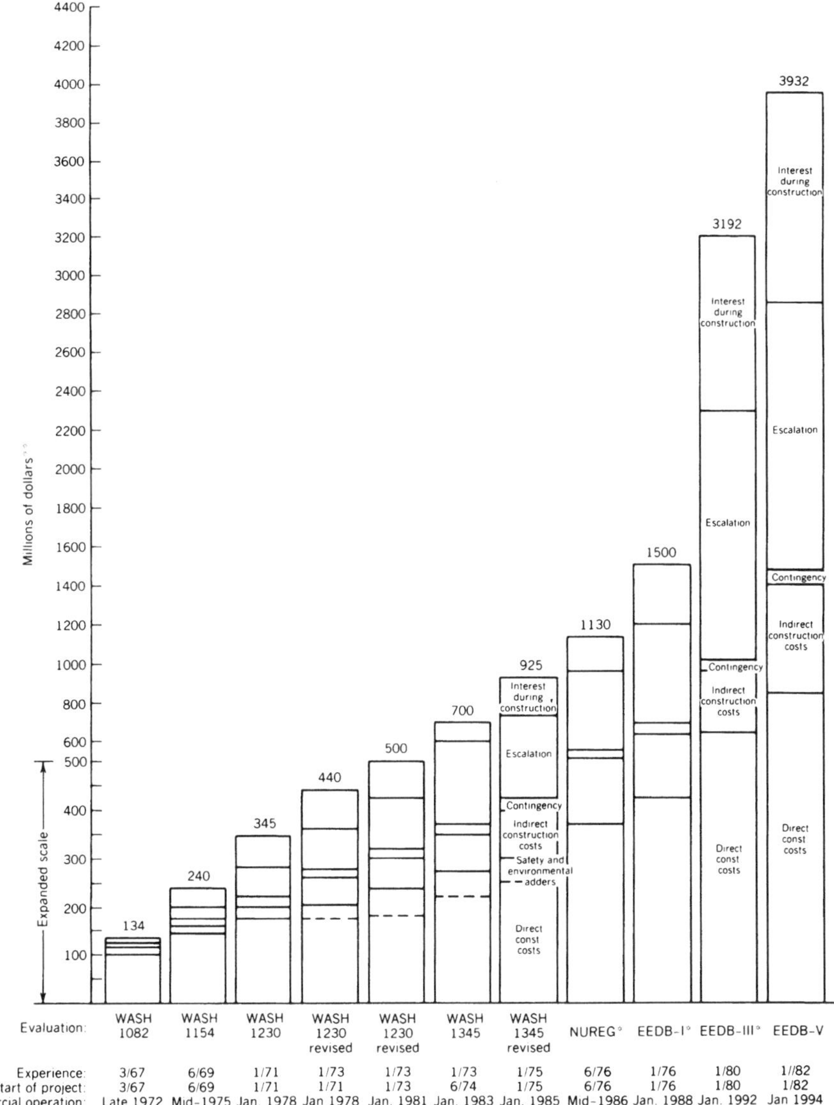

Figure 19.11. Trends of nuclear power plant costs. (From Reference 13.) *Normalized to 1000 MWe. **Dollars are those at year of commercial operation.

1978 \$/kWe could be assigned to plants whose construction permits were issued between 1966 and 1971. Evidence of the leveling off of these cost increases or of economies of scale were found to be statistically insignificant and only a moderate learning-curve effect could be identified.

The total increase in nuclear power plant construction costs was not evenly distributed among all the cost components. This is shown in Figure 19.11. While the direct construction costs have increased in actual dollar amounts, their fraction of the overall costs have shrunk. Time-related capital charges have increased at a much faster rate both in absolute and in fractional terms.

The DOE analysis of future LWR capital-cost trends,[14] indicates an annual cost increment of \$140/kWe in current dollars (a growth rate of 7.2%/yr) for all plants entering commercial service between 1980 and 1987. This reflects utilities' cost estimates. Similar trends will also affect fossil-fuel-fired plant costs.[8,14,15] A large regional cost variation is shown in Figure 19.14. The highest average unit costs occurred in the Middle Atlantic, followed in turn by the Northeast and Far West regional plant costs. Lower costs are reported for the West South Central and the East North

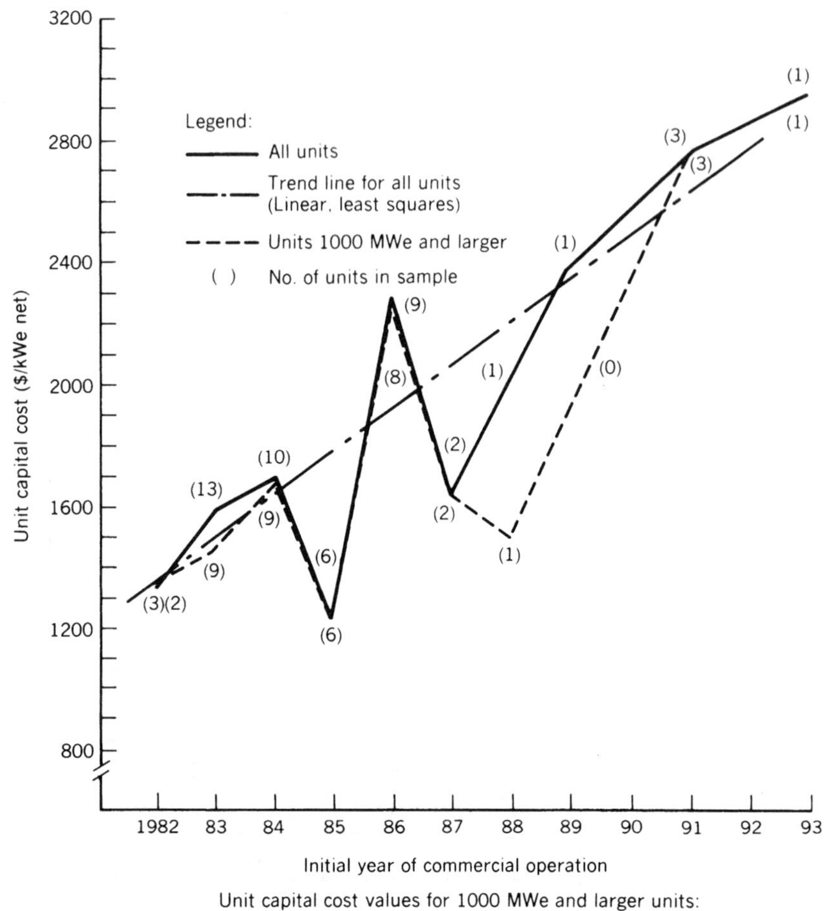

Unit capital cost values for 1000 MWe and larger units:

	1982	83	84	85	86	87	88	89	90	91	92	93
Mean	1350	1456	1670	1231	2251	1659	1500	—	—	2775	—	3062
Std. dev.	368	385	389	175	879	293	—	—	—	300	—	—

Figure 19.12. Average LWR power plant unit capital costs by year of entry into service. (From Reference 14.)

Central regions, with the lowest unit costs occurring in the East South Central and South Atlantic parts of the country. The data in Figure 19.14 relate to all plants entering commercial service in each region over an 8-yr study period. A limited economy of scale effect was found for various plant sizes within each region. Given this history of capital-cost increments and the expected continuation of these trends, it is important to identify the underlying causes for such temporal cost increases.

The increasing plant capital costs mentioned above are closely related to the increasing plant lead times, discussed below. A recent estimation of the increasing plant lead times is shown in Figure 19.15. As seen in this figure, all phases of the nuclear project lead times have lengthened over time: the preconstruction review period, the construction period, and the preoperational testing phase. The lengthening lead times affect the capital costs in different ways. Whereas the increase in the licensing period affects mostly future construction cost escalation, the lengthening preoperational period affects mostly the interest-during-construction cost component, which accumulates until the time the plant starts producing electricity.

The major impact of the longer lead times and the higher capital costs is the increasing vulnerability of nuclear construction periods to public and political criticism, which renders the completion of these projects highly uncertain. Plant completion date and cost are becoming more difficult to forecast and extend beyond normal utility planning horizons. Several power plant licensing reform

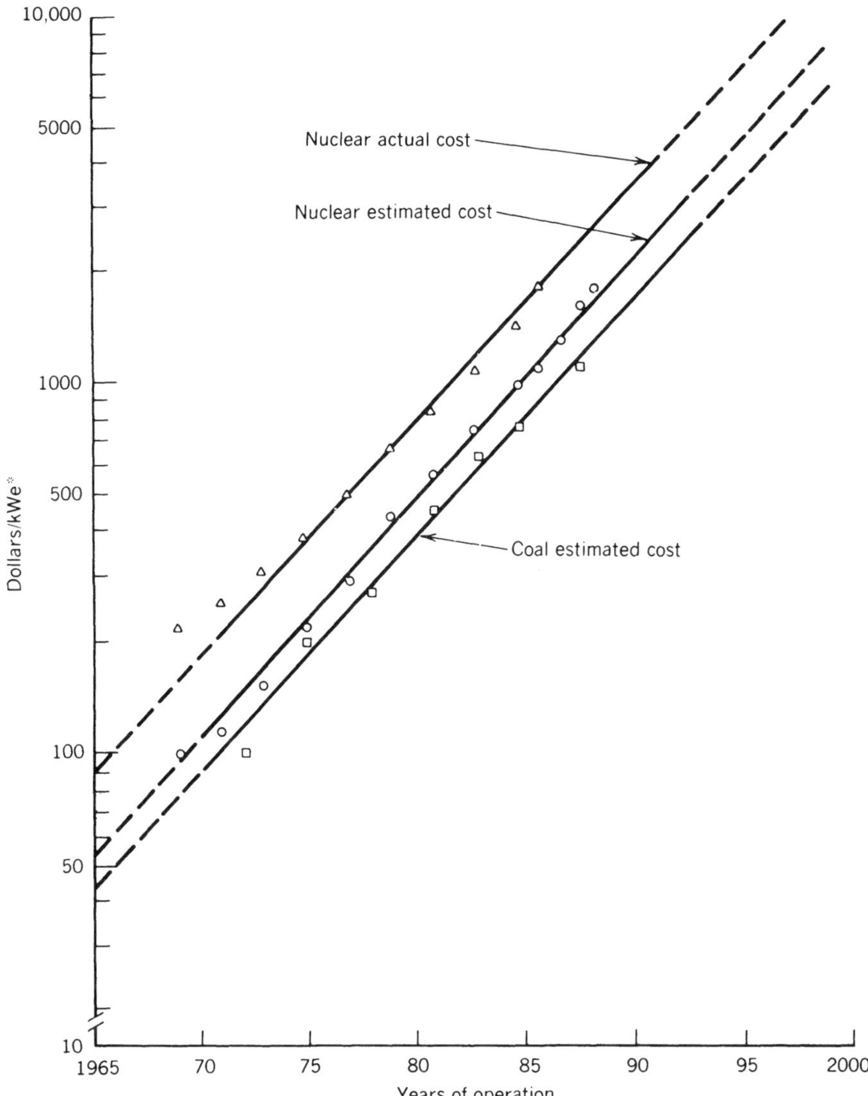

Figure 19.13. Trends in power plant costs in dollars/kWe. (From Reference 15.) *Includes escalation and AFUDC.

measures have recently been proposed, by DOE,[18] by industry, and by the Nuclear Regulatory Commission. These proposals aim at reducing the plant lead times and construction costs, so as to enhance the predictability of nuclear plants schedules and cost estimates. Similar trends are now evident in the construction of coal-fired power plants. Increasingly severe coal plant emission regulations, for example those designed to counter the acid rain problems, tend to increase coal plants' capital costs and lead times and compound the political uncertainties facing coal power generation.

Factors Affecting Capital-Cost Increments

Several factors are responsible for the dramatic rise in nuclear, as well as coal-fired, plant capital costs in the last 15 yr. These factors can be summarized as follows:

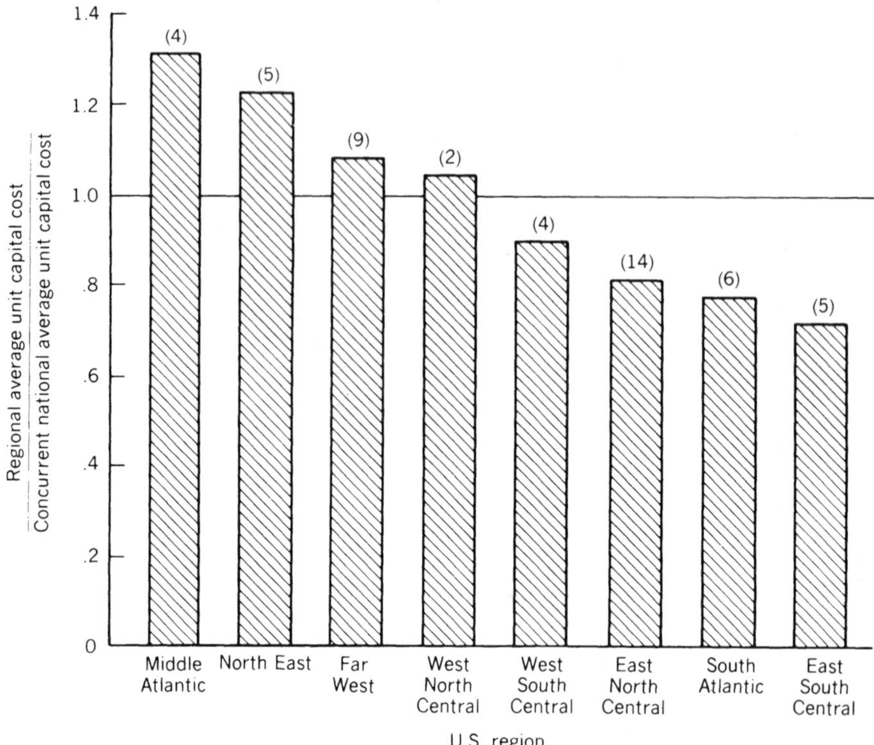

Figure 19.14. Regional LWR power plant capital costs compared to concurrent national LWR capital costs. (From Reference 14.) ( )—Number of units sampled.

1. Significant variations in design. This is caused mostly by the fragmented nature of the supply industry. Most of the nuclear plants in the United States are supplied by four reactor vendors and eight major architect/engineers. In addition, each nuclear plant must be designed and built according to the unique requirements of each utility and each site. This yields so many possible combinations that plant standardization is difficult.
2. Regulatory unpredictability. It has been difficult in the last 15 yr to estimate the number of regulatory requirements for plant redesign, verification, and rework, many of which were promulgated during or after the period of plant design, and required extensive modifications to partially completed plants.
3. Large increase in labor manhours. In the area of construction engineering both at the home office and on site, and in the construction field craft, this has resulted from the need to comply with new regulatory requirements.
4. Increased load of quality control and quality assurance. This is required to monitor compliance with the ever-increasing number of regulatory guides, letters, orders, and questionnaires. The labor hours and size of quality control organizations have risen dramatically.
5. Large increase in plant backfitting, redesign, rework, repeated reanalyses of components, and additions of various seismic protection measures and devices to partially completed plants.
6. Lengthening of construction time due to the increased construction complexity, more elaborate and lengthy licensing process, and utility mandated schedule stretchouts due to financial difficulties or reduced load growth projections.

These points are now further elaborated from a historical point of view.

The initial phase of nuclear plant construction programs in the early to mid-1960s can be referred to as the turnkey phase. This period was characterized by a feeling of confidence in the future of a new technology whose practical implications were not yet realized. Power plant systems design requirements and the real costs of successful projects completion were underestimated

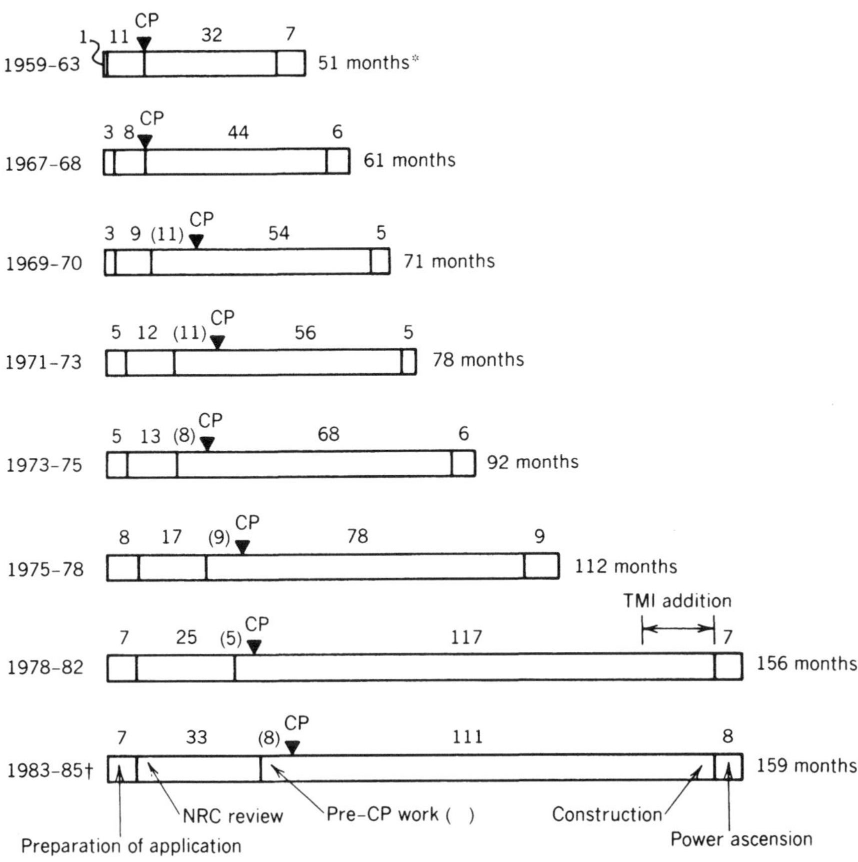

Figure 19.15. Trends in nuclear power plant project schedules. (From Reference 13.) †Year of commercial operation. *All times in months.

during that period. Regulatory control at all levels was minimal. The vendor companies and architect/engineering firms could not anticipate the effects of future regulations on construction lead times and costs. Construction project responsibility was centralized, as implied by the turnkey terminology, with minimal interference from outside regulatory or federal, state, or local supervisory agencies. As a result, short lead times were exhibited, on the order of 4–5 yr.

The second distinct phase in the evolution of nuclear plant capital costs occurred in the mid-1970s. This phase was characterized by a rapid growth in the number of regulatory requirements promulgated and in a resulting increase in materials and personnel demand. This period can be referred to as the standards promulgating phase. The basic federal regulatory guides at this time were followed by a profusion of secondary standards (derived by professional societies) as shown in Figures 19.16 and 19.17. The total body of environmental regulations enacted in Congress is shown in Figure 19.18. The effects of this increase in standards on materials for nuclear plant construction are shown in Figures 19.19, 19.20, and 19.21 as they relate to three generations of power plants. The completed Dresden 2 and 3 Units, and Indian Point 2 and 3 reactors are the PWRs referred to in the document WASH-1230 issued in 1971. The middle bar in Figure 19.21 relates to the Seabrook 1 and 2 units, expected to be completed by 1985. The right-hand side bar corresponds to the Washington Public Power Nuclear Projects 1 to 3, which may be completed by 1985–1992.

The figures above show a doubling and tripling of materials from the early reactors to the current vintage. Several factors are responsible for these increases. The doubling and tripling of concrete occurred in part because of shielding and missile protection requirements. It was assumed that extreme tornado conditions could propel heavy missiles into key safety structures. Additional factors include redundancy and separation of safety equipment, especially those vulnerable to fire or flood. Added criteria to restrict radiation dosage to operators and the public during normal and

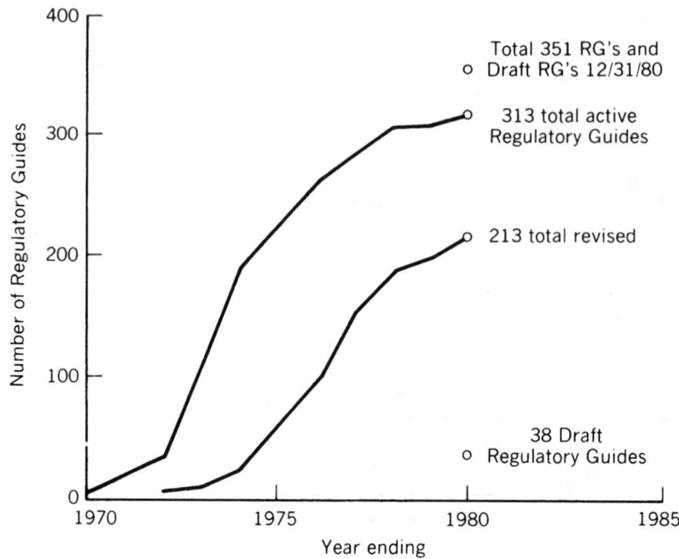

Figure 19.16. Number of NRC Regulatory Guides issued from 1970 to 1980. (From Reference 13.)

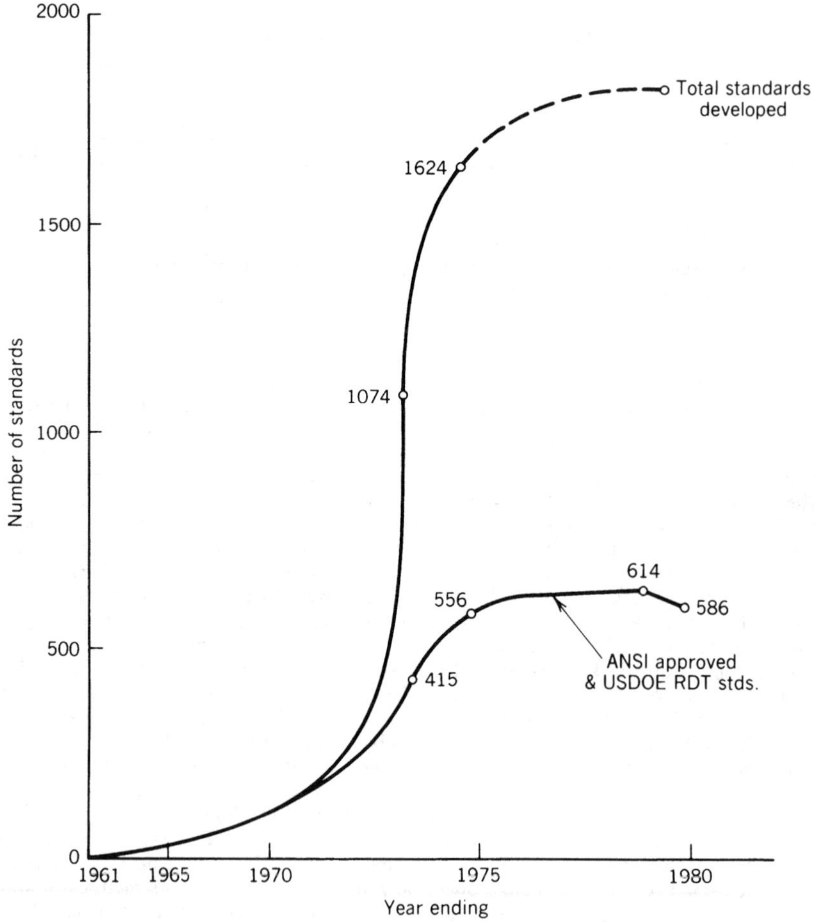

Figure 19.17. Nuclear industry standards 1961–1980. (From Reference 13.)

Early Laws Relating to the Environment	Recent Environmental Laws (69–80)	Future Environmental Issues Subject to Legislation
· Forest Reserve Act (1891) · Rivers and Harbor Act (1899) · Reclamation Act (1902) · Antiquities Act (1906) · Insecticide Act (1910) · Weeks Forestry Act (1911) · Mineral Leasing Act (1920) · Federal Water Power Act (1920) · Clark–McNary Act (1925) · Taylor Grazing Act (1934) · Flood Control Act (1936) · Wildlife Restoration Act (1937) · Federal Insecticide Act (1947) · Communications and Satellite Act (1962) · Dept. of Transportation Act (1966) · Wilderness Act (1964) · Historic Preserv. (1966) · Wild-Scenic Rivers (1966)	[78] · Endangered Species Act (amend.) [78] · Power Plant & Fuel Use Act [77] · Surface Mine and Reclamation Act [77] · Clean Air Act [77] · Clean Water Act (amendments) [76] · Toxic Substances Control Act [76] · Resource Conservation and Recovery Act [75] · Special Energy/Appropriations Act [74] · Federal Energy Admin. Act [74] · Energy Supply and Environmental Coordination [74] · Safe Drinking Water Act [74] · Deep Water Port Act [73] · Endangered Species Act [72] · Water Pollution Control Act [72] · Marine Protection and Sanctuaries Act [72] · Coastal Zone Management Act [70] · Clean Air Act [69] · National Environmental Policy Act	· Acid rain · Non-nuclear radioactivity · Hazardous materials

Figure 19.18. Summary history of environmental regulation. (From Reference 12.)

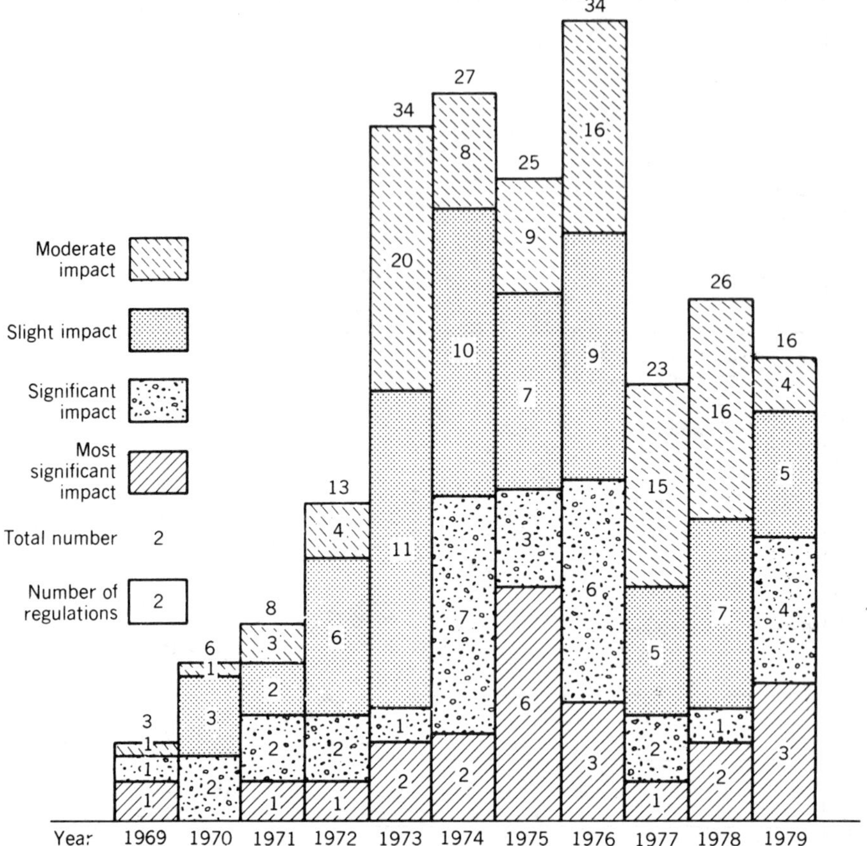

Figure 19.19. Impact of NRC regulations on nuclear steam supply system. (From Reference 12.)

abnormal plant operations have required an increase of wall concrete thicknesses for biological shielding.

Similarly, the large increases in the structural steel for reinforcement are caused by the larger requirement of concrete, stricter seismic design, and the failure assumption of piping systems, which now must be restrained because of a "pipe whip" phenomenon. The IEEE standards require duplicate and multiple electrical supply and signal systems to improve the operational reliability of key safety systems. This results in the doubling and tripling of electrical commodities, as shown in Figure 19.20 and 19.21. Furthermore, the cost of commodities such as valves, heat exchangers, and piping has increased by four to eight times to accommodate the rigid quality assurance and control

	Late 1960s	Early 1970s	Late 1970s	% Increase 1970s
Concrete (CY/kW)[a]	0.11	0.11	0.18	64
Pipe (LF/kW)[b]	0.19	0.18	0.31	72
Wire (LF/kW)[b]	2.90	2.70	5.40	100
Unit size	800	1100	1300	

[a]CY = Cubic Yard.
[b]LF = Linear Feet.

Figure 19.20. Increased construction complexity of nuclear units. (From Reference 13.)

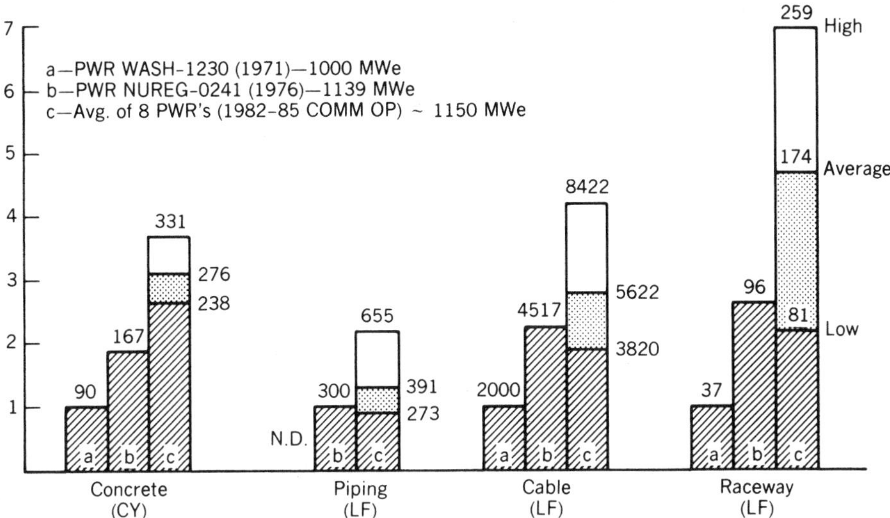

Figure 19.21. Trends in nuclear power plant commodity content. (From Reference 13.) CY = Cubic Yard. LF = Linear Feet.

requirements associated with the manufacture of such equipment. Thus, for the standards promulgating phase, one can identify the substantial increase in the quantity of physical commodities required and the unit prices of each. The cost impact of these increases in commodities was not anticipated for units committed to operation in the mid-to-late 1970s. This contributed to the substantial difference between estimated and realized cost. Adding to these unanticipated increases is the compounding effect of interest rates and price escalation during this same period of time.

The third phase in the evolution of nuclear capital costs is the standards compliance phase; it began approximately in 1977. This phase is characterized by the leveling off of materials cost and significant increase in pesonnel requirements of nuclear projects, driven by engineering design, quality assurance, and construction needs. Figure 19.22 shows the personnel content of several nuclear projects; these are also listed in Figure 19.23. Significant deterioration in labor productivity is evident. This trend is a consequence of many interwoven and complex factors. Among these are an increase in quality assurance criteria, which often cause the reworking of tasks already com-

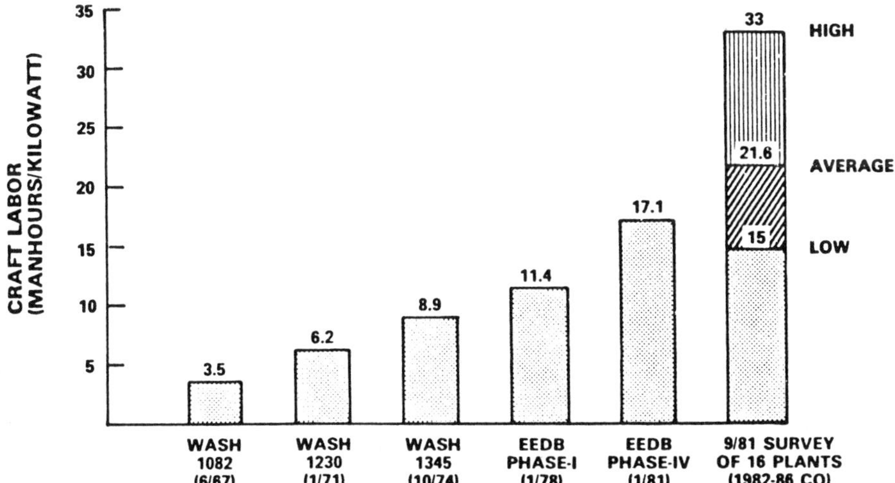

Figure 19.22. Trends in PWR craft labor man-hours per kilowatt. (From Reference 12.)

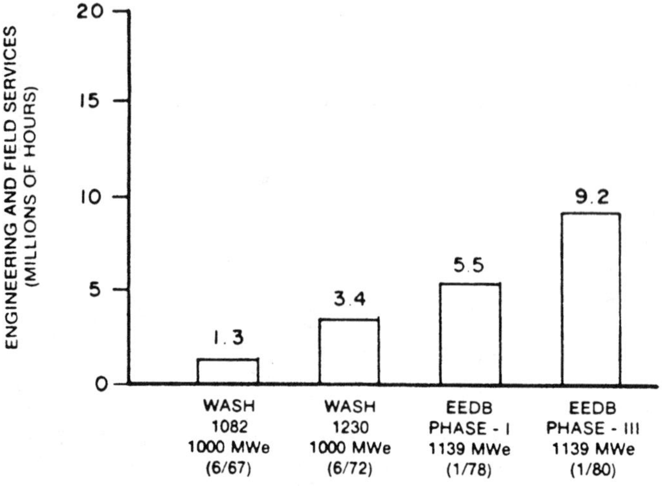

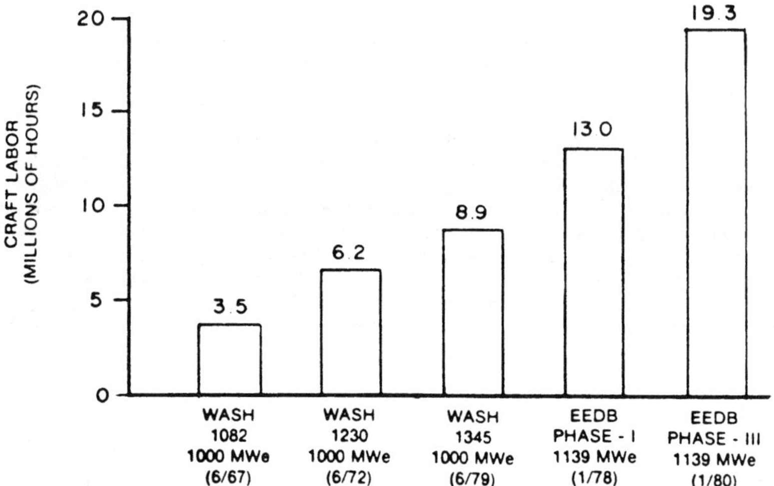

Figure 19.23. Craft and noncraft labor requirements for a PWR nuclear plant: 1967–1980. (From Reference 19.)

pleted. An added factor is the continuing redefinition of engineering detail. This requires work stoppages while changes are made and affects overall job progress. The added work requires a larger supervisory staff. On top of that, new regulations are added as plant experience is accumulated. The effects of increased personnel requirements on nuclear capital costs are shown in Figure 19.24 and Table 19.5. The fastest increasing component of total costs in the last 3 yr has been the cost of noncraft labor which includes all engineering and supervisory manhours. The cost of engineering services for a nuclear plant completed by 1990 will be higher than the total capital cost of a plant completed in 1970, even when measured in constant dollars.

These factors—plant's commodity content and labor productivity—all affect the project schedule. The historic evolution of plant construction schedule is shown in Figure 19.15. This figure shows both the effects of lengthening licensing period prior to construction, and increased actual construction period due to the physical problems cited above. More difficult to isolate are utility-planned construction-period stretchouts due to reduced load growth projections or insufficient funding. The increased construction period, together with the rising inflation rates since the mid-

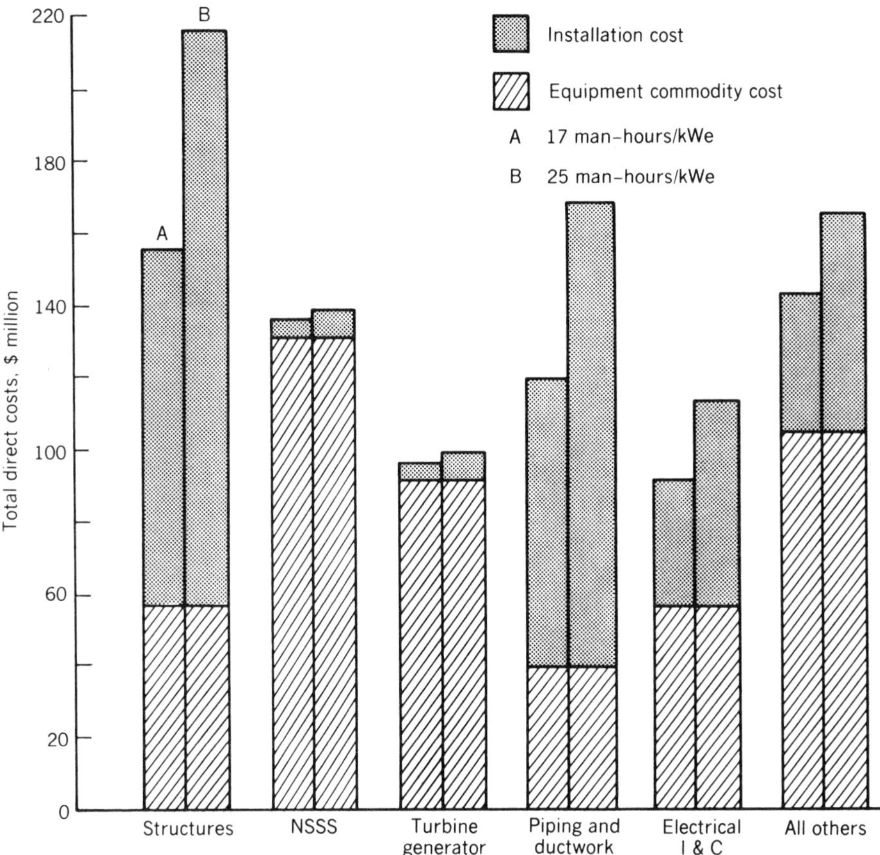

Figure 19.24. Comparison of PWR NPGs cost drivers related to total direct cost. (From Reference 20.)

1970s, significantly increases the time-related components of the nuclear plant capital costs, as shown in Figures 19.9, 19.10, 19.11. The direct construction costs for both coal-fired or nuclear projects could become a small portion of the total plant cost if high inflation continues in the 1980s.

An analysis of the factors contributing to the increasing plant lead times is shown in Figure 19.25. As seen in this figure, the major cause of nuclear construction delays is the regulatory ratcheting phenomenon, which results in plant redesign, rework, and backfitting. Direct increases in labor and materials requirements, or deliberate delays by the owner utilities, have each contributed 20% or less to the total measured lead time delay. It is thus estimated that the combination of various regulatory ratcheting measures, and the utility's ability to respond to the required changes, are the major causes of the increasing plant lead times and capital costs. The effects of a 1-yr reduction in nuclear licensing period on the total plant investment, including inflation, are shown in Figure 19.26.

Economy of Scale and Learning Curves

Economy of scale and learning-curve effects, which reduce power plant construction costs as experience is gained, have long been postulated by the nuclear supply industry. An example of economy of scale for nuclear plant costs at different completion years is shown in Figure 19.27 based on a relative analysis of plant cost components. In the United States, as well as in other industrial nations, the choice now is only between 900 to 1000 MWe plants and 1100 to 1300 MWe class of nuclear reactors. Potential cost savings of the larger plants are yet difficult to prove; no large plant of this class has yet reached commercial operation in the United States. A DOE analysis[14] has identified cost differences between these plant sizes, especially when compared on the same regional conditions. The strong effects of regional conditions on nuclear plants costs was

Table 19.5. Productivity Analysis Based on Unit Rates, Man Hours per Commodity Unit, Nuclear Plants

		Plant Site "A"	Plant Site "B"	Plant Site "C"	Plant Site "D"	Plant Site "X"	Avg. Nucl.	Fossil Site	Factor[b]
Form work	SF	0.78	0.72	1.08	.7	0.72	0.8	0.50	1.6
Reinforcing steel	Ton	47.8	43.3	65.1	41.0	26.3	44.7	—[a]	—[a]
Structural concrete	CY	4.95	3.28	4.43	5.3	4.60	4.5	1.33	3.4
Install pipe over 2 in.	LF	11.2	6.84	8.44	11.0	4.1	8.3	2.76	3.0
Power conduit	LF	1.46	1.18	0.82	2.4	2.1	1.6	0.91	1.7
Cable tray	LF	3.11	3.09	1.08	4.5	4.0	3.2	1.94	1.6
Projected craft labor (manual only) for overall construction	mh/kW	21.3	21.9	18.9	21.3	14.6	19.6	7.00	2.8

Note: These are actual project-to-date unit rates excerpted from late 1981/early 1982 project reports.

Source: From Reference 13.

[a]Fossil plant site data not available.

[b]Factor $= \dfrac{\text{nuclear}}{\text{fossil}}$.

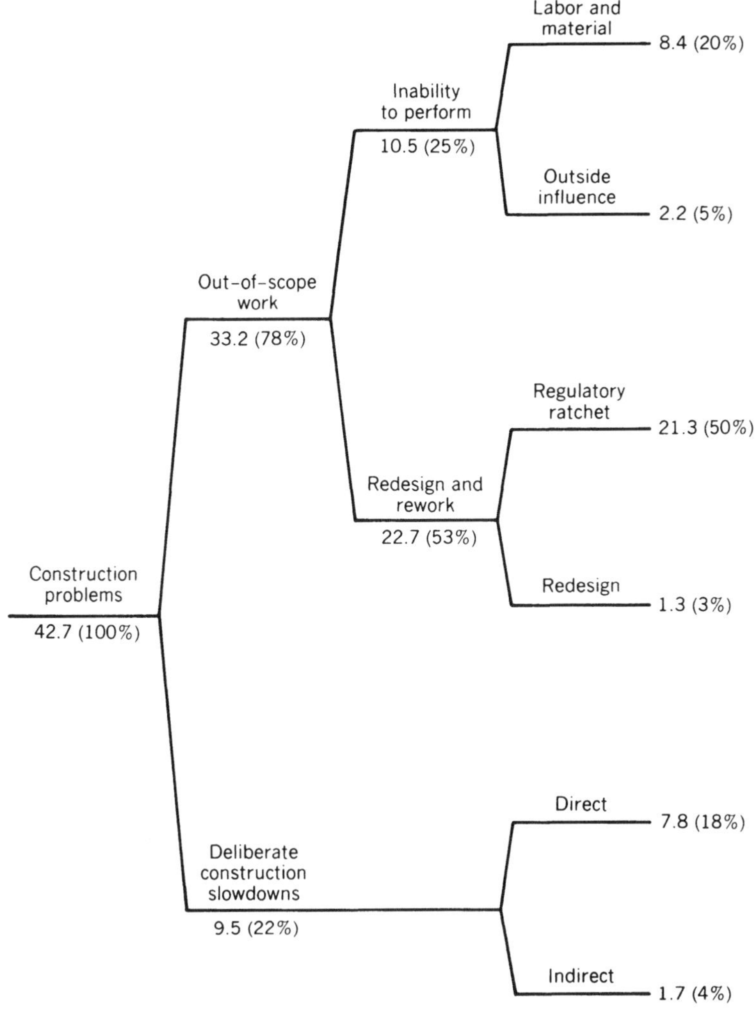

Figure 19.25. Nuclear construction delays—hierarchical classification of causes. Average months of delay per unit. (From Reference 21.)

	Original Schedule	Shortened Schedule	Savings per Unit, 10^6 Dollars
Period from filing of application to receipt of construction permit (months)	31	19	
Nuclear capital investment ($/kW in 1995)			
Base case	4258	4241	18.7
Low inflation	2676	2667	9.8
High inflation	7174	7123	55.2
Nuclear generating costs (levelized ¢/kWh)			
Base case	20.8	20.7	
Low inflation	9.0	9.0	
High inflation	49.9	49.7	

Figure 19.26. Effect of 1-yr reduction in nuclear licensing period. (From Reference 6.)

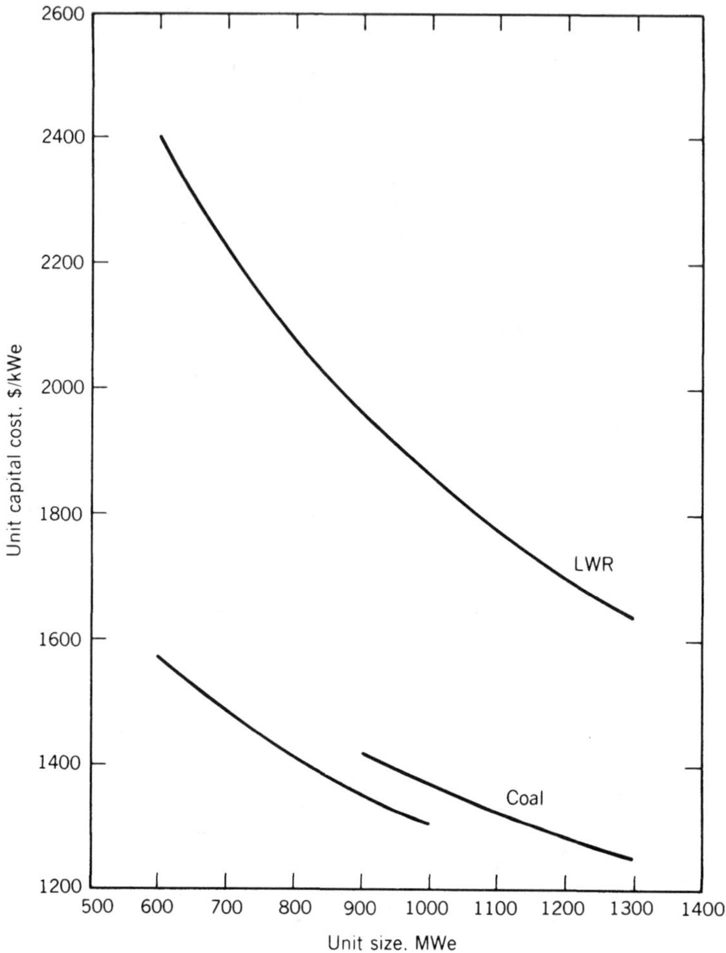

Figure 19.27. Estimated power plant capital investment costs as a function of unit size for 1990 operation. (From Reference 11.)

discussed in Ref. 22. The lack of standardization in plant design, the larger size and complexity of the 1300-MWe units (sometimes referred to as the "mastodon effect"), and the varying regional construction costs still mask any economy-of-scale effects that may be realized when the larger scale plants are brought into operation.

Learning-curve effects are also hard to identify due to the constantly changing regulatory requirement materials and labor inputs and construction time. An attempt to isolate learning-curve effects is shown in Figure 19.28. A modest cost-reduction effect is identified.

Nuclear Plants Decommissioning Costs

Decommissioning is the process by which a nuclear power plant is taken out of service at the end of the plant's useful life and its radioactive material disposed of. Although all types of power plants are decommissioned, nuclear plants are more technically difficult and expensive because of the residual radioactivity in the plant's structures and components. Proper decommissioning of nuclear plants is necessary to protect public health and prevent environmental damage.

The electric utilities' experience with nuclear decommissioning is limited because of the small number of reactors that have so far been decommissioned. To date, barely a dozen facilities have been decommissioned, and these have been primarily small-scale experimental facilities (see Chapter 16). None of the large-scale, commercial reactors now common in industry have yet been

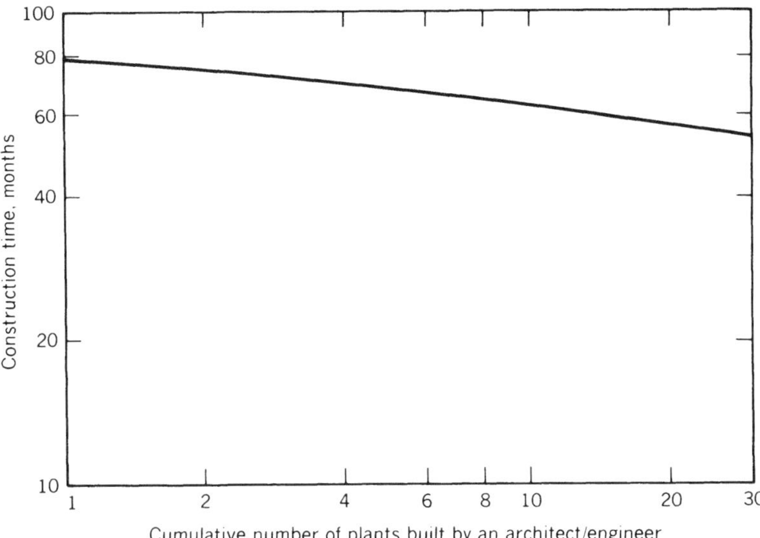

Figure 19.28. Construction-time learning curve. (From Reference 16.)

decommissioned. One result of this is considerable uncertainty about the technology of decommissioning. Several alternatives are being considered and studied, including dismantlement of the facilities, placing the facility in safe storage followed at a later time by dismantlement, and entombment of the facility. Dismantlement would return the site to its original state. All materials would be transported to final disposal areas. Placing the reactor facilities in safe storage is usually viewed as a temporary measure until most radioactivity contained in the structures and components decays sufficiently to permit dismantlement. Placing the facility in safe storage involves removing fuel rods and radioactive liquids and keeping the facility intact and under guard. Entombment involves making the plant more secure physically, perhaps by encasing buildings in concrete.

Technical uncertainty is accompanied by cost uncertainty, although the costs are known to be large. Estimates range from $38 to $97 million for a commercial 1000-MW reactor in 1978 dollars or up to 10% of the original plant cost in constant dollars, accumulated at the year of decommissioning. These costs are uncertain both because of unresolved technical issues and the timing of the decommissioning. Under one plausible scenario, a plant would be placed in safe storage for 100 yr and then finally dismantled. It is difficult to make either technical or economic projections over such a long period.

The subject of nuclear plant decommissioning has been discussed extensively in the technical literature,[24–27] both with respect to the technical options mentioned above and the financing options.

Three basic financing alternatives for nuclear plant decommissioning have been considered: funding at commissioning, sinking fund, and funding at decommissioning using amortization of a negative salvage value. These are characterized by differences in timing, and they yield different costs and risks. In the first strategy, funding at commissioning, the utility raises funds by selling a combination of stocks and bonds at the beginning of the plant's life. These funds are segregated from other utility accounts into a trust fund and invested in low-risk liquid assets (e.g., government bonds), where they remain and accrue interest until needed for decommissioning.

A second approach, a sinking fund, involves the gradual accumulation of funds in a similar trust fund. Each year the utility collects additional revenues, issues additional securities, and contributes the proceeds to the trust fund. The trust therefore increases by the accrued interest as well as the annual utility contributions. The third approach, funding at decommissioning, allows the utility to wait until the end of the plant's life to finance decommissioning. Although the utility collects decommissioning amortization each year based on the plant's negative salvage value, revenues received from customers for decommissioning during the plant's life are not isolated. The funds are treated as a source of internal funds and can be used by the utility for other, unrelated projects.

It is important to realize that each of these options can be designed to raise the same amount of money by the last year of plant operation. This amount equals the total funding required to pay for all of the costs of placing the facility in safe storage, entombing, and/or dismantling the plant at some time after plant closure.

Table 19.6. Cost Comparisons for Three Decommissioning Funding Alternatives

	Net Present Value of Incremental Revenue Streams, 10^6 dollars			
	Baseline	High Interest[a] (Discounted at 9.4%)	High Interest[a] (Discounted at 12%)	High Interest[b] and Inflation
Funding at commissioning	283	388	294	295
Sinking fund	186	240	165	202
Funding at decommissioning	91	68	76	154

Source: From Reference 27.

[a]This scenario assumes a 2% rise in the cost of all forms of capital.

[b]This scenario assumes a 7% return on the decommissioning fund, 10% inflation, and a 2% increase in the cost of common, preferred, and debt financing. A discount rate of 12% was used.

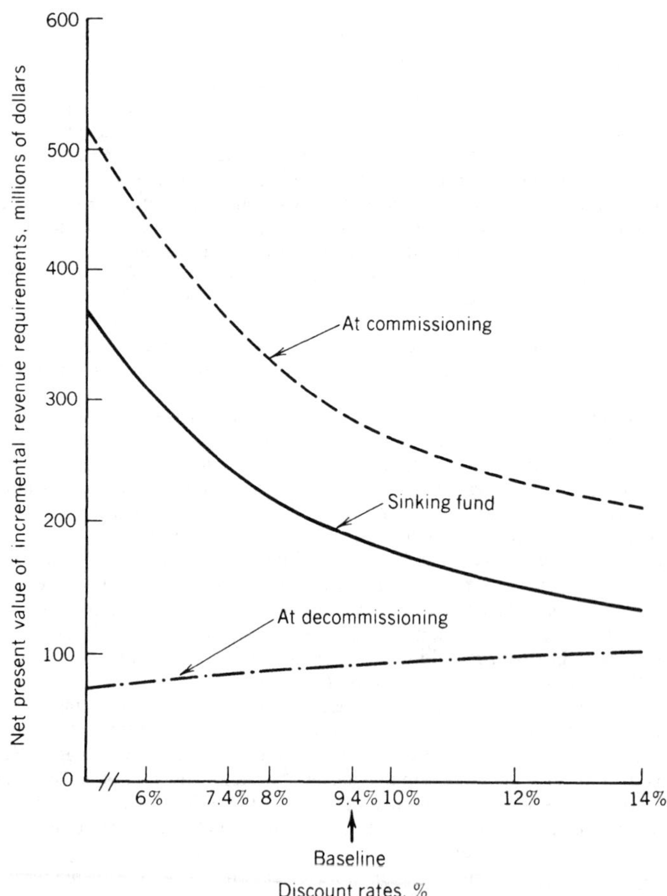

Figure 19.29. Sensitivity analysis of discount rates. (From Reference 27.)

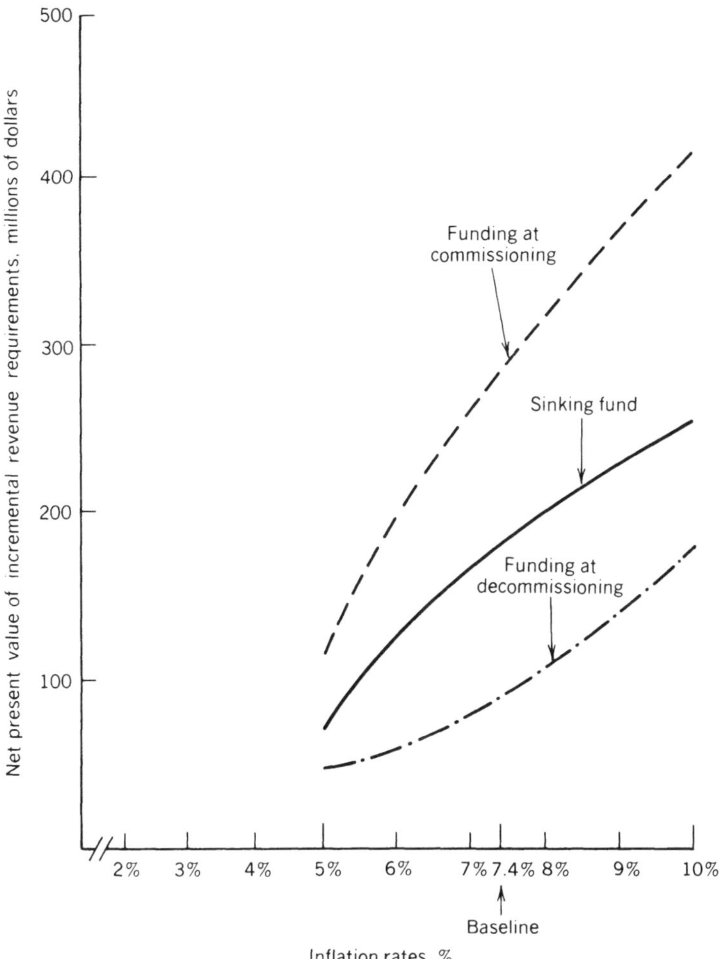

Figure 19.30. Sensitivity analysis of inflation rates. (From Reference 27.)

While the nominal future value of the three funding options will be the same, the net present value will not be the same because of the different cash flow streams. Funding at commissioning will have the highest net present value. Funding at decommissioning has the lowest net present value, and the sinking-fund alternative's present value lies in between. The cost comparison for the three decommissioning funding alternatives is shown in Table 19.6. The sensitivity to the rate of inflation and the discount rate are shown in Figures 19.29 and 19.30. In both figures, the ranking of the three options does not change, but the relative differences in the net present value or revenue requirements vary considerably. The sinking-fund method is found to occupy the middle ground between the two extremes of funding at commissioning or at decommissioning, both in terms of revenue requirements and in terms of a risk of insufficient funds.

Two areas of uncertainty are the exact regulatory requirements for commercial reactors decommissioning[26] and whether the sinking fund using bonds or other investment instruments would be subject to federal income taxes. The results of architect/engineering cost accounting indicate that a uniform annual cost for nuclear plant decommissioning could vary between 0.6 and 3.5 mills/kWh, depending on the inflation rate. These costs are based on a 70% capacity factor. The estimated decommissioning costs are less than 5% of the total bus bar generation costs on either a 10- or 20-yr levelized basis.

The decommissioning costs for PWRs and BWRs are about the same, with BWR costs slightly higher. Only small savings are associated with decommissioning costs of multiunit versus single reactor stations. Mothballing is the lowest cost technical option and prompt dismantling is the most

Table 19.7. Financial Parameters

Plant economic life (yr)	30
Reference year	1982
Inflation rate (%/yr)	6 (3–10)[a]
Escalation rate in excess of inflation rate for power plant construction (%/yr)	2 (0–6)[a]
Capitalization, %	
Debt	51 (55,45)[a]
Preferred stock	12 (15,10)[a]
Equity	37 (30,45)[a]
Return on capitalization (%/yr)	
Debt interest	10 (6–16)[a]
Preferred dividend	10 (6–16)[a]
Equity return	15 (10–18)[a]
Average cost of money (%/yr)	11.9 (7–17)[a]
Federal income tax rate (%/yr)	46
State income tax rate (%/yr)	4
Tax adjusted cost of money (%/yr)	9.4 (6–13)[a]
Local property tax rate[b] (%/yr)	2
Tax depreciation method	ACRS[c]
Tax depreciation life (yr)	
Nuclear	10
Fossil	15
Investment tax credit rate (%)	10
Interim replacement/backfitting rate[d] (%/yr)	1
Decommissioning cost, millions of 1982 dollars	
Fossil	0
Nuclear	120 (60–200)[a]
Interest rate on decommissioning fund (%/yr)	8.5 (5–13)[a]
Fixed charge rates[e] (%/yr)	
Fossil	17.7 (12–25)[a]
Nuclear	17.9 (12–25)[a]

Source: From Reference 3.

[a]Range of variation or uncertainty in parentheses.

[b]Based on initial investment with no escalation due to inflation or decrease due to depreciation.

[c]Accelerated capital recovery system.

[d]Percent of initial investment in constant dollars, escalating at general rate of inflation.

expensive. All other alternatives, including those involving long delays before decommissioning, are bound by the costs of the two alternatives discussed above. The total cost accumulated in the decommissioning sinking fund at the end of the plant lifetime is assumed to vary between 5 and 10% of the initial capital investment, depending on the technical option chosen.

Annualized Capital Charges

The capital investment part of total nuclear power generation cost is obtained by applying an annual fixed-charge rate to the initial capitalized investment. The annual capital-charge rate is the fraction of the initial investment that must be set aside each year to meet charges resulting directly from the investment. These charges include return on investment, depreciation, income taxes, property taxes and insurance, interim replacements, and the sinking fund for plant decommissioning costs. Examples of the financial parameters and of the components of the fixed-charge rate are given in Tables 19.7 and 19.8. Higher inflation expectations would lead to higher fixed-charge rates: for example, 20%/yr as computed for the Commonwealth Edison Co. case[8] or 16% as specified in the EPRI Technical Assessment Guide.[1] The effect of inflation rate on the annual capital charges is also shown in Table 19.9. Fixed-charge rates can be computed for various operating lifetimes, as seen in Table 19.10.

The levelized or the annual fixed-charge rate factors are composite numerical values used to estimate the payment of the required carrying charges on the original plant investment. Carrying

Table 19.8. Levelized Fixed Charge Rate Breakdown, %/yr

Return[a] (effective interest rate)	11.9	11.9
Sinking fund depreciation	0.4	0.4
Income tax	2.9[b]	3.0[b]
Property tax	2.0	2.0
Interim replacement/backfitting[c]	1.8	1.8
Subtotal	19.0	19.1
Less investment tax credit	1.3	1.2
Total	17.7	17.9

Source: From Reference 3.

[a]Capitalization 51% debt at 10%/yr; 12% preferred at 10%/yr; 37% equity at 15%/yr.

[b]Accelerated capital recovery system (ACRS) method, 10-yr tax life for nuclear plants, 15 yr for coal.

[c]Levelized; payments escalate at 6%/yr.

charges are obligations incurred when the plant is placed in service (at the end of the construction period), and they remain an obligation until the plant is retired at the end of its life. Once the plant investment is made, the carrying charges must be collected regardless of how much the plant is actually used, until the plant is fully depreciated. After the capital investment expenditures are made and the plant is in operation, the carrying charges level will not change unless there is a change in the tax laws or unless there is a change in the cost of equity money.

The carrying charges include payments on the following items: return on debt and on equity, book depreciation, income and local property taxes, and insurance. The various charge compo-

Table 19.9. Estimated Carrying Charges for Future Units (See Note)

	Mills/kWh	
	First 10 yr	Full Service Life
With 6% annual escalation:		
Nuclear	78	68
Coal	59	49
Nuclear higher	19	19
With 7½% annual escalation:		
Nuclear	87	76
Coal	68	57
Nuclear higher	19	19
With 10% annual escalation:		
Nuclear	105	91
Coal	87	73
Nuclear higher	18	18

Source: From Reference 8.

Note: Based upon construction costs which assume 1991 and 1992 service dates. Carrying charge factors include (i) annual money cost estimates of 10% for debt, 10.5% for preferred stock and 18% for common equity; (ii) a composite corporate income tax rate of 49.456%; (iii) an Illinois invested capital tax rate of 0.8%; and (iv) a resulting present-value discount rate of 10.8066%—assuming a capital structure of approximately 50% debt, 15% preferred, and 35% common equity.

Table 19.10. Carrying Charge Factors for Several Classes of Electric Utility Plant with and without Tax Preferences[a]

	Book Life (n) 30 yr Tax Recovery (m) 10 yr with Tax Preferences		Current Dollars (i = 12.5%)
f yr	Year by Year Carrying Charge (CC_f)	Cumulative Present Value of Carrying Charge ($V_{f,m,n}$)	Levelized Carrying Charge ($P_{f,m,n}$)
1	0.223	0.198	0.223
2	0.211	0.365	0.217
3	0.190	0.498	0.209
4	0.172	0.606	0.202
5	0.156	0.692	0.194
6	0.141	0.762	0.188
7	0.129	0.819	0.182
8	0.119	0.865	0.177
9	0.110	0.903	0.173
10	0.104	0.935	0.169
11	0.099	0.962	0.166
12	0.096	0.985	0.163
13	0.094	1.006	0.160
14	0.091	1.023	0.158
15	0.088	1.038	0.157
16	0.086	1.051	0.155
17	0.083	1.063	0.154
18	0.081	1.072	0.152
19	0.078	1.081	0.151
20	0.075	1.088	0.150
21	0.073	1.094	0.149
22	0.070	1.099	0.149
23	0.068	1.104	0.148
24	0.065	1.107	0.147
25	0.062	1.111	0.147
26	0.060	1.114	0.146
27	0.057	1.116	0.146
28	0.055	1.118	0.145
29	0.052	1.120	0.145
30	0.049	1.121	0.144

Source: From Reference 1.

[a]Property tax and insurance totaling 2% is included.

nents are discussed below while their contribution to the overall carrying charge rate is shown in Table 19.8.

Return on Plant Investment

The return on investment is the annual amount that the investors are paid for the use of their money, and it is often referred to as the "cost of money." The return payments apply only to funds that the utility currently uses, and not to investments removed from the books through the depreciation charges. In other words, the return obligation is based on the undepreciated investment, after the proper depreciation charges have been deducted.

Investor's money comes to the utility in two forms: debt and equity. Debt money is acquired by mortgaging a portion of the physical assets of the company (mortgage bonds) or by issuing an obligation without the physical asset of the company used as collateral (debentures). In either case, the debt money carries an obligation to pay annual stated return, regardless of the actual utilization of the power plant.

Equity money is acquired by selling ownership in the business through issuing either preferred stock or common stock, and entails higher risk than debt capital. The obligation to pay a return on equity comes after the obligation to return debt investments, but carries a utility ownership feature, the right to vote in annual stockowners meetings, and the promise of higher returns than debt returns as seen in Tables 19.7 and 19.8.

Depreciation

Depreciation is the annual charge against revenue used to repay the original amount from the debt holders. Depreciation also reflects the fact that when the plant is used, it wears out and according to public utility commission practices ratepayers pay for this fact. There are many methods of determining depreciation charges, the most common ones being the straight-line or the sinking-fund methods. The electric utilities industry uses the straight-line method for book depreciation. According to this technique, the annual charge made against revenues is equal to the original cost of the investment divided by the expected years of life. Book depreciation in an expanding utility is usually reinvested in new plant items. It is usually assumed that when a plant is retired the cost of removal is equal to the plant's salvage value. If significant retirement expenditures are required, as in the case of nuclear plant decommissioning, discussed above, separate decommissioning charges are collected. The total remaining investment of a utility is analogous to the allowed "rate base." The total utility book depreciation charged is a composite of the annual payments on the remaining life of each plant item. In order to reflect discrete plant lifetimes, each plant investment is usually assumed to be a separate account and the depreciation rates are based on the individual life of each specific investment, rather than on the composite lifetime of all plant items. This description is, however, a simplification of the real life accounting practices used, and is discussed here for illustrative purposes only.

Income Taxes and Local Property Taxes

Income taxes are computed by multiplying the tax rate by the difference between total revenues and all deductible expenditures. Utility accounting which is based on this general principle, usually assumes 46% federal income tax rate and 6% state tax rate. The state tax rate is of course deductible for federal income tax purposes, yielding a composite tax rate of 49%.

Fuel cost operating and maintenance expenses and interest on debt are all deductible for federal income tax purposes and have no tax obligation. The law also permits a deduction for cost recovery for tax purposes which is similar to book depreciation for rate-making purposes. The Internal Revenue Code now allows tax accounting procedures that will result in greater cost recovery tax deductions during the earlier years of operation than would be computed with a straight-line procedure. This will result in a deferment of tax payments toward the later years of the plant life. The deferred income tax is equal to the tax rate times the difference between the accelerated tax recovery and the straight-line tax recovery, in each year. Based on the Economic Tax Recovery Act of 1981, a 10-yr tax recovery period is assumed for nuclear plants and 15-yr period for coal-fired or hydroelectric plants.

For regulatory purposes there are two methods for handling deferred taxes: the "flow through" and the "normalization" procedures. The normalization method is the one most frequently used by electric utilities. In this procedure the deferred taxes are accumulated in a reserve account and used as a source of internally generated funds, along with retained equity earnings and book depreciation, to pay for new investment items. This method requires that the utility collect revenues as though income taxes were paid based on straight-line tax recovery schedules, hence the "normalization" terminology. This results in the utility having use of the deferred tax funds until they are required to pay the tax obligation later in the life of the plant. There is no return obligation as long as the taxes are deferred, and therefore, the rate base is reduced by the amount of the accumulated reserve.

Another tax incentive available to the electric utilities is the investment tax credit. This credit allows a utility to have an immediate reduction in income taxes proportional to the installed cost of a new plant item. The tax reduction is a credit, rather than a deferral and is realized in the year the plant item goes in service.

The above discussed tax preferences are now in practice and are used in electric utilities' economic analyses; however, they could be withdrawn through a change in the appropriate tax laws in the future. A government owned utility such as Tennessee Valley Authority does not pay federal income taxes; however, a payment in lieu of income taxes is often included in economic analyses related to such utilities. Property taxes and insurance are assumed to be levelized over the lifetime of the power plant at 2% of the installed plant cost level. These charge items are included in the computation of the annual fixed-charge rates.

As evident from Table 19.9, nuclear power plants are penalized for higher capital investment, as compared to coal-fired plants. The economic advantage of nuclear power over coal is in the nuclear fuel cost advantage over coal prices; this more than compensates for the higher nuclear capital charges. The choice of the proper fixed-charge rate to apply depends on the kind of cost analysis required (discussed in the summary section).

Table 19.11. The Effects of Capacity Factor on Unit Cost (Initial Year of Operation 1990, Mills/kWh)

NEW ENGLAND[a]	Nuclear			Coal		
Capacity Factor	50%	65%	80%	50%	65%	80%
Fixed cost	57.76	44.43	36.10	45.79	35.22	28.62
O&M	3.90	3.03	2.49	7.13	6.23	5.67
Fuel[b]	16.08	14.76	13.93	24.70(32.33)	24.70(32.33)	24.70(32.33)
Total[c]	77.74	62.22	52.52	77.62(85.25)	66.15(73.78)	58.99(66.62)
NORTH CENTRAL[d]	**Nuclear**			**Coal**		
Capacity Factor	50%	65%	80%	50%	65%	80%
Fixed Cost	54.16	41.66	33.85	43.52	33.48	27.20
O&M	3.90	3.03	2.49	7.13	6.23	5.67
Fuel[b]	16.08	14.76	13.93	14.48(19.91)	14.48(19.91)	14.48(19.91)
Total[c]	74.14	59.45	50.27	65.13(70.56)	54.19(59.62)	47.35(52.78)

Source: From Reference 29.

[a]One of the regions in which nuclear is favored by a wide margin.
[b]For nuclear, fuel costs are based on the no-recycle case. For coal fuel costs, both the DOE costs and the DOE adjusted costs (those in parentheses) are given.
[c]Figures in parentheses include the DOE adjusted coal costs.
[d]One of the regions in which coal is favored by a wide margin.

If a study on fuel and O&M cost is performed without inflation, the cost of capital and other components of the fixed-charge rate must also be reduced by the inflation component in order to have all costs on a consistent basis. This point is also discussed in Ref. 28. If the electricity generation costs are expressed in annual revenue requirements, the variable production costs must be related to the annual operating hours (the capacity factor). When electricity costs are expressed in mills/kWh, the annual capital charges are divided by the annual generation or, again, the capacity factor. The effects of varying the capacity factor on the annual fixed charges is very pronounced. It affects the relative economies of nuclear versus coal-fired plants when generation costs are expressed on a mills/kWh basis, as seen in Table 19.11.

19.3. ECONOMIC IMPACT OF THE THREE MILE ISLAND ACCIDENT

This section will cover only the economic cost of retrofitting reactors now in operation and the cost of modifying the designs of plants now under construction. The direct cost of TMI plant cleanup or of nuclear electricity loss due to mandated shutdowns and inspections is not considered here. It is known, though, that NRC mandated shutdowns of operating plants reduced the amount of nuclear generated electricity in 1979 by 12% of actual production, based on the NRC "Yellow Book" statistics.[30] Data from Ref. 30 indicate the 30 billion kWh were lost due to NRC restrictions. At an average cost of 20.7 mills/kWh for the actual cost of nuclear generation in 1979, the total loss in 1979 was $625 million, or more than the initial cost of the TMI reactor itself.

Estimates of capital costs due directly to plant modifications required by the NRC *TMI Action Plan* vary considerably. Not all the required guides and regulations have yet been issued, and the impact of the existing and future requirements on plant capital costs is not yet well understood. The NRC estimates that retrofitting costs to existing plants are of the order of $25 million per plant.[31] The Atomic Industrial Forum, however, estimates the added costs to be between $28 and $75 million (1980 dollars) per reactor, and that 100 additional technical person-years would be required.[32] In addition, the AIF estimated an average outage cost for retrofitting of $7.6 million/reactor, as seen in Table 19.12. Table 19.12 shows a breakdown of the range of cost increment on a per unit basis for an operating reactor and for a plant under construction. The AIF report also included figures for a total retrofitting cost in terms of direct capital expenses and outage expenses.

An estimate of the TMI-related cost increments to LWR capital costs is seen in Figure 19.31. A range of costs of $15–75 million (1980 dollars) per unit in direct construction expenses is assumed. This is closer to the AIF estimates than to the NRC estimates.

The effects of TMI related modifications, backfittings, redesigns, and reworks on plant lead-times were investigated in Ref. 21 and are shown in Figure 19.15. As seen in Figure 19.15, the TMI

Table 19.12. Range of Costs and Technical Man-Years Per Unit ($ Millions)

	Priority Group		
	I	II	III
I. Operating units			
A. Minimum Average Cost Per Unit	1.1	22.8	5.1
B. Maximum Average Cost Per Unit	1.4	30.4	6.7
II. Under-construction units			
A. Minimum Average Cost Per Unit	1.1	22.8	5.1
B. Maximum Average Cost Per Unit	232.1	526.8	1,055.1
III. Engineering man-years per unit	8.0	88.0	12.0

Source: From Reference 32.

Note:

1. It is important to recognize that the per-unit figures are indeed *averages* and carry with them all of the potential interpretational hazards inherent with averaged data. Obviously, the cost for any specific unit may be substantially more or less than the averages stated.
2. The costs displayed in the above table were developed in the following manner:
   a. *Minimum average cost per unit* was determined by dividing the total industry capital cost for each priority group by the number of operating and under-construction units considered.
   b. *Maximum average cost per operating unit* was calculated by adding the minimum average cost per unit to the average outage cost per unit.
   c. *Maximum average cost per unit under-construction* was calculated by adding the minimum average cost per unit to the maximum schedule delay cost per unit.

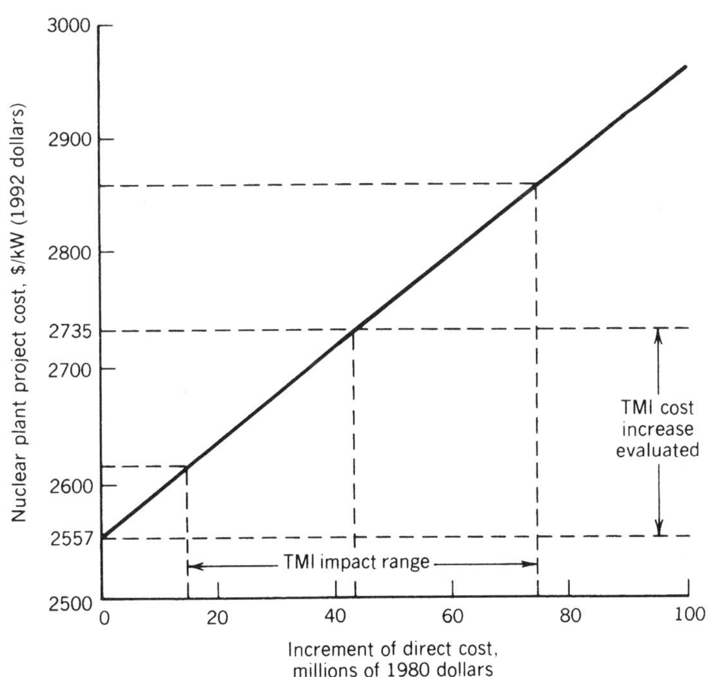

Figure 19.31. Potential investment cost increase associated with the TMI accident. (From Reference 33.)

Table 19.13. Evaluation of Annual Costs for a Single-Unit Nuclear Plant to Implement TMI-2 Corrective Actions

Plant Departments	Number of Personnel Additions
Site operations	1–12
Site training	6–12
Professional/technical	
On-site	12–24
Off-site	12–24
Maintenance	6–12
Personnel totals	37–84
For estimating purposes	40–80
Costs	
Total annual personnel cost, \$1000	3000–6000
Related supplies and expenses, \$1000	1000–2000
Total annual cost, \$1000	4000–8000

Source: From Reference 34.

For a 2-, 3-, and 4-unit plant at the same site, the multiplying factors to adjust costs are ~1.5, 1.9, and 2.3, respectively. It is generally expected that more efficient utilization of technical, professional, and maintenance personnel results at multiple-unit plants.

related leadtime extension is about 20 months, and it mainly affected utilities with partially completed plants, especially those more susceptible to large increments in interest during construction during the schedule stretchout after a large portion of the total plant expenditures had already been paid. In some cases, like the North Anna 3 plant in Virginia, expected modifications due to TMI regulation will increase the estimated direct investment through 1989 by 950 million, out of a total 1.4 billion dollars construction cost. It is assumed that power plants at the initial stages of the construction program will have factored TMI related modifications into their design activities, and will thus require shorter lead times than plants already partly completed. A recent estimate of a backfitting and regulatory cost impact study at a northeast utility includes both NRC mandated and utility initiated backfitting costs for three nuclear plants following the TMI accident.[33] Three of its currently operating plants whose initial capital costs totaled \$620 million have incurred total backfitting costs of \$584 million (all current dollar figures at years of expenditure). The NRC mandated backfits amount to 60% of the total cost increment and \$56 million dollars can directly be attributed to TMI related changes. Other indirectly TMI related backfits amount to about \$100 million.

Additional expenses associated with the TMI accident involve operator training, enhanced technical support, and hiring additional operating personnel. These expenses relate to annual operations charges and not to the initial plant investment. An estimate of the annual costs to implement TMI corrective actions mandated by the NRC is shown in Table 19.13. The incremental annual operating charges could reach \$4–8 million/yr for a single plant, while the plant complement could be increased by up to 80 new operators as seen in this table. The various TMI corrective actions now being implemented are some of the main contributors to the increase in nuclear operating and maintenance charges, as discussed below.

19.4. OPERATING AND MAINTENANCE COSTS

The annual nuclear plant Operating and Maintenance (O&M) costs were until 1979 the smallest of the three components of the total electricity generation costs. While coal plant O&M costs are about one-tenth of the total generation costs, nuclear O&M costs since 1980 comprise 20–25% of total costs, exceeding nuclear fuel expenses. During the last 3 yr nuclear fuel costs did not increase significantly, due to the reduction in uranium fuel prices, while O&M costs have substantially increased, due in part to TMI effects, as discussed above. The relative changes in O&M and fuel expenses for nuclear plants during the 1977–1981 period are shown in Table 19.14, where it is seen that nuclear O&M costs have increased by a factor of 2.5 during the 5-yr period, as measured in

Table 19.14. National Averages of U.S. Investor-owned Nuclear Power Plant Generating Costs

	Average Unit Costs, Mills/kWh				
Cost Category	1981	1980	1979	1978	1977
Fuel (actual)	5.46	4.99	3.92	3.22	2.85
O&M (actual)	6.23	5.69	4.25	2.95	2.46
Capital (estimated)[a]	14.40	14.00	14.03	10.53	9.15
Generating (estimated)	26.09	24.68	22.20	16.70	14.46
Yearly cost increase (%)	5.7	11.2	32.9	15.5	—
Capacity factor (%)[b]	62.4	59.6	58.2	66.6	64.6

Source: From Reference 35.

[a]A Fixed-Charge Rate (FCR) of 18% was used in 1980 and 1981. The fixed-charge rate for previous years was 17%.

[b]Capacity factor is the ratio of the electric energy produced by a generating station over a certain period of time to that which would be produced if the station generated continuously at its full capacity over the whole period (usually expressed as a percent).

current dollars. Coal plant O&M costs vary with the kind of coal burned and the kind of pollution control equipment used. With flue gas scrubbing equipment installed, coal plant O&M costs could reach 20% of total generation costs. As seen in Table 19.3 and discussed in Ref. 35, nuclear O&M costs were more than twice the coal-fired plant operating expenses for the year 1981. A regional variation in O&M costs is evident from utility reports. The highest nuclear O&M expenditures have occurred in the northeast and far-west regions of the country, while the lowest O&M costs were reported in the east north-central region, the range of variation being 4.75 to 8.95 mills/kWh for these regions. Coal plant O&M expenditures show a smaller regional variability, the highest costs occurring in the middle atlantic region.[35]

A summary of annual O&M costs for various power plants in 1982 dollars is shown in Table 19.15, and a breakdown of nuclear and coal-fired plant O&M costs for the years 1978 and 1982 is shown in Table 19.16. As shown in Table 19.15, the O&M charges are grouped into fixed (not dependent on annual operating hours) and variable components. Nuclear plants exhibit high fixed O&M costs and low variable operating expenses. Coal-fired plants exhibit just the reverse cost pattern.

The major components of the O&M costs are:

1. Plant payroll, based on the size of the working staff, including supervision and engineering.
2. Consumable supplies and equipment, including lubricants, chemicals, and other miscellaneous supplies; office, and other incidental expenses; and maintenance renewal parts and materials.
3. Outside support services for certain types of maintenance and other operations.
4. Miscellaneous costs, including training of new staff personnel, requalifying reactor operators, operating fees and licenses, travel, and building maintenance.
5. Liability insurance premiums, some of which are unique to nuclear power plants, due to the very high liability claims and property losses that can accrue in a serious reactor accident.
6. Plant security and physical protection force.

Table 19.15. Nonfuel Operation and Maintenance Costs for Baseload Plants (1982 Dollars)

	Fixed Cost, $/kWe/yr	Variable Cost, Mills/kWh	Total Cost,[a] Mills/kWh
LWR nuclear	35	0.2	6.3
Eastern coal-fired plant with FGD[b]	22	1.5	5.4
Western coal-fired plant with FGD	19	0.6	4.0
Oil-fired plant with FGD	10	0.5	2.3
Natural gas-fired plant without FGD	3	0.3	0.8

Source: From Reference 34.

[a]At 65% capacity factor.

[b]FGD—Flue Gas Desulfurization.

Table 19.16a. Comparison of 1982 and 1978 Annual O&M Cost-Estimating Guidelines for a 1 × 1150-MWe PWR plant at 65% Capacity Factor (Millions of 1982 Dollars)

	1978[a]	1982
On-site staff	6.6	14.8
Maintenance materials	2.3	4.3
Supplies and expenses	6.0	5.5
Regulatory fees, inspections, and reviews	0.1	0.5
Off-site support services	0	3.7
Insurance	0.4	6.0
Administrative and general	2.2	8.6
Total	17.6	43.4

Source: From Reference 34.
[a]ORNL/TM-6467 escalated to 1982 dollars.

Although licensed reactor operators may receive a 5 to 10% wage premium, other fossil-fueled and nuclear plant personnel are assigned the same hourly rates. Nonlicensed jobs in fossil and nuclear work are not significantly different in function. However, more preparation and training may be required to teach nuclear plant procedures for repairs and inspections. These requirements have been upgraded as a result of the TMI accident.

Estimated O&M costs for nuclear plants, while including factors common to conventional plants, most reflect such factors as radioactive waste disposal, personnel radiation dosimetry and record keeping, plant laundry, and maintenance in the presence of radiation. Key supervisory and operating personnel must have valid operating licenses. Nuclear engineers and health physicists have jobs unique to nuclear plants. Furthermore, more technical staff and operators are required for additional systems such as coolant purification, inert gas purification, fuel handling, and fuel and coolant receiving and storage facilities. The number of such additional staff members depends on the type and rating of the plant. Maintenance procedures must take into consideration the problem of workers' exposure to radioactivity at the working location and the permissible radiation dosage, which limits their working time.

Operators of nuclear plants are required to prepare and implement security plans or procedures that meet the approval of the Nuclear Regulatory Commission (NRC). (Currently, security at coal plants is minimal, and some plants have no formal security staff.) Since 1978, security personnel have increased, and the skill requirements are greater. Personnel selection and training have also been upgraded. Contract service is used by many utilities and therefore may not be included in staff numbers. Because of the security nature of this work, the number of personnel is not always reported or is regarded as confidential. It is estimated that a total complement of a physical security force at a nuclear power plant could reach 100 persons, while a coal plant guard force now numbers about one-tenth of that figure.[34]

Table 19.16b. Comparison of 1982 and 1978 Annual O&M Cost-Estimating Guidelines for a 2 × 575-MWe Coal-Fired Plant at 65% Capacity Factor (Millions of 1982 Dollars)

	1978[a]	1982
On-site staff	9.9	9.5
Maintenance materials	4.2	4.0
Supplies and expenses	16.7	13.5
Regulatory fees, inspections, and reviews	0	0
Off-site support services	0	1.1
Insurance	0	0.2
Administrative and general	1.7	8.4
Total	32.5	36.7

Source: From Reference 34.
[a]ORNL/TM-6467 escalated to 1982 dollars.

Testing and maintenance of intrusion alarms, emergency alarms, access control equipment, communication equipment, physical barriers, and other security-related devices add an important amount of work to the annual maintenance costs. Plant maintenance outages also increase security requirements.

In general, NRC review of plant operating procedures following the TMI accident had a significant impact on the training system for plant operators and for technical support. Many more technical people both on-site and off-site are involved in design and procedural activities than were previously involved. As with coal plants, operator teams work similar shift rotation, but key personnel are limited in duration of shift work. More work shifts or teams (six or more) are provided to perform relief, training, and operator functions in nuclear power plants.

While in 1977 only a small group of utilities had in-house simulator facilities for personnel training, now all nuclear utilities are under obligation to provide this feature along with updated training provisions for all their operating plants. The design and use of these training devices are under constant review and analysis. As well as technical and operational upgrades, training and retraining efforts also involve all other work functions including security, maintenance, records, and participation in public and plant emergency functions. Safety, environmental, and health physics inspections for nuclear plants are routinely performed at specified frequencies to assure the NRC that the authorized activities are being conducted in accordance with the Atomic Energy Act of 1954 as amended, NRC regulations, and the terms and conditions of the license. These inspections involve (1) direct observations of operations, (2) personnel interviews, (3) independent measurements and evaluations, and (4) selective record and procedure examinations. The annual NRC facility inspection and review fee amounts to about $400,000, including professional manpower costs.[34]

Price–Anderson Insurance

From the time nuclear fuel is delivered to a nuclear project site, the licensee is required to protect itself from public liability claims arising from a nuclear incident. This protection is provided through a three-layer combination of commercial insurance, self-insurance, and government indemnity, as required. The first layer is commercial nuclear liability insurance, the current maximum amount available being $160 million. The estimated premiums are typical for commercial insurance. Plant sites must be specified before firm rates can be quoted. The second layer is a mandatory industry-wide program of self-insurance, under which nuclear plant licensees can be assessed for each operational reactor owned an amount not to exceed $5 million per reactor year for each nuclear incident and not to exceed $10 million per reactor year in the event of more than one incident. The federal government's long standing role in helping to provide accident liability insurance has ended with the start-up of the San Onofre-3 nuclear plant on November 15, 1982. Liability insurance by utility self-payments now amounts to $400 million, in addition to the private underwriters' contribution mentioned above. Thus the total liability insurance of $570 million, specified by the Price-Anderson Act, is now met without government contribution. The total liability insurance will keep growing beyond the present $570 million as the number of operating reactors exceed 80.

The Price–Anderson Act will expire in 1987. NRC has recommended that the act be renewed with an annual limit on retroactive premium payments instead of the current cap on total liability. Thus after 1987 utilities may have to pay substantially more than the current $570 million limit for total off-site liability in the event of an Extraordinary Nuclear Occurrence (ENO) but could stretch the payments out. In conjunction with the lifting of the liability cap, the NRC recommended that the maximum retroactive premium be increased from the present $5 million to $10 million per reactor year, which would provide roughly the same amount of insurance coverage now available for on-site damage. Also under consideration is the possibility of raising the $160 million primary layer of coverage available through private insurance pools and extending from 20 years to 30 years the statute of limitations for filing a claim under Price–Anderson.

Other Special Nuclear Insurance

In addition to liability insurance, electric utilities carry through private sources nuclear plant property insurance plus coverage against the cost of replacement power needed if an accident causes an extended outage.[36] The NRC has issued a new rule in March 1982 that requires electric utility licensees "to obtain on-site property-damage insurance available at reasonable costs and on reasonable terms."[41] This rule requires, as a minimum, primary nuclear property insurance that is now offered by Nuclear Mutual Limited (NML) and American Nuclear Insurers (ANI) or Mutual Atomic Energy Reinsurance Pool (MAERP), plus excess property insurance offered by either Nuclear Electric Insurance Limited (NEIL) or ANI/MAERP. Primary nuclear property-damage insurance in the amount of $500 million is now available. The nuclear insurance pools and the Edison Electric Institute (EEI) have announced plans to develop additional nuclear property-

Table 19.17. Estimated Annual Premiums for Commercial Property-Damage Insurance

Type of Insurance	Premium Cost for Number of Units 1	2	3	4
Nuclear Plants				
Primary ($500 million)	$2,000,000	$3,600,000	$5,300,000	$7,000,000
Secondary ($500 million)	1,600,000	1,800,000	2,000,000	2,200,000
Total ($1000 million)	$3,600,000	$5,400,000	$7,300,000	$9,200,000
Coal-Fired Plants				
Commercial	$ 100,000	$ 200,000	$ 300,000	$ 400,000

Source: From Reference 34.

damage insurance in the amount of $500 million, which will eventually provide a total of $1 billion in coverage. At present, about $300 million of the excess property-damage insurance is available. Estimated annual premiums for commercial property damage insurance are shown in Table 19.17. Additional costs of about $428,000/yr are required for nuclear liability insurance. NEIL presently covers the cost of buying replacement power for damaged nuclear plants. The premium for a single unit for maximum coverage of $156 million is in the range of $1.5 to 2.0 million/yr.

Administrative and general expenses include the owner's off-site salaries and expenses directly allocable to a specific power production facility. The magnitude of administrative and general expenses is related to fixed O&M costs, minus insurance and operating fees. Values of 10 and 15% of total fixed cost of staff, maintenance materials, and supplies and expenses are used to estimate administrative and general costs for fossil-fuel and nuclear plants, respectively. As seen in Table 19.10, the sum of the insurance and administrative and general expenses now amount to about one-third of the total nuclear plant annual O&M cost.

19.5. NUCLEAR FUEL CYCLE COSTS

The uranium used to fuel present-generation LWRs is in the form of sintered UO_2 pellets, slightly enriched (3%) in the isotope ^{235}U. The cost of fuel, from its mining to the ultimate disposal, is about one-fifth to one-fourth of the total cost of electricity, as seen in Tables 19.1, 19.2, and 19.3. A flow path for the uranium as it moves through the various stages of the fuel cycle is given in Figure 2.20. Cost estimates for each of these stages are presented in the following sections.

The fuel cycle is generally divided into two parts. The front-end includes the mining, milling, conversion, enrichment, and fabrication steps—all these occur before the fuel elements are loaded into the reactor. The back end includes all the unit operations performed after the fuel is discharged from the reactor. These include on-site storage, transportation, off-site storage at an away-from-reactor facility. Several possibilities exist. If the spent fuel elements are sent to a disposal site for ultimate burial, we have a "once-through" or throwaway fuel cycle. This fuel path (not actually a cycle) was advocated by the Carter administration beginning in 1977, while the closed (i.e., recycle) option which was the historic development path pursued over the last 30 yr, was reestablished by the Reagan administration in 1981. All fuel cycles in which the spent fuel is chemically separated to its three major constituents—uranium, plutonium, or fission products—and the remaining fissile elements are recycled back into the front end, are called closed fuel cycles. The "closing" of the cycle has been the goal of all nuclear fuel research and development projects in the United States and abroad since the inception of the nuclear power program. Such a scheme is appealing on engineering grounds due to the recycling of useful constituents of the spent fuel, on resource conservation grounds due to the reduction of new makeup fuel requirements, on waste management grounds due to the concentration and volume reduction of the radioactive waste, and ultimately on economic grounds. Currently, only France and to some extent the United Kingdom operate a closed nuclear reactor fuel cycle. Japan is proceeding toward the establishment of such a cycle and progress toward this scheme in the Federal Republic of Germany has recently resumed. The U.S. government had actively encouraged closing the nuclear fuel cycle until 1977, when a complete reversal of policy was enunciated. The Reagan administration aims at restoring the nuclear fuel cycle operations to their original course and purpose. The formal ban on fuel reprocessing has been lifted by President Reagan; however, commercial reprocessing has not yet commenced, due to uncertain economics and regulatory support.

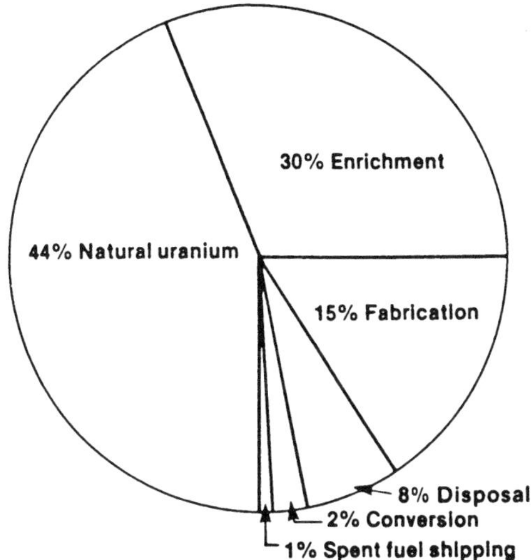

Figure 19.32. Nuclear fuel cost inputs. Distribution of nuclear fuel cost components (based on 30-yr levelized mills/kWh). All prices in 1982 dollars. (1) Yellowcake, \$31/lb U_3O_8. (2) Conversion, \$3.10/lb U. (3) Enrichment, \$130.75/SWU. (4) Fabrication: (a) first core, \$225/kg; (b) reloads, \$200/kg. (5) Spent fuel transportation, \$36/kg. (6) Spent fuel disposal, \$275/kg. (From Reference 6.)

The costs for reprocessing, mixed-oxide† fuel fabrication, and waste disposal are less certain than the costs of other fuel cycle steps due to the lack of commercial experience in these processes. These steps are omitted in the once-through fuel cycle being presently employed. All cost estimates are presented on a levelized basis (constant unit price that must be charged to recover all capital and operating costs by end of plant life). Unlike oil, or other power cycles, nuclear fuel cycle expenditures start several years before the fuel elements are inserted into the reactor and extend for many years after the discharge, until the final disposal of the waste. The coal plant fuel cycle is slowly evolving in the same direction as the nuclear fuel cycle. Front-end steps in the coal fuel cycle may include mining, transportation, precleaning, beneficiation, or oil or water mixture preparations. Back-end cycle steps involve complex waste disposal problems of scrubber sludge streams and other waste products.

There needs to be a separate discussion on each step of the fuel cycle. A summary of the fuel-cycle cost components is shown in Figure 19.32, while the unit electricity costs associated with the fuel cycle are shown in Table 19.18. The time distributions of fuel cycle expenses before, during, and after insertion in the reactor, for once-through and recycle operations, are shown in Figure 19.33.

Mining and Milling

The estimates of uranium resources are broken down into several forward cost (not price) known categories. Forward costs include operating and capital expenditures in constant dollars that would be incurred in producing uranium. These include power, labor, materials, royalties, insurance, severance taxes, and G&A costs. Note that income taxes, interest, profit, and past costs (land expense, exploration) are not included. It is usually assumed that the actual incentive prices could be estimated by multiplying the forward costs by a factor of 1.8 (i.e., 80% higher than forward costs).[39]

The uranium resources versus forward cost in the United States are given in Table 19.19. Uranium reserves range between 205,000 tons at \$30/lb (U_3O_8) and 894,000 tons at \$100/lb. Other resource categories (probable, possible, speculative) are also given in this table. The mean for all categories is 1.25 million tons at \$30/lb and 4.11 million tons for \$100/lb. This does not include secondary recovery of uranium as a by-product through such activities as phosphate production or copper milling. Secondary recovery could add another 150,000 tons/yr of uranium production. The probability distributions of the U.S. uranium reserves are shown in Figure 19.34. For comparison

†"Mixed oxides" denotes a mixture of plutonium and uranium oxides, $(Pu,U)O_2$, used as a fuel in nuclear reactors in place of the usual uranium oxide, UO_2.

Table 19.18. Example Nuclear Fuel Costs (Mills/kWh)

	Levelized Costs			
	Once-Through		Recycle	
	Current $	Constant 1982 $	Current $	Constant 1982 $
U_3O_8	23.6	5.76	16.3	3.96
Conversion	1.1	0.26	0.7	0.18
Enrichment	13.3	3.23	10.3	2.50
LEU fabrication[a]	4.4	1.07	3.4	0.83
MOX fabrication[b]			3.3	0.80
Back end	1.5	0.36	7.9	1.92
Total	43.8	10.7	41.9	10.2

Source: From Reference 3.

[a]LEU—low enriched uranium.

[b]MOX—mixed oxides fuel.

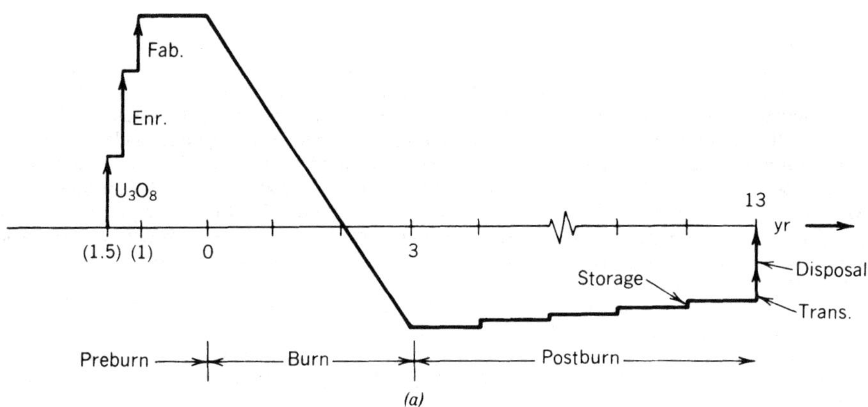

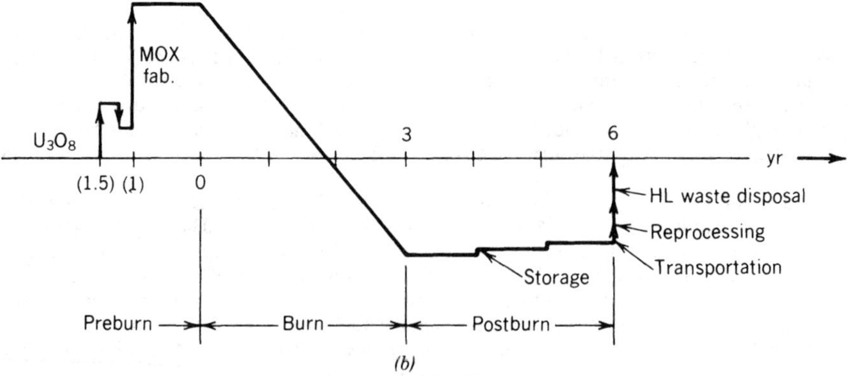

Figure 19.33. (*a*) Batch cash flow—throwaway cycle. (*b*) Batch cash flow—mixed-oxide recycle. (From Reference 38.)

Table 19.19a. Historical and Current Estimates of Uranium Reserves

	Thousand Tons U_3O_8				
Year	\$8/lb U_3O_8	\$15/lb U_3O_8	\$30/lb U_3O_8	\$50/lb U_3O_8	\$100/lb U_3O_8
1/1/65	151	—	—	—	—
1/1/66	145	—	—	—	—
1/1/67	141	—	—	—	—
1/1/68	148	248	—	—	—
1/1/69	161	265	—	—	—
1/1/70	204	317	—	—	—
1/1/71	246	391	—	—	—
1/1/72	273	520	—	—	—
1/1/73	273	520	—	—	—
1/1/74	277	520	634	—	—
1/1/75	200	420	600	—	—
1/1/76	—	430	640	—	—
1/1/77	—	410	680	840	—
1/1/78	—	370	690	890	—
1/1/79	—	290	690	920	—
1/1/80	—	225	645	936	1,122
1/1/81	—	112	470	787	1,034
1/1/82	—	—	205	594	894

Source: From Reference 40.

Table 19.19b. Potential Uranium Resources, 1975–1982

	Thousand Tons U_3O_8						
Forward-Cost Category	1/1/75	1/1/76	1/1/77	1/1/78	1/1/79 and 1/1/80[a]	1/1/81	1/1/82
\$10/lb U_3O_8							
Probable	460	440	275	—	—	—	—
Possible	390	420	115	—	—	—	—
Speculative	110	145	100	—	—	—	—
\$15/lb U_3O_8							
Probable	680	655	585	540	415	295	—
Possible	640	675	490	490	210	87	—
Speculative	210	290	190	165	75	74	—
\$30/lb U_3O_8							
Probable	1,140	1,060	1,090	1,015	1,005	885	596
Possible	1,340	1,270	1,120	1,135	675	346	227
Speculative	410	590	480	415	300	311	236
\$50/lb U_3O_8							
Probable	—	—	1,370	1,395	1,505	1,426	1,080
Possible	—	—	1,420	1,515	1,170	641	473
Speculative	—	—	540	565	550	482	421
\$100/lb U_3O_8							
Probable	—	—	—	—	—	2,080	1,740
Possible	—	—	—	—	—	1,005	784
Speculative	—	—	—	—	—	696	685

Source: From Reference 40.

[a]No new estimates were released for January 1, 1980, since the NURE program was to publish comprehensive potential resource estimates by October 1980.

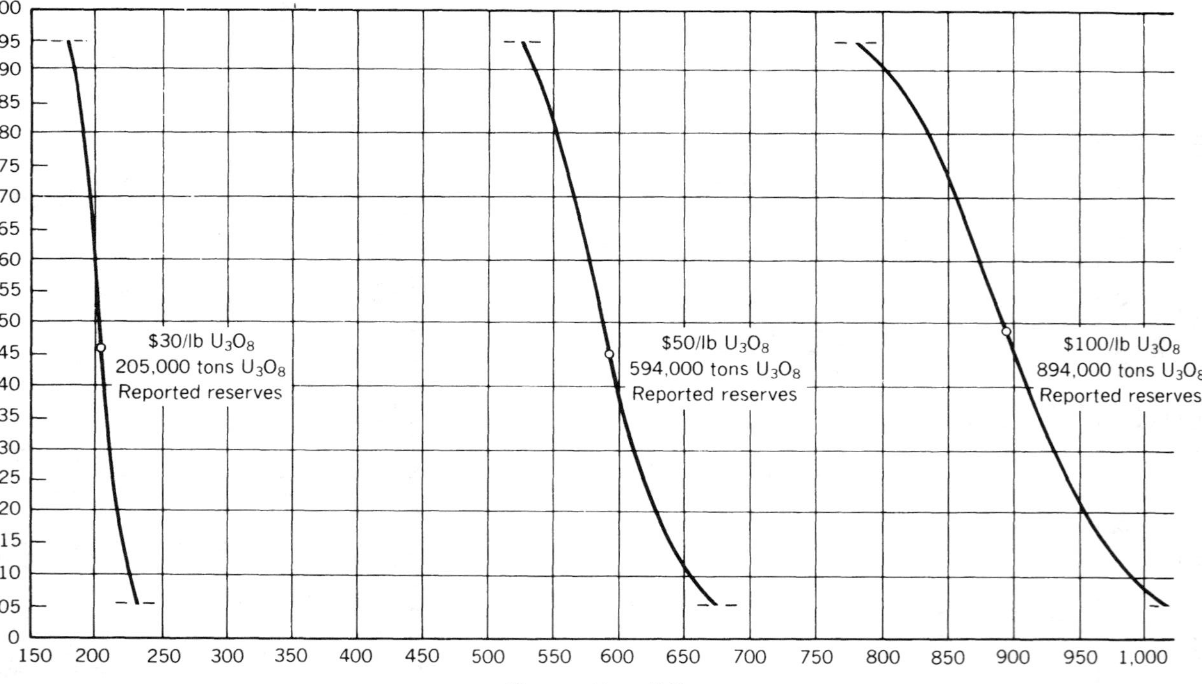

Figure 19.34. Cumulative probability distribution for uranium reserves, January 1982. (From Reference 40.)

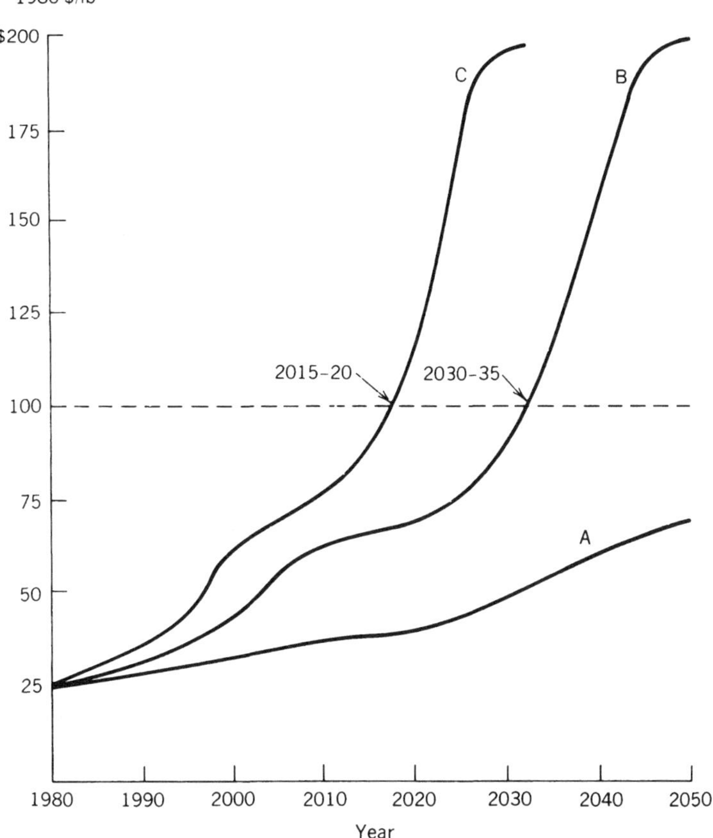

Figure 19.35. Long-term supply schedule. Cost versus time for three production scenarios. A—flat, 10,000 tons/yr. B—linear growth. C—exponential growth. (From Reference 41.)

purposes it takes approximately 6000 tons of uranium to satisfy the lifetime fuel requirements of a single 1000-MWe LWR. Projected uranium supply curves through the year 2050 are shown in Figure 19.35. Additional sources of uranium for power production exist in the 250,000 tons of depleted uranium fluoride or "tails" from the uranium enrichment plants. When burned in breeder reactors, these reserves represent a greater energy source than the entire U.S. uranium resource base in the ground.

It should be recognized that a basic difference exists between uranium reserves and resources. Reserves represent known uranium deposits, clearly delineated in specific mining properties, which can directly be converted to supplies at hand. Resources include inferences to uranium deposits, estimated at various degrees of certainty. The probable resources represent an extension of know uranium deposits. The possible resources represent estimates of uranium occurrences in formations similar to those where actual deposits were found, and are not based on direct evidence. The speculative resources are just such, and are referred to as "uranium found in the computer, rather than in the ground."

It should also be recognized that the existence of uranium reserves in the ground does not correspond to the availability of uranium supplies to power reactors. Lack of capital outlays, experienced miners, or mining permits, and various restrictions and environmental regulations imposed on the uranium mining industry may inhibit the utilization of fuel resources.

Over the years there existed a basic controversy about the true size of the U.S. uranium resource base. This issue has important consequences for the size of the supportable nuclear capacity, the closing of the nuclear fuel cycle, and the need for breeder reactors. On the professional side, there exists a conflict between the conservative resource estimates of uranium geologists and the more optimistic estimates of the energy economists, who believe that with increased prices additional resources will always be found. On the political side the pro- and antinuclear

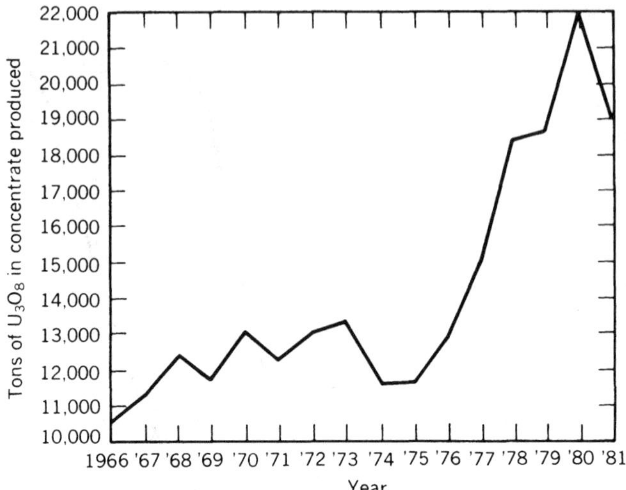

Uranium concentrate production
(includes production from millfeed other than ore)

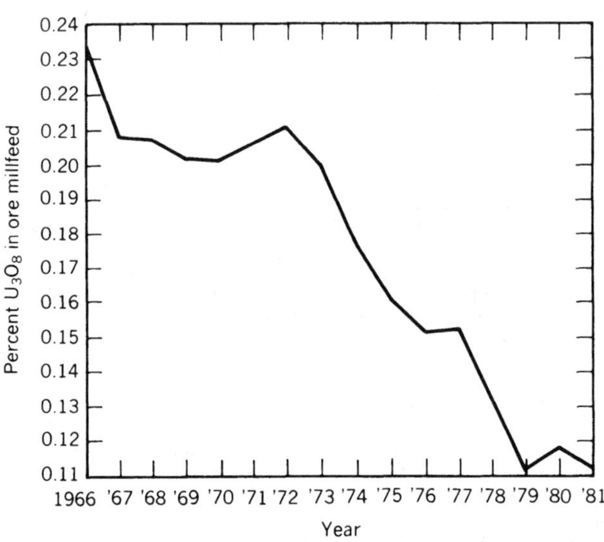

Grade of uranium ore processed

Figure 19.36. Uranium concentrate production and grade of uranium ore processed. (From Reference 40.)

groups have also taken opposite positions. A detailed discussion of these issues can be found in the reports of the Committee on Nuclear and Alternative Energy Systems (CONAES)[42] and the FORD-MITRE[43] study on nuclear power issues and choices.

Since 1950 the average ore grade mined in the United States has decreased from 0.32% U_3O_8 to about 0.11% U_3O_8, as seen in Figure 19.36. The uranium produced in the United States during 1981 was obtained from underground mines (43%), from open pit mines (36%), and from solution mining (11%). By-product, heap leaching, and other mining methods have accounted for the remaining 10% of total production. U_3O_8 concentrate production in the United States peaked in 1980 as seen in Figure 19.36, and then has continuously declined. This is due to the reduced demand for electricity, the slowdown in nuclear capacity expansion, the development of cheaper uranium

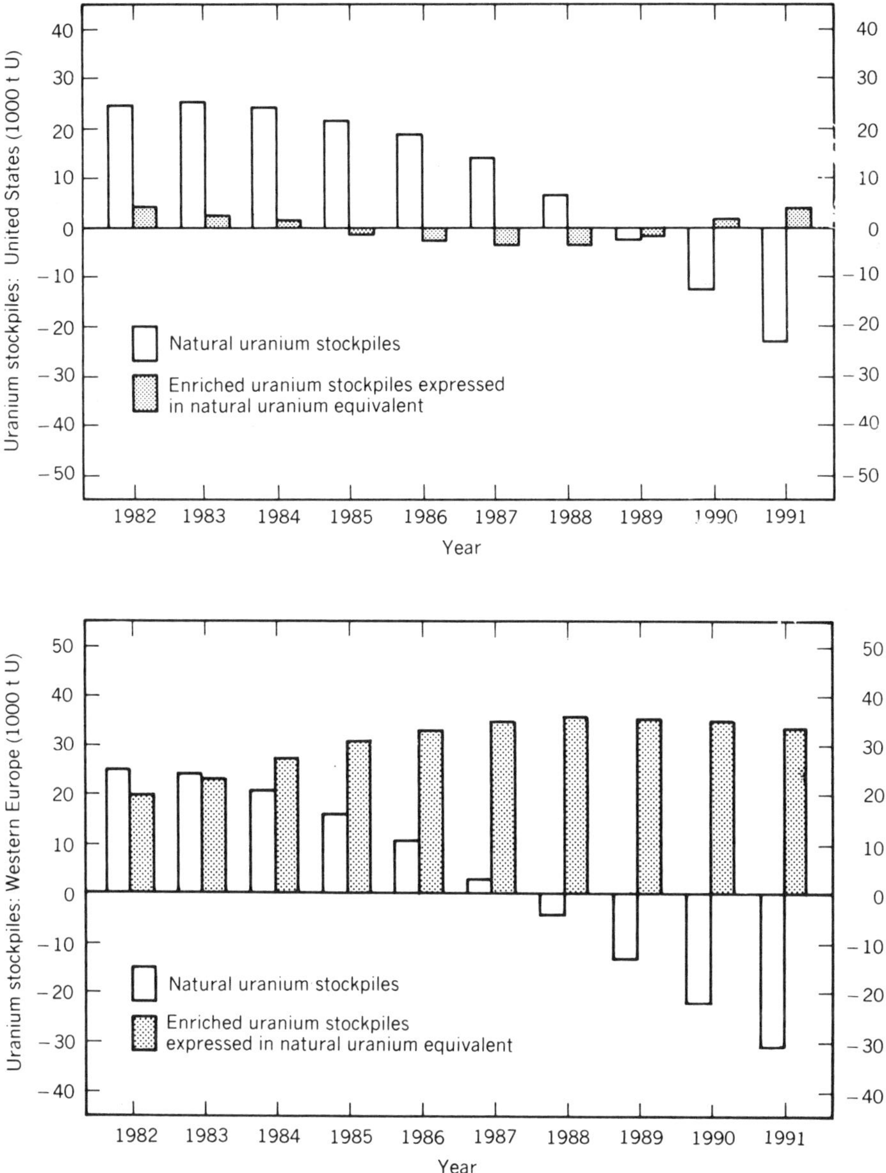

Figure 19.37. Uranium stockpiles: United States and Western Europe. (From Reference 44.)

supplies by foreign producers, and the accumulation of large uranium inventories held by U.S., European, and Japanese utilities, shown in Figure 19.37.

The price of uranium has proved to be quite volatile over the last decade. The uranium spot price rose swiftly to over $40/lb in the period 1975–1979, and then declined to $17/lb in 1982. The evolution of the natural uranium spot price in the recent past is shown in Figure 19.38.

Spot demand for uranium is notoriously difficult to measure or estimate. Actual quantities needed for fueling reactors depend on specific reactor core loadings and power production, enrichment tails assay, and procurement lead times. However, demand may be and often is influenced by price trends, assured supply considerations, and world politics, since mining in many countries (Australia, Canada, etc.) is subject to local political considerations. Demand is also influenced by

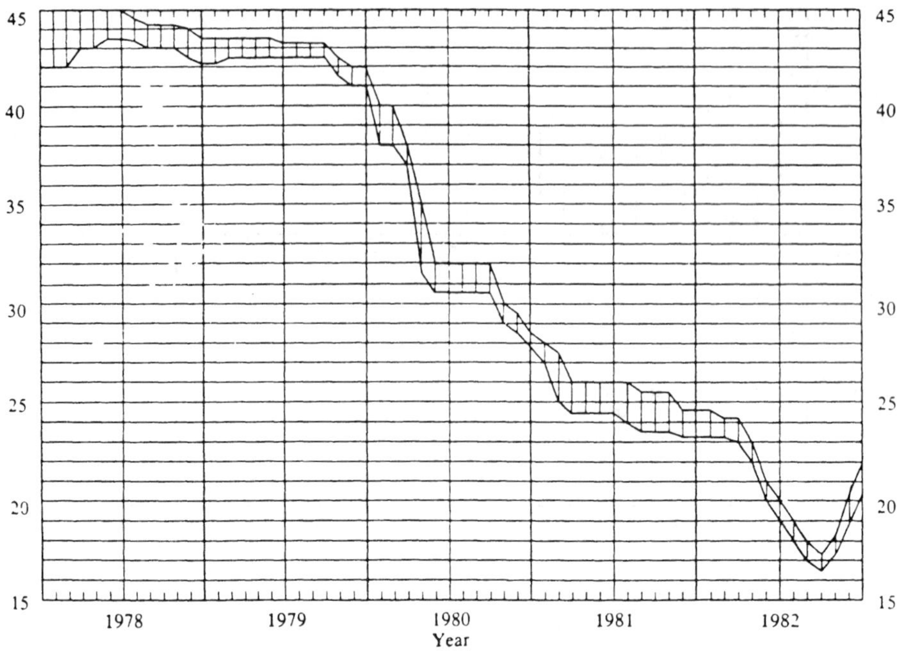

Figure 19.38. Development of the NUKEM spot market price range for natural uranium. (From Reference 44.)

factors such as the accident at TMI and the acceleration/delay of the development schedule of nuclear power in various countries.

The DOE prepares semiannual estimates of uranium requirements and sales commitments for U.S. domestic users. The projected requirements and the contract prices for future delivery through 1990 are shown in Figures 19.39 and 19.40. After 1982, the procurement of uranium via an established contract price mechanism, specifying uranium sale price in the original contract, will probably decrease, and market price arrangements will grow significantly. Market price contracts peg uranium price to an index determined at the year of delivery. Prior to 1975, contract pricing prevailed in the uranium market (market price procurement was less than 15%). As prices rose rapidly, contract pricing terms did not cover cost escalation and remained far below market prices. As a result, such arrangements turned out to be unsatisfactory to uranium producers. Moreover, as prices rose, more uranium came from captive production, that is, utility-controlled operations. By the mid-1980s it is expected that contract price arrangements and captive operations will each have roughly equal shares of the uranium delivery to the utilities in the United States, while market price contracts will account for 45% of all domestic deliveries.[45] In line with the declining uranium production the spot market price for uranium shown in Figure 19.38 has also declined; however, a reversal of this trend is already seen during 1983. It is assumed that the firming of the uranium spot price has to do with the reentrance of U.S. utilities into the market as buyers. This trend is expected to increase as more reactors are started up in the United States during the next 3–5 yr, and as existing inventories are being worked out. Another factor that may increase uranium prices is the threat of an embargo of uranium imports into the United States, which could, if implemented, separate the United States from the rest of the world in terms of uranium production. A uranium imports embargo could result in stratifying a two-tier price structure, with U.S. prices being higher than the rest of the world's, due to the lower-ore-grade, higher-cost domestic mines. The option of uranium import restrictions was proposed as an amendment to the U.S. NRC Appropriations Bill for Fiscal Year 1983; however, it was narrowly defeated during the final voting in December 1982. The U.S. DOE is still required according to the passed legislation to report to Congress on the viability of the U.S. uranium producing industry if foreign uranium import levels exceed a 37.5 percentage of total demand for two consecutive years. Tough measures against cheap uranium imports could then conceivably be imposed. Given current supply and demand trends, such import levels are not expected to be exceeded before 1988, and this time frame could be extended depending on how uranium import percentages are defined.

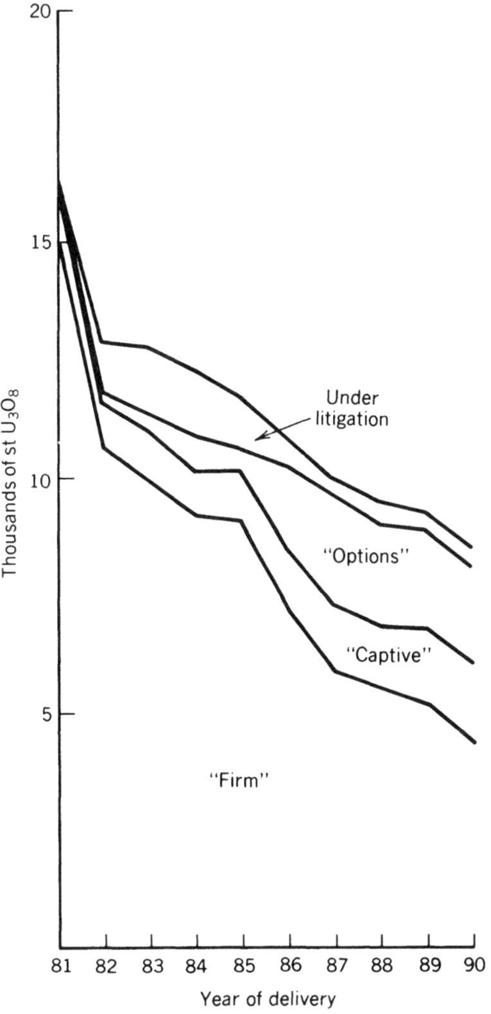

Figure 19.39. Components of domestic uranium delivery components. (From Reference 45.)

Conversion of U_3O_8 to UF_6

To produce feedstock for the gaseous diffusion enrichment process, solid U_3O_8 has to be converted into UF_6, a gas. The current conversion value is about $3.30/lb U as UF_6.[44] The projected need for UF_6 conversion is presented in Figure 5.15 for various growth scenarios. The demand for conversion services can be deduced from the "Deliveries to DOE" curve in Figure 5.15, since this represents the amount of uranium that must be delivered to the DOE enrichment plants, and has to be converted from uranium oxide to uranium hexafluoride in order to be introduced into the enrichment process. The information from Figure 5.15 should, however, be scaled down by the amount of conversion services available on the secondary market. Utilities selling excess inventory of U_3O_8 or of UF_6 to other utilities bypass the direct conversion market. With the role of the utilities in the uranium spot market expected to diminish by 1988, as discussed above, the secondary conversion market is also likely to shrink. When enriched uranium is, however, traded in the secondary market, it has to be reconverted from UF_6 to U_3O_8 or to UO_2. This reconversion demand will increase the total conversion market even though it may not be reflected in the total uranium sales figures. Several companies are now providing conversion services, and this part of the nuclear fuel cycle is handled exclusively by the private sector as a commercial enterprise. The price range

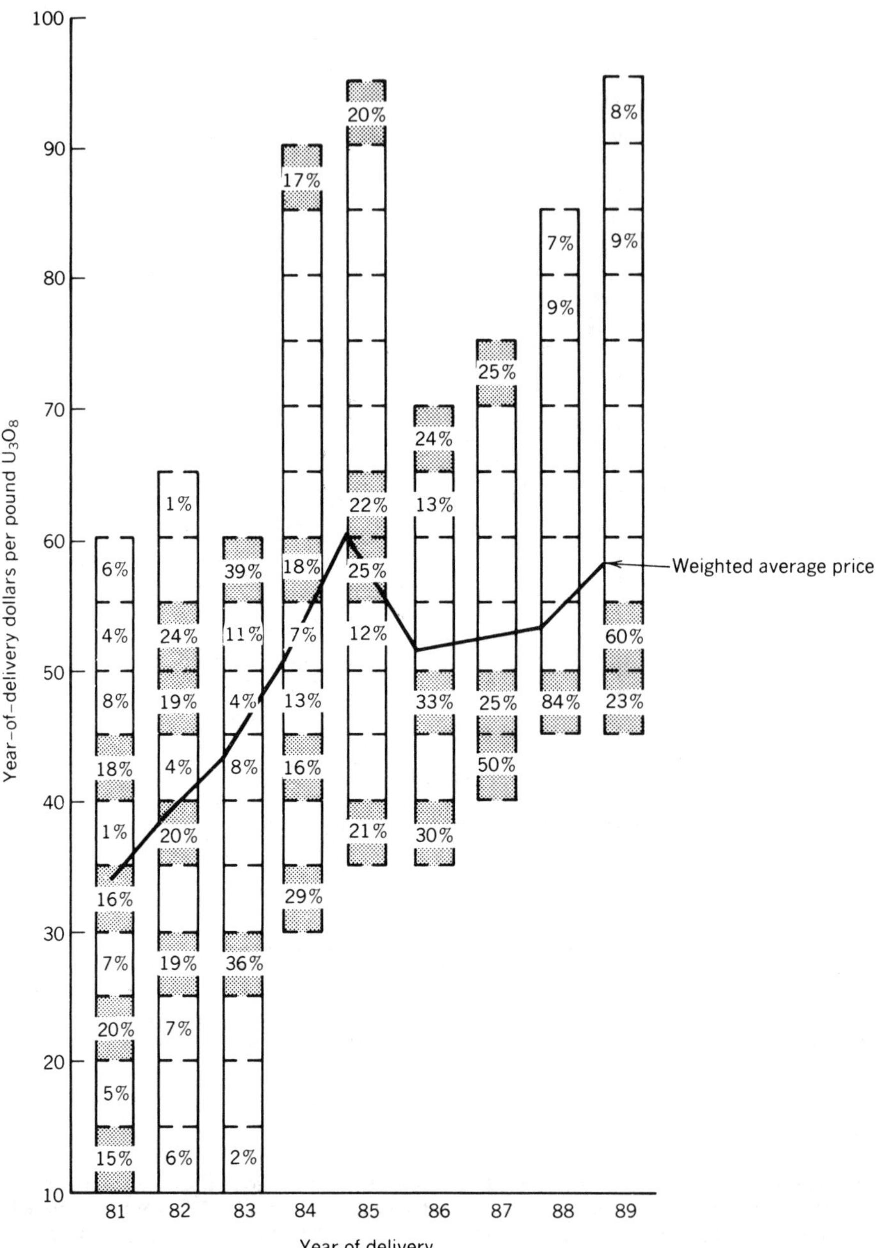

Figure 19.40. Distribution of U.S. contract prices as of January 1982. (From Reference 45.)

for new conversion contracts has increased in 1982 to \$3.00 to 3.30/lb of uranium, and an overcapacity now exists in this market sector.

Enrichment Costs

All the uranium enrichment done in the United States is currently performed by DOE in the government gaseous diffusion enrichment plants at Oak Ridge, Tennessee, Paducah, Kentucky, and Portsmouth, Ohio. These plants are both capital and energy intensive, and require large in-process uranium inventories. The basis of enrichment work is the Separative Work Unit (SWU).

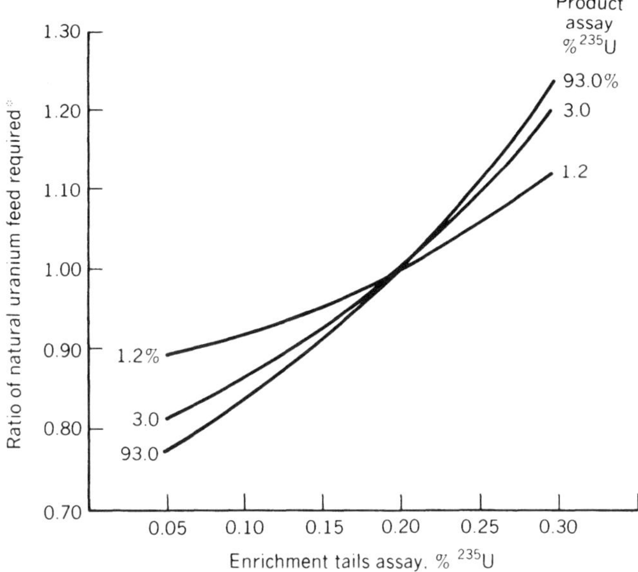

Figure 19.41. Impact of enrichment tails assay on relative natural uranium requirements. Product range from 1.2 to 93% ^{235}U. (From Reference 48.) *At tails assay = 0.20% ^{235}U; ratio = 1.0.

This is the amount of work required to produce uranium of the desired enrichment of ^{235}U from natural uranium feed. It is also a function of the tails assay, or the percentage of ^{235}U in the waste stream. Uranium and enrichment schedules for various product enrichments are shown in Table 6.3. This table shows the relative amounts of natural uranium feed and enrichment services required for various enrichment levels of the product uranium. To a certain extent uranium feed can be interchanged with separative work to provide a given quantity of product, as seen in Figure 19.41. A plant can be operated to optimize the enrichment economics by varying the feed/SWU ratio. Under typical recent price conditions (i.e., about $140/SWU and $40/kg U for normal assay UF_6), the economic optimum tails assay is 0.29%, representing 77% recovery of ^{235}U from the feed. Conversely, lowering the SWU costs would make it advantageous to recover more ^{235}U. For example, at $30/SWU and $120/kg uranium, the optimum tail assay would be 0.10% (89% recovery). The optimum tails assay based on actual recent uranium prices and SWU charges is given in Table 19.20 and in Figure 19.42.

As rough estimators, a 1-GWe nuclear unit requires 30 t/yr of enriched uranium, and 120,000 SWU/yr. The first core requires slightly more enrichment work, about 200,000 SWUs. Presently world enrichment capacity is about 40 million SWU/yr, while actual operational capacity is slightly

Table 19.20. Development of the Optimal Tails Assay (% ^{235}U)

Month	1978	1979	1980	1981	1982
1	0.181	0.198	0.218	0.264	0.296
2	0.181	0.198	0.218	0.268	0.297
3	0.180	0.198	0.221	0.273	0.299
4	0.180	0.198	0.234	0.273	0.302
5	0.179	0.198	0.239	0.273	0.311
6	0.179	0.198	0.239	0.273	0.316
7	0.179	0.198	0.239	0.275	0.321
8	0.180	0.198	0.239	0.275	0.333
9	0.180	0.198	0.239	0.276	0.336
10	0.180	0.198	0.245	0.276	0.331
11	0.181	0.201	0.258	0.295	0.322
12	0.182	0.201	0.261	0.296	0.315

Source: From Reference 44.

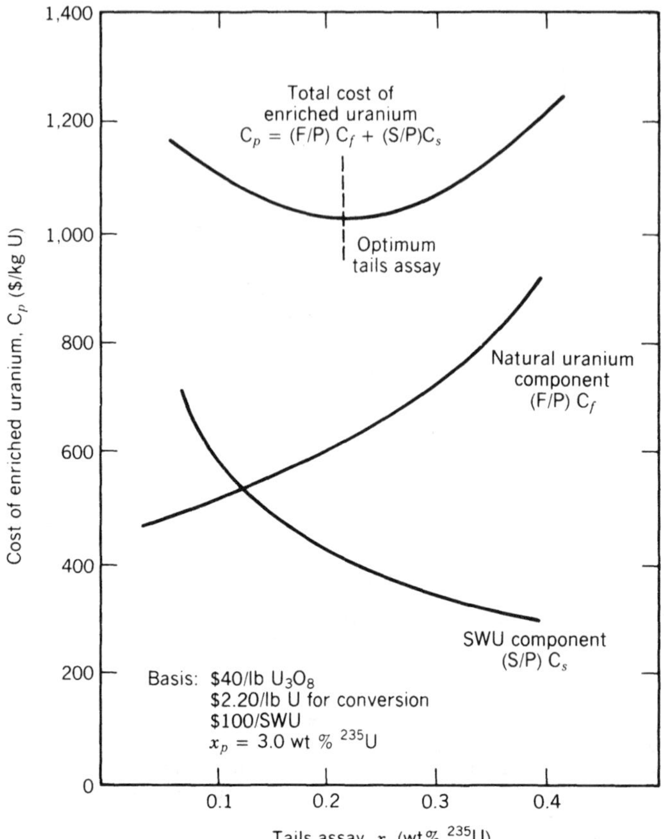

Figure 19.42. Enriched uranium cost as a function of tails assay. (From Reference 47.)

more than one-half of this value. This is due to the currently reduced demand which results in U.S. enrichment plants operating at one-third of capacity. World enrichment capacity may become as large as 83,000,000 SWU/yr by 1995; however, this may represent an oversupply of up to 15,000,000 SWU/yr. Several prospective enrichment projects such as Coredif plant in France, the full-scale expansion of the gas centrifuge enrichment plant in Portsmouth, Ohio, or the Australian UEGA project, may be indefinitely delayed or stretched out. The increase in U.S. enrichment contract prices, shown in Figure 19.43, has resulted for the first time in French enrichment costs being cheaper than U.S. SWU prices, a situation caused in part by the relative strength of the U.S. dollar, vis-à-vis the French franc. This has resulted in foreign enrichment contracts being shifted from the DOE to European suppliers, and even in U.S. utilities applying for French enrichment contracts. The DOE has recently announced that it will forego a scheduled increase in enrichment prices in order to maintain its competitive position,[49] and has offered a discount of about $11/SWU to utilities holding the ore expensive "requirement" enrichment contracts.

Gas diffusion enrichment requires about 2500 kWh of electricity per SWU. This compares with about 100 kWh/SWU for gas centrifuge, and 100 to 200 kWh/SWU for laser enrichment. Both centrifuge and laser enrichment plants have the advantage of allowing for much smaller increments of capacity expansion than does gaseous diffusion. In the United States the next enrichment plant probably will use gas centrifuges. This facility is expected to cost about $1.5 billion for a 2.2-million SWU/yr increment to be built in the 1985–1987 time frame at Portsmouth. A good fraction of this cost will be for development of the centrifuge technology. Most new enrichment capacity throughout the world will also employ gas centrifuge technology. The more modern facilities of this type will therefore set the producer price of enriched uranium. Projected costs for a large (8,800,000 SWU/yr) gas centrifuge facility as well as an existing large gaseous diffusion plant, or a future advanced isotope separation plant based on the atomic vapor laser separation process, are shown in Figure 6.19. As seen in this figure, the price of gaseous diffusion process SWUs is expected to

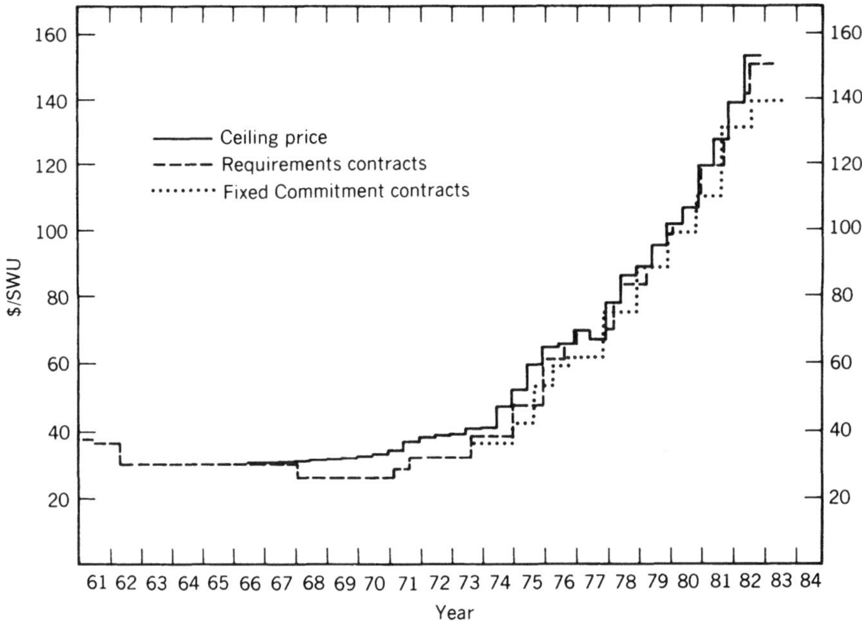

Figure 19.43. Development of U.S. DOE separative work prices ($/SWU). (From Reference 44.)

remain constant (due to process improvements) or to escalate due to higher electricity prices charged to the diffusion plants. Gas centrifuge enrichment cost may decrease in the future with the installation of higher performance centrifuge machines (set IV or V instead of the current set III machines) in the next stages of the Portsmouth enrichment plant. Laser isotope separation processes may yet demonstrate the lowest enrichment prices due to the much higher separation efficiency available with a laser process as compared with the other enrichment options; however, the laser enrichment technology is yet in its infancy and cost projections for the process are still speculative. The overlap in the projected costs of the centrifuge and laser processes shown in Figure 6.19 has raised the issue of the optimal expansion path of the enrichment complex. Should it include advanced centrifuge machines, or should expansion be delayed until the AIS processes are ready for commercialization, bypassing the centrifuge process? This argument has not yet been resolved, however, the DOE plans call for completion of the Portsmouth GCEP facility before installing laser enrichment plants.

Since laser enrichment has a high separation factor (5 to 15), it has another potential advantage: it could be used to strip the depleted uranium stockpile (i.e., uranium already processed for ^{235}U), taking 0.2% tail material and enriching it directly to 3.0% ^{235}U.

The optimal operation of the enrichment complex involves complicated trade-offs between uranium supplies, enrichment capacity and existing stockpiles. The fuel-cycle situation in the early 1980s is characterized by a surplus of enrichment capacity operated at a high cost due to the large specific power requirements, declining uranium prices, and large fuel inventories. The U.S. enrichment complex including all three plants is operated as a single entity and is managed by the U.S. government. The current situation calls for minimizing capital charges for electric power supplies to the enrichment complex. This can be achieved by raising the tails assay, thus requiring more uranium supplies, or a reinstitution of a "split-tails" policy, whereby the government actually operates the enrichment plants on a high-tails basis and draws the incremental uranium requirements from the existing stockpiles. The variable tails assay option, available to holders of adjustable fixed commitment contracts, is a partial solution to the problem of optimal operation of the enrichment complex.

Ultimately, with the rising energy prices, the more energy efficient centrifuge and laser enrichment processes may substitute for the currently existing (and already fully amortized) gaseous diffusion plants. Such a change will result in replacing low-capital-cost/high-operating-cost plants by new high-capital-cost/low-operating-cost centrifuge or laser processes. The point of economic crossover between diffusion and enrichment processes is likely to be reached in the 1988–1993 period. This point is highly sensitive to the centrifuge manufacturing costs, which in turn depend on the volume of centrifuge production and the performance characteristics of the machines produced.

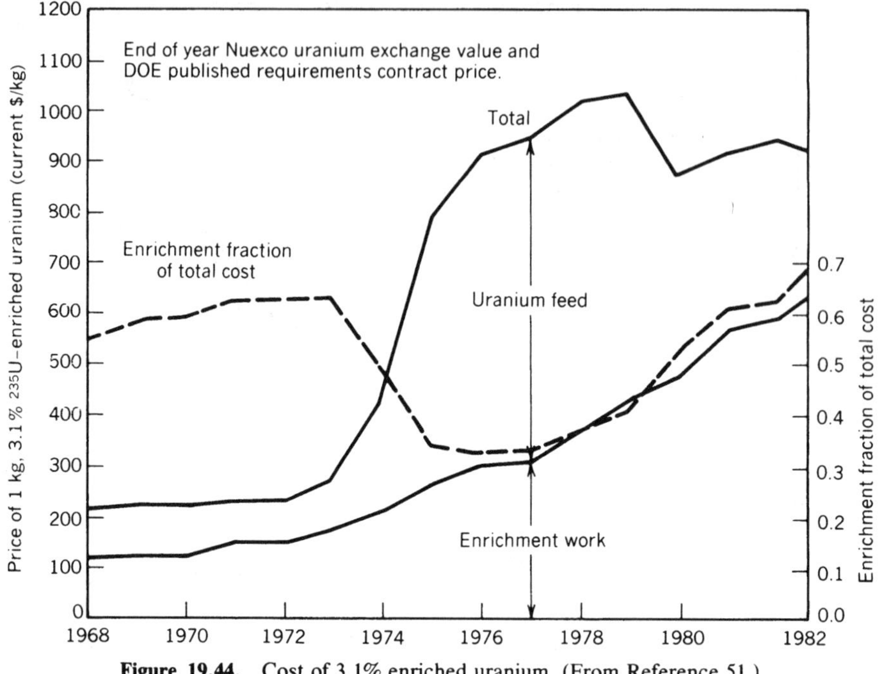

Figure 19.44. Cost of 3.1% enriched uranium. (From Reference 51.)

A major difference between the gaseous diffusion, centrifuge, and laser separation processes is the relative high separation factor of the two laser processes, investigated at the DOE laboratories. It is estimated that one pass through a laser enrichment apparatus can enrich natural uranium to commercially usable proportions. Thus the physical size of the enrichment plant operated on such processes is greatly reduced compared with a gaseous diffusion plant, and enrichment capacity can be installed in smaller increments which better match the increasing demand. These properties, coupled with the low energy demand of the advanced separation processes, will require enhanced security and safeguard measures to prevent the installation of small-scale clandestine enrichment plants dedicated to nuclear weapons material production.

Beyond the optimal operation of the enrichment complex itself, the major problem facing the electric utilities is the cost of the final product—the enriched uranium. Given the currently high SWU costs and low uranium prices, the cost of a 3% ^{235}U enriched uranium fuel for LWRs is on the order of $800–1000/kg enriched uranium, as shown in Figure 19.44. As seen in this figure more than two-thirds of the cost of LWR-enriched uranium fuel is related to enrichment charges and only one-third is related to the natural uranium price. This demonstrates the need for more economic enrichment services or a redistribution of the relative contributions of feed and enrichment, so as to arrest the increase in the cost of enriched uranium fuel.

Fabrication

Commercial fuel fabrication facilities typically have a daily capacity of 2 t of heavy metal (MTHM). A PWR fuel assembly contains about 460 kg of UO_2. The annual capacity of such a plant is about 500 MTHM/yr. Such a plant might cost about $32M, plus an additional $34M for equipment, and have annual operating expenses of $36.5M (1979 dollars). The levelized cost of production would be $138/kg of heavy metal (or about $63,000 per fuel assembly). A more detailed cost breakdown for a large plant is given in Table 19.21.

The fuel fabrication cost consists of about 39% levelized capital charges, and the balance (61%) levelized operating expenses. Of the operating expenses, material accounts for about 50% of the total, and labor another 30%. Several price projections predict that the fabrication costs will vary very little over the next 25 yr when measured in constant dollars. These projections estimate 1989 fabrication costs of $160–$240/kg of heavy metal, and unit costs of $200–225/kg are shown in Figure 19.32. These costs relate to direct contact fabrication of nonradioactive slightly enriched uranium. Fabrication of radioactive recycled fuel will require remote operation, which may double the unit costs shown here, as discussed below.

Table 19.21. UO_2 Fuel Fabrication Expenses for Annual Production of 1040 MTHM (1979 $)

	($ × 1000)
Capital expenses:	
Building	28,800
Land	500
Site preparation	500
Licensing and environmental	400
Security systems	300
Office building	1,600
Engineering and contingencies	7,900
Equipment for UF_6–UO_2 conversion to scrap recovery and waste processing	24,400
Operational support	4,600
Stores	60
Facility support	6,100
Quality control labs	1,500
Ten-yr process equipment replacement	24,400
Total capital expenses	$101,060
Annual operating expenses:	
Labor and supervision	20,900/yr
Overhead and G&A	3,200/yr
Direct and indirect materials	2,200/yr
Supplies	2,400/yr
Hardware	44,700/yr
Utilities	500/yr
Total annual operating expenses	$ 73,900/yr

Source: From Reference 29.

A flow sheet for the different unit operations employed in a PWR fuel refabrication plant is shown in Figure 7.17. The complexity and the costs of the various steps involved will depend on the fuel considered (single or mixed oxides including uranium, plutonium, or thorium), the chemical composition of the fuel (metals, oxides, carbides, or nitrides), the radioactivity of the various fuel constituents, the amount of fissile material in the process (criticality considerations), fuel assembly design, and the cladding material (zirconium, stainless steel, aluminum matrix). The radioactivity and criticality considerations determine the required number of process lines, the level of shielding for radiation protection, and the operation and maintenance method, direct versus remote contact. These considerations will strongly affect the cost of the fabrication process, and a general formulation for computing fabrication charges is shown in Table 19.22.

The equations shown in this table are generalized, and could be applied to any other step in the nuclear fuel cycle, in particular to other industrial operations such as conversion or reprocessing. Application of this general methodology to different fuels used in various nuclear power plants is shown in Table 19.23. As seen in this table, the plant and equipment capital cost components are the dominant contributors to the annual fuel fabrication cost. The variable operation and material expenses account for 10–40% of the total fabrication charge, depending on the complexity of the process. The more complex (and radioactive) recycle mixed-oxide processes result in lower variable cost fractions, while the more conventional uranium oxide fabrication charges require relatively smaller capital investment component. A historic evolution of mixed-oxide fuel fabrication charges is shown in Figure 19.45. As seen in this figure, the constant dollar fabrication charges have almost quadrupled between 1967 and 1982, reflecting greater awareness of the complexity of the commercial scale process, and more stringent operating safety requirements.

LWR uranium fuel fabrication is now a mature commercial process carried out by the private sector. It is estimated that U.S. fuel fabricators will account for over 70% of the worldwide fuel fabrication commitments between 1983 and 1990. A 1000-MWe PWR requires less than 30 t of uranium fuel per annual reload. With the growing worldwide nuclear capacity, the fuel reload demand is expected to increase at a rate of 7–9%/yr until 1990. A new trend which has become evident in 1982 is the fabricators' diversification to different kinds of fuel. Westinghouse Corp., the maker of PWRs, has opened a BWR fabrication line, while ASEA Co. in Sweden, which produces

Table 19.22. Unit Price Analysis Formula

$$\$/\text{kg} = [(C_D + C_O + C_C)R + O + M + E_R + D]/T$$

where[a]

C_D = facility plus equipment costs, $C_F + C_E$
C_F = facility cost (excluding process equipment)
C_E = equipment cost
C_O = owner's cost during construction
C_C = charge on direct capital during construction, $I_OC_O + I_DC_D$
I_D = fractional charge on design and construction cost during construction
I_O = fractional charge on owner's cost during construction
R = annual fixed charge rate on capital, fraction per year
O = annual operating cost
M = annual hardware and expendable material cost
A_R = annual maintenance and replacement rate on equipment, fraction per year
E_R = annual maintenance and replacement cost, A_RC_E
D = annual payment to establish fund for decommissioning
T = annual throughput achieved (Gg/yr), XF
X = design capacity of plant (Gg/yr)
F = average fraction of design capacity achieved

Source: From Reference 52.
[a]All costs in millions of dollars.

BWRs, has qualified its operations to produce PWR fuel elements also. These events signify the importance of the fuel reload business to the fabrication industry. Another trend that is now becoming more pronounced is the shift to higher burnup fuels (greater than the reference 33,000 MWd/t) which is driven by the need to achieve better plant capacity factors when coupled with a longer fuel cycle of 1½ yr between reloads, and by the need to reduce the total amount of spent fuel discharge. Expected burnups of commercial fuels until 1990 are in the range of 38,000 to 44,000 MWd/t, and an average burnup of 50,000 MWd/t could be achieved late in the 1990s.

Spent Fuel Storage and Disposal

Fuel assemblies discharged from reactors are initially stored underwater in storage pools at the reactor site. Originally, pools at the reactors were expected to store only a few years of discharges before the spent fuel would be chemically reprocessed. For various reasons, spent fuel in the United States is not currently being reprocessed, and it continues to be stored in reactor pools. By the end of 1982 there were more than 30,000 fuel assemblies (9,100 t U) in storage.

A summary of the total spent fuel and radioactive waste accumulation by the end of 1981 is shown in Table 19.24a, while a projection of future spent fuel accumulation is shown in Table 19.24b. As seen in Table 19.24a and in Figure 19.46, the spent fuel and high-level radioactive waste form a small component of the total *volume* of waste generated; however, spent fuel is the major component to the *radioactivity* of the total accumulated waste. The relative proportions of waste generated in the various steps of the nuclear power cycle (front end of the fuel cycle, reactor operation, and back end of the fuel cycle) are shown in Table 19.25 and Figure 19.47. The data contained in these tables and figures demonstrate that a significant amount of low-level waste is generated during the reactor operating cycle, thus requiring waste compaction and volume reduction measures at reactors and other sites. On a national level, as indicated in Table 19.24a, a larger amount of low-level waste is generated in the DOE defense program and in various institutional and industrial activities than in the nuclear power industry. This fact indicates that the national radioactive waste disposal problem is related to a large number of waste generators, most of which are unrelated to the power generation industry. A comprehensive national waste management program should address all waste generators and inventories, such as listed in Table 19.23.

As mentioned above, the major radioactive component of the accumulated nuclear waste is the spent nuclear reactors' fuel stockpile. The current stockpile of 9100 tons LWR discharged fuel stored at reactor sites may increase to 60,000 tons by the end of the century, based on nuclear capacity growth projections and achieved capacity factors (Table 19.24b). While the spent fuel generated should be stored at the reactor site to allow cooling before shipment, it is desirable for operational reasons that enough space in the spent fuel storage pools be available, so that all the fuel inside the reactors core can be fully unloaded if desired. This requirement limits the space available in reactor storage pools for storage of routinely discharged fuel. Various methods of dense storage or of fuel assembly transfer between several reactors of a single utility could delay

Table 19.23. Summary of Estimated Costs for Fabrication and Refabrication of LWR, SSCR, HWR, LMFBR, and HTGR Fuels

Fuel Cycle[a]	Estimated Costs ($\$10^6$) Facility	Equipment	Annual Hardware and Material	Annual Operating[b]
LWR/SSCR				
$(^{235}U,U)O_2$	32.0	34.2	23.0	13.4
$(^{235}U,Th)O_2$	34.8	46.5	24.5	13.9
$(^{233}U,U)O_2$	470.5	249.2	27.2	24.4
$(^{233}U,Th)O_2$	509.8	265.7	27.4	24.9
$(Pu,U)O_2$	208.4	208.5	27.6	24.0
$(Pu,U)O_2$*	512.7	267.7	27.8	24.9
$(Pu,Th)O_2$	224.8	211.3	28.2	24.1
$(Pu,Th)O_2$*	519.4	265.7	28.6	24.9
HWR				
UO_2—natural	17.9	27.4	10.8	9.5
$(^{235}U,U)O_2$	21.3	33.2	11.2	11.0
$(^{235}U,Th)O_2$	22.6	44.2	12.5	11.4
$(^{233}U,U)O_2$	414.5	227.0	16.3	17.7
$(^{233}U,Th)O_2$	453.0	247.3	17.7	17.8
$(Pu,U)O_2$	194.5	195.3	16.7	17.4
$(Pu,U)O_2$*	454.1	246.3	16.8	17.8
$(Pu,Th)O_2$	207.0	196.3	18.1	17.4
$(Pu,Th)O_2$*	463.5	246.3	18.5	17.8
LMFBR—oxides				
$(^{235}U,Th)O_2/ThO_2$	50.3	81.5	81.8	15.7
$(^{233}U,Th)O_2/ThO_2$	1000.8	291.5	82.7	26.4
$(Pu,U)O_2/UO_2$	357.5	231.9	76.8	25.1
$(Pu,U)O_2/UO_2$*	938.3	274.4	76.8	26.6
$(Pu,Th)O_2/ThO_2$	357.5	231.9	82.7	25.7
$(Pu,Th)O_2/ThO_2$*	1019.5	309.7	82.7	26.9
UO_2(RB)[c]	24.3	33.6	33.1	13.4
ThO_2(RB)	25.9	36.9	36.3	13.4
ThO_2(RB)*	478.3	333.8	33.5	26.4
HTGR				
OT-1 (LEU-stowaway)[d,e]	87.0	266.0	184.0	22.5
OT-2 (MEU-stowaway)[f]	81.0	260.0	168.0	20.2
OT-3 (MEU-stowaway)	76.0	244.0	157.0	18.9
R-1 (^{235}MEU/Th)[g]	71.0	227.0	146.0	18.9
R-1 (MEU/Th)*	395.0	809.0	113.0	39.7
R-2 (^{233}MEU/Th)*	320.0	807.0	88.0	39.7
R-3 (Pu/Th)*	569.0	807.0	172.0	35.7
R-4 (HEU/Th)[h]	51.0	166.0	94.0	13.4
R-4 (HEU/Th)*	304.0	498.0	89.0	23.6
R-5 (^{233}HEU/Th)*	265.0	450.0	78.4	23.0

Source: From Reference 52.

[a]Fuel descriptions indicate fissile material, fertile material, and axial blanket (if applicable) material. All ^{235}U fuels are fabricated in contact-operated and maintained facilities. ^{233}U fuels are fabricated in remotely operated and maintained facilities, and Pu fuels are fabricated in remotely operated and either contact or remotely maintained facilities. Recycled Th is fabricated in remotely operated and maintained facilities. The asterisks indicate the remotely operated and maintained Pu or Th facilities.

[b]Annual operating costs presented are exclusive of interest on working capital. Operating costs presented in ORNL/TM-6522 include this charge.

[c]RB refers to radial blanket material.

[d]OT = Once Through.

[e]LEU = Low enriched uranium.

[f]MEU = Medium enriched uranium.

[g]R = Recycle.

[h]HEU = High enriched uranium.

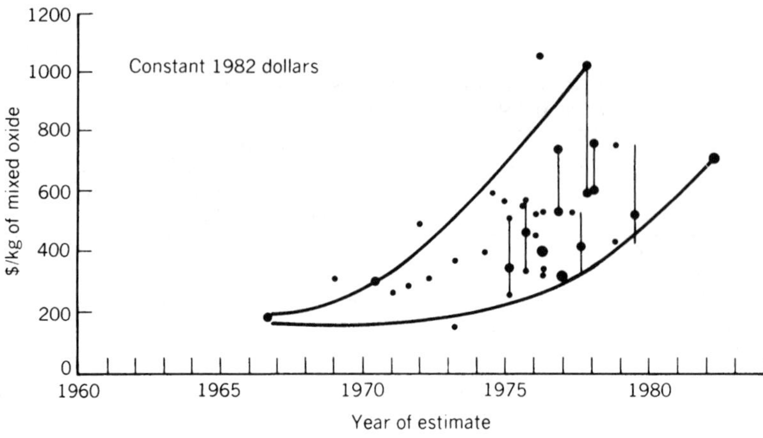

Figure 19.45. Mixed-oxide fabrication cost estimate. (From Reference 53.)

Table 19.24a. Spent Fuel and Radwaste Inventories as of December 31, 1981

Spent fuel	*Mass, t U*	*Activity, kCi*	*Heat, kW*
BWRs (18,700 assemblies)	3,300	3,360,000	12,500
PWRs (10,900 assemblies)	4,500	6,960,000	26,700
High-level waste	*Volume, m^3*	*Activity, kCi*	*Heat, kW*
Savannah River	106,000	982,000	2,900
Idaho CPP	12,000	64,000	210
Hanford	183,000	531,000	1,640
Nuclear Fuel Services	2,190	39,000	115
Transuranic waste	*Volume, m^3*	*Activity, kCi*	*TRU elements, kg*
DOE, buried	299,000	400	1,000
DOE, stored	67,000	1,000	910
Commercial, buried	(in with LLW)	—	130
Low-level waste	*Volume, m^3*	*Activity, kCi*	*Land used, ha*
DOE sites	1,607,000	10,700	159
West Valley (closed 1975)	66,500	580	3
Maxey Flats (closed 1977)	135,000	2,400	6
Sheffield (closed 1978)	88,000	60	4
Barnwell, SC	363,000	3,000	19
Beatty, NV	93,000	370	11
Richland, WA	102,000	1,020	11
Remedial Action Program	*Volume, m^3*	*Activity, kCi*	*No. of sites*
UMTRAP	22,000,000	150	24
FUSRAP	452,000	—	31
SFMP	1,560,000	—	~500
Active mill tailings	*Volume, m^3*	*Activity, kCi*	*Heat, kW*
21 active mills	87,000,000	1,000	20

Source: From Reference 54.

Table 19.24b Nuclear Electric Forecast

Year	Installed Capacity, GWe[a]	Annual Spent Fuel Discharge, t	Cumulative Spent Fuel Discharge, t	Electrical Generation 10^9 kWh
1983	74.4	1601	10,716[b]	399
1984	85.2	1734	12,450	457
1985	91.8	2168	14,618	492
1986	101.0	2598	17,216	545
1987	112.4	2600	19,816	610
1988	114.9	2870	22,685	628
1989	118.4	3224	25,909	651
1990	121.4	3092	29,002	665
1991	122.5	3116	32,118	678
1992	125.8	3526	35,644	696
1993	130.4	3449	39,093	723
1994	132.9	3430	42,523	737
1995	135.3	3576	46,099	747
1996	140.6	3490	49,589	780
1997	146.6	3539	53,127	813
1998	152.6	3900	57,027	846
1999	158.2	3881	60,908	876
2000	165.0	4004	64,912	911
2001	171.2	4386	69,324	945
2002	179.3	4407	73,753	990
2003	188.6	4570	78,361	1041
2004	197.1	4919	83,308	1088
2005	205.3	4841	88,169	1133
2006	213.3	5225	98,434	1177
2007	221.3	6082	99,543	1221
2008	229.2	6043	105,582	1265
2009	237.2	6536	112,158	1309
2010	245.2	6251	118,441	1353
2011	249.2	6228	124,699	1375
2012	253.2	6381	131,121	1397
2013	257.2	6484	137,635	950[c]
2014	261.2	6365	144,000	482[c]
				27,980[d]

Source: From Reference 54.

[a]Gigawatts-electric.

[b]Includes an initial inventory of 9115 t as of the end of 1982. This estimate is about 200 t below more current estimates.

[c]Reduced to compensate for end effect. Part of burnup is fuel that will be emplaced in next repository.

[d]Using the 1.0 mill/kWh fee, this total equals $27.98 billion in revenue in current dollars. Excluded from this total are $1.77 billion in estimated revenues generated from the transfer of discharged spent fuel to the federal government. See Appendix C for the latest official EIA estimates of electricity generation.

the need for Away From Reactor (AFR) storage; however, eventually the optional space in the existing storage pools will be filled up, and thus additional and external storage space will be required. The expected need for off-site storage is shown in Figure 19.48 as a function of year and enhanced on-site storage measures that could be implemented. The basic conclusion from Figure 19.48 is that by the end of the century about one-half of the total generated LWR spent fuel will have to be stored off-site, and that various reracking and transshipment measures will delay the need for off-site storage by a 5-yr interval at most. The regional distribution of the off-site storage demand by the end of the century is shown in Figure 19.49, which indicates that a major need for off-site storage will exist in the Southeast and East North Central regions. The North Central and South Central regions, where nuclear power generation is least economic in comparison with coal

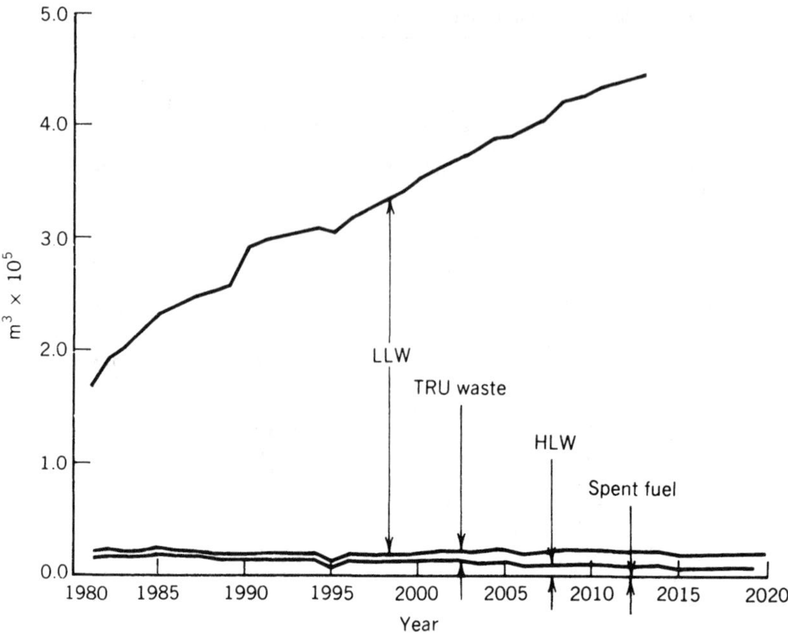

Figure 19.46. Projection of volume generation rates for various waste and spent fuel. (From Reference 54.)

(see Figures 19.1 and 19.6), will require the least off-site spent fuel storage. While spent fuel reprocessing can decrease the amount of accumulated fuel, the logistics and dynamics of reprocessing for the next 20 yrs, as currently perceived, will result in an only modest relaxation of the storage requirements. This point is brought out in Figure 19.50, and has also been discussed by B. Wolfe.[53] The message is that while reprocessing will help, national plans for interim spent fuel storage are also required to handle future spent fuel accumulation. A similar conclusion regarding the French nuclear power program was recently reported by the French High-Level Working Group on Spent Fuel Management (Castaing Report).[57]

Nuclear Waste Policy Act of 1982

Enactment of the Nuclear Waste Policy Act (NWPA) has established a system for disposing of radioactive waste from nuclear power plants and has brought to an end 25 yr of political indecision on how to solve the problem. The legislation, signed into law on January 7, 1983 by President Reagan, has been called the most complicated piece of legislation on nuclear energy ever passed.[58] While a full discussion of this act is beyond the scope of this chapter, a short discussion of the sections relevant to nuclear fuel economics now follows. The general purpose of the act is:

1. To provide a schedule of developing repositories for the disposal of high-level radioactive waste and spent fuel.
2. To set forth a research, development, and demonstration program for disposal of radioactive waste and spent fuel.
3. To establish federal policy and responsibility for disposal of radioactive waste and spent fuel.
4. To devise fees ensuring that the cost of disposal is borne by the owners and generators of radioactive waste and spent fuel.

Within this general framework for spent fuel management, several specific rules regarding nuclear waste charges and the creation of a waste fund to finance the research and development on spent fuel or reprocessing waste storage repositories are included. These rulings specify that:

1. DOE is authorized to enter into contracts with owners and generators for accepting title to, transporting, and disposing of high-level radioactive waste and spent nuclear fuel.

Table 19.25. Basic Rules of Thumb for Waste and Spent Fuel Projections[a]

Facility Type	Waste Type	Annual Waste Volume Generation Rate per Unit Energy Generated, m^3/GWe-yr	Annual Waste Volume per Capita[b], liters/yr Currently Operating Reactors
	Electric Power Generation[c]		
Boiling water reactor	LLW	1,724	0.074
Pressurized water reactor	LLW	931	0.085
Nuclear fuel cycle			
Uranium mill	Mill tailings	112,200	15
Uranium conversion	LLW	20.4	0.003
Uranium enrichment	LLW	4.55	0.0006
Fuel fabrication	LLW	85.2	0.01
Reprocessing	LLW	31.2	0.004
	TRU	52.3	0.007
	HLW	3.19	0.0004
	DOE/Defense Wastes		
		Entire United States (m^3/yr)	DOE/defense
	LLW	62,000	0.28
	TRU	4,900	0.022
	HLW	15,500	0.07
	Institutional and Industrial		
		Entire United States (m^3/yr)	I/I
	LLW	37,900	0.17

Source: From Reference 52.

[a]Volumes given are typical for each operation. Many fuel cycle operations occur years before or after electricity from the nuclear reactor is generated.

[b]Total waste per capita assuming a population of 220 million. Fuel cycle per capita waste volume based on 28.64 GWe-yr of electricity generated from nuclear power plants in 1980 (*Electric World*, April 1981). This is 12.5% of the U.S. electrical demand.

[c]For fuel cycle calculations, assume two-thirds of electricity from a PWR and one-third from a BWR.

2. For electricity generated and sold after 6 April 1983, the fee for these services is 1 mill/kWh, which is equal to $260/kg for 33,000 MWd/t burnup and 33% thermal efficiency.
3. For spent nuclear fuel or high-level waste generated before this date, a one-time charge will be imposed per kilogram of heavy metal that is equivalent to an average charge of 1 mill/kWh.
4. By 5 June 1983, DOE will establish procedures for the collection and payment of these fees.
5. DOE will review these fees annually and propose to Congress adjustments to ensure full cost recovery by the federal government.
6. Once a repository is operating DOE will accept title as expeditiously as practicable and, beginning not later than 31 January 1998, dispose of spent fuel or high-level waste in that facility.
7. The NRC may require as a condition for issuing or renewing a license for a nuclear power reactor that the applicant execute a contract with DOE, or be actively and in good faith negotiating one with DOE.
8. No spent fuel or high-level waste may be disposed of in a repository unless its owner or generator has executed a contract with DOE by 30 June 1983, or by the date on which generation of spent fuel or waste begins or title is accepted.

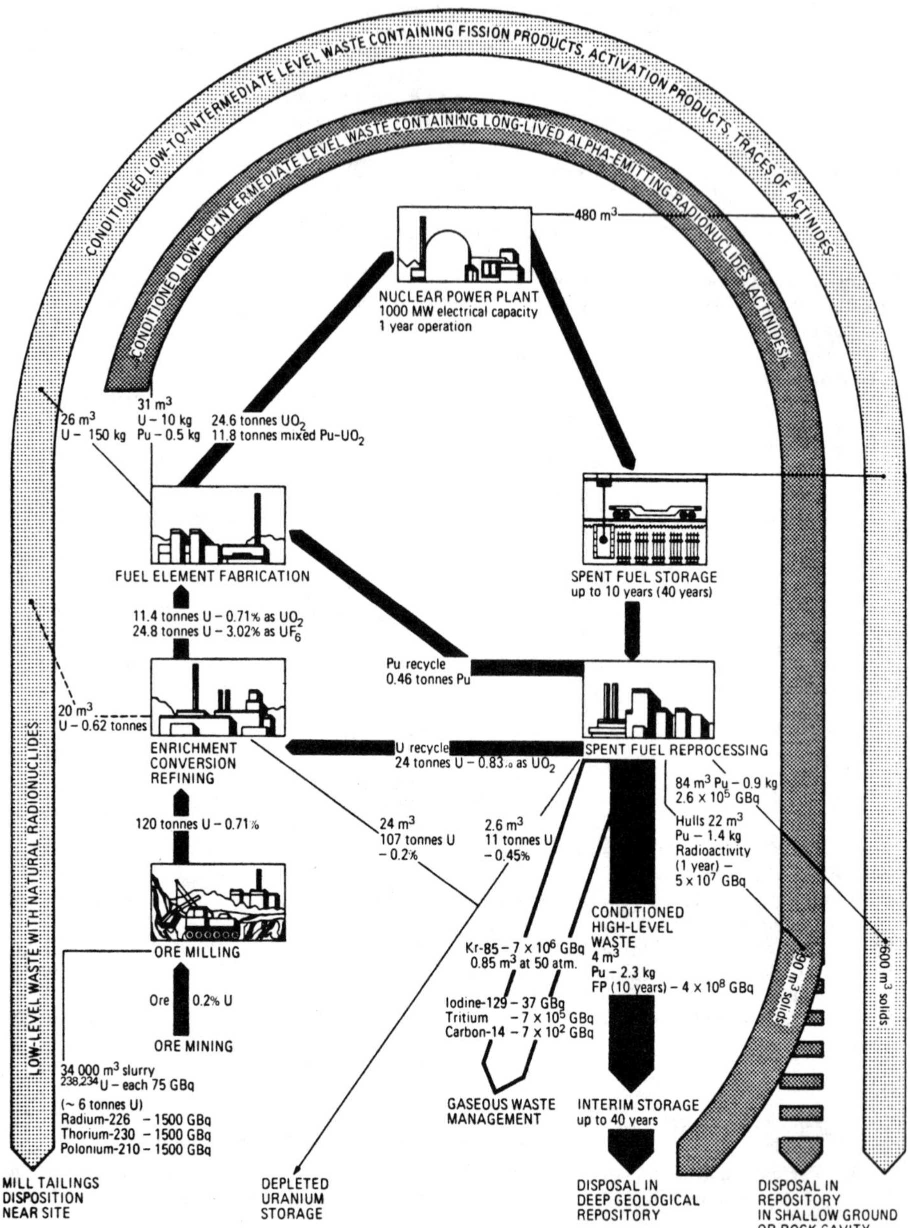

Figure 19.47. Waste arising from the generation of 1 GWe of electrical energy in LWR fuel cycle. GBq = giga becquerel; U − $x\%$ means U with $x\%$ of ^{235}U. (From Reference 55.)

The amount of 1 mill/kWh to be levied against all nuclear power generation will be a relatively small contributor to total nuclear power cost or fuel cycle expenses (Tables 19.1 and 19.18 above, respectively). This will not affect the coal/nuclear economic balance to a great extent. On an equivalent dollars per kilogram spent fuel this amounts to a \$261/kg charge which is similar to the previous DOE charges of \$234/kg in 1980 dollars, as shown in Table 19.26, for the disposal option only. Various measures for interim spent fuel storage by the government, available to utilities that have exhausted their internal fuel storage capabilities, are listed in the Nuclear Waste Policy Act.

The repository research and development charge of \$113/kg shown in Table 19.26 covers the

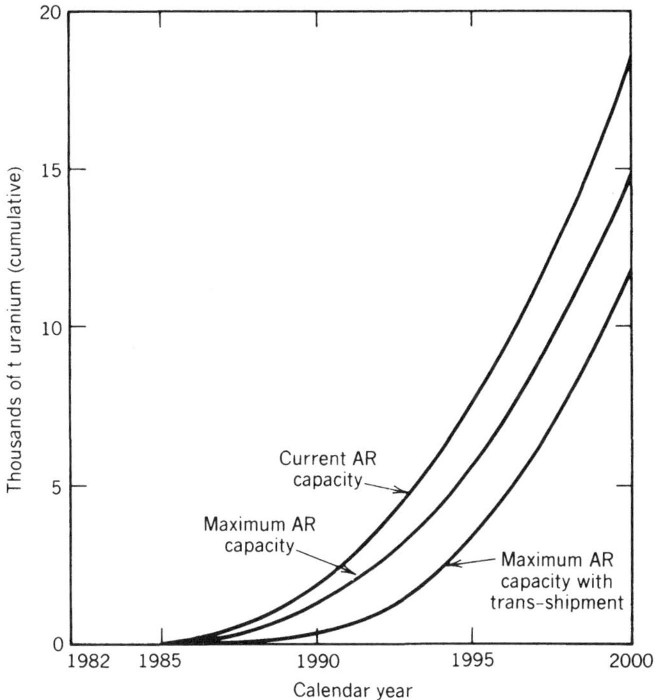

Figure 19.48. Spent fuel storage requirements. Current AR capacity: (1) Current utility plans for pool capacity increases. (2) No trans-shipment except where licensed by NRC. (3) On-site transfers as planned. (4) Full core reserve. Maximum AR capacity: (1) Pool capacities increased to maximum. (2) No transshipment except where licensed by NRC. (3) On-site transfers as planned. (4) Full core reserve. Maximum AR capacity with trans-shipment: (1) Pool capacities increased to maximum. (2) Intra-utility transshipments. (3) On-site transfers as planned. (4) Full core reserve. (From Reference 56.)

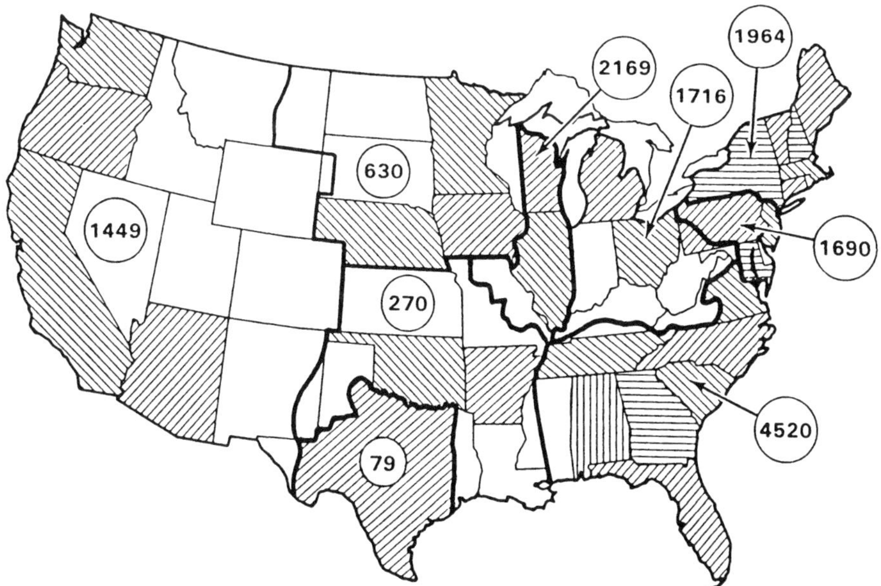

Figure 19.49. Regional requirements for LWR spent fuel storage through 2000, t U. Total U.S. storage requirements 14,487 t U. (From Reference 56.)

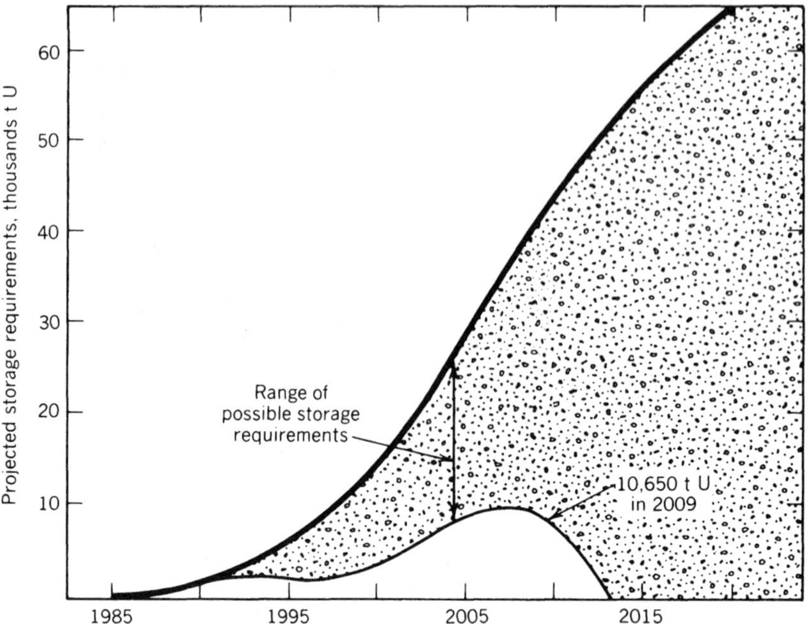

Figure 19.50. Projected spent fuel storage requirements with reprocessing start in 1994. (From Reference 52.)

costs of qualifying sites in several geologic media, engineering development of the repository, and designing and testing appropriate waste packaging concepts. The effects of the various packaging options on repository costs in salt domes, granite, basalt, or tuff environments are shown in Figure 19.51. Three different fuel element packaging options are shown and the repository costs are broken down to several construction related and operating cost categories. As seen in Figure 19.51, the number of fuel elements stored in each packaging mode will strongly affect repository costs; the larger the number of elements, the lower the unit disposal costs.

Table 19.26. Federal Spent Fuel Costs and Fee (1980 Dollars)

	Storage		Disposal		Storage and Disposal	
Cost Center	Discounted Costs, $ M	Unit Cost, $/kg U	Discounted Costs, $ M	Unit Cost, $/kg U	Discounted Costs, $ M	Fee, $/kg U
AFR	666	108	219[a]	13[a]	885	121
Transportation	50	8	23[a]	1[a]	73	9
Encapsulation	—	—	777	40	777	40
Repository	—	—	1,328	65	1,328	65
Research and development[b]	91	15	2,241	113	2,332	128
Government overhead	35	6	37	2	72	8
	842	137	4,625	234	5,467	371

Source: From Reference 59.

[a]Though some limited disposal capacity will be available in 1997, some additional storage capacity is needed for several years.

[b]Research and development for the disposal portion includes costs of multiple site qualification, engineering development and testing, and project management.

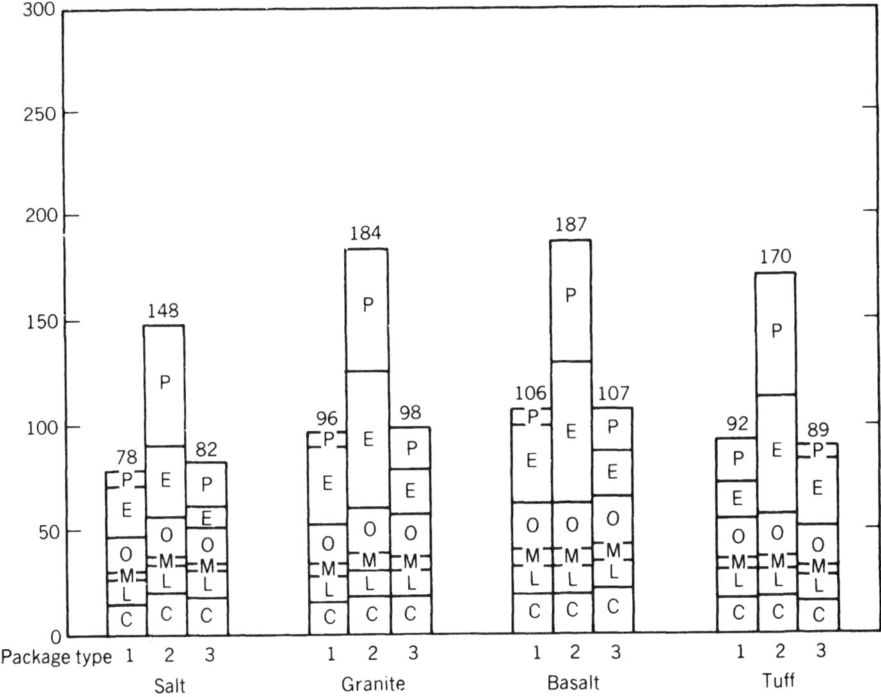

Figure 19.51. The effect of packaging concept on unit repository costs. *Key:* P—packaging, E—emplacement, O—other cost, M—mining, L—labor costs (waste operations), C—construction. Package type: 1 = 1 PWR or 2 BWR in carbon steel package emplaced with carbon steel sleeve. 2 = 1 PWR or 2 BWR in titanium–carbon steel package emplaced with carbon steel sleeve surrounded by bentonite. 3 = 3 PWR or 8 BWR disassembled and packaged in titanium–carbon steel package emplaced with carbon steel sleeve surrounded by bentonite. (From Reference 60.)

The waste management system becomes more complex when spent fuel is reprocessed, the waste streams are segregated, and the useful constituents are recycled. This is due to the fact that several different waste forms are generated during the reprocessing operation, and even though the total volume of the waste is significantly reduced, disposal is needed for several different kinds of radioactive waste. These include high-level waste, cladding hulls, krypton-85 gas, other gaseous waste elements, for example, iodines, as well as various low- or intermediate-level waste streams. The estimated costs of packaging and disposing of reprocessing waste in geologic repositories are shown in Table 19.27. Comparison of Tables 19.26 and 19.27 will indicate that the total repository costs expressed on a per kilogram of uranium fuel basis are about the same for the reprocessing or once-through fuel cycle option. While a larger amount of material is disposed of in the once-through cycle, a more complex waste disposal system is required for the recycle case. Recently published documents by the DOE NWPA Project office[54] list the assumptions and the direct cost figures for the construction and operation of the first two repositories mandated by the NWPA. The assumptions used and the computed unit disposal costs are shown in Tables 19.28 and 19.29, respectively. As seen in Table 19.29 the disposal costs for spent fuel or for reprocessed high-level waste are quite similar. The disposal costs shown here on a \$/kg basis are smaller than the \$260/kg figure derived from the 1.0 mill/kWh charge. The charges are lower in Table 19.29 because the NWPA program cost represents waste storage over a limited period of time in the first two repositories only, and does not deal with the total accumulated waste disposal costs of the national nuclear power program for the next 50 yr or so.

The range of spent fuel shipping charges by various transportation modes is shown in Table 19.30. While the Nuclear Waste Policy Act specifies that the DOE will take title to the spent fuel at the reactor site, the cost of transporting this fuel to an AFR or a final repository will be covered by the utility through the 1 mill/kWh charge which may be extended in the future to cover increasing expenses. Specific provisions of the act deal with the economic aspects of interim spent fuel storage at an AFR facility, prior to emplacement in a repository, should an electric utility require this service after exhausting other alternatives. The NWPA requires that:

Table 19.27. Estimated Costs for Packaging, Storage, and Disposal of Reprocessing Wastes in Mined Geologic Repositories

	Levelized Cost, $/kg HM processed		
	HLW[a]	TRU[b]	Total
Spent fuel storage (reactor)			30
Calcination; vitrification	12.5		12.5
5-yr on-site storage	16.2		16.2
Fuel residue packaging		5.9	5.9
Failed equipment packaging		5.8	5.8
Wet waste fixation		5.2	5.2
Gaseous waste fixation		11.8	11.8
Kr storage		19.7	19.7
Solid waste interim storage	15.6	12.4	28.0
Repository costs[c]	29–61	28–50	57–111
Total[c]	73–105	89–111	192–246

Source: From Reference 54.

[a]HLW = High level wastes.

[b]TRU = Transuranic wastes.

[c]The range shown includes differing costs for repositories in salt, granite, shale, and basalt.

Table 19.28a. Key Reference Case Assumptions

1. Number of geologic repositories—2.
2. Repository design capacity—72,000 t each.
3. Repository design receipt rates—first 5 yr at 1800 t/yr. Next 21 yr at 3000 t/yr.
4. Waste types for disposal—Commercial High-Level Waste (CHLW).
   a. Transuranic Contaminated Waste (TRU).
   b. Spent Fuel (SF).
5. Waste age—10 yr (but a minimum of 5 yr is required).
6. Waste packages—long-lived "Westinghouse Package" for CHLW and SF (not end fittings or intermediate-level waste).
   a. SF disassembly at repository (assumes no predisassembly at reactor) and repackaging using the long-lived (Ticode-12) package.
   b. SF and CHLW packaging at the repository.
   c. TRU (100 nCi/g) in a "thin-walled" package.
   d. TRU incinerated for volume reduction.
7. Waste emplacement—borehole for SF and High-Level Waste (HLW).
   a. No hole liners.
   b. Commingling of TRU with either CHLW or SF.
8. Retrievability—maintained for 50 yr from date of emplacement of first waste package.
   a. Early backfilling not precluded (5 yr).
   b. Retrieval costs are not included.
9. Geologic medium—salt or hard rock.
10. No Monitored Retrievable Storage (MRS).
11. Transportation—from the reprocessing plant and/or reactor to the geologic repository (1500-mile average trip).

Source: From Reference 54.

Table 19.28b. Waste Generation and Repository Content

	Waste Generation, m^3/t U	Package Volume, m^3/t U	Number of Packages per Repository
Spent fuel disposal			
Disssembled spent fuel pins	0.190	0.57	24,374
End fittings	0.047	0.68	5,010
Reprocessing waste disposal			
Solidified high-level waste	0.083	0.19	31,560
Cladding and remote-handled TRU	1.270	1.39	66,000
Contact-handled TRU waste	1.000	0.21	343,000

Source: From Reference 54.

Table 19.29a. Reference Case Results (1982 $/kg for Spent Fuel or Reprocessing Waste Equivalent), Disposal Option

	Spent Fuel Disposal		Reprocessing Waste Disposal	
Cost Center	Salt	Hard Rock	Salt	Hard Rock
Repository	74	78	69	74
Transportation	27	27	23	23
Research and development	32	32	32	32
Total	133	137	124	129

Source: From Reference 54.

Table 19.29b. Discounted Levelized Unit Costs for the Reference Case ($/kg for Spent Fuel or Reprocessing Waste Equivalent)

Disposal Option	Salt	Hard Rock
Spent fuel disposal	122	125
Reprocessing waste disposal	115	119

Source: From Reference 54.

Table 19.30. Approximate Shipping Charges for Spent LWR Fuel[a]

	Constants[b]		Shipping Charges ($/kg U) for One-way Distance of	
	a($)	b($/mile)	500 Miles	1500 Miles
Rail: general freight	3.50	0.0052	5.10	10.30
Truck without escort vehicle	4.10	0.0122	7.80	20.00
Truck with escort vehicle	5.00	0.0155	9.70	25.20
Rail: special train	6.40	0.0173	11.60	28.90

Source: From Reference 54.

[a]Adapted from *Preliminary Estimates of the Charge for Spent-Fuel Storage and Disposal Services*, DOE/ET-0055, U.S. Department of Energy, July 1978. Values were adjusted to mid-1981 dollars.

[b]For estimation of shipping charges from the equation:

$$C = a + b(d - 200)$$

where C is in dollars per kg U, and d is the one-way shipping distance in miles.

1. The DOE is authorized until 1 January 1990 to execute contracts with utilities for taking title to spent fuel at the reactor site, transporting spent fuel to a federally owned and operated AFR, and storing spent fuel until further processing or disposal.
2. Fees for these services were established by 5 July 1983 and took effect on an annual basis by 1 January 1984. These charges will recover full costs of the program including the acquisition, construction, operating, and maintenance of any storage facilities.
3. If spent fuel owned by the government is placed into any storage capacity provided by this program, a fee will be collected equivalent to that charged to utilities.
4. DOE will make annual payments for impact assistance to any state or local government within whose jurisdiction any interim storage capacity is established and operated.
5. Transportation of spent fuel by DOE will remain subject to licensing by NRC and the Department of Transportation and will utilize private industry contacts whenever possible.

The disposal of the entire spent fuel element increases the volume and amount of long-lived actinide activity that has to be emplaced underground since all the uranium and plutonium remain with the fission products waste. The radioactive contamination hazard from the spent fuel over a long period is thus greater than the risk from high-level waste burial. The energy and monetary values in the disposal fuel are also lost to future generations. The major advantage of the spent fuel disposal scheme is the presumed greater ability to safeguard the fissile uranium and plutonium. Such argument has strongly been disputed on the grounds that the disposed spent fuel could ultimately be recovered and separated, and that the best way to eliminate plutonium is to separate and burn it in breeder reactors which are optimized to operate on this nuclear fuel.

Finally the discussion on the economic aspects of nuclear waste disposal should mention low-level waste disposal charges, as this waste form is the largest contributor, by volume, to the total national radioactive waste accumulation, as seen in Figure 19.46. The issues of low-level waste disposal apply to other institutional and industrial end users as well as to the electric utilities industry. They include the availability of disposal sites, transportation routes, and cost of services. A listing of low-level disposal costs as functions of the radiation level of the waste and distance to the currently available sites is shown in Table 19.31. (See also Chapter 15.)

Chemical Reprocessing

Chemical reprocessing aims at recovering the fissile values in the spent reactor fuel, while separating the harmful wastes. As of 1980, fuel residing in storage pools had an effective enrichment of 1.0% ^{235}U. This represented approximately \$800M in uranium value and \$200M in SWU content. In addition, fissile plutonium contained in the fuel has a value of \$20 to \$30/g. The value of the plutonium depends on its end use in the avoided production method. It is assumed that recycling LWR plutonium in breeder reactors rather than in LWRs will double the value of this material because of the improved energy extraction efficiency of the breeder as compared to that of LWRs. LWR-generated plutonium could be used for the breeder R&D project commitments made by the DOE. Should the DOE have to provide the plutonium it is obligated to deliver out of the defense stockpile, the price of plutonium could reach as much as \$200/g.[61] Provision of plutonium supplies for breeder R&D programs from civilian LWR fuel reprocessing avoids the need to produce very high-cost plutonium in dedicated government facilities.

One of the major problems adversely affecting the prospects for chemical reprocessing is the potential misuse of the separated plutonium for weapons production purposes. Every commercial nuclear power reactor unavoidably creates a by-product fissionable material, plutonium, which can be separated from the spent fuel. The isotopic quality of this product from present commercial power reactors greatly differs from that desired for optimum weapons manufacture, performance, and use; however, small nuclear weapons explosions can be produced even from these poorer grades of material. Such weapons would have uncertain effectiveness, reduced confidence in initial performance, and added handling difficulties. A weapons program using spent fuel from power reactors is so complicated, costly, uncertain, and time-consuming that it is far easier to invest the resources required to produce good weapons-grade plutonium from systems dedicated to that purpose.

The (not yet operated) reprocessing plant at Barnwell, South Carolina, cost about \$360 million 1980 dollars. It has a capacity of 1500 t/yr. A new plant probably would cost about five times as much. At an earlier time the market for reprocessing services, the cost and price of services, and applicable regulation and public policy resulted in commercial reprocessing ventures. These were thought to be attractive investments, and financing was readily available. Changing regulatory requirements caused increases in costs and uncertainties, followed by prohibitive public policy which destroyed the value of large investments. Subsequently, the market for reprocessing services and by-products has diminished or disappeared, and alternative means of disposing of spent fuel have been developed, as discussed above. Thus, private financing of reprocessing at this time

Table 19.31. Basic Commercial LLW Disposal Charges[a]

Facility:	Barnwell Low-Level Radioactive Waste Disposal Facility[b]			Washington Nuclear Center[c,d]			Nevada Nuclear Center[c,e]		
Rate Schedule Effective Date:	January 1, 1982			August 1, 1982			March 15, 1982		
Container Type:	Drums and Boxes	Disposable Liners in Shielded Cask		Drums and Boxes	Disposable Liners in Shielded Cask		Drums and Boxes	Disposable Liners in Shielded Cask	
Radiation Level Surface of Container, R/hr	Total, $/m^3$	Volume, $/m^3$	Radiation Surcharge, $/liner	Total, $/m^3$	Volume, $/m^3$	Radiation Surcharge, $/liner	Total, $/m^3$	Volume, $/m^3$	Radiation Surcharge, $/liner
0–0.20	494	494	None	555	555	None	340	340	None
0.20–1.00	609	494	175	598	555	118	370	340	132
1.00–2.00	741	494	500	663	555	462	416	340	324
2.00–5.00	741	494	500	794	555	650	508	340	456
5.00–10.0	891	494	700	926	555	940	600	340	659
10.0–20.0	1,138	494	1,000	1,180	555	1,200	778	340	841
20.0–25.0	1,138	494	1,000	1,448	555	1,490	965	340	1,045
25.0–40.0	1,492	494	1,275	1,448	555	1,490	965	340	1,045
40.0–50.0	1,492	494	1,275	2,182	555	1,767	1,479	340	1,239
50.0–60.0	1,889	494	1,550	2,182	555	1,767	1,479	340	1,239
60.0–75.0	1,889	494	1,550	2,606	555	2,038	1,776	340	1,430
75.0–80.0	2,242	494	1,700	2,606	555	2,038	1,776	340	1,430
80.0–100	2,242	494	1,700	2,868	555	2,315	1,959	340	1,624
100–125	2,489	494	1,800	By special request only			By special request only		
>125	By special request only								

Source: From Reference 54.

[a]In addition to the basic charge, there are surcharges for heavy loads, high curie activity, special wastes, and other items. Data taken from cost sheets provided by the burial ground operators.

[b]Operated by Chem-Nuclear. In addition to the charges shown, there is a 2.4% Barnwell Co. business tax on the total of all fees.

[c]Operated by U.S. Ecology.

[d]Includes a 30% tax.

[e]Third-party inspection is required, at the shipper's expense.

Table 19.32. Unit Costs for Reprocessing in AGNS-Type Plant and Sensitivity Thereof to Changes in Select Conditions ($/kg U, 1982)[a]

	Commercial Financing 17% After-Tax Return	Utility Financing	Debt Financing
Base case—20-yr depreciation	$391	$283	$235
$100 million change in capital cost	±26	±18	±14
1% change in escalation during construction	±21	±15	±11
2-yr delay in licensing	+4	+3	+2
10% decrease in planned capacity	+44	+31	+26

Source: From Reference 62.

[a]This assumes that de facto utility financing is achieved by advanced payments for reprocessing from utility companies. However, if the owner-operator of the reprocessing facility were able to finance the plant through the sale of debt and equity as utilities normally do, no contract operator would be involved, and the cost of reprocessing would be reduced by about $7/kg U.

would require guarantees or indemnification against further untoward U.S. government actions in the area of public policy and regulation. Also, there are many other potentially controlling issues, such as demand for reprocessing services and by-products, as well as regulatory requirements governing the design, construction, and operation of facilities and their related costs, and so on. These and other issues would probably have to be dealt with before financing may become limiting on reinstitution. The expected reprocessing unit cost in a Barnwell-like new reprocessing plant is shown in Table 19.32, assuming a total plant investment of 1.35 billion 1982 dollars. A unit price range of $235–391/kg is shown for various plant financing arrangements, and several sensitivity analyses are also included.

The evolution of unit reprocessing charges over the last 10 yr is shown in Figure 19.52. As seen in this figure a sevenfold increase in reprocessing costs took place between 1970 and 1980, with the mean unit charge for the 1980s exceeding $500/kg. This figure is higher than the numbers presented in Table 19.32, and may reflect more conservative assumptions regarding the reprocessing plant capital costs requirements and achievable capacity factors. The reprocessing cost figures shown for U.S. conditions in Figure 19.53 are lower yet than the assumed unit charges for the European nations nuclear power programs. A review of fuel cycle cost parameters for six European countries is shown in Table 19.33. Cost figures in Table 19.33 are presented in European Currency Units

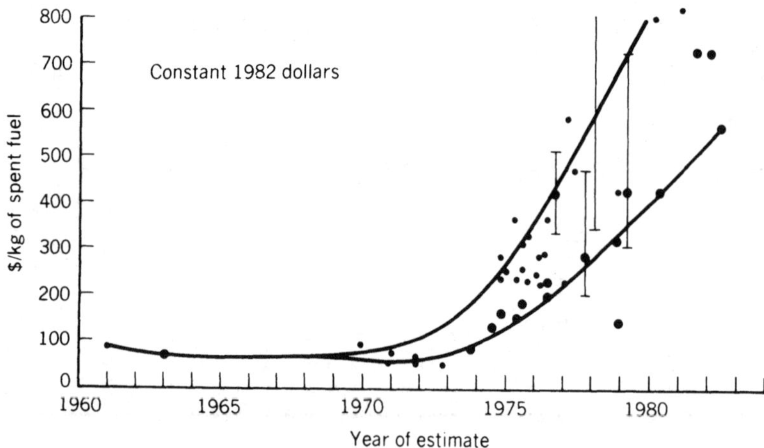

Figure 19.52. Reprocessing cost estimates. (From Reference 53.)

Table 19.33. Price Assumptions Concerning Nuclear Fuel

PHASES	*FRG*		*Italy*		*Belgium*		*France*		Average		Agreed Common Assumption	
	Price at 1.1.81	Relative Price Change, %/yr	Price at 1.1.81	Relative Price Change	Price at 1.1.81	Relative Price Change	Price at 1.1.81	Relative Price Change	1981	1990	1990	Relative Price Change, %/yr after 1990
Uranium concentrates (ECU/kg U)	70.2	0.48	85.45	0	76.96	0	81: 78.8 90: 88.3	2 (after: 90)	77.9	81	75	1%
Conversion into UF_6 (ECU/kg U)	4.6	0.48	4.93	0	5.92	0	4.94	0	5.1	5.15	5	0%
Enrichment (ECU/kg SWU)	95.3	−0.95	131.4	0	126.86	0	121.3	81–90: −1 after 90: 0	118.7	114.1	120	0%
Manufacture of assemblies (ECU/kg U)	233.5	0	238.2	0	164.32	0	177.5	2% until a limit of 115	203.4	196	200	0%
Reprocessing and storage of wastes (ECU/kg U)	856.1	1.9	780.2	0	676.6	0	875	0	797	836	850	0%
Value of Pu (ECU/g fissile Pu)	1990: 8 2000: 8.4	0.48	12.3	0	8.46	0	1990: 20.5 2000: 26.5	—	1990: 12.3 2000: 13.9		12 15	

Source: From Reference 63.
ECU = European Currency Unit.

(ECUs) which are roughly equivalent to the exchange value of the U.S. dollar. As seen from this table, European reprocessing charges vary between $670 and 860/kg with the average being $836/kg in 1990 (assuming parity between the U.S. dollar and the ECU at that time). The European reprocessing unit charges are thus viewed as 50–100% higher than the corresponding U.S. values. Since Europe has more experience with commercial LWR fuel reprocessing than the United States, it seems that a greater validity should be placed on their cost figures. The increasing costs of unit operations at the back end of the closed nuclear fuel cycle, at a time of relatively low uranium prices, has cast a doubt on the economics of the recycle versus the once-through fuel cycle. An analysis of the total fuel cycle costs with and without recycle is shown in Table 19.34. This table includes both material requirements and unit charges for each step of the once-through and recycle fuel cycles. As seen in Table 19.34, the once-through cycle is slightly less costly on a total annual cost basis than the recycle option. The results of this table are quite sensitive to the economic assumptions employed. Uranium prices higher than $25/lb will favor recycling, while reprocessing costs higher than $283/kg would favor once-through operation. The basic conclusion is that no compelling economic rationale for reprocessing and closure of the fuel cycle exists at this time. A similar conclusion was discussed by Wolfe in Ref. 53.

The reasons for attempting closure of the nuclear fuel cycle in the United States, based on the operation of the Barnwell plant and reprocessing of a limited amount of spent fuel in that plant, include:

1. Spent fuel congestion, which will be experienced by some, but not all, U.S. reactors beginning in the mid-1980s.
2. A demand for substantial amounts of plutonium for breeder research, development, and demonstration.
3. A need to develop and demonstrate reprocessing, which is viewed as the preferable or only acceptable approach by most countries, as a step in one of the alternative ways of managing nuclear waste (i.e., fission product isolation, vitrification, and disposal).
4. A need to regain international leadership in reprocessing as an essential element in the achievement of U.S. nonproliferation and other international nuclear policy objectives.
5. Reprocessing of civilian power reactor fuel must be developed and demonstrated on an industrial scale as an integral part of breeder reactor development and demonstration. Without reprocessing, there is no breeder option.
6. The lead times for the development and demonstration of industrial-scale reprocessing are of the same order as those for breeder reactors themselves. Therefore, work on this process must get underway soon.
7. The reprocessing operation, by separating most of the actinides from the high-level waste, cuts by several orders of magnitude the amount of very long-lived activity present in the disposed waste.

19.6. GENERAL SUMMARY AND DISCUSSION

The economic benefits of fuel recycling are highly dependent on the expectation of increasing cost of uranium fuel and on the unit costs of spent fuel processing. In time, with the depletion of easily accessible uranium supplies and rise in fuel prices, the net benefits of recycling will increase.

Other major operating options that affect the cost structure of the fuel cycle are the change in fuel burnup and the change in residence time in the reactor. These are not independent of each other and are in fact concomitant on some occasions. The purpose of increased fuel burnup is to extract more energy values from a given fuel; this will increase enrichment requirements and fabrication costs and may deplete the remaining plutonium content and reprocessing benefits. A schematic representation of the effects of fuel burnup on the various fuel-cycle cost components is shown in Figure 19.53.

Increasing the fuel resident time in the reactor involves a trade-off between enrichment requirements, reduced uranium demand, and savings on annual reactor shutdown times. Longer residence periods can be achieved by discharging the same fraction of the reactor core at each refueling and increasing the fuel enrichment and burnup, or by increasing the refueling fraction without changing the design burnup. A potential economic trade-off of various operating schemes is shown in Figure 19.54 and Table 19.35.

The discussion of nuclear fuel cycle issues shows that most of the problems now affecting nuclear power generation stem from plant construction and economics. Fuel cycle issues, while complex and important in their own right, contribute little to the difficulties affecting nuclear plants. The increase in the base construction cost of nuclear power plants has significantly deteriorated the competitive position of nuclear power with respect to other forms of electric energy generation. The problem has two aspects. The first is an industry-wide trend due to external forces

Table 19.34. Comparison of Annual Fuel Cycle Costs for Once-Through Fuel Cycle and Recovery and Recycle of Uranium and Sale of Plutonium—1000-MWe PWR[a] (1982 Dollars)

	Once-Through Fuel Cycle			Recovery and Recycle of Uranium and Sale of Plutonium		
	Quantity	Unit Price, $	Total Cost, $K	Quantity	Unit Price, $	Total Cost, $K
Uranium concentrates	181,345 kg U	$65.00	$11,787	149,140 kg U	$65.00	$ 9,694
Transport—U_3O_8	181,345 kg U	0.14	25	149,140 kg U	0.14	21
Conversion	180,438 kg U	5.50	992	148,394 kg U	5.50	816
Transport—UF_6 (nat)	180,428 kg U	0.21	38	148,394 kg U	0.21	31
Enrichment	120,219 kg SWU	138.65	16,668	117,314 kg SWU	138.65	16,266
Transport—UF_6 (enr)	27,273 kg U	0.75	20	27,273 kg U	0.75	20
Fuel fabrication	27,000 kg U	165.00	4,455	27,000 kg U	165.00	4,455
Transport—fresh fuel	27,000 kg U	1.71	46	27,000 kg U	1.71	46
Transport—spent fuel	27,000 kg U	30.80	832	27,000 kg U	22.00	594
Reprocessing	—	—	—	27,000 kg U	283.00[b]	7,641
Transport—recovered U product	—	—	—	25,527 kg U	0.21	5
Transport—repr. waste	—	—	—	27,000 kg U	18.00	486
Waste disposal	27,000 kg U	283.00	7,641	27,000 kg U	226.00	6,102
Total			$42,504			$46,177

Source: From Reference 62.

[a]Excludes interim storage of spent fuel in AFR storage facilities or expanded reactor facilities.
[b]Based on utility financing method.

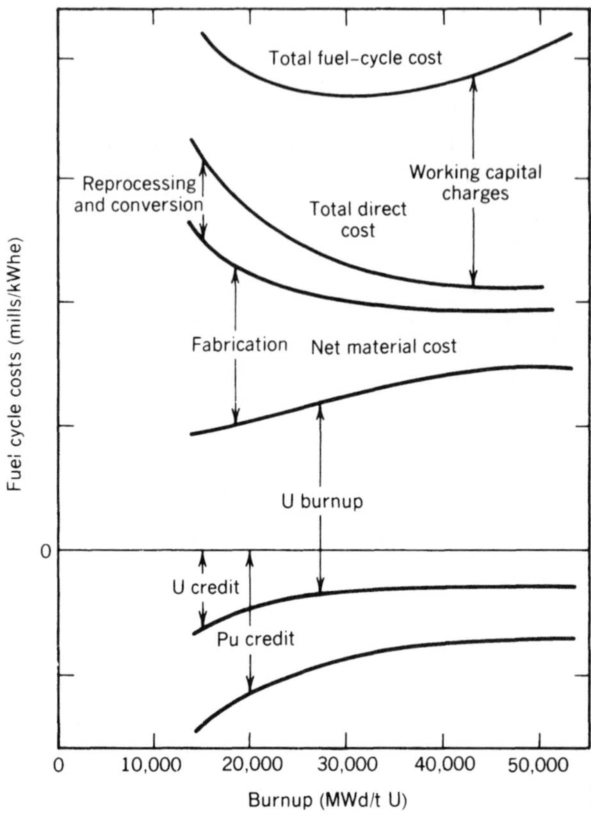

Figure 19.53. Fuel-cycle costs versus discharge burnup. (From Reference 47.)

including evolving regulatory requirements. The second aspect is a wide range in project performance because of factors internal to the projects themselves.

The deteriorating trend affecting the nuclear power industry results from the following external factors:

1. Continuously increasing regulatory requirements for safety and environmental concerns and variations in the level of regulatory attention given to different projects.
2. An advancing state-of-the-art associated with the evolution of larger sized nuclear plants and increasingly complex regulatory requirements.
3. The reduced load growth projections resulting from the nation's response to the 1973 oil crisis and from a change in the nature of the nation's production infrastructure.
4. Financial pressures from a deteriorating national economy, reduced load growth, and from the impact of (1) and (2) on the ultimate cost of the plant itself.

The initial impact of reduced load growth is to defer the in-service date of planned generating capacity. However, if that in-service date is moved far enough into the future, a point is reached where the annual costs of maintaining a construction restart capability, combined with the increased uncertainty surrounding the ultimate cost of the new capacity relative to its alternatives, prescribe project cancellation as the most economic choice. Furthermore, the inability of most investor-owned utilities plants to earn rates of return on investment at least equal to their respective costs of capital during much of the past decade substantially limited their access to debt capital and also made additional investment of equity capital unattractive. As a result, many investor-owned utilities appear to have adopted a strategy of restricting new investment to just those projects that are absolutely necessary to fulfill the utilities' service obligation. In light of this, nuclear plants and other major projects, such as coal-fired or hydroelectric plants, in early stages of planning or construction are vulnerable targets for cancellation, particularly since the sunk costs of

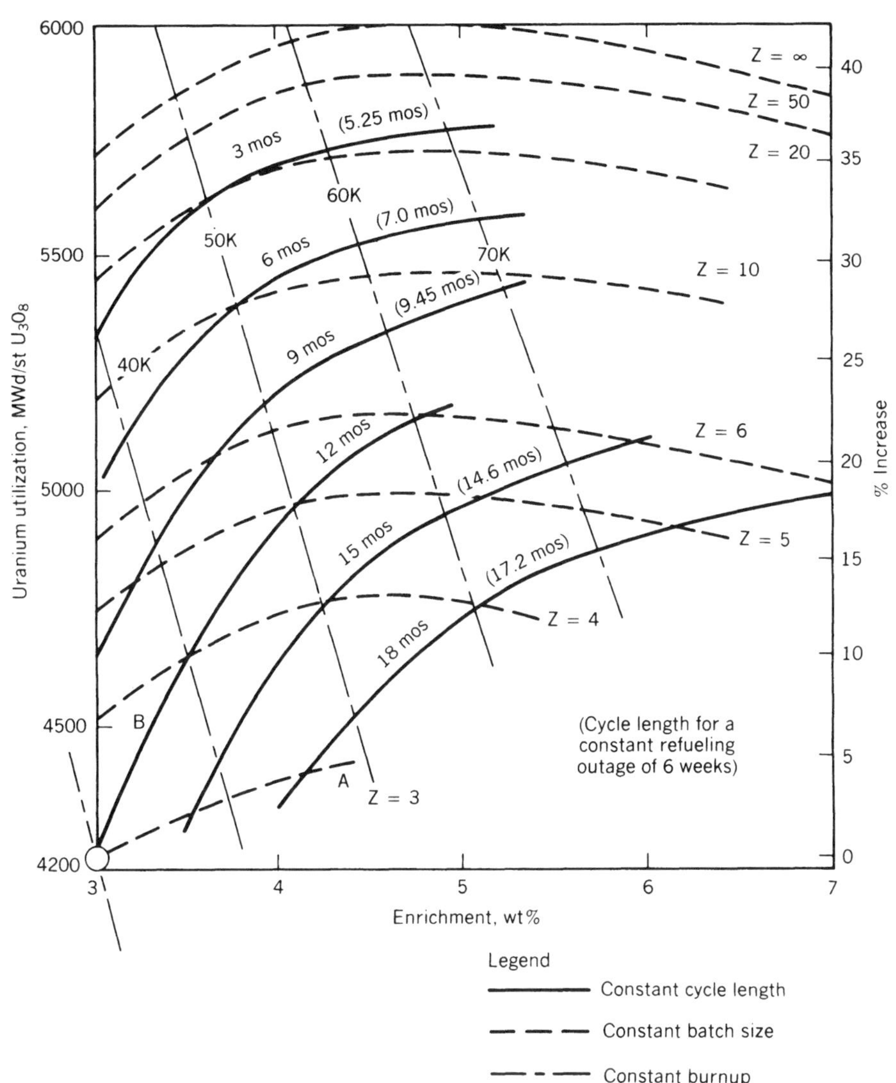

Figure 19.54. Uranium utilization as a function of enrichment and cycle length. (From Reference 64.)

Table 19.35. Thirty-Year Levelized Costs for PWR Fuel Cycles, mills/kWh[a]

Fuel Management	UF_6	SWU	FAB	Back-End Direct[b]	Indirect	Total
Three-batch out–in	2.47	1.76	0.60	0.58	0.82	6.23
	(6.05)	(1.76)	(0.52)	(0.58)	(1.53)	(10.44)
Five-batch out–in	2.15	1.73	0.39	0.35	1.02	5.63
	(5.26)	(1.73)	(0.33)	(0.35)	(1.87)	(9.53)
Five-batch low-leakage[c]	2.11	1.70	0.41	0.33	0.98	5.54
	(5.15)	(1.70)	(0.35)	(0.33)	(1.80)	(9.38)

Source: From Reference 64.

[a]Values without parentheses are for near-term assumptions, while those with parentheses are for the long-term assumptions.

[b]Disposal costs.

[c]Includes extra cost for fabrication of shimmed assemblies.

Table 19.36. Components of Coal and Nuclear Electricity Costs for Electric Generating Units in Western Europe and the United States

Country	Capital Costs,[a] 1982 $/kW	Levelized Annual Costs (1982 ¢/kWh)			
		Capital	O&M	Fuel	Total
		Nuclear Units			
Britain	$2,352	3.15	0.31	0.91	4.37
France	1,309	1.75	0.31	0.91	2.97
United States	1,375	2.06	0.31	0.91	3.28
		Coal Units			
Britain	$1,294	1.73	0.24	3.02	4.99
France	822	1.10	0.24	3.02	4.36
United States	988	1.34	0.34	2.24	3.92

Source: From Reference 65.

[a]Estimates of capital costs for coal and nuclear units in Britain were taken from *Nuclear Engineering International,* "News Review," June 1982, p. 3. For France, 1982 estimates were obtained from information supplied by the Paris European Nuclear Society.

the canceled plants would be mostly borne by parties other than utility investors. However, nuclear plants have been among the most vulnerable because of their long lead times, high capital intensity, and the uncertainties shrouding their ultimate costs and completion dates.

Except for units canceled specifically because of a reversal in the comparative generation economics, the completion of nuclear units under construction could offer the cheapest alternatives to meeting future increases in baseload demand. Furthermore, in those regions projected to be still dependent on oil- or natural gas-fired generation for baseload power in the 1990s, the on-schedule completion of some nuclear units could probably be cost justified on the basis of displacing generation from those expensive fuels. Also, the adverse secondary effects of higher electricity prices on regional economic development and the balance-of-payments effects of greater oil imports† must be considered.

A number of studies conducted in the past 5 yr for utilities or government agencies support a consensus that utility systems with heavy reliance on oil or natural gas as boiler fuels could lower the cost of electricity to their customers by placing in service nuclear or coal-fired capacity in excess of that needed for service reliability alone. It is thus important to identify the lessons from the better nuclear construction projects, relative to timely and on-budget completion of nuclear power plants, so that the benefits from these plants could be realized.

The key to superior project performance, in a given regulatory climate, is the effective utilization of craft, nonmanual, and engineering labor in a specific plant. Intrinsic to this utilization is the interaction of regulatory and industry staffs with respect to regulatory requirements and their interpretation, the amount of sophisticated engineering analysis, the Q/A requirements and procedures, the information and communication documentation requirements, and the engineering and construction sequencing strategies. Superior project performance depends on the regulatory and industry infrastructure learning from previous plants, standardizing design aspects and procedures, optimizing Q/A–Q/C's relationship to production, optimizing engineering and construction pacing, and managing "impacts" from regulatory or technical "change."

The foregoing discussion is mostly related to nuclear power experience in the United States. An intercomparison of coal and nuclear electricity generation economics between the United States and other countries is now in order. A cross-national economic comparison is complicated by several factors.

1. Variations in the rates of exchange among the different currencies which extend over the construction and operation periods.

†In the northeastern United States, electricity is being increasingly imported from Canada. Certain regions of the United States seem to have made a decision to be net importers of electricity, e.g., California now looks to nearby states for new electrical power.

Table 19.37. Summary of Costs, Discounted Average Cost per kWh (0.01 ECU/kWh) (Excluding Taxes and Similar Charges) (Prepared 1/1/81)

COUNTRY	*U.K.*		*FRG*		*Italy*		*Netherlands*		*Belgium*		*France*	
Discount rate	5%	10%	5%	10%	5%	10%	5%	10%	5%	10%	5%	10%
Nuclear plant	2 × 622 MW		1 × 1285 MW		2 × 1000 MW				2 × 1000 MW		2 × 1275 MW	
Investment	2.88	4.79	1.58	2.65	0.99	1.59			1.26	2.07	1.02	1.64
Operation	0.29	0.29	0.47	0.46	0.22	0.22			0.57	0.57	0.36	0.36
Fuel	1.45	1.61	0.82	0.80	0.78	0.83			0.68	0.71	0.69	0.74
TOTAL		6.69		3.91		2.64				3.35		2.74
	4.62		2.87		1.99				2.51		2.07	
Cool-fired plant	3 × 630 MW		2 × 675 MW		4 × 627 MW		1 × 600 MW		2 × 600 MW		2 × 580 MW	
Investment	1.50	2.58	0.79	1.25	0.56	0.85	0.74	1.22	0.59	0.94	0.83	1.35
Operation	0.36	0.35	0.60	0.60	0.19	0.19	0.31	0.31	0.32	0.33	0.29	0.28
Fuel	4.21	4.21	4.02	3.93	2.38	2.38	3.61	3.51	2.59	2.55	2.50	2.48
TOTAL		7.14		5.78		3.42		5.04		3.82		4.11
	6.07		5.41		2.13		4.66		3.50		3.62	
Oil-fired plant											2 × 580 MW	
Investment											0.71	1.16
Operation											0.25	0.25
Fuel											7.03	7.07
TOTAL												8.48
											7.99	
Discount rate used in each country	5%		4%		5%		4%		8.6%		9%	

Source: From Reference 63.
ECU = European Currency Unit.

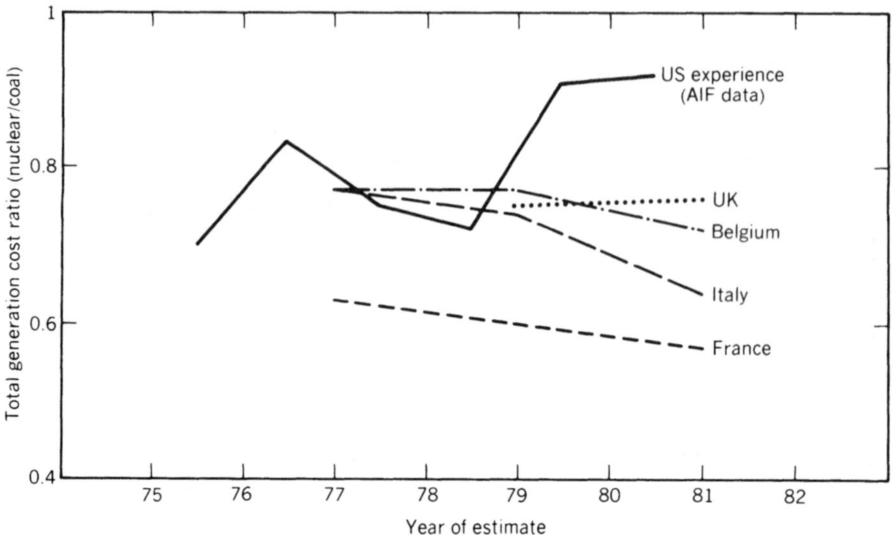

Figure 19.55. Trends in relative total generation costs for nuclear and coal plants. (From Reference 66.)

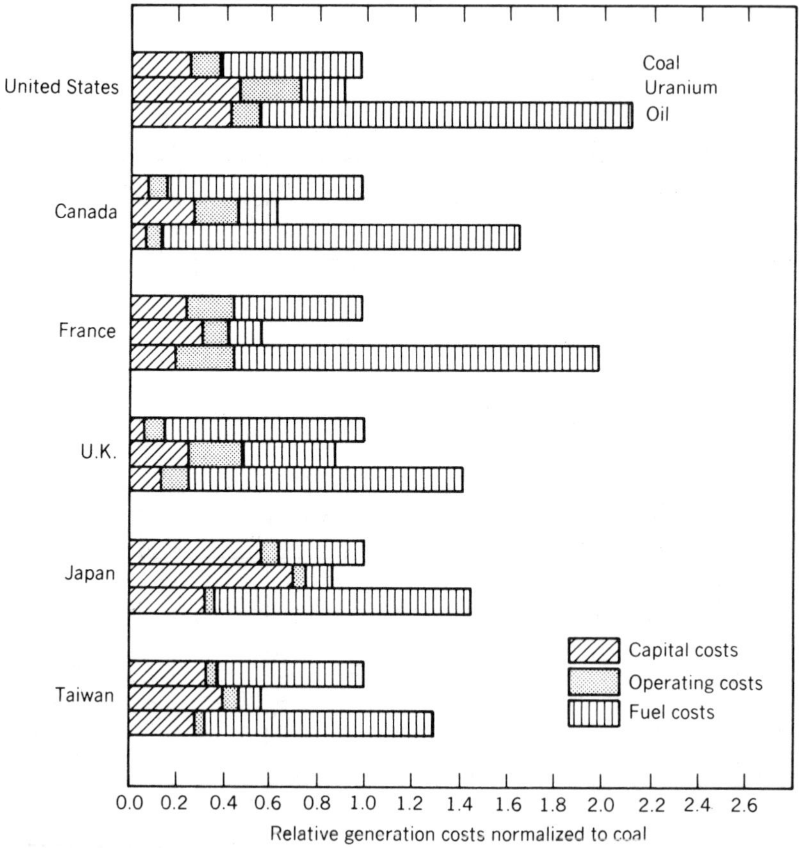

United States
Canada
France
U.K.
Japan
Taiwan
Coal
Uranium
Oil
Capital costs
Operating costs
Fuel costs
0.0 0.2 0.4 0.6 0.8 1.0 1.2 1.4 1.6 1.8 2.0 2.2 2.4 2.6
Relative generation costs normalized to coal

Figure 19.56. Relative generation costs of uranium-, coal-, and oil-fired power plants, 1980–1981. (From Reference 67.)

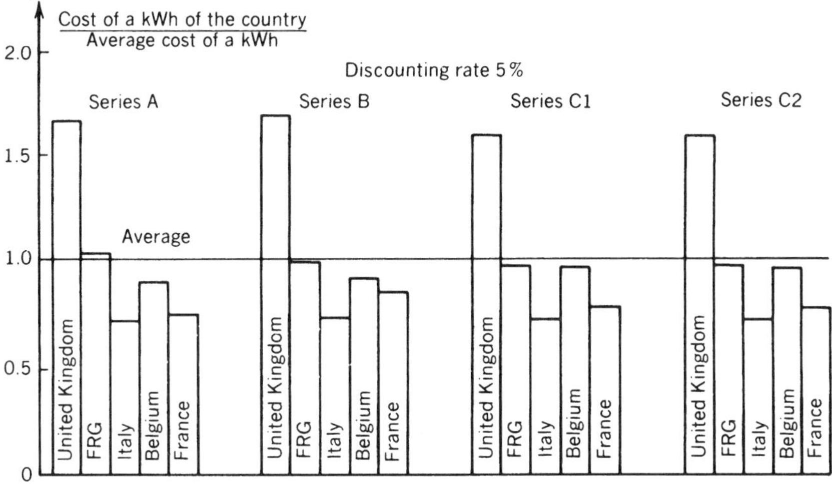

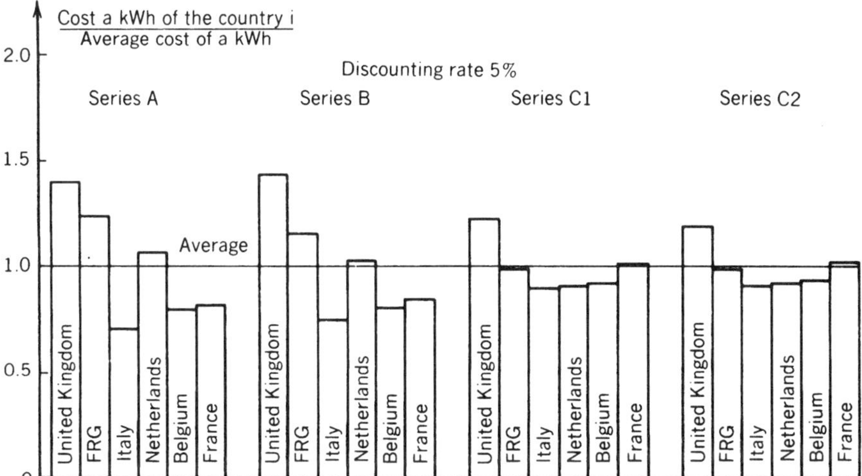

Figure 19.57. Comparison of the discounted average cost of nuclear kWh (top) and coal-fired kWh (bottom) between the various countries. (From Reference 63.)

2. Differing national practices regarding tax obligations, financing methods, subsidies, rate making and accounting procedures.
3. Varying plant capacity factors among both the nuclear or the coal-fired plants in each country, when expressed either on an annual or a lifetime basis.

Within the above limits several recent cross-national economic comparisons have recently been prepared, and selected results are shown in Tables 19.36[65] and 19.37,[63] and in Figures 19.55,[66] 19.56,[67] and 19.57.[63] Reference 63 is a very detailed and periodically updated study of power generation costs among European countries which is now being expanded to include Canada and the United States.

The results of these cross-national comparisons lead to several basic conclusions:

1. The highest capital cost differentials between nuclear and coal-fired power plants occur in countries which have not standardized their plant designs, or which operate a multitiered regulatory process with a potential for disagreement between national and regional interests. Thus the United States, United Kingdom, and the FRG demonstrate high capital costs ratios whereas

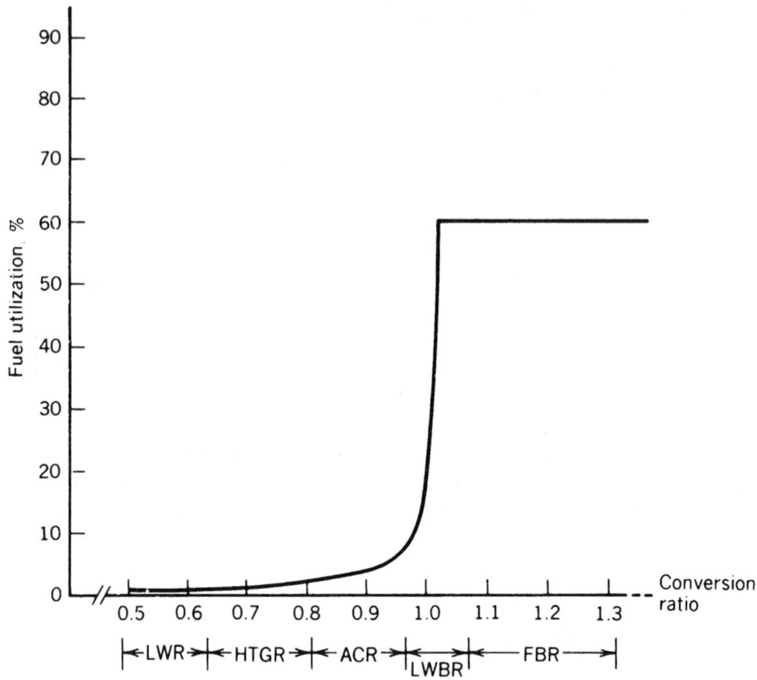

Figure 19.58. Fuel utilization in reactors as a function of conversion ratio. *Key:* LWR—light-water reactor. HTGR—high-temperature gas-cooled reactor. ACR—advanced converter reactor. LWBR—light-water breeder reactor. FBR—fast breeder reactor. (From Reference 68.)

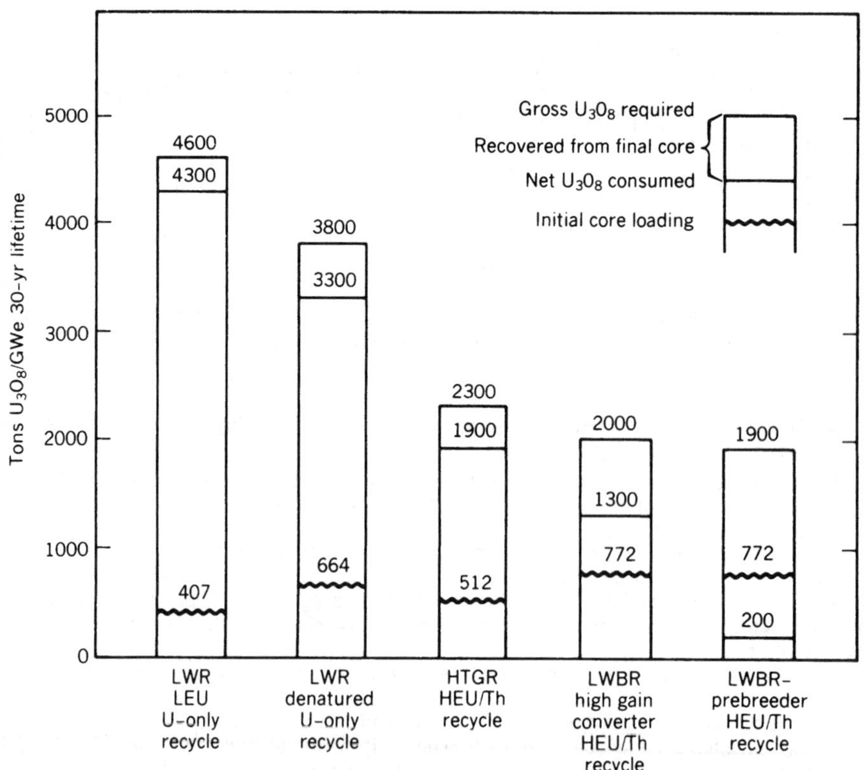

Figure 19.59. U_3O_8 resource utilization in $^{235}U/^{233}U$ fueled systems. (From Reference 48.)

France, Belgium, and Italy demonstrate low nuclear–coal cost ratios. Lack of standardization in power plant design may lead to plant redesign and backfitting requirements imposed by the regulatory agencies which will increase capital costs.

2. Nations with large domestic coal resources and relatively low coal extraction prices will exhibit smaller nuclear–coal generation cost differentials. Thus the United States, United Kingdom, and Belgium show lower economic advantage of nuclear plants over coal, whereas France and the FRG, which are endowed with large domestic resources but highly expensive coal extraction operations and prices, show a greater nuclear advantage.

3. Countries that have to import most of their energy fuels will exhibit a greater economic advantage for nuclear power generation. This is due to the high cost and complicated logistics of importing large amounts of steam coal or residual oil, versus natural or enriched uranium. A 1000-MWe oil-fired plant will burn 30,000 barrels of oil per day. A 1000-MWe coal-fired plant will consume 10,000 tons of coal per day, whereas a similar sized LWR will require less than 6000 tons of natural uranium per a 30-yr lifetime. Nations like Taiwan and Japan, which import oil, coal, and uranium, show the highest nuclear economic advantage.

4. The international comparisons are thus summarized in Table 19.36 and in Figure 19.55. The United States shows the highest nuclear/coal generation cost ratio, and France shows the lowest costs ratio.

Finally, a discussion on nuclear power economics would be incomplete without mentioning the nuclear power alternatives. Some of these might in time prove economically attractive, due to their improved performance characteristics. A major criterion for a nuclear reactor's performance is its uranium utilization efficiency, which could be measured as a dimensionless figure as a function of a reactor's conversion ratio, or in physical units such as tons U_3O_8 consumed per unit electricity produced. Both representations, shown here in Figures 19.58 and 19.59 respectively, are useful in comparing different nuclear reactor concepts. Advanced nuclear reactors such as the High-Temperature Gas-Cooled Reactor (HTGR), the Light-Water Breeder Reactor (LWBR), or the Fast Breeder Reactor (FBR) show better utilization efficiency expressed in terms of higher conversion ratio and lower uranium consumption. Breeder reactors do not require any natural uranium supply, and thus avoid all the mining, milling, and enrichment problems that affect the front end of the current LWR fuel cycles. In time, with the increasing cost of uranium extraction, advanced nuclear power systems which are more capital intensive than the current LWRs may become competitive due to their lower fuel costs. It will then be possible to trade off higher initial capital costs for reduced fuel supply requirements. This improved fuel utilization efficiency will allow for a significantly larger amount of electricity to be produced by advanced nuclear power plants, turning nuclear technology effectively into a renewable energy resource for the benefit of humankind.

REFERENCES

1. EPRI Planning and Evaluation Division, *TAG-Technical Assessment Guide,* EPRI Report P-2410-SR, Palo Alto, California, May 1982.
2. Ashley, R. L., "Power Plant Generation Costs," ANS Topical Meeting on Power Plant Construction Operation and Maintenance, Charleston, South Carolina, March 1982.
3. Delene, J. G., et al., *Reference Data Base for Nuclear/Fossil Power Generation Cost Analysis,* Report DOE/NE-0044 Version 1, Washington, D.C., October 1982.
4. Dillon, T., U.S. DOE, *Nuclear Economics, A Presentation,* Washington, D.C., June 1982.
5. Behnke, W. B., Jr., "Economics and Technical Experience of Nuclear Power Production in the U.S.," IAEA International Conference on Nuclear Power Experience, Paper IAEA-CN-42/81, Vienna, Austria, September 1982.
6. Brandfon, W. W., "A Comparison of Future Nuclear and Coal Fired Electric Generation," *Trans. Am. Nuclear Soc.* **43,** 536 (1982).
7. Reynolds, A., *Projected Costs of Electricity from Nuclear and Coal Fired Power Plants,* Report DOE/EIA-0356/1, Washington, D.C., August 1982.
8. Corey, G. R., *An Economic Comparison of Nuclear and Coal Fired Generation,* Commonwealth Edison Co., December 1980.
9. Atomic Industrial Forum, "U.S. Average Electrical Generating Costs and Plant Performance in 1981," Press Release, Washington, D.C., November 1982.
10. Nuclear Utility Services Corporation, *Guide for Economic Evaluation of Nuclear Reactor Plant Designs,* Report No. NUS-531, Washington, D.C., January 1969.
11. U.S. Department of Energy, Office of Nuclear Reactors Programs, *Power Plant Capital Investment Cost Estimates: Current Trends and Sensitivity to Economic Parameters,* Report No. DOE/NE-0009, Washington, D.C., June 1980.

12. Bechtel Power Corporation, *Electricity: Can We Produce Enough For America's Future*, San Francisco, California, October 1982.
13. Crowley, J. H., United Engineers and Construction Co., "Commercial Light Water Reactor Nuclear Power Generating Station Experience," private communication, January, 1983.
14. U.S. DOE Office of Nuclear Reactor Programs, *Analysis of Utility Reports on Nuclear Power Plant Capital Costs*, Update, July–September 1982.
15. Crowley, J. H., "Trends Influencing the Continuing Rise in Costs for Nuclear and Coal Fired Electric Generating Stations," Presentation to the State of Washington Senate Energy Committee, Seattle, Washington, 1980.
16. Mooz, W. E. *Cost Analysis of Light Water Reactor Power Plants*, Report No. R-2304-DOE, Rand Corporation, Los Angeles, California, June 1978.
17. Mooz, W. E., *A Second Cost Analysis of Light Water Reactor Power Plants*, Report No. R-2504-RC, Rand Corporation, Los Angeles, California, December 1979.
18. U.S. DOE, "Energy Department Considers New Licensing Reform Proposals for Nuclear Power Plant Construction," *DOE News*, Washington, D.C., October 15, 1982.
19. Crowley, J. H., "Nuclear Energy—What's Next?," Atomic Industrial Forum Workshop on the Electric Imperative, Monterey, California, June 1981.
20. Crowley, J. H., and J. D. Griffith, "U.S. Construction Cost Rise Threatens Nuclear Option," *Nuclear Engineering International*, **27,** 25 (June 1982).
21. Bauman, D. S., et al., *An Analysis of Power Plant Construction Leadtimes. Volume 1: Analysis and Results*, EPRI Report EA-2880, Palo Alto, California, March 1983.
22. Brandfon, W. W., "Cost Impact of Nuclear Project Duration," AIF Workshop on Nuclear Power Financing, Las Vegas, Nevada, February 9, 1982.
23. Budwani, R., "Power Plants Scheduling, Construction and Costs: 10 Years Analysis," *Power Engineering*, **86,** 36 (August 1982).
24. McLeod, B. N., and Y. M. Park, *Methods of Power Reactor Decommissioning Cost Recovery*, NUS Corporation Report, Washington, D.C., September 1979.
25. Atomic Industrial Forum, Inc., *An Engineering Evaluation of Nuclear Power Reactor Decommissioning—Summary Report*, Washington, D.C., November 1976.
26. Moore, E. B., Jr., *Facilitation of Decommissioning Light Water Reactors*, NUREG/CR-0569, Washington, D.C., December 1979.
27. Temple, Barker and Sloane, Inc., *Financing Strategies for Nuclear Power Plant Decommissioning*, NUREG/CR-1484, Washington, D.C., July 1980.
28. Roberts, J. O., et al., *Treatment of Inflation in the Development of Discount Rates and Levelized Costs in NEPA Analyses for the Electric Utility Industry*, NUREG-0670, Washington, D.C., January 1980.
29. U.S. Nuclear Regulatory Commission, *Total Generating Costs: Coal and Nuclear Plants*, Vol. 8 of *Commercial Electric Power Cost Studies*, NUREG-0248 (also COO-2477-12), Washington, D.C., February 1979.
30. U.S. Nuclear Regulatory Commission, *NRC Operating Units Status Report: Licensed Operating Reactors*, NUREG-0020, monthly issues, Nos. 1–12, Vol. 3, Washington, D.C., 1979.
31. U.S. Nuclear Regulatory Commission, *Three Mile Island Action Plan (Draft)*, NUREG-0660, Washington, D.C., May 1980.
32. Lee, Byron, Jr., Atomic Industrial Forum letter to Dr. H. Denton, U.S. NRC, and attached enclosure titled: "Report to the AIF Policy Committee on Follow Up to the TMI Accident," by the Working Group on Action Plan Priorities and Resources, Washington, D.C., February 1980.
33. Kettler, D. J., "Nuclear vs. Fossil Cost Post TMI," New York, N.Y., September 1980. See also Olds, F. C., "Backfitting and Regulatory Impact Costs," *Power Engineering* **12,** 15 (August 1983).
34. Myers, M. L., et al., *Non Fuel Operation and Maintenance Costs for Large Steam-Electric Power Plants-1982*, ORNL/TM-8324 (NUREG/CR-2844), Oak Ridge, Tennessee, September 1982.
35. U.S. DOE, Office of Converter Reactor Deployment, *Comparison of Utility Nuclear and Coal Fired Plant Generation Costs (Form 1) in 1981*, Washington, D.C., April–June 1982.
36. Long, J. D., *Nuclear Property Insurance: Status and Outlook*, Report NUREG-0891, Washington, D.C., May 1982.
37. Clark, L. L., and A. D. Chockie, *Fuel Cycle Cost Projections*, Report NUREG/CR-1041, Washington, D.C., December 1979.

38. Brandfon, W. W., and D. F. Hang, "LWR Recycle, Economic at What Price U_3O_8?," Paper presented at the Atomic Industrial Fuel Cycle Conference 80, New Orleans, Louisiana, April 17, 1980.

39. Douglas, H., "Summary and Conclusion Section," in the *Proceedings of the EPRI Symposium on Fissile Fuel Supply Assurance,* C. H. Waldman, Ed., Palo Alto, California, May 20, 1982.

40. U.S. DOE, *Statistical Data on the Uranium Industry,* Report GJO-100 (82), Grand Junction, Colorado, January 1, 1982.

41. Bleistein, S., "Long Term Uranium Supply Schedules," *Proceedings of the EPRI Symposium on Fissile Fuel Supply Assurance,* C. H. Waldman, Ed., Palo Alto, California, May 20, 1982.

42. National Academy of Science, "Problems of U.S. Uranium Resources and Supply to the Year 2010," Supporting Paper 1, Study of Nuclear and Alternative Energy Systems, Washington, D.C., 1978.

43. Ford Foundation/MITRE Corporation, *Nuclear Power Issues and Choices: Report of the Nuclear Energy Policy Study Group,* Ballinger, Cambridge, Massachusetts, 1977.

44. NUKEM GmbH, *The NUKEM Market Report on the Nuclear Fuel Cycle,* monthly issues of 11/82 to 3/83, Hanau, FRG.

45. U.S. DOE, *Survey of United States Uranium Marketing Activities,* Report DOE/NE-0013/1, Washington, D.C., June 1982.

46. Clark, R. G., DOE, "Survey of U.S. Uranium Marketing Activities," Paper presented at the Uranium Colloquium V, Grand Junction, Colorado, April 6, 1982.

47. Park, Y., NUS Corporation, "Fundamentals of Light Water Reactor Fuel Cycle (An Overview of Its Economics)," Presentation before the 1981 Continuing Education Course, Philadelphia Section of the ASME, Philadelphia, Pennsylvania, April 14, 1981.

48. U.S. DOE, *Nuclear Proliferation and Civilian Nuclear Power. Report of the Non-Proliferation Alternative Systems Assessment Program,* Document DOE/NE-0001, Vol. 3, Washington, D.C., June 1980.

49. "DOE Holds Line on SWU Price with New Look at Imputed Interested and Stockpile Charges," *Nuclear Fuel* **8,** 5 (1983).

50. Voigt, W. R., Jr., and S. E. Peske, "United States Enrichment Supply—Policy and Direction," Paper presented at the 9th Annual Meeting of the World Nuclear Fuel Market, Nice, France, October 17, 1982.

51. C. Braun, "Comparison of Various Measures and Options for Nuclear Fuel Supply Assurance," Paper presented at the ANS Winter Meeting, Washington, D.C., November 14, 1983.

52. Judkins, R. R., and A. R. Olsen, *Nuclear Fuel Fabrication and Refabrication Cost Estimation Methodology,* Report ORNL/TM-6640, Oak Ridge, Tennessee, November 1979.

53. Wolfe, B., and B. F. Judson, "Closing the Fuel Cycle," Paper presented at the ANS Executive Conference on Technical Aspects of International Nuclear Commerce, San Diego, California, January 1983.

54. U.S. DOE, Office of Nuclear Energy, *Spent Fuel and Radioactive Waste Inventories, Projection and Characteristics,* Report DOE/NE-0017-1, Washington, D.C., October 1982. See also U.S. DOE, Office of Nuclear Waste Policy Act Project Office, *Report on Financing the Disposal of Commercial Spent Nuclear Fuel and Reprocessed High Level Radioactive Waste,* Report DOE/S-0020/1, Washington, D.C., July 1983.

55. International Atomic Energy Agency, *Nuclear Power, The Environment and Man,* Report STI/PUB/635, IAEA Vienna, Austria, August 1982.

56. Fletcher, J. F., B. M. Cole, W. L. Purcell, and R. G. Rau, *Projections of U.S. LWR Spent Fuel Storage Requirements,* Report PNL-SA-10585, Richland, Washington, November 1982. See also U.S. DOE Richland Operations Office, *Spent Fuel Storage Requirements,* Report DOE/RL-82-1, Richland, Washington, June 1982.

57. French Ministry of Research and Industry, *Report of the Working Group on Spent Fuel Management,* Paris, France, November 1982.

58. U.S. Congress—Congressional Record/House, Nuclear Waste Policy Act of 1982, pp.H-10525–H-10544, *Congressional Record,* Washington, D.C., December 20, 1982. See also U.S. Government Federal Register, Standard Contract for Disposal of Nuclear Fuel and/or High Level Radioactive Waste, 10CFR961, *Federal Register* **48,** No. 25, Part IV, pp. 5458–5471, Washington, D.C., February 4, 1983.

59. U.S. DOE, *Department of Energy Report on Fee for Spent Nuclear Fuel Storage and Disposal Services,* Report DOE/SR-006, Washington, D.C., October 1980.

60. Clark, L. L., and B. M. Cole, *An Analysis of the Cost of Mixed Geologic Repositories in Alternative Media,* Report PNL-3949, Richland, Washington, February 1982.

61. U.S. General Accounting Office, *Interim Letter Report in GAO's Review of the Total Cost Estimate for the Clinch River Breeder Reactor Project,* Report GAO/EMD-82-131, Washington, D.C., September 23, 1982.

62. Johnson, E. R., "The Economics of Reprocessing," Paper presented at the Seminar on Spent Fuel Management and Waste Disposal, INMM, Washington, D.C., October 1982.

63. Moynet, G., et al., "Generation Costs, Assessment Made in 1981," UNIPEDE Report, Brussels, Belgium, June 1982.

64. Matzie, R. A., Ed., *Uranium Resources Utilization Improvements in the Once-Through PWR Fuel Cycle,* Report CEND-380 (COO-2426-199), Windsor, Connecticut, April 1980.

65. Perl, L. J., "The Current Economics of Electric Generation from Coal in the U.S. and Western Europe," Paper presented at the International Scientific Forum on Reassessing the World Energy Prospects, Paris, France, October 20, 1982.

66. Bennett, L. L., P. M. Karousakis, and G. Moynet, "Review of Nuclear Power Costs Around the World," Paper presented at the IAEA International Conference on Nuclear Power Experience, Vienna, Austria, September, 1982.

67. Starr, C., "Electrification, Economic Growth and Uranium Power," Paper presented at the 7th Annual Symposium of the Uranium Institute, London, U.K., September, 1982.

68. U.S. House of Representatives, Committee on Science and Technology, *The Energy Content of Nuclear Fuels: Technical Comparisons and Computations,* Report prepared by J. R. LaMarsh and the Congressional Research Service, U.S. Government Printing Office, Washington, D.C., April 1980.

CHAPTER 20

PROLIFERATION ISSUES

20.1. INTRODUCTION AND OVERVIEW

Historical Background

Nuclear power is burdened by the fact that its first use was in an explosive device used for destructive purposes. The nuclear weapons era was launched abruptly upon the world with the first test explosion of a nuclear weapon at Alamogordo, New Mexico on July 16, 1945 which was followed by two detonations in the war against Japan. Other nations followed suit† and by the early 1960s there were five nuclear weapons countries: the United States, the Soviet Union, the United Kingdom, France, and the Peoples' Republic of China.

In the first three nuclear weapons states, the United States, the Soviet Union, and the United Kingdom, civilian power was an offshoot of their weapons programs. Fear of the use of scientific knowledge in the manufacture of weapons squelched early attempts at scientific and technical exchanges in the hope of stopping the spread of weapons development by denial of scientific knowledge. In 1946, President Truman broke off exchanges on civilian power development with the United Kingdom. A few months later, however, the Acheson–Lilienthal plan outlined an ambitious scheme for international development for nuclear power. For a number of years, the policy of secrecy and denial was continued in hopes of stemming the further spread of nuclear explosives. These hopes were shattered by the Soviet explosion in 1949 and the policy of an embargo on nuclear scientific information was dead. In 1955, the First Geneva Conference on the Peaceful Uses of Atomic Energy was organized and in 1957, the International Atomic Energy Agency (IAEA) was created. Both actions presupposed an open exchange of scientific information for peaceful nuclear power.

At the time, all three weapons states had demonstrated their capability and had established facilities for weapons grade material production. In the United States, diffusion plants, first established during World War II, were used to produce highly enriched uranium for weapons, nuclear submarine fuels, and research reactors: the Hanford reactors produced plutonium, and the Savannah River plants produced plutonium, tritium, and uranium-233, all weapons materials. The United Kingdom had established the Calder Hall production reactor and was building the Capenhurst enrichment facility. The Soviet Union had built equivalent facilities.

The Geneva Conference of 1955 gave the opportunity to the three leading nuclear nations to announce the first civilian applications of nuclear power. Although the first production of electric power from a nuclear reactor was from the Experimental Breeder Reactor (EBR-1) in 1951, almost all other civilian reactors were adaptations of military reactor designs.

The Canadian civilian power program followed the route of natural uranium heavy-water reactors which were developed during World War II as a backup to the Hanford plutonium production plants. France joined the nuclear club in 1960. Although it is not clear whether the military motivation preceded the civilian one, France declared itself a nation with nuclear weapons and a nuclear navy before any civilian power development. The feat was accomplished in spite of discouragement by the United States, thus proving that nuclear explosives can be manufactured by a determined country (even weakened by war) without outside assistance. In the period of 1955 to the mid-1960s, France was the only additional country to join the nuclear club. The regime promoted by the IAEA and followed by the major weapons states consisted of the following trade-off. Scientific and technological assistance would be provided in exchange for an obligation, with

†The USSR exploded its first fission-type bomb on August 29, 1949; the United Kingdom on October 3, 1952; France on February 13, 1960; and China in 1964.

safeguards provisions attached, to eschew the development of nuclear weapons (more on this in Section 20.5).

China, which detonated its first nuclear weapon in 1964, built its technological capability with assistance from the Soviet Union, beginning in 1957. The Soviets subsequently terminated their assistance program, possibly out of fear that it was helping the Chinese toward weapons capability, among other reasons. The explosion of a "peaceful" nuclear device by India in May 1974, made the latest confirmed addition to the nuclear club. Material for the Indian explosion was plutonium, apparently obtained from a low-power experimental reactor supplied by Canada by using heavy water from the United States, and separated in a small chemical processing facility. Severe strains in the relations between India on one hand and Canada and the United States on the other resulted from the explosion, which India has insisted was for peaceful purposes.

With a number of conflicts besetting several areas of the world, and with the potential emergence (or actual existence) of irresponsible leaders or other political instability, the threat of additional countries entering the "nuclear club" became a haunting preoccupation for many. This spread is called "horizontal" as opposed to the "vertical" proliferation which occurs when the numbers of weapons increase within the nuclear-weapons states.

The questions that were posed were: To what extent does the development of nuclear power facilitate the proliferation of nuclear weapons? Is it prudent to promote or even to allow the transfer of scientific and technical know-how to an increasing number of countries, particularly developing countries with potentially unstable political regimes, or those countries in sensitive areas of the world? Should possessors of the technology impose conditions on buyers and users and should they set examples of "good behavior"? Are there any secrets left in the business of nuclear explosives or "are the horses out of the barn?" Is horizontal proliferation the only risk or should one also worry (perhaps even to a larger degree) about vertical proliferation? Is the training of foreign nationals by technologically advanced states contributing to the proliferation risk? Are there technical and/or institutional measures that can be applied to tighten existing conditions, and to render proliferation more difficult if not impossible? Are the existing regimes of international treaties and safeguards adequate? What can be done to improve and strengthen them? The subject is large and multifaceted. In this chapter we shall concentrate on "the weapons connection," that is, on the possibilities for civilian nuclear power becoming a means for the proliferation of nuclear weapons.

There are many "do's" and "don'ts" in the nuclear power business and many different views have been expressed on its various aspects. Our effort here will be to provide the background and facts needed for a better understanding of the issue, rather than advocacy of a certain view. As with many other policy questions, proliferation lies greatly in the domain of political decisions although it has many technical aspects. The understanding of the latter is essential to a sound position on the proliferation question.

Technical Aspects

To assemble a nuclear explosive device, one needs first and foremost a certain amount of fissile material. The materials of interest are enriched uranium-235, plutonium, and uranium-233. Many aspects of nuclear bomb making are still classified. However, quite a few technical facts are known. Perhaps too much technical information is already known through publication of scientific papers, disclosure of previously classified documents, easy access to a number of government documents in public libraries, or through inquiries to government authorities.†

Fissile material can be used to construct explosive devices, if a sufficient fissile mass (critical mass) can be assembled and a chain reaction can be supported at a very fast rate. This latter is very important because if heat produced in the nuclear fission reaction has the time to cause expansion of the fissile mass, the reaction stops prematurely and the device "fizzles." For this reason, explosive devices are constructed as balls of metallic fissile material where neutrons remain fast (no moderation occurs) and the successive generations of fissions proceed in very rapid succession.

The basic principle in producing a nuclear explosion is to bring together two or more subcritical amounts of fissile material to form a critical mass and hold it together long enough for a supercritical state to be achieved. The fast succession of fast fissions spreads to a good portion of the nuclei present and releases a very large amount of heat in a very short time, which causes a detonation.

At least two designs have been devised for the triggering of a bomb. The first is a gun-type device in which a conventional explosive is used to propel one subcritical piece (a plug) into

†A number of student papers were written on how to construct an explosive device, using information available in public libraries and government document rooms. Notorious among them is the one written by Aristotle Phillips at Princeton University, which created a national furor in 1976. Nuclear bomb experts who examined the design argued that the device, if properly constructed, had a good chance of detonation with reasonably high efficiency.

another (the sphere), thus forming a supercritical mass. The second type is an implosive device where again a conventional explosive charge is placed symmetrically around the subcritical sphere and compresses it uniformly by implosion. The imploding wave raises the density of the sphere to a point where criticality is reached and a detonation follows.

Thermonuclear devices are based on the fusion reaction of deuterium and tritium and utilize a fissionable charge to achieve the high temperatures required for the fusion reaction to occur. Since proliferation concerns have focused on fission devices, we shall not discuss thermonuclear devices further.

In order to understand the potential connection between fuels in commercial reactors and weapons proliferation, a discussion on materials is necessary. Materials suitable for nuclear explosive devices are commonly uranium-235 or plutonium-239; uranium-233 can also be used. ^{233}U extracted from short irradiation of thorium is suitable for small weapons such as tactical nuclear warheads or priming devices for hydrogen bombs.

The quality of the material is very important for the construction of an explosive device. Uranium used for this purpose is typically more than 90% enriched in ^{235}U. Since ^{238}U undergoes fast fission, it can contribute to the fission process. Lower enrichment material can be used, but it becomes progressively more difficult to achieve a sustained multiplication factor higher than prompt critical.† With lower enrichment, the critical mass of ^{235}U increases sharply as shown in Figure 20.1. The increase is not as great in the case of ^{239}Pu. Values for reflected and unreflected spheres for the three fissile isotopes are also given in Table 20.1. Plutonium seems, at first sight, an easier way to an explosive device. However, plutonium presents other difficulties: (1) it is a harder material than uranium to machine and to shape into a bomb; and (2) it requires the difficult implosion technique for detonation, while the simpler gun concept can be used with ^{235}U. Hence, the first ^{235}U bomb was used without testing, while the first ^{239}Pu bomb had to be tested first.

The lowest fissile content for the construction of a nuclear weapon is in the range of 10–20%. The figure 20% has been, somewhat arbitrarily, adopted for ^{235}U by international organizations as a threshold. Materials having an enrichment of about 20% are called Special Nuclear Materials (SNM) and are subject to special treatment. Since the proliferation concerns were heightened, an effort was mounted to reduce to below 20% the fissile content of a number of experimental reactors, which were previously designed to operate with highly enriched uranium. Similarly, the quality of plutonium affects the ease of construction and the efficiency of a plutonium bomb. The undesirable isotopes are ^{238}Pu, ^{240}Pu, and ^{241}Pu which build up with irradiation.‡ ^{238}Pu, with its particularly high heating effect due to alpha decay, raises the temperature of the metal, and causes a metallurgical phase transition that hampers the explosion of the device. ^{240}Pu causes two problems: first it dilutes the fissile ^{239}Pu; second, it is a strong source of spontaneous fission neutrons, which makes for a much less efficient and less predictable device. The third contaminant, ^{241}Pu, even though a superior fissile isotope, presents yet another problem. It decays, by beta decay, to americium with a half-life of 14.5 yr, which in turn decays by alpha emission with half-life of 433 yr. Therefore, both ^{241}Pu and ^{238}Pu affect the "shelf life" of a weapon because of the heat and helium gas released in the decay. Since plutonium is a relatively weak and brittle material, the alpha decay of contaminants leads to rapid deterioration of the weapon and hence to the need for periodic replacement.

Weapons manufacturing is still secret; a few details are, however, well known. The quantities of pure fissile materials required to make an explosive device depend not only on the material purity, but also on the design. The use of a reflector (called "tamper"), a metallic shell surrounding the fissile material, minimizes the leakage of fast neutrons and reduces the amount of material required. Similarly, the use of conventional explosives increases the density of the imploded sphere and hence reduces the mass needed for detonation. Nominally, the following figures can be used for pure metallic fissile materials: 10–11 kg of ^{235}U, 5 kg of ^{239}Pu, and 4.5 kg of ^{233}U. The size of these devices is very small indeed, as shown in Table 20.2. A nuclear explosive made of pure ^{239}Pu is approximately the size of an orange. If oxide is used instead, the quantities needed increase by about 50%. If additional isotopes are included in the mixture (such as are produced in reactor irradiation), the amount needed increases. For plutonium with a 80% fissile content, the amount needed is still quite low, about 8 kg, but as the fissile content decreases the total material mass needed increases rapidly.

Given the simple technical data above and the availability of fissile materials in various points of the nuclear fuel cycle in many countries, what is the potential and the risks of nuclear weapons proliferation? Ten kilograms of fissile material is not a large amount, and if one considers that a typical LWR plant discharges about 200 kg of plutonium in its spent fuel each year, it appears that a potential problem exists. With these concerns in mind, many have proposed a wide variety of

†1.00 plus the delayed neutron fraction. See Chapter 2.

‡See also Chapter 11, Figure 11.5, for buildup of higher isotopes. Plutonium discharged from reactors may contain 2% ^{238}Pu, 25% ^{240}Pu, and 10% ^{241}Pu (the balance is ^{239}Pu).

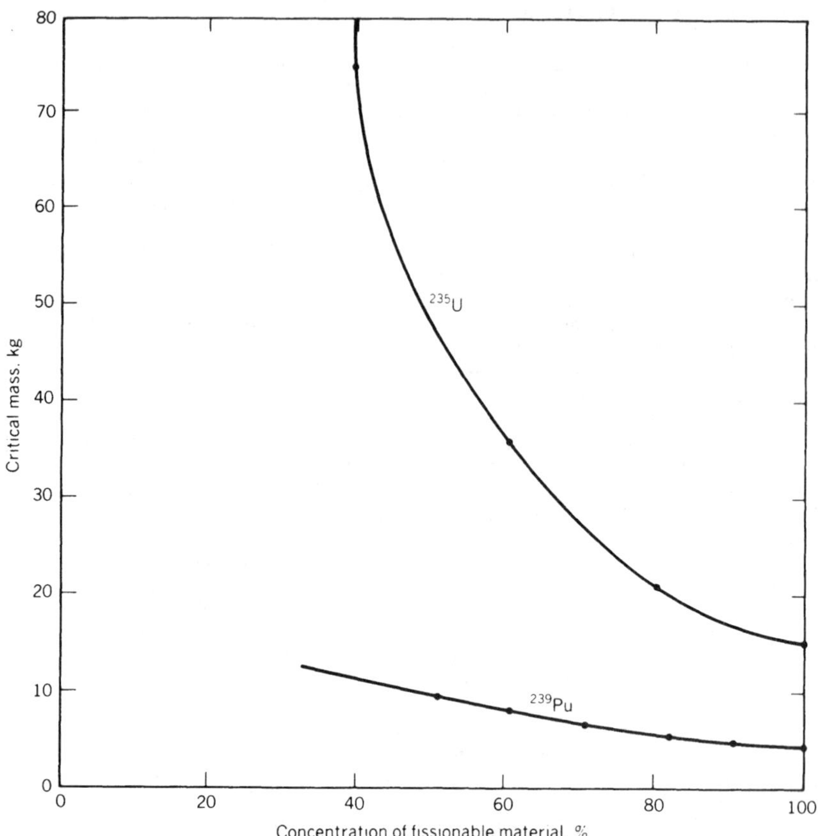

Figure 20.1. A "critical" mass of fissile material is necessary to produce an explosive device. This mass depends on the purity of the material and the specific design. The use of a reflector surrounding the fissile material, such as natural uranium, iron, or beryllium, reduces the loss of fast neutrons through leakage and reduces the critical mass. The graph shows the variation of the critical mass with fissile content for reflected spheres. At 100% purity, about 15 kg ^{235}U is required. The amount rises sharply as the enrichment is lowered. For a plutonium explosive about 4.5 kg of pure ^{239}Pu is sufficient. At lower purities, the increase is not as sharp in ^{239}Pu as in ^{235}U.

Table 20.1. Fast Critical Masses of Fissile Material for Nuclear Explosives

	Percent Fissile Isotope						
	20	50	60	70	80	90	100
U metal (^{235}U)							
Without reflector (kg U)		145	105	82	66	54	50
With Be reflector (kg U)	250	50					15
Pu metal (^{239}Pu)							
Without reflector (kg Pu)				23			15
With Be reflector (kg Pu)				6			4
U metal (^{233}U)							
Without reflector (kg U)							17
With Be reflector (kg U)							4–5

Source: G. Hildenbrand, "Nuclear Energy, Nuclear Exports and the Nonproliferation of Nuclear Weapons," AIF Conference on International Commerce and Safeguards for Civil Nuclear Power, March 1977.

Note: Critical masses of oxides are 1.5 × critical masses of metals. Weapon uranium = 90% or more enrichment; reactor uranium = 3%, spent fuel 0.8%. Weapon plutonium = Pu-239 of 98% or more purity.

Table 20.2. Radii of Critical Spheres

Fissile Material	With an Iron Reflector (15 cm thick)	With a Beryllium Reflector (15 cm thick)
^{235}U (metal)	6.53 cm	5.02 cm
^{239}Pu (metal)	3.80 cm	3.32 cm

Source: NUREG/CR-0095, June 1978.

changes in the nuclear power area (if not stopping nuclear development altogether). The question must be considered in a broader framework of technical and institutional considerations. These are: technical difficulties in acquiring, handling, and processing the materials necessary; the wide variety of skills and resources required to design an efficient device with all its accessories (conventional explosives and electronic timing devices); the alternate means available to achieving the intended objective; the potential advantages of the proposed alternatives; and finally, the disincentives inherent in a network of international institutions. If we agree that it is highly desirable to prevent the further spread of nuclear weapons countries, it is not entirely clear how to achieve this goal while taking into account the legitimate needs of nonweapons countries in terms of energy sufficiency and technological development.

The following discussion will attempt to clarify some of these issues. Certain facts must, however, be stated. Historical experience shows that most countries that developed nuclear weapons obtained the necessary material from dedicated military facilities where the production could be optimized and kept secret. India, however, which successfully detonated an underground explosive device, obtained the plutonium in a small reprocessing plant using fuel from an experimental heavy-water moderated reactor. Second, as talk of nonproliferation continues, the number of nuclear warheads continues to proliferate unabated in the weapons states. In the United States alone, it is estimated that two to three nuclear weapons are manufactured daily using materials from specially designed plutonium production plants or recycled from old bombs that have deteriorated. Such dedicated production facilities remain a distinct possibility for a potential proliferator quite apart from any civilian power production system.

20.2. MODES OF NUCLEAR EXPLOSIVES SPREAD

As we proceed to examine the various paths of proliferation and methods of prevention, it is important to distinguish among the different kinds of risks. The methods of preventing them are also different.

Theft and terrorism refers to the possibility that one or more individuals manages to acquire amounts of fissile material through illicit means. It could be done quietly, for example, at a processing plant or elsewhere by slow removal of small quantities of material over a long period of time. Measures against such quiet theft are careful material accounting, adequate supervision and surveillance of personnel, installation of detectors at plant exits, and the like. Robberies could also occur by groups of thieves or terrorists who may use assault weapons. This is called "forced diversion." The probability of such a terrorist attack and probability of its success are difficult to assess because so much depends on the size of the terrorist group, the number and power of their weapons, and other circumstances. Security forces and physical plant security are used to guard against this risk, but how much is enough? If a plutonium storage bank (national or international) is constructed, heavy arms and security forces may be required. Transportation is a point of the fuel cycle particularly vulnerable to "forced diversion."

National diversion of nuclear materials is a altogether different case. A nation, even under the regime of international treaties and safeguards, may decide to divert in a clandestine manner quantities of nuclear materials (e.g., spent fuel bundles) from a civilian installation to a weapons application. The approach to deterrence is different in this case since prevention is not possible. The application of effective safeguards (to be discussed later) would ensure timely detection of the diversion with possible diplomatic and economic sanctions, which might disrupt not only the particular nuclear project but the country's economy also. But what is actually a "timely" detection and whether the time available would be enough for effective action are matters for debate. It depends on the country's technological development, the preexistence of processing and fabricating facilities, its resources, and so on.

Open proliferation is the overt and explicit decision of a state to proceed with the development of a nuclear weapon in the pursuit of its perceived national interests. International obligations, like those under the Nonproliferation Treaty, can be abrogated with three-months notice. Open proliferation is easier to pursue than clandestine diversion but substantial barriers exist here too as we shall see later. The term proliferation is usually applied somewhat loosely to the two last categories.

20.3. MEASURES OF PROLIFERATION POTENTIAL

In order to make judgments regarding the potential for proliferation of various materials, technologies, or phases of a fuel cycle, some standards should be established. In fact, quantitative measures have been developed, which take into account various partial contributions, apply weighting factors, and aggregate them into a composite single proliferation index. Such aggregation may be subject to objections and even to misinterpretations. In this section, we shall limit the discussion to a qualitative understanding of the criteria to be applied in making assessments on relative merit of proliferation resistance or relative risk of proliferation.

The assessment of proliferation potential depends to a great extent on the specific proliferation scenario. Whether it is to be accomplished by a state or by a terrorist group, by a technologically developed or by a developing or undeveloped nation, through a sudden and open national decision or through gradual diversion to a clandestine facility, these different scenarios are associated with different degrees of difficulty and detectability. The number of possible combinations of systems, activities, potential proliferators, and specific circumstances is large, and cannot be examined explicitly. One can, however, enumerate a number of basic considerations, predominantly technical in nature, which could adequately characterize a system, or a situation. These considerations can be narrowed down to the following categories:

1. Quantity and quality produced versus quantity and quality needed. As described in the previous section, these parameters vary depending on type of fissile material, chemical form, admixtures, and so on.
2. The relative ease of stealing or diverting the material from a fuel cycle facility. This characteristic is related to the probability of detection of an illicit or unauthorized activity by the plant operator, or by monitoring and safeguarding organizations (such as the IAEA) or by other national entities, depending on the scenario. Detection can occur at the removal or transportation stage or even later when accounting and containment procedures are applied to reveal suspected activities.
3. The relative ease of converting the stolen or diverted material into an explosive device. Does the material require isotopic enrichment or only chemical separation? How easy would it be to perform either of these two operations? Does the radioactivity level present serious hazards for the potential proliferator and does it require remote handling and heavily shielded facilities?

Two of the factors enumerated above (mass needed and ease of conversion) determine the time required from the moment of diversion to the moment of completion of an explosive device (details depending on the scenario). This time is important since it provides a chance for detection and/or for appropriate countermeasures to thwart the proliferation attempt. This time includes preparation of facilities, removal of fuel, processing, conversion, and manufacture.

Resources needed to accomplish the manufacture of an explosive device are also determined by the three factors above. The resources needed are human, material, industrial, and financial. The higher the resources needed, the greater the barrier will be to individuals, and to national, or subnational groups.

Although it is difficult to quantify all these factors, they can be used, in a qualitative sense, as indicators of relative proliferation resistance and as pointers toward increasing the proliferation resistance of various technologies and fuel cycles, within the realm of practical considerations. A number of alternate systems have been proposed to this effect. Their potential must be judged in terms of the factors discussed above but also in the broader context of international institutional measures, such as safeguards, international treaties, bilateral agreements, and the like, as well as in the context of industrial capability and economic reality.

20.4. NUCLEAR TECHNOLOGIES AND PROLIFERATION

Reactors with Highly Enriched Uranium

Since highly enriched uranium is a suitable material for an explosive device, such fuel could be a target for theft or diversion. Unirradiated fuel is obviously much preferable to irradiated fuel; it is safe to handle in a hands-on mode because no radioactivity is present. Irradiated fuel, which still contains a high amount of fissile ^{235}U, is contaminated with ^{236}U which is a neutron poison that significantly degrades the quality of ^{235}U. A number of experimental reactors around the world and the HTGR use highly enriched uranium. Only one HTGR is in operation in the United States at the

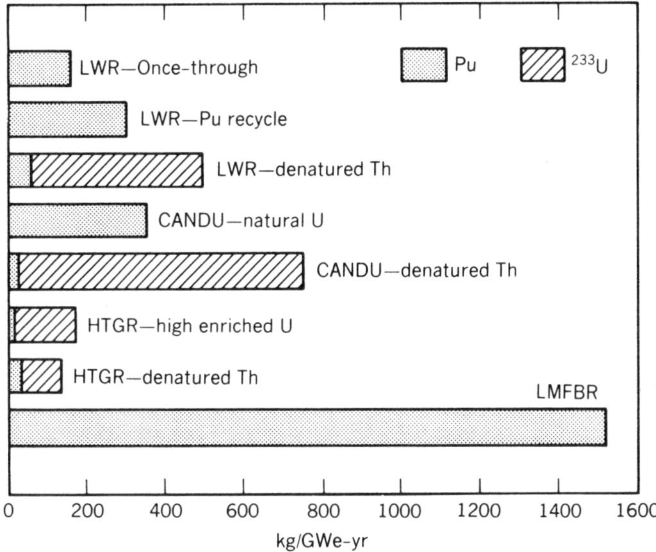

Figure 20.2. The fissile element discharged from various types of reactor systems (existing and proposed) is shown. Quantities are normalized to 1 GWe-yr of electric energy production for comparison. Cycles of denatured thorium fuel still discharge considerable amounts of fissile element but this is mixed with nonfissile isotopes and cannot be chemically separated (hence the term "denatured"). However, they could be obtained with isotope separation methods such as the centrifuge. The breeder discharges a large amount but this is intended for refueling. (From EPRI.)

time of this writing (the 250-MWe Fort St. Vrain plant); there are no plans to deploy more in the near future.

Regarding the experimental reactors, measures have been taken to limit fresh fuel shipments to quantities below what is considered a "significant amount," usually restricted to 5 kg of fissile uranium, only enough for partial refueling in order to maintain criticality. In most cases, the highly enriched uranium is being replaced by medium-enriched fuel (20% or lower) if severe performance degradation can be avoided. The French have developed a special fuel design for experimental reactors, with a view toward proliferation resistance. The fuel, called "caramel," will be described later in this section.

The HTGR uses thorium as fertile material. Neutrons absorbed in thorium produce, through a nuclear reaction chain, the fissile element ^{233}U, which is at least as good as ^{235}U as weapons material.† Since ^{233}U is chemically different than thorium, only a chemical separation of spent fuel would be necessary for obtaining the ^{233}U fissile material. The presence of ^{232}U and of a hard gamma emitter in the chain (^{208}Tl) requires that the reprocessing facility be remotely operated. The amount of fissile material discharged per year from a 1000 MWe HTGR plant is shown in Figure 20.2 for comparison with other types of reactors. The highly enriched uranium HTGR discharges somewhat less than 200 kg ^{233}U/yr (and a small amount of plutonium from fertile ^{238}U contained in the fuel).

As part of the effort to limit the proliferation potential of nuclear power technologies, a number of denatured cycles have been proposed. "Denaturing" refers to the mixing of a nonfissile isotope in the fuel so that separation of the desired fissile isotope would be impossible without an isotope enrichment plant. In the case of the HTGR "denaturing" consists of mixing fertile ^{238}U with thorium in the fertile rods. When ^{233}U is produced, it is intimately mixed and diluted with ^{238}U which greatly diminishes its suitability as weapons material. However, two consequences result from such denaturing. First, plutonium is produced from the admixed ^{238}U, and could be separated out by chemical means. The quantities involved, however, are low (Figure 20.2) and the amount of fuel to be processed large. Second, the separative work required for separating ^{233}U from ^{238}U is significantly lower than the equivalent work required to separate ^{235}U from ^{238}U as will be explained later. If one considers the recycling of fissile materials recovered from spent fuel, the picture is

†In fact, the minimum amount for a ^{233}U weapon is about half the amount of ^{235}U. Also, the enrichment threshold for ^{233}U material is 12% as compared with 20% for ^{235}U.

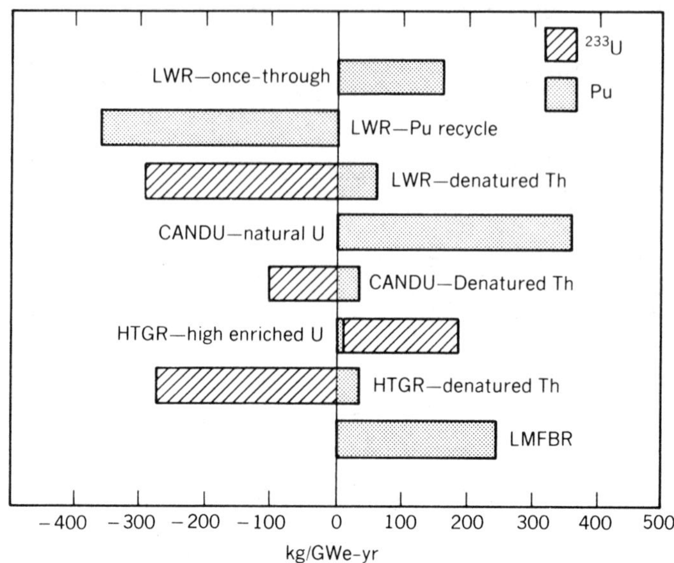

Figure 20.3. The net production of fissile element in each reactor system is shown, assuming that reprocessing and recycling are allowed. The bars to the right of the zero line indicate a net production whereas the bars to the left of the line show a net consumption. It is assumed here that fuel from CANDU is not reprocessed (not advantageous economically), hence, the plutonium formed in the fuel is shown as a net production of about 350 kg/GWe-yr. The LWR with recycle is a net consumer of fissile material, but the breeder is a net producer. (From EPRI.)

quite different, as shown in Figure 20.3. In this case, the net production (or consumption) must be considered. The HTGR consumes (a negative net production) close to 300 kg/GWe-yr of ^{233}U while producing a relatively small quantity (less than 50 kg) of ^{239}Pu.

LWRs and Fuel Cycle

The fuel used in LWRs is enriched to 3–4%, an amount unsuitable for explosive devices. It is, of course, easier to reach higher enrichments starting from 3 or 4% than it is when starting with natural uranium (0.71%). The main concern about LWRs is rooted in the production of plutonium contained in spent fuel as seen in Figure 20.2. The annual spent fuel discharge from a 1000-MWe reactor contains an amount of the order of 200-kg plutonium. A number of possible scenarios can be envisioned, from theft by terrorist groups from the reactor fuel pool or during transportation, to surreptitious diversion of fuel assemblies rod by rod (with substitution of dummies), to open and flagrant proliferation with abrogation of safeguards.

Several considerations are important here. First, the quality of fissile material in spent fuel is far from optimum as explained in Figure 20.4. Because of the high burnup to which the fuel is typically exposed in a reactor, higher isotopes build up which "degrade" the plutonium for weapons purposes. Nevertheless, it has been stated that the manufacture of an explosive is possible, albeit more difficult and less reliable, with reactor grade plutonium.† The second important consideration is that proliferation must be considered in the context of the entire fuel cycle. Figure 20.5 shows the part of a nuclear fuel cycle (with variations) and approximate estimate of sensitivity to diversion. In this respect, the single most important item in the cycle is the existence of a reprocessing and refabrication facility where plutonium (and fissile uranium) are separated from fission products and

†One of the arguments cited in evidence of this fact is that in late 1981 the U.S. government announced that it was considering purchases of commercial-reactor spent fuel as the source of plutonium for a new round of nuclear warheads. The government, however, may have had in mind to separate out undesirable isotopes with new and much more efficient enrichment methods like Laser Isotope Separation (LIS). Also, both France and the U.K. stated in INFCE meetings and elsewhere that they did not have the capacity to make weapons out of reactor-grade plutonium and that the probability of either national or subnational groups to do the same was judged extremely low.

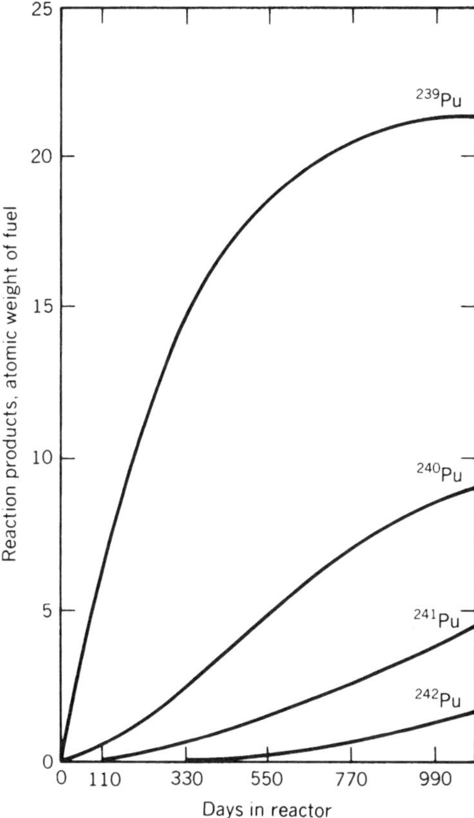

Figure 20.4. The graph shows the growth of various plutonium isotopes in LWR nuclear fuel as a function of residence time in a reactor. Plutonium-239 is produced by neutron absorptions in uranium-238, which is the largest constitutent (~96–97%) in LWR fuel. Plutonium-239 is one of the three fissile isotopes that can be used in making weapons. However, as exposure increases, higher isotopes are formed by additional neutron absorptions. Plutonium-241 is also fissile but the even isotopes plutonium-240 and plutonium-242 are poisons and degrade the mix for weapons production. For this latter purpose, plutonium-239 is obtained from specially designed facilities where exposure is kept low and the proportion of even isotopes to plutonium-239 small. "Reactor-grade" plutonium, obtained from fuel burned for 3 yr, can also be used for weapons manufacture but the task is more difficult. Spent fuel must, therefore, be safeguarded if its diversion is to be prevented. The other solution is, of course, to extract the plutonium, place it in new fuel, and burn it in reactor, thus reducing the amount of plutonium residing inspent fuel pools.

refabricated for recycle in the reactor. It is these concerns that led to the ban of reprocessing and plutonium recycle by Presidents Ford and Carter, which was later lifted by President Reagan. The weapons states already own facilities in the entire fuel cycle. Attempts by other nonweapons states to build them have become notorious cases of international friction and disputes. Japan has proceeded with plans for a reprocessing and refabrication plant at Tokai-Mura; Pakistan has contracted with France for the construction of a reprocessing plant with no apparent economic incentive; Brazil has negotiated with West Germany for the importation of the entire fuel cycle technology; and South Africa has established a uranium enrichment plant, mostly on its own technology and resources. All these nations claimed to be pursuing the goal of energy independence. But the fact that India separated its plutonium in a pilot scale reprocessing plant from fuel irradiated in an experimental reactor kept the international anxiety at a high level.

It seems prudent to try to separate the reactor from its fuel cycle. While the exportation of reactor technology could be relatively unrestrained, the transfer of fuel cycle technology needs to be strictly regulated. In addition, if the weapons states (plus perhaps Japan and West Germany where the technological know-how and industrial capability is undoubtedly in existence) provided

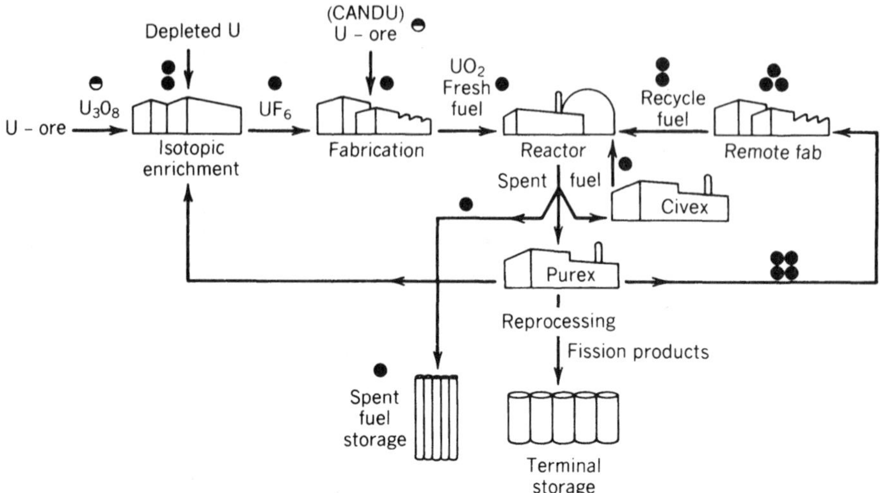

Figure 20.5. A generic nuclear fuel cycle is shown with its major components and loops. The PUREX reprocessing system separates chemically pure plutonium for recycling. The scheme also shows a potential alternative of reprocessing and recycle, called CIVEX, which could be tailored to fit any imposed requirements of hardening, radioactivity in the fuel, etc., to increase the barriers to diversion for proliferation purposes. The black dots indicate the relative sensitivity of a facility or route to diversion.

fuel cycle services, the incentives for other nations to develop their own facilities would be greatly reduced. The possibility, nevertheless, exists that a plutonium separation facility could be built within a few months, with available information and reasonable resources, by a determined nation. If such a separation facility were available, the total amount that would have to be diverted for one weapon equivalent of fissile material is two LWR spent fuel assemblies weighing about 1 t. This weight is compared with the amounts that need to be diverted from other fuel cycles in Figure 20.6.

The CANDU Reactor

Operating on a once-through cycle, the CANDU reactor utilizes natural uranium as feed fuel and discharges spent fuel containing plutonium. The equivalent of about 300 kg of plutonium is discharged annually from a 1000-MWe plant (Figure 20.2).

The advantages cited in favor of the CANDU in terms of proliferation potential are: (1) that it uses natural uranium and, therefore, does not necessitate an enrichment technology which is itself a sensitive technology; and (2) that since it offers a higher fuel utilization than a LWR (see Figure 11.18), it could be used to forestall the use of reprocessing and recycle in LWRs. However, the CANDU has proliferation problems compared to LWRs, even apart from economic and industrial potential considerations. These are:

1. The very fact of natural uranium use as fuel means that a country could procure or manufacture the fuel much more easily than the slightly enriched uranium and, conceivably, even be free of fuel safeguards. Since only three or four countries are currently in the market of providing enrichment services, the imposition of restrictions and other guarantees by the supplying country is much easier. India, for example, has had to accept a serious penalty (lower output) in its two Tarapur reactors (2 × 210-MWe BWRs) because of the U.S. embargo on fuel, following the May 1974 explosion. Only recently (1983) have French suppliers negotiated to substitute the United States as fuel suppliers for India, undoubtedly with their own terms and restrictions.

2. The fuel discharged from a CANDU is of a low burnup, typically 7000–8000 MWd/t. Therefore, the plutonium contained has a lower proportion of higher isotopes and is, therefore, of higher grade. The reactors used in the United States for the production of weapons-grade plutonium were, in fact, heavy-water reactors fueled with natural uranium burned to a few thousand MWd/t.

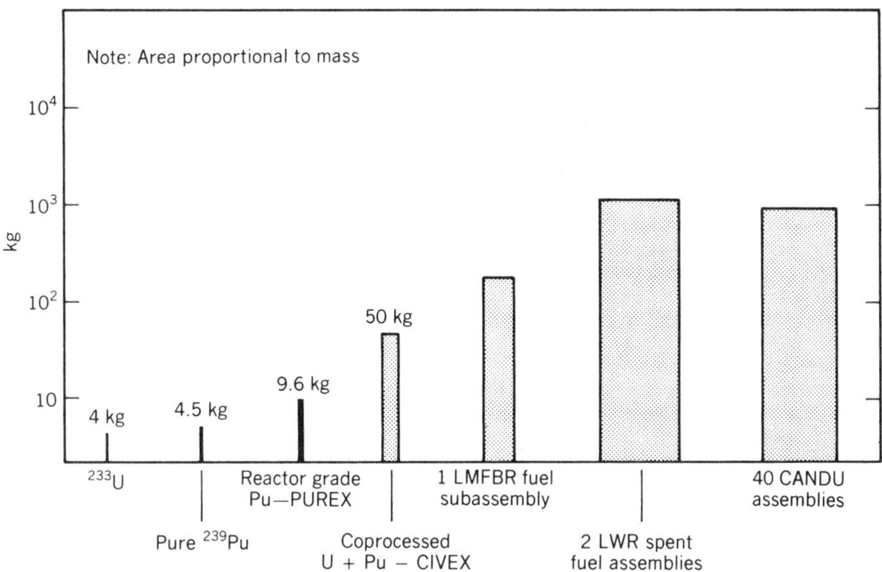

Figure 20.6. The graph shows the minimum material necessary to construct an explosive device. The three bars on the left correspond to pure fissile isotopes. The thicker bars to the right indicate the amounts of fuel that would have to be diverted so that enough fissile material for a weapon could be obtained. The mass of material is one barrier to diversion.

3. The most worrisome aspect of CANDU in a possible proliferation scenario is the feature of on-line continuous fueling. Obviously, safeguards measures (to be described later) are harder to apply. Keeping an account of number and location of fuel assemblies that are handled continuously is more taxing than the same task in a LWR where refueling is a major operation occurring once a year. Measures have been proposed to enhance the monitoring activities at CANDU reactors to provide a continuous accounting and surveillance system which would give timely warning of any diversion activity. It should also be noted that the plutonium in CANDU spent fuel is more dilute than in LWR discharged fuel. Since the effects of dilution and of higher quality balance out, the total spent fuel mass necessary for a weapon is comparable in the two systems.

Breeders

Perhaps the most acute proliferation anxieties were created by the prospect of large-scale deployment of breeders. This type of reactor produces more fissile material than it consumes, enough to refuel itself and to fuel an additional reactor. The most developed breeder is the Liquid-Metal Fast Breeder Reactor (LMFBR) of which a number of prototypes and commercial demonstration units are in operation or in advanced construction stage in several countries (see also Chapter 13). The LMFBR operates normally on the uranium/plutonium cycle taking advantage of the superior neutronic characteristics of plutonium in the fast spectrum. It can be initially loaded with either uranium or plutonium, but the ultimate goal is, of course, to eliminate the need for additional natural uranium and to depend on recycled plutonium.

If one considers the amount of plutonium discharged annually from a breeder, it is very large, on the order of 1500 kg. But if the recycling of plutonium into the reactor is taken into account then the net amount produced is much lower, on the order of 250 kg (Figures 20.2 and 20.3). These values correspond to a high breeding gain. If the demand for additional plutonium is not perceived to be high (as is the case at the time of this writing, due to large amounts of plutonium residing in spent LWR fuel), the design can be adjusted and the breeding gain lowered.

The proliferation potential of the breeder stems primarily from the existence of large amounts of purified plutonium in the fuel cycle, the so-called "plutonium economy." A number of facts are pertinent to this discussion. The fuel burnup in the breeder is about three times as high as in LWRs. Consequently, the assemblies discharged from the breeder core contain a higher amount of fission products, and hence are much more radioactive. This in itself is a serious barrier to at least certain kinds of proliferation. Higher burnup also means larger percentage of higher isotopes, which degrade the quality of plutonium. Breeder technology is more sophisticated than LWR technology

Table 20.3. Criteria for Terrorist Proofing

1. No pure plutonium in storage.
2. No pure plutonium at any intermediate point.
3. No way to produce pure plutonium by simple process adjustment.
4. No way to produce pure plutonium without equipment modifications.
5. No way to carry out equipment modifications with facilities and components normally on site.
6. No way to carry out the required equipment modifications without plant decontamination or entry into extremely high radiation fields.
7. Length of time required for successful diversion should be such that adequate time is available for national and/or international responses to occur.
8. Any alternative proposed must be technically credible.

and requires a higher level of resources. Consequently, deployment of breeders is envisioned in only a relatively small number of industrially developed countries. Finally, the easing of pressure from competition of energy resources, which is the most dramatic feature of the breeder, should be considered as a factor in easing international tensions, which in turn may lower the motivations toward weapons acquisition.

Since the concerns of weapons proliferation from the breeder originated in the fuel cycle, a proposal was made (called CIVEX) in February, 1978† to modify the presently used PUREX chemical separation system and to tailor it to the actual needs of a commercial breeder cycle, including proliferation concerns. The concept was called CIVEX (*CIV*ilian *EX*traction) and was proposed as an example of a process tailored to meet a set of criteria. Given that technology could do very little to deter a sovereign nation from going the nuclear weapons route, the scheme was proposed to deter terrorists or subnational groups.

The criteria used in the design of the system are shown in Table 20.3. The CIVEX concept increases the proliferation resistance of the breeder cycle (it was not proposed for the LWR cycle) by a fuel-reprocessing arrangement in which the recovered plutonium is mixed with a substantial fraction of short-lived radioactive fission products present in the spent fuel. The change in potential risk from PUREX to CIVEX is shown in Figure 20.7. Although the scheme makes it much more difficult to divert plutonium from the cycle, it does not entirely prevent the owner of the plant from modifying it to diversion purposes. The criterion used here was that the time and effort required to do so via the CIVEX cycle should not be less than that required by a small clandestine and dedicated facility to produce pure plutonium. Thus, a CIVEX plant would not have increased the probability of or shortened the time to weapons capability. Other related concepts, such as SAFER, have subsequently been proposed (see Chapter 14).

Alternate Fuel Cycles

The proliferation concerns of nuclear power focused primarily (whether rightly or wrongly is left up to reader to judge) on the reprocessing and recycling of plutonium in LWRs in the short run and on the large-scale plutonium economy envisaged for the breeder reactor in the longer run. A number of proposals were put forward in the late 70s to stymie the deployment of both these routes. The first group of proposals was based on a strategy for the deployment of Advanced Converter Reactors (ACRs) which make, cumulatively and in the long run, better use of uranium resources on a once-through cycle, which was judged by the advocates of this strategy to be more proliferation resistant than the existing LWRs with reprocessing and recycle. Others pointed out that once-through cycles produce progressively larger stores of plutonium in spent fuel pools or repositories. As the spent fuel assemblies cool down with time, they become more accessible by potential proliferators. In that respect, an underground spent fuel disposal site has been called a "plutonium mine." The various proposals for ACRs and their fuel utilization features were discussed in Chapter 11. The second group of proposals included the ACRs with reprocessing and recycle (in case demand for uranium increased substantially) but with denatured fuel. "Denaturing" consists in mixing of a percentage of an additional isotope so that chemical separation of the fissile material is no longer possible; isotope separation is necessary.‡

†Papers on CIVEX were presented at the 5th Energy Technology Conference, February 27, 1978 in Washington, D.C. by Chauncey Starr, Floyd Culler, Milton Levenson, and Ed Zebroski of the United States and Walter Marshall and R. H. Flowers et al. of the United Kingdom.

‡Another group examined included a number of "advanced concepts" such as the fast-mixed-spectrum reactor, the denatured molten-salt reactor, the mixed-flow gaseous-core reactor, the linear accelerator fuel-regenerator reactor, fission-fusion hybrids, and so on.

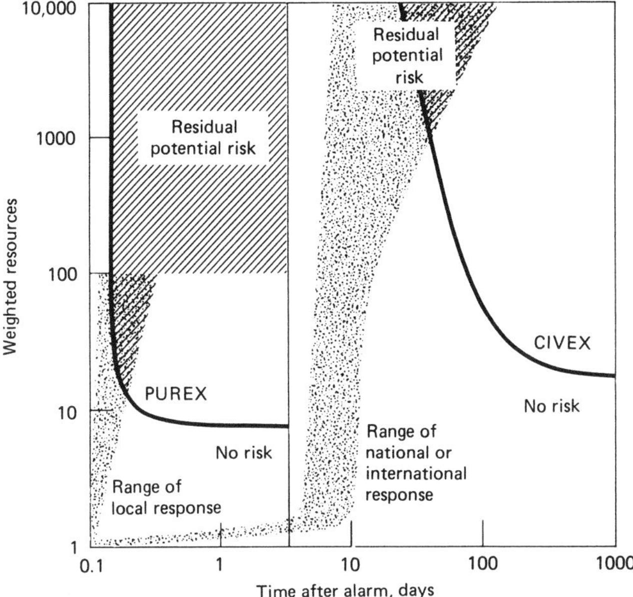

Figure 20.7. The risks of forced diversion from terrorist and subnational groups is graphically represented for the PUREX and CIVEX reprocessing systems. A certain combination of resources and time the alarm has been sounded after diversion determines the risk. The area above the solid curves represents the original potential risk. For example, given one day or more, a weighted resource of 10 or more would constitute a potential risk for PUREX while a time of 100 days and a resource of 100 would result in potential risk for CIVEX. The ranges of local and national and international responses are also shown, as dotted areas. These responses would be used to counter the diversion threat, resulting in smaller residual potential risks.

Simplified diagrams of the straight uranium and thorium cycles and the denatured versions are shown in Figures 20.8 and 20.9. The relative merits of the proposed systems have been discussed at great length in many papers (see Bibilography) and in the NASAP and INFCE† studies, taking into account proliferation resistance, fuel utilization, economics, potential for market penetration, and so on.

A sample of these considerations can be obtained in the figures shown in Table 20.4, where the material flows of the current LWR with and without recycle are compared with the uranium/thorium and the denatured cycles. Denatured fuel cycles feature a smaller quantity of discharged plutonium (70 kg versus 200–300 in the standard cycle) that are still adequate for several explosive devices, however. Thorium substitutes ^{238}U as a fertile material, necessitating an entirely new commercial thorium fuel cycle including thorium mining and reprocessing. The cycle also discharges a large amount of ^{233}U, also a weapons-usable material. But separation of fissile ^{233}U for weapons manufacture requires isotope separation facilities. However, since the separative work needed varies in inverse relation to the square of the mass difference, it is considerably easier to separate ^{233}U from ^{238}U than it is to separate ^{235}U. The availability of enrichment technologies should not be discounted, particularly with the development and spread in recent years of centrifuge and laser enrichment methods. It has been estimated that separating fissile ^{233}U from a denatured cycle could be an order of magnitude easier than separating an equivalent amount of ^{235}U from slightly enriched fuel of standard LWRs. The contamination of the recycle material by an energetic gamma-ray source (originating in the ^{232}U chain) is a significant barrier to recycling and to subnational diversion but no effective deterrent to a weapons effort on a national scale.

The extensive NASAP and INFCE studies concluded in 1980 and a number of additional detailed assessments concluded that, although individual schemes may offer specific advantages with respect to specific scenarios, none is clearly immune to the proliferation potential. The annual quantities of fissile isotopes handled do not vary by large factors from cycle to cycle. Furthermore,

†NASAP: Nonproliferation Alternative Systems Assessment Program.
INFCE: International Nuclear Fuel Cycle Evaluation.

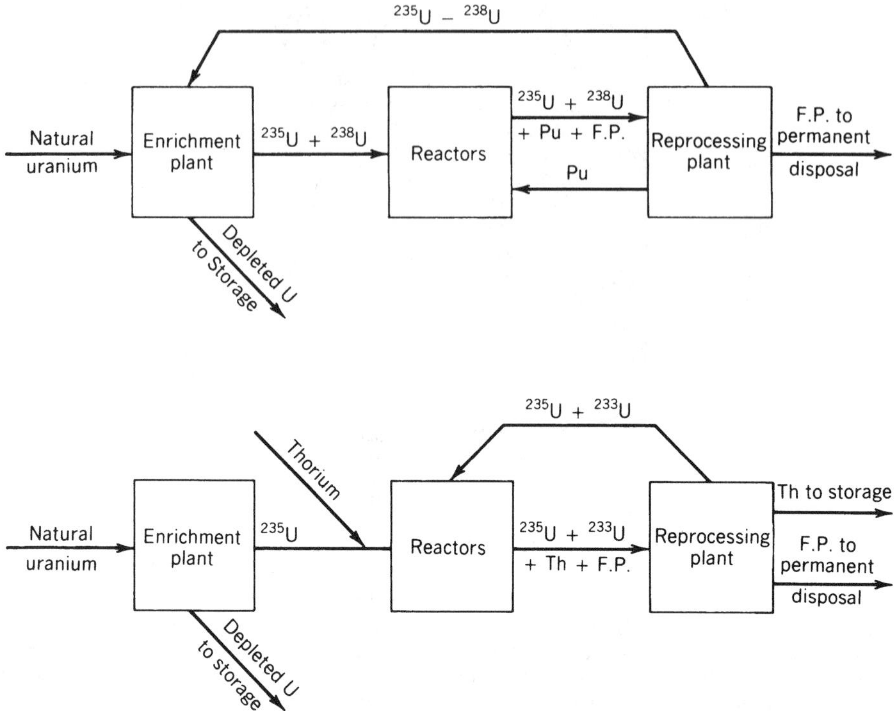

Figure 20.8. The uranium (top) and thorium (bottom) cycles with reprocessing and recycle are shown in simplified form. The sensitive part of the first is the reprocessing plant where purified plutonium is separated, refabricated, and recycled in the reactor. The sensitive parts of the thorium cycle are the highly enriched uranium required for reactor fueling and the reprocessing plant where purified ^{233}U and ^{235}U are separated and refabricated for recycling in the reactor. The enrichment plant itself is additionally a sensitive facility. Colocation of the facilities in nuclear energy parks would concentrate one reprocessing plant with many reactors and facilitate the task of inspection, surveillance, and control.

all cycles yield materials that are amenable to chemical separation of fissile isotopes. A 1000-MWe nuclear plant could yield weapons-usable (if not weapons-grade) material enough for several weapons annually. Denatured thorium cycles do reduce the amount of chemically separable plutonium by a factor of 4 to 5 relative to the standard uranium/plutonium cycle but involve large amounts of ^{233}U-bearing materials which could be treated with relative ease with isotopic separation methods to yield weapons-usable fissile ^{233}U.

The final, and perhaps more pertinent, question regarding alternate technologies and fuel cycles is their practicality and likelihood of adoption and sizable market penetration. The international consensus is that they present no decisive advantage. In view of a stagnant market for new plant orders and plentiful uranium supplies, the necessary incentives for commercialization are also absent.

Proliferation-Resistant "Caramel" Fuel

The Caramel fuel was designed by the French Commissariat à l'Energie Atomique (CEA) for replacement of the highly enriched fuel (90–93% in ^{235}U) used in low- and medium-power research reactors installed around the world.† The design was intended to replace the fuel assemblies of the MTR (Material Testing Reactor) type which uses flat or slightly curved thin plates of highly enriched uranium alloyed with aluminum and sandwiched between two aluminum plates. The

†It was proposed for use in the Tammuz reactor constructed in Iraq by the French CEA, which is a 70-MWe test reactor, modeled after the French Osiris reactor.

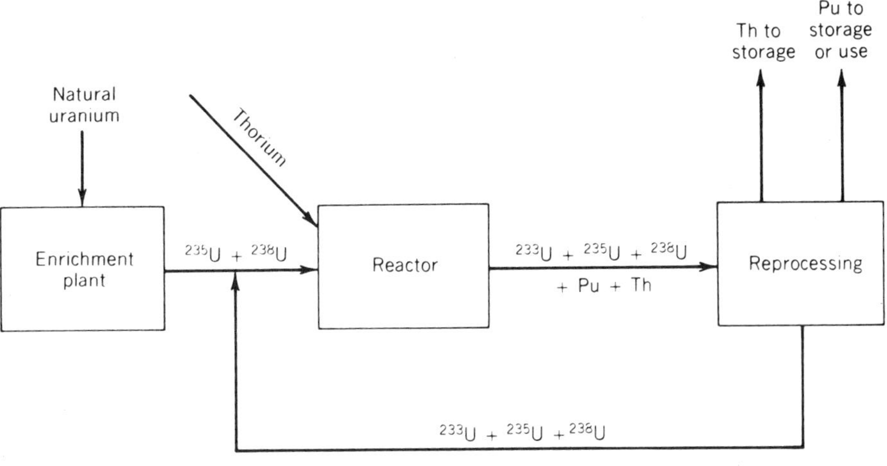

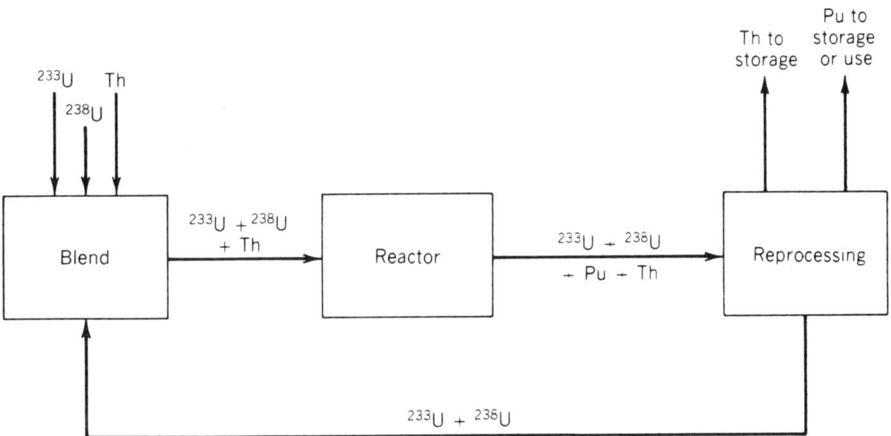

Figure 20.9. In the denatured cycles the fissile isotopes ^{233}U (bottom) and ^{235}U (top) are always mixed with nonfissile ^{238}U by deliberate addition of natural or depleted uranium to the thorium rods. This precludes the use of chemical separation of fissile material. However, plutonium is still produced at the reprocessing plants and left mixed (spiked) with radioactive fission products. ^{233}U is a weapons material but can only be separated from ^{238}U by isotope separation techniques.

Caramel design, shown in Figure 20.10, utilizes uranium enriched to 7% in the form of uranium oxide (UO_2). The sintered pellets, with dimensions 0.4 × 2 × 2 cm are first encased in a Zircaloy box and then welded between two Zircaloy plates in a checkered pattern as shown, to produce a long rectangular fuel plate. Several plates are grouped together to form an assembly.

Prototype fuel assemblies have been irradiated in the Osiris reactor to a maximum burnup of 30,000 MWd/t and specific power of 3000 W/cm³ of oxide. For full core loading, it is calculated that with 7% enriched fuel, certain modifications are necessary: coolant flow must be increased by 30%; core volume must be increased from 39 to 45 assemblies; and fast and thermal fluxes must be decreased by 20%. For higher performance the fuel design has evolved to thinner plate, of about 1.5 cm thickness.

Although the fuel fabrication cost is expected to be somewhat higher than the conventional design cost, it appears that the Caramel fuel has a good potential for adoption in a class of experimental reactors to allay the fears of weapons proliferation.

Table 20.4. Annual Material Flows for a 1000-MWe PWR

Fertile/fissile feed materials		$^{235}U/^{238}U$	$^{235}U/^{238}U$	$^{235}U/Th$	$^{235}U/^{238}U$, Th	$^{233}U/^{238}U$, Th
Recycled materials		None	Pu, ^{235}U	^{233}U, ^{235}U	^{233}U, ^{235}U	^{235}U
Charge (kg)	^{233}U	0	0	414	352	772
	^{235}U	809	636	520	735	55
	Pu[a]	0	287	0	0	0
	Total fissile	809	923	934	1,087	827
	^{238}U	26,000	26,000	40	4,646	6,128
	Th	0	0	23,000	18,300	17,358
Discharge (kg)	^{233}U	0	0	422	373	468
	^{235}U	219	176	186	305	59
	Pu[a]	178	303	3	64	70
	Total fissile	397	479	611	742	597
	^{238}U	25,400	25,400	34	4,463	5,909
	Th	0	0	22,400	17,800	16,915

Source: J. Dietrich, NRC Briefing, December 1978.
[a]Fissile Pu isotopes only.

Enrichment Technologies

Two important aspects have shrouded the enrichment process for most of the past three decades. Secrecy, imposed originally because of the weapons applications, is still applied to certain aspects of the technology. High cost was also thought to be a prohibitive barrier to any potential user of the technology. What has raised the proliferation potential of enrichment technologies is the introduction of the centrifuge enrichment process and the advent of the laser (see Chapter 6).

To consider the technical information on enrichment secret is, however, an oversimplification. For example, the electromagnetic separation process, used to produce the Hiroshima bomb, has been declassified some time ago.

Figure 20.10. Caramel fuel. The picture shows two fuel plates with their flat uranium oxide square pellets. On the right, an assembly of fuel plates (made for the Osiris reactor) can be seen. The component in the back is a fitting to be located at the bottom of the core for the installation of the assembly. The fuel design was made specifically to be proliferation resistant. (Courtesy Commissariat à L'Energie Nucléaire, France.)

The centrifuge technology has become the object of increasing proliferation concern because of its compact size and its low power requirements (which could help avoid detection). Some of the technology largely developed in Germany on an unclassified basis has been in the public domain for a long time. It is widely believed that a moderately industrialized country, using information available in the open literature, could build and operate a small centrifuge enrichment plant at reasonable cost.†

The material from an operating commercial centrifuge enrichment plant might conceivably be diverted for weapons-grade material. The ability to safeguard such a plant must be examined. A plant designed for production of low enriched fuel has inherent characteristics for safeguard protection. Since major modifications in piping, valving, and instrumentation would be required for a departure of purpose toward highly enriched fuel, the probability of detection by plant security is quite high on account of mechanical, electrical, and procedural safeguards. In addition, an overlapping system of audits, accountability checks, and other controls, plus, perhaps, the presence of a resident inspector would provide adequate safeguards satisfying a national or international program.

Another enrichment technology (see Chapter 6) already in commercial operation is the one based on the Becker nozzle process, developed in West Germany. It remains unclassified but technological details are under proprietary restrictions. South Africa is well advanced in the installation of an enrichment plant, based on a variation of this principle, claimed by this nation to be an element of its civilian nuclear power program. West Germany sold the technology to Brazil as part of a large contract covering the entire fuel cycle, but further exports have been effectively stopped.

Finally, laser isotope separation (LIS), of which several variations exist, has aroused nonproliferation concern because of its purported capability to produce significant amounts of highly enriched material in extremely compact facilities. An important motivation for LIS development is the possibility of economic extraction of significant amounts of fissile material from the enrichment plant tails (containing an average of 0.25% uranium, compared with the original 0.71% in natural uranium). This recovery, which cannot be done economically with current technology, holds the promise of extending uranium resources up to 20%.

However, proliferation concerns have accompanied LIS development, particularly when Israel announced in 1974 that it had successfully used lasers to produce 7 g of 60% enriched uranium in 24 hr. Other countries, notably Australia and France, have claimed success with the technique in laboratory tests. The U.S. government has selected the Atomic Vapor Laser Isotope Separation (AVLIS) technique for further development but has clamped a tight security lid on the technology.

Some have argued that LIS is a "garage technology" with dangerous potential consequences and have asked for a complete moratorium on further development. Others have countered that the technology is highly sophisticated, requires large amounts of energy and investment (for laser, optics, and electronics), and has inherent limitations that would prevent its use for illicit purposes. For example, a single-stage LIS plant designed to strip the uranium tailings would be designed to produce uranium of 3% enrichment, and have a separation factor about 15 (3 ÷ 0.2). Production of 96% enriched material from 3% material (the most likely route) would require a further separation factor of 32 (96 ÷ 3). To achieve this, the plant would have to either be redesigned or be shifted to a batch recycle mode of operation. It appears that such modifications are not easier to accomplish than modifications and replumbing of a centrifuge plant for batch recycling.

It is clear that enrichment technologies cannot be ignored as potential routes toward weapons proliferation. In this context, the nonproliferation scenarios based on denatured cycles are faulted, particularly in view of the much lower separative work needed to perform the $^{233}U/^{238}U$ separation in comparison to the $^{235}U/^{238}U$ one, and the superior "quality" of ^{233}U as a weapons-grade material. These concerns have produced an almost general concensus that enrichment technologies are sensitive and their dissemination must be tightly controlled. The consensus has been assisted by the large size and required investment of an economic plant which can only be justified in the service of a large number of nuclear plants. The other side of the coin is that reliability of supply of enrichment services by nations already in possession of large enrichment plants would greatly remove any incentives for development of additional plants by countries or groups of countries seeking assurance of energy sources.

An overall assessment of the various technologies and fuel cycles discussed in this section is given in Table 20.5, where the degree of blackness indicates proliferation resistance. The alternate technologies were assessed as potential routes to weapons proliferation in terms of resources needed, the difficulty of route, cost and schedule, risk to personnel and risk of detection, and finally, the weapon's capability. As seen from the table, the commecial reactors of present design have a high proliferation resistance by most of the assessment criteria.

†An international furor resulted from the news that a Pakistani scientists working in the Netherlands for a subcontractor to URENCO, the German–British–Dutch enrichment consortium, returned home with complete plans, and other information, for a centrifuge enrichment plant.

Table 20.5. Evaluation of Alternate Proliferation Routes

	Centrifuge Isotope Separation Uranium	Research Reactors Plutonium	Mass Spectrograph Isotope Separation Uranium	Graphite Pile Plutonium	Heavy Water Reactor Plutonium	Diffusion Isotope Separation Uranium	Laser Isotope Separation Uranium	COMMERCIAL REACTORS CANDU Plutonium	COMMERCIAL REACTORS HTGR Uranium	COMMERCIAL REACTORS PWR/BWR Plutonium	COMMERCIAL REACTORS LMFBR Plutonium
RESOURCES											
Technological Sophistication	High	Moderate	Moderate	Moderate	Moderate	Moderate	Very High	High	High	High	Very High
Facilities Requirement	Moderate	Low	Moderate	Low	Moderate	Moderate	Low	High	High	High	Very High
Instrumentation Capability	Moderate	Moderate	High	High	High	High (Many Stages)	Moderate	Very High (Reprocessing)	Moderate	Very High (Reprocessing)	Very High
Personnel Requirement	Moderate (200 – 500)	Low (~ 50)	Moderate (200 – 500)	Low (~ 100)	Moderate (100 – 200)	Moderate (200 – 500)	Low (10 – 50)	High (2000 – 10,000)	High (2000 – 10,000)	High (2000 – 10,000)	High (2000 – 10,000)
DIFFICULTY OF ROUTE											
Availability of Information	Moderate	Very High	Very High	Very High	Very High	Moderate	Very Low	Very High	Very High	Very High	Very High
Accessibility of Fissile Mass	High (Nat. U)	Moderate	High (Nat. U)	Moderate (Low Burnup Pu)	Moderate (Low Burnup Pu)	High (Nat. U)	High (Nat. U)	Very Low (Reprocessing)	High (1st Core)	Very Low (Reprocessing)	Very Low
COST AND SCHEDULE											
Cost	Moderate ($\$10^8$)	Low ($\$10^7$)	Moderate ($\$10^8$)	Low ($\$10^7$)	Moderate ($\$10^8$)	Moderate ($\$10^8$)	Low ($\$10^7$)	Very High ($\$10^9$)	Very High ($\$10^9$)	Very High ($\$10^9$)	Very High ($\$10^9$)
Schedule (yrs. to completion)	Very High (>12)	Very Low (Now)	Very High (>12)	Moderate (4 – 7)	Moderate (4 – 7)	Moderate (4 – 7)	Very High (>12)	High (8 – 12)	High (8 – 12)	High (8 – 12)	Very High (>12)
RISKS											
Risk to Personnel	Low	High	Low	High	High	Low	Low	High	Low (1st Core)	Very High	Very High
Risk of Project Detection	Moderate	Low (Low Accountability)	High	Low	High	Moderate	Very Low	Moderate	High (1st Core)	High (Recycle)	High
WEAPON CAPABILTY											
Rate of Fissile Production	High	Very Low	Very Low	Low (1 wpn/yr)	Low (1 wpn/yr)	Low (Small Plant 3 wpns/yr)	High (23 wpns/yr)	Moderate (8 wpns/yr)	Very High (1st Core)	High (14 wpns/yr)	High (11 wpns/yr)
Weapon Reliability	Very High (Enr. U)	High (Low Pu^{240})	Very High (Enr. U)	High (Low Pu^{240})	High (Low Pu^{240})	Very High (Enr. U)	Very High (Enr. U)	Low (Much Pu^{240})	Very High (Enr. U)	Low (Much Pu^{240})	Low (Coprocessed Pu)

Proliferation Resistance: Low — High

20.5. NATIONAL AND INTERNATIONAL MEASURES

The Non-Proliferation Treaty (NPT)

Anxieties stemming from the possibility of an increasing number of weapons states particularly in an atmosphere of intense regional conflicts and internal political instability along with the realization that technical barriers alone do not suffice, led to a number of institutional arrangements. One of the most important measures was the signing, in July of 1968, of the Treaty on the Nonproliferation of Nuclear Weapons, known widely as the NPT, by over 100 sovereign nations. The treaty, placed in force in 1970, sought to limit the number of weapons states to the then existing five (China, France, the United Kingdom, the United States, and the USSR). As of April, 1983, the status of membership in the NPT and participation in the safeguards agreements with the IAEA are shown in Table 20.6. A full discussion of the NPT is beyond the scope of this chapter. Its essential parts, however, must be mentioned in a discussion of nonproliferation. The signatories to the treaty agreed not to transfer to and not to receive nuclear weapons or other explosive devices from any party. Non-nuclear weapons states undertook not to manufacture or otherwise acquire nuclear weapons and any assistance to this end was banned. A system of safeguards was set up to be administered by the International Atomic Energy Agency (IAEA) for the verification of compliance with the treaty's provisions, in order to prevent any diversion of nuclear materials from peaceful nuclear applications to nuclear weapons. In return for this obligation on the part of nonweapon states, the treaty guarantees the "inalienable right of all Parties to the Treaty to develop research, production and use of nuclear energy for peaceful purposes without discrimination." In fact, the "fullest possible exchange of equipment, materials and scientific and technological information for peaceful uses" is encouraged. The second important provision balancing its inherent discriminatory nature was that an effort will be made for the "cessation of the nuclear arms race" and for "a general and complete disarmament under strict and effective international control."

The treaty implicitly recognized that erstwhile barriers to the proliferation of nuclear weapons, namely the technical and economic ones, were no longer effective. Scientific and technical knowledge in the various aspects of weapons manufacture became widely known, even at open scientific meetings (notably in the four Geneva Conferences) and in the international literature. The economic barrier was similarly not insurmountable, since any country with a significant peaceful nuclear program could dedicate enough financial and manpower resources to produce an explosive device, as the Indian explosion in May of 1974 dramatically proved. The NPT provided a voluntary international mechanism by which the risk of proliferation could be significantly lowered in a broader context of reduced international tensions, a lower competition for energy resources, and greater attention to the needs and desires of nonweapons (developed or developing) countries by the weapons countries.

Although some of these lofty aspirations have yet to be fulfilled, the NPT provided a means of separating the development of peaceful nuclear power from weapon development particularly through Article III which provides for international safeguards.

Safeguards and the IAEA

Safeguards were first instituted to govern international transfers of fissile materials through the use of bilateral agreements between the providing country (United States, United Kingdom, and Canada) and the receiving country. The tendency, over time, has been for the exporting countries to rely on the IAEA to provide safeguards. The United States which has bilateral agreements with over 20 countries, has transferred this responsibility to the agency. The bilateral system, practiced by the United States, stemmed from the 1953 Atoms for Peace program, which anticipated a more comprehensive international system. Later, trilateral agreements were used (the first of which was between the United States, Japan, and the IAEA). The agency took over responsibility for U.S. supplied nuclear material and facilities. In the late 1950s, regional safeguards agreements were instituted by two international groups: the European Atomic Energy Commission (Euratom) and the Nuclear Energy Agency, a branch of the Organization for Economic Cooperation and Development (OECD).

The administration of safeguards became the main activity of the IAEA. Its mandate is to "administer safeguards designed to ensure that special fissionable and other materials services, equipment, facilities and information or control are not used in such a way as to further any military purpose" (NPT, Article III, 5 of the IAEA Statute). The nonproliferation treaty espoused safeguards and made it an important part of its objectives. Each NPT signatory has accepted safeguards in order to verify adherence to its treaty obligation "with a view to preventing diversion of nuclear energy from peaceful uses to nuclear weapons or other nuclear explosive devices" (NPT, Article III.1).

Although the NPT did not specify the nature of the safeguards to be adopted, a new safeguards system was instituted, to be applicable to NPT conditions and to amend previous deficiencies.

Table 20.6. NPT and NPT Safeguards Status as of April 83[a]

Non-Nuclear-Weapon States Party to NPT with NPT Safeguards Agreements in Force		
Afghanistan	Honduras	Netherlands
Australia	Hungary	(including Neth. Antilles)
Austria	Iceland	New Zealand
Bangladesh	Indonesia	Nicaragua
Belgium	Iran	Norway
Bulgaria	Iraq	Paraguay
Canada	Ireland	Peru
Costa Rica	Italy	Philippines
Cyprus	Jamaica	Poland
Czechoslovakia	Japan	Portugal
Denmark	Jordan	Romania
Dominican Republic	Korea, Republic of	Samoa
Ecuador	Lebanon	Senegal
Egypt	Lesotho	Singapore
El Salvador	Libyan Arab Jamahiriya	Sudan
Ethiopia	Liechtenstein	Suriname
Fiji	Luxembourg	Swaziland
Finland	Madagascar	Sweden
Gambia	Malaysia	Switzerland
German Democratic Republic	Maldives	Thailand
Germany, Federal Republic of	Mauritius	Turkey
Ghana	Mexico	Venezuela
Greece	Mongolia	Uruguay
Guatemala	Morocco	Yugoslavia
Holy See	Nepal	Zaire

Non-Nuclear-Weapon States Party to NPT for Which NPT Safeguards Agreements Are Not Yet in Force	
Antigua and Barbuda	Mali
Bahamas	Malta
Barbados	Nigeria
Benin	Papua New Guinea
Bolivia	Panama
Botswana	Rwanda
Burundi	St. Lucia
Cape Verde	San Marino
Central African Republic	Sierra Leone
Chad	Solomon Islands
Congo	Somalia
Democratic Kampuchea	Sri Lanka
Democratic Yemen	Syrian Arab Republic
Gabon[a]	Togo
Guinea-Bissau	Tonga[a]
Grenada	Tunisia
Haiti[a]	Tuvalu
Ivory Coast	United Republic of Cameroon
Kenya	Upper Volta
Lao People's Democratic Republic	Taiwan
Liberia	

Non-Nuclear-Weapon States Not Party to NPT in Which IAEA Safeguards Agreements Are in Force on All Operating and Planned Nuclear Activities	
Argentina	Cuba
Brazil	Democratic People's Republic of Korea
Chile	Spain
Colombia	

Table 20.6. (Continued)

Non-Nuclear-Weapon States Not Party to NPT Having No Significant Nuclear Activities		
Albania	Guinea	Sao Tome and Principe
Algeria	Guyana	Saudi Arabia
Andorra	Kuwait	Seychelles
Angola	Malawi	Trinidad and Tobago
Bahrain	Mauritania	Uganda
Belize	Monaco	United Arab Emirates
Bhutan	Mozambique	United Republic of Tanzania
Burma	Nauru	Yemen Arab Republic
Comoros	Niger	Zambia
Djibouti	Oman	Zimbabwe
Equatorial Guinea	Qatar	

Non-Nuclear-Weapon States Not Party to NPT in Which Certain Nuclear Activities are Not Under IAEA Safeguards
India
Israel
Pakistan
South Africa

Nuclear-Weapon States Party to NPT
Union of Soviet Socialist Republics
United Kingdom
United States of America

Nuclear-Weapon States Not Party to NPT
China
France

Source: IAEA.

[a]Safeguards agreement approved by the IAEA Board and awaiting entry into force.

Member states of the NPT must sign a separate agreement with the agency agreeing to safeguards implementation. Safeguards cover "nuclear materials," a term used to mean any radioactive source or special fissionable material as defined in the IAEA Statute. The term "source material" does not apply to ore or ore residue. An increasing number of reactors, bulk-handling facilities, and special nuclear materials (highly enriched uranium and plutonium) have come under safeguards over the years, as shown in Figures 20.11, 20.12, and 20.13.

The means utilized in the application of safeguards measures are: accountancy, containment, and surveillance. Accountancy deals with the amounts of material entering in, residing in, and exiting from a "materials balance area." This term defines an area in or outside a nuclear facility where the material flows and physical inventory can be determined when necessary according to specified procedures to produce a balance. The difference between book inventory and physical inventory is called Material Unaccounted For (MUF). With due account for material losses, material stuck inside pipes and vessels, and so on, the material unaccounted for would give an indication of diversion. Material accountancy is greatly assisted by an array of scientific instruments that can estimate (produce an assay of) the amount of fissile material contained in a package without opening it or otherwise disturbing it. The process is called Non-Destructive Analysis (NDA). A sample of such a sophisticated safeguards instrument is the High-Level Neutron Coincidence Counter (HLNCC), shown in Figure 20.14, which can be used in conjunction with other instruments (Figure 20.15) to measure the concentration of ^{240}Pu in a sample. The instrument uses coincident pulses from neutrons emitted by the process of spontaneous fission in the isotope ^{240}Pu, thus discriminating out pulses from other sources. The procedure allows the measurement of the relative concentration of ^{240}Pu to be made, and hence, with calculations, of total plutonium.

"Containment" is a series of measures such as locks, seals, or other devices designed to assure the inspectors that material has not been tampered with or removed from a certain vessel or area between inspections. "Surveillance," performed by means of instruments (e.g., TV cameras) or human observation is intended to provide a backup to material accounting by keeping track of material flows, locations of stored material, processing activities, and so on. Such surveillance

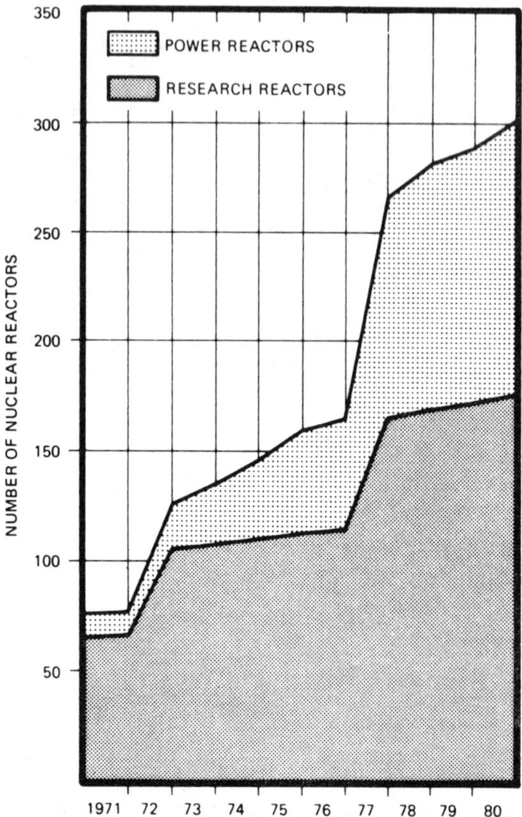

Figure 20.11. The number of reactors under safeguards.

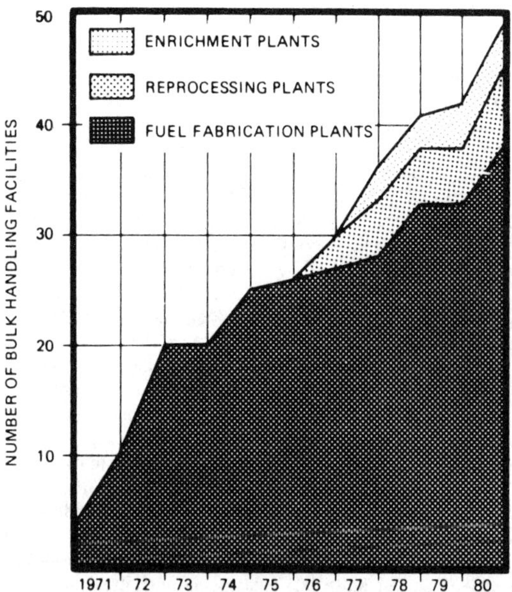

Figure 20.12. The number of bulk-handling facilities under safeguards.

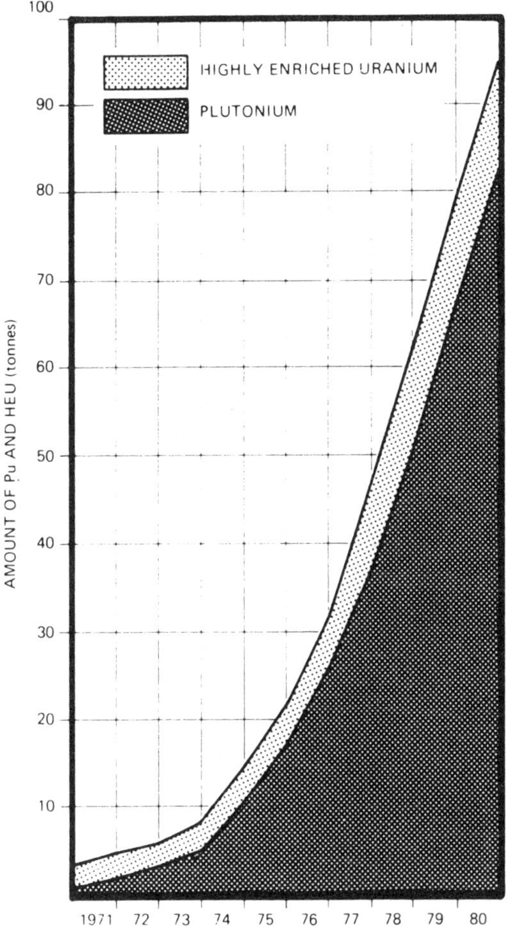

Figure 20.13. The amounts of plutonium and highly enriched uranium under safeguards. (From IAEA.)

devices are shown in Figures 20.16 and 20.17. Although the IAEA depends to a great extent on the national system for keeping material balances, it also applies its own independent checks and procedures in order to give its safeguarding activity the necessary international credibility.

Safeguards do not apply to materials in mining or ore-processing plants. Nevertheless, when the transfer is to a non-nuclear weapons state and unless it is to be used in non-nuclear applications, the IAEA must be informed of the quantity, composition, and destination of any imported or exported material containing uranium or thorium even before it reaches a point in the fuel cycle.

Are the safeguards measures of the IAEA adequate in preventing the proliferation of nuclear weapons? Many criticisms have been voiced regarding the system's loopholes and the need for improvement. Some countries, notably India, have sharply criticized the NPT and have refused to submit all its facilities to international safeguards claiming the institution is unfair and discriminatory to nonweapons states while giving free reign to weapons states.

It is useful to summarize what safeguards can and what they cannot do. They can provide a technical verification of materials balance, but they cannot prevent diversion of material or allow for searches for clandestine material or facilities. They do provide assurance of compliance, but they cannot serve to apprehend a violator or to provide credible sanctions. In case of noncompliance, a report is made to agency members and to other international bodies; assistance provided by the IAEA or by its members may be curtailed or suspended; the recipient member may be asked to return the materials and equipment made available to it; and the membership of the violating state to the IAEA may be suspended.

Clearly, the formal sanctions are not a sufficient deterrent to a determined violator. Moreover,

Figure 20.14. The High-Level Neutron Coincidence Counter (HLNCC) shown in this figure counts neutron pulses that are coincident. Such pulses come from spontaneous fission in ^{240}Pu and hence the instrument can determine the concentration of this isotope (and by extension the total plutonium) in a sample when used in conjunction with a multichannel spectrometer such as the one shown in Figure 20.15. (From IAEA.)

each member of the NPT has the right to withdraw from the treaty in the face of extraordinary events when its supreme interests have been jeopardized, with a three-month notice.

The safeguards regime provides two main benefits. The first is a timely warning, once a violation has been detected or suspicious signals have been given that a country may be embarking on the road to nuclear weapons development. This would allow diplomacy to take a lead in appropriate action. Second, it provides a deterrent to diversion since the diverting country would have to anticipate the possibility of substantive sanctions which might be costly to its development and to its standing among other nations. The experience of India following the May 1974 explosion and its difficulty in securing the flow of technology and fuel from the United States and Canada attests to this point. It seems fair to say that safeguards are a necessary but not sufficient element in the nonproliferation effort.

Other Institutional Measures

Other institutional arrangements worth mentioning are national legislation and regional treaties. The Nonproliferation Act of 1978, passed by the Congress at the height of the proliferation concerns, imposes severe restrictions and conditions on the exportation of nuclear technology and materials. One of its most important provisions is that the recipient nonweapons nation must agree to "full-scope safeguards," that is, it must allow safeguards inspection at *all* its nuclear facilities. To provide a good example and an inducement (however weak or dubious it may be) the United States and the United Kingdom, although weapons states themselves, have agreed to subject *some* selected civilian nuclear facilities to international safeguards. Since these countries remain unrestricted in the production of nuclear weapons in their military programs, this is a symbolic gesture.

Among the notable regional agreements is the Treaty of Tlatelolco, known also as the Treaty for

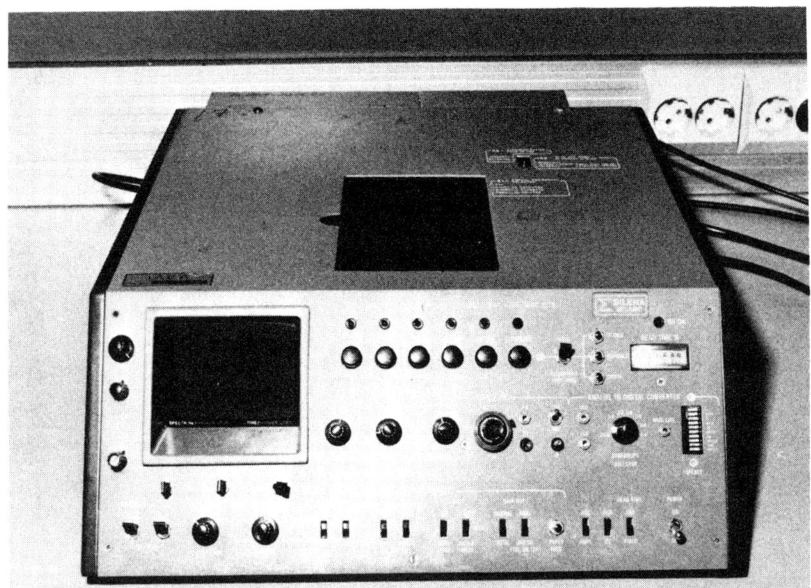

Figure 20.15. This multichannel analyzer (1024 channels), called Silena, is a portable instrument used by inspection teams in order to determine the amounts of fissile material in various packages without destroying or otherwise disturbing them, a process called Non-Destructive Assay (NDA). This gamma-ray spectrometer used in conjunction with the high-level neutron coincidence counter (Figure 20.14) can provide sufficient knowledge on the fuel to assay its fissile content. It has been successfully used in measuring fast reactor fuel assemblies. (From IAEA.)

Figure 20.16. The device shown is sensitive to the Cherenkov radiation characteristically emitted by irradiated fuel in spent fuel water pools. This radiation is normally visible to the naked eye as blue-green glow. This device, however, allows the viewer to view spent fuel in adverse lighting conditions, even in total darkness. A built-in electronic converter provides an amplified image and allows the examination of the fuel to the detail of individual pins and segments. This method has supplemented containment and surveillance approaches which were not always successful and has provided additional means to safeguards-inspect spent fuel. (From IAEA.)

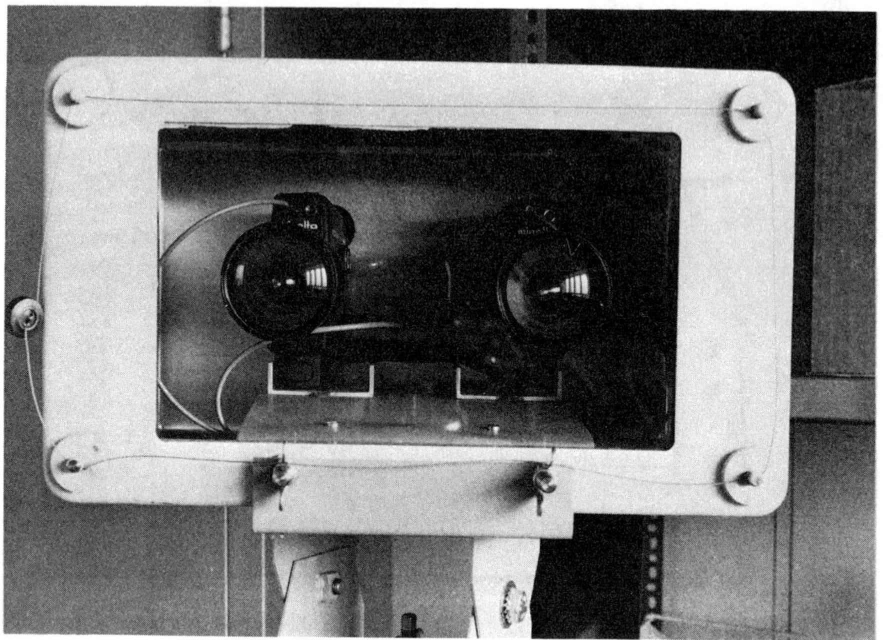

Figure 20.17. A double camera system is used by the IAEA to keep an eye on activities in sensitive areas of a nuclear installation. The system could be used to provide on-line information and timely warning for diversion-suspicious moves. The system is also equipped with an installation that makes it tamper-proof. (From IAEA.)

the Prohibition of Nuclear Weapons in Latin America. The pact was signed in 1967 by an overwhelming majority of Latin American and Caribbean countries and by the five weapons states. It totally excludes nuclear weapons from the areas's 22 countries (including Puerto Rico and the Virgin Islands) and prohibits even subterranean bomb explosions. It permits verification by the IAEA and special inspections by a regional control group. The only countries that have not ratified the treaty are Argentina, Brazil, Cuba, and Chile. The two former countries are considered rivals in the region and have substantial nuclear development programs. If the Tlatelolco Treaty becomes fully effective it would establish the first nuclear weapons free zone outside the sparsely populated Antarctica.

20.6. BARRIERS TO DIVERSION

It is generally agreed that the basic technical information needed to manufacture weapons is already available and widespread. It is also agreed that there are ways other than civilian power production facilities to proceed with the production of weapons-grade materials. Nuclear power is a reality and already constitutes an important component of the energy mix. Despite the fact that only a handful of nations have, so far, decided to pursue weapons development, concerns of proliferation linger. The connection of civilian power boils down to the question: to what extent could a nuclear power program lower the barriers and push a nation over the fence?

A combination of technical and institutional barriers seems the only realistic approach to this question. These barriers should be always considered in proportion to the already existing ones which stand in the way to proliferation. These are related to dedicated small and clandestine plutonium production facilities operating either with heavy water or graphite in association with small dedicated chemical separation facilities; or small enrichment plants most probably of the centrifuge type. A summary of what is needed to operate a dedicated processing facility to produce either 10 or 100 kg of plutonium is given in Table 20.7.

A list of barriers that have or can be employed to enhance the distance of civilian nuclear power from weapons is given in Table 20.8. They are essentially technical barriers but a national or international consensus may be necessary for their adoption, as for example, in the last item of Table 20.8 which requires the installation of technical means by which an inspector (either local or remote) could disable the plant upon a suspicious signal of diversion. The barriers are of four basic

Table 20.7. Summary of Information on Dedicated Processing Facilities

	Millions of Dollars Capital Cost	Operating Manpower	Development Time, Months	Cold-Test Time,[a] Weeks	Time for 10-kg Pu, Weeks	Time for 100-kg Pu, Weeks
Spent Fuel (cooled)[b]	12–24	100	12–24	4–8	1–3	25–35
PuO_2	$\frac{1}{2}$–1	20	6–9	1–3	$\frac{1}{2}$–1	9–12
PuO_2–UO_2 (cold) MOX	1–2	20	8–12	2–4	$\frac{1}{2}$–1	10–20
Fresh-fuel (cold MOX)	1–2	30	8–12	2–4	$\frac{1}{2}$–1	10–20
assemblies	5–10	50	10–15	3–6	$\frac{1}{2}$–1	15–30[d]
PuO_2–UO_2 (hot) MOX[c]	5–10	50	10–15	3–6	$\frac{1}{2}$–1	15–30[d]
Fresh-fuel (hot MOX) assemblies[c]	6–12	80	10–15	3–6	$\frac{1}{2}$–1	15–30[d]

Source: DOE/NE-0001/8, June 1980.

[a]Time assumes training of operating personnel using cold materials during construction phase.
[b]"Cooled" means radioactive at levels 1 yr after discharge.
[c]Hot means partially decontaminated (or preirradiated, in the case of fresh fuel assemblies).
[d]Time is that allowed for remote maintenance not required for cold facilities.

Table 20.8. Barriers to Diversion

1. Bulk—including weight of shielding
2. Radiation—inherent and added
3. Lack of purity (U or Th dilution)
4. Decay heat—^{238}Pu production
5. Ease of detection
6. Hardening
7. Physical isolation by barriers
8. Single monitored facility which receives and ships fuel elements
9. Guards and physical security
10. Means for inspector to intentionally disable plant

categories. *Time* required to divert from a civilian facility and process for weapons material production should be greater than the time needed to do the same job through a quick and secret plant. The fuel should have inherent characteristics that make it *dangerous* to handle. Additional *physical barriers* and *protective systems* should be provided as deterrents to diversion, and the *cost* of overcoming the barrier must be higher than the cost of clandestine systems. But the cost of the barrier to the legitimate operator must be acceptable.

One of the barriers, that is, quantity of spent fuel needed for the production of one weapon equivalent, is shown in Figure 20.6. The figure shows how the use of a CIVEX cycle, where uranium, plutonium, and some fission products are processed together (coprocessed), raised the amount needed compared to the PUREX process (50 kg versus 9.6 kg). The amount of LWR spent fuel assemblies (2) and the amount of CANDU fuel assemblies (40) is already a considerable barrier to the potential diverter. The exposure to personnel handling this material is another important

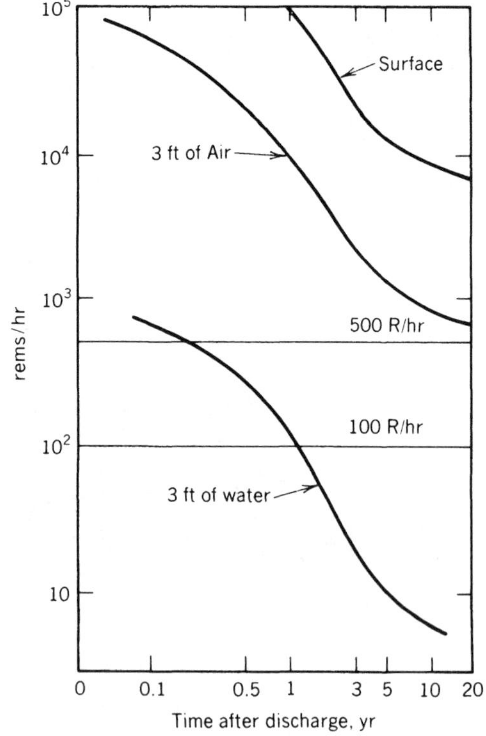

Figure 20.18. The dose rate or exposure rate to personnel caused by a LWR spent fuel assembly is shown as a function of time after discharge from the reactor (also called cooling time). Even after 1 yr of cooling and with about 1 m (3 ft) of water shielding, the rate is 100 rems/hr. A few hours of work in that environment would be enough to give a person a lethal dose of radiation.

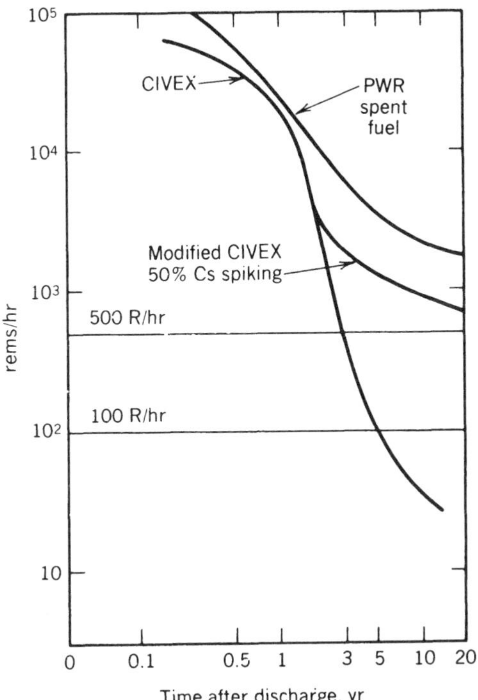

Figure 20.19. Comparison of dose rate at a distance of 2 ft in air from a LWR spent fuel assembly and from fresh breeder assemblies using the CIVEX and modified CIVEX design. Dose rate drops off with time since the radioactivity of fission products decays. Both the LWR and the 50% Cs spiked breeder assemblies still produce a dose rate of more than 500 rems/hr after 20 yr of cooling which prohibits any crude, hands-on handling of the material. (From EPRI.)

barrier. Exposure, in rems/hr as a function of time after discharge of a LWR spent fuel assembly, is shown in Figure 20.18. Even though the radiation emitted from a spent fuel assembly drops off with cooling time, it remains at sufficiently high levels to give a person working in the vicinity a lethal dose of radiation within a few hours. The way the radiation exposure barrier can be used to tailor designs to requirements is shown in Figure 20.19. Fresh fuel assemblies for the breeder containing pure plutonium could be a target for diverters because of its high plutonium content and its low radioactivity. Use of the CIVEX scheme, described earlier, and "spiking" of the fresh fuel with additional radioactive cesium can make fresh breeder fuel comparably dangerous to a LWR spent fuel assembly. One can convert the dose rate figures to the working time when onset of physical disability occurs to a worker at a certain distance from the assembly. These times are shown in Figure 20.20. A method of denaturing plutonium has been proposed† based on admixture of ^{238}Pu. ^{238}Pu has an unusually high specific power of 567 W/kg of material.‡ When the temperature of metallic plutonium exceeds 115°C, it undergoes a metallurgical phase transition from the alpha to the delta phase. This thermal effect is very significant because it means that from 50–100% more source material is needed to form a critical mass. Consequently, a percentage of ^{238}Pu ranging from 2–5% would cause the weapon to heat up, resulting in a phase transition and an unreliable, excessively large weapon as shown in Figure 20.21. The amount of ^{238}Pu is quite low in fuel discharged from the first fuel cycle of a nuclear reactor and grows in successive cycles. Therefore, first cycle fuel would have to be denatured with plutonium obtained from several cycles in other reactors. The denaturing of plutonium with even plutonium isotopes has been reexamined in recent years and appears to be viable as a proliferation barrier. The effect of various denaturing schemes on average weapon yield and total mass required is shown in Table 20.9.

†Proposal was advanced by the Allied General Nuclear (AGNS) and by De Volpi of Argonne National Laboratory.
‡This property of ^{238}Pu has made it suitable for application in space power sources using the thermoelectric principle.

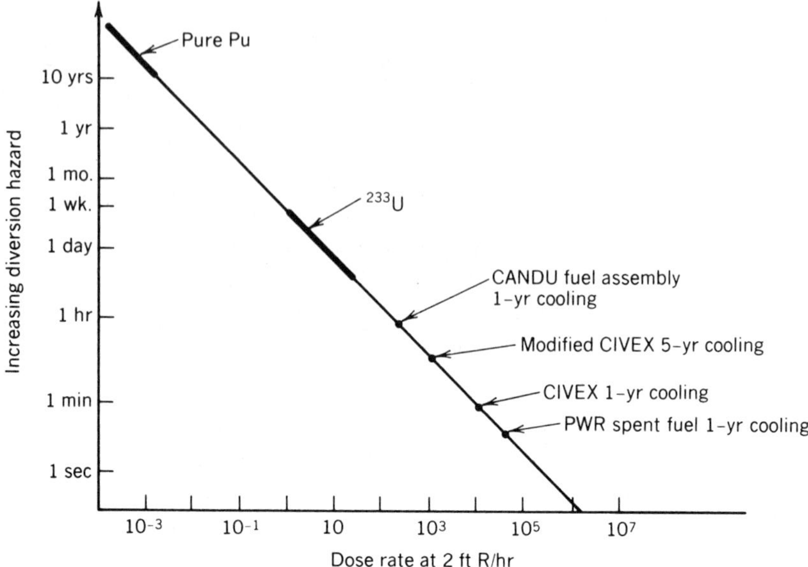

Figure 20.20. The graph shows the time at which disability-onset is expected to occur to a person working at a distance of 60 cm (2 ft) from various spent fuel assemblies. It is assumed that disability-onset occurs at a dose of 150 rems. The longer the time, the lower the diversion resistance. (From EPRI.)

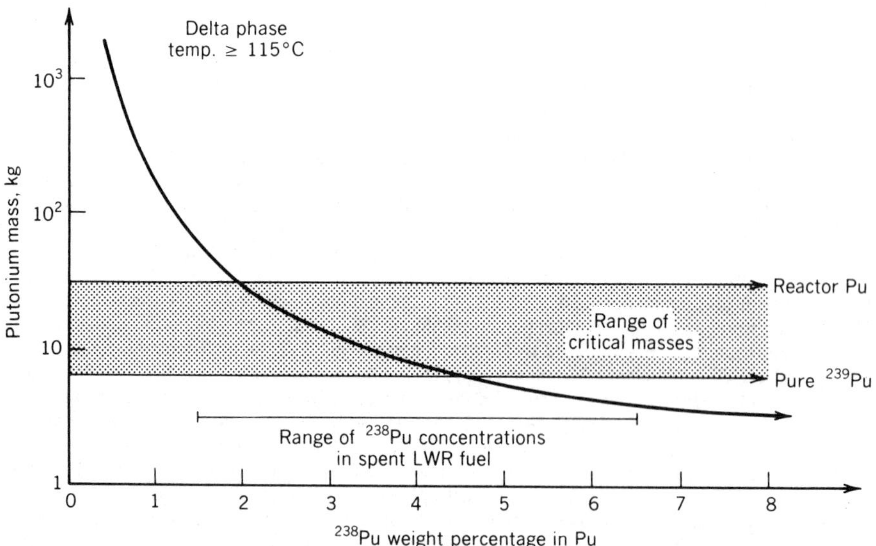

Figure 20.21. A possible scheme of denaturing plutonium is by using an admixture of ^{238}Pu which is produced in a reactor from ^{237}Np. The 2–5% of ^{238}Pu, found in reactor grade Pu, produces a large amount of heat from alpha decay, raises the temperature of a weapon to above 115°C and causes a transition to the delta phase. This raises the amount of mass needed by 50–100%, degrades the weapon's yield, and introduces a difficult-to-overcome uncertainty concerning how much Pu is needed. (From EPRI.)

Table 20.9. Mass-Normalized Fission Energy Yields[a]

Grade	Core	Fissile Fraction, %	Average Yield, kt (TNT)	Total Mass,[b] kg	Yield/Mass, kt (TNT)/kg
Pure	^{233}U	100	20	~200	0.1
Denatured	$^{233/8}U$	10	0.16	~1000	0.0002
Pure	^{235}U	100	20	~300	0.06
Denatured	$^{235/8}U$	20	0.08	~1500	0.00005
Pure	^{239}Pu	100	20	~200	0.1
Reactor	Pu	70	8	~250	0.03
Pure	^{240}Pu	0	0.1	~375	0.0003
Pure	^{242}Pu	0	0.004	~800	0.0000005
Reactor	Pu	50	2	~300	0.007
Denatured	Pu	20	0.03	~450	0.00007
Denatured	Pu	5	0.001	~700	0.000001

Source: A. DeVolpi, "Denaturing Fissile Materials," *Progress in Nuclear Energy* **10,** No. 2, 161–220 (1982).

[a]For high-technology systems; yields normalized to 20 kt (TNT).

[b]Heavy-metal content only: 10-cm ^{238}U reflector assumed.

Detectability of diversion is another effective barrier to the diversion of material from civilian facilities. Portal monitors and/or monitors at a facility's perimeter can be effective means of detecting diversion. The dose rate from 1 g of material is a measure of detectability, shown in Figure 20.22.

The combination of technical and institutional measures that are possible to increase the proliferation resistance of civilian nuclear installations further include enhanced security at the plants, colocation of facilities, coprocessing and coprecipitation, nuclear energy parks, multinational energy centers, international plutonium storage, and other measures. Many of these are fraught with difficulties of a political nature relating to questions of fairness, discrimination among nations, national sovereignty versus the powers of international entities, enforcement procedures, and assurances of supply. Even so, the general concensus is that technical barriers alone do not suffice and institutional arrangements are needed to erect additional barriers and disincentives to the spread of nuclear weapons.

20.7. ARE THE HORSES OUT OF THE BARN?

This question expresses the view that it is futile to attempt the control of nuclear technology through secrecy and denial. A different viewpoint is given by: "it matters how many horses have gone out of the barn and how many more and how fast." The extensive investigations of recent years have concluded that all reactor cycles have some diversion potential which does not dramatically differ from one cycle to the other. Various technical measures can be used to harden the facilities and raise the barriers of proliferation potential. While risks from terrorist organizations or subnational groups are easier to cope with, the more intractable risk stems from a calculated national decision toward either covert or open weapons development. Given the independent and intractable routes open to this end, the strategy of civilian nuclear technology is to raise the barriers toward proliferation to at least the same level as those of the independent secret route. This can be done through a variety of means such as denaturing or spiking of fuel, more effective inspection and surveillance, and more refined accountability means that can provide adequate warning time. Technology should address all phases of the nuclear cycle including the enrichment phase which presents a separate threat, even independently from civilian applications.

On the other hand, the risks should not be blown out of proportion. The nature and size of the barriers are considerable. Going the weapons route requires specialized skills and resources which are largely different from those needed for plant operation. Practical knowledge comes from direct development experience, which is lacking in the large majority of countries. The number of countries that have developed nuclear weapons has been limited to perhaps half a dozen compared to over one hundred that have elected to abstain from it.

International arrangements regarding present and future civilian facilities can greatly remove mutual suspicions and fears (which often prompt the flirting with the nuclear weapons idea), and thus eliminate incentives in this direction. These arrangements will inevitably have to be coupled with assurances of fuel supply and of transfer of technology to meet the needs of nonweapons states. In this respect, the commercial availability of reprocessing services and the continued

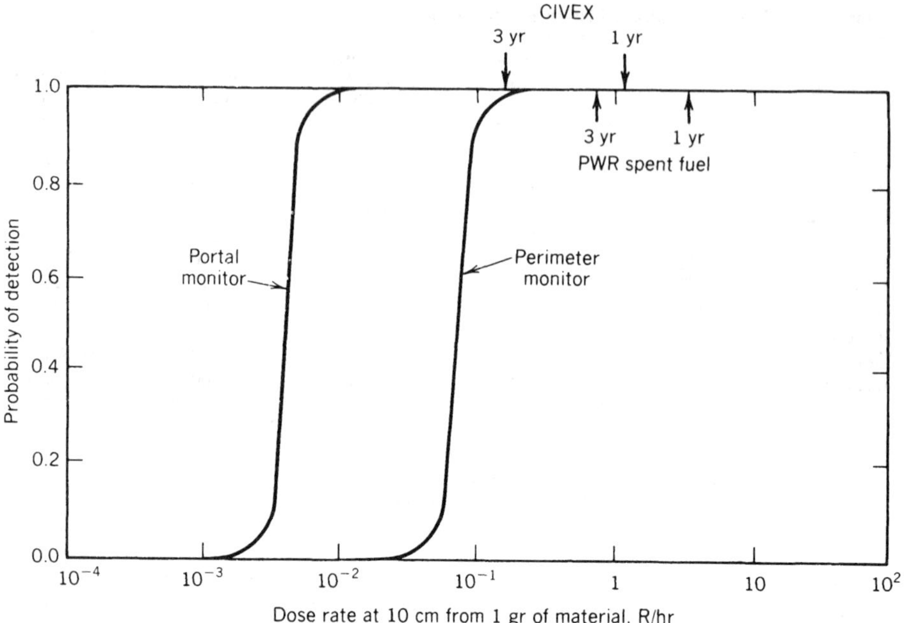

Figure 20.22. The probability for detection of 1 g of diverted fuel is plotted against dose rate at a distance of 10 cm from the detector. For a 90% certain detection, a portal monitor requires a dose rate of about 6 mrems/hr while a perimeter monitor requires 100 mrems/hr. The dose rates from 1 g of PWR spent fuel and CIVEX fuel at 1 and 3 yr cooling are also shown at the upper right. They are either higher or (at worst) equal to the threshold values. (From EPRI.)

assurance of enrichment services would reduce or even eliminate the need for independent national development of such sensitive facilities.

Technology can provide considerable assistance as was shown in this chapter. Its capability is, however, limited, a fact technologists recognize. A problem with political dimensions clearly needs political solutions. In a world where nuclear power is already a sizable reality, where many countries consider it indispensable to their energy future, technical measures must be combined with international treaties, regional agreements, fuel supply assurances, and perhaps more importantly, with a general effort toward reduction of tensions and the removal of other causes of competition for natural resources.

BIBLIOGRAPHY

History and Technical Aspects

DeVolpi, A., "Denaturing Fissile Materials," *Progress in Nuclear Energy* **10,** No. 2, 161–220 (1982).

Foster, J. S., "Nuclear Weapons," *Encyclopedia Americana,* Vol. 20, pp. 520–522, Americana Corp., New York, 1973.

Heising-Goodman, C., "An Evaluation of the Plutonium Denaturing Concept as an Effective Safeguards Method," *Nuclear Technology* **50,** 242 (1980).

Meyer, W., et al., "The Home-Made Nuclear Bomb Syndrome," *Nuclear Safety* **18,** 427–438 (1977).

Sahin, S., and J. Ligou, "The Effect of the Spontaneous Fission of Plutonium-240 on the Energy Release in a Nuclear Explosive," *Nuclear Technology* **50,** 88 (1980).

Starr, C., and E. Zebroski, "Nuclear Power and Weapons Proliferation." *American Power Conference,* Chicago, Illinois, Vol. 39, 1977, pp. 26–33.

The Los Alamos Primer, based on lectures by R. Serber, Los Alamos National Laboratory, LA-1, 1943.

Thomas, J. T., Ed., *Nuclear Safety Guide*, Rev. 2, NUREG/CR-0095, ORNL/NUREG/CSD-6, June 1978.

General

Dunn, L. A., *Nuclear-Weapons Pathways, Scenarios, and Possible Institutional Responses*, HI-2786-D, Croton-on-Hudson, New York, Hudson Institute, February 1978 (CNSI).

Dunn, L. A., and H. Kahn, *Trends in Nuclear Proliferation, 1975–1995*, Hudson Institute Croton-on-Hudson, New York, 1976.

Epstein, W., "The Proliferation of Nuclear Weapons," *Scientific American* **232,** (April 1975).

Ford Foundation, "Nuclear Power Issues and Choices," S. Keeny, Ed., *Report on the Nuclear Energy Policy Study Group*, Cambridge, Massachusetts, Ballinger, 1977.

Kratzer, M. B., "Nuclear Power: Problems and Prospects," International Symposium on "Energy-What Now?," The Royal Tropical Institute, Amsterdam, The Netherlands, Oct. 22, 1979.

Nye, J., "Non Proliferation: A Long Term Strategy," *Foreign Affairs*, 601–623 (April 1978).

Quester, G. H., "Can Proliferation Now be Stopped?," *Foreign Affairs* **53,** 77–97 (October 1974).

Rathjens, G. W., and A. Carnesale, "The Nuclear Fuel Cycle and Nuclear Proliferation," *Int'l Arrangements for Nuclear Fuel Reprocessing"*, edited by A. Chayes and W. B. Lewis, Ballinger, Cambridge, Massachusetts, 1977, pp. 3–16.

Stockholm International Peace Research Institute, *Nuclear Proliferation Problems*, MIT Press, Cambridge, Massachusetts, 1974.

The Atlantic Council, *Nuclear Power and Nuclear Weapons Proliferation*, Vols. 1 and 2, Westview Press, Boulder, Colorado, 1978.

U.S. Congress, Senate Committee on Government Operations, *Peaceful Nuclear Exports and Weapons Proliferation, A Compendium*, Government Printing Office, 1975.

Wohlsletter, A., et al., *Moving Toward Life in a Nuclear Armed Crowd?*, Pan Heuristics, Los Angeles, California, 1976.

International Treaties—Safeguards

dell'Acqua, F., et al., "The Development and Function of the IAEA's Safeguards Information System," *IAEA Bulletin* **23,** No. 4 (December 1981).

Donnely, W. H., and B. Rather, *Nuclear Weapons Proliferation and the International Atomic Energy Agency*, Congressional Research Service, Government Printing Office, Washington, D.C., 1976.

Fisher, D. A. V., "Safeguards and Non-Proliferation: Geography, Prospects, Problems," *IAEA Bulletin* **23,** No. 4, (December 1981).

Gruemm, H., "Safeguards and Tamuz: Setting the Record Straight," *IAEA Bulletin* **23,** No. 4 (December 1981).

Johnson, B., *Whose Power to Choose?, International Institutions and the Control of Nuclear Energy*, The International Institute for Environment, 1977.

Klik, F., "Field Experience of Safeguards Inspectors," *IAEA Bulletin* **23,** No. 4 (December 1981).

"Nuclear Energy and World Order: Implications for International Organizations," Proc. of an Int'l Conf. with a report by R. N. Gardner, The Institute of Man and Science, Rensselaerville, New York, 1976.

Persiani, P. J., *Diversion Analysis and Safeguards Measures for Liquid Metal Fast Breeder Reactors*, Argonne National Laboratory, ANL-81-48, October, 1981.

Persiani, P. J., et al., *Nuclear Material Safeguards, Surveillance, and Accountancy by Isotope Correlation Techniques*, Argonne National Laboratory, ANL-81-80, November 1981.

Stockholm International Peace Research Institute, *Safeguards Against Nuclear Proliferation*, MIT Press, Cambridge, Massachusetts, 1975.

Stockholm International Peace Research Institute, *The Nuclear Age*, MIT Press, Cambridge, Massachusetts, 1974.

Subrahmanyam, K., "Nuclear Weapons and India's Security," *The Institute for Defense Studies and Analysis Journal* **3,** No. 1 (July 1979).

U.S. Congress Office of Technology Assessment, *Nuclear Proliferation and Safeguards*, 1977.

Yager, J. A., Ed., *Nonproliferation and U.S. Foreign Policy*, Brookings Institution, Washington, D.C., 1980.

Civilian Power and Nuclear Proliferation—Alternate Nuclear Cycles

Atomic Industrial Forum, *Technical Deterrents to Proliferation,* November 1978.

Casper, B. M., "Laser Enrichment: A New Path to Proliferation?," *Bulletin of the Atomic Scientists* **33,** No. 1, 28 (January 1977).

Committee for Economic Development, *Nuclear Energy and National Security,* CED, Washington, D.C., 1976.

Department of Energy, *Nuclear Proliferation and Civilian Nuclear Power,* Report of the Nonproliferation Alternative Systems Assessment Program, 9 Vols., DOE/NE-0001/8, Government Printing Office, June 1980.

DeVolpi, A., "Investigation of Isotopically Denatured Plutonium," *Trans. Am. Nuclear Soc.* **30,** 298 (1978).

Feiveson, H. A., and T. B. Taylor, "Security Implications of Alternative Fission Futures," *Bull. of Atomic Scientists,* 14 (December 1976).

General Atomic, *Nonproliferation Studies of Low-Enriched High Temperature Gas Cooled Reactors,* General Atomic Co., San Diego, California, 1978.

Glancy, J., et al., *Diversion Analysis of a Uranium Enrichment Facility,* ISPO-22, SAI-78-694-LJ, Science Applications, La Jolla, California, June 1978.

Glancy, J., et al., *Diversion Analysis of a Light Water Reactor Facility,* ISPO-28, SAI-78-704-LJ, La Jolla, California: Science Applications, Inc., June 1978.

Guhin, M. A., *Nuclear Paradox: Security Risks of the Peaceful Atom,* American Enterprise Institute, Washington, D.C., 1976.

Holdren, J. P., "Nuclear Power and Nuclear Weapons: The Connection is Dangerous," *The Bulletin of the Atomic Scientist* **39,** No. 1, 40 (January 1983).

International Nonproliferation Fuel Cycle Evaluation, INFCE.

Kapur, A., *India's Nuclear Option, Atomic Diplomacy and Decision Making,* Praeger, New York, 1976.

Krass, A. S., "Laser Enrichment of Uranium: The Proliferation Connection," *Science* **196,** 721 (1977).

Liner, R. T., et al., *A Methodology for Evaluating the Proliferation Resistance of Alternative Nuclear Power Systems,* SAI-78-673-WA., McLean, Virginia: Science Applications, Inc., November 1, 1977.

Miller, M., "International Management of Spent Fuel: Technical Alternatives and Constraints," MIT-EL 78-012, Cambridge, Massachusetts, June 1978.

Moniz, E. J., and T. L. Neff, "Nuclear Power and Nuclear Weapons Proliferation," *Physics Today,* 42–51 (April 1978).

Nacht, M., *Nuclear Energy and Nuclear-Weapons,* Report on the 1975 Aspen Workshop on Arms Control, Aspen Institute on Humanistic Studies, Princeton, 1976.

Papazoglou, I. A., et al., *A Methodology for the Assessment of the Proliferation Resistance of Nuclear Power Systems,* MIT-EL-78-021, Cambridge, Massachusetts, MIT, September 1978.

Schwartz, J. P., "Uranium Dioxide Caramel Fuel, An Alternative Fuel Cycle for Research and Test Reactors, Int'l Conf. on Nucl. Nonproliferation and Safeguards," Atomic Industrial Forum, Oct. 22–25, 1978, New York. Also, *Trans. Am. Nuclear Soc.* **30,** 729 (1978).

Science Applications, Inc., *Analysis of Facility Requirements for the Processing of Nuclear Weapon Material,* SAL-77-768, LJ, LaJolla, California, Science Applications, Inc., June 24, 1977.

Spinrad, B., "Nuclear Power and Nuclear Weapons: The Connection is Tenuous," *The Bulletin of the Atomic Scientists* **39,** No. 2, 44 (February 1983).

Stockholm International Peace Research Institute, *The Nuclear Age,* MIT Press, Cambridge, Massachusetts, 1974.

U.S. Congress, Congressional Research Service, *Nuclear Proliferation Factbook,* Government Printing Office, Washington, D.C., 1977. Of particular interest in this volume are three reports prepared by the late John Lamarsh for the CRS titled: "The Production of Plutonium Isotopes and ^{233}U in American and Canadian Power Reactors"; "On the Construction of Plutonium-Producing Reactors by Small and/or Developing Countries"; "On the Extraction of Plutonium from Reactor Fuel by Small and/or Developing Nations."

U.S. Congress, House International Relations Committee Hearing: *Nuclear Proliferation and Reprocessing,* 94th Congress, 2nd Session, Government Printing Office, Washington, D.C., 1976.

Wohlstetter, A., et al. *Nuclear Alternatives and Proliferation Risks,* PH-78-06-858-36, Los Angeles, California: Dan Heuristics, June, 1978.

Proliferation and Breeders

Ermakov, S., and D. Tolchenkov, *Safeguards Approach for Fast Breeder Reactors (Preliminary Approach),* IAEA-STR-85, May 1979, Revision, 1979.

Gray, J., et al., *International Cooperation on Breeder Reactors,* New York, New York, The Rockefeller Foundation, May, 1978.

Krinninger, H., et al., "Status of the Safeguards System Developed for the LMFBR Prototype Power Plant SNR-300 (KKW Kalkar)," Proc. Int'l Symp. on Nuclear Safeguards Technology, Vienna, October 1978, IAEA-SM-231/5.

Lawroski, S., "Fuel Cycles and the Fast Breeder Reactor," *Chemical Engineering Progress* **68,** No. 5 (May 1972).

Levenson, M., and F. Zebroski, "A Fast Breeder System Concept, A Diversion Resistant Fuel Cycle," 5th Energy Technology Conference, Washington, D.C., February 27, 1978.

Persiani, P. J., and M. Gundy, *NDA Safeguards Techniques for LMFBR Assemblies,* Argonne National Laboratory, 1981.

APPENDIX A
STATISTICS

Table A.1. Nuclear Electricity Generation Through January 31, 1984 by Country

Country	Plant	Capacity, MWe Gross	Lifetime Total MWh Gross
ARGENTINA	Atucha	357	22,704,492
BELGIUM	Doel-1	412	26,740,460
	Doel-2	412	22,174,660
	Doel-3	936	9,173,645
	Tihange-1	920	51,838,900
	Tihange-2	941	5,603,570
BRAZIL	Angra-1	657	187,569
BRITAIN	Berkeley (2 units)	334.4	41,174,040
	Bradwell (2 units)	374.1	39,393,870
	Dungeness A (2 units)	576.6	50,932,770
	Dungeness B-1	660	401,050
	Hartlepool-1	660	3,000
	Heysham-1	660	16,250
	Hinkley Point A (2 units)	663.9	63,596,670
	Hinkley Point B (2 units)	1,320	39,173,780
	Oldbury (2 units)	633.5	47,901,520
	Sizewell (2 units)	652.5	61,083,590
	Trawsfynydd (2 units)	584.8	57,638,210
	Wylfa (2 units)	1,352	64,913,640
	Calder Hall (4 units)	240	40,975,427
	Chapelcross (4 units)	240	41,356,210
	Hunterston A-1	169	23,753,142
	Hunterston A-2	169	24,139,110
	Hunterston B-1	660	18,677,670
	Hunterston B-2	660	14,482,340
	Dounreay PFR	250	1,424,000
	Winfrith SGHWR	100	7,916,458
CANADA	Gentilly-2	685	2,682,507
	Point Lepreau	680	4,959,283
	Douglas Point	220	15,836,238
	Pickering-1	542	47,911,946
	Pickering-2	542	46,803,376
	Pickering-3	542	42,901,793
	Pickering-4	542	41,013,825
	Pickering-5	540	3,041,360
	Bruce-1	826	38,975,958
	Bruce-2	826	37,434,334
	Bruce-3	826	36,354,167
	Bruce-4	826	29,805,670
FINLAND	Loviisa-1	465	20,327,836
	Loviisa-2	465	9,711,283
	Olkiluoto-1	683	22,493,816
	Olkiluoto-2	683	13,759,699

Table A.1. (Continued)

Country	Plant	Capacity, MWe Gross	Lifetime Total MWh Gross
FRANCE	Blayais-1	957	11,161,100
	Blayais-2	957	6,850,250
	Blayais-3	957	1,486,670
	Blayais-4	957	2,164,425
	Bugey-1	560	35,128,810
	Bugey-2	957	25,465,023
	Bugey-3	957	26,840,917
	Bugey-4	937	26,835,590
	Bugey-5	937	24,687,940
	Chinon-A2	242	24,502,276
	Chinon-A3	500	26,500,958
	Chinon-B1	924	3,556,600
	Chinon-B2	924	50
	Chooz (Sena)	325	27,518,000
	Cruas-1	928	449,174
	Dampierre-1	942	18,838,610
	Dampierre-2	942	14,434,330
	Dampierre-3	942	14,635,590
	Dampierre-4	942	11,571,841
	Fessenheim-1	930	30,100,127
	Fessenheim-2	930	33,127,869
	Gravelines-B1	957	15,757,590
	Gravelines-B2	957	15,606,270
	Gravelines-B3	957	14,759,446
	Gravelines-B4	957	12,068,530
	Marcoule	43	6,123,881
	Monts d'Arree	75	6,088,562
	Phenix	250	12,071,630
	St. Laurent-des-Eaux-A1	500	33,885,294
	St. Laurent-des-Eaux-A2	530	29,603,640
	St. Laurent-des-Eaux-B1	928	4,818,751
	St. Laurent-des-Eaux-B2	928	6,460,542
	Tricastin-1	957	18,348,828
	Tricastin-2	957	17,685,237
	Tricastin-3	957	16,406,620
	Tricastin-4	957	14,168,940
INDIA	Rapp-1	220	6,095,409
	Rapp-2	220	2,153,095
	Tarapur-1	210	13,026,848
	Tarapur-2	210	13,406,124
ITALY	Caorso	860	14,360,811
	Latina	200	22,573,660
JAPAN	Fukushima I-1	460	22,320,291
	Fukushima I-2	784	31,591,894
	Fukushima I-3	784	34,179,939
	Fukushima I-4	784	27,013,832
	Fukushima I-5	784	28,951,559
	Fukushima I-6	1,100	29,675,160
	Fukushima II-1	1,100	14,689,290
	Genkai-1	559	30,217,198
	Genkai-2	559	13,330,567
	Hamaoka-1	540	22,215,204
	Hamaoka-2	840	28,368,256
	Ikata-1	566	23,473,387
	Ikata-2	566	1,183,740
	Mihama-1	340	8,960,903
	Mihama-2	500	26,290,407
	Mihama-3	826	34,597,534

Table A.1. (Continued)

Country	Plant	Capacity, MWe Gross	Lifetime Total MWh Gross
	Ohi-1	1,175	28,995,252
	Ohi-2	1,175	31,227,795
	Takahama-1	826	33,085,557
	Takahama-2	826	36,641,358
	Shimane	460	27,076,607
	Tokai-1	166	16,489,712
	Tokai-2	1,100	34,739,970
	Tsuruga	357	25,470,783
	Fugen	165	4,168,836
NETHERLANDS	Borssele-1	480.9	34,244,620
	Dodewaard	54	5,689,245
PAKISTAN	Kanupp	137	3,512,070
SOUTH KOREA	Kori-1	587	18,611,803
	Kori-2	650	2,044,397
	Wolsung-1	678.7	2,716,852
SPAIN	Almaraz-1	930	7,982,060
	Almaraz-2	930	207,780
	Asco-1	930	305,630
	Garona	460	31,371,610
	Vandellos	497.4	37,428,029
	Zorita	160	14,229,400
SWEDEN	Barsebaeck-1	590	30,210,487
	Barsebaeck-2	590	26,233,596
	Forsmark-1	940	18,059,897
	Forsmark-2	940	13,497,115
	Oskarshamn-1	460	32,446,601
	Oskarshamn-2	615	37,249,099
	Ringhals-1	780	31,984,143
	Ringhals-2	840	37,751,982
	Ringhals-3	980	7,224,617
	Ringhals-4	980	2,216,727
SWITZERLAND	Beznau-1	364	34,020,940
	Beznau-2	364	32,765,830
	Goesgen	970	30,265,800
	Muehleberg	336	28,003,107
TAIWAN	Chinshan-1	636	21,997,425
	Chinshan-2	636	19,953,005
	Kuosheng-1	985	10,270,899
	Kuosheng-2	985	6,050,785
WEST GERMANY	Biblis A	1,215	64,912,250
	Biblis B	1,300	53,215,486
	Brunsbuettel	806	17,859,952
	Grafenrheinfeld	1,290	17,640,657
	Isar (Ohu)	907	25,273,746
	MZFR	57	5,556,132
	Neckar	855	40,591,570
	Obrigheim	345	35,689,080
	Philippsburg-1	900	15,117,155
	Stade-1	662	57,153,232
	Unterweser	1,300	46,193,431
	Wuergassen	670	26,971,690
YUGOSLAVIA	Krsko	664	5,854,707
U.S.			
New England	Connecticut Yankee	616	65,665,394
	Millstone-1	690	50,860,096
	Millstone-2	881	37,963,895
	Pilgrim	685	39,691,808
	Yankee	185	25,591,103

Table A.1. (Continued)

Country	Plant	Capacity, MWe Gross	Lifetime Total MWh Gross
	Vermont Yankee	540	36,896,821
	Maine Yankee	864	54,961,120
Middle Atlantic	Indian Point-2	1,022	44,535,106
	Indian Point-3	1,022	27,649,980
	Ginna	496	40,790,858
	FitzPatrick	850	37,156,686
	Nine Mile Point-1	640	45,172,498
	Oyster Creek	650	46,287,120
	Salem-1	1,136	32,606,870
	Salem-2	1,158	12,188,980
	Susquehanna-1	1,152	5,503,840
	Peach Bottom-2	1,098	57,014,410
	Peach Bottom-3	1,098	53,078,070
	Three Mile Island-1	871	26,029,947
	Beaver Valley	923	20,824,100
South Altantic	Calvert Cliffs-1	890	47,942,583
	Calvert Cliffs-2	880	41,156,795
	Surry-1	824	43,131,712
	Surry-2	824	43,955,562
	North Anna-1	947	26,691,131
	North Anna-2	947	16,937,171
	Brunswick-1	849	22,838,020
	Brunswick-2	849	26,920,374
	Robinson-2	739	52,106,566
	Oconee-1	911	50,469,000
	Oconee-2	911	45,497,680
	Oconee-3	911	46,743,204
	McGuire-1	1,220	9,261,198
	McGuire-2	1,220	1,929,331
	Summer	954	4,508,817
	Hatch-1	813	34,336,861
	Hatch-2	820	20,201,071
	Farley-1	861	27,079,598
	Farley-2	861	14,453,212
	Turkey Point-3	728	43,224,142
	Turkey Point-4	728	41,647,936
	St. Lucie-1	853	35,687,125
	St. Lucie-2	853	2,212,913
	Crystal River-3	868	28,277,999
East South Central	Browns Ferry-1	1,098	48,474,797
	Browns Ferry-2	1,098	47,919,498
	Browns Ferry-3	1,098	44,496,240
	Sequoyah-1	1,183	18,304,260
	Sequoyah-2	1,183	11,545,624
East North Central	Big Rock Point	75	7,367,016
	Palisades	810	35,753,430
	Cook-1	1,089	53,689,130
	Cook-2	1,133	37,438,660
	Davis-Besse	934	21,727,995
	Dresden-2	834	55,963,717
	Dresden-3	832	51,952,919
	LaSalle-1	1,122	2,346,578
	Quad Cities-1	833	52,662,195
	Quad Cities-2	833	49,436,317
	Zion-1	1,085	55,914,389
	Zion-2	1,085	52,085,990
	Kewaunee	563	35,830,071
	LaCrosse	55	3,057,232

Table A.1. (Continued)

Country	Plant	Capacity, MWe Gross	Lifetime Total MWh Gross
	Point Beach-1	524	41,395,980
	Point Beach-2	524	40,582,600
West North Central	Monticello	580	44,785,519
	Prairie Island-1	560	35,886,420
	Prairie Island-2	560	33,696,770
	Arnold	566	24,015,639
	Fort Calhoun	501	28,272,854
	Cooper	801	41,226,223
	Fort St. Vrain	342	4,181,109
West South Central	Arkansas Nuclear I-1	910	39,971,239
	Arkansas Nuclear I-2	943	18,489,381
Pacific	Hanford-1 (N reactor)	862	57,555,305
	Rancho Seco	967	36,786,742
	San Onofre-1	456	37,203,434
	San Onofre-2	1,127	3,929,127
	San Onofre-3	1,127	560,047
	EBR-2	16.0	1,501,961
	Trojan	1,216	38,359,918

1. In instances where reactors of similar or higher power capacity have a significantly lower lifetime kWh output, the explanation is usually that the latter unit was completed a year or several years later. This is frequently noted in the case of units bearing the same name but different numerical designations (e.g. Cook-1, Cook-2).
2. This table gives a good approximation of the total amount of electricity generated by uranium power by different countries—but only an approximation, because the table includes only plants in operation as of January 31, 1984, and does not include some early small plants that have been retired.
3. The electricity production numbers are presented by courtesy of, and with the permission of, *Nucleonics Week*, a McGraw-Hill publication. The plants' capacity ratings are the turbine nameplate ratings, except in a few cases where *Nucleonics Week* has evidence that some other figure more justly represents what the seller and buyer felt the unit was bought, designed, built, and intended to produce.

Table A.2. Status of U.S. Nuclear Power Plants Under Construction as of January 31, 1984

Electric utility companies expect to be able to begin to load nuclear fuel into power plants still under construction at the present time in the years and months shown:

Unit	Utility	Net MWe	Current
Beaver Valley 2	Duquesne Light	852	12/85
Bellefonte 1	TVA	1,235	—
Bellefonte 2	TVA	1,235	—
Braidwood 1	Commonwealth Edison	1,120	4/85
Braidwood 2	Commonwealth Edison	1,120	4/86
Byron 1	Commonwealth Edison	1,120	—
Byron 2	Commonwealth Edison	1,120	5/85
Callaway 1	Union Electric	1,150	4/84
Catawba 1	Duke Power	1,145	5/84
Catawba 2	Duke Power	1,145	10/86
Clinton 1	Illinois Power	950	1/86
Clinton 2	Illinois Power	950	Canceled
Comanche Peak 1	Texas Utilities	1,150	—
Comanche Peak 2	Texas Utilities	1,150	—
Diablo Canyon 1	Pacific G&E	1,084	Low-power license suspension lifted
Diablo Canyon 2	Pacific G&E	1,106	—
Fermi 2	Detroit Edison	1,123	—
Grand Gulf 1	Mississippi P&L	1,250	
Grand Gulf 2	Mississippi P&L	1,250	Low-power licensed issued 6/82
Harris 1	Carolina P&L	900	6/85
Harris 2	Carolina P&L	900	6/89
Hope Creek 1	PSE&G	1,067	1/86
LaSalle 2	Commonwealth Edison	1,078	2/84
Limerick 1	Philadelphia Elec.	1,065	—
Limerick 2	Philadelphia Elec.	1,065	—
Marble Hill 1	Public Serv. of Indiana	1,130	Canceled
Marble Hill 2	Public Serv. of Indiana	1,130	Canceled
McGuire 2	Duke Power	1,180	Low-power license issued 3/83
Midland 1	Consumers Power	492	—
Midland 2	Consumers Power	818	—
Millstone 3	Northeast Nuclear Energy	1,150	—
Nine Mile Pt. 2	Niagara Mohawk	1,080	3/86
Palo Verde 1	Arizona Public Serv.	1,270	8/84
Palo Verde 2	Arizona Public Serv.	1,270	—
Palo Verde 3	Arizona Public Serv.	1,270	—
Perry 1	Cleveland Electric	1,205	—
Perry 2	Cleveland Electric	1,205	—
River Bend 1	Gulf States Utilities	934	4/85
River Bend 2	Gulf States Utilities	934	Delayed
Seabrook 1	Public Serv. Co. of N.H.	1,194	9/84
Seabrook 2	Public Serv. Co. of N.H.	1,194	4/87
Shoreham	L.I. Lighting	854	5/84
South Texas 1	Houston Lighting & Power	1,250	12/86
South Texas 2	Houston Lighting & Power	1,250	12/88
Susquehanna 2	Pennsylvania P&L	1,050	1/84
Vogtle 1	Georgia Power	1,100	9/86
Vogtle 2	Georgia Power	1,100	3/88
Wash. Nuclear Proj. 1	WPPSS	1,267	Delayed
Wash. Nuclear Proj. 2	WPPSS	1,267	Low-power license issued 12/83
Wash. Nuclear Proj. 3	WPPSS	1,242	6/86
Waterford 3	Louisiana P&L	1,165	3/84
Watts Bar 1	TVA	1,165	4/84
Watts Bar 2	TVA	1,165	10/85
Wolf Creek	Kansas G&E	1,150	—
Yellow Creek 1	TVA	1,285	Delayed
Yellow Creek 2	TVA	1,285	Delayed
Zimmer 1	Cincinnati G&E	810	Canceled

Table A.3. Summary of Status of U.S. Nuclear Power Plants as of December 31, 1983

	Units	MW
Plants in operation	75	58,456
Plants with OLs near operation	3	3,180
Plants with OLs shut down	4	2,090
Plants awaiting OLs through 1985	29	31,981
Plants awaiting OLs beyond 1985	20	22,869
Plants awaiting CPs	2	2,576
Other planned plants	2	2,240
Plants indefinitely deferred	7	8,573
Plants canceled in 1983 through 2/84	4	4,350
Grand total, summary	145	136,315

Source: The information in this and the previous table was compiled by, and is presented here by courtesy of and with the permission of the Utility Data Institute, Inc., Washington, D.C.

Table A.4. U.S. Nuclear Power Plant Cancelations

1972	6 units	5,738 MWe
1973	0	0
1974	8 units	8,290 MWe
1975	11 units	12,291 MWe
1976	2 units	2,328 MWe
1977	9 units	9,862 MWe
1978	13 units	13,333 MWe
1979	8 units	9,476 MWe
1980	16 units	18,085 MWe
1981	6 units	5,811 MWe
1982	18 units	19,500 MWe
1983	1 unit	1,280 MWe
1984	3 units[a]	3,070 MWe

[a]Through 2/84.

Table A.5. Forecast of Nuclear Generating Capacity Outside the United States. (Showing expected net installed capacity, and percent of total installed capacity contributed by uranium-fueled plants, at or near century's end.)

	Net MWe Installed	Nuclear % of Total	Year
	Noncommunist World		
Argentina	3,442	23.0	2000
Belgium	5,427	38.0	1985
Brazil	10,586	11.0	2000
Canada	14,502	13.0	1990
Egypt	8,400	28.6	2000
Finland	3,160	25.0	1995
France	n.a.	85.0	2000
Germany (West)	37,000	50.0	2000
Greece	600–900	5.0	1990
India	10,000	9.3	2000
Israel	4,750	50.0	2000
Italy	4,711	6.4	1990
Japan	90,000	30.0	2000
Korea (South)	11,215	n.a.	1990
Mexico	1,308	4.0	1990
Netherlands	450	n.a.	2000
Pakistan	725	n.a.	1985
Philippines	620	7.9	1990
Portugal	2,700	18.0	2000
South Africa	1,844	7.0	1985
Spain	27,000	40.0	2000
Sweden	9,450	28.0	1990
Switzerland	2,882	19.1	1985
Taiwan	(4,928	31.0	1985
	(11,578	n.a.	1995
Thailand	900	10.1	1995
Turkey	1,000	n.a.	1995
United Kingdom	10,267	n.a.	1985
	Communist Bloc Countries		
Bulgaria	4,760	35.0	1990
China	16,000	n.a.	2000
Cuba	1,320	n.a.	1990
Czechoslovakia	6,280	n.a.	1990
Germany (East)	(9,000	n.a.	1990
	(n.a.	50.0	2000
Hungary	11,000	48.0	2000
Poland	3,860	n.a.	1995
Romania	3,960	20.0	1990
U.S.S.R.	(90,000	25.0	1990
	(n.a.	33.0	2000
Yugoslavia	632	n.a.	1982

In addition to the countries shown in the list above, Iran has two plants under construction at Bushehr on the Persian Gulf; and the following countries are planning to install one nuclear unit each:

Algeria	Libya
Bangladesh	Kenya
Chile	Luxembourg
Colombia	Morocco
Iraq	Syria
Ireland	Venezuela

(*Note:* The information and figures in this table have been supplied by the nuclear authorities of the countries concerned, in response to a survey conducted annually by the Atomic Industrial Forum. They are presented here by courtesy of and with the permission of the Forum.)

Table A.6. Known Nuclear Power Plants in Communist Bloc Countries as of First Half 1983

		Capacity, MWe	
Bulgaria			
*	Kozloduy 1	440	
*	Kozloduy 2	440	
*	Kozloduy 3	440	
*	Kozloduy 4	440	
#	Kozloduy 5, 6	1,000 each	
#	Belene 1, 2, 3, 4	1,000 each	
China			
UC	Qing Shan 1, 2 (Zhejiang province)	300 each	
#	Guangdong 1, 2	900 each	
Cuba			
UC	Cienfuegos 1, 2	440 each	
#	Holguin 1, 2	440 each	
#	Unnamed, 1–7	n.a.	
Czechoslovakia			
*	Bohunice V-1, 1	440	
*	Bohunice V-1, 2	440	
UC	Bohunice V-2, 1 and 2	440 each	
UC	Dukovany 1, 2, 3, 4	440 each	
UC	Mochovce 1, 2, 3, 4	440 each	
@	Temelin 1, 2	1,000 each	
#	Temelin 3, 4	1,000 each	
#	North Moravia 1, 2, 3, 4	1,000 each	
East Germany			
*	Rheinsberg	80	
*	Bruno Leuschner 1, 2, 3	440	
UC	Bruno Leuschner 4	440	
UC	Magdeburg 1, 2, 3, 4	440 each	
#	Magdeburg 5, 6, 7, 8	440 each	
Hungary			
*	Paks 1	440	
UC	Paks 2, 3, 4	440 each	
#	Paks 5, 6, 7	1,000 each	
Poland			
UC	Zarnowiec 1, 2	465	
#	Zarnowiec 3, 4	465	
#	Kujawy 1, 2, 3, 4	1,000 each	
Rumania			
*	Olt	440	
UC	Cernavoda 1, 2	700 each	
#	Cernavoda 3, 4	700 each	
#	Unnamed 1, 2	700 each	
USSR			
*	Obninsk	5	
*	Troitsk 1, 2, 3, 4, 5, 6	100 each	(Siberia)
*	Beloyarsk 1	200	(Near Sverdlovsk, Urals)
*	Beloyarsk 2	100	
*	Beloyarsk 3 (BN-600)	600	
*	Novovoronezh 1	210	(At Voronezh on Don)
*	Novovoronezh 2	365	
*	Novovoronezh 3, 4	440 each	

Table A.6. (Continued)

		Capacity, MWe	
USSR			
*	Novovoronezh 5	1,000	
*	Kola 1, 2, 3, 4	440 each	(Near Murmansk)
*	Armenia 1, 2	400 each	(Ararat Valley near Yerevan)
*	Shevchenko (BN-350)	350	(On Caspian shore)
*	Leningrad 1, 2, 3, 4	1,000 each	
*	Kursk 1, 2, 3	1,000 each	(South Russia, 125 miles west of Voronezh)
UC	Kursk 4	1,000	
*	West Ukraine 1, 2	1,000 each	(Near Khmeltnitski)
*	West Ukraine 3, 4	1,000 each	
UC	South Ukraine	1,000	(Near Nikolayev)
#	South Ukraine 2, 3, 4	1,000 each	
*	Smolensk 1	1,000	
UC	Smolensk 2	1,000	
#	Smolensk 3, 4	1,000 each	
*	Chernobyl 1, 2, 3	1,000 each	
UC	Chernobyl 4	1,000	
UC	Kalinin 1, 2, 3, 4	1,000 each	(100 miles north Moscow)
#	Zaporozhe 1–6	1,000 each	(On Dnieper R., Ukraine)
#	Chernobyl 5–12	1,000 each	
*	Bilibin 1, 2, 3, 4	12 each	
*	Ulyanovsk (VK-50)	50	
*	Ulyanovsk (BOR-60)	12	
*	Rovno 1	440	
UC	Rovno 2	440	
UC	Ingolinka 1, 2	1,500 each	(Near Ingolinka, Lithuania)
#	Aktash 1–6	1,000 each	(At Aktash, Crimea)
#	Odessa	1,000	
#	Odessa (BN-800)	800	
#	unknown site (BN-1600)	1,600	

Note: Reactors designated "BN" are fast breeders, "BN" standing for "Bystrye Neiytrony," or fast neurons.
* = in operation.
UC = Under Construction.
# = planned.
@ = ordered.

APPENDIX B
GLOSSARY

ABOUT THIS GLOSSARY

Most of the commonly used technical terms, such as "half-life," "curie," "rem," "rad," and so on, have already been defined in the text of this book where first introduced.

To try to present here a complete glossary or dictionary giving precise and complete definitions of all such terms would require a book in itself, and moreover would duplicate the many such books already in print and readily available.

Therefore we have thought it more useful to present a glossary of the many—and often confusing—acronyms so commonly used in trade talk and trade jargon, together with a bibliography of a few, only, of the standard dictionaries of technical terms.

We have not aimed in this glossary to list nuclear acronyms completely, but rather to include all the important, and most commonly encountered ones.

Regarding the arrangement: rather than throwing all the acronyms into one pot by alphabetical order, we have made an attempt at classifying them into three groups. The context in which the acronym appears will usually give the reader ample clues to which of the three lists to look in first; in any event the reader will have at worst no more than three lists to check.

We hope this list and arrangement will prove useful.

—THE AUTHORS

B.1. INSTITUTIONAL TERMS (GOVERNMENTAL)

Note: Names of governmental bodies and national laboratories are in all CAPITAL letters; regulatory terms and other expressions are in Capital and Lowercase letters.

ACRS	ADVISORY COMMITTEE ON REACTOR SAFEGUARDS
ANL	ARGONNE NATIONAL LABORATORY
ASLAB	ATOMIC SAFETY & LICENSING APPEALS BOARD (of NRC)
ASLB	ATOMIC SAFETY & LICENSING BOARD (of NRC)
ASLP	ATOMIC SAFETY & LICENSING BOARD PANEL (experts' pool from which members of ASLBs and ASLABs are drawn)
ATOG	Abnormal Transient Operating Guidelines (NRC)
B&O	Bulletins & Orders (of NRC)
CEQ	COUNCIL ON ENVIRONMENTAL QUALITY (Federal)
CP	Construction Permit (issued by NRC)
DOE	U.S. DEPARTMENT OF ENERGY
EIS	Environmental Impact Statement (required under National Environmental Protection Act)
FRC	FEDERAL RADIATION COUNCIL
FSAR	Final Safety Analysis Report (to NRC)
GEIS	Generic Environmental Impact Statement (variety of EIS)
I&E	INSPECTION & ENFORCEMENT OFFICE (of NRC)
ICRP	INTERNATIONAL COMMISSION ON RADIOLOGICAL PROTECTION
ICRU	INTERNATIONAL COMMISSION ON RADIATION UNITS & MEASUREMENTS
INFCE	INTERNATIONAL NUCLEAR FUEL CYCLE EVALUATION (initiated by President Carter)

INEL	IDAHO NATIONAL ENGINEERING LABORATORY (formerly NRTS)
IREP	Interim Reliability Evaluation Program
LASL	LOS ALAMOS SCIENTIFIC LABORATORY
LER	Licensee Event Report (from reactor owners to NRC)
LLL	LAWRENCE LIVERMORE (NATIONAL) LABORATORY
ML	Manufacturing License (NRC. Only one ever applied for, by Offshore Power Systems)
NBS	NATIONAL BUREAU OF STANDARDS
NCRM	NATIONAL COUNCIL ON RADIATION MEASUREMENT
NCRP	NATIONAL COMMISSION FOR RADIATION PROTECTION
NPDES	National Pollution Discharge Elimination System
NRC	U.S. NUCLEAR REGULATORY COMMISSION
NRR	OFFICE OF NUCLEAR REACTOR REGULATION (of NRC)
NRTS	NATIONAL REACTOR TESTING STATION (now INEL, q.v.)
NTCP	Near-Term Construction Permit (NRC) } expected to be issued shortly
NTOL	Near-Term Operating License (NRC) } expected to be issued shortly
OL	Operating License (issued by NRC)
ORNL	OAK RIDGE NATIONAL LABORATORY
PNO	Preliminary Notification of event or unusual Occurrence
PSAR	Preliminary Safety Analysis Report (to NRC; cf. FSAR)
RO	Reportable Occurrence (NRC)
SALP	Systematic Assessment of Licensee Performance
SNM	Special Nuclear Material [early AEC code words for fissionable material, fertile (convertible to fissionable) material, or other controlled substances; used in 1946 and 1954 Atomic Energy Acts]
UOR	Unusual Occurrence Report (to NRC)
USI	Unresolved Safety Issue (NRC, ACRS)

B.2 NUCLEAR POWER PLANT TERMS

Note: Technical, operational, and component terms are in Capital and Lowercase letters; reactor types and classifications are in all CAPITAL letters; individual reactor names are in all *CAPITAL* italics.

ALARA	As Low As Reasonably Achievable (i.e., radiation levels: an NRC goal)
ANO	*ARKANSAS NUCLEAR ONE* station
ANP	AIRCRAFT NUCLEAR PROPULSION, an AEC program covering many land prototypes
ARE	*AIRCRAFT REACTOR EXPERIMENT*, a molten-salt reactor built at ORNL in ANP program
ATWS	Anticipated Transient Without Scram (a routine, minor malfunction such as occurs in all power plants, which in a nuclear plant should result in automatic reactor shutdown, or "scram," but does not)
BONUS	*BOILING NUCLEAR SUPERHEAT* Reactor, an experimental reactor built at Mayaguez, Puerto Rico
BORAX	*BOILING REACTOR EXPERIMENT*, A small early experimental BWR to test BWR stability, tested to destruction
BWR	BOILING WATER REACTOR
CANDU	CANADIAN DEUTERIUM (natural)-URANIUM Reactor, developed, perfected, used by Canada
CRBR, CRBRP	*CLINCH RIVER BREEDER REACTOR* Project
CVTR	*CAROLINAS-VIRGINIA* (pressure)-*TUBE REACTOR*
CY	*CONNECTICUT YANKEE* station
DBA	Design Basis Accident (the worst technically expectable accident for that particular reactor design)
DHR	Decay Heat Removal (cf. RHR)

DASS	Disturbance Analysis & Surveillance System (a computerized diagnostic aid to analyze certain plant conditions, alert operators to disturbing trends)
DNB	Departure from Nucleate Boiling (in a BWR, when local boiling turns to bulk boiling)
ECCS	Emergency Core Cooling System
EFWS	Emergency Feedwater System
ECP	Emergency Communications Plan
ERV	Electromatic Relief Value
EFPH	Effective Full-Power Hours (of operation of a plant)
EBWR	*EXPERIMENTAL BOILING WATER REACTOR* (first BWR to produce power)
EBOR	*EXPERIMENTAL BERYLLIUM OXIDE* (moderated) *REACTOR*
EBR-1, 2	*EXPERIMENTAL BREEDER REACTOR* nos. *1, 2* (EBR-1 was the first nuclear power unit to produce usable quantity of electricity. Both EBR-1 and EBR-2 are at INEL, Idaho.)
EGCR	*EXPERIMENTAL GAS-COOLED REACTOR* (built at ORNL but never operated)
FNP	FLOATING NUCLEAR POWER PLANT
FGCR	FAST GAS-COOLED REACTOR (helium-cooled breeder, proposed alternative to LMFBR q.v.)
FPR	Fission Product Release
GCRE	*GAS-COOLED REACTOR EXPERIMENT* (small pilot plant built at Idaho INEL)
GDP	Gaseous Diffusion Plant (for enrichment of uranium)
HEPA	High-Efficiency Particulate Air Filter
HLW	High-Level (radioactive) Waste
HPCI	High-Pressure Coolant Injection (usually pronounced "Hipsy")
HPI	High-Pressure Injection (of additional coolant water)
HRE-1, 2	*HOMOGENEOUS REACTOR EXPERIMENT* nos. *1, 2* (both built at ORNL)
HTGR	HIGH-TEMPERATURE GAS-COOLED REACTOR
ICPP	Idaho Chemical Processing Plant (the first reprocessing plant for spent fuel)
IGSCC	Intergranular Stress-Corrosion Cracking (in stainless steel)
LAMPRE	*LOS ALAMOS MOLTEN PLUTONIUM REACTOR EXPERIMENT*
LAPRE	*LOS ALAMOS POWER REACTOR EXPERIMENT*, nos. *1, 2*
LLW	Low-Level (radioactive) Waste
LOCA	Loss of Coolant Accident (usually thought of as a postulated catastrophic break in a main coolant pipe, letting all coolant escape and leaving the reactor core uncovered)
LOFT	*LOSS OF FLUID TEST* Reactor (a safety test reactor to investigate effects of a postulated LOCA)
LMFBR	LIQUID-METAL FAST BREEDER REACTOR (the choice of breeder-reactor type of most of the world today)
LWR	LIGHT-WATER REACTOR (a combining term for PWR and BWR)
LWBR	LIGHT-WATER BREEDER REACTOR (a water-cooled, thermal-neutron breeder type championed by VADM. H. G. Rickover—unsuccessfully)
MSIV	Main Steam Isolation Valve (characteristic of BWRs)
MY	*MAINE YANKEE* station
MUF	Material Unaccounted For (fissionable material shortage in material-accountability bookkeeping, usually attributed to powdery fines too small to collect, remaining in process-plant piping, on floor, or deposited on walls or ceiling)
MWd	MegaWatt days (the unit in which nuclear fuel burnup is measured)
MTU	Metric Tons of Uranium (the unit in which uranium fuel processed is measured)
NCC	Natural Circulation Cooldown (of a reactor)

NDL	Nuclear Data Link (between each nuclear station and NRC, proposed by NRC)
NMP	*NINE MILE POINT* station
NSSS	Nuclear Steam Supply System
OTSG	Once-Through Steam Generator (in which the coolant water makes only one pass through the steam generator)
OMRE	*ORGANIC MODERATOR REACTOR EXPERIMENT* (experimental plant built at INEL)
ORALLOY	The wartime code word between the U.S. and Britain designating uranium
PBF	*POWER BURST FACILITY* (safety test reactor at INEL)
PCM	Power-Cooling Mismatch
PORV	Power-Operated Relief Valve (a principal cause of the TMI-2 accident: it jammed and failed to close although control-room indication was that it had closed)
PRA	Probability Risk Assessment
PWR	PRESSURIZED WATER REACTOR
QA	Quality Assurance; sometimes also called: QC
QC	Quality Control
RCP	Reactor Coolant Pump
RCS	Reactor Coolant System
RCB	Reactor Containment Building
REM	Roentgen Equivalent Man (the unit for measuring biological effect of radiation exposure)
RHR	Residual Heat Removal (c.f. DHR)
RO	Reactor Operator (c.f. SRO)
RPS	Reactor Protection System (the automatic computerized system that cuts back power or shuts down the reactor to prevent damage to it in case of low flow, over-pressure, excessive temperature, or other parameters)
RTD	Resistance Temperature Detector
RWST	Refueling Water Storage Tank
RV or RPV	Reactor Vessel/Reactor Pressure Vessel
SOE	Sequence Of Events
SPDS	Safety Panel Display System (reactor operator aid that displays principal parameters showing state of an operating plant at operator's console for quick overview)
SPND	Self-Powered Neutron Detector
SRE	SODIUM REACTOR EXPERIMENT (one of the five units in AEC's first reactor demonstration program)
SRO	Senior Reactor Operator (q.v. RO)
STA	Shift Technical Adviser (new position since TMI-2: an experienced graduate engineer in control room to advise operator when necessary)
TBP	Tributyl Phosphate (most commonly used solvent used to extract U and Pu from fission products in a spent fuel reprocessing plant)
TSC	Technical Support Center (similar post-TMI-2 measure to back up reactor operators as needed)
TREAT	TRANSIENT REACTOR TEST EXPERIMENT
UT	Ultrasonic Testing
VR	Volume Reduction (of low-level radioactive waste)

B.3. INDUSTRY AND PRIVATE SECTOR TERMS

Note: Names of electric utilities, other companies, and private laboratories are in CAPITAL letters; other private industry terms are in Capital and Lowercase letters; foreign company names are in *CAPITAL* italics.

AECL	*ATOMIC ENERGY OF CANADA LTD.*
AIF	Atomic Industrial Forum

ANS	American Nuclear Society
APPA	American Public Power Association
APDA	ATOMIC POWER DEVELOPMENT ASSOCIATES (c.f. PRDC)
AFEI	Americans For Energy Independence
ANEC	American Nuclear Energy Council
ANSI	American National Standards Institute
AP&L	ARKANSAS POWER & LIGHT Co.
ASME	American Society of Mechanical Engineers
BBC	*BROWN, BOVERI et Cie.* (Baden, Switzerland, & Mannheim, Germany)
B&W	BABCOCK & WILCOX Co.
BNFL	*BRITISH NUCLEAR FUELS LTD.*
C-E	COMBUSTION ENGINEERING Inc.
CESSAR	Combustion Engineering Standard Safety Analysis Report (c.f. Gessar, Resar)
CPFF	Cost Plus Fixed Fee (type of contract; opposite, in practice, of turnkey contract)
COM ED, or CECo	COMMONWEALTH EDISON CO. (Chicago)
CON ED	CONSOLIDATED EDISON CO. OF NEW YORK
CP&L	CAROLINA POWER & LIGHT CO.
CRIEPI	Central Research Institute of the Electric Power Industry (Japan)
EEI	Edison Electric Institute
ENS	European Nuclear Society
EDF	*ELECTRICITE DE FRANCE*
EPRI	Electric Power Research Institute
EURATOM	The European Atomic Energy Community
ETH	Eidgenossische Technische Hochschule (the Swiss Federal Polytechnic Institute at Zurich)
GE	GENERAL ELECTRIC CO. (U.S.)
GEC	*GENERAL ELECTRIC CO. LTD.* (U.K.)
GESSAR	GENERAL ELECTRIC STANDARD SAFETY ANALYSIS REPORT (c.f. Cessar, Resar)
GKSS	*GESELLSCHAFT FÜR KERNENERGIEVERWERTUNG IN SCHIFFBAU UND SCHIFFAHRT* (company for nuclear energy application in ship construction and ship operation, Hamburg, West Germany)
GPU	GENERAL PUBLIC UTILITIES
HPS	Health Physics Society
IAEA	International Atomic Energy Agency (headquartered in Vienna)
IAG	Industry Advisory Group (first months after TMI-2)
IEEE	Institute of Electrical & Electronic Engineers
IEL&P	IOWA ELECTRIC LIGHT & POWER
INPO	Institute for Nuclear Power Operation (headquarters, Atlanta, Ga.)
JAERI	Japanese Atomic Energy Research Institute
KRB	*KERNKRAFTWERK RWE-BAYERNWERK GmbH* (joint nuclear power subsidiary of West German utilities RWE and Bayernwerk)
KWU	KRAFTWERK UNION, AG (West German reactor manufacturer)
NFS	NUCLEAR FUEL SERVICES INC.
NUS	NUCLEAR UTILITY SERVICE CORP.
NEU	NORTHEAST UTILITIES INC.
NEIL	NUCLEAR ELECTRIC INSURANCE LTD. (another by-product of TMI-2)
NPRDS	Nuclear Plant Reliability Data System
NPRDC	National Public Resources Defense Council
NSAC	Nuclear Safety Analysis Center (of EPRI, q.v.)
NRECA	National Rural Electric Cooperative Association
PASNY	Power Authority of the State of New York (state agency, not privately owned)

PGE	PORTLAND GAS & ELECTRIC CO.
PG&E	PACIFIC GAS & ELECTRIC CO.
PP&L	PENNSYLVANIA POWER & LIGHT CO.
also	PACIFIC POWER & LIGHT CO.
PRDC	POWER REACTOR DEVELOPMENT CORP. (the utility consortium that was the builder and owner of the Enrico Fermi Breeder Reactor, for which APDA (q.v.), another utility syndicate, was the design agent)
P.S.E.&G.	PUBLIC SERVICE ELECTRIC & GAS CO. (of Newark, N.J.)
PSI	PUBLIC SERVICE CORP. OF INDIANA
PSC	PUBLIC SERVICE CO. OF COLORADO
PSNH	PUBLIC SERVICE CO. OF NEW HAMPSHIRE
S.C.E.&G.	SOUTH CAROLINA ELECTRIC & GAS CO.
SCE or So-Cal-Ed	SOUTHERN CALIFORNIA EDISON CO.
RESAR	Reactor Safety Analysis Report (the Westinghouse analogue to Cessar, Gessar)
RWE	*RHEINISCH-WESTFÄLISCHES ELEKTRIZITÄTSWERK* (of Essen, West Germany's largest power utility company)
UCS	Union of Concerned Scientists
VEPCO	VIRGINIA ELECTRIC & POWER CO.
WPPSS	WASHINGTON PUBLIC POWER SUPPLY SYSTEM (a syndicate of many small public power utilities in Washington state)
W	WESTINGHOUSE ELECTRIC CO.
YAEC	YANKEE ATOMIC ELECTRIC CO.

BIBLIOGRAPHY

A Glossary of Terms in Nuclear Science & Technology, ASME (ASA N1.1-1957).

A Handbook of Acronyms and Initialisms, NUREG 0544, anonymous, U.S. NRC, Washington, 1981.

Béné, G. J., R. Beeler, and M. Golub, *Nuclear Physics and Atomic Energy: Terms of Nuclear Physics and Nuclear Technology in English, French, German, Russian*, Elsevier, Amsterdam, London, New York, Princeton, 1960. (2117 terms cross-indexed four ways.)

Concise Dictionary of Atomics, A. Del Vecchio, Ed., Philosophical Library, New York, 1964.

Dictionary of Atomic Terminology, L. Lettenmeyer, Ed., Philosophical Library, New York. 1959.

Glossary of Terms, Nuclear Power & Radiation, NUREG 0770, compiled by J. G. Hanchett and F. W. Hasselberg, edited by M. H. Singh, Ed., U.S. NRC, Washington, 1981.

INDEX